THE ANATOMY OF MELANCHOLY

THE

ANATOMY

OF

MELANCHOLY

By

R O B E R T   B U R T O N

Now for the first time
With the *Latin* completely given in translation
And embodied in an *All-English* text

Edited by
FLOYD DELL
and
PAUL JORDAN–SMITH, B.A., B.D.,
(Sometime Fellow in the University of California)

TUDOR PUBLISHING COMPANY
NEW YORK

PREFACE

URTON'S great book, always the delight of the wise and the curious, has had for modern readers the difficulty of being largely couched in a language no longer generally current, being liberally interspersed, according to scholarly seventeenth-century custom, with Latin passages, quoted or original, and adorned with so many scraps of Latin poetry that it is a veritable Roman anthology; and though various editors have attempted to supply, in footnotes, English translations of these passages and scraps, the huge task was never completely accomplished: so that a great English classic has suffered the strange fate of becoming partly unintelligible to readers of our language. By transmuting the Latin parts directly into English, and presenting a straightforward all-English text, the present editors have undertaken to restore to this work the unhindered appreciation which it had in its author's own day.

In translating the Latin passages, we have only followed to its full extent the example set by Burton himself, who frequently enough, after quoting from some medico or traveller, or from one of his favourite poets, proceeded with a partial translation or paraphrase in his own robust prose or quaint verse. Where his translation or paraphrase has fairly covered the others' ground, we have simply left out the Latin, and let Burton speak for them; and we have pieced it out where needful, with much aid from other translators. We owe a large debt to two previous editors of Burton, the pseudonymous " Democritus Minor " who partially anticipated us in his London edition of 1845, and the Rev. A. R. Shilleto, editor of the scholarly 1893 edition; and we have drawn upon various translations, chiefly in verse, of Latin poets, by Sandys, Harrington, Phaer, Stapylton, Dryden, Martin, Connington, Gifford, Hodgson, Bryce, with, of course, the assistance of the Loeb classics. We have tried to preserve, in this cento-work, if not Burton's own authentic flavour, at least a seventeenth-century air, which will, we hope, except to the practiced and familiar eye, blend sufficiently with the original text, or at least not betray our handiwork by any modern incongruities. Charles Lamb would have been able to do perfectly what we have here attempted; he so loved the " fantastic old great man " that he could — as he did, upon occasion — write perfect Burtonese.

v

In presenting for the first time a complete Burton all in English, we have preferred to dispense with the elaborate apparatus of footnotes in which Burton gave credit (not always, it would seem, accurately) to the sources of his vagarious and compendious wisdom. For the reader who reads Burton for enjoyment, these references possess little meaning and in general no interest. We have abbreviated likewise the textual references to chapter and book of forgotten medical and other authorities. " Struthius, Stigmat. artis. l. 4. c. 9 saith " becomes " Struthius saith " for our purposes. A few footnotes have been added to clear up verbal difficulties. The most interesting of Burton's notes have been retained, and in a few instances, where the notes represent afterthoughts on the subject being dealt with, it has seemed permissible to incorporate them into the text, in parentheses; as on pp. 83–84 and 93 of Vol. I. The translation of the Latin parts of sentences into English has of course made necessary some slight changes in punctuation.

This edition is based upon the text of the sixth edition of the Anatomy, posthumously published in 1651, and containing Burton's final revisions: it has, however, been necessary to correct this text in certain passages by comparison with that of the earlier folios and the first edition, the quarto of 1621. We have freely made use of the modern Shilleto edition of 1893, which is based upon the 1651 folio, with some slight changes of spelling, which we have retained in the interests of intelligibility. The Shilleto edition is sometimes spoken of as giving a complete English translation of all Burton's Latin; but such is not the fact. It does represent much valuable editorial labour, and it gives the English of many of the Latin passages, though not with infallible accuracy, as we have discovered. In correcting some of Shilleto's errors, inevitable in so vast a work, we have taken advantage of the painstaking critical notes of Professor Edward Bensly, published in the 9th and 10th Series of Notes and Queries. It is to these notes that we owe such important corrections as " parasites " for the mysterious " parats " of the 1651 folio (Democritus to the Reader, p. 100 of this edition).

In all the early editions, italics are used for the purpose of indicating quoted or paraphrased matter; in the medical portions of the work we have sometimes followed this style, but in the main we have felt obliged by our purposes to use a more readable Roman type; though we leave Biblical quotations and paraphrases generally in italics, and an occasional phrase which for clearness needs to be set off from the rest of one of Burton's long, leisurely, " land-leaping " sentences. It has seldom seemed necessary to modernize the appearance of the page by the use of quotation-marks. When all that Burton has borrowed is put in quotation-marks, as in some modern reprints, there seems little of Burton left; but these quotations are actually not what one means by that word, but rather paraphrases, which owe their peculiar flavour somewhat to Burton's own verbal seasoning. "The matter is theirs most part, and yet mine," as he says of his work, " whence it is taken appears (which Seneca approveth), yet it appears as something different from what 'tis taken from; which nature doth with the aliment of our bodies, incorporate, digest, assimulate, I do dispose of what I take." He says again: " I have laboriously collected this Cento out of divers Writers, and that without injury, I have wronged no authors, but given every man his own; which Hierome so much commends in Nepotian, he stole not whole verses, pages, tracts, as some do nowadays, concealing their Authors' names, but still said, this was Cyprian's, that Lactantius', that Hilarius', so said Minucius Felix, so Victorinus, thus far Arnobius: I cite and quote mine Authors (which howsoever some illiterate scribblers account pedantical, as a cloak of ignorance, and opposite to their affected style, I must and will use), I have borrowed, not stolen, and what Varro speaks of bees, *they are by no means malicious, because they hurt nothing they take honey from,* I can say of myself, whom have I injured?" Usually it is made clear enough in the text from whom Burton is borrowing for the nonce. But sometimes a sentence begins, " As o one saith," leaving that little letter to guide the eye to the margin, where his debt is paid to Seneca, or Nevisanus, or whomever. Leaving off these marginal references, as we have done, has made it necessary at times to present such a passage in this shape: " As one [Tully] saith," or again to replace the pronoun boldly with the name: " As Cardan saith "; yet there are times when it has seemed so unimportant to any modern reader who it is that saith it, that the passage has been left to stand thus: " As one saith," not telling whether 'tis Joh. Struthius or Lod. Mercatus to whom Burton is here indebted. But Burton has paid his debts to these, the illustrious of his day, long since; some of them have been saved from dusty oblivion only by his borrowings from them; and it is the marvellous borrower with whom we are chiefly concerned, leaving the lenders to shift as best they can in the Index — which is also a biographical and bibliographical dictionary, designed to illuminate the text in lieu of notes.

The spelling, it has been said, has been sometimes changed, for the sake of intelligibility; yet it has not lost its pleasantly archaic savour, and, but for an explanatory note, the modern reader might peruse many opinions of Hierome and Austin before recognizing them as St. Jerome and St. Augustine. From the Latinized form it may not easily be guessed that Nevisanus the Lawyer was called Nevizanni in his own country, though it may be more readily apparent that the Mat. Riccius, from whose Christian Campaign in China Burton learned so many fascinating things about the " Chinenses " was none other than the Jesuit missionary, Matteo Ricci. Such information will be found in the Index, in which biographical data are briefly given concerning some five hundred or more of the obscurer or less recognizable of his authorities, chiefly medical. Further than that, even if our scholarship were equal to the task of illuminating all, including the most obscure, of Burton's multitudinous sources, more extensive notes would mar what we have most in mind, an Anatomy that may be read easily for its own sake. It has been our aim to produce a Burton that, in despite of any feats of future Burtonian scholarship, will still remain the edition preferred for popular and pleasurable reading.

Burton's large, genial, tolerant mind had its prejudices and its squeamishnesses. His chief prejudice was that against " Papists," his chief squeamishness was in regard to certain of the sexual aspects of Melancholia ; and sometimes these traits are rather in conflict, for he does dearly love to relate scandal against the " Papists." Concerning all the pleasant, or odd and amusing, or impressively terrible, of " erotick " matters, he has a robust curiosity, which puts his discussion of the symptoms of " Heroical Love " among the most delightful things written on that subject in our language. But there were matters in connection with his theme which he found distasteful, and could not bring himself to deal with in English ; indeed, to one such passage he appends the note, " Good Master Schoolmaster, do not English this " — an injunction which we have broken with the less compunction inasmuch as the matters with which it deals are not nowadays so frightful. It is such traits that remind us that we are after all dealing with a " melancholy " bachelor whose acquaintance with the other sex was gained chiefly from his books. Nevertheless, bearing in mind our Author's feelings about these matters, we have been studious not to overemphasize such expressions as he himself disliked to see written in plain English.

The reader may, then, rest assured that he is here getting all of Burton's text, as unencumbered as possible by notes and references. For the liberties which we have wittingly or unwittingly taken, may his shade forgive us!

　　　　　　　　　　　　　　　　　　　　　F. D. & P. J.-S.

INTRODUCTION

I

N DECEMBER FIFTH, three hundred and more years ago, in his study at Christ Church, Oxford, a curious, middle-aged scholar wrote the last lines of one of the most entertaining and amazing books in the world. When one considers the rather forbidding title — Anatomy of Melancholy — its immediate and lasting popularity is not among the least astonishing facts of its singular history. Five editions appeared before Robert Burton's death, and it had gone into nine when Dr. Johnson's famous dictum quickened it into new life.

If we are to believe Burton, his quaint masterpiece would have never been put into " the vulgar tongue " had it not been that " mercenary Stationers " were beginning to frown upon the use of the more elegant Latin. Had the author been permitted to have his way, the book-lovers of our own non-classical age might well have been deprived of many hours of quiet satisfaction; even Samuel Johnson might have lingered in bed to enjoy his morning sleep, and his great dictionary have lacked its caustic reference to the uses of oats; Tristram Shandy might have lacked some of its wit and learning; Charles Lamb would have lost an essay, Milton his Il Penseroso, and Keats his Lamia. Fortunate vulgarity of those mercenary Stationers! And 'twas a happy heresy that prompted the stationers of 1811 to issue the handy volumes which drew from Lamb the protest: " What need was there of unearthing the bones of that fantastic old great man, to expose them in a winding-sheet of newest fashion to modern censure? " For that edition, says Mr. Middleton Murry, is the one which introduced Keats to Burton.

The present editors, while respecting Lamb's opinion concerning the desirability of treasuring a stout calf folio of an early issue, do not share his notion of the limited appeal of this work. For the Anatomy is a sort of literary cosmos, an omnium gatherum; a compendium of everything that caught the fancy of a fine and lusty scholar who lived in an unspecialized age. Poetry, medicine, psychology, philosophy, old wives' tales, philology, wars, antiquarian lore, theology, morals, history, cli⸗

matology, food, travel, love, hate, ambition, pride, astrology, art, politics, and a scheme for the establishment of Utopia — all these and more,
are poured forth, helter-skelter, by this 17th century mathematician,
vicar, rector, and reckoner of nativities, in a style abounding in quaint
conceits, sly Rabelaisian humour, and not without a certain vein of un-
malicious satire.

Prevented by circumstance from taking that place in the world of
affairs for which his extraordinary talents and training fitted him,
Burton turned to books, and was without doubt one of the greatest
readers of his time. Dipping into the Anatomy we find that its author
was conversant with Seneca, Horace, Plato, Aristotle, Apuleius, Ariosto,
Aretino, Erasmus, Rabelais, Montaigne, Cardan, Scaliger, Bodine,
Jason Pratensis, Delrio, Cornelius Agrippa, Marlowe, Chaucer, Lydgate,
and Galen; that he was familiar with nearly all the medical, astrological, and magical books then extant, and that he was well enough acquainted with Ovid, Juvenal, Martial, Lucian and a host of others to
venture innumerable quotations from unaided memory. That he frequently misquotes is very true, but it is none the less a marvel that in
so vast a work, filled with thousands of excerpts from classical and
post-classical writers, the man was able, so neatly, to recall the perti-
nent and apposite with such approximate accuracy. As an artist in
quotation, Samuel Johnson alone in all the range of English letters can
approach him.

One of the happy things about the Anatomy is the fact that while its
formidable Synopses promise a most minute and logical analysis of
mental pathology, the text that follows is enlivened by unexpectedly
romantic digressions into every strange field that chanced to catch the
writer's fancy: while the book proposes to anatomize Melancholy, it
really celebrates all the wonders of the earth and all the curious moods
of mankind. Not even Nathaniel Wanley's " Wonders " (1678), is more
delightfully wayward.

Nevertheless, to speak fairly, there is a continual recurrence to the
theme of melancholy, its causes and its cures; and, since the personality
of Burton must ever charm the reader far more than his ostensible
theme, it is but natural to ask why so genial a man, so widely read a
scholar, happily situated in the very heart of such an idyllic spot as
Oxford, the possessor of two livings and a kindly patron, should be preoccupied with the disaffections of the human spirit, and devote the
better part of his life to the making of a vast anthology of depression.

One may get a hint of the answer by musing upon such meagre biographical odds and ends as have come down to us, and by noting certain peculiarly emphasised passages in his book.

Robert Burton was born February 8th, 1576–7, at Lindley, Leicester‑ shire, the son of Ralph Burton, Esq., and his wife Dorothy — who seems to have been a kindly soul, much given to ministrations among the sick. His preparatory schooling was done at Sutton Coldfield, Warwickshire, and at Nuneaton Grammar School. In 1593 he entered Brasenose Col‑ lege, Oxford. In 1599 he was elected to Christ Church, from which, in 1614, he received the degree of B.D. Two years later he was made vicar of St. Thomas in Oxford, and in 1630 his patron, Lord Berkeley, pre‑ sented him with the living of Seagrave. From the year 1599 to the day of his death, January 25, 1640, he lived at Christ Church College, read‑ ing mathematics, divinity, astrology, magic, medicine and the classics. A man, if one may believe the testimony of his colleagues, of charm, wit and vivacity, who was suited to occupy a place of power among states‑ men and makers of history. And the only outlets for his creative energy, afforded by his time, means and position, he found in composing an unpublished comedy, Philosophaster, written in 1606–15, and by com‑ piling the Anatomy of Melancholy. He is said to have amused himself during this period — in imitation of Democritus, whose name he ap‑ propriated — by hearkening (enviously, perhaps?) to the profanities of near-by bargemen.

It would appear that, hedged within his cloister, his heart yearned after the romance of adventure, and a life of action. We may, indeed, have reason to rejoice that the author of the Anatomy was thwarted to so noble a purpose, — for the liberated man would not then have done this chronicle of his discontent; but that which has contributed to the pleasure of generations of readers was without a doubt the child of his own fantastic dreams.

Evidences of his ungratified wanderlust are to be found on many of his best pages: " Methinks it would well please any man to look upon a Geographical Map, because of the unbelievable variety and delight‑ someness of the subject, & would stimulate him to further steps . . ." (Part. 2, Sect. 2, Memb. 3) ; or the entire chapter (Memb. 3), " Air rectified," beginning: " As a long-winged hawk, when he is first whistled off the fist, mounts aloft, and for his pleasure fetcheth many a circuit in the Air, still soaring higher and higher, till he come to his full pitch, and in the end, when the game is sprung, comes down amain, and stoops upon a sudden: so will I, having now come at last into these ample fields of Air, wherein I may freely expatiate and exercise myself for

my recreation, a while rove, wander round about the world, mount aloft
to those etherial orbs and celestial spheres. . . . In which progress I
will first see whether that relation of the Friar of Oxford be true, concerning those Northern parts under the Pole, (if I meet on the way with
the Wandering Jew, Elias Artifex, or Lucian's Icaromenippus, they
shall be my guides) . . . Whether Hudson's discovery be true of a
new found Ocean. . . . I would see those inner parts of America,
whether there be any such great City of Manoa or Eldorado in that
golden Empire. . . . I would examine the true seat of that terrestrial
Paradise, and where Ophir was, whence Solomon did fetch his gold."

Again (Memb. 4) after an expression of his love of husbandry, the
Oxford recluse jots down this plaintive note : " No man ever took more
delight in Springs, Woods, Groves, Gardens, Walks, Fishponds, &c. But

> *Thus Tantalus catches at the waves*
> *That fly his parched lips.* (HORACE)

And so do I: I may long; I may not have."

Burton's more positive discontent with the immediate circumstances
of his life is very forcibly expressed in the section on " Study " (Part. 1,
Sect. 1, Memb. 3, Subs. 15) : " University men, like so many hide-
bound calves in a pasture, tarry out our time, wither away as a flower
ungathered in a garden, & are never used: or, as too many candles, illuminate ourselves alone, obscuring one another's light, & are not discerned here at all . . . if after long expectation, much expense, travail,
earnest suit of ourselves and friends, we obtain a small Benefice at last,
our misery begins afresh . . . we change a quiet life for an ocean of
troubles, we come to a ruinous house . . . else we are insulted over and
trampled on . . . fleeced by those greedy Harpies to get more fees
. . . confined to a country village . . . and daily converse with a
company of idiots and clowns."

The Anatomy, then, was, in part, a product of the man's rebellion
against his limitations. The same might be said of many books. The
quiet scholar dreams of what he might have done as soldier, statesman,
explorer; of what a devil of a fellow he might have been: the active
man, in his later years, sets it down that if he had been left the leisure
he might have made a stir in the world of letters. 'Tis an ordinary complaint, but none the less especially notable in the case of Robert Burton.

Perhaps our Author's amusing preoccupation with love-melancholy
is but another of his mutinies. Certainly he has addressed to this theme
more study than might be deemed strictly necessary; and the Partition

that contains his somewhat voluminous observations is written with a lightness and verve which do not comport with an abstract detachment. Gusto is there, and if there be likewise some malice against women, and some fear of them, the pages are relieved by just the right seasoning of romanticism and gallantry. The apology itself gives a clue to the vigorous instincts that stirred the pulses of the scholar. He approaches his text with hesitating self-consciousness, and in the attempt to justify his honest frankness through high precedent his protestations grow loud. " Condemn me not, good Reader . . . " " I need not blush and hide mine eyes . . . " etc. He confesses that he is but a novice here, and anticipates those who might question his right to knowledge concerning these matters; but once he is done with anxious excuses his pen seems to leap to its joyful task, and more than three hundred pages of wit, jocundity, satire, and mellow wisdom are poured out for the delectation of mankind.

The Anatomy is one of the most comfortable books that ever graced a library, as entrancing as Rabelais, or its own step-child, Tristram Shandy; the " bed book " par excellence; the true companion of every honest pipe and homely pewter mug; a source of incomparable literary pleasure, as he who reads will find.   P. J.-S.

II

Translated into modern terminology, Burton's title, The Anatomy of Melancholy, would read, An Analysis of Morbid Psychology. Burton was, indeed, a scholarly and humanistic precursor of Freud. The range of his interest, so far as the facts of human behaviour are concerned, was identical with that of our great modern analyst of the psyche. But early 17th-century medicine, at the time Burton wrote (before Harvey had discovered the circulation of the blood), was humbly relying upon the authority of the great Greek and Arabian physicians, Galen, Hippocrates, Avicenna, etc.; there was no new scientific knowledge to serve as the basis of any large and illuminating generalizations upon the subject of morbid psychology. In its scientific aspect, therefore, Burton's work is merely a quaint curiosity. He patiently rehearsed all the remedies known to the times, from taking hellebore to boring a hole in the skull to let out the " fuliginous vapours," adding such philosophic consolations as he could by way of giving full measure. But his interest in the subject was actually not so scientific as artistic.

Doubtless he had a temperamental attraction to this theme, for he was an eccentric bachelor, of " melancholy " disposition, a bookworm, a recluse, who found consolation for himself in the study of people as ill at ease with life as himself. At all events, he was profoundly fascinated by the spectacle of human queernesses of all sorts, and a vast reading enriched his mind with data from Latin and English poetry, from history, legend, travelers' tales and medical lore. All this is spread before us in his three Partitions, the first two dealing respectively with the causes and the cures of Melancholy; but it is in his Third Partition, " Love-Melancholy," that his interest is fully released from its pseudo-scientific trammels.

Here, drawn from history, poetry and legend, is a pageant of all the mad lovers of the world. Erotic psychology is set forth in its wealth of familiar symptoms — leanness, waking, sighing, fear, sorrow, suspicion, wantonness, strange actions, gestures, looks, speeches, locking up, outrages, severe laws, prodigious trials, despair, madness, frenzy, murder, suicide — and illustrated with a thousand anecdotes.

" Give me but a little leave," says our author, " and I will set before your eyes in brief a stupend, vast, infinite Ocean of incredible madness and folly: a Sea full of shelves and rocks, sands, gulfs, Euripuses, and contrary tides, full of fearful monsters, uncouth shapes, roaring waves, tempests, and Siren calms, Halcyonian Seas, unspeakable misery, such Comedies and Tragedies, such absurd and ridiculous, feral and lamentable fits, that I know not whether they are more to be pitied or derided, or may be believed, but that we daily see the same still practiced in our days, fresh examples, new news, fresh objects of misery and madness in this kind, that are still represented to us, abroad, at home, in the midst of us, in our bosoms."

These words, from the Section on " Religious Melancholy," might serve as a motto for his whole work. It is a promise that he has nobly kept; and this panorama of " incredible madness and folly," with its revelations of the tragic and ridiculous depths of our human nature, remains permanently impressive.

Burton grew up during the age of Shakespeare. It was an age that was frankly interested in the passionately unreasonable aspects of human nature. Between that time and our own there have intervened two periods, the eighteenth century and the Victorian era, in which a great emphasis was laid upon, and perhaps an undue confidence reposed in, man's reasonableness. Today, again, and not without cause, we are interested in the " unreasonable " part of man's mind. And Burton, who is not the least of the great Elizabethans, can speak to us across the centuries.   F. D.

CONTENTS OF VOLUME I

THE FIRST PARTITION

THE SECOND PARTITION

The Cure of Melancholy

THE THIRD PARTITION

Love-Melancholy

ACKNOWLEDGEMENTS

The editors are particularly indebted to Professor Edward Bensly, not only for his valuable commentaries on the text of Burton in " Notes and Queries," but also for research at the British Museum generously undertaken in response to our inquiries ; to Mr. Gordon Ray Young of Los Angeles for the use of his library and for his help in philological problems ; to Prof. Adolph Elwyn of the Medical School of Columbia University for help in identifying early medical writers ; to the officials of the Huntington Library in Los Angeles for the privilege of reproducing LeBlon's Frontispiece (from the folio of 1628, where it appeared for the first time) — the reproduction being from the famous Hoe copy ; besides the many friends who have so generously assisted us with old books, maps and information in preparing this edition, and the courteous officials of the public libraries in New York and Los Angeles, and of Columbia University Library.

TO THE RIGHT HONOURABLE,

NO LESS FOR HIS OWN

VIRTUE THAN ON ACCOUNT OF

THE EXCELLENCE OF HIS BIRTH, THE

MOST ILLUSTRIOUS,

LORD GEORGE BERKELEY,

KNIGHT OF THE BATH,

BARON OF BERKELEY,

MOWBRAY, SEGRAVE,

&

MASTER OF BREUSE,

TO HIS LORDSHIP, *honoured with*

many titles,

DEMOCRITUS, Jr., HATH

PRESENTED THIS HIS ANATOMY OF MELANCHOLY,

Now revised for the sixth time.

THE ARGUMENT OF THE FRONTISPIECE

TEN distinct Squares here seen apart,
Are joined in one by Cutter's art.

I

Old *Democritus* under a tree,
Sits on a stone with book on knee;
About him hang there many features,
Of Cats, Dogs, and such like creatures,
Of which he makes Anatomy,
The seat of Black Choler to see.
Over his head appears the sky,
And Saturn, Lord of Melancholy.

II

To th' left a landscape of *Jealousy*,
Presents itself unto thine eye.
A Kingfisher, a Swan, an Hern,
Two fighting-Cocks you may discern;
Two roaring Bulls each other hie,
To assault concerning Venery.
Symbols are these; I say no more,
Conceive the rest by that's afore.

III

The next of *Solitariness*
A portraiture doth well express,
By sleeping Dog, Cat: Buck and Doe,
Hares, Conies in the desert go:
Bats, Owls the shady bowers over,
In melancholy darkness hover.
Mark well: If't be not as't should be,
Blame the bad Cutter, and not me.

IV

I' th' under Column there doth stand
Inamorato with folded hand;
Down hangs his head, terse and polite,
Some ditty sure he doth indite.
His lute and books about him lie,
As symptoms of his vanity.
If this do not enough disclose,
To paint him, take thyself by th' nose.

V

Hypochondriacus leans on his arm,
Wind in his side doth him much harm,
And troubles him full sore, God knows,
Much pain he hath and many woes.
About him pots and glasses lie,
Newly brought from's Apothecary.
This Saturn's aspects signify,
You see them portray'd in the sky.

VI

Beneath them kneeling on his knee,
A *Superstitious* man you see:
He fasts, prays, on his Idol fixt,
Tormented hope and fear betwixt:
For hell perhaps he takes more pain,
Than thou dost heaven itself to gain.
Alas poor Soul, I pity thee,
What stars incline thee so to be?

VII

But see the *Madman* rage down right
With furious looks, a ghastly sight.
Naked in chains bound doth he lie,
And roars amain he knows not why!
Observe him; for as in a glass,
Thine angry portraiture it was.
His picture keeps still in thy presence;
'Twixt him and thee, there's no difference.

VIII–IX

Borage and *Hellebore* fill two scenes,
Sovereign plants to purge the veins
Of Melancholy, and cheer the heart,
Of those black fumes which make it smart;
To clear the Brain of misty fogs,
Which dull our senses, and Soul clogs.
The best medicine that e'er God made
For this malady, if well assay'd.

X

Now last of all to fill a place,
Presented is the *Author's* face;
And in that habit which he wears,
His image to the world appears.
His mind no art can well express,
That by his writings you may guess.
It was not pride, nor yet vain glory,
(Though others do it commonly,)
Made him do this: if you must know,
The Printer would needs have it so.

Then do not frown or scoff at it,
Deride not, or detract a whit.
For surely as thou dost by him,
He will do the same again.
Then look upon't, behold and see,
As thou like'st it, so it likes thee.
And I for it will stand in view,
Thine to command, Reader, Adieu!

2

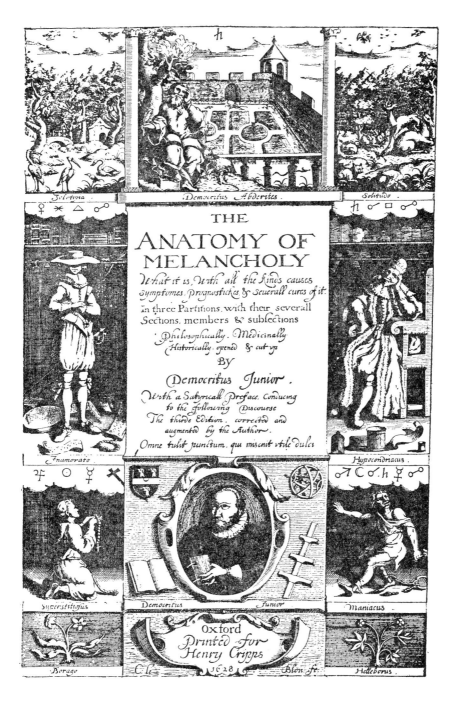

Zelotypia .   Democritus Abderites .   Solitudo .

THE
ANATOMY OF
MELANCHOLY

What it is, With all the kinds causes
symptomes, Prognostickes, & severall cures of it.
In three Partitions, with their severall
Sections, members & subsections.

Philosophically, Medicinally,
Historically, opened & cut vp.

By

Democritus Junior.

With a Satyricall Preface, Conducing
to the following Discourse.
The thirde Edition, corrected and
augmented by the Author.

Omne tulit punctum, qui miscuit vtile dulci.

Inamorato .   Hypocondriacus .

Superstitiosus .   Democritus Junior .   Maniacus .

Oxford
Printed for
Henry Cripps

Borago .   1628   Blon fe.   Helleborus .

Democritus Junior to His Book

GO FORTH, my book, into the open day;
    Happy, if made so by its garish eye.
O'er earth's wide surface take thy vagrant way,
    To represent thy master's genius try.
The Graces three, the Muses nine salute,
    Should those who love them try to con thy lore.
The country, city seek, grand thrones to boot,
    With gentle courtesy humbly bow before.
Should nobles gallant, soldiers frank and brave
    Seek thy acquaintance, hail their first advance:
From twitch of care thy pleasant vein may save,
    May laughter cause or wisdom give perchance.
Some surly Cato, Senator austere,
    Haply may wish to peep into thy pages:
Seem very nothing — tremble and revere:
    No forceful eagle the light fly engages.
They love not thee: of them then little seek,
    And wish for readers triflers like thyself.
Of haughty dame be quick to catch the beck,
    Or gorgeous countess full of pride and pelf.
They may say " pish! " and frown, and yet read on:
    Cry odd, and silly, coarse, and yet amusing.
Should dainty damsels seek thy page to con,
    Spread thy best stores: to them be ne'er refusing:
Say, Fair one, would my master on thy face
    Might gaze, for such a one he loveth dearly! *
Should known or unknown student, for a space
    Free from the schools, thy trifling jests severely
Con, then cry mercy, and thy page withhold:
    Be some few errors pardon'd though observ'd:
An humble author to implore makes bold,
    Thy kind indulgence, even undeserv'd.
Should melancholy wight or pensive lover,

    * 'Tis said in jest, pray do not take it ill.

Courtier, snug cit, or carpet knight so trim
Our blossoms cull, he'll find himself in clover,
   Gain sense from precept, laughter from our whim.
Should learnéd leech with solemn air unfold
   Thy leaves, beware, be civil, and be wise:
Thy volume many precepts sage may hold,
   His well fraught head may find no trifling prize.
Should crafty lawyer trespass on our ground,
   Caitiffs avaunt! disturbing tribe away!
Unless (white crow) an honest one be found;
   He'll better, wiser go for what we say.
Should some ripe scholar, gentle and benign,
   With candour, care, and judgment thee peruse:
Thy faults to kind oblivion he'll consign;
   Nor to thy merit will his praise refuse.
Thou may'st be searched for polish'd words and verse
   By flippant spouter, emptiest of praters:
Bid him seek elsewhere something to rehearse —
   My periods all are rough as nutmeg graters.
The popular poet, wishing thee to read,
   Reject not; let him glean thy jests and stories.
His brother I, of lowly sembling breed:
   Apollo grants to few Parnassian glories.
Menac'd by critic with sour furrowed brow,
   Momus or Zoilus or grim reviewer:
Before they've time to snap at thee, snarl thou;
   Frighten away the hateful misconstruer.
When foul-mouth'd senseless railers cry thee down,
   Reply not: fly, and show the rogues thy stern:
They are not worthy even of a frown:
   Good taste or breeding they can never learn;
Or let them clamour, turn a callous ear,
   As though in dread of some harsh donkey's bray.
If chid by censor, friendly though severe,
   To such explain and turn thee not away.
Thy vein, says he perchance, is all too free;
   Thy smutty language suits not learned pen:
Reply, Good Sir, throughout, the context see;
   Thought chastens thought; so prithee judge again.
Besides, although my master's pen may wander

Through devious paths, by which it ought not stray,
His life is pure, beyond the breath of slander :
　So pardon grant ; 'tis merely but his way.
If some rank cynick on thy garner fall,
　Brandish thy cudgel, drive him far away ;
And fools I bid thee suffer not at all. —
　To dunces, what indeed have we to say?
And yet bar none : bid all and sundry in :
　Strangers be doubly welcome, friend or foe !
For if they blame, that shall be discipline,
　To make us mend ; and if they praise bestow,
We will not be puffed up ; contented so
　Good things to set against what ill there be.
Thus would I charge thee, book, before thou go :
　So saith the Author, taking leave of thee.*

* This poem of Burton's was in Latin, and the present translation is from the edition of " Democritus Minor " with some corrections.

The Author's Abstract of Melancholy

A DIALOGUE

HEN I go musing all alone,
Thinking of divers things fore-known,
When I build Castles in the air,
Void of sorrow and void of fear,
Pleasing my self with phantasms sweet,
Methinks the time runs very fleet.
   All my joys to this are folly,
   Naught so sweet as Melancholy.
When I lie waking all alone,
Recounting what I have ill done,
My thoughts on me then tyrannise,
Fear and sorrow me surprise,
Whether I tarry still or go,
Methinks the time moves very slow.
   All my griefs to this are jolly,
   Naught so sad as Melancholy.
When to my self I act and smile,
With pleasing thoughts the time beguile,
By a brook side or wood so green,
Unheard, unsought for, or unseen,
A thousand pleasures do me bless,
And crown my soul with happiness.
   All my joys besides are folly,
   None so sweet as Melancholy.
When I lie, sit, or walk alone,
I sigh, I grieve, making great moan,
In a dark grove, or irksome den,
With discontents and Furies then,
A thousand miseries at once
Mine heavy heart and soul ensconce.
   All my griefs to this are jolly,
   None so sour as Melancholy.

Methinks I hear, methinks I see,
Sweet musick, wondrous melody,
Towns, Palaces, and Cities fine;
Here now, then there; the world is mine.
Rare beauties, gallant Ladies shine,
Whate'er is lovely or divine.
 All other joys to this are folly,
 None so sweet as Melancholy.
Methinks I hear, methinks I see
Ghosts, goblins, fiends: my phantasy
Presents a thousand ugly shapes,
Headless bears, black men, and apes,
Doleful outcries, and fearful sights,
My sad and dismal soul affrights.
 All my griefs to this are folly,
 None so damn'd as Melancholy.
Methinks I court, methinks I kiss,
Methinks I now embrace my mistress,
O blessed days, O sweet content,
In Paradise my time is spent.
Such thoughts may still my fancy move,
So may I ever be in love.
 All my joys to this are folly,
 Naught so sweet as Melancholy.
When I recount love's many frights,
My sighs and tears, my waking nights,
My jealous fits; O mine hard fate
I now repent, but 'tis too late.
No torment is so bad as love,
So bitter to my soul can prove.
 All my griefs to this are jolly,
 Naught so harsh as Melancholy.
Friends and Companions get you gone,
'Tis my desire to be alone;
Ne'er well but when my thoughts and I
Do domineer in privacy.
No Gem, no treasure like to this,
'Tis my delight, my Crown, my bliss.
 All my joys to this are folly,
 Naught so sweet as Melancholy.

'Tis my sole plague to be alone,
I am a beast, a monster grown,
I will no light nor company,
I find it now my misery.
The scene is turn'd, my joys are gone;
Fear, discontent, and sorrows come.
   All my griefs to this are jolly,
   Naught so fierce as Melancholy.
I'll not change life with any King,
I ravisht am: can the world bring
More joy than still to laugh and smile,
In pleasant toys time to beguile?
Do not, O do not, trouble me,
So sweet content I feel and see.
   All my joys to this are folly,
   None so divine as Melancholy.
I'll change my state with any wretch,
Thou canst from gaol or dunghill fetch.
My pain's past cure, another Hell,
I may not in this torment dwell,
Now desperate I hate my life,
Lend me a halter or a knife.
   All my griefs to this are jolly.
   Naught so damn'd as Melancholy.

DEMOCRITUS JUNIOR TO THE READER

ENTLE READER, I presume thou wilt be very inquisitive to know what antick or personate actor this is that so insolently intrudes upon this common theatre to the world's view, arrogating another man's name; whence he is, why he doth it, and what he hath to say. Although, as he * said, *In the first place, supposing I do not wish to answer, who shall make me?* I am a free man born, and may choose whether I will tell; who can compel me? If I be urged, I will as readily reply as that Egyptian in Plutarch, when a curious fellow would needs know what he had in his basket, *When you see the cover, why ask about the thing hidden?* It was therefore covered, because he should not know what was in it. Seek not after that which is hid; if the contents please thee, and be for thy use, suppose the Man in the Moon, or whom thou wilt to be the Author; I would not willingly be known.† Yet in some sort to give thee satisfaction, which is more than I need [do], I will shew a reason, both of this usurped name, title, and subject. And first of the name of *Democritus;* lest any man by reason of it should be deceived, expecting a pasquil, a satire, some ridiculous treatise (as I myself should have done), some prodigious tenent, or paradox of the Earth's motion, of infinite Worlds in an infinite waste, so caused by an accidental collision of Motes in the Sun, all which Democritus held, Epicurus and their Master Leucippus of old maintained, and are lately revived by Copernicus, Brunus, and some others. Besides, it hath been always an ordinary custom, as Gellius observes, for later writers and impostors to broach many absurd and insolent fictions under the name of so noble a philosopher as Democritus, to get themselves credit and by that means the more to be respected; as artificers usually do, ascribing a new statue to Praxitiles himself. 'Tis not so with me.

> *No Centaurs here, or Gorgons look to find,*
> *My subject is of man, and human kind.* (MARTIAL)

Thou thyself art the subject of my discourse.

* The philosopher Seneca, in his Satire on the Death and Pumpkinification of Claudius Cæsar.

† Burton revealed his identity, however, in an epilogue to the first edition, " The Conclusion of the Author to the Reader," which is given here in the Appendix.

Whate'er men do, vows, fears, in ire, in sport,
Joys, wand'rings, are the sum of my report. (JUVENAL)

My intent is no otherwise to use his name, than Mercurius Gallobelgicus, Mercurius Britannicus, use the name of Mercury, Democritus Christianus, &c. Although there be some other circumstances for which I have masked myself under this visard, and some peculiar respects, which I cannot so well express, until I have set down a brief character of this our Democritus, what he was, with an Epitome of his life.

Democritus, as he is described by Hippocrates and Laertius, was a little wearish old man, very melancholy by nature, averse from company in his latter days, and much given to solitariness, a famous Philosopher in his age, coeval with Socrates, wholly addicted to his studies at the last, and to a private life: writ many excellent works, a great Divine, according to the divinity of those times, an expert Physician, a Politician, an excellent Mathematician, as Diacosmus and the rest of his works do witness. He was much delighted with the studies of Husbandry, saith Columella, and often I find him cited by Constantinus and others, treating of that subject. He knew the natures, differences, of all beasts, plants, fishes, birds; and, as some say, could understand the tunes and voices of them. In a word, he was learned in everything, a general scholar, a great student; and to the intent [that] he might better contemplate, I find it related by some, that he put out his eyes and was in his old age voluntarily blind, yet saw more than all Greece besides, and writ of every subject: *Nothing there is in all the contriving of nature, of which he hath not written.* A man of an excellent wit, profound conceit; and to attain knowledge the better in his younger years, he travelled to Egypt and Athens, to confer with learned men, admired of some, despised of others. After a wandering life, he settled at Abdera, a town in Thrace, and was sent for thither to be their Lawmaker, Recorder, or Town-clerk, as some will; or as others, he was there bred and born. Howsoever it was, there he lived at last in a garden in the suburbs, wholly betaking himself to his studies and a private life, saving that sometimes he would walk down to the haven, and laugh heartily at such variety of ridiculous objects, which there he saw. Such a one was Democritus.

But in the mean time, how doth this concern me, or upon what reference do I usurp his habit? I confess indeed that to compare myself unto him for ought I have yet said, were both impudency and arrogancy: I do not presume to make any parallel; he outranks me by countless numbers; I am inconsiderable, nothing at all; I do not aspire to great-

ness, nor hope for it. Yet thus much I will say of myself, & that I hope
without all suspicion of pride, or self-conceit, I have lived a silent,
sedentary, solitary, private life, with myself and the Muses in the University as long almost as Xenocrates in Athens, nearly to old age, to
learn wisdom as he did, penned up most part in my study. For I have
been brought up a student in the most flourishing College of Europe,
the most august College,* and can brag with Jovius, almost, *in that
splendor of Vaticanish retirement, confined to the company of the
distinguished, I have spent thirty-seven full and fortunate years;* for
thirty years I have continued (having the use of as good Libraries † as
ever he had) a scholar, and would be therefore loth, either by living as
a drone, to be an unprofitable or unworthy Member of so learned and
noble a society, or to write that which should be any way dishonorable
to such a royal and ample foundation. Something I have done, though
by my profession a Divine, yet *being carried away by a giddy disposition,* as he [Scaliger] said, out of a running wit, an unconstant, un-
settled mind, I had a great desire (not able to attain to superficial skill
in any) to have some smattering in all, to be Somebody in everything,
Nobody in anything, which Plato commends, out of him Lipsius approves and furthers, *as fit to be imprinted in all curious wits, not to be a
slave of one science, or dwell altogether in one subject, as most do, but to
rove abroad,* the servant of a hundred arts, *to have an oar in every man's
boat, to taste of every dish, and sip of every cup,* which saith Montaigne,
was well performed by Aristotle, and his learned countryman Adrian
Turnebus. This roving humor (though not with like success) I have
ever had, & like a ranging spaniel, that barks at every bird he sees,
leaving his game, I have followed all, saving that which I should, and
may justly complain, and truly (for who is everywhere is nowhere).
which Gesner did in modesty, that I have read many books, but to
little purpose, for want of good method; I have confusedly tumbled
over divers authors in our Libraries, with small profit, for want of art,
order, memory, judgement. I never travelled but in Map or Card, in
which my unconfined thoughts have freely expatiated, as having ever
been especially delighted with the study of Cosmography. Saturn was
the Lord of my geniture, culminating, &c., and Mars principal significa-
tor of manners, in partile conjunction with mine Ascendant; both fortunate in their houses, &c. I am not poor, I am not rich, nothing's here

* Christ Church, in Oxford. — Burton's note.
† Keeper of our college library, lately revived by Otho Nicholson, Esquire. —
Burton's note.

but nothing's lacking, I have little, I want nothing: all my treasure is
in Minerva's tower. Greater preferment, as I could never get, so am
I not in debt for it; I have a competency (praise God) from my noble
and munificent Patrons, though I live still a Collegiate student, as
Democritus in his garden, and lead a monastick life, a theatre to myself,
sequestered from those tumults & troubles of the world, as he [Heinsius]
said, and in some high place above you all, like the wise Stoick, seeing
all ages, past and present, as at one glance: I hear & see what is done
abroad, how others run, ride, turmoil, & macerate themselves in court
and country; far from those wrangling lawsuits, courts of vanity, marts
of ambition, I am wont to laugh with myself: I laugh at all, [each]
only secure lest my suit go amiss, my ships perish, corn and cattle miscarry, trade decay. *I have no wife nor children, good or bad, to provide
for.* A mere spectator of other men's fortunes and adventures, and how
they act their parts, which methinks are diversely presented unto me, as
from a common theatre or scene. I hear new news every day, and those
ordinary rumours of war, plagues, fires, inundations, thefts, murders,
massacres, meteors, comets, spectrums, prodigies, apparitions, of towns
taken, cities besieged in France, Germany, Turkey, Persia, Poland, &c.,
daily musters and preparations, and such like, which these tempestuous
times afford, battles fought, so many men slain, monomachies, shipwrecks, piracies, and sea-fights, peace, leagues, stratagems, and fresh
alarms. A vast confusion of vows, wishes, actions, edicts, petitions, law-
suits, pleas, laws, proclamations, complaints, grievances, are daily
brought to our ears. New books every day, pamphlets, currantoes,
stories, whole catalogues of volumes of all sorts, new paradoxes, opinions, schisms, heresies, controversies in philosophy, religion, &c. Now
come tidings of weddings, maskings, mummeries, entertainments, jubilees, embassies, tilts and tournaments, trophies, triumphs, revels, sports,
plays: then again, as in a new shifted scene, treasons, cheating tricks,
robberies, enormous villanies in all kinds, funerals, burials, deaths of
Princes, new discoveries, expeditions; now comical then tragical matters. To-day we hear of new Lords and officers created, to-morrow of
some great men deposed, and then again of fresh honours conferred; one
is let loose, another imprisoned; one purchaseth, another breaketh; he
thrives, his neighbour turns bankrupt; now plenty, then again dearth
and famine; one runs, another rides, wrangles, laughs, weeps &c. Thus
I daily hear, and such like, both private and publick news. Amidst the
gallantry and misery of the world; jollity, pride, perplexities and cares,
simplicity and villany; subtlety, knavery, candour and integrity, mu-

tually mixed and offering themselves, I rub on in a strictly private life; as I have still lived, so I now continue, as I was from the first, left to a solitary life, and mine own domestick discontents: saving that sometimes, not to tell a lie, as Diogenes went into the city, and Democritus to the haven, to see fashions, I did for my recreation now and then walk abroad, look into the world, and could not choose but make some little observation, not so wise an observer as a plain rehearser, not as they did to scoff or laugh at all, but with a mixed passion.

Oft have your passions rous'd my rage or mirth. (HORACE)

I did sometimes laugh and scoff with Lucian, and satirically tax with Menippus, lament with Heraclitus, sometimes again I was bitterly mirthful, and then again burning with rage; I was much moved to see that abuse which I could not amend. In which passion howsoever I may sympathise with him or them, 'tis for no such respect I shroud myself under his name, but either in an unknown habit, to assume a little more liberty and freedom of speech, or if you will needs know, for that reason and only respect, which Hippocrates relates at large in his Epistle to Damagetus, wherein he doth express, how coming to visit him one day, he found Democritus in his garden at Abdera, in the suburbs, under a shady bower, with a book on his knees, busy at his study, sometimes writing, sometimes walking. The subject of his book was melancholy and madness, about him lay the carcasses of many several beasts newly by him cut up and anatomized, not that he did contemn God's creatures, as he told Hippocrates, but to find out the seat of this black bile, or melancholy, whence it proceeds, and how it was engendered in men's bodies, to the intent he might better cure it in himself, and by his writings & observations teach others how to prevent and avoid it. Which good intent of his Hippocrates highly commended: Democritus Junior is therefore bold to imitate, and because he left it unperfect, and it is now lost, as a substitute for Democritus, to revive again, prosecute and finish, in this treatise.

You have had a reason of the name. If the title and inscription offend your gravity, were it a sufficient justification to accuse others, I could produce many sober treatises, even sermons themselves, which in their fronts carry more phantastical names. Howsoever it is a kind of policy in these days to prefix a phantastical title to a book which is to be sold. For as Larks come down to a day-net, many vain readers will tarry and stand gazing, like silly passengers, at an antick picture in a painter's shop, that will not look at a judicious piece. And indeed, as Scaliger observes, *nothing more invites a reader than an argument unlooked for,* *unthought of, and sells better then a scurrile pamphlet,* especially when its novelty whets the palate. Many men, saith Aulus Gellius, *are very conceited in their inscriptions,* and able (as Pliny quotes out of Seneca) to make him loiter by the way *that went in haste to fetch a mid-wife for his daughter, now ready to lie down.* For my part I have honourable precedents for this which I have done: I will cite one for all, Anthony Zara, his Anatomy of Wit, in four sections, members, subsections, &c., to be read in our Libraries.*

If any man except against the matter or manner of treating of this my subject, & will demand a reason of it, I can allege more than one. I writ of melancholy, by being busy to avoid melancholy. There is no greater cause of melancholy than idleness, no better cure than business, as Rhasis holds: and howbeit to be busied in toys is to small purpose, yet hear that divine Seneca: Better do to no end than nothing. I writ therefore, and busied myself in this playing labour that I might avoid the torpor of laziness, with Vectius in Macrobius, and turn my leisure to purpose.

> *At once to profit and to please*
> *And teach the reader at his ease.* (HORACE)

To this end I writ, like them, saith Lucian, that recite to trees, & declaim to pillars, for want of auditors: as Paulus Ægineta ingeniously confesseth, not that any thing was unknown or omitted, but to exercise myself, which course if some took, I think it would be good for their bodies, and much better for their souls; or peradventure as others do, for fame, to show myself: (Your knowledge is nothing unless it be proclaimed to others). I might be of Thucydides' opinion: To know a thing and not express it, is all one as if he knew it not. When I first took this task in hand, & as he saith, undertook the work, my genius impelling me, this I aimed at: to ease my mind by writing, for I had a heavy heart and an ugly head, a kind of imposthume in my head, which I was very desirous to be unladen of, & could imagine no fitter evacuation than this. Besides I might not well refrain, for one must needs scratch where it itches. I was not a little offended with this malady, shall I say my Mistress Melancholy, my Egeria, or my Evil Genius? & for that cause, as he that is stung with a scorpion, I would expel one nail with another, comfort one sorrow with another, idleness with idleness, the antidote from the Viper, make an Antidote out of that which was the prime cause of my disease. Or as he did, of whom Felix Plater

---

* In a footnote Burton cites the following " precedents ": Anatomy of Popery, Anatomy of Immortality, Angelus Salas, Anatomy of Antimony. For Zara, see Index.

speaks, that thought he had some of Aristophanes' frogs in his belly, still crying *Brececcex, coax, coax, oop, oop,* and for that cause studied physick seven years, and travelled over most part of Europe to ease himself. To do myself good I turned over such physicians as our Libraries would afford, or my private friends impart, and have taken this pains. And why not? Cardan professeth he writ his book on Consolation after his son's death, to comfort himself; so did Tully write of the same subject with like intent after his daughter's departure, if it be his at least, or some impostor's put out in his name, which Lipsius probably suspects. Concerning myself, I can peradventure affirm with Marius in Sallust: That which others hear or read of, I felt & practised myself, they get their knowledge by books, I mine by melancholizing. Believe Robert, who speaketh from experience. Something I can speak out of experience, painful experience hath taught me, and with her in the Poet:

Not unschool'd in woe, I have learned to succour the woeful.

(VIRGIL)

I would help others out of a fellow-feeling, and as that virtuous Lady did of old, being a Leper herself, bestow all her portion to build an Hospital for Lepers, I will spend my time and knowledge, which are my greatest fortunes, for the common good of all.

Yea but you will infer that this is doing what is already done, an unnecessary work, serving a warmed over dish; the same again & again, in other words. To what purpose? Nothing is omitted that may well be said, so thought Lucian in the like theme. How many excellent Physicians have written just Volumes and elaborate Tracts of this subject! no news here, that which I have is stolen from others. And my page says to me, thou'rt a thief! If that severe doom of Synesius be true, *it is a greater offense to steal dead men's labours than their clothes,* what shall become of most Writers? I hold up my hand at the bar amongst others, and am guilty of felony in this kind, I confess, I am content to be pressed with the rest. 'Tis most true that many are possessed by an incurable itch to write, and there is no end of writing of books, as the Wise-man found of old, in this scribbling age especially, wherein the number of books is without number (as a worthy man saith), presses be oppressed, & out of an itching humor, that every man hath to show himself, desirous of fame and honor (we all write, learned and unlearned) he will write no matter what, & scrape together it boots not whence. Bewitched with this desire of fame, even in the thick of illness, to the disparagement of their health, & scarce able to hold a pen, they must say something, & get themselves a name, saith Scaliger, though it be to the downfall and ruin of many others. To be counted writers, that they may hear applause, to be thought and held Polymaths & Polyhistors, toiling for a frothy name among the vulgar masses, to get a paper kingdom; from no hope of gain, but great hope of fame, in this precipitate ambitious age, and they that are scarce auditors, must be masters & teachers ('tis Scaliger's censure), before they be capable & fit hearers. They will rush into all learning, gowned, armed, divine, human authors, rake over all Indexes & Pamphlets for notes, as our merchants do strange havens for traffick, write great Tomes, when as they are not thereby better scholars, but greater praters. They commonly pretend publick good, but, as Gesner observes, 'tis pride and vanity that eggs them on, no news or ought worthy of note, but the same in other terms. They turn authors lest peradventure the printers should have a holiday; or they must write something to prove they have existed. As Apothecaries we make new mixtures every day, pour out of one vessel into another; and as those old Romans robbed all the cities of the world, to set out their bad-sited Rome, we skim off the cream of other men's wits, pick the choice flowers of their tilled gardens to set out our own sterile plots. They lard their lean books (so Jovius inveighs) with the fat of others' works, the blundering thieves. A fault that every Writer finds, as I do now, and yet faulty themselves. *Men of three letters,** all thieves; they pilfer out of old Writers to stuff up their new Comments, scrape Ennius' dung-hills, and out of Democritus' pit, as I have done. By which means it comes to pass, that not only libraries & shops are full of our putrid papers, but every close-stool and jakes are well supplied with privy-poetry; they serve to put under pies, to lap spice in, and keep roast-meat from burning. With us in France, saith Scaliger, every man hath liberty to write, but few ability. Heretofore learning was graced by judicious scholars, but now noble sciences are vilified by base and illiterate scribblers, that either write for vain-glory, need, to get money, or as Parasites to flatter and collogue with some great men, they put out trifles, rubbish and trash. Amongst so many thousand Authors you shall scarce find one, by reading of whom you shall be any whit better, but rather much worse; by which he is rather infected than any way perfected.

> *What hath he learn'd who cons such themes?*
> *What doth he know but trifling dreams?*   (PALINGENIUS)

---

* *Fur,* a word of three letters, meaning "thief." A pun on "men of letters," from Plautus.

So that oftentimes it falls out (which Callimachus taxed of old) a great Book is a great mischief. Cardan finds fault with Frenchmen & Germans, for their scribbling to no purpose; he doth not bar them to write, so that it be some new invention of their own; but we weave the same web still, twist the same rope again and again, or if it be a new invention, 'tis but some bauble or toy which idle fellows write, for as idle fellows to read, and who so cannot invent? He must have a barren wit, that in this scribbling age can forge nothing. Princes show their armies, rich men vaunt their buildings, soldiers their man-hood, and scholars vent their toys, they must read, they must hear whether they will or no.

What once is said and writ, all men must know,
Old wives and children as they come and go. (HORACE)

What a company of Poets hath this year brought out! as Pliny complains to Sossius Senecio, *this April every day some or other have recited!* What a catalogue of new books all this year, all this age (I say) have our Frank-furt Marts, our domestick Marts, brought out! Twice a year we stretch our wits out, and set them to sale; after great toil we attain nothing. So that, which Gesner much desires, if a speedy reformation be not had, by some Princes' Edicts and grave Supervisors, to restrain this liberty, it will run on to infinity. What a glut of books! who can read them? As already, we shall have a vast Chaos and confusion of Books, we are oppressed with them, our eyes ache with reading, our fingers with turning. For my part I am one of the number, — one of the many —, I do not deny it; I have only this of Macrobius to say for myself, *'tis all mine and none mine.* As a good house-wife out of divers fleeces weaves one piece of cloth, a bee gathers wax and honey out of many flowers, and makes a new bundle of all,

As bees in flowery glades sip every plant, (LUCRETIUS)

I have laboriously collected this Cento * out of divers Writers, and that without injury, I have wronged no authors, but given every man his own; which Hierome so much commends in Nepotian, he stole not whole verses, pages, tracts, as some do nowadays, concealing their Authors' names, but still said, this was Cyprian's, that Lactantius', that Hilarius', so said Minucius Felix, so Victorinus, thus far Arnobius: I cite and quote mine Authors (which howsoever some illiterate scribblers account pedantical, as a cloak of ignorance, and opposite to their affected fine style, I must and will use) ; I have borrowed, not stolen; and what Varro speaks of bees, *they are by no means malicious, because they injure nothing they take honey from,* I can say of myself, whom have I in-

* Patch-work

jured? The matter is theirs most part, and yet mine, whence it is taken appears (which Seneca approves), yet it appears as something different from what 'tis taken from; which nature doth with the aliment of our bodies, incorporate, digest, assimulate, I do dispose of what I take. I make them pay tribute, to set out this my Macaronicon,* the method only is mine own, I must usurp that of Wecker: We can say nothing but what hath been said, the composition and method is ours only, & shows a Scholar. Oribasius, Aetius, Avicenna, have all out of Galen, but to their own method; different styles, but the same reliability. Our Poets steal from Homer; he spews, saith Ælian, they lick it up. Divines use Austin's words verbatim still, and our Story-dressers do as much, he that comes last is commonly best,

Till a later age and a happier lot
Produce a tale with a grander plot.

Though there were many Giants of old in Physick and Philosophy, yet I say with Didacus Stella: A dwarf standing on the shoulders of a Giant may see farther than a Giant himself; I may likely add, alter, and see farther than my predecessors. And it is no greater prejudice for me to indite after others, than for Ælianus Montaltus, that famous Physician, to write about ailments of the head after Jason Pratensis, Heurnius, Hildesheim, &c., many horses to run in a race, one Logician, one Rhetorician, after another. Oppose then what thou wilt, —

Although at me you bark forever,
Your wanton snarling ceasing never, (MARTIAL)

I solve it thus. And for those other faults of barbarism, Dorick dialect, extemporanean style, tautologies, apish imitation, a rhapsody of rags gathered together from several dung-hills, excrements of authors, toys and fopperies confusedly tumbled out, without art, invention, judgement, wit, learning, harsh, raw, rude, phantastical, absurd, insolent, indiscreet, ill-composed, indigested, vain, scurrile, idle, dull and dry, I confess all ('tis partly affected), thou canst not think worse of me then I do of myself. 'Tis not worth the reading, I yield it, I desire thee not to lose time in perusing so vain a subject, I should be peradventure loth myself to read him or thee so writing, 'tis not worth while. All I say, is this, that I have precedents for it, which Isocrates calls a shelter for sinners; others as absurd, vain, idle, illiterate, &c. Others have done as much, it may be more, and perhaps thou thyself; we have all our faults, we know it, and this liberty we claim for ourselves. Thou censurest me, so have I done others, and may do thee; 'tis the law of

* Medley.

retaliation, one thing for another. Go now, censure, criticize, scoff and
rail.

Wert thou all scoffs and flouts, a very Momus:
Than we ourselves, thou canst not say worse of us. (MARTIAL)

Thus, as when women scold, have I cried whore first, and in some men's
censures I am afraid I have overshot myself; the vain praise themselves,
the foolish blame; as I do not arrogate, I will not derogate. I am none
of the best, I am none of the meanest of you. As I am an inch, or so many
feet, or so many parasangs, after him or him, I may be peradventure an
ace before thee. Be it therefore as it is, well or ill, I have assayed, put
myself upon the stage, I must abide the censure, I may not escape it.
It is most true, our style bewrays us, and as hunters find their game
by the trace, so is a man's *genius* descried by his works; we judge much
better of a man's character by his words than by his features; 'twas old
Cato's rule. I have laid myself open (I know it) in this treatise, turned
mine inside outward, I shall be censured, I doubt not, for to say truth
with Erasmus, there's naught so peevish as men's judgments, yet this
is some comfort, our censures are as various as our palates.

They seem to me to differ like three guests
Whose palates each require different food. (HORACE)

Our writings are as so many dishes, our readers guests, our books like
beauty, that which one admires, another rejects; so are we approved as
men's fancies are inclined.

The reader's fancy makes the fate of books. (TERENTIANUS MAURUS)
That which is most pleasing to one is as marjoram to a sow, — most
harsh to another. So many men, so many minds: that which thou con-
demnest he commends.

What you wish, that the other two detest. (HORACE)
He respects matter, thou art wholly for words, he loves a loose and free
style, thou art all for neat composition, strong lines, hyperboles, alle-
gories; he desires a fine frontispiece, enticing pictures, such as Hierony.
mus Natali the Jesuit hath cut to the Dominicals, to draw on the
reader's attention, which thou rejectest; that which one admires, another explodes as most absurd & ridiculous. If it be not pointblank to
his humour, his method, his conceit, if ought be omitted or added, which
he likes, or dislikes, thou art a sorry fellow of scant reading, an idiot,
an ass, not worth reading, or a plagiarist, a trifler, a trivant, thou art an
idle fellow; or else 'tis a thing of mere industry, a collection without wit
or invention, a very toy. People deem things easy that are already done,
nor do they consider the rough places after the road is made; so men are

valued, their labours vilified, as things of nought, by fellows of no worth themselves, who could not have done as much. Every man abounds in his own sense; and whilst each particular party is so affected, how should one please all?

What shall I give my guests? For you refuse
What he demands. (HORACE)

How shall I hope to express myself to each man's humour & conceit, or to give satisfaction to all? Some understand too little, some too much, some value books by the authors, as people judge of men by their clothes, as Austin observes, not regarding what, but who writes, the fame of the author sells the book; not valuing the metal but the stamp that is upon it, they can't see the liquor for the tankard. If he be not rich, in great place, polite and brave, a great doctor, or full-fraught with grand titles, though never so well qualified, he is a dunce; but, as Baronius hath it of Cardinal Caraffa's works, he is a mere hog that rejects any man for his poverty. Some are too partial, as friends, to overween, others come with a prejudice to carp, vilify, detract, and scoff; (who judge, perhaps, whatever I produce as unworthy of aught but contempt) some as bees for honey, some as spiders to gather poison. What shall I do in this case? As a Dutch Host, if you come to an Inn in Germany, & dislike your fare, diet, lodging, &c., replies, in a surly tone: If you like not this, get you to another Inn: I resolve, if you like not my writing, go read something else. I do not much esteem thy censure, take thy course, 'tis not as thou wilt, nor as I will, but when we have both done, that of Pliny the Younger to Trajan will prove true: Every man's witty labour takes not, except the matter, subject, occasion, & some commending favourite happen to it. If I be taxed, exploded, by thee and some such, I shall haply be approved and commended by others, & so have been (I speak from experience), & may truly say with Jovius in like case, (let me not speak boastfully): *I have had the intimacy and friendship of some eminent men, Pontiffs, and Nobles, and had pleasant favours from them, and been praised by many who were themselves highly esteemed;* as I have been honoured by some worthy men, so have I been vilified by others, and shall be. At the first publishing of this book (which Probus [saith] of Persius' Satires), men began both to admire and eagerly tear to pieces,* I may in some sort apply to this my work. The first, second, and third editions were suddenly gone,

* The word here translated " tear to pieces," when referring to an edition of a book, meant " buy up rapidly ": but the context seems to indicate that Burton had the other meaning in mind.

eagerly read, & as I have said, not so much approved by some, as scornfully rejected by others. But it was Democritus his fortune that he was both admired and jeered at. 'Twas Seneca's fate, that superintendent of wit, learning, judgment, learned to a marvel, the best of Greek and Latin writers in Plutarch's opinion: that renowned corrector of vice, as Fabius terms him, and painful omniscious philosopher, that writ so excellently and admirably well, could not please all parties, or escape censure. How is he vilified by Caligula, A. Gellius, Fabius, and Lipsius himself, his chief propugner! For the most part pernicious, saith the same Fabius, many childish tracts and sentences he hath, unwrought speech, too negligent often and remiss, as A. Gellius observes, vulgar speech, trite phrases, inept thoughts, plebeian learning, an homely shallow writer as he is. In some of his works he has difficulties and inspires disgust, saith Lipsius, & as in all his other works, so especially in his epistles, he jumbles up many things together immethodically, after the Stoicks' fashion; he accumulated much, gave form to very little, &c. If Seneca be thus lashed, and many famous men that I could name, what shall I expect? How shall I, that am scarce the shadow of so great a philosopher, hope to please? No man so absolute, Erasmus holds, to satisfy all, except antiquity, prescription, &c., set a bar. But as I have proved in Seneca, this will not always take place, how shall I evade? 'Tis the common doom of all writers, I must (I say) abide it, I seek not applause; I seek not the suffrage of the windy crowd; again, I am not so unsightly, I would not be vilified.

> *I shall have praise enough if, gentle reader,*
> *You do not despise me.* (OVID)

I fear good men's censures, and to their favourable acceptance I submit my labours,

> *But I despise the tongues of slaves.* (JUVENAL)

As the barking of a dog, I securely contemn those malicious and scurrile obloquies, flouts, calumnies of railers and detractors. I scorn the rest. What therefore I have said, in my poor fashion, I have said.

One or two things yet I was desirous to have amended, if I could, concerning the manner of handling this my subject, for which I must apologize, deprecate, and upon better advice give the friendly reader notice: it was not mine intent to prostitute my muse in English, or to divulge the secrets of Minerva, but to have exposed this more contract in Latin, if I could have got it printed. Any scurrile pamphlet is welcome to our mercenary Stationers in *English,* they print all, and pound out pamphlets on the leaves of which even a poverty-stricken monkey would not wipe; but in *Latin* they will not deal; which is one of the reasons Nicholas Car, in his oration of the paucity of English writers, gives, that so many flourishing wits are smothered in oblivion, lie dead and buried in this our nation. Another main fault is, that I have not revised the copy, and amended the style, which now flows remissly, as it was first conceived, but my leisure would not permit. I confess it is neither as I would, nor as it should be.

> *When I peruse this tract which I have writ,*
> *I am abash'd, and much I hold unfit.* (OVID)

And, what is most important, in the matter itself, many things I disallow at this present, which when I writ, my years are not what they were, nor yet my tastes; I would willingly retract much, &c., but 'tis too late, I can only crave pardon now for what is amiss.

I might indeed (had I wisely done) have observed that precept of the poet, let them be kept quiet until the ninth year, and have taken more care: or as Alexander the Physician would have done by *Lapis Lazuli*, fifty times washed before it be used, I should have revised, corrected, and amended this tract; but I had not as (I said) that happy leisure, no amanuenses or assistants. Pancrates in Lucian, wanting a servant as he went from Memphis to Coptos in Egypt, took a door-bar, and after some superstitious words pronounced (Eucrates the relator was then present) made it stand up like a serving-man, fetch him water, turn the spit, serve in supper, and what work he would besides; and when he had done that service he desired, turn'd his man to a stick again. I have no such skill to make new men at my pleasure, or means to hire them, no whistle to call like the master of a ship, and bid them run, &c. I have no such authority, no such benefactors, as that noble Ambrosius was to Origen, allowing him six or seven amanuenses to write out his dictates; I must for that cause do my business myself, and was therefore enforced, as a bear doth her whelps, to bring forth this confused lump, I had not time to lick it into form, as she doth her young ones, but even so to publish it, as it was first written, whatever came uppermost, in an extemporean style, as I do commonly all other exercises; I put forth what my genius dictated, out of a confused company of notes, and writ with as small deliberation as I do ordinarily speak, without all affectation of big words, fustian phrases, jingling terms, tropes, strong lines, that like Acestes' arrows caught fire as they flew, strains of wit, brave heats, elogies, hyperbolical exornations, elegancies, &c., which many so much affect. I am a water-drinker, drink no wine at all, which so much improves our modern wits, a loose, plain,

rude writer, & as free as loose, I call a spade a spade, I write for minds,
not ears, I respect matter, not words; remembering that of Cardan,
Words exist for things, not things for words; and seeking, with Seneca,
rather what than how to write. For as Philo thinks, He that is conversant about matter, neglects words, and those that excel in this art
of speaking, have no profound learning.

Words may sound fine, yet have no inner meaning. (PALINGENIUS)

Besides, it was the observation of that wise Seneca, When you see a
fellow careful about his words, and neat in his speech, know this for
a certainty, that man's mind is busied about toys, there's no solidity
in him. Prettiness of style is not a manly distinction: as he said of a
nightingale, A voice you are, and nothing else,* &c. I am therefore in
this point a professed disciple of Apollonius, a scholar of Socrates, I
neglect phrases, and labour wholly to inform my reader's understanding,
not to please his ear; 'tis not my study or intent to compose neatly,
which an Orator requires, but to express myself readily & plainly as it
happens. So that as a River runs, sometimes precipitate and swift, then
dull and slow; now direct, then winding; now deep, then shallow; now
muddy, then clear; now broad, then narrow; doth my style flow: now
serious, then light; now comical, then satirical; now more elaborate,
then remiss, as the present subject required, or as at that time I was
affected. And if thou vouchsafe to read this treatise, it shall seem no
otherwise to thee than the way to an ordinary Traveller, sometimes fair,
sometimes foul; here champaign, there inclosed; barren in one place,
better soil in another: by woods, groves, hills, dales, plains, &c. I shall
lead thee over steep mountains, through treacherous valleys, dew-clad
meadows and rough plowed fields, through variety of objects, that
which thou shalt like and surely dislike.*

For the matter itself or method, if it be faulty, consider I pray
you that of Columella, nothing is to be made perfect, even with the
most unparalleled and consummate industry, no man can observe all,
much is defective no doubt, may be justly taxed, altered and avoided
in Galen, Aristotle, those great Masters. He is a good Huntsman (one
[Nannius] holds) can catch some, not all; I have done my endeavour.
Besides, I dwell not in this study, plow not this furrow, sweat not in
this field; I am but a smatterer, I confess, a stranger, here and there I
pull a flower; I do easily grant, if a rigid censurer should criticize on
this which I have writ, he should not find three sole faults, as Scaliger in

* It was Plutarch, in his Laconic Apothegms, who said that of the nightingale,
quoted above.

Terence, but 300: so many as he hath done in Cardan's Subtleties, as many notable errors as Gulielmus Laurembergius, a late Professor of Rostock, discovers in that Anatomy of Laurentius, or Barocius the Venetian in Sacroboscus. And although this be a Sixth Edition, in which I should have been more accurate, corrected all those former escapes, yet it was so difficult and tedious a work that, as Carpenters do find out of experience, 'tis much better build a new sometimes than repair an old house; I could as soon write as much more, as alter that which is written. If ought therefore be amiss (as I grant there is) I require a friendly admonition, no bitter invective,

So be the Graces friend the Muse,
Furies all their venom lose.

Otherwise as in ordinary controversies, we may contend, and likely misuse each other, but to what purpose? We are both scholars, say,

Arcadians both, and adepts in part-singing. (VIRGIL)

If we do wrangle, what shall we get by it? Trouble & wrong ourselves, make sport to others. If I be convict of an error, I will yield, I will amend. If I have said anything contrary to good morals or truth, let it be supposed unsaid. In the mean time I require a favourable censure of all faults omitted, harsh compositions, pleonasms of words, tautological repetitions (though Seneca bear me out: It can never be repeated too often, since it can never be learned too well), perturbations of tenses, numbers, printers' faults, &c. My translations are sometimes rather paraphrases than interpretations, not word for word, but, as an author, I use more liberty, and that's only taken which was to my purpose. Quotations are often inserted in the Text, which make the style more harsh, or in the margin, as it happened. Greek authors, Plato, Plutarch, Athenæus, &c., I have cited out of their interpreters, because the original was not so ready. I have mingled the Sacred with the Profane, but I hope not profaned, and in repetition of authors' names, ranked them willy-nilly, not according to Chronology; sometimes Neotericks before Ancients, as my memory suggested. Some things are here altered, expunged in this Sixth Edition, others amended, much added, because many good authors in all kinds are come to my hands since, and 'tis no prejudice, no such *indecorum,* or oversight.

Ne'er was ought yet at first contriv'd so fit,
But use, age, or something would alter it ;
Advise thee better, and upon peruse,
Make thee not say, and what thou takest refuse. (TERENCE)

But I am now resolv'd never to put this treatise out again, not too much of anything, I will not hereafter add, alter, or retract; I have done. The last and greatest exception is, that I being a divine have meddled with physick, which Menedemus objected to Chremes; have I so much leisure, or little business of mine own, as to look after other men's matters which concern me not? What have I to do with physick? What belongs to doctors let doctors undertake. The Lacedæmonians were once in counsel about state matters, a debauched fellow spake excellent well, and to the purpose, his speech was generally approved: a grave Senator steps up, and by all means would have it repealed, though good, because it had no better an author; let some good man relate the same, and then it should pass. This counsel was embraced, the thing was done, and it was registered forthwith. And so the good advice was taken, the bad adviser was changed. Thou sayest as much of me, peevish fellow as thou art, & grantest peradventure this which I have written in physick, not to be amiss, had another done it, a professed physician, or so; but why should I meddle with this tract? Hear me speak. There be many other subjects, I do easily grant, both in humanity and divinity, fit to be treated of, of which had I written only to show myself, I should have rather chosen, and in which I have been more conversant, I could have more willingly luxuriated, and better satisfied myself and others; but that at this time I was fatally driven upon this rock of melancholy, and carried away by this by-stream, which, as a rillet, is deducted from the main channel of my studies, in which I have pleased and busied myself at idle hours, as a subject most necessary and commodious. Not that I prefer it before Divinity, which I do acknowledge to be the Queen of professions, and to which all the rest are as handmaids, but that in Divinity I saw no such great need. For had I written positively, there be so many books in that kind, so many commentators, treatises, pamphlets, expositions, sermons, that whole teams of oxen cannot draw them; and had I been as forward and ambitious as some others, I might have haply printed a Sermon at Paul's Cross, a Sermon in St. Mary's, Oxford, a Sermon in Christ-Church, or a Sermon before the Right Honourable, Right Reverend, a Sermon before the Right Worshipful, a Sermon in Latin, in English, a Sermon with a name, a Sermon without, a Sermon, a Sermon, &c. But I have been ever as desirous to suppress my labours in this kind, as others have been to press and publish theirs. To have written in controversy had been to cut off an *Hydra's head,* litigation begets litigation, one begets another, so many duplications, triplications, & swarms of questions, in this sacred war which is fought with the pen's point, that, having once begun, I should never make an

end. One had much better, as Pope Alexander the Sixth long since observed, provoke a great Prince than a begging Friar; a Jesuit, or a
Seminary Priest, I will add, for they are an irrefragable society, they
must & will have the last word; and that with such eagerness, impudence, abominable lying, falsifying, and bitterness in their questions
they proceed, that as he said, Is it madness or some overmastering power
that hastens you on? or wickedness? Make answer! Blind fury, or
error, or rashness, or what it is that eggs them, I know not. I am sure
many times, which Austin * perceived long since, with this tempest of
contention the serenity of charity is over-clouded, & there be too many
spirits conjured up already in this kind in all sciences, and more than
we can tell how to lay which do so furiously rage, and keep such a racket,
that as Fabius said, *It had been much better for some of them to have
been born dumb and altogether illiterate, than so far to dote to their own
destruction.*

> *It had been better not to write, for silence*
> *Is always safe.*

'Tis a general fault, so Severinus the Dane complains in physick, *unhappy men as we are, we spend our days in unprofitable questions &
disputations,* intricate subtleties, about goat's wool, about moonshine in
the water, *leaving in the mean time those chiefest treasures of nature
untouched, wherein the best medicines for all manner of diseases are to
be found, & do not only neglect them ourselves, but hinder, condemn,
forbid, and scoff at others, that are willing to enquire after them.* These
motives at this present have induced me to make choice of this medicinal subject.

If any physician in the mean time shall infer, let no cobbler go beyond his last, and find himself grieved that I have intruded into his profession, I will tell him in brief, I do not otherwise by them, than they
do by us. If it be for their advantage, I know many of their sect which
have taken orders in hope of a benefice, 'tis a common transition, and
why not a melancholy divine, that can get nothing but by Simony, profess physick? Drusianus an Italian (Crusianus, but corruptly, Trithemius calls him) because he was not fortunate in his practice, forsook his
profession, and writ afterwards in divinity. Marcilius Ficinus was a
priest & a physician at once, & T. Linacre in his old age took orders.
The Jesuits profess both at this time, divers of them by the permission
of their superiors, chirurgeons, panders, bawds, and midwives, &c. Many
poor country-vicars, for want of other means, are driven to their shifts;

---

* St. Augustine.

to turn mountebanks, quacksalvers, empiricks, and if our greedy patrons hold us to such hard conditions, as commonly they do, they will make most of us work at some trade, as Paul did, at last turn taskers, malsters, costermongers, graziers, sell Ale as some have done, or worse. Howsoever, in undertaking this task, I hope I shall commit no great error or *indecorum,* if all be considered aright, I can vindicate myself with Georgius Brunnius, and Hieronymus Henninges, those two learned Divines; who (to borrow a line or two of mine elder brother *) drawn by a *natural love, the one of pictures and maps, prospectives and chorographical delights, writ that ample Theatre of Cities; the other to the study of genealogies, penned The Theatre of Genealogies.* Or else I can excuse my studies with Lessius the Jesuit in like case. It is a disease of the soul on which I am to treat, and as much appertaining to a Divine as to a Physician; and who knows not what an agreement there is betwixt these two professions? A good Divine either is or ought to be a good physician, a spiritual physician at least, as our Saviour calls himself, and was indeed. They differ but in object, the one of the body, the other of the soul, and use divers medicines to cure: one amends the soul through the body, the other the body through the soul, as our Regius Professor of Physick † well informed us in a learned lecture of his not long since. One helps the vices and passions of the soul, anger, lust, desperation, pride, presumption, &c., by applying the spiritual physick; as the other uses proper remedies in bodily diseases. Now this being a common infirmity of body and soul, and such a one that hath as much need of a spiritual as corporal cure, I could not find a fitter task to busy myself about, a more apposite theme, so necessary, so commodious, and generally concerning all sorts of men, that should so equally participate of both, and require a whole physician. A Divine in this compound mixed malady can do little alone, a Physician in some kinds of melancholy much less, both make an absolute cure. Thus does the one thing require the help of the other. And 'tis proper to them both, and I hope not unbeseeming me who am by my profession a Divine, and by mine inclination a Physician. I had Jupiter in my Sixth House; I say with Beroaldus, *I am not a physician, and yet not altogether ignorant of physick;* in the theorick of physick I have taken some pains, not with an intent to practise, but to satisfy myself, which was a cause likewise of the first undertaking of this subject.

* Mr. W. Burton, Preface to his Description of Leicestershire, printed at London by W. Jaggard for J. White, 1622. — Burton's note.
  † Dr. Clayton, 1621, according to Burton's note.

If these reasons do not satisfy thee, Good Reader, as Alexander Munificus, that bountiful Prelate sometime Bishop of Lincoln, when he had built six Castles, to take away the envy of his work, saith Mr. Camden, (which very words Nubrigensis hath of Roger the rich Bishop of Salisbury, who in King Stephen's time built Sherborne Castle, and that of Devizes) to divert the scandal or imputation which might be thence inferred, built so many Religious Houses; if this my discourse be over medicinal, or savour too much of humanity, I promise thee that I will hereafter make thee amends in some treatise of divinity. But this I hope shall suffice, when you have more fully considered of the matter of this my subject, melancholy, madness, and of the reasons following, which were my chief motives, the generality of the disease, the necessity of the cure, and the commodity or common good that will arise to all men by the knowledge of it, as shall at large appear in the ensuing preface. And I doubt not but that in the end you will say with me, that to anatomize this humour aright through all the members of this our *Microcosmos,* is as great a task as to reconcile those chronological errors in the Assyrian monarchy, find out the quadrature of a circle, the creeks and sounds of the north-east or north-west passages, & all out as good a discovery as that hungry Spaniard's * of the Unknown Austral Land, as great a trouble as to perfect the motion of Mars & Mercury, which so crucifies our Astronomers, or to rectify the Gregorian Calendar. I am so affected for my part, and hope as Theophrastus did by his Characters, *that our posterity, O friend Polycles, shall be the better for this which we have written, by correcting and rectifying what is amiss in themselves by our examples, and applying our precepts and cautions to their own use.* As that great Captain Zisca would have a drum made of his skin when he was dead, because he thought the very noise of it would put his enemies to flight, I doubt not but that these following lines, when they shall be recited, or hereafter read, will drive away melancholy (though I be gone) as much as Zisca's drum could terrify his foes. Yet one caution let me give by the way to my present or future reader, who is actually melancholy, that he read not the symptoms or prognosticks in this following tract, lest by applying that which he reads to himself, aggravating, appropriating things generally spoken to his own person (as melancholy men for the most part do), he trouble or hurt himself, and get in conclusion more harm than good. I advise them therefore warily to peruse that tract: he speaks stones (so said Agrippa †) and let

* Ferdinand de Quiros. See Index.
† Cornelius Agrippa, in his Occult Philosophy.

his readers beware lest he break their heads. The rest I doubt not they may securely read, and to their benefit. But I am over-tedious, I proceed.

Of the necessity and generality of this which I have said, if any man doubt, I shall desire him to make a brief survey of the world, as Cyprian advised Donatus, *supposing himself to be transported to the top of some high mountain, and thence to behold the tumults and chances of this wavering world, he can't choose but either laugh at, or pity it.* S. Hierom,* out of a strong imagination, being in the wilderness, conceived with himself that he then saw them dancing in Rome; and if thou shalt either conceive, or climb to see, thou shalt soon perceive that all the world is mad, that it is melancholy, dotes: that it is (which Epichthonius Cosmopolites expressed not many years since in a map) made like a fool's head (with that Motto, A head requiring hellebore), a crazed head, a fool's Paradise, or, as Apollonius, a common prison of gulls, cheaters, flatterers, &c., and needs to be reformed. Strabo, in the Ninth Book of his Geography, compares Greece to the picture of a man, which comparison of his Nicholas Gerbelius, in his exposition of Sophianus' map, approves; the breast lies open from those Acroceraunian hills in Epirus to the Sunian promontory in Attica; Pagæ & Megara are the two shoulders; that Isthmus of Corinth the neck; and Peloponnesus the head. If this allusion hold, 'tis sure a mad head, Morea may be *Moria* [Folly]; and to speak what I think, the inhabitants of modern Greece swerve as much from reason & true religion at this day, as that Morea doth from the picture of a man. Examine the rest in like sort, and you shall find that Kingdoms and Provinces are melancholy, cities and families, all creatures, vegetal, sensible, and rational, that all sorts, sects, ages, conditions, are out of tune, as in Cebes' † Table, before they come into the world, they are intoxicated by error's cup, from the highest to the lowest have need of physick, and those particular actions in Seneca, where father & son prove one another mad, may be general; Porcius Latro shall plead against us all. For indeed who is not a fool, melancholy, mad? — Who attempts nothing foolish, who is not brainsick? Folly, melancholy, madness, are but one disease, *delirium* is a common name to all. Alexander, Gordonius, Jason Pratensis, Savanarola, Guianerius, Montaltus, confound them as differing according to great or small, so doth David, *I said unto the fools, deal not so madly,* & 'twas an

* St. Jerome.

† Cebes was a Greek philosopher, a friend and pupil of Socrates. He, or someone later under his name, wrote a work called The Picture (or The Table, in the old pictorial sense of that word), a disquisition upon the vicissitudes and dangers of human life.

old Stoical paradox, all fools are mad, though some madder than others. And who is not a fool? Who is free from melancholy? Who is not touched more or less in habit or disposition? If in disposition, *ill disposi-tions beget habits, if they persevere,* saith Plutarch, habits either are or turn to diseases. 'Tis the same which Tully maintains in the Second of his Tusculans, fools are sick, and all that are troubled in mind: for what is sickness, but as Gregory Tholosanus defines it, *a dissolution or per-turbation of the bodily league which health combines.* And who is not sick, or ill disposed? In whom doth not passion, anger, envy, discontent, fear, and sorrow, reign? Who labours not of this disease? Give me but a little leave, & you shall see by what testimonies, confessions, argu-ments, I will evince it, that most men are mad, that they had as much need to go a pilgrimage to the Anticyræ * (as in Strabo's time they did) as in our days they run to Compostella, our Lady of Sichem, or Loretto, to seek for help; that it is like to be as prosperous a voyage as that of Guiana, and that there is much more need of Hellebore than of Tobacco.

That men are so misaffected, melancholy, mad, giddy-headed, hear the testimony of Solomon, *And I turned to behold wisdom, madness, and folly,* &c. And *All his days are sorrow, his travail grief, & his heart taketh not rest in the night.* So that take melancholy in what sense you will, properly or improperly, in disposition or habit, for pleasure or for pain, dotage, discontent, fear, sorrow, madness, for part, or all, truly, or metaphorically, 'tis all one. Laughter itself is madness according to Solomon, and, as S. Paul hath it, *worldly sorrow brings death. The hearts of the sons of men are evil, & madness is in their hearts while they live. Wise men themselves are no better. In the multitude of wisdom is much grief, & he that increaseth wisdom increaseth sorrow.* He hated life itself, nothing pleased him, he hated his labour, all, as he concludes, is *sorrow, grief, vanity, vexation of spirit.* And though he were the wisest man in the world, & had wisdom in abundance, he will not vindicate himself, or justify his own actions. *Surely I am more foolish than any man, and have not the understanding of a man in me.* Be they Solomon's words, or the words of Agur, the son of Jakeh, they are canonical. David, a man after God's own heart, confesseth as much of himself, *So foolish was I & ignorant, I was even as a beast before thee:* and condemns all for fools. He compares them to *beasts, horses and mules, in which there is no understanding.* The Apostle Paul accuseth himself in like sort,

---

* Several towns in Greece were named Anticyra, and all were famed for their black hellebore, a plant which was used by physicians to " purge the head." To say " Go to Anticyra " was a way of saying " You are mad."

I would you would suffer a little my foolishness, I speak foolishly. The whole head is sick, saith Esay,* *and the heart is heavy,* and makes lighter of them than of oxen and asses, *the ox knows his owner, &c.* Read Deut., 32 : 6 ; Jer. 4., Amos, 3 : 1 ; Ephes., 5 : 6. *Be not mad, be not deceived, foolish Galatians, who hath bewitched you?* How often are they branded with this epithet of madness and folly! No word so frequent amongst the Fathers of the Church and Divines ; you may see what an opinion they had of the world, and how they valued men's actions.

I know that we think far otherwise, and hold them most part wise men that are in authority, Princes, Magistrates, rich men, they are wise men born, all Politicians and Statesmen must needs be so, for who dare speak against them? And on the other, so corrupt is our Judgement, we esteem wise and honest men fools. Which Democritus well signified in an Epistle of his to Hippocrates: the *Abderites account virtue madness,* and so do most men living. Shall I tell you the reason of it? Fortune and Virtue, Wisdom and Folly, their seconds, upon a time contended in the Olympicks ; every man thought that Fortune and Folly would have the worst, and pitied their cases. But it fell out otherwise. Fortune was blind and cared not where she stroke, nor whom, without laws, after the fashion of blinded gladiators, &c. Folly, rash and inconsiderate, esteemed as little what she said or did. Virtue and Wisdom gave place, were hissed out, and exploded by the common people, Folly and Fortune admired, & so are all their followers ever since. Knaves and fools commonly fare and deserve best in worldlings' eyes & opinions. Many good men have no better fate in their ages. Achish held David for a mad man. Elisha & the rest were no otherwise esteemed, David was derided of the common people, *I am become a monster to many.* And generally we are accounted fools for Christ. *We fools thought his life madness, and his end without honour.* Christ and his Apostles were censured in like sort. And so were all Christians in Pliny's time, insane like others, and called not long after, followers of madness, upsetters of men, vicious innovators, fanatics, dogs, evil-doers, poisoners, Galilaean mannikins, &c. 'Tis an ordinary thing with us to account honest, devout, orthodox, divine, religious, plain-dealing men, idiots, asses, that cannot or will not lie and dissemble, shift, flatter, cut the coat according to their cloth, make good bargains, supplant, thrive, fawn upon their patrons, practise the usual arts of climbing, duly observe laws, manners, customs, praise openly, defend through thick and thin, give in to opinions, doubt nothing, believe everything, stand everything, blame nothing, and

* Isaiah.

do all the other things which bring promotion & security, and, without roundabout ways, make a man happy and truly wise amongst us; that cannot temporize as other men do, hand and take bribes, &c., but fear God, and make a conscience of their doings. But the Holy Ghost, that knows better how to judge, he calls them fools. *The fool hath said in his heart ——— And their ways utter their folly.* For what can be more mad, than for a little worldly pleasure to procure unto themselves eternal punishment? as Gregory and others inculcate unto us.

Yea, even all those great philosophers the world hath ever had in admiration, whose works we do so much esteem, that gave precepts of wisdom to others, inventors of Arts & Sciences, Socrates [declared] the wisest man of his time by the Oracle of Apollo, whom his two Scholars, Plato and Xenophon, so much extol and magnify with those honourable titles, best and wisest of all mortal men, the happiest, and most just; & as Alcibiades incomparably commends him; Achilles was a worthy man, but Brasidas and others were as worthy as himself; Antenor and Nestor were as good as Pericles, and so of the rest; but none present, before or after Socrates, none of the ancients or of those who now are, were ever such, will match, or come near him. Those seven wise men of Greece, those British Druids, Indian Brachmanni, Æthiopian Gymnosophists, Magi of the Persians, Apollonius, of whom Philostratus [said that he was] not learned but born wise, Epicurus so much admired by his Scholar Lucretius;

> *Whose wit excell'd the wits of men as far*
> *As the Sun rising doth obscure a Star.* (LUCRETIUS)

Or that so much renowned Empedocles,

> *That he scarce seems to be of mortal stock.* (LUCRETIUS)

All those of whom we read such hyperbolical eulogiums, as of Aristotle, that he was wisdom itself in the abstract, a miracle of nature, breathing libraries, as Eunapius of Longinus, lights of nature, giants for wit, quintessence of wit, divine spirits, eagles in the clouds, fallen from heaven, gods, spirits, lamps of the world, dictators,

> *No future ages will produce such men:* (BESSARION)

monarchs, miracles, superintendents of wit and learning, Oceanus, Phoenix, Atlas, a marvel and wonder of a man, the museum of the whole world, the last effort of human nature, the husband of Nature,

> *To whom the learned world deservedly*
> *Lowering the fasces brings imperial sway.*

As Ælian writ of Protagoras and Gorgias, we may say of them all, that they were as devoid of wisdom as children are, they were children in respect, infants, not eagles but kites, novices, illiterate, eunuchs of wisdom. And although they were the wisest, and most admired in their age, as he censured Alexander, I do them, there were 10,000 in his army as worthy Captains (had they been in place of command) as valiant as himself; there were myriads of men wiser in those days, & yet all short of what they ought to be. Lactantius, in his Book of Wisdom, proves them to be dizzards, fools, asses, mad-men, so full of absurd and ridiculous tenents and brain-sick positions, that to his thinking never any old woman or sick person doted worse. Democritus took all from Leucippus, and left, saith he, the inheritance of his folly to Epicurus, witless wisdom, &c. The like he holds of Plato, Aristippus, and the rest, making no difference *betwixt them and beasts, saving that they could speak.* Theodoret in his tract manifestly evinces as much of Socrates, whom though that Oracle of Apollo confirmed to be the wisest man then living, and saved him from the plague, whom 2,000 years have admired, of whom some will as soon speak evil as of Christ, yet in reality he was an illiterate idiot, as Aristophanes calls him, a mocker and ambitious, as his Master Aristotle terms him, an Attic buffoon, as Zeno, an enemy to all arts & sciences, as Athenæus, to Philosophers & Travellers, an opinionative ass, a caviller, a kind of Pedant; for his manners, as Theod. Cyrensis describes him, a Sodomite, an Atheist, (so convict by Anytus) hot tempered, and a drunkard, and prater, &c., a pot companion, by Plato's own confession, a sturdy drinker; and that of all others he was most sottish, a very mad-man in his actions and opinions. Pythagoras was part philosopher, part magician, or part witch. If you desire to hear more of Apollonius, a great wise man, sometime parallel'd by Julian the Apostate to Christ, I refer you to that learned tract of Eusebius against Hierocles, & for them all to Lucian's Piscator, Icaromenippus, Necyomantia: their actions, opinions, in general were so prodigious, absurd, ridiculous, which they broached and maintained, their books and elaborate treatises were full of dotage, which Tully long since observed, writers generally rave in their books, their lives being opposite to their words, they commended poverty to others, and were most covetous themselves, extolled love and peace, and yet persecuted one another with virulent hate and malice. They could give precepts for verse and prose, but not a man of them (as Seneca tells them home) could moderate his affections. Their musick did shew us tearful measures, &c. how to rise and fall, but they could not so contain themselves as in adversity not to make a lamentable tone. They will measure ground by Geometry, set down limits, divide and subdivide, but cannot yet prescribe what is proper for a man, or keep within compass of reason and discretion. They can square circles, but understand not the state of their own souls; describe right lines and crooked, &c., but know not what is right in this life, so that, as he said, I think all the Anticyræ will not restore them to their wits. If these men now that held Zenodotus' heart, Crates' liver, Epictetus' lanthorn, were so sottish, and had no more brains than so many beetles, what shall we think of the commonalty? what of the rest?

Yea, but will you infer, that is true of *heathens,* if they be conferred with Christians. *The wisdom of this world is foolishness with God, earthly and devilish,* as James calls it. *They were vain in their imaginations, and their foolish heart was full of darkness. When they professed themselves wise, they became fools.* Their witty works are admired here on earth, whilst their souls are tormented in hell fire. In some sense Christians are Crassians, and if compared to that wisdom, no better than fools. Who is wise? Pythagoras replies, God is only wise. Paul determines *only good,* as Austin well contends, *and no man living can be justified in his sight. God looked down from heaven upon the children of men to see if any did understand,* but all are corrupt, err. *None doth good, no not one.* Job aggravates this, *Behold he found no stedfastness, in his servants, and laid folly upon his angels: How much more on them that dwell in houses of clay!* In this sense we are all as fools, and the Scripture alone is the tower of Minerva; we and our writings are shallow and imperfect. But I do not so mean; even in our ordinary dealings we are no better than fools. All our actions, as Pliny told Trajan, *upbraid us of folly,* our whole course of life is but matter of laughter: we are not soberly wise; and the world itself, which ought at least to be wise by reason of his antiquity, as Hugo de Prato Florido will have it, *is every day more foolish than other ; the more it is whipped, the worse it is, and as a child, will still be crowned with roses and flowers.* We are apish in it, & every place is full of metamorphosed and two-legged asses, transformed Silenuses, childish, like a two-year old baby rocked asleep in his father's arms. Jovianus Pontanus brings in some laughing at an old man, that by reason of his age was a little fond,* but as he admonisheth there, marvel not at him only, for all our town dotes in like sort; we are a company of fools. Ask not with him in the Poet, What madness ghosts this old man, but what madness ghosts us all? For we are all mad, not once, but always so, & ever and altogether as bad as he; & not " old man, twice childish," " crazy old woman," but say it of us all, young & old, all dote, as Lactantius proves out of Seneca; & no

* Silly.

difference betwixt us and children, saving that they play with babies of clouts & such toys, we sport with greater baubles. We cannot accuse or condemn one another, being faulty ourselves, " You talk idly," or as Micio upbraided Demea, " You are mad, take yourself off! " for we are as mad our own selves, and it is hard to say which is the worst. Nay, 'tis universally so, Chance governs our lives, not wisdom.

When Socrates had taken great pains to find out a wise man, and to that purpose had consulted with philosophers, poets, artificers, he concludes all men were fools; and though it procured him both anger and much envy, yet in all companies he would openly profess it. When Supputius, in Pontanus, had travelled all over Europe to confer with a wise man, he returned at last without his errand, and could find none. Cardan concurs with him, *Few there are (for ought I can perceive) well in their wits.* So doth Tully, *I see every thing to be done foolishly and unadvisedly.*

> *One reels to this, another to that wall,*
> *'Tis the same error that deludes them all.* (HORACE)

They dote all, but not alike, not in the same kind. *One is covetous, a second lascivious, a third ambitious, a fourth envious,* etc., as Damasippus the Stoick hath well illustrated in the poet,

> *All dote as much as you.* (HORACE)

'Tis an inbred malady in every one of us, there is a seminary of folly, *which, if it be stirred up, or get ahead, will run to infinity, & infinitely varies, as we ourselves are severally addicted,* saith Balthasar Castilio. & cannot so easily be rooted out, it takes such fast hold, as Tully holds, deep are the roots of folly, so we are bred, & so we continue. Some say there be two main defects of wit, error and ignorance, to which all others are reduced; by ignorance we know not things necessary, by error we know them falsely. Ignorance is a privation, error a positive act. From ignorance comes vice, from error heresy, &c. But make how many kinds you will, divide and subdivide, few men are free, or that do not impinge on some one kind or other. So ignorance commonly dominates the foolish, as he that examines his own and other men's actions shall find.

Charon in Lucian, as he wittily feigns, was conducted by Mercury to such a place, where he might see all the world at once; after he had sufficiently viewed, and looked about, Mercury would needs know of him what he had observed. He told him that he saw a vast multitude, and a promiscuous, their habitations like mole-hills, the men as emmets, *he could discern Cities like so many hives of Bees, wherein every Bee had a sting, & they did nought but sting one another, some domineering like Hornets, bigger than the rest, some like filching wasps, others as drones.* Over their heads were hovering a confused company of perturbations, hope, fear, anger, avarice, ignorance, &c. and a multitude of diseases hanging, which they still pulled on their pates. Some were brawling, some fighting, riding, running, anxiously canvassing, cunningly litigating for toys, and trifles, and such momentany things; their Towns and Provinces mere factions, rich against poor, poor against rich, nobles against artificers, they against nobles, and so the rest. In conclusion, he condemned them all for mad-men, fools, idiots, asses, O fools, where indeed is folly? O fools, O mad-men, he exclaims, mad endeavours, mad actions, mad, mad, mad, O giddy-headed age! Heraclitus the Philosopher, out of a serious meditation of men's lives, fell a weeping, and with continual tears bewailed their misery, madness, and folly. Democritus on the other side burst out a laughing, their whole life seemed to him so ridiculous, and he was so far carried with this ironical passion, that the citizens of Abdera took him to be mad, and sent therefore Embassadors to Hippocrates the physician, that he would exercise his skill upon him. But the story is set down at large by Hippocrates, in his Epistle to Damagetus, which because it is not impertinent to this discourse, I will insert word for word almost, as it is delivered by Hippocrates himself, with all the circumstances belonging unto it.

When Hippocrates was now come to Abdera, the people of the City came flocking about him, some weeping, some intreating of him that he would do his best. After some little repast, he went to see Democritus, the people following him, whom he found (as before) in his garden in the suburbs all alone, *sitting upon a stone under a plane tree, without hose or shoes, with a book on his knees, cutting up several beasts, and busy at his study.* The multitude stood gazing round about to see the congress. Hippocrates, after a little pause, saluted him by his name, whom he resaluted, ashamed almost that he could not call him likewise by his, or that he had forgot it. Hippocrates demanded of him what he was doing. He told him that he was *busy in cutting up several beasts, to find out the cause of madness and melancholy.* Hippocrates commended his work, admiring his happiness and leisure. And why, quoth Democritus, have not you that leisure? Because, replied Hippocrates, domestic affairs hinder, necessary to be done for ourselves, neighbors, friends, — expenses, diseases, frailties and mortalities which happen, — wife, children, servants, & such businesses that deprive us of our time. At this speech Democritus profusely laughed, (his friends and the people standing by weeping in the mean time, and lamenting his madness.) Hippocrates asked the reason why he laughed. He told him at the vanity and fopperies of the time, to see men so empty of all virtuous actions, to hunt so far after gold, having no end of ambition; to take such infinite pains for a little glory, and to be favoured of men; to make such deep mines into the earth for gold, and many times to find nothing, with loss of their lives and fortunes. Some to love dogs, others horses, some to desire to be obeyed in many provinces, and yet themselves will know no obedience. Some to love their wives dearly at first, and after a while to forsake and hate them, begetting children with much care & cost for their education, yet when they grow to man's estate, to despise, neglect, and leave them naked to the world's mercy. Do not these behaviours express their intolerable folly? When men live in peace, they covet war, detesting quietness, deposing Kings, and advancing others in their stead, murdering some men to beget children of their wives. How many strange humours are in men! When they are poor and needy, they seek riches, and when they have them, they do not enjoy them, but hide them under ground, or else wastefully spend them. O wise Hippocrates, I laugh at such things being done, but much more when no good comes of them, & when they are done to so ill purpose. There is no truth or justice found amongst them, for they daily plead one against another, the son against the father and the mother, brother against brother, kindred and friends of the same quality, and all this for riches, whereof after death they cannot be possessors. And yet notwithstanding they will defame & kill one another, commit all unlawful actions, contemning God & men, friends & country. They make great account of many senseless things, esteeming them as a great part of their treasure, statues, pictures, and such like moveables, dear bought, & so cunningly wrought, as nothing but speech wanteth in them, & yet they hate living persons speaking to them. Others affect difficult things; if they dwell on firm land, they will remove to an island, and thence to land again, being no way constant to their desires. They commend courage & strength in wars, & let themselves be conquered by lust and avarice; they are in brief, as disordered in their minds, as Thersites was in his body. And now, methinks, O most worthy Hippocrates, you should not reprehend my laughing, perceiving so many fooleries in men; for no man will mock his own folly, but that which he seeth in a second, & so they justly mock one another. The drunkard calls him a glutton, whom he knows to be sober. Many men love the sea, others husbandry; briefly they cannot agree in their own trades & professions, much less in their lives and actions.

When Hippocrates heard these words so readily uttered, without premeditation, to declare the world's vanity, full of ridiculous contrariety, he made answer, that necessity compelled men to many such actions, and divers wills ensuing from divine permission, that we might not be idle, seeing nothing is so odious to them as sloth & negligence. Besides, men cannot foresee future events, in this uncertainty of human affairs; they would not so marry, if they could foretell the causes of their dislike and separation; or parents, if they knew the hour of their children's death, so tenderly provide for them; or an husbandman sow, if he thought there would be no increase; or a merchant adventure to sea, if he foresaw shipwreck; or be a magistrate, if presently to be deposed. Alas, worthy Democritus, every man hopes the best, and to that end he doth it, and therefore no such cause, or ridiculous occasion, of laughter!

Democritus, hearing this poor excuse, laughed again aloud, perceiving he wholly mistook him, and did not well understand what he had said concerning perturbations and tranquillity of the mind; insomuch that, if men would govern their actions by discretion and providence, they would not declare themselves fools, as now they do, and he should have no cause of laughter; but (quoth he) they swell in this life, as if they were immortal and demi-gods, for want of understanding. It were enough to make them wise, if they would but consider the mutability of this world, and how it wheels about, nothing being firm and sure. He that is now above, to-morrow is beneath; he that sate on this side to-day, to-morrow is hurled on the other: and, not considering these matters they fall into many inconveniences and troubles, coveting things of no profit, and thirsting after them, tumbling headlong into many calamities. So that if men would attempt no more than what they can bear, they should lead contented lives, &, learning to know themselves, would limit their ambition, they would perceive then that Nature hath enough without seeking such superfluities, & unprofitable things, which bring nothing with them but grief and molestation. As a fat body is more subject to diseases, so are rich men to absurdities and fooleries, to many casualties and cross inconveniences. There are many that take no heed what happeneth to others by bad conversation, & therefore overthrow themselves in the same manner through their own fault, not foreseeing dangers manifest. These are things (O more than mad, quoth he) that give me matter of laughter, by suffering the pains of your impieties, as your avarice, envy, malice, enormous villanies, mutinies, unsatiable desires, conspiracies, and other incurable vices, besides your dissimulation and hypocrisy, bearing deadly hatred one to the other, and yet shadowing it with a good face, flying out into all filthy lusts, and transgressions of all laws, both of nature and civility. Many things, which they have left off, after a while they fall to again, husbandry, navigation, and leave again, fickle and unconstant as they are. When they are young, they would be old, and old, young. Princes commend a private life, private men itch after honour: a magistrate commends a quiet life, a quiet man would be in his office, and obeyed as he is: and what is the cause of all this, but that they know not themselves? Some delight to destroy, one to build, another to spoil one country to enrich another and himself. In all these things they are like children, in whom is no judgment or counsel, and resemble beasts, saving that beasts are better than they, as being contented with nature. When shall you see a Lion hide gold in the ground, or a Bull contend for a better pasture? When a Boar is thirsty, he drinks what will serve him, and no more; and when his belly is full, he ceaseth to eat, but men are immoderate in both; as in lust, they covet carnal copulation at set times, men always, ruinating thereby the health of their bodies. And doth it not deserve laughter to see an amorous fool torment himself for a wench; weep, howl for a misshapen slut, a dowdy, sometimes, that might have his choice of the finest beauties? Is there any remedy for this in physick? I do anatomize and cut up these poor beasts, to see these distempers, vanities, and follies, yet such proof were better made on man's body, if my kind nature would endure it: who from the hour of his birth is most miserable, weak, and sickly; when he sucks he is guided by others, when he is grown great practiseth unhappiness, and is sturdy, and when old, a child again, and repenteth him of his life past. And here being interrupted by one that brought books, he fell to it again, that all were mad, careless, stupid. To prove my former speeches, look into courts, or private houses. Judges give judgement according to their own advantage, doing manifest wrong to poor innocents to please others. Notaries alter sentences, and for money lose their deeds. Some make false monies, others counterfeit false weights. Some abuse their parents, yea corrupt their own sisters, others make long libels and pasquils, defaming men of good life, and extol such as are lewd and vicious. Some rob one, some another; magistrates make laws against thieves, and are the veriest thieves themselves. Some kill themselves, others despair, not obtaining their desires. Some dance, sing, laugh, feast and banquet, whilst others sigh, languish, mourn and lament, having neither meat, drink, nor clothes. Some prank up their bodies, and have their minds full of execrable vices. Some trot about to bear false witness, and say any thing for money; and though judges know of it, yet for a bribe they wink at it, and suffer false contracts to prevail against equity. Women are all day a dressing, to pleasure other men abroad, and go like sluts at home, not caring to please their own husbands whom they should. Seeing men are so fickle, so sottish, so intemperate, why should not I laugh at those, to whom folly seems wisdom, will not be cured, and perceive it not?

It grew late, Hippocrates left him, and no sooner was he come away, but all the citizens came about flocking, to know how he liked him. He told them in brief, that, notwithstanding those small neglects of his attire, body, diet, the world had not a wiser, a more learned, a more honest man, and they were much deceived to say that he was mad.

Thus Democritus esteemed of the world in his time, and this was the cause of his laughter: and good cause he had.

> *Democritus did well to laugh of old,*
> *Good cause he had, but now much more,*
> *This life of ours is more ridiculous*
> *Than that of his, or long before.*

Never so much cause of laughter as now, never so many fools and mad-men. 'Tis not one Democritus will serve [the] turn to laugh in these days, we have now need of a *Democritus to laugh at Democritus,* one jester to flout at another, one fool to fleer at another: a great Stentorian Democritus, as big as that Rhodian Colossus. For now, as Sarisburiensis said in his time, the whole world plays the fool; we have a new theatre, a new scene, a new Comedy of Errors, a new company of personate actors; the rites of Pleasure, (as Calcagninus wittily feigns in his Apologues) are celebrated all the world over, where all the actors were mad-men and fools, and every hour changed habits, or took that which came next. He that was a mariner to-day, was an apothecary to-morrow; a smith one while, a philosopher another, in these games of Pleasure; a king now with his crown, robes, sceptre, attendants, by and by drove a loaded ass before him like a carter, &c. If Democritus were alive now, he should see strange alterations, a new company of counterfeit vizards, whifflers, Cuman * asses, maskers, mummers, painted puppets, outsides, phantastick shadows, gulls, monsters, giddyheads, butterflies. And so many of them are indeed (if all be true that I have read). For when Jupiter and Juno's wedding was solemnized of

---

* It was an ass of Cumæ that wore the lion's skin in Æsop, in the old versions. Erasmus, in his Praise of Folly, also speaks of "Cuman asses."

old, the Gods were all invited to the feast, and many noble men besides. Amongst the rest came Chrysalus, a Persian Prince, bravely attended, rich in golden attires, in gay robes, with a majestical presence, but otherwise an ass. The Gods, seeing him come in such pomp and state, rose up to give him place, judging the fellow by his dress; but Jupiter perceiving what he was, a light, phantastick, idle fellow, turned him and his proud followers into butterflies: and so they continue still (for ought I know to the contrary) roving about in pied coats, and are called *Chrysalides* by the wiser sort of men: that is, golden outsides, drones, flies, and things of no worth. Multitudes of such, &c.

> *The wasteful toady and the grasping fool*
> *You 'meet them everywhere, for 'tis the rule.*

Many additions, much increase of madness, folly, vanity, should Democritus observe, were he now to travel, or could get leave of Pluto to come see fashions, as Charon did in Lucian, to visit our cities of Moronia Pia and Moronia Felix *; sure I think he would break the rim of his belly with laughing.

A satirical Roman in his time thought all vice, folly, and madness were all at full sea; Josephus the Historian taxeth his country-men Jews for bragging of their vices, publishing their follies, and that they did contend amongst themselves who should be most notorious in villanies; but we flow higher in madness, far beyond them,

> *Soon sure a faultier offspring to produce,* (HORACE)

and the latter end (you know whose oracle it is), is like to be worst. 'Tis not to be denied, the world alters every day, cities fall, kingdoms are transferred; as Petrarch observes: We change language, habits, laws, customs, manners, but not vices, not diseases, not the symptoms of folly and madness, — they are still the same. And as a River, we see, keeps the like name and place, but not water, and yet ever runs, our times and persons alter, vices are the same, and ever will be. Look how nightingales sang of old, cocks crowed, kine lowed, sheep bleated, sparrows chirped, dogs barked, so they do still; we keep our madness still, play the fools still, the play's not finished yet, we are of the same humours and inclinations as our predecessors were, you shall find us all alike, much at one, we and our sons, and so shall our posterity continue to the last. But to speak of times present.

If Democritus were alive now, and should but see the superstition of our age, our religious madness, as Meteran calls it, so many professed Christians, yet so few imitators of Christ, so much talk of Religion, so

* See Index.

much science, so little conscience, so much knowledge, so many preachers, so little practise, such variety of sects, such have and hold of all
sides, banner against banner, such absurd and ridiculous traditions and
ceremonies. If he should meet a Capuchin, a Franciscan, a Pharisaical
Jesuit, a man-serpent, a shave-crowned Monk in his robes, a begging
Friar, or see their three-crown'd Sovereign Lord the Pope, poor Peter's
successor, the slave of the slaves of God, to depose Kings with his foot,
to tread on Emperors' necks, make them stand bare-foot and bare-legg'd
at his gates, hold his bridle and stirrup, &c., (O that Peter and Paul
were alive to see this!), if he should observe a Prince creep so devoutly
to kiss his toe, and those Red-cap Cardinals, poor parish priests of old,
now Princes' companions, what would he say? In our folly we storm the
very heavens. Had he met some of our devout pilgrims going barefoot
to Jerusalem, Our Lady of Loretto, Rome, S. Iago, S. Thomas' Shrine,
to creep to those counterfeit and maggot-eaten Reliques; had he been
present at a Mass, and seen such kissing of Paxes, Crucifixes, cringes,
duckings, their several attires and ceremonies, pictures of saints, indulgences, pardons, vigils, fastings, feasts, crossing, knocking, kneeling at
Ave-Marias, bells, with many such Spectacles pleasing to the ignorant
masses, praying in gibberish, and mumbling of beads. Had he heard an
old woman say her prayers in Latin, their sprinkling of holy water, and
going a procession,

> *A thousand bands of monks go on procession;*
> *Why should I mention banners, crosses, idols?* (NAUGER)

their breviaries, bulls, hallowed beans, exorcisms, pictures, curious
crosses, fables, and baubles. Had he read the Golden Legend, the Turks'
Alcoran, or Jews' Talmud, the Rabbins' Comments, what would he have
thought? How dost thou think he might have been affected? Had he
more particularly examined a Jesuit's life amongst the rest, he should
have seen an hypocrite profess poverty, and yet possess more goods and
lands than many Princes, to have infinite treasures & revenues; teach
others to fast, and play the gluttons themselves; like watermen, that
row one way and look another. Vow virginity, talk of holiness, and yet
indeed a notorious bawd, and famous fornicator, lascivious beast, a very
goat. Monks by profession, such as give over the world and the vanities
of it, and yet a Machiavellian rout interested in all matters of state:
holy men, peace-makers, and yet composed of envy, lust, ambition,
hatred & malice, fire-brands, overgrown pests of the country, traitors,
assassinates, thus do men reach the stars. and this is to supererogate, and
merit heaven for themselves and others. Had he seen, on the adverse

side, some of our nice and curious schismaticks in another extreme abhor all ceremonies, and rather lose their lives and livings than do or admit anything Papists have formerly used, though in things indifferent (they alone are the true Church, the salt of the earth, whereas they have the least savour of all:), formalists, out of fear and base flattery, like so many weather-cocks turn round, a rout of temporisers, ready to embrace and maintain all that is or shall be proposed in hope of preferment: another Epicurean company, lying at lurch as so many vultures, watching for a prey of Church goods, and ready to rise by the down-fall of any: as Lucian said in like case, what dost thou think Democritus would have done, had he been spectator of these things; or had he but observed the common people follow like so many sheep, one of their fellows drawn by the horns over a gap, some for zeal, some for fear, wherever the storm drives them, to credit all, examine nothing, and yet ready to die before they will abjure any of those ceremonies to which they have been accustomed; others out of hypocrisy frequent sermons, knock their breasts, turn up their eyes, pretend zeal, desire reformation, and yet professed usurers, gripers, monsters of men, harpies, devils in their lives, to express nothing less?

What would he have said to see, hear, and read so many bloody battles, so many thousand slain at once, such streams of blood able to turn mills: because of one man's mad offense, or to make sport for princes, without any just cause, *for vain titles* (saith Austin), *precedency, some wench, or such like toy, or out of desire of domineering, vain-glory, malice, revenge, folly, madness,* ———— (goodly causes all for which the whole world should be laid waste with blood and slaughter!), whilst statesmen themselves in the mean time are secure at home, pampered with all delights & pleasures, take their ease, and follow their lusts, not considering what intolerable misery poor soldiers endure, their often wounds, hunger, thirst, &c., the lamentable cares, torments, calamities & oppressions, that accompany such proceedings, they feel not, take no notice of it. *So wars are begun, by the persuasion of a few debauched, hair-brain, poor, dissolute, hungry captains, parasitical fawners, unquiet Hotspurs, restless innovators, green heads, to satisfy one man's private spleen, lust, ambition, avarice, &c.;* such causes lead folk to accursed battles. Proper men, well proportioned, carefully brought up, able both in body and mind, sound, led like so many beasts to the slaughter, in the flower of their years, pride, and full strength, without all remorse and pity, sacrificed to Pluto, killed up as so many sheep, for devil's food, 40,000 at once. At once, said I? — that were tolerable, but these wars last always, and for many ages; nothing so familiar as this hacking and hewing, massacres, murders, desolations;

The sky re-echoes with the unknown clangor,

they care not what mischief they procure, so that they may enrich themselves for the present; they will so long blow the coals of contention, till all the world be consumed with fire. The siege of Troy lasted ten years eight months, there died 870,000 Grecians, 670,000 Trojans, at the taking of the City, and after were slain 276,000 men, women, and children, of all sorts. Cæsar killed a million, Mahomet the Second Turk 300,000 persons: Sicinius Dentatus fought in an hundred battles, eight times in single combat he overcame, had forty wounds before, was rewarded with 140 crowns, triumphed nine times for his good service. M. Sergius had 32 wounds; Scæva, the Centurion, I know not how many; every nation hath their Hectors, Scipios, Cæsars, and Alexanders. Our Edward the Fourth was in 26 battles afoot: and as they do all, he glories in it, 'tis related to his honour. At the siege of Jerusalem 1,100,000 died with sword and famine. At the battle of Cannæ 70,000 men were slain, as Polybius records, and as many at Battle Abbey with us; and 'tis no news to fight from sun to sun, as they did; as Constantine and Licinius, &c. At the siege of Ostend (the Devil's Academy) a poor town in respect, a small fort, but a great grave, 120,000 men lost their lives, besides whole towns, dorps, and hospitals, full of maimed soldiers; there were engines, fire-works, and whatsoever the Devil could invent to do mischief with 2,500,000 iron bullets shot of 40 pound weight, three or four millions of gold consumed. *Who* (saith mine Author) *can be sufficiently amazed at their flinty hearts, obstinacy, fury, blindness, who, without any likelihood of good success, hazard poor soldiers, and lead them without pity to the slaughter, which may justly be called the rage of furious beasts, that run without reason upon their own deaths:* what plague, what fury brought so devilish, so brutish a thing as war first into men's minds? Who made so soft & peaceable a creature, born to love, mercy, meekness, so to rave, rage like beasts, & run on to their own destruction? How may Nature expostulate with mankind, I made thee a harmless, quiet, a divine creature! How may God expostulate, and all good men! Yet (as one condoles), these are the brave spirits, the gallants of the world, these admired alone, triumph alone, have statues, crowns, pyramids, obelisks, to their eternal fame, that immortal Genius attends on them, thus do men reach the stars. When Rhodes was beseiged the ditches were full of dead carcasses; and as when the said Solyman, great Turk, beleaguered Vienna, they lay level with the top,

of the walls. This they make sport of, and will do it to their friends
and confederates, against oaths, vows, promises, by treachery or otherwise; who, fighting with an enemy, cares if he acts with stratagem
or valor? leagues and laws of arms, (for the laws are silent during war),
for their advantage God's and men's laws are trampled under foot, the
sword alone determines all; to satisfy their lust and spleen, they care
not what they attempt, say, or do.

> *Scarce are faith and honour 'mongst the scamps*
> *Whose trade it is to follow camps.* (LUCAN)

Nothing so common as to have father fight against the son, brother
against brother, kinsman against kinsman, kingdom against kingdom,
province against province, Christians against Christians, of whom they
never had offense in thought, word, or deed. Infinite treasures consumed,
towns burned, flourishing cities sacked and ruinated, and, what the
mind shudders to recall, goodly countries depopulated and left desolate,
old inhabitants expelled, trade and traffick decayed, maids deflowered,
virgins and lads with unshorn locks; chaste matrons cry out with
Andromache, they shall be compelled peradventure to lie with them that
erst killed their husbands: to see rich, poor, sick, sound, Lords, servants,
consumed all or maimed, &c., saith Cyprian, and whatsoever torment,
misery, mischief, hell itself, the devil, fury and rage, can invent to their
own ruin and destruction! So abominable a thing is war, as Gerbelius
concludes, the destroyer of man, the scourge of God, cause, effect, fruit
and punishment of sin, and not the shearing of the human race, as
Tertullian calls it, but absolute ruin. Had Democritus been present at
the late Civil Wars in France, those abominable wars, hated of mothers,
where, in less than ten years, ten hundred thousand men were consumed,
saith Collignius, 20 thousand Churches overthrown; nay, the whole
kingdom subverted (as Richard Dinoth adds:) so many myriads of the
Commons were butchered up, with sword, famine, war, with such feral
hatred, the world was amazed at it: or at our late Pharsalian fields, in
the time of Henry the Sixth, between the houses of Lancaster and York,
an hundred thousand men slain, one writes, another, ten thousand families were rooted out, *that no man can but marvel,* saith Commines, *at
that barbarous immanity, feral madness, committed betwixt men of the
same nation, language, and religion!* What fury moves you, O citizens?
Why do the Gentiles so furiously rage, saith the Prophet David. But
we may ask, why do the Christians so furiously rage? Do not the young
men within the same hour desire, demand and seize the sword? Unfit
for Gentiles, much less for us so to tyrannize, as the Spaniards in the

West Indies, that killed up in 42 years (if we may believe Bartholomæus à Casa, their own Bishop) 12 millions of men, with stupend &
exquisite torments; neither should I lie (said he) if I said 50 millions.
I omit those French Massacres, Sicilian Evensongs, the Duke of Alva's
tyrannies, our gunpowder machinations, and that fourth fury, as one
calls it, the Spanish Inquisition, which quite obscures those 10 * persecutions; impious war rages throughout the whole earth. Is not this a mad
world, as he terms it, is not war madness? are not these madmen, as
Scaliger concludes, which leave so frequent battles as perpetual memorials of their madness to all succeeding ages? Would this, think you,
have enforced our Democritus to laughter, or rather made him turn his
tune, alter his tone, and weep with Heraclitus, or rather howl, roar, and
tear his hair in commiseration, stand amazed; or as the Poets feign, that
Niobe was for grief quite stupified, and turned to a stone? I have not
yet said the worse, that which is more absurd and mad, in their tumults,
seditions, civil and unjust wars, begun in folly, carried on in sin, and
finished in wretchedness; such wars I mean, for all are not to be condemned, as those fantastical Anabaptists vainly conceive. Our Christian
Tacticks are all out as necessary as the Roman Acies,† or Grecian Pha-
lanx; to be a soldier is a most noble and honourable profession (as the
world is), not to be spared, they are our best walls and bulwarks, and
I do therefore acknowledge that of Tully to be most true, *all our civil
affairs, all our studies, all our pleading, industry, and commendation,
lies under the protection of warlike virtues, and whensoever there is any
suspicion of tumult, all our arts cease.* Wars are most behoveful, and
warriors are more useful to a state than farmers, as Tyrius defends:
and valour is much to be commended in a wise man, but they mistake
most part ('twas Galgacus' observation in Tacitus), they term theft,
murder, and rapine, virtue, by a wrong name; rapes, slaughters, massacres, &c., are jests & games, pretty pastimes, as Ludovicus Vives notes.
*They commonly call the most hair-brain blood-suckers, strongest
thieves, the most desperate villains, treacherous rogues, inhuman murderers, rash, cruel and dissolute caitiffs, courageous and generous spirits,
heroical and worthy Captains, brave men at arms, valiant and renowned
soldiers, possessed with a brute persuasion of false honour,* as Pontus
Heuter in his Burgundian History complains. By means of which it
comes to pass that daily so many voluntaries offer themselves, leaving
their sweet wives, children, friends, for six pence (if they can get it)

* The ten persecutions of Christians under the Roman emperors.
† Battle-line.

a day, prostitute their lives and limbs, desire to enter upon breaches, lie sentinel, perdu, give the first onset, stand in the fore-front of the battle, marching bravely on, with a cheerful noise of drums and trumpets, such vigour and alacrity, so many banners streaming in the air, glittering armours, motions of plumes, woods of pikes and swords, variety of colours, cost and magnificence, as if they went in triumph, now victors to the Capitol, and with such pomp, as when Darius' army marched to meet Alexander at Issus. Void of all fear they run into eminent dangers, cannon's mouth, &c., that they may blunt the sword of their enemies by their own wounds, saith Barletius, to get a name of valour, honour and applause, which lasts not neither, for it is but a mere flash this fame, and like a rose 'tis gone in an instant. Of 15,000 proletaries slain in a battle, scarce fifteen are recorded in history, or one alone, the General perhaps, and after a while his and their names are likewise blotted out, the whole battle itself is forgotten. Those Grecian Orators, with the greatest force of genius and eloquence, set out the renowned overthrows at Thermopylæ, Salamis, Marathon, Mycale, Mantinea, Chæronea, Platæa. The Romans record their battle at Cannae, & Pharsalian fields, but they do but record, & we scarce hear of them. And yet this supposed honour, popular applause, desire of immortality by this means, pride and vain-glory spurs them on many times rashly and unadvisedly to make away themselves and multitudes of others. Alexander was sorry because there were no more worlds for him to conquer, he is admired by some for it; 'twas spoken like a Prince; but as wise Seneca censures him, 'twas spoken like a bedlam fool: and that sentence which the same Seneca appropriates to his father Philip and him, I apply to them all, they did as much mischief to mortal men as fire and water, those merciless elements when they rage. Which is yet more to be lamented, they persuade them this hellish course of life is holy, they promise heaven to such as venture their lives in holy war, and that by these bloody wars, (as Persians, Greeks, and Romans of old, as modern Turks do now their Commons, to encourage them to fight, that they may die in bliss), *if they die in the field, they go directly to heaven, & shall be canonized for saints,* (O diabolical invention!) put in the Chronicles to their eternal memory: when as in truth, as some hold it, it were much better (since wars are the scourge of God for sin, by which he punisheth mortal mens' peevishness & folly) such brutish stories were suppressed, because they conduce not at all to manners, or good life. But they will have it thus nevertheless, & so they put a note of *divinity upon the most cruel, & pernicious plague of hu-*

man kind, adore such men with grand titles, degrees, statues, images, honour, applaud, & highly reward them for their good service, no greater glory than to die in the field! So Africanus is extolled by Ennius: Mars, and Hercules, and I know not how many besides of old, were deified, went this way to heaven, that were indeed bloody butchers, wicked destroyers, and troublers of the world, prodigious monsters, hell-hounds, feral plagues, devourers, common executioners of human kind, as Lactantius truly proves, & Cyprian to Donatus, such as were desperate in wars, & precipitately made away themselves (like those Celts in Damascene, with ridiculous valour, so that they thought it a disgrace to run away for a rotten wall, now ready to fall on their heads). Such as will not rush on a sword's point, or seek to shun a cannon's shot, are base cowards, & no valiant men. By which means the earth wallows in her own blood, lust of the sword rages in him, the accursed madness of war, & for that which, if it be done in private, a man shall be rigorously executed, *and which is no less than murder itself, if the same fact be done in publick in wars, it is called manhood, and the party is honoured for it.* — Crime, when it is prosperous and successful, is called virtue. — We measure all, as Turks do, by the event, and most part, as Cyprian notes, in all ages, countries, places, the foulness of the fact vindicates the offender. One is crowned for that for which another is tormented; made a Knight, a Lord, an Earl, a great Duke, (as Agrippa notes), for which another should have hung in gibbets, as a terror to the rest. A poor sheep-stealer is hanged for stealing of victuals, compelled peradventure by necesity of that intolerable cold, hunger, & thirst, to save himself from starving: but a great man in office may securely rob whole provinces, undo thousands, pill and poll, oppress at his pleasure, flea, grind, tyrannize, enrich himself by the spoils of the Commons, be uncontrollable in his actions, and, after all, be recompensed with turgent titles, honoured for his good service, and no man dare to find fault, or mutter at it.

How would our Democritus have been affected, to see a wicked caitiff or *fool, a very idiot, a funge, a golden ass, a monster of men, to have many good men, wise men, learned men, to attend upon him with all submission, as an appendix to his riches, for that respect alone, because he hath more wealth and money, and to honour him with divine titles and bombast epithets,* to smother him with fumes & eulogies, whom they know to be a dizzard, a fool, a covetous wretch, a beast, &c., *because he is rich!* To see an ass dressed in the skin of a lion, a filthy loathsome carcass, a Gorgon's head puffed up by parasites, assume this unto him self, glorious titles, in worth an infant, a Cuman ass, a painted sepulchre, an Egyptian Temple! To see a withered face, a diseased, deformed, cankered complexion, a rotten carcass, a viperous mind, and Epicurean soul, set out with orient pearls, jewels, diadems, perfumes, curious elaborate works, as proud of his clothes as a child of his new coats; and a goodly person, of an angel-like divine countenance, a Saint, an humble mind, a meek spirit, clothed in rags, beg, and now ready to be starved! To see a silly contemptible sloven in apparel, ragged in his coat, polite in speech, of a divine spirit, wise; another neat in clothes, spruce, full of courtesy, empty of grace, wit, talk nonsense!

To see so many lawyers, advocates, so many tribunals, so little justice; so many magistrates, so little care of the common good; so many laws, yet never more disorders; the Tribunal a Labyrinth, so many thousand suits in one court sometimes, so violently followed! To see often a most unjust man preside over justice, an impious man over religion, a most ignorant man decide questions of learning, a most lazy man questions of labor, a monster questions of humanity! To see a lamb executed, a wolf pronounce sentence, a robber arraigned, and a thief sit on the bench, the Judge severely punish others, and do worse himself! Laws altered, misconstrued, interpreted *pro* and *con,* as the Judge is made by friends, bribed, or otherwise affected as a nose of wax, good to-day, none to-morrow; or firm in his opinion, cast in his! Sentence prolonged, changed according to the judge's whim, still the same case, *one thrust out of his inheritance, another falsely put in by favour, false forged deeds or wills.* Laws are made and not kept; or if put in execution, they be some silly ones that are punished. As put case it be fornication, the father will disinherit or abdicate his child, quite cashier him (out, villain, begone, come no more in my sight): a poor man is miserably tormented with loss of his estate perhaps, goods, fortunes, good name, for ever disgraced, forsaken, and must do penance to the utmost; a mortal sin, and yet, make the worst of it, saith Tranio in the Poet, he hath done no more than what Gentlemen usually do; neither new, startling, nor out of the ordinary. For in a great person, Right Worshipful Sir, a Right Honourable Grandee, 'tis not a venial sin, no not a *peccadillo,* 'tis no offence at all, a common and ordinary thing, no man takes notice of it; he justifies it in publick, and peradventure brags of it. For what would be base in good men — in Titius and Seius — was becoming to Crispinus.

Many poor men, younger brothers, &c., by reason of bad policy and idle education (for they are likely brought up in no calling), are com-

pelled to beg or steal, and then hanged for theft; than which what can
be more ignominious? For many punishments are not less a disgrace to
the governor than many funerals to a physician, — 'tis the governor's
fault; as Schoolmasters do rather correct their pupils, than teach them
when they do amiss. *They had more need provide there should be no
more thieves and beggars, as they ought with good policy, and take away
the occasions, than let them run on, as they do, to their own destruction:*
root out likewise those causes of wrangling, a multitude of lawyers, and
compose controversies by some more compendious means. Whereas
now for every toy and trifle they go to law, they are ready to pull out
one another's throats; and for commodity *to squeeze blood,* saith
Hierome, *out of their brothers' heart,* defame, lie, disgrace, backbite,
rail, bear false witness, swear, forswear, fight and wrangle, spend their
goods, lives, fortunes, friends, undo one another, to enrich an Harpy
Advocate, that preys upon them both, and cries Up, Socrates! up, Xanthippe! or some corrupt Judge, that like the kite in Æsop, while the
mouse & frog fought, carried both away. Generally they prey one upon
another, as so many ravenous birds, brute beasts, devouring fishes, no
medium, [all] either deceive or be deceived; tear others, or be torn in
pieces themselves; like so many buckets in a well, as one riseth another
falleth, one's empty, another's full; his ruin is a ladder to the third;
such are our ordinary proceedings. What's the market? A place, according to Anacharsis, wherein they cozen one another, a trap, nay, what's
the world itself? A vast Chaos, a confusion of manners, as fickle as the
air, a crazy house, a turbulent troop full of impurities, a mart of walking spirits, goblins, the theatre of hypocrisy, a shop of knavery, flattery,
a nursery of villainy, the scene of babbling, the school of giddiness, the
academy of vice; a warfare where, willing or unwilling, one must
fight and either conquer or succumb, in which kill or be killed; wherein
every man is for himself, his private ends, & stands upon his own guard.
No charity, love, friendship, fear of God, alliance, affinity, consanguinity, Christianity, can contain them, but if they be any ways
offended, or that string of commodity be touched, they fall foul. Old
friends become bitter enemies on a sudden for toys and small offences,
and they that erst were willing to do all mutual offices of love and kindness, now revile, & persecute one another to death, with more than
Vatinian hatred, & will not be reconciled. So long as they are behoveful, they love, or may bestead each other, but when there is no more
good to be expected, as they do by an old dog, hang him up or cashier
him: which Cato counts a great *indecorum,* to use men like old shoes

or broken glasses, which are flung to the dunghill; he could not find in his heart to sell an old ox, much less to turn away an old servant: but they instead of recompense, revile him, and when they have made him an instrument of their villainy, as Bajazet the Second, Emperor of the Turks, did by Achmet Bassa, make him away, or, instead of reward, hate him to death, as Silius was served by Tiberius. In a word, every man for his own ends. Our greatest good is commodity, and the goddess we adore Queen Money, to whom we daily offer sacrifice, which steers our hearts, hands, affections, all: that most powerful Goddess, by whom we are reared, depressed, elevated, esteemed the sole commandress of our actions, for which we pray, run, ride, go, come, labour and contend as fishes do for a crumb that falleth into the water. It's not worth, virtue, (that's a theatrical value), wisdom, valour, learning, honesty, religion, or any sufficiency for which we are respected, but money, greatness, office, honour, authority; honesty is accounted folly; knavery, policy; men admired out of opinion, not as they are, but as they seem to be: such shifting, lying, cogging, plotting, counterplotting, temporizing, flattering, cozening, dissembling, *that of necessity one must highly offend God, if he be conformable to the world,* be a Cretan with the Cretans, *or else live in contempt, disgrace, and misery.* One takes upon him temperance, holiness, another austerity, a third an affected kind of simplicity, when as indeed he, and he, and he, and the rest are hypocrites, ambodexters, out-sides, so many turning pictures, a lion on the one side, a lamb on the other. How would Democritus have been affected to see these things!

To see a man turn himself into all shapes like a Chameleon, or as Proteus transform himself into all that is monstrous; to act twenty parts & persons at once for his advantage, to temporize & vary like Mercury the Planet, good with good, bad with bad; having a several face, garb, & character, for every one he meets; of all religions, humours, inclinations; to fawn like a spaniel, with lying and feigned obsequiousness, rage like a lion, bark like a cur, fight like a dragon, sting like a serpent, as meek as a lamb, & yet again grin like a tiger, weep like a crocodile, insult over some, & yet others domineer over him, here command, there crouch, tyrannize in one place, be baffled in another, a wise man at home, a fool abroad to make others merry!

To see so much difference betwixt words and deeds, so many parasangs betwixt tongue and heart, men like stage-players act variety of parts, give good precepts to others, soar aloft, whilst they themselves grovel on the ground!

To see a man protest friendship, kiss his hand, whom he would wish slain, smile with an intent to do mischief, or cozen him whom he salutes, magnify his friend unworthy with hyperbolical elogiums; his enemy, albeit a good man, to vilify and disgrace him, yea, all his actions, with the utmost livor and malice can invent!

To see a servant able to buy out his master, him that carries the mace more worth than the magistrate, which Plato absolutely forbids, Epictetus abhors. An horse that tills the land fed with chaff, an idle jade have provender in abundance; him that makes shoes go barefoot himself, him that sells meat almost pined; a toiling drudge starve, a drone flourish!

To see men buy smoke for wares, castles built with fools' heads, men like apes follow the fashions in tires, gestures, actions: if the King laugh, all laugh;

Laugh you? a louder laugh shakes him; weep,
And with his friend in tears he'll company keep. (JUVENAL)

Alexander stooped, so did his Courtiers; Alphonsus turned his head, and so did his parasites. Sabina Poppæa, Nero's wife, wore amber-colour'd hair, so did all the Roman Ladies in an instant, her fashion was theirs.

To see men wholly led by affection, admired and censured out of opinion without judgment; an inconsiderate multitude, like so many dogs in a village, if one bark, all bark without a cause: as fortune's fan turns, if a man be in favour, or commended by some great one, all the world applauds him; if in disgrace, in an instant all hate him, & as at the Sun when he is eclipsed, that erst took no notice, now gaze, and stare upon him!

To see a man wear his brains in his belly, his guts in his head, an hundred oaks on his back, to devour 100 oxen at a meal, nay more, to devour houses and towns, or as those *Anthropophagi,* to eat one another!

To see a man roll himself up, like a snow ball, from base beggary to Right Worshipful and Right Honourable titles, unjustly to screw himself into honours and offices; another to starve his *genius,* damn his soul, to gather wealth, which he shall not enjoy, which his prodigal son melts and consumes in an instant!

To see the dishonourable ambition of our times, a man bend all his forces, means, time, fortunes, to be a favourite's favourite's favourite, &c., a parasite's parasite's parasite, that may scorn the servile world as having enough already!

To see an hirsute beggar's brat, that lately fed on scraps, crept and whin'd, crying to all, and for an old jerkin ran on errands, now ruffle in silk and satin, bravely mounted, jovial and polite, now scorn his old friends and familiars, neglect his kindred, insult over his betters, domineer over all!

To see a scholar crouch and creep to an illiterate peasant for a meal's meat; a scrivener better paid for an obligation; a falconer receive greater wages than a student: a lawyer get more in a day than a philosopher in a year, better reward for an hour than a scholar for a twelvemonth's study; him that can paint Thais, play on a fiddle, curl hair, &c., sooner get preferment than a philologer or a poet!

To see a fond mother, like Æsop's ape, hug her child to death, a wittol wink at his wife's honesty, and too perspicuous in all other affairs; one stumble at a straw, and leap over a block; rob Peter, and pay Paul; scrape unjust sums with one hand, purchase great manors by corruption, fraud, and cozenage, and liberally to distribute to the poor with the other, give a remnant to pious uses, &c.; penny wise, pound foolish; blind men judge of colours; wise men silent, fools talk; find fault with others, and do worse themselves; denounce that in publick which he doth in secret; and which Aurelius Victor gives out of Augustus, severely censure that in a third, of which he is most guilty himself!

To see a poor fellow, or an hired servant, venture his life for his new master, that will scarce give him his wages at year's end; a country colone* toil and moil, till and drudge, for a prodigal idle drone, that devours all the gain, or lasciviously consumes with phantastical expences; a noble man in a bravado to encounter death, and for a small flash of honour to cast away himself; a worldling tremble at an executioner, and yet not fear hell-fire; to wish and hope for immortality, desire to be happy, and yet by all means avoid death, a necessary passage to bring him to it!

To see a fool-hardy fellow like those old Danes, who would die rather than be punished, in a sottish humour embrace death with alacrity, yet scorn to lament his own sins and miseries, or his dearest friends' departures!

To see wise men degraded, fools preferred; one govern towns and cities, and yet a silly woman over-rules him at home; command a Province, and yet his own servants or children prescribe laws to him, as Themistocles' son did in Greece; *What I will* (said he) *my mother wills, and what my mother wills, my father doth.* To see horses ride in a coach, men draw it; dogs devour their masters; towers build masons;

* A farmer on shares, serf, or peasant.

children rule; old men go to school; women wear the breeches, sheep demolish towns, devour men, &c., and in a word, the world turned upside downward! O that Democritus were but alive again!

To insist in every particular were one of Hercules' Labours, there's so many ridiculous instances, as motes in the Sun. What emptiness there is in human affairs! And who can speak of all? From one offense learn all; take this for a taste.

But these are obvious to sense, trivial and well-known, easy to be discerned. How would Democritus have been moved, had he seen the secrets of their hearts! If every man had a window in his breast, which Momus would have had in Vulcan's man, or, that which Tully so much wished, it were written in every man's forehead what he thought about the Republic; or that it could be effected in an instant, which Mercury did by Charon in Lucian, by touching of his eyes, to make him discern,

Blind hopes and wishes, their thoughts and affairs,
Whispers and rumours, and those flying cares:

that he could bring forth what is concealed behind bed room doors, and discover the secrets of hearts, which Cyprian desired, open doors and locks, shoot bolts, as Lucian's Cock did with a feather of his tail: or Gyges' invisible ring, or some rare perspective glass, or Otacousticon, which would so multiply appearances, that a man might hear and see all at once (as Martianus Capella's Jupiter did in a spear which he held in his hand, which did present unto him all that was daily done upon the face of the earth), observe cuckolds' horns, forgeries of alchemists, the philosopher's stone, new projectors, &c., and all those works of darkness, foolish vows, hopes, fears, and wishes, what a deal of laughter would it have afforded! He should have seen wind-mills in one man's head, an hornet's nest in another! Or had he been present with Icaromenippus, in Lucian, at Jupiter's whispering place, and heard one pray for rain, another for fair weather, one for his wife's, another for his father's, death, &c., *to ask that at God's hand which they are abashed any man should hear:* how would he have been confounded! Would he, think you, or any man else, say that these men were well in their wits?

That mad Orestes, if he saw the show,
Would swear thou wert the madder of the two. (PERSIUS)

Can all the Hellebore in the Anticyræ cure these men? No, sure, *an acre of Hellebore will not do it!*

That which is more to be lamented, they are mad like Seneca's blind woman, and will not acknowledge, or seek for any cure of it, for few see their malady, all love it. If our leg or arm offend us, we covet by all means possible to redress it; and if we labour of a bodily disease, we send for a physician; but for the diseases of the mind we take no notice of them: lust harrows us on the one side, envy, anger, ambition, on the other. We are torn in pieces by our passions, as [by] so many wild horses, one in disposition, another in habit; one is melancholy, another mad; and which of us all seeks for help, doth acknowledge his error, or knows he is sick? As that stupid fellow put out the candle, because the biting fleas should not find him; he shrouds himself in an unknown habit, borrowed titles, because nobody should discern him. Every man thinks with himself, I seem quite sane, I am well, I am wise; and laughs at others. And 'tis a general fault amongst them all, that which our forefathers have approved, diet, apparel, opinions, humours, customs, manners, we deride and reject in our time as absurd. Old men account juniors all fools, when they are mere dizzards; and as to sailors, they move, the land stands still, the world hath much more wit, they dote themselves. Turks deride us, we them; Italians Frenchmen, accounting them light-headed fellows; the French scoff again at Italians, and at their several customs; Greeks have condemned all the world but themselves of *barbarism,* the world as much vilifies them now; we account Germans heavy, dull, fellows, explode many of their fashions; they as contemptibly think of us; Spaniards laugh at all, and all again at them. So are we fools and ridiculous, absurd in our actions, carriages, diet, apparel, customs, and consultations; we scoff and point one at another, when as in conclusion all are fools, *and they the veriest asses that hide their ears most.* A private man, if he be resolved with himself, or set on an opinion, accounts all idiots and asses that are not affected as he is,

There's nothing right except what pleases them, (HORACE)
that are not so minded, (for what men wish, they think they wish wisely), all fools that think not as he doth. He will not say with Atticus, let every man enjoy his own spouse; but his alone is fair, &c., and scorns all in respect of himself, will imitate none, hear none, but himself, as Pliny said, [be] a law and example to himself. And that which Hippocrates, in his Epistle to Dionysius, reprehended of old, is verified in our times, that which he hath not himself, or doth not esteem, he accounts superfluity, an idle quality, a mere foppery, in another: like Æsop's fox, when he had lost his tail, would have all his fellow foxes cut off theirs. The Chinese say, that we Europeans have one eye, they themselves two, all the world else is blind (though

Scaliger accounts them brutes too, mere cattle); so thou and thy sectaries are only wise, others indifferent, the rest beside themselves, mere idiots and asses. Thus, not acknowledging our own errors and imperfections, we securely deride others, as if we alone were free, and spectators of the rest, accounting it an excellent thing, as indeed it is, to profit ourselves by the madness of others, to make ourselves merry with other men's obliquities, when as he himself is more faulty than the rest, change the name and you're the man, he may take himself by the nose for a fool; and which one calls the height of folly, to be ridiculous to others, and not to perceive or take notice of it, as Marsyas was when he contended with Apollo, not understanding that he was being made game of, saith Apuleius; 'tis his own cause, he is a convict mad-man, as Austin well infers, *In the eyes of wise men and Angels he seems like one, that to our thinking walks with his heels upward.* So thou laughest at me, and I at thee, both at a third; and he returns that of the Poet upon us again, they call me insane when they themselves are the most insane. We accuse others of madness, of folly, and are the veriest dizzards ourselves. For it is a great sign and property of a fool (which Ecclesiastes points at) out of pride and self-conceit to insult, vilify, condemn, censure, and call other men fools (We see not what's in the wallet on our back), to tax that in others of which we are most faulty; teach that which we follow not ourselves: for an inconstant man to write of constancy, a profane liver prescribe rules of sanctity and piety, a dizzard himself make a treatise of wisdom, or with Sallust to rail down right at spoilers of countries, and yet in office to be a most grievous poller himself. This argues weakness, and is an evident sign of such parties' indiscretion. *Who is the fool now?* Or else peradventure in some places we are all mad for company, and so 'tis not seen, the fre-quency of fault and madness removes both the wonder and the absurd-ity they excite. 'Tis with us, as it was of old (in Tully's censure at least), with C. Fimbria in Rome, a bold, hair-brain, mad fellow, and so es-teemed of all, such only excepted, that were as mad as himself: now in such a case there is no notice taken of it.

> *When all are mad, where all are like opprest,*
> *Who can discern one mad man from the rest?*   (HORACE)

But put case they do perceive it, and some one be manifestly convict of madness, he now takes notice of his folly, be it in action, gesture, speech, a vain humour he hath in building, bragging, jangling, spending, gaming, courting, scribbling, prating, for which he is ridiculous to others, on which he dotes, he doth acknowledge as much: yet with all the

Rhetorick thou hast, thou canst not so recall him, but to the contrary notwithstanding, he will persevere in his dotage? 'Tis the insanity of love, & the dearest delusion of an enraptured mind; so pleasing, so delicious, that he cannot leave it. He knows his error, but will not seek to decline it, tell him what the event will be, beggary, sorrow, sickness, disgrace, shame, loss, madness, yet *an angry man will prefer vengeance, a lascivious his whore, a thief his booty, a glutton his belly, before his welfare.* Tell an Epicure, a covetous man, an ambitious man, of his irregular course, wean him from it a little, By Pollux! my friend, he cries anon, you have undone him, and, as a *dog to his vomit,* he returns to it again: no persuasion will take place, no counsel, say what thou canst,

> *Though you call out, confound the sky and sea,*
> *You address a deaf man when you call out to me;*

demonstrate as Ulysses did to Elpenor and Gryllus, and the rest of his companions, *those swinish men,* he is irrefragable in his humour, he will be a hog still; bray him in a mortar, he will be the same. If he be in an heresy, or some perverse opinion, settled as some of our ignorant Papists are, convince his understanding, shew him the several follies, and absurd fopperies, of that sect, force him to say, I am convinced by the truth, make it as clear as the sun, he will err still, peevish and obstinate as he is; and as he said, If I err in this, I willingly err, nor will I have this error taken away from me, I will do as I have done, as my predecessors have done, and as my friends now do, I will dote for company. Say now, are these men mad or no? Answer me, are they ridiculous? Bring any judge, are they of sound mind, sober, wise, and discreet? have they common sense?

> *Which of these is the more mad?* (HORACE)

I am of Democritus' opinion for my part, I hold them worthy to be laughed at; a company of brain-sick dizzards as mad as Orestes and Athamas, that they may go *ride the ass,* and all sail along to the Anticyræ in the *ship of fools* for company together. I need not much labour to prove this which I say otherwise than thus, make any solemn protestation, or swear, I think you will believe me without an oath; say at a word, are they fools? I refer it to you, though you be likewise fools and madmen yourselves, and I as mad to ask the question; for what said our comical Mercury?

> *I'll stand to your censure yet, what think you?* (PLAUTUS)

But, forasmuch as I undertook at first, that Kingdoms, Provinces, families, were melancholy as well as private men, I will examine them in particular, and that which I have hitherto dilated at random, in more general terms, I will particularly insist in, prove with more special and evident arguments, testimonies, illustrations, and that in brief.

Now hear why all are fools as much as you. (HORACE)

My first argument is borrowed from Solomon, an arrow drawn out of his sententious quiver, *Be not wise in thine own eyes.* And *Seest thou a man wise in his own conceit? more hope is of a fool than of him.* Isaiah pronounceth a woe against such men, *that are wise in their own eyes and prudent in their own sight.* For hence we may gather, that it is a great offence, and men are much deceived that think too well of themselves, an especial argument to convince them of folly. Many men (saith Seneca) *had been without question wise, had they not had an opinion that they had attained to perfection of knowledge already, even before they had gone halfway,* too forward, too ripe, too quick and ready, they had too good a conceit of themselves, and that marred all; of their worth, valour, skill, art, learning, judgement, eloquence, their good parts; all their geese are swans, and that manifestly proves them to be no better than fools. In former times they had but seven wise men, now you can scarce find so many fools. Thales sent the golden Tripos, which the Fisherman found, & the oracle commanded to be *given to the wisest,* to Bias, Bias to Solon, &c. If such a thing were now found, we should all fight for it, as the three Goddesses did for the golden apple, we are so wise: we have women politicians, children metaphysicians; every silly fellow can square a circle, make perpetual motions, find the philosopher's stone, interpret *Apocalypsis,* make new Theoricks, a new system of the world, new Logick, new Philosophy, &c. Saith Petronius, *our country is so full of deified spirits, divine souls, that you may sooner find a God than a man amongst us,* we think so well of ourselves, and that is an ample testimony of much folly.

My second argument is grounded upon the like place of Scripture, which though before mention'd in effect, yet for some reasons is to be repeated (and by Plato's good leave, I may do it, a good thing is no worse for repetition). *Fools* (saith David) *by reason of their transgressions, &c.* Hence Musculus infers all transgressors must needs be fools. So we read, *Tribulation and anguish on the soul of every man that doth evil;* but all do evil. And Isaiah, *My servants shall sing for joy, and ye shall cry for sorrow of heart, and vexation of mind.* 'Tis ratified by the common consent of all philosophers. *Dishonesty* (saith Cardan) *is nothing else but folly and madness.* Who can find a faithful man? Shew me an honest man. There is no bad man who is not a fool, 'tis

Fabius' aphorism to the same end. If none honest, none wise, then all fools. And well may they be so accounted: for who will account him otherwise, that goes backward all his life, westward, when he is bound to the east? or hold him a wise man (saith Musculus) *that prefers momentany pleasures to eternity, that spends his Master's goods in his absence, forthwith to be condemned for it?* He is wise to no purpose who is not wise for himself. Who will say that a sick man is wise, that eats & drinks to overthrow the temperature of his body? Can you account him wise or discreet that would willingly have his health, and yet will do nothing that should procure or continue it? Theodoret, out of Plotinus the Platonist, *holds it a ridiculous thing for a man to live after his own laws, to do that which is offensive to God, and yet to hope that He should save him; and when he voluntarily neglects his own safety, and contemns the means, to think to be delivered by another.* Who will say these men are wise?

A third argument may be derived from the precedent. All men are carried away with passion, discontent, lust, pleasures, &c.; they generally hate the virtues they should love, and love such vices they should hate. Therefore more than melancholy, quite mad, brute beasts, and void of reason, so Chrysostom contends; *or rather dead and buried alive,* as Philo Judaeus concludes it for a certainty, *of all such that are carried away with passions, or labour of any disease of the mind. Where is fear and sorrow,* there, Lactantius stiffly maintains, *wisdom cannot dwell.*

> *He who desires will, certes, also fear,*
> *And he who lives in fear will ne'er be free*
> *In my opinion.* (HORACE)

Seneca & the rest of the Stoicks are of opinion, that, where is any the least perturbation, wisdom may not be found. *What more ridiculous,* as Lactantius urgeth, than to hear how Xerxes whipped the Hellespont, threatened the Mountain Athos, and the like? To speak pointedly, who is free from passion? As Tully determines out of an old Poem, no mortal man can avoid sorrow & sickness; and sorrow is an inseparable companion of melancholy. Chrysostom pleads farther yet, that they are more than mad, very beasts, stupefied, and void of common sense. *For how* (saith he) *shall I know thee to be a man, when thou kickest like an ass, neighest like a horse after women, ravest in lust like a bull, ravenest like a bear, stingest like a scorpion, rakest like a wolf, as subtle as a fox, as impudent as a dog? shall I say thou art a man, that hast all the symptoms of a beast? how shall I know thee to be a man?*

By thy shape? that affrights me more, when I see a beast in likeness of a man.

Seneca calls that of Epicurus an heroical speech, *A fool still begins to live,* and accounts it a filthy lightness in men, every day to lay new foundations of their life, but who doth otherwise? One travels, another builds; one for this, another for that business; and old folks are as far out as the rest; O mad old age! Tully exclaims. Therefore young, old, middle age, all are stupid, and dote.

Æneas Sylvius, amongst many others, sets down three special ways to find a fool by. He is a fool that seeks that he cannot find: he is a fool that seeks that, which being found will do him more harm than good: he is a fool, that, having variety of ways to bring him to his journey's end, takes that which is worst. If so, methinks most men are fools; examine their courses, and you shall soon perceive what dizzards and mad men the major part are.

Beroaldus will have drunkards, afternoon men, and such as more than ordinarily delight in drink, to be mad. The first pot quencheth thirst, so Panyasis the Poet determines in Athenæus, the second makes merry, the third for pleasure, the fourth makes them mad. If this position be true, what a catalogue of mad men shall we have! what shall they be that drink four times four? Does not drink make men insane above all fury and madness? I am of his opinion, they are more than mad, much worse than mad.

The Abderites condemned Democritus for a mad man, because he was sometimes sad, and sometimes again profusely merry. His countrymen (saith Hippocrates), hold him mad because he laughs; and therefore *he desires him to advise all his friends at Rhodes, that they do not laugh too much, or be over-sad.* Had those Abderites been conversant with us, and but seen what fleering and grinning there is in this age, they would certainly have concluded, we had been all out of our wits!

Aristotle in his Ethicks holds to be wise and happy are reciprocal terms. Goodness and wisdom are one to the honourable. 'Tis Tully's paradox, *wise men are free, but fools are slaves,* liberty is a power to live according to his own laws, as we will ourselves. Who hath this liberty? Who is free?

He is wise that can command his own will,
Valiant and constant to himself still,
Whom poverty nor death, nor bands can fright,
Checks his desires, scorns honours, just and right.   (HORACE)

But where shall such a man be found? If no where, then on the contrary, we are all slaves, senseless, or worse. No bad man is happy. But no man is happy in this life, none good, therefore no man wise. The good are scarce. For one virtue you shall find ten vices in the same party. There are few Prometheuses, many Epimetheuses. We may peradventure usurp the name, or attribute it to others for favour, as Charles the Wise, Philip the Good, Louis the Pious, &c., and describe the properties of a wise man, as Tully doth an Orator, Xenophon Cyrus, Castilio a Courtier, Galen Temperament, an Aristocracy is described by Politicians. But where shall such a man be found?

> *A wise, a good man in a million,*
> *Apollo consulted could scarce find one.* (AUSONIUS)

A man is a miracle of himself, but Trismegistus adds, a wise man is the greatest wonder: many Bacchantes, but few Bacchuses. Alexander when he was presented with that rich and costly casket of King Darius, and every man advised him what to put in it, he reserved it to keep Homer's works, as the most precious jewel of human wit, and yet Scaliger upbraids Homer's Muse as a nursery of madness, impudent as a Court Lady, that blushes at nothing. Jacobus Mycillus, Gilbertus Cognatus, Erasmus, and almost all posterity admire Lucian's luxuriant wit, yet Scaliger rejects him in his censure, and calls him the Cerberus of the Muses. Socrates, whom all the world so much magnified, is by Lactantius and Theodoret condemned for a fool. Plutarch extols Seneca's wit beyond all the Greeks, second to none, yet Seneca saith of himself, *when I would solace myself with a fool, I reflect upon myself, and there I have him.* Cardan, in his 16th Book of Subtleties, reckons up twelve supereminent, acute Philosophers, for worth, subtlety, and wisdom: Archimedes, Galen, Vitruvius, Archytas Tarentinus, Euclid, Geber, that first inventor of Algebra, Alkindus the Mathematician, both Arabians, with others. But his three great men of the world, far beyond the rest, are Ptolemæus, Plotinus, Hippocrates. Scaliger scoffs at this censure of his, calls some of them carpenters and mechanicians, he makes Galen a skirt of Hippocrates: & the said Cardan himself elsewhere condemns both Galen and Hippocrates for tediousness, obscurity, confusion. Paracelsus will have them both mere idiots, infants in physick and philosophy. Scaliger and Cardan admire Suisset the Calculator, who well nigh exceeded the bounds of human genius, and yet Lod. Vives calls them Suisset's trifles: and Cardan, opposite to himself in another place, contemns those ancients in respect of times present and says that our ancestors, compared with our contemporaries, may be justly called children. In conclusion, the said Cardan and Saint Bernard will admit none into this Catalogue of wise men, but only Prophets and Apostles; how they esteem themselves, you have heard before. We are worldly-wise, admire ourselves, and seek for applause: but hear Saint Bernard, *the more wise thou art to others, the more fool to thyself*. I may not deny but that there is some folly approved, a divine fury, a holy madness, even a spiritual drunkenness, in the Saints of God themselves; holy madness Bernard calls it (though not as blaspheming Vorstius, would infer it as a passion incident to God himself, but) familiar to good men, as that of Paul, *he was a fool*, &c., and he wisheth himself *to be anathematized for them*. Such is that drunkenness which Ficinus speaks of, when the soul is elevated and ravished with a divine taste of that heavenly Nectar, which poets deciphered by the sacrifice of Dionysus, and in this sense with the Poet, as Austin exhorts us, let's all be mad and drunk. But we commonly mistake, and go beyond our commission, we reel to the opposite part, we are not capable of it, and as he said of the Greeks, You Greeks, British, Gauls, Germans, Italians, are forever no more than boys, &c., you are a company of fools.

Proceed now from the parts to the whole or from the whole to [the] parts, and you shall find no other issue, the parts shall be sufficiently dilated in this following Preface. The whole must needs follow by a *Sorites* or Induction. Every multitude is mad, precipitate and rash, without judgment, a roaring rout. Roger Bacon proves it out of Aristotle, that which the commonalty accounts true is most part false, they are still opposite to wise men, but all the world is of this humour (*vulgar*), and thou thyself art one of the commonalty, and he, and he, and so are all the rest; and therefore, as Phocion concludes, to be approved in nought you say or do, mere idiots and asses. Begin then where you will, go backward or forward, choose out of the whole pack, wink and choose, you shall find them all alike, *never a barrel better herring*.

Copernicus, Atlas his successor, is of opinion the earth is a planet, moves and shines to others, as the moon doth to us. Digges, Gilbert, Kepler, Origanus, and others, defend this *hypothesis* of his in sober sadness, and that the moon is inhabited: if it be so that the earth is a moon, then are we also giddy, vertiginous and lunatick within this sublunary maze.

I could produce such arguments till dark night: if you should hear the rest,

> *The night would come upon us ere 'twas finished,*
>
> (VIRGIL)

but, according to my promise, I will descend to particulars. This melancholy extends itself not to men only, but even to vegetals and sensibles. I speak not of those creatures which are *saturnine,* melancholy by nature, (as lead, and such like minerals, or those plants, rue, cypress, &c. and hellebore itself, of which Agrippa treats, fishes, birds, and beasts, hares, conies, dormice, &c. owls, bats, nightbirds,) but that artificial, which is perceived in them all. Remove a plant, it will pine away, which is especially perceived in date trees, as you may read at large in Constantine's husbandry, that antipathy betwixt the vine and the cabbage, wine and oil. Put a bird in a cage, he will die for sullenness, or a beast in a pen, or take his young ones or companions from him, and see what effect it will cause. But who perceives not these common passions of sensible creatures, fear, sorrow, &c.? Of all other, dogs are most subject to this malady, insomuch some hold they dream as men do, and through violence of melancholy run mad; I could relate many stories of dogs that have died for grief, and pined away for loss of their masters, but they are common in every author.

Kingdoms, provinces, and politick bodies are likewise sensible and subject to this disease, as Boterus in his Politicks hath proved at large. *As in human bodies* (saith he) *there be divers alterations proceeding from humours, so there be many diseases in a commonwealth, which do as diversely happen from several distempers,* as you may easily perceive by their particular symptoms. For where you shall see the people civil, obedient to God and Princes, judicious, peaceable and quiet, rich, fortunate, and flourish, to live in peace, in unity and concord, a country well tilled, many fair built and populous cities, as old Cato said, the people are neat, polite and terse, where they live well and happily, which our politicians make the chief end of a common-wealth; and which Aristotle calls a general blessing, Polybius a desirable and favorable condition, that country is free from melancholy; as it was in Italy in the time of Augustus, now in China, now in many other flourishing kingdoms of Europe. But whereas you shall see many discontents, common grievances, complaints, poverty, barbarism, beggary, plagues, wars, rebellions, seditions, mutinies, contentions, idleness, riot, epicurism, the land lie untilled, waste, full of bogs, fens, deserts, &c., cities decayed, base and poor towns, villages depopulated, the people squalid, ugly, uncivil; that kingdom, that country, must needs be discontent, melancholy, hath a sick body, and had need to be reformed.

Now that cannot well be effected, till the causes of these maladies be first removed, which commonly proceed from their own default, or some accidental inconvenience: as to be sited in a bad clime, too far

North, sterile, in a barren place, as the desert of Libya, deserts of Arabia, places void of waters, as those of Lop and Belgian in Asia, or in a bad air, as at Alexandretta, Bantam, Pisa, Durazzo, S. John de Ullua, &c., or in danger of the sea's continual inundations, as in many places of the Low Countries, and elsewhere, or near some bad neighbours, as Hungarians to Turks, Podolians to Tartars, or almost any bordering countries, they live in fear still, and by reason of hostile incursions are oftentimes left desolate. So are cities by reason of wars, fires, plagues, inundations, wild beasts, decay of trades, barred havens, the sea's violence, as Antwerp may witness of late, Syracuse of old, Brundusium in Italy, Rye & Dover with us, and many that at this day suspect the sea's fury and rage, and labour against it, as the Venetians, to their inestimable charge. But the most frequent maladies are such as proceed from themselves, as first when religion & God's service is neglected, innovated or altered, where they do not fear God, obey their Prince, where Atheism, Epicurism, Sacrilege, Simony, &c., and all such impieties are freely committed, that country cannot prosper. When Abraham came to Gerar, and saw a bad land, he said, sure the fear of God was not in that place. Cyprian Echovius, a Spanish Chorographer, above all other Cities of Spain commends Barcino, *in which there was no beggar, no man poor, &c., but all rich and in good estate, and he gives the reason, because they were more religious than their neighbours.* Why was Israel so often spoiled by their enemies, led into captivity, &c., but for their idolatry, neglect of God's word, for sacrilege, even for one Achan's fault? And what shall we expect that have such multitudes of Achans, Church-robbers, Simoniacal Patrons, &c.? How can they hope to flourish, that neglect divine duties, that live most part like Epicures?

Other common grievances are generally noxious to a body politick; alteration of laws and customs, breaking privileges, general oppressions, seditions, &c., observed by Aristotle, Bodine, Boterus, Junius, Arniseus, &c. I will only point at some of the chiefest. Confusion, ill government, which proceeds from unskilful, slothful, griping, covetous, unjust, rash, or tyrannizing magistrates, when they are fools, idiots, children, proud, wilful, partial, indiscreet, oppressors, giddy heads, tyrants, not able or unfit to manage such offices. Many noble cities and flourishing kingdoms by that means are desolate, the whole body groans under such heads, and all the members must needs be misaffected, as at this day those goodly provinces in Asia Minor, &c., groan under the burden of a Turkish government; and those vast kingdoms of Muscovia, Russia, under a tyrannizing Duke. Who ever heard of more civil and rich populous countries than those of Greece, Asia Minor, *abounding with all wealth, multitude of inhabitants, force, power, splendour, and magnificence?* and that miracle of countries, the Holy Land, that in so small a compass of ground could maintain so many towns, cities, produce so many fighting men? Egypt, another Paradise, now barbarous and desert, and almost waste, by the despotical government of an imperious Turk, sent into an intolerable slavery (one saith); not only fire and water, goods or lands, but such is their slavery, their lives and souls depend upon his insolent will and command: a tyrant that spoils all wheresoever he comes, insomuch that an Historian complains, *if an old inhabitant should now see them, he would not know them, if a traveller, or stranger, it would grieve his heart to behold them.* Where, as Aristotle notes, new burdens and exactions daily come upon them, like those of which Zosimus [speaks], so grievous, as that men prostituted their wives, fathers their sons, for the profit of overseers, &c., they must needs be discontent, as Tully holds, hence come those complaints and tears of cities, poor, miserable, rebellious, and desperate subjects, as Hippolytus adds: and as a judicious countryman of ours observed not long since in a survey of that great Duchy of Tuscany, the people lived much grieved and discontent, as appeared by their manifold and manifest complainings in that kind; *that the State was like a sick body which had lately taken physick, whose humours were not yet well settled, and weakened so much by purging, that nothing was left but melancholy.*

Whereas the Princes and Potentates are immoderate in lust, hypocrites, epicures, of no religion, but in show: what so brittle and unsure? what sooner subverts their estates than wandering & raging lusts on their subjects' wives, daughters, to say no worse? They that should lead the way to all virtuous actions, are the ringleaders oftentimes of all mischief and dissolute courses, and by that means their countries are plagued, *and they themselves often ruined, banished or murdered by conspiracy of their subjects,* as Sardanapulus was, Dionysius Junior, Heliogabalus, Periander, Pisistratus, Tarquinius, Timocrates, Childericus, Appius Claudius, Andronicus, Galeazzo Sforza, Alexander de Medici, &c.

Whereas the Princes or great men are malicious, envious, factious, ambitious, emulators, they tear a commonwealth asunder, as so many *Guelphs* and *Ghibelines,* disturb the quietness of it, and with mutual murders let it bleed to death. Our histories are too full of such barbarous inhumanities, and the miseries that issue from them.

Whereas they be like so many horse-leeches, hungry, griping, corrupt, covetous, greedy for property, ravenous as wolves, (for as Tully writes, Whoso rules is a benefit, and he who rules cattle should study their interests,) or such prefer their private before the publick good (for as he said long since, private interests always interfere with publick benefits), — or whereas they be illiterate, ignorant, empiricks in policy,* lacking in capacity, courage, & knowledge, wise only by inheritance, and in authority by birth-right, favour, or for their wealth and titles; there must needs be a fault, a great defect: because, as an old Philosopher affirms, such men are not always fit: *of an infinite number few alone are Senators, and of those few fewer good, and of that small number of honest good and noble men, few that are learned, wise, discreet and sufficient, able to discharge such places;* it must needs turn to the confusion of a State.

For as the Princes are, so are the people; and which Antigonus right well said of old, he that teacheth the King of Macedon, teacheth all his subjects, is a true saying still.

For Princes are the glass, the school, the book,
Where subjects' eyes do learn, do read, do look. (SHAKESPEARE)

——— *Swiftly, in a trice,*
We are corrupted by domestic vice;
When precedents of sin our great ones give,
Few are the youths that free from vice can live. (JUVENAL)

Their examples are soonest followed, vices entertained; if they be profane, irreligious, lascivious, riotous, epicures, factious, covetous, ambitious, illiterate, so will the commons most part be idle, unthrifts, prone to lust, drunkards, and therefore poor and needy (for poverty begets sedition and villainy), upon all occasions ready to mutiny and rebel, discontent still, complaining, murmuring, grudging, apt to all outrages, thefts, treasons, murders, innovations, in debt, shifters, cozeners, outlaws, men of evil life and reputation. It was an old Politician's Aphorism, *they that are poor and bad envy rich, hate good men, abhor the present government, wish for a new, and would have all turned topsy turvy.* When Catiline rebelled in Rome, he got a company of such debauched rogues together, they were his familiars and coadjutors; and such have been your rebels most part in all ages, Jack Cade, Tom Straw, Kett, and his companions.

---

* For most part we mistake the name of Politicians, accounting such as read Machiavel and Tacitus great statesmen, that can dispute of political precepts, supplant and overthrow their adversaries, enrich themselves, get honours, dissemble; but what is this to the benefit, or preservation of a Commonwealth? — Burton's note.

Where they be generally riotous and contentious, where there be many discords, many laws, many law-suits, many lawyers, and many physicians, it is a manifest sign of a distempered, melancholy state, as Plato long since maintained: for where such kind of men swarm, they will make more work for themselves, and that body politick diseased, which was otherwise sound. A general mischief in these our times, an insensible plague, and never so many of them: *which are now multiplied* (saith Mat. Geraldus, a Lawyer himself,) *as so many locusts, not the parents, but the plagues of the Country, & for the most part a supercilious, bad, covetous, litigious generation of men;* a purse-milking nation, a clamorous company, gowned vultures, who live by violence and bloodshed, thieves and seminaries of discord; worse than any pollers by the high-way side, gold-hawks, gold-borers, money-fishers, temple thieves, market-jinglers, horrible wretches, slave-traders, &c., that take upon them to make peace, but are indeed the very disturbers of our peace, a company of irreligious Harpies, scraping, griping catchpoles (I mean our common hungry pettifoggers; I love and honour in the mean time all good laws, and worthy lawyers, that are so many oracles and pilots of a well-governed commonwealth), without art, without judgment, that do more harm, as Livy said, than sickness, wars, hunger, diseases; *and cause a most incredible destruction of a Commonwealth,* saith Sesellius, a famous Civilian sometime in Paris. As ivy doth by an oak, embrace it so long, until it hath got the heart out of it, so do they by such places they inhabit, no counsel at all, no justice, no speech to be had, he must be fee'd still, or else he is as mute as a fish, better open an oyster without a knife. *I speak out of experience* (saith Sarisburiensis), *I have been a thousand times amongst them, & Charon himself is more gentle than they; he is contented with his single pay, but they multiply still, they are never satisfied:* besides, they have pernicious tongues, as he terms it, they must be fee'd to say nothing, and get more to hold their peace than we can to say our best. They will speak their clients fair, and invite them to their tables, but, as he follows it, *of all injustice there is none so pernicious as that of theirs, which, when they deceive most, will seem to be honest men.* They take upon them to be peace-makers, and to espouse the cause of the humble, to help them to their right, they play patron to the afflicted, but all is for their own good, that they may drain the money-bags of the rich, they plead for poor men free, but they are but as a stale to catch others. If there be no jar, they can make a jar, out of the law itself find still some quirk or other, to set them at odds, and continue causes so

long, I know not how many years before the cause is heard, and when
'tis judged and determined, by reason of some tricks and errors it is as
fresh to begin, after twice seven years sometimes, as it was at first;
and so they prolong time, delay suits, till they have enriched themselves, and beggared their clients. And as Cato inveighed against
Isocrates' scholars, we may justly tax our wrangling lawyers, they
do grow old in lawsuits, are so litigious & busy here on earth, that I
think they will plead their clients' causes hereafter, some of them
in hell. Simlerus complains, amongst the Suissers, of the Advocates
in his time, that when they should make an end, they begin controversies, and *protract their causes many years, persuading them their title
is good, till their patrimonies be consumed, and that they have spent
more in seeking than the thing is worth, or they shall get by the recovery.* So he that goes to law, as the proverb is, holds a wolf by the
ears, or, as a sheep in a storm runs for shelter to a briar, if he prosecute
his cause he is consumed, if he surcease his suit he loseth all; what
difference? They had wont, heretofore, saith Austin, to end matters by
common arbitrators, and so in Switzerland, (we are informed by Simlerus,) *they had some common arbitrators, or daysmen in every town,
that made a friendly composition betwixt man and man; and he much
wonders at their honest simplicity, that could keep peace so well, and
end such great causes by that means.* At Fez, in Africa, they have neither
lawyers nor advocates; but if there be any controversies amongst them,
both parties, plaintiff and defendant, come to their *Alfakins* or chief
Judges, *& at once, without any further appeals or pitiful delays, the
cause is heard and ended.* Our forefathers, as a worthy Chorographer
of ours observes, had wont with a few golden crosses, and lines in verse,
[to] make all conveyances, assurances. And such was the candour & integrity of succeeding ages, that a Deed (as I have oft seen), to convey
a whole Manor, was succinctly contained in some twenty lines or thereabouts; like that Schede or *Scytala Laconica,* so much renowned of old
in all contracts, which Tully so earnestly commends to Atticus, Plutarch
in his Lysander, Aristotle, Thucydides, Diodorus, and Suidas, approve
and magnify for that Laconick brevity in this kind; and well they
might, for, according to Tertullian, there is much more certainty in
fewer words. And so was it of old throughout: but now many skins of
parchment will scarce serve turn; he that buys and sells a house, must
have a house full of writings, there be so many circumstances, so many
words, such tautological repetitions of all particulars (to avoid cavilla-
tion, they say), but we find, by our woful experience, that to subtle wits

it is a cause of much more contention and variance, and scarce any con-
veyance so accurately penned by one, which another will not find a
crack in, or cavil at; if any one word be misplaced, any little error, all
is disannulled. That which is law to-day is none to-morrow, that which
is sound in one man's opinion, is most faulty to another; that, in conclusion, here is nothing amongst us but contention and confusion, we
band one against another. And that which long since Plutarch complained of them in Asia, may be verified in our times. *These men here
assembled, come not to sacrifice to their gods, to offer Jupiter their first
fruits, or merriments to Bacchus; but a yearly disease exasperating
Asia hath brought them hither, to make an end of their controversies
and law suits.* 'Tis a destructive rout that seek one another's ruin. Such
most part are our ordinary suitors, termers, clients; new stirs every
day, mistakes, errors, cavils, and at this present, as I have heard, in
some one Court, I know not how many thousand causes: no person
free, no title almost good, with such bitterness in following, so many
slights, procrastinations, delays, forgery, such cost (for infinite sums
are inconsiderately spent), violence and malice, I know not by whose
fault, lawyers, clients, laws, both or all: but as Paul reprehended the
Corinthians long since, I may more appositely infer now: *There is a
fault amongst you, & I speak it to your shame; is there not a wise
man amongst you, to judge between his brethren; but that a brother
goes to law with a brother?* And Christ's counsel concerning law-suits
was never so fit to be inculcated, as in this age: *Agree with thine adversary quickly, &c.*

I could repeat many such particular grievances, which must disturb
a body politick. To shut up all in brief, where good government is, prudent and wise Princes, there all things thrive and prosper, peace and
happiness is in that land: where it is otherwise, all things are ugly to
behold, incult, barbarous, uncivil, a Paradise is turned to a wilderness.
This Island amongst the rest, our next neighbours the French and Germans, may be a sufficient witness, that in a short time, by that prudent
policy of the Romans, was brought from barbarism; see but what Cæsar
reports of us, and Tacitus of those old Germans; they were once as uncivil as they in Virginia, yet by planting of colonies and good laws, they
became, from barbarous outlaws, to be full of rich and populous cities,
as now they are, and most flourishing kingdoms. Even so might Virginia,
and those wild Irish, have been civilized long since, if that order had
been heretofore taken, which now begins, of planting colonies, &c. I
have read a discourse, printed in the year 1612, *discovering the true*

causes why Ireland was never entirely subdued, or brought under obedi-
ence to the Crown of England, until the beginning of his Majesty's
happy reign. Yet if his reasons were thoroughly scanned by a judicious
politician, I am afraid he would not altogether be approved, but that it
would turn to the dishonour of our nation, to suffer it to lie so long
waste. Yea, and if some travellers should see (to come nearer home)
those rich United Provinces of Holland, Zealand, &c., over against us;
those neat cities and populous towns, full of most industrious artificers,
so much land recovered from the sea, and so painfully preserved by
those artificial inventions, so wonderfully approved, as that of Bemster
in Holland, so that you would find nothing equal to it or like it in the
whole world, saith Bertius the Geographer, all the world cannot match
it, so many navigable channels from place to place, made by men's
hands, &c., and on the other side so many thousand acres of our fens lie
drowned, our cities thin, and those vile, poor, and ugly to behold in respect of their's, our trades decayed, our still running rivers stopped, and
that beneficial use of transportation wholly neglected, so many havens
void of ships and towns, so many parks and forests for pleasure, barren
heaths, so many villages depopulated, &c., I think sure he would find
some fault.

I may not deny but that this nation of ours doth bear a good name
amongst foreigners, is a most noble, a most flourishing kingdom, by
common consent of all Geographers, Historians, Politicians, 'tis an
unique stronghold, and which Quintius in Livy said of the inhabitants
of Peloponnesus, may be well applied to us, we are like so many tor-
toises in our shells, safely defended by an angry sea, as a wall on all
sides. Our Island hath many such honorable elogiums; and as a learned
countryman * of ours right well hath it, *Ever since the Normans' first*
coming into England, this country both for military matters, and all
other of civility, hath been paralleled with the most flourishing king-
doms of Europe & our Christian world, a blessed, a rich country, and
one of the fortunate Isles: and for some things preferred before other
countries, for expert seamen, our laborious discoveries, art of navigation, true merchants, they carry the bell away from all other nations,
even the Portugals and Hollanders themselves; *without all fear,* saith
Boterus, *furrowing the ocean winter and summer, and two of their cap-*
tains, with no less valour than fortune, have sailed round about the
world. We have besides many particular blessings, which our neighbours want, the Gospel truly preached, Church discipline established,

* Camden, in his Brittania.

long peace and quietness, free from exactions, foreign fears, invasions, domestical seditions, well manured, fortified by art and nature, and now most happy in that fortunate union of England and Scotland, which our forefathers have laboured to effect, and desired to see. But in which we excel all others, a wise, learned, religious King, another Numa, a second Augustus, a true Josiah, most worthy senators, a learned clergy, an obedient commonalty, &c. Yet amongst many roses some thistles grow, some bad weeds and enormities, which much disturb the peace of this body politick, eclipse the honour and glory of it, fit to be rooted out, and with all speed to be reformed.

The first is idleness, by reason of which we have many swarms of rogues and beggars, thieves, drunkards, and discontented persons (whom Lycurgus in Plutarch calls the boils of the commonwealth), many poor people in all our towns; low born citizens, as Polydore calls them, base built cities, inglorious, poor, small, rare in sight, ruinous, and thin of inhabitants. Our land is fertile, we may not deny, full of all good things, and why then doth it not abound with cities, as well as Italy, France, Germany, the Low Countries? Because their policy hath been otherwise, and we are not so thrifty, circumspect, industrious. Idleness is the evil genius of our nation. For as Boterus justly argues, fertility of a country is not enough, except art and industry be joined unto it. According to Aristotle, riches are either natural or artificial; natural are good land, fair mines, &c.; artificial are manufactures, coins, &c. Many kingdoms are fertile, but thin of inhabitants, as that Duchy of Piedmont in Italy, which Leander Albertus so much magnifies for corn, wine, fruits, &c., yet nothing near so populous as those which are more barren. England, saith he (*London only excepted*), *hath never a populous city, and yet a fruitful country.* I find 46 cities and walled towns in Alsatia, a small province in Germany, 50 castles, an infinite number of villages, no ground idle, no not rocky places nor tops of hills are untilled, as Munster informeth us. In Greichgea, a small territory on the Necker, 24 Italian miles over, I read of 20 walled towns, innumerable villages, each one containing 150 houses most part, besides castles and noblemen's palaces. I observe in Turinge, in Dutchland (twelve miles over by their scale), 12 counties, and in them 144 cities, 2,000 villages, 144 towns, 250 castles. In Bavaria 34 cities, 46 towns, &c. Portugal-between-the-rivers, a small plot of ground, hath 1460 parishes, 130 monasteries, 200 bridges. Malta, a barren Island, yields 20,000 inhabitants. But of all the rest, I admire Lues Guicciardini's relations of the Low Countries. Holland hath 26 cities, 400 great villages; Zealand 10 cities, 102 parishes; Brabant 26 cities, 102 parishes; Flanders 28 cities, 90 towns, 1154 villages, besides abbies, castles, &c. The Low Countries generally have three cities at least for one of ours, and those far more populous and rich: and what is the cause, but their industry and excellency in all manner of trades; their commerce, which is maintained by a multitude of tradesmen, so many excellent channels made by art, and opportune havens, to which they build their cities? all which we have in like measure, or at least may have. But their chiefest loadstone which draws all manner of commerce and merchandize, which maintains their present estate, is not fertility of soil, but industry that enricheth them, the gold mines of Peru or New Spain may not compare with them. They have neither gold nor silver of their own, wine nor oil, nor scarce any corn growing in those United Provinces, little or no wood, tin, lead, iron, silk, wool, any stuff almost, or metals; and yet Hungary, Transylvania, that brag of their mines, fertile England, cannot compare with them. I dare boldly say, that neither France, Tarentum, Apulia, Lombardy, or any part of Italy, Valentia in Spain, or that pleasant Andalusia, with their excellent fruits, wine and oil, two harvests, no nor any part of Europe, is so flourishing, so rich, so populous, so full of good ships, of well-built cities, so abounding with all things necessary for the use of man. 'Tis our Indies, an epitome of China, and all by reason of their industry, good policy, and commerce. Industry is a loadstone to draw all good things; that alone makes countries flourish, cities populous, and will enforce by reason of much manure, which necessarily follows, a barren soil to be fertile and good, as sheep, saith Dion, mend a bad pasture.

Tell me, Politicians, why is that fruitful Palestine, noble Greece, Egypt, Asia Minor, so much decayed, and (mere carcasses now) fallen from that they were? The ground is the same, but the government is altered, the people are grown slothful, idle, their good husbandry, policy, and industry, is decayed. The soil is not tired nor exhausted, as Columella well informs Sylvinus, but barren through our own laziness, &c. May a man believe that which Aristotle in his Politicks, Pausanias, Stephanus, Sophianus, Gerbelius relate of old Greece? I find heretofore 70 cities in Epirus overthrown by Paulus Æmilius, a goodly Province in times past, now left desolate of good towns and almost inhabitants: 62 cities in Macedonia in Strabo's time: I find 30 in Laconia, but now scarce so many villages, saith Gerbelius. If any man from Mount Taygetus should view the country round about, and see so many delicate and brave cities built with such cost and exquisite cunning, so neatly set out in Peloponnesus, he should perceive them now ruinous and overthrown, burnt, waste, desolate, and laid level with the ground. Incredible to say, &c. And as he laments, Who telling such a tale could keep from tears? Who is so hard, so iron-hearted? (so he prosecutes it). Who is he that can sufficiently condole and commiserate these ruins? Where are those 4000 cities of Egypt, those 100 cities in Crete? Are they now come to two? What saith Pliny and Ælian of old Italy? There were in former ages 1166 cities: Blondus and Machiavel both grant them now nothing near so populous, and full of good towns, as in the time of Augustus (for now Leander Albertus can find but 300 at most), and if we may give credit to Livy, not then so strong and puissant as of old: *They mustered 70 Legions in former times, which now the known world will scarce yield.* Alexander built 70 cities in a short space for his part, our Sultans and Turks demolish twice as many, and leave all desolate. Many will not believe but that our Island of Great Britain is now more populous than ever it was; yet let them read Bede, Leland, and others, they shall find it most flourished in the Saxon Heptarchy, and in the Conqueror's time was far better inhabited than at this present. See that Doomsday-Book, and show me those thousands of parishes, which are now decayed, cities ruined, villages depopulated, &c. The lesser the territory is, commonly the richer it is. A little but well-tilled estate. As those Athenian, Lacedæmonian, Arcadian, Elean, Sicyonian, Messenian, &c., Common-wealths of Greece make ample proof, as those Imperial Cities and free States of Germany may witness, those Cantons of Switzers, Rheti, Grisons, Walloons, Territories of Tuscany, Lucca and Sienna of old, Piedmont, Mantua, Venice in Italy, Ragusa, &c.

That Prince, therefore, as Boterus adviseth, that will have a rich country, and fair cities, let him get good trades, privileges, painful inhabitants, artificers, and suffer no rude matter unwrought, as tin, iron, wool, lead, &c., to be transported out of his country; a thing in part seriously attempted amongst us, but not effected. And because industry of men, and multitude of trade, so much avails to the ornament and enriching of a kingdom; those ancient Massilians would admit no man into their city that had not some trade. Selym the First, Turkish Emperor, procured a thousand good artificers to be brought from Tauris to Constantinople. The Polanders indented with Henry Duke of Anjou, their new chosen King, to bring with him an hundred families of artificers into Poland. James the First in Scotland (as Buchanan writes) sent for the best artificers he could get in Europe, and gave them great rewards to teach his subjects their several trades. Edward the Third, our most renowned King, to his eternal memory brought clothing first into this Island, transporting some families of artificers from Ghent hither. How many goodly cities could I reckon up, that thrive wholly by trade, where thousands of inhabitants live singular well by their fingers' ends! As Florence in Italy by making cloth of gold; great Milan by silk, and all curious works; Arras in Artois by those fair hangings; many cities in Spain, many in France, Germany, have none other maintenance, especially those within the land. Mecca, in Arabia Petræa, stands in a most unfruitful country, that wants water, amongst the rocks (as Vertomannus describes it), and yet it is a most elegant and pleasant city, by reason of the traffick of the East and West. Ormus in Persia is a most famous Mart-Town, hath nought else but the opportunity of the haven to make it flourish. Corinth, a noble city (Tully calls it the Eye of Greece) by reason of Cenchrea and Lechæum, those excellent ports, drew all that traffick of the Ionian and Ægean seas to it; and yet the country about it was, as Strabo terms it, rugged and harsh. We may say the same of Athens, Actium, Thebes, Sparta, and most of those towns in Greece. Nuremberg in Germany is sited in a most barren soil, yet a noble Imperial city, by the sole industry of artificers, and cunning trades; they draw the riches of most countries to them, so expert in manufactures, that as Sallust long since gave out of the like, their soul, or active mind, was placed in their fingers' ends; & so we may say of Basil, Spires, Cambray, Frankfurt, &c. It is almost incredible to speak what some write of Mexico and the cities adjoining to it, no place in the world at their first discovery more populous, [and what] Mat. Riccius, the Jesuit, and some others, relate of the industry of the Chinese, most populous countries, not a beggar or an idle person to be seen, and how by that means they prosper and flourish. We have the same means, able bodies, pliant wits, matter of all sorts, wool, flax, iron, tin, lead, wood, &c., many excellent subjects to work upon, only industry is wanting. We send our best commodities beyond the seas, which they make good use of to their necessities, set themselves a work about, and severally improve, sending the same to us back at dear rates, or else make toys and baubles of the tails of them, which they sell to us again, at as great a reckoning as they bought the whole. In most of our cities, some few excepted, like Spanish loiterers, we live wholly by tippling; inns and ale-houses, malting, are their best ploughs; their greatest traffick to sell ale. Meteran and some others object to us, that we are no whit so industrious as the Hollanders: *Manual trades* (saith he) *which are more curious or troublesome, are wholly exercised by strangers: they dwell in a sea full of fish, but they are so idle they will not catch so much as shall serve their own turns, but buy it of their neighbours.* Tush! The sea is free, they fish under our noses, and sell it to us when they have done, at their own prices. I am ashamed to hear this objected by strangers, and know not how to answer it.

Amongst our Towns, there is only London that bears the face of a City, Epitome of Britain, a famous market-place, second to none beyond seas, a noble mart: but it only grows at the expense of other cities; and yet, in my slender judgement, defective in many things. The rest (some few excepted), are in mean estate, ruinous most part, poor and full of beggars, by reason of their decayed trades, neglected or bad policy, idleness of their inhabitants, riot, which had rather beg or loiter, and be ready to starve, than work.

I cannot deny but that something may be said in defence of our Cities, that they are not so fair built, (for the sole magnificence of this Kingdom, concerning buildings, hath been of old in those Norman Castles and Religious Houses) so rich, thick sited, populous, as in some other countries; besides the reasons Cardan gives, we want wine and oil, their two harvests, we dwell in a colder air, and for that cause must a little more liberally feed of flesh, as all Northern Countries do. Our provision will not therefore extend to the maintenance of so many: yet notwithstanding we have matter of all sorts, an open sea for traffick, as well as the rest, goodly havens. And how can we excuse our negligence, our riot, drunkenness, &c., and such enormities that follow it? We have excellent laws enacted, you will say, severe statutes, houses of correction, &c., to small purpose it seems, it is not houses will serve, but cities of correction, our trades generally ought to be reformed, wants supplied. In other countries they have the same grievances, I confess, but that doth not excuse us, wants, defects, enormities, idle drones, tumults, discords, contention, law-suits, many laws made against them to repress those innumerable brawls and law-suits, excess in apparel, diet, decay of tillage, depopulations, especially against rogues, beggars, Egyptian vagabonds (so termed at least) which have swarmed all over Germany, France, Italy, Poland, as you may read in Munster, Cranzius, and Aventinus; as those Tartars and Arabians at this day do in the Eastern Countries; yet, such hath been the iniquity of all ages, as it seems to small purpose. Let no one in our state be a beggar, saith Plato, he will have them purged from a Common-wealth, *as a bad humour from the body,* that are like so many ulcers and boils, and must be cured before the melancholy body can be eased.

What Charlemagne, the Chinese, the Spaniards, the Duke of Saxony, and many other States, have decreed in this case, read **Arniseus,** Boterus, Osorius. When a country is over-stored with people, as a pasture is oft overlaid with cattle, they had wont in former times to disburden themselves by sending out colonies, or by wars, as those old Romans, or by employing them at home about some publick buildings, as bridges, roadways, for which those Romans were famous in this Island : as Augustus Cæsar did in Rome, the Spaniards in their Indian Mines, as at Potosi in Peru, where some 30,000 men are still at work, 6,000 furnaces ever boiling, &c.; aqueducts, bridges, havens, those stupend works of Trajan, Claudius, at Ostia, the baths of Dioclesian, the Lake Fucinus, that Piraeus in Athens, made by Themistocles, Amphitheatres of curious Marble, as at Verona, the city of Philip, and Heraclea in Thrace, those Appian and Flaminian Ways, prodigious works all, may witness : and rather than they should be idle, as those Egyptian Pharaohs, Mæris and Sesostris did, to task their subjects to build unnecessary Pyramids, Obelisks, Labyrinths, Channels, Lakes, Gigantean works all, to divert them from rebellion, riot, drunkenness, whereby they might be supported, and not become vagrants and cease from labour.

Another eye-sore is that want of conduct and navigable rivers, a great blemish, as Boterus, Hippolytus a Collibus, and other Politicians hold, if it be neglected in a Commonwealth. Admirable cost and charge is bestowed in the Low Countries on this behalf, in the Duchy of Milan, Territory of Padua, in France, Italy, China, and so likewise about corrivations of waters to moisten and refresh barren grounds, to drain fens, bogs, and moors. Massinissa made many inward parts of Barbary and Numidia in Africa, before his time incult and horrid, fruitful and bartable by this means. Great industry is generally used all over the Eastern Countries in this kind, especially in Egypt, about Babylon, and Damascus, as Vertomannus and Gotardus Arthus relate; about Barcelona, Segovia, Murcia, and many other places of Spain, Milan in Italy; by reason of which their soil is much improved, and infinite commodities arise to the inhabitants.

The Turks of late attempted to cut that Isthmus betwixt Africa and Asia, which Sesostris and Darius, and some Pharaohs of Egypt, had formerly undertaken, but with ill success, as Diodorus Siculus records, and Pliny, for that the Red Sea, being three cubits higher * than Egypt, would have drowned all the country, they left off; yet, as the same

* Contrary to that of Archimedes, who holds the superficies of all waters even. — Burton's note.

Diodorus writes, Ptolemy renewed the work many years after, and ab-solved it in a more opportune place.

That Isthmus of Corinth was likewise undertaken to be made navi-gable by Demetrius, by Julius Cæsar, Nero, Domitian, Herodes Atticus, to make a speedy passage, and less dangerous, from the Ionian and Ægean seas; but because it could not be so well effected, the Pelopon-nesians built a wall, like our Picts' wall, about Schænus, where Nep-tune's Temple stood, and in the shortest cut over the Isthmus, of which Diodorus, Herodotus. Our later writers call it Hexamilium, which Amurath the Turk demolished, the Venetians, in the year 1453, repaired in 15 days with 30,000 men. Some, saith Acosta, would have a passage cut from Panama to Nombre de Dios in America, but Thuanus & Serres, the French Historians, speak of a famous aqueduct in France, intended in Henry the Fourth's time, from the Loire to the Seine, and from Rhone to Loire. The like to which was formerly assayed by Domitian the Em-peror, from Arar to Moselle, which Cornelius Tacitus speaks of in the 13th of his Annals, after by Charles the Great and others. Much cost hath in former times been bestowed in either new making or mending channels of rivers, and their passages, (as Aurelianus did by Tiber to make it navigable to Rome to convey corn from Egypt to the City, saith Vopiscus, he cut fords, made banks, &c.) decayed havens, which Claudius the Emperor with infinite pains and charges attempted at Ostia, as I have said, the Venetians at this day to preserve their City. Many excellent means to enrich their Territories have been fostered, invented in most Provinces of Europe, as planting some Indian plants amongst us, silk-worms, the very mulberry leaves in the Plains of Granada yield 30,000 crowns a year to the King of Spain's coffers, be-sides those many trades and artificers that are busied about them in the kingdom of Granada, Murcia, and all over Spain. In France a great benefit is raised by salt, &c. Whether these things might not be as hap-pily attempted with us, and with like success, it may be controverted, silk-worms (I mean) vines, fir-trees, &c. Cardan exhorts Edward the Sixth to plant olives, and is fully persuaded they would prosper in this Island. With us navigable rivers are most part neglected; our streams are not great, I confess, by reason of the narrowness of the Island, yet they run smoothly and even, not headlong, swift, or amongst rocks and shelves, as foaming Rhone and Loire in France, Tigris in Mesopotamia, violent Douro in Spain, with cataracts and whirl-pools, as the Rhine, and Danube, about Schaffhausen, Lausenburgh, Linz, and Cremmes, to endanger navigators; or broad shallow, as Neckar in the Palatinate,

Tiber in Italy; but calm and fair as Arar in France, Hebrus in Macedonia, Eurotas in Laconia, they gently glide along, and might as well
be repaired many of them (I mean Wye, Trent, Ouse, Thames at Oxford, the defect of which we feel in the mean time) as the river of Lee
from Ware to London. B. Atwater of old, or as some will Henry I.,
made a channel from Trent to Lincoln, navigable; which now, saith
Mr. Camden, is decayed, and much mention is made of anchors, & such
like monuments, found about old Verulamium, good ships have formerly
come to Exeter, and many such places, whose channels, havens, ports,
are now barred and rejected. We contemn this benefit of carriage by
waters, & are therefore compelled in the inner parts of this Island, because portage is so dear, to eat up our commodities ourselves, & live like
so many boars in a sty, for want of vent and utterance.

We have many excellent havens, royal havens, Falmouth, Ports-
mouth, Milford, &c., equivalent, if not to be preferred to that Indian
Havanna, old Brundusium in Italy, Aulis in Greece, Ambracia in
Acarnania, Suda in Crete, which have few ships in them, little or no
traffick or trade, which have scarce a village on them, able to bear great
cities, but let our statesmen look to it. I could here justly tax many
other neglects, abuses, errors, defects among us, and in other countries,
depopulations, riot, drunkenness, &c., & many such, which would give
offense now even to whisper in the air. But I must take heed that I do
not overshoot myself. The sow teaches Minerva, I am forth of my element, as you peradventure suppose, and sometimes truth arouses hatred, as he said, *verjuice and oatmeal is good for a parrot.** For as
Lucian said of an Historian, I say of a politician, he that will freely
speak and write, must be for ever no subject, under no prince or law,
but lay out the matter truly as it is, nor caring what any can, will, like
or dislike.

We have good laws, I deny not, to rectify such enormities, and so in
all other countries, but it seems not always to good purpose. We had
need of some general visitor in our age, that should reform what is
amiss; a just army of Rosy-Cross men,† for they will amend all matters, (they say) religion, policy, manners, with arts, sciences, &c.; another Attila, Tamerlane, Hercules, to strive with Achelous, to clean the
Augean stables, to subdue tyrants, as he did Diomedes and Busiris: to
expel thieves, as he did Cacus & Lacinius: to vindicate poor captives,

* This phrase is apparently some schoolboy's " howler," or comic " translation " of
the Latin *veritas odium parit* (truth begets hatred), which came just previously in
the text.
† Rosicrucians, Utopian reformers.

as he did Hesione: to pass the Torrid Zone, the deserts of Libya, and purge the world of monsters and Centaurs; or another Theban Crates to reform our manners, to compose quarrels and controversies, as in his time he did, and was therefore adored for a god in Athens. *As Hercules purged the world of monsters, and subdued them, so did he fight against envy, lust, anger, avarice, &c., and all those feral vices and monsters of the mind.* It were to be wished we had some such visitor, or (if wishing would serve) one had such a ring or rings, as Timolaus desired in Lucian, by virtue of which he should be as strong as 10,000 men, or an army of giants, go invisible, open gates & castle doors, have what treasure he would, transport himself in an instant to what place he desired, alter affections, cure all manner of diseases, that he might range over the world, and reform all distressed states and persons, as he would himself. He might reduce those wandering Tartars in order, that infest China on the one side, Muscovy, Poland, on the other; and tame the vagabond Arabians that rob and spoil those Eastern Countries, that they should never use more Caravans, or Janisaries to conduct them. He might root out barbarism out of America, and fully discover *Terra Australis Incognita,** find out the North-East, and North-West passages, drain those mighty Mæotian fens, cut down those vast Hercynian Woods, irrigate those barren Arabian deserts, &c., cure us of our epidemical diseases, scurvy, plica, the Neapolitan disease, &c., end all our idle controversies, cut off our tumultuous desires, inordinate lusts, root out atheism, impiety, heresy, schism, and superstition, which now so crucify the world, catechise gross ignorance, purge Italy of luxury and riot, Spain of superstition and jealousy, Germany of drunkenness, all our Northern countries of gluttony and intemperance, castigate our hard-hearted parents, masters, tutors; lash disobedient children, negligent servants; correct these spendthrifts and prodigal sons, enforce idle persons to work, drive drunkards off the alehouse, repress thieves, visit corrupt and tyrannizing magistrates, &c. But as L. Licinius taxed Timolaus, you may us. These are vain, absurd, and ridiculous wishes not to be hoped: all must be as it is, Bocchalinus may cite Commonwealths to come before Apollo, and seek to reform the world itself by Commissioners, but there is no remedy, it may not be redressed, men will only cease to be fools when they cease to be, so long as they can wag their beards, they will play the knaves and fools.

Because therefore it is a thing so difficult, impossible, and far beyond Hercules' Labours to be performed; let them be rude, stupid, ignorant,

* Here synonymous with Oceania.

incult, let stone sit above stone, and as the Apologist will, let the State suffer from coughing and short breath, the world from vice, let them be barbarous as they are, let them tyrannize, epicurize, oppress, luxuriate, consume themselves with factions, superstitions, law-suits, wars and contentions, live in riot, poverty, want, misery; rebel, wallow as so many swine in their own dung, with Ulysses' companions, let them be fools, since that's their wish. I will yet, to satisfy and please myself, make an Utopia of my own, a new Atlantis, a poetical Commonwealth of mine own, in which I will freely domineer, build cities, make laws, statutes, as I list myself. And why may I not?

> *Poets and painters — sure you know the plea —,*
> *Have always been allowed their fancy free, &c.*

You know what liberty Poets ever had, and besides my predecessor Democritus was a Politician, a Recorder of Abdera, a law-maker as some say, and why may I not presume so much as he did? Howsoever I will adventure. For the site, if you will needs urge me to it, I am not fully resolved, it may be in the Unknown Austral Land, there is room enough (for of my knowledge neither that hungry Spaniard, nor Mercurius Britannicus, have yet discovered half of it) or else one of those floating Islands in the South Sea which, like the Cyanean Isles in the Euxine Sea, alter their place, and are accessible only at set times, and to some few persons; or one of the Fortunate Isles, for who knows yet where, or which they are? There is room enough in the inner parts of America, and northern coasts of Asia. But I will choose a site, whose latitude shall be 45 degrees (I respect not minutes) in the midst of the Temperate Zone, or perhaps under the Equator, that Paradise of the world, *where the laurel is ever green, &c.*, where is a perpetual Spring: the longitude for some reasons I will conceal. Yet *be it known to all men by these presents,* that if any honest gentleman will send in so much money, as Cardan allows an Astrologer for casting a Nativity, he shall be a sharer, I will acquaint him with my project, or if any worthy man will stand for any temporal or spiritual office or dignity, (for as he * said of his Archbishoprick of Utopia, tis a holy ambition, and not amiss to be sought after) it shall be freely given without all intercession, bribes, letters, &c., his own worth shall be the best spokesman; & because we shall admit of no deputies or advowsons, if he be sufficiently qualified, and as able as willing to execute the place himself, he shall have present possession. It shall be divided into 12 or 13 provinces, and those by hills, rivers, road-ways, or some more eminent limits exactly

* Sir Thomas More.

bounded. Each province shall have a *metropolis,* which shall be so placed as a centre almost in a circumference, and the rest at equal distances, some 12 Italian miles asunder, or thereabout; and in them shall be sold all things necessary for the use of man, at stated hours and days, no market towns, markets or fairs, for they do but beggar cities (no village shall stand above 6, 7, or 8 miles from a city) except those emporiums which are by the sea side, general staples, marts, as Antwerp, Venice, Bergen of old, London, &c. Cities most part shall be situate upon navigable rivers or lakes, creeks, havens, and for their form, regular, round, square, or long square, with fair, broad and straight streets, houses uniform, built of brick and stone, like Bruges, Brussels, Rhegium Lepidi, Berne in Switzerland, Milan, Mantua, Crema, Cambalu in Tartary described by Marco Polo, or that Venetian Palma. I will admit very few or no suburbs, & those of baser building, walls only to keep out man and horse, except it be in some frontier towns, or by the sea side, & those to be fortified after the latest manner of fortification, and sited upon convenient havens, or opportune places. In every so built city, I will have convenient churches, and separate-places to bury the dead in, not in church-yards; a citadel (in some, not all) to command it, prisons for offenders, opportune market-places of all sorts, for corn, meat, cattle, fuel, fish, &c. commodious courts of justice, publick halls for all societies, bourses, meeting places, armouries, in which shall be kept engines for quenching of fire, artillery gardens, publick walks, theatres, and spacious fields allotted for all gymnicks, sports, and honest recreations, hospitals of all kinds, for children, orphans, old folks, sick men, mad men, soldiers, pest-houses, &c., not built propitiatorily, or by gouty benefactors, who, when by fraud & rapine they have extorted all their lives, oppressed whole provinces, societies, &c., give something to pious uses, build a satisfactory alms-house, school, or bridge, &c., at their last end, or before perhaps, which is no otherwise than to steal a goose, and stick down a feather, rob a thousand to relieve ten: and those hospitals so built and maintained, not by collections, benevolences, donaries, for a set number (as in ours), just so many and no more at such a rate, but for all those who stand in need, be they more or less, and that at publick expense, & so still maintained; we are not born for ourselves alone, &c. I will have conduits of sweet and good water, aptly disposed in each town, common granaries, as at Dresden in Misnia [Saxony], Stettin in Pomerland, Nuremberg, &c., colleges of mathematicians, musicians, and actors, as of old at Lebedos in Ionia, alchemists, [in a footnote Burton adds: Not to make gold, but for matters of physick], physicians, artists, and philosophers; that all arts and sciences may sooner be perfected & better learned; and publick historiographers, as amongst those ancient Persians, informed and appointed by the state to register all famous acts, & not by each insufficient scribbler, partial or parasitical pedant, as in our times. I will provide publick schools of all kinds, singing, dancing, fencing, &c. especially of grammar & languages, not to be taught by those tedious precepts ordinarily used, but by use, example, conversation, as travellers learn abroad, & nurses teach their children. As I will have all such places, so will I ordain publick governors, fit officers to each place, treasurers, ædiles,* quæstors,† overseers of pupils, widows' goods, and all publick houses, &c. and those once a year to make strict accounts of all receipts, expenses, to avoid confusion, & so they will waste no money, (as Pliny to Trajan,) which is a shameful thing to have to mention. They shall be subordinate to those higher officers and governors of each city, which shall not be poor tradesmen, and mean artificers, but noblemen and gentlemen, which shall be tied to residence in those towns they dwell next, at such set times and seasons: for I see no reason (which Hippolytus complains of) *that it should be more dishonourable for noblemen to govern the city than the country, or unseemly to dwell there now than of old.*

I will have no bogs, fens, marshes, vast woods, deserts, heaths, commons, but all inclosed, (yet not depopulated, and therefore take heed you mistake me not), for that which is common, and every man's, is no man's; the richest countries are still inclosed,‡ as Essex, Kent, with us, &c., Spain, Italy; and where inclosures are least in quantity, they are best husbanded, as about Florence in Italy, Damascus in Syria, &c., which are liker gardens than fields. I will not have a barren acre in all my territories, not so much as the tops of mountains: where nature fails, it shall be supplied by art: lakes and rivers shall not be

---

* Commissioners of buildings.

† Deputies.

‡ Mr. Carew, in his Survey of Cornwall, saith that before that country was inclosed, the husbandmen drank water, did eat little or no bread, their apparel was coarse, they went bare-legged, their dwelling was correspondent; but since inclosure, they live decently, and have money to spend; when their fields were common, their wool was coarse Cornish hair; but since inclosure, it is almost as good as Cotswold, and their soil much mended. Tusser, chapter 52 of his Husbandry, is of his opinion, one acre inclosed is worth three common:

> *The country incloséd I praise;*
> *The other delighteth not me;*
> *For nothing of wealth it doth raise, &c.*

left desolate. All common high-ways, bridges, banks, corrivations of waters, aqueducts, channels, publick works, buildings, &c. out of a common stock curiously maintained and kept in repair; no depopulations, engrossings, alterations of wood, arable, but by the consent of some supervisors that shall be appointed for that purpose, to see what reformation ought to be had in all places, what is amiss, how to help it; and what each clime produces, and what each rejects, what ground is aptest for wood, what for corn, what for cattle, gardens, orchards, fishponds, &c., with a charitable division in every village, (not one domineering house greedily to swallow up all, which is too common with us), what for lords, what for tenants: and because they shall be better encouraged to improve such lands they hold, manure, plant trees, drain, fence, &c., they shall have long leases, a known rent, and known fine, to free them from those intolerable exactions of tyrannizing landlords. These supervisors shall likewise appoint what quantity of land in each manor is fit for the lord's demesnes, what for holding of tenants, how it ought to be husbanded,

As the Magnesians famous are for horses,
The Argonauts for rowing, (LUCAN)

how to be manured, tilled, rectified; here you see corn crops, there grapes have kindlier growth, — other spots are green with young trees and unbidden grass; and what proportion is fit for all callings, because private possessors are many times idiots, ill husbands, oppressors, covetous, and know not how to improve their own, or else wholly respect their own, and not publick good.

Utopian parity is a kind of government to be wished for rather than effected, the Christianopolitan Republic,* Campanella's City of the Sun, and that New Atlantis, witty fictions, but mere Chimeras, and Plato's Community in many things is impious, absurd and ridiculous, it takes away all splendour and magnificence. I will have several orders, degrees of nobility, and those hereditary, not rejecting younger brothers in the meantime, for they shall be sufficiently provided for by pensions, or so qualified, brought up in some honest calling, they shall be able to live of themselves. I will have such a proportion of ground belonging to every barony, he that buys the land shall buy the barony, he that by riot consumes his patrimony, & ancient demesnes, shall forfeit his honours. As some dignities shall be hereditary, so some again by election, or by gift (besides free offices, pensions, annuities), like our Bishopricks, Prebends, the Bassas' palaces in Turkey, the Procurator's

* Johann Valentin Andrea's Utopia. See Index.

houses and offices in Venice, which, like the golden apple, shall be given to the worthiest & best deserving both in war and peace, as a reward of their worth and good service, as so many goals for all to aim at, (honour nourishes the arts), and encouragements to others. For I hate those severe, unnatural, harsh, German, French, and Venetian decrees, which exclude plebeians from honours, be they never so wise, rich, virtuous, valiant, and well qualified, they must not be patricians, but keep their own rank; this is to war against nature, — odious to God and men, I abhor it.

My form of government shall be monarchical;

> *If to sweet freedom you would cling*
> *Submit unto a righteous King.* (CLAUDIAN)

few laws, but those severely kept, plainly put down, and in the mother tongue, that every man may understand. Every city shall have a peculiar trade or privilege, by which it shall be chiefly maintained: and parents shall teach their children, one of three at least, bring up and instruct them in the mysteries of their own trade. In each town these several tradesmen shall be so aptly disposed, as they shall free the rest from danger or offence: fire-trades, as smiths, forge-men, brewers, bakers, metal-men, &c. shall dwell apart by themselves: dyers, tanners, fell-mongers, and such as use water, in convenient places by themselves: noisome or fulsome for bad smells, as butchers' slaughter-houses, chandlers, curriers, in remote places, & some back lanes. Fraternities and companies I approve of, as merchants' bourses, colleges of druggers, physicians, musicians, &c., but all trades to be rated in the sale of wares, as our clerks of the market do bakers and brewers; corn itself, what scarcity soever shall come, not to exceed such a price. Of such wares as are transported or brought in, if they be necessary, commodious, and such as nearly concern man's life, as corn, wood, coals, &c., and such provision we cannot want, I will have little or no custom paid, no taxes; but for such things as are for pleasure, delight, or ornament, as wine, spice, tobacco, silk, velvet, cloth of gold, lace, jewels, &c. a greater impost. I will have certain ships sent out for new discoveries every year, & some discreet men appointed to travel into all neighbour Kingdoms by land, which shall observe what artificial inventions and good laws are in other countries, customs, alterations, or ought else, concerning war or peace, which may tend to the common good. Ecclesiastical discipline in the hands of Bishops, subordinate as the other. No impropriations, no lay patrons of church livings, or one private man, but common societies, corporations, &c. and those Rectors of Benefices to be chosen out of the Universities, examined and approved, as the *Literati* in China. No Parish to contain above a thousand auditors. If it were possible, I would have such Priests as should imitate Christ, charitable Lawyers should love their neighbours as themselves, temperate and modest Physicians, Politicians contemn the world, Philosophers should know themselves, Noblemen live honestly, Tradesmen leave lying and cozening, Magistrates corruption, &c.; but this is impossible, I must get such as I may. I will therefore have of lawyers, judges, advocates, physicians, chirurgeons, &c. a set number, and every man, if it be possible, to plead his own cause, to tell that tale to the judge, which he doth to his advocate, as at Fez in Africa, Bantam, Aleppo, Ragusa, those advocates, chirurgeons and physicians, which are allowed, to be maintained out of the common treasure, no fees to be given or taken upon pain of losing their places, or if they do, very small fees, and when the cause is fully ended. He that sues any man shall put in a pledge, which, if it be proved he hath wrongfully sued his adversary, rashly or maliciously, he shall forfeit, and lose. Or else, before any suit begin, the plaintiff shall have his complaint approved by a set delegacy to that purpose; if it be of moment, he shall be suffered as before to proceed, if otherwise, they shall determine it. All causes shall be pleaded with the parties' names concealed, if some circumstances do not otherwise require. Judges and other officers shall be aptly disposed in each Province, Villages, Cities, as common arbitrators to hear causes, and end all controversies, and those not single, but three at least on the bench at once, to determine or give sentence, and those again to sit by turns or lots, and not to continue still in the same office. No controversy to depend above a year, but without all delays and further appeals to be speedily dispatched, and finally concluded in that time allotted. These & all other inferior Magistrates to be chosen as the *Literati* * in China, or by those exact suffrages of the Venetians, and such again not be eligible, or capable of magistracies, honours, offices, except they be sufficiently qualified for learning, manners, and that by the strict approbation of deputed examinators: first Scholars to take place, then Soldiers; for I am of Vegetius his opinion, a Scholar deserves better than a Soldier, because a Soldier's work lasts for an age, a Scholar's for ever. If they misbehave themselves, they shall be deposed, and accordingly punished; & whether their offices be annual or otherwise, once a year they shall be called in question, and give an account; for men are partial, and passionate, merciless, covetous, corrupt, subject to love, hate,

* By competitive examinations.

fear, favour, &c. Every kingdom is under a greater kingdom. Like
Solon's Areopagites, or those Roman Censors, some shall visit others,
and be visited in turn themselves, they shall oversee that no prowling
officer, under colour of authority, shall insult over his inferiors, as so
many wild beasts, oppress, domineer, flea, grind, or trample on, be partial or corrupt, but that there be justice equally done, live as friends and
brethren together; and, which Sesellius would have and so much desires
in his Kingdom of France, *a diapason and sweet harmony of Kings,
Princes, Nobles, and Plebeians, so mutually tied and involved in love,
as well as laws and authority, as that they never disagree, insult, or
encroach one upon another.* If any man deserve well in his office he
shall be rewarded; Who values virtue but for its reward? He that in-
vents anything for publick good in any Art or Science, writes a Treatise,
or performs any noble exploit at home or abroad, shall be accordingly
enriched, honoured, and preferred. I say with Hannibal in Ennius, He
who shall slay an enemy shall be to me a Carthaginian; let him be of
what condition he will, in all offices, actions, he that deserves best shall
have best.

Tilianus, in Philonius, out of a charitable mind no doubt, wished all
his books were gold and silver, jewels and precious stones, to redeem
captives, set free prisoners, and relieve all poor distressed souls that
wanted means; religiously done, I deny not, but to what purpose?
Suppose this were so well done, within a little after, though a man had
Crœsus' wealth to bestow, there would be as many more. Wherefore I
will suffer no beggars, rogues, vagabonds, or idle persons at all, that cannot give an account of their lives how they maintain themselves. If they
be impotent, lame, blind, and single, they shall be sufficiently maintained in several hospitals, built for that purpose; if married and infirm, past work, or by inevitable loss, or some such like misfortune, cast
behind, by distribution of corn, house-rent free, annual pensions or
money, they shall be relieved, and highly rewarded for their good service they have formerly done; if able, they shall be enforced to work.
For I see no reason (as he * said) *why an epicure or idle drone, a rich
glutton, a usurer, should live at ease, and do nothing, live in honour, in
all manner of pleasures, and oppress others, when as in the mean time a
poor labourer, a smith, a carpenter, an husbandman, that hath spent
his time in continual labour, as an ass to carry burdens, to do the commonwealth good, and without whom we cannot live, shall be left in his
old age to beg or starve, & lead a miserable life worse than a jument!*

* Sir Thomas More.

As all conditions shall be tied to their task, so none shall be over-tired, but have their set times of recreations & holidays, to indulge their humour, feasts and merry meetings, even to the meanest artificer, or basest servant, once a week to sing or dance, (though not all at once) or do whatsoever he shall please; like that Sacred Festival amongst the Persians, those Saturnalia in Rome, as well as his master. If any be drunk, he shall drink no more wine or strong drink in a twelvemonth after. A bankrupt shall be publickly shamed, and he that cannot pay his debts, if by riot or negligence he have been impoverished, shall be for a twelvemonth imprisoned; if in that space his creditors be not satisfied, he shall be hanged. He that commits sacrilege shall lose his hands; he that bears false witness, or is of perjury convict, shall have his tongue cut out, except he redeem it with his head. Murder, adultery, shall be punished by death, but not theft, except it be some more grievous offence, or notorious offenders: otherwise they shall be condemned to the gallies, mines, be his slaves whom they offended, during their lives. I hate all hereditary slaves, and that hard law of the Persians, as Brisonius calls it; or as Ammianus, hard law that wife and children, friends and allies, should suffer for the father's offence!

No man shall marry untill he be 25, no woman till she be 20, unless it is otherwise arranged. If one die, the other party shall not marry till 6 months after; and because many families are compelled to live niggardly, exhaust and undone by great dowers, none shall be given at all, or very little, and that by supervisors rated; they that are foul shall have a greater portion; if fair, none at all, or very little: howsoever, not to exceed such a rate as those supervisors shall think fit. And when once they come to those years, poverty shall hinder no man from marriage, or any other respect, but all shall be rather enforced than hindered, except they be dismembered, or grievously deformed, infirm, or visited with some enormous hereditary disease in body or mind; in such cases, upon a great pain or mulct, man or woman shall not marry, other order shall be taken for them to their content. If people overabound, they shall be eased by colonies.

No man shall wear weapons in any city. The same attire shall be kept, and that proper to several callings, by which they shall be distinguished. Funeral display shall be taken away, that intempestive expense moderated, and many others. Brokers, takers of pawns, biting usurers, I will not admit; yet because we converse here with men not with gods, and for the hardness of men's hearts, I will tolerate some kind of usury. If we were honest, I confess, we should have no use of it, but being as it is, we must necessarily admit it. Howsoever most Divines contradict it,

We say No, but 'tis but a word with us,

it must be winked at by Politicians. And yet some great Doctors approve of it, Calvin, Bucer, Zanchius, P. Martyr, because by so many grand Lawyers, decrees of Emperors, Princes' Statutes, customs of Commonwealths, Churches' approbations, it is permitted, &c. I will therefore allow it. But to no private persons, nor to every man that will, to orphans only, maids, widows, or such as by reason of their age, sex, education, ignorance of trading, know not otherwise how to employ it, and those so approved not to let it out apart, but to bring their money to a common bank which shall be allowed in every city, as in Genoa, Geneva, Nuremberg, Venice, at 5, 6, 7, not above 8 *per cent.,* as the supervisors, or managers of the treasury shall think fit. And as it shall not be lawful for each man to be an usurer that will, so shall it not be lawful for all to take up money at use, not to prodigals and spendthrifts, but to merchants, young trades-men, such as stand in need, or know honestly how to employ it, whose necessity, cause, and condition, the said supervisors shall approve of.

I will have no private monopolies, to enrich one man, and beggar a multitude, multiplicity of offices, of supplying by deputies; weights and measures the same throughout, and those rectified by the *Primum mobile,** and Sun's motion, threescore miles to a degree according to observation, 1000 Geometrical paces to a mile, five foot to a pace, twelve inches to a foot, &c., & from measures known it is an easy matter to rectify weights &c., to cast up all, and resolve bodies by Algebra, Stereometry. I hate wars if they be not for the welfare of the people upon urgent occasion.

We hate the hawk, because it lives by war.   (OVID)

Offensive wars, except the cause be very just, I will not allow of. For I do highly magnify that saying of Hannibal to Scipio, in Livy, *It had been a blessed thing for you and us, if God had given that mind to our predecessors, that you had been content with Italy, we with Africa. For neither Sicily nor Sardinia are worth such cost and pains, so many fleets & armies, or so many famous Captains' lives.* Fair means shall first be tried. Power exercised with moderation, can effect that which violence could never accomplish. I will have them proceed with all moderation: but hear you, Fabius my General, not Minucius, for he who acts wisely

---

* Primum mobile: in the Ptolemaic system of astronomy, the tenth or outermost of the revolving spheres of the universe.

hurts his enemy far more than by violence. And in such wars to abstain as much as is possible from depopulations, burning of towns, massacring of infants, &c. For defensive wars, I will have forces still ready at a small warning, by land and sea, a prepared navy, soldiers, as handy, Bonifinius wishes, as a rod of iron, & money, which is the nerve of war, still in a readiness, and a sufficient revenue, a third part, as in old Rome & Egypt, reserved for the Commonwealth, to avoid those heavy taxes and impositions, as well to defray this charge of wars, as also all other publick defalcations, expenses, fees, pensions, reparations, chaste sports, feasts, donaries, rewards, and entertainments. All things in this nature especially I will have maturely done, & with great deliberation: that nothing be done rashly, or remissly and timidly. But where am I rushing to, a mere novice? To prosecute the rest would require a volume. But hands off the picture! I have been over-tedious in this subject; I could have here willingly ranged, but these straits wherein I am included will not permit.

From commonwealths and cities I will descend to families, which have as many corrosives & molestations, as frequent discontents, as the rest. Great affinity there is betwixt a political and economical body; they differ only in magnitude and proportion of business (so Scaliger writes), as they have both likely the same period, as Bodine and Peucer hold, out of Plato, six or seven hundred years, so many times they have the same means of their vexation and overthrows; as, namely, riot, a common ruin of both, riot in building, riot in profuse spending, riot in apparel, &c. be it in what kind soever, it produceth the same effects. A Chorographer * of ours, speaking incidentally of ancient families, why they are so frequent in the North, continue so long, are so soon extinguished in the South, and so few, gives no other reason but this, riot hath consumed all. Fine clothes and curious buildings came into this Island, as he notes in his Annals, not so many years since, to the decay of hospitality. Howbeit, many times that word is mistaken, and under the name of bounty and hospitality is shrouded riot and prodigality; and that which is commendable in itself well used, hath been mistaken heretofore, is become by his abuse the bane & utter ruin of many a noble family. For some men live like the rich glutton, consuming themselves and their substance by continual feasting and invitations, — with Axylus in Homer, keep open house for all comers, giving entertainment to such as visit them, keeping a table beyond their means, and a company of idle servants (though not so frequent as of old) — are blown

* William Camden in his Brittania.

up on a sudden, and, as Actæon was by his hounds, devoured by their kinsmen, friends, and multitude of followers. It is a wonder that Paulus Jovius relates of our Northern Countries, what an infinite deal of meat we consume on our tables: that I may truly say, 'tis not bounty, not hospitality, as it is often abused, but riot in excess, gluttony, and prodigality, a mere vice; it brings in debt, want, and beggary, hereditary diseases, consumes their fortunes, and overthrows the good temperature of their bodies. To this I might here well add their inordinate expense in building, those phantastical houses, turrets, walks, parks, &c., gaming, excess of pleasure, & that prodigious riot in apparel, by which means they are compelled to break up house, and creep into holes. Sesellius, in his Commonwealth of France, gives three reasons why the French Nobility were so frequently bankrupts. *First, because they had so many lawsuits and contentions, one upon another, which were tedious and costly: by which means it came to pass, that commonly lawyers bought them out of their possessions. A second cause was their riot; they lived beyond their means, and were therefore swallowed up by merchants.* (La Nove, a French writer, yields five reasons of his countrymen's poverty, to the same effect almost, and thinks verily, if the Gentry of France were divided into ten parts, eight of them would be found much impaired, by sales, mortgages, and debts, or wholly sunk in their estates.) *The last was immoderate excess in apparel, which consumed their revenues.* How this concerns and agrees with our present state, look you. But of this elsewhere. As it is in a man's body, if either head, heart, stomach, liver, spleen, or any one part be misaffected, all the rest suffer with it; so is it with this economical body. If the head be nought, a spendthrift, a drunkard, a whoremaster, a gamester, how shall the family live at ease? It is beyond the power of Providence itself to save this household, as Demea said in the Comedy, safety herself cannot save it. A good, honest, painful man many times hath a shrew to his wife, a sickly, dishonest, slothfull, foolish, careless woman to his mate, a proud, peevish flirt, a liquorish, prodigal quean, and by that means all goes to ruin: or if they differ in nature, he is thrifty, she spends all, he wise, she sottish and soft; what agreement can there be? what friendship? Like that of the thrush and swallow in Æsop, instead of mutual love, kind compellations, whore and thief is heard, they fling stools at one another's heads. What madness vexes this family? All enforced marriages commonly produce such effects, or if on their behalfs it be well, as to live & agree lovingly together, they may have disobedient & unruly children, that take ill courses to disquiet them, *their son is a thief, a spendthrift, their daughter a whore;* a step mother, or a daughter in law, distempers all; or else for want of means, many tortures arise, debts, dues, fees, dowries, jointures, legacies to be paid, annuities issuing out; by means of which they have not wherewithal to maintain themselves in that pomp as their predecessors have done, bring up or bestow their children to their callings, to their birth and quality, and will not descend to their present fortunes. (When pride and beggary meet in a family, they roar and howl, and cause as many flashes of discontents, as fire and water, when they concur, make thunder-claps in the skies.) Oftentimes, too, to aggravate the rest, concur many other inconveniences, unthankful friends, decayed friends, bad neighbours, negligent servants, slaves thievish, cunning, crafty, such as open doors seal'd with a thousand keys, and stealthily snatch, and consume, and live on naught but dainties; casualties, taxes, mulcts, chargeable offices, vain expenses, entertainments, loss of stock, enmities, emulations, frequent invitations, losses, suretyship, sickness, death of friends, and that which is the gulf of all, improvidence, ill husbandry, disorder and confusion; by which means they are drenched on a sudden in their estates, and at unawares precipitated insensibly into an inextricable labyrinth of debts, cares, woes, want, grief, discontent, and melancholy itself.

I have done with families, and will now briefly run over some few sorts and conditions of men. The most secure, happy, jovial, and merry, in the world's esteem are Princes and great men, free from melancholy: but for their cares, miseries, suspicions, jealousies, discontents, folly, and madness, I refer you to Xenophon's Tyrannus, where King Hiero discourseth at large with Simonides the Poet of this subject. Of all others they are most troubled with perpetual fears, anxieties, insomuch that, as he said in Valerius, If thou knewest with what cares and miseries this robe were stuffed, thou wouldst not stoop to take it up. Or put case they be secure and free from fears and discontents, yet they are void of reason too oft, and precipitate in their actions. Read all our histories, which fools have writ of fools, Iliads, Æneids, Annals, and what is the subject?

The rage of foolish kings and populations. (HORACE)

How mad they are, how furious, and upon small occasions, rash and inconsiderate in their proceedings, how they dote, every page almost will witness,

When kings are mad, the people have to pay for't. (HORACE)

Next in place, next in miseries and discontents, in all manner of harebrain actions, are great men; *far from Jupiter, far from his thunder-*

bolts, the nearer the worse. If they live in Court, they are up and down, ebb and flow with their Prince's favours; their face, not merit, makes or mars their fortunes; now aloft, to-morrow down, as Polybius describes them, *like so many casting counters, now of gold, to-morrow of silver, that vary in worth as the computant will; now they stand for units, to-morrow for thousands; now before all, and anon behind.* Beside, they torment one another with mutual factions, emulations: one is ambitious, another enamoured, a third in debt, a prodigal, over-runs his fortunes, a fourth, solicitous with cares, gets nothing, &c. But for these men's discontents, anxieties, I refer you to Lucian's Tract, The Hire of Servants, Æneas Sylvius (slaves to lust and folly, he calls them), Agrippa, and many others.

Of Philosophers and Scholars, Dictators of ancient wisdom, I have already spoken in general terms, those superintendents of wit and learning, men above men, those refined men, minions of the Muses,

> *To whom 'tis given to have brains and intellects.* (DOUSA)

These acute & subtle Sophisters, so much honoured, have as much need of hellebore as others; —— *O physicians, open the middle vein.* Read Lucian's Piscator, and tell how he esteemed them; Agrippa's Tract of the Vanity of Sciences; nay read their own works, their absurd tenents, prodigious paradoxes, & " Could you keep from laughing, my friends? " You shall find that of Aristotle true: There is no great genius without a touch of madness. They have a worm as well as others; you shall find a phantastical strain, a fustian, a bombast, a vain-glorious humour, an affected style, &c., like a prominent thread in an uneven woven cloth, run parallel throughout their works. And they that teach wisdom, patience, meekness, are the veriest dizzards, harebrains, and most discontent. *In the multitude of wisdom is grief, & he that increaseth wisdom increaseth sorrow.* I need not quote mine author. They that laugh and contemn others, contemn the world of folly, deserve to be mocked, are as giddy-headed, and lie as open as any other. Democritus, that common flouter of folly, was ridiculous himself, barking Menippus, scoffing Lucian, satirical Lucilius, Petronius, Varro, Persius, &c., may be censured with the rest. Let the shapely man deride the bandy-legg'd, the white man the blackamoor. Bale, Erasmus, Hospinian, Vives, Kemnisius, explode, as a vast Ocean of Obs and Sols,* School Divinity. A labyrinth of inextricable questions, unprofitable contentions, incredible folly, one calls it. If School Divinity be so censured, — subtle Scotus, the file of truth; invincible Ockham, surpassing all previous

---

* Objections and Solutions.

thought, &c., Baconthorpe, (Doctor Resolute, and the Heart of Theology), Thomas * himself, (Doctor Seraphic, who was called Angelic), &c., what shall become of humanity? Foolish Art, what can she plead? what can her followers say for themselves? Much learning hath crackt their sconce, and taken such root, that they are too crazy for three Anticyras, — hellebore itself can do no good, nor that renowned Lanthorn of Epictetus, by which if any man studied, he should be as wise as he was. But all will not serve; rhetoricians out of their volubility of tongue will talk much to no purpose; orators can persuade other men what they will, move, pacify, &c., but cannot settle their own brains. What saith Tully? I prefer silent Wisdom to talkative Folly; and, as Seneca seconds him, a wise man's oration should not be polite or solicitous. Fabius esteems no better of most of them, either in speech, action, gesture, than as men beside themselves; so doth Gregory, I esteem a man wise, not according to his words but to his deeds. Make the best of him, a good orator is a turn-coat, an evil man, his tongue is set to sale, he is a mere voice, as he said of a nightingale, gives a voice without thought, an hyperbolical liar, a flatterer, a parasite, and, as Ammianus Marcellinus will, a corrupting cozener, one that doth more mischief by his fair speeches, than he that bribes by money; for a man may with more facility avoid him that circumvents by money, than he that deceives with glozing terms; which made Socrates so much abhor and explode them. Fracastorius, a famous Poet, freely grants all Poets to be mad; so doth Scaliger, and who doth not? Either mad or making verses (saith Horace); (saith Virgil) it pleases one to be mad, i.e., to make verses; so Servius interprets it, all Poets are mad, a company of bitter satirists, detractors, or else parasitical applauders: and what is poetry itself, but, as Austin holds, the wine of error administered by drunken teachers? You may give that censure of them in general, which Sir Thomas More once did of Germanus Brixius' Poems in particular: they are borne in the bark of folly, and dwell in the grove of madness.

Budæus, in an Epistle of his to Lupsetus, will have civil law to be the tower of wisdom; another honours physick, the quintessence of nature; a third tumbles them both down, and sets up the flag of his own peculiar science. Your supercilious criticks, grammatical triflers, notemakers, curious antiquaries, find out all the ruins of wit, gutters of folly, amongst the rubbish of old writers; and what they take they spoil, all fools with them that cannot find fault; they correct others, & are hot in a cold cause, puzzle themselves to find out how many streets in Rome,

* Thomas Aquinas.

houses, gates, towers, Homer's country, Æneas' mother, Niobe's daughters, whether Sappho was a public woman? which came first, the egg or the hen? &c. & other things which you would try to forget if you ever knew them, as Seneca holds; what clothes the Senators did wear in Rome, what shoes, how they sat, where they went to the close stool, how many dishes in a mess, what sauce; which for the present for an historian to relate, according to Lodovic. Vives, is very ridiculous, is to them most precious elaborate stuff, they admired for it, and as proud, as triumphant, in the mean time for this discovery, as if they had won a City, or conquered a Province; as rich as if they had found a mine of gold ore. One saith, they bewray & daub a company of books and good authors with their absurd comments, dung-hill reformers, Scaliger calls them, and shew their wit in censuring others, a company of foolish notemakers, humble bees, dors * or beetles, they rake over all those rubbish and dunghills, and prefer a manuscript many times before the Gospel itself, the critic's treasure-house, before any treasure, and with their *Omit so and so, some read so and so, my MS. has so and so,* with their latest editions, annotations, castigations, &c. make books dear, themselves ridiculous, and do nobody good; yet if any man dare oppose or contradict, they are mad, up in arms on a sudden, how many sheets are written in defence, how bitter invectives, what apologies? These are a poor vintage and mere trifles. But I dare say no more of, for, with, or against them, because I am liable to their lash as well as others. Of these and the rest of our Artists and Philosophers, I will generally conclude, they are a kind of mad men, as Seneca esteems of them, to make doubts & scruples, how to read them truly, to mend old authors, but will not mend their own lives, or teach us to keep our wits in order, or rectify our manners. Is not he mad that draws lines with Archimedes, whilst his house is ransacked, and his city besieged, when the whole world is in combustion, or we whilst our souls are in danger, (Death follows, life flies), to spend our time in toys, idle questions, and things of no worth?

That lovers are mad, I think no man will deny. To love and be wise, why, Jupiter himself cannot intend both at once. Majesty and love do not well agree, nor do they dwell in the same place. Tully, when he was invited to a second marriage, replied, he could not be wise and love both together. Love is madness, a hell, an incurable disease; Seneca calls it an impotent and raging lust. I shall dilate this subject apart; in the mean time let lovers sigh out the rest.

* Cockchafers.

Nevisanus the lawyer holds it for an axiom, *most women are fools,* of feeble judgment; Seneca men, be they young or old; who doubts it? Youth is mad, as Elius in Tully, old age little better, &c. Theophrastus, in the 107th year of his age, said he then began to be wise, & therefore lamented his departure. If wisdom come so late, where shall we find a wise man? Our old ones dote at threescore and ten. I would cite more proofs, and a better author; but for the present, let one fool point at another. Nevisanus hath as hard an opinion of rich men, *wealth and wisdom cannot dwell together,* wealth permits folly, and they do commonly besot men; &, as we see it, *fools have fortune.* Wisdom is not found in the world among the rich. For besides a natural contempt of learning, which accompanies such kind of men, innate idleness (for they will take no pains) and, which Aristotle observes, where the greatest brains are is the least luck, where most luck there are very poor brains; great wealth & little wit go commonly together: they have as much brains some of them in their heads as in their heels; besides this inbred neglect of liberal sciences, and all arts, which should polish the mind, they have most part some gullish humour or other, by which they are led; one is an Epicure, an Atheist, a second a gamester, a third a whoremaster, (fit subjects all for a Satirist to work upon),

One burns for married women, one for boys;   (HORACE)
one is mad of hawking, hunting, cocking; another of carousing, horse-riding, spending; a fourth of building, fighting, &c.

Mad is Damasippus, buying up old statues,   (HORACE)
Damasippus hath an humour of his own, to be talked of: Heliodorus, the Carthaginian, another. In a word, as Scaliger concludes of them all, they are the very statues or pillars of folly. Choose out of all stories him that hath been most admired, you shall still find much to praise, much to blame, as Berosus of Semiramis; mankind march to victory, wealth, honor, &c., on the other hand, to excess, bloodshed, crime; as she had some good, so had she many bad parts.

Alexander, a worthy man, but furious in his anger, overtaken in drink: Cæsar and Scipio valiant and wise, but vain-glorious, ambitious: Vespasian a worthy Prince, but covetous: Hannibal, as he had mighty virtues, so had he many vices; one virtue to a thousand vices was joined, as Machiavel of Cosmo de Medici, he had two distinct persons in him. I will determine of them all, they are like these double or turning pictures; stand before which, you see a fair maid on the one side, an ape on the other, an owl; look upon them at the first sight, all is well; but farther examine, you shall find them wise on the one side, and fools on the other; in some few things praiseworthy, in the rest incomparably faulty. I will say nothing of their diseases, emulations, discontents, wants, and such miseries; let Poverty plead the rest in Aristophanes' Plutus.

Covetous men, amongst others, are most mad, they have all the symptoms of melancholy, fear, sadness, suspicion, &c. as shall be proved in his proper place.

Most hellebore to misers must be given. (HORACE)

And yet methinks prodigals are much madder than they, be of what condition they will, that bear a publick or private purse; as a Dutch writer censured Richard, the rich Duke of Cornwall, suing to be Emperor, for his profuse spending, that scattered money like water; I do censure them. Foolish England, that has been deprived of so much money, foolish rulers of Germany, who have sold their noble privilege for gold. Spend-thrifts, bribers, and bribe-takers are fools, and so are all they that cannot keep, disburse, or spend, their monies well.

I might say the like of angry, peevish, envious, ambitious; drink a purer hellebore; Epicures, Atheists, Schismaticks, Hereticks; all these have a faulty imagination (saith Nymannus), *and their madness shall be evident.* Fabatus, an Italian, holds sea-faring men all mad; *the ship is mad, for it never stands still: the mariners are mad, to expose themselves to such imminent danger: the waters are raging mad, in perpetual motion: the winds are as mad as the rest, they know not whence they come, whither they would go: and those men are maddest of all that go to sea; for one fool at home, they find forty abroad.* He was a mad man that said it, and thou peradventure as mad to read it. Felix Plater is of opinion all Alchemists are mad, out of their wits; Athenæus saith as much of fiddlers, nightingales of the Muses, and musicians, pipers, who, when they blow blow out their brains, in comes musick at one ear, out goes wit at another. Proud and vain-glorious persons are certainly mad; and so are lascivious; I can feel their pulses beat hither, horn-mad some of them, to let others lie with their wives, and wink at it.

To insist in all particulars were an Herculean task, to reckon up mad labours, mad books, endeavours, carriages, gross ignorance, ridiculous actions, absurd gestures; as Tully terms them [in his letters to Quintus], madness of villages [villas], stupend structures, as those Egyptian pyramids, Labyrinths & Sphinxes, which a company of crowned asses, in the ostentation of riches, vainly built, when neither the Architect nor King that made them, or to what use and purpose, are yet known. To insist in their hypocrisy, inconstancy, blindness, rashness, fraud, cozenage, malice, anger, impudence, ingratitude, ambition gross superstition, as in Tiberius' times, such base flattery, stupend, parasitical, fawning and colloguing, &c. brawls, conflicts, desires, contentions, it would ask an expert Vesalius to anatomise every member. Shall I say Jupiter himself, Apollo, Mars, &c., doted; and monster-conquering Hercules, that subdued the world, & helped others, could not relieve himself in this, but mad he was at last. And where shall a man walk, converse with whom, in what Province, City, and not meet with Signior Deliro, or Hercules Furens, Mænades, & Corybantes? Their speeches say no less. They were men sprung from mushrooms, or else they fetched their pedigree from those that were struck by Samson with the jawbone of an ass; or from Deucalion and Pyrrha's stones, for we are stony-hearted, and savour too much of the stock: as if they had all heard that enchanted horn of Astolpho, that English Duke in Ariosto, which never sounded but all his auditors were mad, & for fear ready to make away themselves; or landed in the mad haven in the Euxine sea of Daphne Insana, which had a secret quality to dementate; they are a company of giddy-heads, afternoon men, it is Midsummer moon still, & the Dog-days last all the year long, they are all mad. Whom shall I then except? Ulric Hutten saith, Nemo [No-body] is wise at all hours, Nemo is born without faults, Nemo is free from crime, Nemo is content with his lot, Nemo in love is wise, Nemo is good, Nemo's a wise man, and perfectly happy &c., and therefore *Nicholas Nemo,* or Monsieur *No-body* shall go free. But whom shall I except in the second place? such as are silent, the wise man speaks but little; no better way to avoid folly and madness than by taciturnity. Whom in a third? all Senators, Magistrates; for all fortunate men are wise, and conquerors valiant, and so all great men, it is not well to trifle with the gods, they are wise by authority, good by their office and place, (some say) we must not speak ill of them, neither is it fit; let me hasten to speak favorably, I will not think amiss of them. Whom next? Stoicks? The Stoick is the wise man, and he alone is subject to no perturbations, as Plutarch scoffs at him, *he is not vexed with torments, or burnt with fire, foiled by his adversary, sold of his enemy. Though he be wrinkled, sand-blind, toothless, and deformed; yet he is most beautiful, and like a god, a king in conceit, though not worth a groat. He never dotes, [is] never mad, never sad, [never] drunk, because virtue cannot be taken away,* as Zeno holds, *by reason of strong apprehension,* but he was mad to say so. For this sort of thing an Anticyrian operation is needful; he had need to be bored, & so had all his fellows, as wise as they would seem to be. Chry-

sippus himself liberally grants them to be fools as well as others, at
certain times, upon some occasions; a man's power may be lost by
drunkenness or melancholy, he may be sometimes crazed as well as the
rest: " above all, he is sound, save when the phlegm troubles him." I
should here except some Cynicks, Menippus, Diogenes, that Theban
Crates; or, to descend to these times, that omniscious, only wise fraternity of the Rosy Cross, those great Theologues, Politicians, Philosophers, Physicians, Philologers, Artists, &c., of whom S. Bridget, Abbas
Joacchimus, Leicenbergius, & such divine spirits, have prophesied, &
made promise to the world, if at least there be any such (Hen. Neuhu-
sius makes a doubt of it, Valentinus Andreas, & others), or an Elias
Artifex, their Theophrastian master; whom though Libavius & many
deride & carp at, yet some will have to be *the renewer of all arts &
sciences,* reformer of the world, & now living; for so Johannes Montanus Strigoniensis, that great Patron of Paracelsus, contends, and certainly avers, *a most divine man,* & the quintessence of wisdom, wheresoever he is; for he, his fraternity, friends, &c. are all *betrothed to
wisdom,* if we may believe their disciples and followers. I must needs
except Lipsius & the Pope, and expunge their names out of the catalogue of fools. For besides that parasitical testimony of Dousa,

> *From the Mæotid Lake to the rising sun,*
> *Of men like Justus there's not one;*

Lipsius saith of himself that he was a grand Signior, a Master, a Tutor
of us all, and for 13 years he brags how he sowed wisdom in the Low
Countries, as Ammonius the philosopher sometime did in Alexandria,
combining humanism with letters & science with common-sense; the
High Priest of wisdom, he shall be the eighth wise man. The Pope is
more than a man, as his parasites make him, a demi-god, and besides his
Holiness cannot err, from the Throne belike: and yet some of them have
been Magicians, Hereticks, Atheists, children, and as Platina saith of
John, he showed himself a scholar sufficient, yet many things he did
foolishly, lightly. I can say no more then in particular, but in general
terms to the rest, they are all mad, their wits are evaporated, and as
Ariosto feigns, kept in jars above the Moon.

> *Some lose their wits with love, some with ambition,*
> *Some following Lords and men of high condition.*
> *Some in fair jewels rich and costly set,*
> *Others in Poetry their wits forget,*
> *Another thinks to be an Alchemist,*
> *Till all be spent, and he his number mist.* (ARIOSTO)

Convict fools they are, mad men upon record; and I am afraid past cure many of them; their bowels rumble, the symptoms are manifest, they are all of Gotham * parish. What remains then but to send for Lorarios,† those Officers to carry them all together for company to Bedlam, & set Rabelais to be their physician.

If any man shall ask in the mean time, who I am, that so boldly censure others, have I no faults? Yes more than thou hast, whatsoever thou art. We are the merest ciphers, I confess it again, I am as foolish, as mad as any one.

I seem to you insane, I pray you think so. (PETRONIUS)

I do not deny it, let the mad man be removed from the people. My comfort is, I have more fellows, and those of excellent note. And though I be not so right, or so discreet as I should be, yet not so mad, so bad neither, as thou perhaps takest me to be.

To conclude, this being granted, that all the world is melancholy, or mad, dotes, and every member of it, I have ended my task, and sufficiently illustrated that which I took upon me to demonstrate at first. At this present I have no more to say. *Democritus to Sanity!* I can but wish myself and them a good Physician, and all of us a better mind.

And although, for the above-named reasons, I had a just cause to undertake this subject, to point at these particular species of dotage, that so men might acknowledge their imperfections, and seek to reform what is amiss; yet I have a more serious intent at this time; and to omit all impertinent digressions, to say no more of such as are improperly melancholy, or metaphorically mad, lightly mad, or in disposition, as stupid, angry, drunken, silly, sottish, sullen, proud, vain-glorious, ridiculous, beastly, peevish, obstinate, impudent, extravagant, dry, doting, dull, desperate, harebrain, &c., mad, frantick, foolish, heteroclites, which no new Hospital can hold, no physick help: my purpose & endeavour is, in the following discourse, to anatomize this humour of melancholy, through all his parts and species, as it is an habit, or an ordinary disease, and that philosophically, medicinally, to shew the causes, symptoms, and several cures of it, that it may be the better avoided; moved thereunto for the generality of it, and to do good, it being a disease so frequent, as Mercurialis observes, *in these our days; so often happening,* saith Laurentius, *in our miserable times,* as few there are that feel not the smart of it. Of the same mind is Ælian Montaltus, Melancthon, and

* A Nottingham village proverbially rated for stupidity.
† Or to send for a cook to the Anticyræ, to make hellebore pottage, settle-brain pottage. — Burton's note.

others; Julius Cæsar Claudinus calls it the *fountain of all other diseases, and so common in this crazed age of ours, that scarce one of a thousand is free from it:* and that splenetick hypochondriacal wind especially, which proceeds from the spleen and short ribs. Being then it is a disease so grievous, so common, I know not wherein to do a more general service, and spend my time better, than to prescribe means how to prevent and cure so universal a malady, an epidemical disease, that so often, so much, crucifies the body and mind.

If I have overshot myself in this which hath been hitherto said, or that it is, which I am sure some will object, too fantastical, *too light and comical, for a Divine, too satirical for one of my profession,* I will presume to answer with Erasmus, in like case, 'Tis not I, but Democritus who said it: you must consider what it is to speak in one's own or another's person, an assumed habit and name; a difference betwixt him that affects or acts a Prince's, a Philosopher's, a Magistrate's, a Fool's part, and him that is so indeed; and what liberty those old Satirists have had, it is a *Cento* collected from others, not I, but they, that say it.

> *If I shall speak too freely, grant to me*
> *Both pardon and indulgency.* (HORACE)

Take heed you mistake me not. If I do a little forget myself, I hope you will pardon it. And to say truth, why should any man be offended, or take exceptions at it?

> *It lawful was of old, and still will be,*
> *To speak of vice, but let the name go free.*

I hate their vices, not their persons. If any be displeased, or take ought unto himself, let him not expostulate or cavil with him that said it (so did Erasmus excuse himself to Dorpius, if I may compare small things with great, and so do I); *but let him be angry with himself, that so betrayed and opened his own faults in applying it to himself. If he be guilty and deserve it, let him amend, whoever he is, and not be angry.* He that hateth correction is a fool. If he be not guilty, it concerns him not; it is not my freeness of speech, but a guilty conscience, a galled back of his own that makes him winch.

> *Himself distrusts who error makes,*
> *And what is general to him takes;*
> *The silly man, his conscience quakes.*

I deny not this which I have said savours a little of Democritus; but one may speak in jest, & yet speak truth. It is somewhat tart, I grant it, as he said, sharp sauces increase appetite, even victuals are tasteless without a little vinegar. Object then and cavil what thou wilt, I ward all with Democritus' buckler, his medicine shall salve it; where thou wilt, and when; Democritus has said it, Democritus will answer it. It was written by an idle fellow, at idle times, about our Saturnalian or Dionysian feasts, when as he said, " there is no danger in freedom: " servants in old Rome had liberty to say and do what they list. When our countrymen sacrificed to their goddess Vacuna, and sat tippling by their Vacunal fires, I writ this, and published this. One alone is not wanton, it is every one. The time, place, persons, and all circumstances, apologize for me, and why may I not then be idle with others, speak my mind freely? If you deny me this liberty, upon these presumptions I will take it: I say again, I will take it. If there be a man who thinks that hard words are applied to him, let him reflect that this is not in attack but in self-defence. If any man take exceptions, let him turn the buckle of his girdle, I care not. I owe thee nothing (Reader), I look for no favour at thy hands, I am independent, I fear not.

No, I recant, I will not, I care, I fear, I confess my fault, acknowledge a great offence,

> *But 'tis well first to calm the troubled billows.* (VIRGIL)

I have overshot myself, I have spoken foolishly, rashly, unadvisedly, absurdly, I have anatomized mine own folly. And now, methinks, upon a sudden I am awaked as it were out of a dream, I have had a raving fit, a phantastical fit, ranged up and down, in and out; I have insulted over most kind of men, abused some, offended others, wronged myself; and now being recovered, and perceiving mine error, cry with Orlando, Absolve me, pardon (O kind readers), that which is past, and I will make you amends in that which is to come; I promise you a more sober discourse in my following treatise.

If through weakness, folly, passion, discontent, ignorance, I have said amiss, let it be forgotten and forgiven. I acknowledge that of Tacitus to be true, a bitter jest leaves a sting behind it: and as an honourable man observes, *They fear a Satirist's wit, he their memories.* I may justly suspect the worst; and though I hope I have wronged no man, yet in Medea's words I will crave pardon,

> *And in my last words this I do desire,*
> *That what in passion I have said, or ire,*
> *May be forgotten, and a better mind*
> *Be had of us, hereafter as you find.* (SENECA)

I earnestly request every private man, as Scaliger did Cardan, not to take offence. I will conclude in his lines: Didst know me well, thou wouldst not only pardon these my witticisms, but would even consider it unmeet that so kindly a soul as I should find it necessary to avert even the slightest suspicion. If thou knewest my modesty and simplicity, thou wouldst easily pardon and forgive what is here amiss, or by thee misconceived. If hereafter, anatomizing this surly humour, my hand slip, as an unskilful prentice I lance too deep, and cut through skin and all at unawares, make it smart, or cut awry, pardon a rude hand, an unskilful knife, 'tis a most difficult thing to keep an even tone, a perpetual tenor, and not sometimes to lash out; not to write satire is the difficulty, there be so many objects to divert, inward perturbations to molest, and the very best may sometimes err; if Homer, usually so good, takes a nap, it is impossible not in so much to overshoot: it is no great sin if over a long work, sleep should steal at times. But what needs all this? I hope there will no such cause of offence be given: if there be,

Let none take these to himself, they're fables all,   (PLAUTUS)

I'll deny all (my last refuge), recant all, renounce all I have said, if any man except, and with as much facility excuse, as he can accuse; but I presume of thy good favour, and gracious acceptance (gentle reader.) Out of an assured hope and confidence thereof, I will begin.

TO THE MISCHIEVOUSLY IDLE READER

WHOEVER you may be, I caution you against rashly defaming the Author of this work, or cavilling in jest against him. Nay, (to be brief), neither tacitly reproach him because of others' censure, nor employ your wit in foolish disapproval, or false accusation. For, should Democritus Junior prove to be what he professes, akin at least to his elder namesake, or smack ever so little of his genius, it is all over with you: he will become both accuser and judge of you (being reckless with spleen), will dissipate you in jests, pulverize you with wit, and, finally, sacrifice you to the God of Mirth.

I further advise you, not to asperse, or calumniate, or slander, Democritus Junior, who possibly does not think ill of you, lest you may hear from some discreet friend, the same remark the people of Abdera did from Hippocrates, of their worthy and familiar fellow-citizen Democritus, whom they had looked on as a madman: Not that you, Democritus, are wise, but the people of Abdera be fools and mad.

Thou hast thyself an Abditerian soul. (MARTIAL)

And having thus briefly warned you, O mischievously idle Reader, farewell.

*   *   *   *   *

WEEP, Heraclitus, for this wretched age,
  Nought dost thou see that is not base and sad:
Laugh on, Democritus, thou laughing sage,
Nought dost thou see that is not vain and bad.
Let one delight in tears and one in laughter,
Each shall find his occasion ever after.
There needs, since mankind's now in madness hurled,
A thousand weeping, laughing sages more:
And best (such madness doth prevail) the world
Should go to Anticyra, feed on hellebore.

*   *   *   *   *

THE FIRST PARTITION

THE SYNOPSIS OF THE FIRST PARTITION

In diseases consider *Sec.* 1. *Memb.* 1.

Their Causes. *Subs.* 1.
- Impulsive;
  - Sin, concupiscence, &c.
- Instrumental;
  - Intemperance, all second causes, &c

Or

Definition, Member, Division, *Subs.* 2.
- Of the body 300, which are
  - Epidemical, as Plague, Plica, &c. Or
  - Particular; as Gout; Dropsy, &c.

Or

of the head or mind. *Subs.* 3.
- In disposition; as all perturbations, evil affection, &c.

Or

Habits, as *Subs.* 4.
- Dotage.
- Phrensy.
- Madness.
- Extasy.
- Lycanthropia.
- Chorus Sancti Viti.
- Hydrophobia.
- Possession or obsession of Devils.
- Melancholy. See ♈.

♈ Melancholy: in which consider

Its Æquivocations, in Disposition, Improper, &c. *Subsect.* 5.

Memb. 2. To its explication, a digression of anatomy, in which observe parts of *Subs.*1.

Body hath parts *Subs.* 1.
- contained as
  - Humours, 4. Blood, Phlegm, &c.
  - Spirits; vital, natural, animal.
- or containing
  - Similar; spermatical, or flesh, bones, nerves, &c.
  - Dissimilar; brain, heart, liver, &c. *Subs.* 4.

Or

Soul & his faculties, as
- Vegetal. *Subs.* 5.
- Sensible. *Subs.* 6, 7, 8.
- Rational. *Subsect.* 9, 10, 11.

Memb. 3.
Its definition, name, difference, *Sub.* 1.
The part and parties, affected, affection, &c. *Sub.* 2.
The matter of melancholy, natural, unnatural, &c. *Sub.* 4.

Species, or kinds, which are
- Proper to parts, as
  - Of the head alone, Hypochondriacal, or windy melancholy. Of the whole Body.
  - with their several causes, symptoms, prognosticks, cures.
- Or
- Indefinite; as Love-melancholy, the subject of the third Partition.

Its Causes in general. *Sect.* 2. A.
Its Symptoms or signs. *Sect.* 3. B.
Its Prognosticks or Indications. *Sect.* 4.
Its Cures; the subject of the second Partition.

A.
Sect. 2.
Causes of
Melancholy
are either

General, as *Memb.* 1.

Supernatural

As from God immediately, or by second causes, *Sub.* 1.
Or from the devil immediately, with a digression of the nature of spirits and devils, *Sub.* 2.
Or mediately by Magicians, Witches, *Sub.* 3.
Primary as stars, proved by Aphorisms, signs from Physiognomy, Metoposcopy, Chiromancy, *Subs.* 4.

Or

Natural

Congenite, inward from

Old age, temperament, *Sub.* 5.
Parents, it being an hereditary disease, *Sub.* 6.

or

Secondary, as

Or

Evident, outward, remote, adventitious, as,

Necessary, see 8.

Not necessary, as *M. 4. S.* 2.

Nurses, *Sub.* 1.
Education, *Sub.* 2.
Terrors, affrights, *Sub.* 3.
Scoffs, calumnies, bitter jests, *Sub.* 4.
Loss of liberty, servitude, imprisonment, *Sub.* 5.
Poverty and want, *Sub.* 6.
An heap of other accidents, death of friends, loss, &c. *Sub.* 7.

Outward, or adventitious, which are

Or

Contingent inward, antecedent, nearest. *Memb.* 5. *Sect.* 2.

In which the body works on the mind, and this malady is caused by precedent diseases; as agues, pox, &c. or temperature innate, *Sub.* 1.
Or by particular parts distempered, as brain, heart, spleen, liver, Mesentery, Pylorus, stomach, &c. *Sub.* 2.

Particular to the three Species. See **Π**.

Π
Particular causes.
Sect. 2.
Memb. 5.

Of head Melancholy are. *Sub.* 3.

Inward

Innate humour, or from distemperature adust.
A hot brain, corrupted blood in the brain.
Excess of Venery, or defect.
Agues, or some precedent disease.
Fumes arising from the stomach, &c.

Or

Outward

Heat of the Sun immoderate.
A blow on the head.
Overmuch use of hot wines, spices, garlick, onions, hot baths, overmuch waking, &c.
Idleness, solitariness, or overmuch study, vehement labour, &c.
Passions, perturbations, &c.

Of hypochondriacal, or windy Melancholy are,

Inward

Or

Outward

Default of spleen, belly, bowels, stomack, mesentery, meseraick veins, liver, &c.
Months, or hemrods stopt, or any other ordinary evacuation.

Those six non-natural things abused.

Over all the body are, *Subs.* 5.

Inward

Or

Outward

Liver distempered, stopped, over-hot, apt to ingender melancholy, temperature innate.
Bad diet, suppression of hemrods, &c. and such evacuations, passions, cares, &c. those six non-natural things abused.

8 Necessary causes, as those six non-natural things, which are, Sect. 2. Mem. 2.

Diet offending in *Sub.* 3.

Substance

Bread; coarse and black, &c.
Drink; thick, thin, sour, &c.
Water unclean, milk, oil, vinegar, wine, spices, &c.

Flesh — Parts; heads, feet, entrails, fat, bacon, blood, &c.
Kinds { Beef, Pork, Venison, Hares, Goats, Pigeons, Peacocks, Fen fowl, &c.

Fish, Of fish; all shell-fish, hard and slimy fish, &c.
Herbs, Of herbs; pulse, cabbage, melons, garlick, onions, &c.
&c. All roots, raw fruits, hard and windy meats.

Quality, as in
Preparing, dressing, sharp sauces, salt meats, indurate, soused fried, broiled, or made dishes, &c.

Quantity
Disorder in eating, immoderate eating, or at unseasonable times, & *Subsect.* 2.

Custom; delight, appetite, altered, &c. *Subs.* 3.

Retention and evacuation, *Subs.* 4.
Costiveness, hot baths, sweating, issues stopped, Venus in excess, or in defect, phlebotomy, purging, &c.

Air; hot, cold, tempestuous, dark, thick, foggy, moorish, &c. *Subs.* 5.

Exercise, *Sub.* 6.
Unseasonable, excessive or defective, of body and mind, solitariness, idleness, a life out of action, &c.

Sleep and waking, unseasonable, inordinate, overmuch, overlittle, &c. *Subs.* 7.

Memb. 3. *Sect.* 2. Passions and perturbations of the mind, *Subsect.* 2. With a digression of the force of imagination. *Sub.* 2. & division of passions into *Sub.* 3.

Irascible

Sorrow, cause and symptom, *Sub.* 4. Fear, cause & symptom, *Sub.* 5. Shame, repulse, disgrace, &c. *Sub.* 6. Envy and malice, *Sub.* 7. Emulation, hatred, faction, desire of revenge, *Sub.* 8. Anger a cause, *Sub.* 9. Discontents, cares, miseries, &c. *Sub.* 10.

or

concupiscible.

Vehement desires, ambition, *Sub.* 11. Covetousness, φιλαργυρία, *Sub.* 12. Love of pleasures, gaming in excess, &c. *Sub.* 13. Desire of praise, pride, vainglory, &c. *Sub.* 14. Love of learning, study in excess, with a digression of the misery of Scholars, and why the Muses are melancholy, *Sub.* 15.

B. Symptoms of melancholy are either. Sect. 3.

General, as of *Memb.* 1.

or

Body, as ill digestion, crudity, wind, dry brains, hard belly, thick blood, much waking, heaviness and palpitation of heart, leaping in many places, &c. *Sub.* 1.

Common to all or most
Fear and sorrow without a just cause, suspicion, jealousy, discontent, solitariness, irksomeness, continual cogitations, restless thoughts, vain imaginations, &c. *Subs.* 2.
Celestial influences, as ♄ ♃ ♂, &c. parts of the body, heart, brain, liver, spleen, stomach, &c.

Or

Humours
Sanguine are merry still, laughing, pleasant, meditating on plays, women, musick, &c.
Phlegmatick, slothful, dull, heavy, &c.
Cholerick, furious, impatient, subject to hear and see strange apparitions, &c.
Black, solitary, sad, they think they are bewitcht, dead, &c.

Or mixt of these four humours adust, or not adust, infinitely varied.

Mind

Particular to private persons, according to *Sub.* 3. 4.

Their several customs, conditions, inclinations, discipline, &c.
Ambitious thinks himself a King, a Lord; covetous runs on his money, lascivious on his mistress; religious hath revelations, visions, is a Prophet, or troubled in mind, a scholar on his book, &c.

Continuance of time as the humour is intended or remitted, &c.
Pleasant at first, hardly discerned, afterwards harsh and intolerable, if inveterate.
Hence some make three degrees, { 1. *Falsa cogitatio.* 2. *Cogitata loqui.* 3. *Exsequi locutum.* }
By fits, or continuate, as the object varies, pleasing, or displeasing.

Simple, or as it is mixt with other Diseases, Apoplexies, Gout, *caninus appetitus*, &c. so the symptoms are various.

Particular symptoms to the three distinct species. *Sect.* 3. *Memb.* 2.

Head-melancholy. *Sub.* 1.

- *In body* — Headache, binding, heaviness, vertigo, lightness, singing of the ears, much waking, fixed eyes, high colour, red eyes, hard belly, dry body, no great sign of melancholy in the other parts.
- *Or*
- *In mind* — Continual fear, sorrow, suspicion, discontent, superfluous cares, solicitude, anxiety, perpetual cogitation of such toys they are possessed with, thoughts like dreams, &c.

Hypochondriacal or windy melancholy. *Sub.* 2.

- *In body* — Wind, rumbling in the guts, belly-ache, heat in the bowels, convulsions, crudities, short wind, sour and sharp belchings, cold sweat, pain in the left side, suffocation, palpitation, heaviness of the heart, singing in the ears, much spittle, and moist, &c.
- *Or*
- *In mind* — Fearful, sad, suspicious, discontent, anxiety, &c. Lascivious by reason of much wind, troublesome dreams, affected by fits, &c.

Over all the body. *Sub.* 3.

- *In body* — Black, most part lean, broad veins, gross, thick blood, their hemrods commonly stopped, &c.
- *Or*
- *In mind* — Fearful, sad, solitary, hate light, averse from company, fearful dreams, &c.

Symptoms of Nuns, Maids, and Widows, melancholy, in body and mind, &c.

A reason of these symptoms. *Memb.* 3.

- Why they are so fearful, sad, suspicious without a cause, why solitary, why melancholy men are witty, why they suppose they hear and see strange voices, visions, apparitions.
- Why they prophesy, and speak strange languages, whence comes their crudity, rumbling, convulsions, cold sweat, heaviness of heart, palpitation, cardiaca, fearful dreams, much waking, prodigious phantasies.

C. Prognosticks of melancholy. *Sect.* 4.

Tending to good, as

- Morphew, scabs, itch, breaking out, &c.
- Black jaundice.
- If the hemrods voluntarily open.
- If varices appear.

Tending to evil, as

- Leanness, dryness, hollow-eyed, &c.
- Inveterate melancholy is incurable.
- If cold, it degenerates often into epilepsy, apoplexy, dotage, or into blindness.
- If hot, into madness, despair, and violent death.

Corollaries and questions.

- The grievousness of this above all other diseases.
- The diseases of the mind are more grievous than those of the body.
- Whether it be lawful in this case of melancholy, for a man to offer violence to himself. *Neg.*
- How a melancholy or mad man, offering violence to himself, is to be censured.

THE FIRST PARTITION

THE FIRST	{ SECTION MEMBER SUBSECTION

Man's Excellency, Fall, Miseries, Infirmities; the causes of them

AN, the most excellent and noble creature of the World, *the principal and mighty work of God, wonder of Nature,* as Zoroaster calls him; *the marvel of marvels,* as Plato; *the Abridgement and Epitome of the World,* as Pliny; a Microcosm, a little world, Sovereign Lord of the Earth, Viceroy of the World, sole Commander and Governor of all the Creatures in it: to whose Empire they are subject in particular, and yield obedience; far surpassing all the rest, not in body only, but in soul; created in God's own *Image,* to that immortal and incorporeal substance, with all the faculties and powers belonging unto it; was at first pure, divine, perfect, happy, created after God in true holiness and righteousness; Like God, free from all manner of infirmities, and put in Paradise, to know God, to praise and glorify him, to do his will: So that God might bring forth the Godlike, (as an old Poet saith) to propagate the Church.

But this most noble creature, (one exclaims) O pitiful change! is fallen from that he was, and forfeited his estate, become a wretched mannikin, a castaway, a caitiff, one of the most miserable creatures of the world, if he be considered in his own nature, an unregenerate man, and so much obscured by his fall (that some few reliques excepted) he is inferior to a beast: *man in honour that understandeth not, is like unto beasts that perish,* so David esteems him: a monster by stupend metamorphosis, a fox, a dog, a hog, what not? How much altered from that he was; before blessed and happy, now miserable and accursed! *He must eat his meat in sorrow,* subject to death & all manner of infirmities, all kinds of calamities. *Great travail is created for all men, and an heavy yoke on the sons of Adam, from the day that they go out of their mother's womb, unto that day they return to the mother of all things. Namely their thoughts, and fear of their hearts, and their imagination of things they wait for, and the day of death. From him that sitteth in*

the glorious throne, to him that sitteth beneath in the earth and ashes; from him that is clothed in blue silk, and weareth a Crown, to him that is clothed in simple linen. Wrath, envy, trouble, and unquietness, and fear of death, and rigour, and strife, and such things come to both man and beast, but sevenfold to the ungodly. All this befalls him in this life, and peradventure eternal misery in the life to come.

The impulsive cause of these miseries in man, this privation or destruction of God's image, the cause of death and diseases, of all temporal and eternal punishments, was the sin of our first parent Adam, in eating of the forbidden fruit, by the devil's instigation and allurement. His disobedience, pride, ambition, intemperance, incredulity, curiosity; from whence proceeded original sin, and that general corruption of mankind, as from a fountain flowed all bad inclinations, and actual transgressions, which cause our several calamities inflicted upon us for our sins. And this belike is that which our fabulous Poets have shadowed unto us in the tale of Pandora's box, which, being opened through her curiosity, filled the world full of all manner of diseases. It is not curiosity alone, but those other crying sins of ours, which pull these several plagues and miseries upon our heads. For where there is sin, there is a storm, as Chrysostom well observes. *Fools by reason of their transgression, and because of their iniquities, are afflicted. Fear cometh like sudden desolation, and destruction like a whirlwind, affliction and anguish, because they did not fear God.* Are you shaken with wars? (as Cyprian well urgeth to Demetrius,) are you molested with dearth and famine? is your health crushed with raging diseases? is mankind generally tormented with epidemical maladies? *'tis all for your sins.* God is angry, punisheth, and threateneth, because of their obstinacy and stubbornness, they will not turn unto him. If the earth be barren then for want of rain, if, dry and squalid, it yield no fruit, if your fountains be dried up, your wine, corn, and oil blasted, if the air be corrupted, & men troubled with diseases, 'tis by reason of their sins: which, like the blood of Abel, cry aloud to heaven for vengeance. *That we have sinned, therefore our hearts are heavy. We roar like bears, and mourn like doves, and want health, &c., for our sins and trespasses.* But this we cannot endure to hear, or to take notice of: *We are smitten in vain, and receive no correction;* and *Thou hast stricken them, but they have refused to receive correction, they have not returned. Pestilence he hath sent, but they have not turned to him.* Herod could not abide John Baptist, nor Domitian endure Apollonius to tell the causes of the plague at Ephesus, his injustice. incest, adultery and the like.

To punish therefore this blindness and obstinacy of ours, as a concomitant cause, and principal agent, is God's just judgement, in bringing these calamities upon us, to chastise us, I say, for our sins, and to satisfy God's wrath. For the law requires obedience or punishment, as you may read at large: *If they will not obey the Lord, and keep his commandments and ordinances, then all these curses shall come upon them. Cursed in the town and in the field, &c. Cursed in the fruit of the body, &c. The Lord shall send thee trouble and shame, because of thy wickedness.* And a little after, *The Lord shall smite thee with the botch of Egypt, and with emrods, and scab, and itch, and thou canst not be healed. With madness, blindness, and astonishing of heart.* This Paul seconds, *Tribulation and anguish on the soul of every man that doth evil.* Or else these chastisements are inflicted upon us for our humiliation, to exercise and try our patience here in this life, to bring us home, to make us to know God and ourselves, to inform & teach us wisdom. *Therefore is my people gone into captivity, because they had no knowledge, therefore is the wrath of the Lord kindled against his people, & he hath stretched out his hand upon them.* He is desirous of our salvation, saith Lemnius, and for that cause pulls us by the ear many times, to put us in mind of our duties: *that they which erred might have understanding,* (as Isaiah speaks) *and so to be reformed. I am afflicted, and at the point of death,* so David confesseth of himself, *mine eyes are sorrowful through mine affliction:* and that made him turn unto God. Great Alexander, in the midst of all his prosperity, by a company of parasites deified, and now made a God, when he saw one of his wounds bleed, remembered that he was but a man, and remitted of his pride. As Pliny well perceived, in sickness the mind reflects upon itself, with judgement surveys itself, and abhors its former courses; insomuch that he concludes to his friend Maximus, that it were the period of all philosophy, if we could so continue sound, or perform but a part of that which we promised to do, being sick. *Whoso is wise, then, will consider these things,* as David did, and whatsoever fortune befall him, make use of it. If he be in sorrow, need, sickness, or any other adversity, seriously to recount with himself, why this or that malady, misery, this or that incurable disease, is inflicted upon him; it may be for his good, truly it is well, as Peter said of his daughter's ague. Bodily sickness is for his soul's health, had he not been visited, he had utterly perished; for *the Lord correcteth him whom he loveth, even as a father doth his child in whom he delighteth.* If he be safe and sound, on the other side, and free from all manner of infirmity;

And that he have grace, beauty, favour, health,
A cleanly diet, and abound in wealth;   (HORACE)

yet in the midst of his prosperity, let him remember that caveat of
Moses, *beware that he do not forget the Lord his God;* that he be not
puffed up, but acknowledge them to be his good gifts and benefits, and
the more he hath, to be more thankful, (as Agapetianus adviseth) & use
them aright.

Now the instrumental causes of these our infirmities are as divers as
the infirmities themselves. Stars, heavens, elements, &c. and all those
creatures which God hath made, are armed against sinners. They were
indeed once good in themselves, and that they are now many of them
pernicious unto us, is not in their nature, but our corruption, which hath
caused it. For, from the fall of our first parent Adam, they have been
changed, the earth accursed, the influence of stars altered, the four
elements, beasts, birds, plants, are now ready to offend us. *The prin-*
cipal things for the use of man are water, fire, iron, salt, meal, wheat,
honey, milk, oil, wine, clothing, good to the godly, to the sinners turned
to evil. Fire, and hail, and famine, and dearth, all these are created for
vengeance. The heavens threaten us with their comets, stars, planets,
with their great conjunctions, eclipses, oppositions, quartiles, and such
unfriendly aspects; the air with his meteors, thunder and lightning,
intemperate heat and cold, mighty winds, tempests, unseasonable
weather; from which proceed dearth, famine, plague, and all sorts of
epidemical diseases, consuming infinite myriads of men. At Cairo in
Egypt, every third year, (as it is related by Boterus, and others) 300,-
000 die of the plague; and 200,000 in Constantinople, every fifth or
seventh at the utmost. How doth the earth terrify and oppress us with
terrible earthquakes, which are most frequent in China, Japan, and
those Eastern Climes, swallowing up sometimes six cities at once! How
doth the water rage with his inundations, irruptions, flinging down
towns, cities, villages, bridges, &c. besides shipwrecks; whole Islands
are sometimes suddenly overwhelmed with all their inhabitants in
Zealand, Holland, and many parts of the Continent drowned, as the
Lake Erne in Ireland! And we behold naught but the remains of cities
in the open sea. In the fens of Friesland, 1230, by reason of tempests,
the sea drowned all the country almost, men and cattle in it. How doth
the fire rage, that merciless element, consuming in an instant whole
cities! what town, of any antiquity or note, hath not been once, again
and again, by the fury of this merciless element, defaced, ruinated, and
left desolate? In a word,

Whom fire spares, sea doth drown; whom sea,
Pestilent air doth send to clay;
Who war scapes, sickness takes away.   (BUCHANAN)

To descend to more particulars, how many creatures are at deadly feud with men! Lions, wolves, bears, &c. some with hoofs, horns, tusks, teeth, nails. How many noxious serpents and venomous creatures, ready to offend us with stings, breath, sight, or quite kill us! How many pernicious fishes, plants, gums, fruits, seeds, flowers, &c. could I reckon up on a sudden, which by their very smell, many of them, touch, taste, cause some grievous malady, if not death itself! Some make mention of a thousand several poisons: but these are but trifles in respect. The greatest enemy to man is man, who by the Devil's instigation is still ready to do mischief, his own executioner, a wolf, a Devil to himself and others. We are all brethren in Christ, or at least should be, members of one body, servants of one Lord, and yet no fiend can so torment, insult over, tyrannize, vex, as one man doth another. Let me not fall therefore, (saith David, when wars, plague, famine were offered) into the hands of men, merciless, and wicked men:

Scarce are they worthy of the name of men,
For fiercer far are they than ravening wolves.   (OVID)

We can most part foresee these epidemical diseases, and likely avoid them. Dearths, tempests, plagues, our Astrologers foretell us; earthquakes, inundations, ruins of houses, consuming fires, come by little and little, or make some noise before-hand; but the knaveries, impostures, injuries, and villanies, of men no art can avoid. We can keep our professed enemies from our cities, by gates, walls, and towers, defend ourselves from thieves and robbers by watchfulness and weapons; but this malice of men, and their pernicious endeavours, no caution can divert, no vigilancy foresee, we have so many secret plots and devices to mischief one another.

Sometimes by the Devil's help, as Magicians, Witches: sometimes by impostures, mixtures, poisons, stratagems, single combats, wars, we hack and hew, as if we were, like Cadmus' soldiers, born to consume one another. 'Tis an ordinary thing to read of a hundred and two hundred thousand men slain in a battle; besides all manner of tortures, brazen bulls, racks, wheels, strappadoes, guns, engines, &c. We have invented more torturing instruments than there be several members in a man's body, as Cyprian well observes. To come nearer yet, our own parents by their offences, indiscretion, and intemperance, are our mortal enemies. *The fathers have eaten sour grapes, and the children's teeth are*

set on edge. They cause our grief many times, and put upon us hereditary diseases, inevitable infirmities: they torment us, & we are ready to
injure our posterity;

> *Like to produce still more degenerate stock,*   (HORACE)

and the latter end of the world, as Paul foretold, is still like to be worst.
We are thus bad by nature, bad by kind, but far worse by art, every
man the greatest enemy unto himself. We study many times to undo
ourselves, abusing those good things which God hath bestowed upon us,
health, wealth, strength, wit, learning, art, memory, to our own destruction; you owe to yourself your own ruin. As Judas Maccabaeus killed
Apollonius with his own weapons, we arm our selves to our own overthrows; and use reason, art, judgement, all that should help us, as so
many instruments to undo us. Hector gave Ajax a sword, which, so long
as he fought against enemies, served for his help and defence; but after
he began to hurt harmless creatures with it, turned to his own hurtless
bowels. Those excellent means God hath bestowed on us, well employed,
cannot but much avail us; but if otherwise perverted, they ruin and confound us: and so by reason of our indiscretion and weakness they commonly do, we have too many instances. This S. Austin acknowledgeth
of himself in his humble Confessions, *promptness of wit, memory,
eloquence, they were God's good gifts, but he did not use them to his
glory.* If you will particularly know how, and by what means, consult
Physicians, and they will tell you, that it is in offending in some of those
six non-natural things, of which I shall after dilate more at large; they
are the causes of our infirmities, our surfeiting, and drunkenness, our
immoderate insatiable lust, and prodigious riot. It is a true saying, the
board consumes more than the sword. Our intemperance it is that pulls
so many several incurable diseases upon our heads, that hastens old age,
perverts our temperature, and brings upon us sudden death. And last of
all, that which crucifies us most, is our own folly, madness (Whom
Jupiter would destroy, he first drives mad; by subtraction of his assisting grace God permits it), weakness, want of government, our facility
and proneness in yielding to several lusts, in giving way to every passion and perturbation of the mind: by which means we metamorphose
ourselves, and degenerate into beasts. All which that Prince of Poets
observed of Agamemnon, that when he was well pleased, and could moderate his passion, he was — like Jupiter in feature, Mars in valour,
Pallas in wisdom, another God; but when he became angry, he was a
lion, a tiger, a dog, &c. there appeared no sign or likeness of Jupiter in
him; so we, as long as we are ruled by reason, correct our inordinate ap-

petite, and conform ourselves to God's word, are as so many living saints: but if we give reins to lust, anger, ambition, pride, and follow our own ways, we degenerate into beasts, transform ourselves, overthrow our constitutions, provoke God to anger, and heap upon us this of *Melancholy,* and all kinds of incurable diseases, as a just and deserved punishment of our sins.

SUBSECTION 2 — *The Definition, Number, Division of Diseases*

What a disease is, almost every Physician defines. Fernelius calleth it an *affection of the body contrary to nature;* Fuschius and Crato, *an hindrance, hurt, or alteration of any action of the body, or part of it;* Tholosanus, *a dissolution of that league which is between body and soul, and a perturbation of it: as health is the perfection, and makes to the preservation of it;* Labeo, in A. Gellius, *an ill habit of the body, opposite to nature, hindering the use of it;* others otherwise, all to this effect.

How many diseases there are, is a question not yet determined. Pliny reckons up 300 from the crown of the head to the sole of the foot: elsewhere he saith [that] their number is infinite. Howsoever it was in those times, it boots not; in our days I am sure the number is much augmented: *Wasting sickness and strange hosts of fevers dire brood o'er the earth.* For besides many epidemical diseases unheard of, and altogether unknown to Galen and Hippocrates, as *scurvy, small-pox, plica, sweating sickness, syphilis, &c.,* we have many proper and peculiar almost to every part. No man amongst us so sound, of so good a constitution, that hath not some impediment of body or mind. We have all our infirmities, first or last, more or less. There will be peradventure one in an age, or one of a thousand, like Zenophilus the Musician in Pliny, that may happily live 105 years without any manner of impediment; a Pollio Romulus, that can preserve himself *with wine and oil;* a man as fortunate as Q. Metellus, of whom Valerius so much brags; a man as healthful as Otto Herwardus, a Senator of Augsburg in Germany, whom Leovitius the Astrologer brings in for an example and instance of certainty in his art; who, because he had the significators in his geniture fortunate, and free from the hostile aspects of Saturn and Mars, being a very old man, *could not remember that ever he was sick.* Paracelsus may brag that he could make a man live 400 years or more, if he might bring him up from his infancy, and diet him as he list; and some Physicians hold that there is no certain period of man's life, but it may still by temperance and physick be prolonged. We find in the mean time, by common experience, that no man can escape, but that of Hesiod is true:

Th' earth's full of maladies, and full the sea,
Which set upon us both by night and day.

If you require a more exact division of these ordinary diseases which
are incident to men, I refer you to Physicians; they will tell you of
acute and *chronick, first* and *secondary, lethal, salutary, errant, fixed,
simple, compound, connexed,* or *consequent,* belonging to *parts* or the
whole, in *habit* or in *disposition,* &c. My division at this time (as most
befitting my purpose) shall be into those of the body and mind. For
them of the body, a brief catalogue of which Fuschius hath made, I refer you to the voluminous tomes of Galen, Aretæus, Rhasis, Avicenna,
Alexander, Paulus, Aetius, Gordonius, and those exact Neotericks,
Savanarola, Capivaccius, Donatus Altomarus, Hercules de Saxonia,
Mercurialis, Victorius Faventinus, Wecker, Piso, &c. that have method-
ically and elaborately written of them all. Those of the mind and head
I will briefly handle, and apart.

SUBSECTION 3 — *Division of the Diseases of the Head*

These diseases of the mind, forasmuch as they have their chief seat
and organs in the head, are commonly repeated amongst the diseases of
the head, which are divers, & vary much according to their site. For in
the head, as there be several parts, so there be divers grievances, which,
according to that division of Heurnius, (which he takes out of Arculanus), are inward or outward (to omit all others which pertain to eyes
and ears, nostrils, gums, teeth, mouth, palate, tongue, wesel,* chops,
face, &c.), belonging properly to the brain, as baldness, falling of hair,
furfaire,† lice, &c. Inward belonging to the skins next to the brain,
called *dura* and *pia mater,* as all head-aches, &c., or to the ventricles,
cauls, kells, tunicles, creeks, and parts of it, and their passions, as *caro,
vertigo, incubus, apoplexy, falling sickness.* The diseases of the *nerves,
cramps, stupor, convulsion, tremor, palsy:* or belonging to the excrements of the brain, *catarrhs, sneezing, rheums, distillations:* or else
those that pertain to the substance of the brain itself, in which are conceived *phrenzy, lethargy, melancholy, madness, weak memory, sleeping-
sickness,* or *insomnia.* Out of these again I will single such as properly
belong to the *phantasy,* or *imagination,* or *reason* itself, which Laurentius calls the diseases of the mind; & Hildesheim, diseases of the imagination, or loss of reason, which are three or four in number, *phrenzy,
madness, melancholy, dotage,* and their kinds: *Hydrophobia, Lycan-*

* Windpipe.
† Dandruff.

thropia, St. Vitus' Dance, demoniacal possession, which I will briefly touch and point at, insisting especially in this of *Melancholy,* as more eminent than the rest, and that through all his kinds, causes, symptoms, prognosticks, cures: as Lonicerus hath done concerning apoplexy, and many others of such particular diseases. Not that I find fault with those which have written of this subject before, as Jason Pratensis, Laurentius, Montaltus, T. Bright, &c., they have done very well in their several kinds and methods; yet that which one omits, another may haply see; that which one contracts, another may enlarge. To conclude with Scribanius, *that which they had neglected, or perfunctorily handled, we may more thoroughly examine; that which is obscurely delivered in them, may be perspicuously dilated and amplified by us:* and so made more familiar and easy for every man's capacity, and the common good; which is the chief end of my discourse.*

SUBSECTION 4 — *Dotage, Phrenzy, Madness, Hydrophobia, Lycanthropia, St. Vitus' Dance, Extasis*

Dotage, fatuity, or folly, is a common name to all the following species, as some will have it. Laurentius and Altomarus comprehended *madness, melancholy,* and the rest under this name, and call it the most inclusive of them all. If it be distinguished from them, it is *natural* or inborn, which comes by some defect of the organs, and over-much brain, as we see in our common fools; and is for the most part intended or remitted in particular men, and thereupon some are wiser than others: or else it is acquisite, an appendix or symptom of some other disease, which comes or goes; or, if it continue, a sign of *melancholy* itself.

Phrenitis, which the Greeks derive from the word Phren, is a disease of the mind, with a continual madness or dotage, which hath an acute fever annexed, or else an inflammation of the brain, or the membranes or kells of it, with an acute fever, which causeth madness and dotage. It differs from *melancholy* and *madness,* because their dotage is without an ague; this continual, with waking, or memory decayed, &c. *Melancholy* is most part silent, this clamorous; and many such like differences are assigned by Physicians.

Madness, phrenzy, and *melancholy,* are confounded by Celsus and many Writers; others leave out *phrenzy,* and make *madness* and *melan-*

* Of those who preceded Burton in writing of Melancholy, the most significant was Dr. Timothy Bright (1551–1615). His book, A Treatise of Melancholie (London, 1586), was the most important work on the subject in English prior to this one by Burton, who was greatly indebted to it. Bright is known as the Father of modern shorthand.

choly but one disease, which Jason Pratensis especially labours, and that they differ only in the more or less, in quantity alone, the one being a degree to the other, and both proceeding from one cause. They differ, saith Gordonius, as the humour is intended or remitted. Of the same mind is Aretæus, Alexander Trallianus, Guianerius, Savanarola, Heurnius; and Galen himself writes promiscuously of them both by reason of their affinity: but most of our neotericks do handle them apart, whom I will follow in this treatise. *Madness* is therefore defined to be a vehement *dotage,* or raving without a fever, far more violent than *melancholy,* full of anger and clamour, horrible looks, actions, gestures, troubling the patients with far greater vehemency both of body and mind, without all fear and sorrow, with such impetuous force & boldness, that sometimes three or four men cannot hold them. Differing only in this from *phrenzy,* that it is without a fever, and their memory is most part better. It hath the same causes as the other, as choler adust, and blood incensed, brains inflamed, &c. Fracastorius adds, *a due time, and full age, to this definition, to distinguish it from children, & will have it confirmed impotency, to separate it from such as accidentally come and go again, as by taking henbane, nightshade, wine, &c.* Of this fury there be divers kinds; *ecstasy,* which is familiar with some persons, as Cardan saith of himself, he could be in one when he list; in which the Indian priests deliver their oracles, and the witches in Lapland, as Olaus Magnus writeth, answer all questions in an ecstasy you will ask; what your friends do, where they are, how they fare, &c. The other *species* of this fury are *enthusiasms, revelations,* and *visions,* so often mentioned by Gregory and Bede in their works; obsession or possession of devils, Sibylline Prophets, and poetical Furies; such as come by eating noxious herbs, tarantula's stinging, &c. which some reduce to this. The most known are these, *Lycanthropia, Hydrophobia, Chorus Sancti Viti* [St. Vitus Dance].

Lycanthropia, which Avicenna calls *Cucubuth,* others Wolf-madness, when men run howling about graves and fields in the night, and will not be persuaded but that they are wolves, or some such beasts. Aetius and Paulus call it a kind of *Melancholy;* but I should rather refer it to *Madness,* as most do. Some make a doubt of it whether there be any such disease. Donatus Altomarus saith, that he saw two of them in his time: Wierus tells a story of such a one at Padua, 1541, that would not believe to the contrary, but that he was a wolf. He hath another instance of a Spaniard, who thought himself a bear: Forestus confirms as much by many examples; one amongst the rest of which he was an eye-witness, at Alkmaar in Holland, a poor husbandman that still hunted about graves, & kept in churchyards, of a pale, black, ugly, & fearful look. Such belike, or little better, were King Prætus' daughters, that thought themselves kine. And Nebuchadnezzar in Daniel, as some interpreters hold, was only troubled with this kind of madness. This disease perhaps gave occasion to that bold assertion of Pliny, *some men were turned into wolves in his time, and from wolves to men again:* and to that fable of Pausanias, of a man that was ten years a wolf, and afterwards turned to his former shape: to Ovid's tale of Lycaon, &c. He that is desirous to hear of this Disease, or more examples, let him read Austin in his 18th Book, The City Of God, Mizaldus, Sckenkius, Hildesheim on Manias, Forestus, Diseases of The Brain, Olaus Magnus, Vincentius Bellavicensis, Pierius, Bodine, Zuinger, Zeilger, Peucer, Wierus, Springer, &c. This malady, saith Avicenna, troubleth men most in February, and is now-a-days frequent in Bohemia and Hungary, according to Heurnius. Schernitzius will have it common in Livonia. They lie hid most part all day, and go abroad in the night, barking, howling, at graves and deserts; *they have usually hollow eyes, scabbed legs and thighs, very dry and pale,* saith Altomarus; he gives a reason there of all the symptoms, and sets down a brief cure of them.

Hydrophobia is a kind of madness, well known in every village, which comes by the biting of a mad dog, or scratching, saith Aurelianus; touching or smelling alone sometimes, as Sckenkius proves, and is incident to many other creatures as well as men, so called because the parties affected cannot endure the sight of water, or any liquor, supposing still they see a mad dog in it. And which is more wonderful, though they be very dry, (as in this malady they are) they will rather die than drink. Cælius Aurelianus. an ancient writer, makes a doubt whether this *Hydrophobia* be a passion of the body or the mind. The part affected is the brain: the cause, poison that comes from the mad dog, which is so hot and dry, that it consumes all the moisture in the body. Hildesheim relates of some that died so mad, and, being cut up, had no water, scarce blood, or any moisture left in them. To such as are so affected, the fear of water begins at 14 days after they are bitten, to some again not till 40 or 60 days after: commonly, saith Heurnius, they begin to rave, fly water and glasses, to look red, and swell in the face, about 20 days after (if some remedy be not taken in the mean time) to lie awake, to be pensive, sad, to see strange visions, to bark and howl, to fall into a swoon, and oftentimes fits of the falling sickness. Some say, little things like whelps will be seen in their urine. If any of these signs appear, they are past recovery. Many times these symptoms will not appear till six or seven months after, saith Codronchus; and sometimes not till 7 or 8 years, as Guianerius; 12, as Albertus; 6 or 8 months after, as Galen holds. Baldus the great lawyer died of it: an Augustine Friar, and a woman in Delft, that were Forestus' patients, were miserably consumed with it. The common cure in the country (for such at least as dwell near the sea-side) is to duck them over head and ears in sea-water; some use charms; every good wife can prescribe medicines. But the best cure to be had in such cases, is from the most approved Physicians. They that will read of them, may consult with Dioscorides, Heurnius, Hildesheim, Capivaccius, Forestus, Sckenkius, and before all others Codronchus, an Italian, who hath lately written two exquisite books on this subject.

S. Vitus' Dance; the lascivious dance, Paracelsus calls it, because they that are taken with it, can do nothing but dance till they be dead, or cured. It is so called, for that the parties so troubled were wont to go to S. Vitus for help, & after they had danced there a while, they were certainly freed. 'Tis strange to hear how long they will dance, & in what manner, over stools, forms, tables; even great-bellied women sometimes (and yet never hurt their children) will dance so long that they can stir neither hand nor foot, but seem to be quite dead. One in red clothes they cannot abide. Musick above all things they love, & therefore Magistrates in Germany will hire Musicians to play to them, and some lusty sturdy companions to dance with them. This disease hath been very common in Germany, as appears by those relations of Sckenkius, and Paracelsus in his book of Madness, who brags how many several persons he hath cured of it. Felix Platerus reports of a woman in Basle whom he saw, that danced a whole month together. The Arabians call it a kind of *palsy*. Bodine, in his 5th Book, On The Republic, speaks of this infirmity; Monavius in his last Epistle to Scoltzius, and in another to Dudithus, where you may read more of it.

The last kind of madness or melancholy, is that demoniacal (if I may so call it) obsession or possession of devils, which Platerus & others would have to be preternatural: stupend things are said of them, their actions, gestures, *contortions*, fasting, prophesying, speaking languages they were never taught, &c. Many strange stories are related of them, which because some will not allow, (for Deacon and Darrel have written large volumes on this subject *pro & con*,) I voluntarily omit.

Fuschius, Felix Plater, Laurentius, add to these another *fury* that proceeds from *love*, & another from *study*, another divine or *religious fury;* but these more properly belong to *Melancholy;* of all which I will speak apart, intending to write a whole book of them.

SUBSECTION 5 — *Melancholy in Disposition, improperly so called.*
Equivocations

Melancholy, the subject of our present discourse, is either in disposition or habit. In disposition, is that transitory *Melancholy* which goes and comes upon every small occasion of sorrow, need, sickness, trouble, fear, grief, passion, or perturbation of the mind, any manner of care, discontent, or thought, which causeth anguish, dulness, heaviness and vexation of spirit, any ways opposite to pleasure, mirth, joy, delight, causing frowardness in us, or a dislike. In which equivocal and improper sense, we call him melancholy, that is dull, sad, sour, lumpish, ill-disposed, solitary, any way moved, or displeased. And from these melancholy dispositions no man living is free, no Stoick, none so wise, none so happy, none so patient, so generous, so godly, so divine, that can vindicate himself; so well-composed, but more or less, some time or other, he feels the smart of it. Melancholy in this sense is the character of Mortality. *Man that is born of a woman, is of short continuance and full of trouble.* Zeno, Cato, Socrates himself, whom Ælian so highly commends for a moderate temper, that *nothing could disturb him; but going out, and coming in, still Socrates kept the same serenity of countenance, what misery soever befell him,* (if we may believe Plato his Disciple) was much tormented with it. Q. Metellus, in whom Valerius gives instance of all happiness, *the most fortunate man then living, born in that most flourishing city of Rome, of noble parentage, a proper man of person, well qualified, healthful, rich, honourable, a Senator, a Consul, happy in his wife, happy in his children, &c.,* yet this man was not void of Melancholy, he had his share of sorrow. Polycrates Samius, that flung his ring into the sea, because he would participate of discontent with others, and had it miraculously restored to him again shortly after by a fish taken as he angled, was not free from melancholy dispositions. No man can cure himself; the very gods had bitter pangs,* & frequent passions, as their own Poets put upon them. In general, *as the heaven, so is our life, sometimes fair, sometimes overcast, tempestuous and serene; as in a rose, flowers and prickles; in the year itself, a temperate summer sometimes, a hard winter, a drowth, and then again pleasant showers: so is our life intermixt with joys, hopes, fears, sorrows, calumnies.* There is a succession of pleasure and pain.

* Homer, Iliad. — Burton's note.

From the heart of this fount of joy there wells
Some bitter that, e'en mid flowers, their pleasure quells. (SENECA)
Even in the midst of laughing there is sorrow, (as Solomon holds) : even
in the midst of all our feasting and jollity, as Austin infers in his Commentary on the 41st Psalm, there is grief and discontent. Amid our en-
joyments there is always some vexation to torment us; for a pint of
honey thou shalt here likely find a gallon of gall, for a dram of pleasure
a pound of pain, for an inch of mirth an ell of moan; as ivy doth an
oak, these miseries encompass our life; and 'tis most absurd & ridiculous for any mortal man to look for a perpetual tenor of happiness in
this life. Nothing so prosperous & pleasant, but it hath some bitterness
in it, some complaining, some grudging; 'tis all bitter-sweet, a mixt
passion, and like a Chequer table, black & white men; families, cities,
have their falls and wanes, now trines, sextiles, then quartiles and oppositions. We are not here, as those Angels, celestial powers and bodies,
sun and moon, to finish our course without all offence, with such constancy, to continue for so many ages: but subject to infirmities, miseries, interrupt, tossed & tumbled up and down, carried about with every
small blast, often molested & disquieted upon each slender occasion,
uncertain, brittle, & so is all that we trust unto. *And he that knows not
this, & is not armed to endure it, is not fit to live in this world* (as one
condoles our time) : *he knows not the condition of it, where with a reciprocal tie pleasure & pain are still united, and succeed one another in a
ring.* Get thee gone hence, if thou canst not brook it; there is no way to
avoid it, but to arm thyself with patience, with magnanimity, to oppose
thyself unto it, to suffer affliction as a good soldier of Christ, as Paul adviseth, constantly to bear it. But forasmuch as so few can embrace this
good counsel of his, or use it aright, but rather, as so many brute beasts,
give a way to their passion, voluntarily subject & precipitate themselves
into a Labyrinth of cares, woes, miseries, & suffer their souls to be overcome by them, cannot arm themselves with that patience as they ought
to do, it falleth out oftentimes that these *dispositions* become *habits,*
and *many affects contemned* (as Seneca notes) *makes a disease. Even
as one distillation, not yet grown to custom, makes a cough, but continual and inveterate causeth a consumption of the lungs :* so do these
our melancholy provocations: and, according as the humour itself is intended, or remitted in men, as their temperature of body, or rational
soul, is better able to make resistance; so are they more or less affected.
For that which is but a flea-biting to one, causeth insufferable torment
to another; & which one by his singular moderation and well-composed

carriage can happily overcome, a second is no whit able to sustain; but upon every small occasion of misconceived abuse, injury, grief, disgrace, loss, cross, rumour, &c., (if solitary, or idle) yields so far to passion, that his complexion is altered, his digestion hindered, his sleep gone, his spirits obscured, and his heart heavy, his hypochondries misaffected; wind, crudity, on a sudden overtake him, and he himself overcome with *Melancholy*. As it is with a man imprisoned for debt, if once in the gaol, every creditor will bring his action against him, and there likely hold him: if any discontent seize upon a patient, in an instant all other per-turbations (for — where a door is opened they rush) will set upon him, and, then, like a lame dog or broken-winged goose, he droops and pines away, and is brought at last to that ill habit or malady of Melan-choly itself. So that as the Philosophers make eight degrees of heat and cold, we may make 88 of *Melancholy*, as the parts affected are diversely seized with it, or have been plunged more or less into this infernal gulf, or waded deeper into it. But all these *melancholy* fits, howsoever pleas-ing at first, or displeasing, violent & tyrannizing over those whom they seize on for the time; yet these fits I say, or men affected, are but im-properly so called, because they continue not, but come and go, as by some objects they are moved. This *Melancholy* of which we are to treat, is an habit, a serious ailment, a chronick or continuate disease, a settled humour, as Aurelianus and others call it, not errant, but fixed: and as it was long increasing, so, now being (pleasant or painful) grown to an habit, it will hardly be removed.

MEMBER 2

SUBSECTION 1 — *Digression of Anatomy*

Before I proceed to define the disease of *Melancholy*, what it is, or to discourse farther of it, I hold it not impertinent to make a brief di-gression of the anatomy of the body and faculties of the soul, for the better understanding of that which is to follow; because many hard words will often occur, as *myrach, hypochondries, hemrods, &c., im-agination, reason, humours, spirits, vital, natural, animal, nerves, veins, arteries, chylus, pituita;* which of the vulgar will not so easily be per-ceived, what they are, how sited, and to what end they serve. And, be-sides, it may peradventure give occasion to some men, to examine more accurately, search farther into this most excellent subject, and there-upon with that Royal Prophet to praise God, (for a man is fearfully and wonderfully made, and curiously wrought), that have time and leisure

enough, and are sufficiently informed in all other worldly businesses, as
to make a good bargain, buy and sell, to keep and make choice of a fair
hawk, hound, horse, &c. But for such matters as concern the knowledge
of themselves, they are wholly ignorant and careless, they know not
what this body and soul are, how combined, of what parts and faculties
they consist, or how a man differs from a dog. And what can be more
ignominious and filthy (as Melancthon well inveighs) *than for a man
not to know the structure and composition of his own body, especially
since the knowledge of it tends so much to the preservation of his health,
and information of his manners?* To stir them up therefore to this study,
to peruse those elaborate works of Galen, Bauhinus, Plater, Vesalius,
Falopius, Laurentius, Remelinus, &c., which have written copiously in
Latin; or that which some of our industrious countrymen have done in
our mother tongue, not long since, as that translation of Columbus, and
Microcosmographia,* in 13 books, I have made this brief digression.
Also because Wecker, Melancthon, Fernelius, Fuschius, and those
tedious Tracts on Life (which have more compendiously handled and
written of this matter) are not at all times ready to be had, to give
them some small taste or notice of the rest, let this epitome suffice.

SUBSECTION 2 — *Division of the Body, Humours, Spirits*

Of the parts of the Body, there be many divisions: the most approved
is that of Laurentius, out of Hippocrates: which is, into parts *contained,*
or *containing. Contained* are either *humours* or *spirits.*

A humour is a liquid or fluent part of the body, comprehended in it,
for the preservation of it; and is either innate or born with us, or adventitious and acquisite. The radical or innate is daily supplied by
nourishment, which some call *cambium,* and make those secondary humours of *ros* and *gluten* to maintain it: or acquisite, to maintain these
four first primary humours, coming and proceeding from the first concoction in the liver, by which means chyle is excluded. Some divide
them into profitable and excrementitious. But Crato out of Hippocrates
will have all four to be juice, and not excrements, without which no living creature can be sustained: which four, though they be comprehended in the mass of *blood,* yet they have their several affections, by
which they are distinguished from one another, and from those adventitious, *peccant, or diseased humours,* as Melancthon calls them.

Blood is a hot, sweet, temperate, red humour, prepared in the *meseraick* veins, and made of the most temperate parts of the *chylus* in the

* See Index.

liver, whose office is to nourish the whole body, to give it strength and colour, being dispersed by the veins through every part of it. And from it *spirits* are first begotten in the heart, which afterwards by the *arteries* are communicated to the other parts.

Pituita, or phlegm, is a cold and moist humour, begotten of the colder parts of the *chylus* (or white juice coming out of the meat digested in the stomack) in the liver; his office is to nourish and moisten the members of the body, which, as the tongue, are moved, that they be not over dry.

Choler is hot and dry, bitter, begotten of the hotter parts of the *chylus,* and gathered to the gall: it helps the natural heat and senses, and serves to the expelling of excrements.

Melancholy, cold and dry, thick, black, and sour, begotten of the more fæculent part of nourishment, and purged from the spleen, is a bridle to the other two hot humours, *blood* and *choler,* preserving them in the blood, and nourishing the bones. These four humours have some analogy with the four elements, and to the four ages in man.

To these humours you may add *serum,* which is the matter of urine, & those excrementitious humours of the third concoction, sweat & tears.

Spirit is a most subtle vapour, which is expressed from the *blood,* and the instrument of the soul, to perform all his actions; a common tie or *medium* betwixt the body and the soul, as some will have it; or, as Paracelsus, a fourth soul of itself. Melancthon holds the fountain of these spirits to be the *heart;* begotten there, and afterwards conveyed to the brain, they take another nature to them: Of these spirits there be three kinds, according to the three principal parts, *brain, heart, liver; natural, vital, animal.* The *natural* are begotten in the *liver,* and thence dispersed through the veins, to perform those natural actions. The *vital spirits* are made in the heart of the *natural,* which by the arteries are transported to all the other parts: if these *spirits* cease, then life ceaseth. as in a *syncope* or swooning. The *animal* spirits formed of the *vital,* brought up to the brain, and diffused by the nerves, to the subordinate members, give sense and motion to them all.

SUBSECTION 3 — *Similar Parts*

Containing parts, by reason of their more solid substance, are either *homogeneal* or *heterogeneal, similar* or *dissimilar;* so Aristotle divides them, Hist. Animal; Laurentius. *Similar,* or *homogeneal,* are such as, if they be divided, are still severed into parts of the same nature, as water into water. Of these some be *spermatical,* some *fleshy* or carnal.

Spermatical are such as are immediately begotten of the seed, which are *bones, gristles, ligaments, membranes, nerves, arteries, veins, skins, fibres* or *strings, fat.*

The bones are dry and hard, begotten of the thickest of the seed, to strengthen and sustain other parts: some say there be 304, some 307, or 313, in a man's body. They have no nerves in them, and are therefore without sense.

A *gristle* is a substance softer than bone, and harder than the rest, flexible, and serves to maintain the parts of motion.

Ligaments are they that tie the bones together, and other parts to the bones, with their subserving tendons. *Membranes'* office is to cover the rest.

Nerves, or sinews, are membranes without, and full of marrow within; they proceed from the brain, & carry the animal spirits for sense and motion. Of these some be harder, some softer; the softer serve the senses, and there be 7 pair of them. The first be the optick *nerves,* by which we see; the second move the eyes; the third pair serve for the tongue to taste; the fourth pair for the taste in the palate; the fifth belong to the ears; the sixth pair is most ample, and runs almost over all the bowels; the seventh pair moves the tongue. The harder sinews serve for the motion of the inner parts, proceeding from the marrow in the back, of whom there be thirty combinations, seven of the neck, twelve of the breast, &c.

Arteries are long and hollow, with a double skin to convey the vital spirits; to discern which the better, they say that Vesalius the Anatomist was wont to cut up men alive. They * arise in the left side of the heart, & are principally two, from which the rest are derived, *aorta,* and *venosa. Aorta* is the root of all the other, which serve the whole body; the other goes to the lungs, to fetch air to refrigerate the heart.

Veins are hollow and round like pipes, arising from the liver, carrying blood and natural spirits; they feed all the parts. Of these there be two chief, *vena porta,* and *vena cava,* from which the rest are corrivated. That *vena porta* is a vein coming from the concave of the liver, and receiving those meseraical veins, by whom he takes the *chylus* from the stomack and guts, and conveys it to the liver. The other derives blood from the liver to nourish all the other dispersed members. The branches of that *vena porta* are the *meseraical* and *hæmorrhoids.* The branches of the *cava [porta]* are *inward* or *outward. Inward, seminal* or *emulgent. Outward,* in the head, arms, feet, &c. and have several names.

* In these they observe the beating of the pulse. — Burton's note.

Fibræ are strings, white and solid, dispersed through the whole member, and right, oblique, transverse, all which have their several uses. *Fat* is a similar part, moist, without blood, composed of the most thick and unctuous matter of the blood. The skin covers the rest, and hath cuticle, or a little skin, under it. *Flesh* is soft and ruddy, composed of the congealing of blood, &c.

SUBSECTION 4 — *Dissimilar Parts*

Dissimilar parts are those which we call *organical* or *instrumental*, and they be *inward* or *outward*. The chiefest outward parts are situate forward or backward. *Forward,* the crown and foretop of the head, skull, face, forehead, temples, chin, eyes, ears, nose, &c., neck, breast, chest, upper and lower part of the belly, hypochondries, navel, groin, flank, &c. *Backward,* the hinder part of the head, back, shoulders, sides, loins, hip bones, *os sacrum,* buttocks, &c. Or joints, arms, hands, feet, legs, thighs, knees, &c. Or common to both, which, because they are obvious and well known, I have carelessly repeated, and the more important: what remains, from the book of life, whoso wishes may read.

Inward organical parts, which cannot be seen, are divers in number, and have several names, functions, and divisions; but that of Laurentius is most notable, into *noble* or *ignoble* parts. Of the *noble* there be three principal parts, to which all the rest belong, and whom they serve, *brain, heart, liver;* according to whose site, three regions, on a threefold division, is made of the whole body. As first of the *head,* in which the animal organs are contained, and brain itself, which by his nerves give sense and motion to the rest, and is (as it were) a Privy Counsellor, and Chancellor, to the *Heart.* The second region is the chest, or middle *belly,* in which the *Heart* as King keeps his Court, and by his arteries communicates life to the whole body. The third region is the lower *belly,* in which the liver resides as a hidden governor with the rest of those natural organs, serving for concoction, nourishment, expelling of excrements. This lower region is distinguished from the upper by the *midriff,* or *diaphragm,* and is subdivided again by some into three concavities or regions, upper, middle, and lower; the upper of the hypochondries, in whose right side is the *liver,* the left the *spleen,* from which is denominated *hypochondriacal Melancholy;* the second of the navel and flanks, divided from the first by the *rim;* the last of the watercourse, which is again subdivided into three other parts. The Arabians make two parts of this region, *epigastrium* and *hypogastrium;* upper and lower. *Epigastrium* they call *myrach,* from whence comes *myrachialis melancholia,* sometimes mentioned of them. Of these several regions I will treat in brief apart : and first of the third region, in which the natural organs are contained.

But you that are readers in the mean time, *suppose you were now brought into some sacred temple, or majestical palace* (as Melancthon saith) *to behold not the matter only, but the singular art, workmanship, and counsel, of this our great Creator. And 'tis a pleasant and profitable speculation, if it be considered aright.* The parts of this *region,* which present themselves to your consideration and view, are such as serve to *nutrition* or *generation.* Those of *nutrition* serve to the first or second concoction : as the *œsophagus* or gullet, which brings meat and drink into the *stomack.* The *ventricle* or stomack, which is seated in the midst of that part of the belly beneath the *midriff,* the kitchen (as it were) of the first concoction, and which turns our meat into *chylus.* It hath two mouths, one above, another beneath. The upper is sometimes taken for the stomack itself ; the lower and nether door (as Wecker calls it) is named *pylorus.* This stomack is sustained by a large kell or caul, called *omentum ;* which some will have the same with *peritoneum,* or rim of the belly. From the *stomack* to the very *fundament* are produced the *guts,* or *intestina,* which serve a little to alter and distribute the *chylus,* and convey away the excrements. They are divided into small and great, by reason of their site and substance, slender or thicker : the slender is *duodenum,* or whole gut, which is next to the stomack, some twelve inches long (saith Fuschius) ; *jejunum,* or empty gut, continuate to the other, which hath many *meseraick veins* annexed to it, which take part of the *chylus* to the liver from it ; *ilion* the third, which consists of many crinkles, which serves with the rest to receive, keep, and distribute the *chylus* from the *stomack.* The thick guts are three, the *blind gut, colon,* and *right gut.* The *blind* is a thick and short gut, having one mouth, in which the *ilion* and *colon* meet : it receives the excrements, and conveys them to the *colon.* This *colon* hath many windings, that the excrements pass not away too fast : the *right gut* is straight, and conveys the excrements to the *fundament,* whose lower part is bound up with certain *muscles* called *sphincters,* that the excrements may be the better contained, until such time as a man be willing to go to the stool. In the midst of these guts is situated the *mesenterium* or *midriff,* composed of many veins, arteries, & much fat, serving chiefly to sustain the guts. All these parts serve the first concoction. To the second, which is busied either in refining the good nourishment or expelling the bad, is chiefly belonging the liver, like in colour to congealed blood, the shop of blood, situate in the right *hypochondry,* in figure like to an half-moon, the noble member Melancthon styles it, a general part; it serves to turn the *chylus* to blood, for the nourishment of the body. The excrements of it are either *cholerick* or *watery,* which the other subordinate parts convey. The *gall,* placed in the concave of the *liver,* extracts *choler* to it: the *spleen, melancholy;* which is situate on the left side, over against the *liver,* a spongy matter, that draws this black *choler* to it by a secret virtue, and feeds upon it, conveying the rest to the bottom of the stomack, to stir up appetite, or else to the guts as an excrement. That watery matter the two kidneys expurgate by those emulgent veins and *ureters.* The emulgent draw this superfluous moisture from the blood; the two *ureters* convey it to the *bladder,* which, by reason of his site in the lower belly, is apt to receive it, having two parts, neck and bottom: the bottom holds the water, the neck is constringed with a muscle, which, as a porter, keeps the water from running out against our will.

Members of generation are common to both sexes, or peculiar to one; which, because they are impertinent to my purpose, I do voluntarily omit.

Next in order is the *middle region,* or chest, which comprehends the vital faculties & parts: which (as I have said) is separated from the lower belly by the *diaphragm* or *midriff,* which is a skin consisting of many nerves, membranes; and amongst other uses it hath, is the instrument of laughing. There is also a certain thin membrane, full of sinews, which covereth the whole chest within, and is called *pleura,* the seat of the disease called *pleurisy,* when it is inflamed. Some add a third skin, which is termed *mediastinus,* which divides the chest into two parts, right and left. Of this region the principal part is the *Heart,* which is the seat and fountain of life, of heat, of spirits, of pulse, and respiration; the Sun of our body, the King and sole commander of it: the seat and organ of all passions and affections; (it lives first, and dies last, in all creatures); of a pyramidical form, and not much unlike to a pine-apple; a part worthy of admiration, that can yield such variety of affections, by whose motion it is dilated or contracted, to stir and command the humours in the body: as in sorrow, melancholy; in anger, choler; in joy, to send the blood outwardly; in sorrow, to call it in; moving the humours, as horses do a chariot. This *heart,* though it be one sole member, yet it may be divided into two creeks *right* and *left.* The *right* is like the Moon increasing, bigger than the other part, and receives blood from *vena cava,* distributing some of it to the *lungs* to nourish them, the rest to the left side, to engender spirits. *The left creek* hath the form of a *cone*, & is the seat of life, which, as a torch doth oil, draws blood into it, begetting of it spirits and fire; and, as fire in a torch, so are spirits in the blood, & by that great *artery* called *aorta* it sends vital spirits over the body, and takes air from the lungs by that *artery* which is called *venosa;* so that both creeks have their vessels; the right two veins, the left two arteries, besides those two common anfractuous ears, which serve them both, the one to hold blood, the other air, for several uses. The *lungs* is a thin spongy part, like an ox-hoof, (saith Fernelius), the Town-Clerk, or Cryer (one terms it), the instrument of voice, as an Orator to a King; annexed to the heart, to express his thoughts by voice. That it is the instrument of voice is manifest, in that no creature can speak or utter any voice, which wanteth these lights. It is besides the instrument of respiration, or breathing; & its office is to cool the *heart,* by sending air unto it by the *venosal artery,* which vein comes to the lungs by that *aspera arteria,* which consists of many gristles, membranes, nerves, taking in air at the nose and mouth, and by it likewise exhales the fumes of the *heart.*

In the upper *region* serving the animal faculties, the chief organ is the *brain,* which is a soft, marrowish, & white substance, engendered of the purest part of seed and spirits, included by many skins, and seated within the skull or brain-pan, and it is the most noble organ under heaven, the dwelling-house and seat of the soul, the habitation of wisdom, memory, judgement, reason, and in which man is most like unto God: and therefore nature hath covered it with a skull of hard bone, and two skins or membranes, whereof the one is called *dura mater,* or *meninx,* the other *pia mater.* The *dura mater* is next to the skull, above the other, which includes and protects the brain. When this is taken away, the *pia mater* is to be seen, a thin membrane, the next and immediate cover of the brain, and not covering only, but entering into it. The *brain* itself is divided into two parts, the *fore* and *hinder part;* the *fore part* is much bigger than the other, which is called the *little brain* in respect of it. This *fore part* hath many concavities distinguished by certain ventricles, which are the receptacles of the spirits, brought hither by the arteries from the heart, and are there refined to a more heavenly nature, to perform the actions of the soul. Of these ventricles there be three, *right, left,* & *middle.* The *right* and *left* answer to their site, and beget animal spirits; if they be any way hurt, sense and motion ceaseth. These ventricles, moreover, are held to be the seat of the common sense. The *middle ventricle* is a common concourse and cavity of them both, and hath two passages, the one to receive *pituita,* and the other extends itself to the fourth creek: in this they place *imagination* and *cogitation;* and so the three ventricles of the fore part of the *brain* are used. The fourth creek behind the head is common to the *cerebel* or little brain, and marrow of the backbone, the last, and most solid of all the rest, which receives the animal spirits from the other ventricles, and conveys them to the marrow in the back, and is the place where they say the memory is seated.

SUBSECTION 5 — *Of the Soul and her Faculties*

According to Aristotle, the soul is defined to be the Actual Being, the perfection or first act of an organical body, having power of life, which most Philosophers approve. But many doubts arise about the *essence, subject, seat, distinction,* and subordinate faculties of it. For the essence and particular knowledge, of all other things it is most hard (be it of man or beast) to discern, as Aristotle himself, Tully, Picus Mirandula, Tolet, and other Neoterick Philosophers confess. *We can understand all things by her, but what she is we cannot apprehend.* Some therefore make one *soul,* divided into three principal faculties: others, three distinct *souls:* (which question of late hath been much controverted by Picolomineus, and Zabarel): Paracelsus will have four *souls,* adding to the three granted faculties a *spiritual soul:* which opinion of his Campanella, in his book The Meaning Of Things, much labours to demonstrate and prove, because carcasses bleed at the sight of the murderer; with many such arguments; and some again one soul of all creatures whatsoever, differing only in organs; and that beasts have reason as well as men, though, for some defect of organs, not in such measure. Others make a doubt whether it be all in all, and all in every part; which is amply discussed in Zabarel amongst the rest. The common division of the *soul* is into three principal faculties, *vegetal, sensitive,* and *rational,* which make three distinct kinds of living creatures: *vegetal* plants, *sensible* beasts, *rational* men. How these three principal faculties are distinguished and connected, is beyond human capacity, as Taurellus, Philip, Flavius, and others, suppose. The inferior may be alone, but the superior cannot subsist without the other; so *sensible* includes *vegetal, rational* both; which are contained in it (saith Aristotle) as a triangle in a quadrangle.

Vegetal, the first of the three distinct faculties, is defined to be *a substantial act of an organical body, by which it is nourished, augmented, and begets another like unto itself;* in which definition, three several operations are specified, sustainer, producer, creator. The first is nutrition, whose object is nourishment, meat, drink, and the like; his organ the liver in sensible creatures, in plants the root or sap. His office is to turn the nutriment into the substance of the body nourished, which he performs by natural heat. This nutritive operation hath four other subordinate functions, or powers belonging to it, *attraction, retention, digestion, expulsion. Attraction* is a ministering faculty, which, as a loadstone doth iron, draws meat into the stomack, or as a lamp doth oil; and this attractive power is very necessary in plants, which suck up moisture by the root, as another mouth, into the sap, as a like stomack. *Retention* keeps it, being attracted unto the stomack, until such time it be concocted; for if it should pass away straight, the body could not be nourished. *Digestion* is performed by natural heat; for as the flame of a torch consumes oil, wax, tallow, so doth it alter and digest the nutritive matter. Indigestion is opposite unto it, for want of natural heat. Of this *digestion* there be three differences, *maturation, elixation, assation. Maturation* is especially observed in the fruits of trees: which are then said to be ripe, when the seeds are fit to be sown again. *Crudity* is opposed to it, which gluttons, epicures, and idle persons are most subject unto, that use no exercise to stir up natural heat, or else choke it, as too much wood puts out a fire. *Elixation* is the seething of meat in the stomack by the said natural heat, as meat is boiled in a pot; to which corruption or putrefaction is opposite. *Assation* is a concoction of the inward moisture by heat; his opposite is *semiustulation.* Besides these three several operations of *digestion,* there is a fourfold order of concoction: *mastication,* or chewing in the mouth; *chylification* of this so chewed meat in the stomack; the third is in the *liver,* to turn this *chylus* into blood, called *sanguification;* the last is *assimulation,* which is in every part. *Expulsion* is a power of *nutrition,* by which it expels all superfluous excrements, and reliques of meat and drink, by the guts, bladder, pores; as by purging, vomiting, spitting, sweating, urine, hairs, nails, *&c.*

As this *nutritive faculty* serves to nourish the body, so doth the *augmenting faculty* (the second operation or power of the *vegetal faculty*) to the increasing of it in quantity, according to all dimensions, long, broad, thick, and to make it grow till it come to his due proportion and perfect shape: which hath his period of augmentation, as of consumption: and that most certain, as the Poet observes:

> *A term of life is set to every man,*
> *Which is but short, and pass it no one can.* (VIRGIL)

The last of these *vegetal faculties* is *generation,* which begets another by means of seed like unto itself, to the perpetual preservation of the *species.* To this faculty they ascribe three subordinate operations: the first to turn nourishment into seed, &c.

Necessary concomitants or affections of this *vegetal faculty* are life, and his privation, death. To the preservation of life the natural heat is most requisite, though siccity and humidity, and those first qualities, be not excluded. This heat is likewise in plants, as appears by their increasing, fructifying, &c., though not so easily perceived. In all bodies it must have radical moisture to preserve it, that it be not consumed; to which preservation our clime, country, temperature, and the good or bad use of those six non-natural things, avail much. For as this natural heat and moisture decays, so doth our life itself: and if not prevented before by some violent accident, or interrupted through our own default, is in the end dried up by old age, and extinguished by death for want of matter, as a lamp for defect of oil to maintain it.

SUBSECTION 6 — *Of the Sensible Soul*

Next in order is the *sensible faculty,* which is as far beyond the other in dignity, as a beast is preferred to a plant, having those vegetal powers included in it. 'Tis defined *an act of an organical body, by which it lives, hath sense, appetite, judgement, breath, and motion.* His object in general is a sensible or passible quality, because the sense is affected with it. The general organ is the brain, from which principally the sensible operations are derived. This *sensible soul* is divided into two parts, *apprehending* or *moving.* By the *apprehensive* power we perceive the species of sensible things, present or absent, and retain them as wax doth the print of a seal. By the *moving* the body is outwardly carried from one place to another, or inwardly moved by spirits & pulse. The *apprehensive* faculty is subdivided into two parts, *inward* or *outward;* *outward,* as the five senses, of *touching, hearing, seeing, smelling, tasting,* to which you may add Scaliger's sixth sense of *titillation,* if you please; or that of *speech,* which is the sixth external sense according to Lullius; *inward* are three, *common sense, phantasy, memory.* Those five outward senses have their object in outward things only, and such as are present, as the eye sees no colour except it be at hand, the ear no sound. Three of these senses are of commodity, *hearing, sight,* and *smell:* two of necessity, *touch* and *taste,* without which we cannot live. Besides the *sensitive* power is *active* or *passive; active* in sight, the eye sees the colour; *passive* when it is hurt by his object, as the eye by the sun-beams; according to that Axiom, *too bright an object destroys the organ;* or if the object be not pleasing, as a bad sound to the ear, a stinking smell to the nose, &c.

Of these five senses, *sight* is held to be most precious, and the best, and that by reason of his object: it sees the whole body at once; by it we learn and discern all things, a sense most excellent for use. To the *sight* three things are required, the *object,* the *organ,* and the *medium.* The *object* in general is *visible,* or that which is to be seen, as colours, and all shining bodies. The *medium* is the illumination of the air, which comes from light, commonly called *diaphanum;* for in dark we cannot see. The *organ* is the eye, and chiefly the apple of it, which by those optick nerves, concurring both in one, conveys the sight to the common sense. Betwixt the organ and object a true distance is required, that it be not too near, or too far off. Many excellent questions appertain to this sense, discussed by Philosophers: as whether this sight be caused by receiving in the visible species, or sending of them out; which Plato, Plutarch, Macrobius, Lactantius, and others dispute. And besides it is the subject of the *perspectives,* of which Alhazen the Arabian, Vitellic, Roger Bacon, Baptista Porta, Guidus Ubaldus, Aquilonius, &c., have written whole volumes.

Hearing, a most excellent outward sense, *by which we learn and get knowledge.* His object is sound, or that which is heard; the *medium,* air; the *organ* the ear. To the sound, which is a collision of the air, three things are required: a body to strike, as the hand of a musician; the body strucken, which must be solid and able to resist, as a bell, lute-string, not wool, or sponge; the *medium,* the air, which is *inward,* or *outward;* the outward, being struck or collided by a solid body, still strikes the next air; until it come to that inward natural air, which, as an exquisite organ, is contained in a little skin formed like a drum-head, and struck upon by certain small instruments like drum-sticks, conveys the sound, by a pair of nerves appropriated to that use, to the *common sense,* as to a judge of sounds. There is great variety and much delight in them; for the knowledge of which consult with Boethius, and other Musicians.

Smelling is an *outward sense, which apprehends by the nostrils drawing in air;* and of all the rest it is the weakest sense in men; the organ is the nose, or two small hollow pieces of flesh a little above it: the *medium* the air to men, as water to fish: the *object, smell,* arising from a mixed body resolved, which whether it be a quality, fume, vapour, or exhalation, I will not now dispute, or of their differences, and how they are caused. This sense is an organ of health, as sight and hearing, saith A. Gellius, are of discipline; and that by avoiding bad smells, as by choosing good, which do as much alter and affect the body many times as *diet* itself.

Taste, a necessary sense, *which perceives all savours by the tongue and palate, and that by means of a thin spittle, or watery juice.* His *organ* is the *tongue* with his tasting nerves; the *medium,* a watery juice; the *object, taste* or savour, which is a quality in the juice, arising from the mixture of things tasted. Some make eight species or kinds of savour, bitter, sweet, sharp, salt, &c., all which sick men (as in an ague) cannot discern, by reason of their organs misaffected.

Touch, the last of the senses, and most ignoble, yet of as great necessity as the others, and of as much pleasure. This sense is exquisite in men, and by his nerves dispersed all over the body, perceives any tactile quality. His *organ* the *nerves;* his *object* those first qualities, hot, dry, moist, cold; and those that follow them hard, soft, thick, thin, &c. Many delightsome questions are moved by Philosophers about these five senses, their organs, objects, mediums, which for brevity I omit.

SUBSECTION 7 — *Of the Inward Senses*

Inner senses are three in number, so called, because they be within the brain-pan, as *common sense, phantasy, memory.* Their objects are not only things present, but they perceive the sensible species of things to *come, past, absent,* such as were before in the sense. This *common sense* is the judge or moderator of the rest, by whom we discern all differences of objects; for by mine eye I do not know that I see, or by mine ear that I hear, but by my *common sense,* who judgeth of sounds and colours: they are but the organs to bring the species to be censured; so that all their objects are his, and all their offices are his. The forepart of the brain is his organ or seat.

Phantasy, or imagination, which some call *estimative, or cogitative,* (confirmed, saith Fernelius, by frequent meditation) is an inner sense which doth more fully examine the species perceived by *common sense,* of things present or absent, and keeps them longer, recalling them to mind again, or making new of his own. In time of sleep this faculty is free, and many times conceives strange, stupend, absurd shapes, as in sick men we commonly observe. His *organ* is the middle cell of the brain; his *objects* all the species communicated to him by the *common sense,* by comparison of which he feigns infinite others unto himself. In *melancholy* men this faculty is most powerful and strong, and often hurts, producing many monstrous and prodigious things, especially if it be stirred up by some terrible object, presented to it from *common sense* or *memory*. In Poets and Painters *imagination* forcibly works, as appears by their several fictions, anticks, images: as Ovid's House of Sleep, Psyche's Palace in Apuleius, &c. In men it is subject and governed by *reason,* or at least should be; but in brutes it hath no superior, and is the reason of brutes, all the reason they have.

Memory lays up all the species which the senses have brought in, and records them as a good *register,* that they may be forth-coming when they are called for by *phantasy* and *reason*. His object is the same with *phantasy,* his seat and *organ* the back part of the brain.

The affections of these senses are *sleep* and *waking,* common to all sensible creatures. *Sleep is a rest or binding of the outward senses, and of the common sense, for the preservation of body and soul,* (as Scaliger defines it), for when the common sense resteth, the outward senses rest also. The phantasy alone is free, and his commander, reason: as appears by those imaginary dreams, which are of divers kinds, *natural, divine, demoniacal, &c.,* which vary according to humours, diet, actions, objects, &c., of which, Artemidorus, Cardan, and Sambucus, with their several interpretators, have written great volumes. This ligation of senses proceeds from an inhibition of spirits, the way being stopped by which they should come; this stopping is caused by vapours arising out of the stomack, filling the nerves, by which the spirits should be conveyed. When these vapours are spent, the passage is open, and the spirits perform their accustomed duties; so that *waking is the action and motion of the senses, which the spirits, dispersed over all parts, cause.*

SUBSECTION 8 — *Of the Moving Faculty*

This *moving faculty* is the other power of the *sensitive soul,* which causeth all those *inward and outward animal motions in the body*. It is divided into two faculties, the power of *appetite,* and of *moving from place to place*. This of *appetite* is threefold, so some will have it; *natural,* as it signifies any such inclination, as of a stone to fall downward, and such actions as *retention, expulsion,* which depend not on sense, but are *vegetal,* as the appetite of meat and drink, hunger and thirst. *Sensitive* is common to men and brutes. *Voluntary,* the third, or intellective, which commands the other two in men, and is a curb unto them, or at least should be, but for the most part is captivated and over-ruled by them: and men are led like beasts by sense, giving reins to their concupiscence and several lusts. For by this appetite the soul is led or inclined to follow that good which the senses shall approve, or avoid that which they hold evil. His object being good or evil, the one he embraceth, the other he rejecteth: according to that Aphorism, all things seek their own good, or at least seeming good. This power is inseparable from sense; for where sense is, there is likewise pleasure and pain. His *organ* is the same with the *common sense,* and is divided into two powers, or inclinations, *concupiscible* or *irascible:* or (as one translates it) *coveting, anger invading,* or impugning. *Concupiscible* covets always pleasant and delightsome things, and abhors that which is distasteful, harsh, and unpleasant. *Irascible,* as avoiding it with anger and indignation. All affections and perturbations arise out of these two fountains, which although the Stoicks make light of, we hold natural, and not to be resisted. The good affections are caused by some object of the same nature; and, if present, they procure joy, which dilates the heart, & preserves the body; if absent, they cause hope, love, desire, and concupiscence. The *bad* are *simple* or *mixed: simple* for some bad object present, as sorrow, which contracts the heart, macerates the soul, subverts the good estate of the body, hindering all the operations of it, causing melancholy, and many times death itself: or future, as fear. Out of these two arise those mixed affections and passions of anger, which is a desire of revenge; hatred, which is inveterate anger; zeal, which is offended with him who hurts that he loves; and epichairekakia, a compound affection of joy and hate, when we rejoice at other men's mischief, and are grieved at their prosperity; pride, self-love, emulation, envy, shame, &c., of which elsewhere.

Moving from place to place is a faculty necessarily following the other. For in vain were it otherwise to desire and to abhor, if we had not likewise power to prosecute or eschew, by moving the body from place to place: by this faculty therefore we locally move the body, or any part of it, and go from one place to another. To the better performance of which, three things are requisite: that which moves; by what it moves; that which is moved. That which moves is either the efficient cause, or end. The end is the object, which is desired or eschewed, as in a dog to catch a hare, &c. The efficient cause in man is *reason,* or his subordinate *phantasy,* which apprehends good or bad objects: in brutes, *imagination* alone, which moves the *appetite,* the *appetite* this faculty, which, by an admirable league of nature, and by mediation of the spirit commands the organ by which it moves: and that consists of nerves, muscles, cords, dispersed through the whole body, contracted and relaxed as the spirits will, which move the muscles, or nerves in the midst of them, and draw the cord, and so, by consequence the joint, to the place intended. That which is moved is the body or some member apt to move. The motion of the body is diverse, as going, running, leaping, dancing, sitting, & such like, referred to the predicament of *situs.* Worms creep, birds fly, fishes swim; and so of parts, the chief of which is *respiration* or breathing, and is thus performed. The outward air is drawn in by the *vocal artery,* and sent by mediation of the *midriff* to the lungs, which, dilating themselves as a pair of bellows, reciprocally fetch it in, and send it out to the heart to cool it: and from thence, now being hot, convey it again, still taking in fresh. Such a like motion is that of the *pulse,* of which, because many have written whole books, I will say nothing.

SUBSECTION 9 — *Of the Rational Soul*

In the precedent subsections I have anatomized those inferior faculties of the soul; the *rational* remaineth, *a pleasant, but a doubtful subject* (as one terms it), and with the like brevity to be discussed. Many erroneous opinions are about the essence & original of it; whether it be fire, as Zeno held; harmony, as Aristoxenus; number, as Xenocrates; whether it be organical, or inorganical; seated in the brain, heart or blood; mortal or immortal; how it comes into the body. Some hold that it is extraduced, as Philip, Tertullian, Lactantius. Hugo, Vincent of Beauvais, Hippocrates, Avicenna, and many late writers, that one man begets another, body & soul: or as a candle from a candle, to be produced from the seed: otherwise, say they, a man begets but half a man, and is worse than a beast, that begets both matter and form; and besides, the three faculties of the soul must be together infused, which is most absurd, as they hold, because in beasts they are begot, the two inferior I mean, and may not be well separated in men. Galen supposeth the soul to be the temperature itself; Trismegistus, Musæus, Orpheus, Homer, Pindar, Pherecydes Syrius, Epictetus, with the Chaldees and Egyptians, affirmed the soul to be immortal, as did those British Druids of old. The Pythagoreans defend Metempsychosis and Palingenesia, that souls go from one body to another, after having first drunk the water of Lethe, as men into wolves, bears, dogs, hogs, as they were inclined in their lives, or participated in conditions;

> *Guest of all bodies: out of beasts it flies*
> *To men, from men to beasts, — and never dies.*   (OVID)

Lucian's Cock was first Euphorbus, a Captain,

> *In Trojan wars I, (I remember well),*
> *Euphorbus was, Panthous' son, and fell ;*   (OVID)

a horse, a man, a sponge. Julian the Apostate thought Alexander's soul was descended into his body : Plato in his Timæus, and in his Phædo (for ought I can perceive) differs not much from this opinion, that it was from God at first, and knew all, but being inclosed in the body, it forgets, and learns anew, which he calls *reminiscence* or *recalling,* and that it was put into the body for a punishment, and thence it goes into a beast's, or man's, as appears by his pleasant fiction of drawing lots for a soul, and after 10,000 years is to return into the former body again,

> *After countless years in countless shapes,*
> *Back home 'tis borne from dogs and apes.*   (CLAUDIAN)

Others deny the immortality of it, which Pompanatius of Padua decided out of Aristotle not long since, Pliny the Elder, Seneca, Dicæarchus, Epicurus, Aratus, Hippocrates, Galen, Lucretius :

> *The mind is born with the body, wakes and wanes with it,*

Averroes, and I know not how many Neotericks. This question of the immortality of the soul is diversely and wonderfully impugned *and disputed, especially among the Italians of late,* saith Jab. Colerus. The Popes themselves have doubted of it, Leo X, that Epicurean Pope, as some record of him, caused this question to be discussed *pro* and *con* before him, and concluded at last, as a profane and atheistical *moderator,* with that verse of Cornelius Gallus : It began of nothing, and in nothing it ends. Zeno and his Stoicks, as Austin quotes him, supposed the soul so long to continue, till the body was fully putrefied, and resolved into primary substance : but after that, to be extinguished and vanish ; and in the mean time, whilst the body was consuming, it wandered all abroad, and (as that Clazomenian Hermotimus averred) saw pretty visions, and suffered I know not what.

> *The bloodless shades without bones or body wander.*   (OVID)

Others grant the immortality thereof, but they make many fabulous fictions in the mean time of it, after the departure from the body, like Plato's Elysian Fields, and that Turkey Paradise. The souls of good men they deified, the bad (saith Austin) *became devils,* as they supposed ; with many such absurd tenents, which he hath confuted. Hierome, Austin, and other Fathers of the Church, hold that the *soul* is immortal, created of nothing, and so infused into the child or *embryo* in his mother's womb six months after the conception ; not as those of brutes, which are carried over, and dying with them vanish into nothing. To whose divine treatises, and to the Scriptures themselves, I rejourn [refer] all such Atheistical spirits, as Tully did Atticus, doubting of this point, to Plato's Phædo. Or, if they desire Philosophical proofs and demonstrations, I refer them to Niphus, Faventinus' tracts of this subject: to Francis and John Picus, Tholosanus, Eugubinus, to Soto, Canas, Thomas, Peresius, Dandinus, Colerus, to that elaborate tract in Zanchius, to Tolet's 60 reasons, and Lessius' 22 arguments, to prove the immortality of the soul. Campanella is large in the same discourse, Albertinus the School-man, Jacob Nactantus, handleth it in four questions, Antony Brunus, Aonius Palearius, Marinus Marcennus, with many others. This *reasonable soul*, which Austin calls a spiritual substance moving itself, is defined by Philosophers to be *the first substantial act of a natural, human, organical body, by which a man lives, perceives, and understands, freely doing all things, and with election.* Out of which definition we may gather, that this *rational soul* includes the powers, and performs the duties of the two other, which are contained in it, and all three faculties make one *soul*, which is inorganical of itself, although it be in all parts, and incorporeal, using their organs, and working by them. It is divided into two chief parts, differing in office only, not in essence; the *understanding*, which is the *rational* power *apprehending;* the *will*, which is the *rational* power *moving:* to which two all the other *rational* powers are subject and reduced.

SUBSECTION 10 — *Of the Understanding*

Understanding is a power of the soul, by which we perceive, know, remember, and judge, as well singulars as universals, having certain innate notices or beginnings of arts, a reflecting action, by which it judgeth of his own doings, and examines them. Out of this definition (besides his chief office, which is to apprehend, judge, all that he performs, without the help of any instruments or organs) three differences appear betwixt a man and a beast; at first, the sense only comprehends *singularities,* the understanding *universalities;* secondly, the sense hath no innate notions; thirdly, brutes cannot reflect upon themselves. Bees indeed make neat and curious works, and many other creatures besides; but when they have done, they cannot judge of them. His object is God, *Ens,** all nature, and whatsoever is to be understood: which successively it apprehends. The object first moving the *understanding,* is some sensible thing; after, by discoursing, the mind finds out the corporeal

* Pure being.

substance, and from thence the spiritual. His actions (some say) are *apprehension, composition, division, discoursing, reasoning, memory,* which some include in *invention,* and *judgement.* The common divisions are of the understanding, *agent* and *patient; speculative,* and *practick;* in *habit,* or in *act; simple,* or *compound.* The *agent* is that which is called the *wit* of man, *acumen* or subtlety, *sharpness* of invention, when he doth invent of himself without a teacher, or learns anew, which abstracts those intelligible species from the phantasy, and transfers them to the passive understanding, *because there is nothing in the understanding, which was not first in the sense.* That which the imagination hath taken from the sense, this *agent* judgeth of, whether it be true or false; and being so judged h~~   ~~ s it to the *possible* to be kept. The *agent*
 ve a scholar; and his office is to keep and
 are committed to his charge: as a bare
 le of all forms and notions. Now these
 habits: actions, by which we take no-
 habits, which are durable lights and
 1 we will. Some reckon up eight kinds
 igence, faith, suspicion, error, opinion,
 prudence, wisdom: as also *synteresis,**
 ꜱ that in all there be fourteen species
 me are *innate,* as the three last men-
 octrine, learning, and use. Plato will
 :kons up but five intellectual habits:
 ꜱnd is to practise, to fabricate; *wis-*
 :periments of all notions and habits
 totle (if it be considered aright) is
 being innate, and five acquisite, the
 1 more strict examination excluded.
 ꜰ-ꜰ ꜱꜱate, but my subject will not permit.
 . ꜱ. ꜱꜱem 1 will only point at, as more necessary to my following discourse.

Synteresis, or the purer part of the conscience, is an innate habit, and doth signify *a conversation of the knowledge of the law of God and Nature, to know good or evil.* And (as our Divines hold) it is rather in the *understanding* than in the *will.* This makes the *major* proposition in a practick *syllogism.* The *dictamen rationis*† is that which doth admonish us to do good or evil, and is the *minor* in the *syllogism.* The *conscience*

---

* The pure part of the conscience.
† The Dictator of reason.

is that which approves good or evil, justifying or condemning our actions, and is the conclusion of the *syllogism*: as in that familiar example of Regulus the Roman, taken prisoner by the Carthaginians, and suffered to go to Rome, on that condition he should return again, or pay so much for his ransom. The *synteresis* proposeth the question; his word, oath, promise, is to be religiously kept, although to his enemy, and that by the law of nature. Do not that to another, which thou wouldst not have done to thyself. *Dictamen* applies it to him, and dictates this or the like: Regulus, thou wouldst not another man should falsify his oath, or break promise with thee: *conscience* concludes, Therefore, Regulus, thou dost well to perform thy promise, and oughtest to keep thine oath. More of this in *Religious Melancholy*.

SUBSECTION 11 — *Of the Will*

Will is the other power of the *rational soul, which covets or avoids such things as have been before judged and apprehended by the understanding.* If good, it approves; if evil, it abhors it: so that his object is either good or evil. Aristotle calls this our *rational appetite;* for as in the *sensitive* we are moved to good or bad by our *appetite,* ruled and directed by sense; so in this we are carried by *reason.* Besides, the *sensitive appetite* hath a particular object, good or bad: this an universal immaterial; that respects only things delectable and pleasant, this honest. Again, they differ in liberty. The *sensual appetite* seeing an object, if it be a convenient good, cannot but desire it; if evil, avoid it: but this is free in his essence, *much now depraved, obscured, and fallen from his first perfection; yet in some of his operations still free,* as to go, walk, move at his pleasure, and to choose whether it will do or not do, steal or not steal. Otherwise in vain were laws, deliberations, exhortations, counsels, precepts, rewards, promises, threats, and punishments: and God should be the author of sin. But in spiritual things we will no good, prone to evil (except we be regenerate, and led by the Spirit), we are egged on by our natural concupiscence, and there is a confusion in our powers, *our whole will is averse from God and his law,* not in natural things only, as to eat and drink, lust, to which we are led headlong by our temperature and inordinate appetite, we are neither able to make head against them, nor struggle as we should; we cannot resist, our concupiscence is originally bad, our heart evil, the seat of our affections captivates and enforceth our will; so that in voluntary things we are averse from God and goodness, bad by nature, by ignorance worse, by art, discipline, custom, we get many bad habits: suffering them to domineer and tyrannize over us; and the devil is still ready at hand with his evil suggestions, to tempt our depraved will to some ill-disposed action, to precipitate us to destruction, except our *will* be swayed and counterpoised again with some divine precepts, and good motions of the spirit, which many times restrain, hinder, and check us, when we are in the full career of our dissolute courses. So David corrected himself, when he had Saul at a vantage. Revenge and malice were as two violent oppugners on the one side; but honesty, religion, fear of God, withheld him on the other.

The actions of the *will* are to will and nill: which two words comprehend all, and they are good or bad, accordingly as they are directed: and some of them freely performed by himself; although the Stoicks absolutely deny it, and will have all things inevitably done by *destiny,* imposing a fatal necessity upon us, which we may not resist; yet we say that our will is free in respect of us, and things contingent, howsoever (in respect of God's determinate counsel) they are inevitable and necessary. Some other actions of the *will* are performed by the inferior powers, which obey him, as the *sensitive & moving appetite;* as to open our eyes, to go hither and thither, not to touch a book, to speak fair or foul: but this *appetite* is many times rebellious in us, and will not be contained within the lists of sobriety and temperance. It was (as I said) once well agreeing with reason, and there was an excellent consent and harmony betwixt them, but that is now dissolved, they often jar, *reason* is overborne by *passion:* as so many wild horses run away with a chariot, and will not be curbed. We know many times what is good, but will not do it, as she said,

> *A new-felt force my striving powers invades:*
> *Affection this, discretion that, persuades;* (OVID)

lust counsels one thing, reason another, there is a new reluctancy in men.

> *I hate, yet can't but be the thing I hate.* (OVID)

We cannot resist, but, as Phædra confessed to her nurse, she said well and true, she did acknowledge it, but headstrong passion and fury made her to do that which was opposite. So David knew the filthiness of his fact, what a loathsome, foul, crying sin adultery was, yet, notwithstanding, he would commit murder, and take away another man's wife, enforced against reason, religion, to follow his appetite.

Those *natural* and *vegetal* powers are not commanded by *will* at all; for who can add one cubit to his stature? These other may, but are not: and thence come all those headstrong passions, violent perturbations of the mind; and many times vicious habits, customs, feral diseases, because we give so much way to our *appetite,* and follow our inclination, like so many beasts. The principal *habits* are two in number, *virtue* and *vice,* whose peculiar definitions, descriptions, differences and kinds, are handled at large in the *Ethicks,* and are indeed the subject of *Moral Philosophy.*

MEMBER 3

SUBSECTION 1 — *Definition of Melancholy, Name, Difference*

HAVING thus briefly anatomized the body and soul of man, as a preparative to the rest, I may now freely proceed to treat of my intended object to most men's capacity, and after many ambages perspicuously define what this *Melancholy* is, shew his *name* and *differences.* The *name* is imposed from the matter, and disease denominated from the material cause, as Bruel observes, Melancholia, a sort of melaina (black) chole (choler), from black Choler. And whether it be a cause or an effect, a disease, or symptom, let Donatus Altomarus and Salvianus decide, I will not contend about it. It hath several descriptions, notations, and definitions. Fracastorius, in his second book of intellect, calls those *melancholy, whom abundance of that same depraved humour of black choler hath so misaffected, that they become mad thence, and dote in most things, or in all, belonging to election, will, or other manifest operations of the understanding.* Melanelius (out of Galen, Ruffus, Aetius) describes it to be *a bad and peevish disease, which makes men degenerate into beasts:* Galen, *a privation or infection of the middle cell of the head, &c.,* defining it from the part affected, which Hercules de Saxonia approves, calling it *a depravation of the principal function:* Fuschius, Arnoldus, Guianerius, and others: *by reason of black choler,* Paulus adds. Halyabbas simply calls it a *commotion of the mind;* Aretæus, *a perpetual anguish of the soul, fastened on one thing, without an ague;* which definition of his Mercurialis taxeth: but Ælianus Montaltus defends for sufficient and good. The common sort define it to be *a kind of dotage without a fever, having for his ordinary companions fear and sadness, without any apparent occasion.* So doth Laurentius, Piso, Donatus Altomarus, Jacchinus (on Rhasis), Valesius, Fuchsius, &c., which common definition, howsoever approved by most, Hercules de Saxonia will not allow of, nor David Crusius; he holds it insufficient, *as rather shewing what it is not, than what it is:* as omitting the specific difference, the phantasy and brain: but I descend to particulars. The most general class is *dotage, or anguish of the mind,* saith Aretæus, *of a principal part,* Hercules de Saxonia adds, to distinguish it from cramp and palsy, and such diseases as belong to the outward sense and motions; *depraved,* to distinguish it from folly and madness (which Montaltus makes the suffocation of the mind, to separate) in which those functions are not depraved, but rather abolished; *without an ague,* is added by all, to sever it from *phrenzy,* and that *melancholy* which is in a pestilent fever. *Fear* and *Sorrow* make it differ from *madness: without a cause* is lastly inserted, to specify it from all other ordinary passions of *Fear* and *Sorrow.* We properly call that *dotage,* as Laurentius interprets it, *when some one principal faculty of the mind, as imagination, or reason, is corrupted, as all melancholy persons have.* It is without a fever, because the humour is most part cold and dry, contrary to putrefaction. *Fear & Sorrow* are the true characters, and inseparable companions, of most melancholy, not all, as Hercules de Saxonia well excepts; for to some it is most pleasant, as to such as laugh most part; some are bold again, and free from all manner of fear and grief, as hereafter shall be declared.

SUBSECTION 2 — *Of the part affected. Affection. Parties affected*

SOME difference I find amongst writers about the principal part affected in this disease, whether it be the *brain,* or *heart,* or some other member. Most are of opinion that it is the *brain:* for, being a kind of *dotage,* it cannot otherwise be but that the *brain* must be affected, a similar part, be it by *consent* or *essence,* not in his ventricles, or any obstructions in them, for then it would be an apoplexy or epilepsy, as Laurentius well observes, but in a cold dry distemperature of it in his substance, which is corrupt and becomes too cold, or too dry, or else too hot, as in mad-men, and such as are inclined to it, and this Hippocrates confirms, Galen, Arabians, and most of our new writers. Marcus de Oddis (in a consultation of his, quoted by Hildesheim), and five others there cited are of the contrary part, because fear and sorrow, which are passions, be seated in the heart. But this objection is sufficiently answered by Montaltus, who doth not deny that the heart is affected (as Melanelius proves out of Galen) by reason of his vicinity; & so is the *midriff* and many other parts. They do sympathize, & have a fellow-feeling, by the law of nature: but forasmuch as this malady is caused by precedent *imagination,* with the *appetite,* to whom spirits obey, and are subject to those principal parts, the *brain* must needs primarily be misaffected, as the seat of *reason;* and then the *heart,* as the seat of *affection*. Cappivaccius and Mercurialis have copiously discussed this question, and both conclude the subject is the inner *brain*, and from thence it is communicated to the *heart*, and other inferior parts, which sympathize and are much troubled, especially when it comes by consent, and is caused by reason of the *stomack*, or *myrach*, as the Arabians term it, whole body, liver, or spleen, which are seldom free, *pylorus, meseraick veins, &c.* For our body is like a clock; if one wheel be amiss, all the rest are disordered, the whole fabrick suffers: with such admirable art and harmony is a man composed, such excellent proportion, as Lodovicus Vives, in his Fable of Man, hath elegantly declared.

As many doubts almost arise about the *affection*, whether it be *imagination* or *reason* alone, or both. Hercules de Saxonia proves it out of Galen, Aetius, and Altomarus, that the sole fault is in *imagination;* Bruel is of the same mind. Montaltus confutes this tenent of theirs, and illustrates the contrary by many examples: as of him that thought himself a shell-fish, of a Nun, & of a desperate Monk that would not be persuaded but that he was damned. *Reason* was in fault as well as *imagination,* which did not correct this error. They make away themselves oftentimes, and suppose many absurd & ridiculous things. Why doth not *reason* detect the fallacy, settle and persuade, if she be free? Avicenna therefore holds both corrupt, to whom most Arabians subscribe. The same is maintained by Aretæus, Gordonius, Guianerius, &c. To end the controversy, no man doubts of *imagination,* but that it is hurt and misaffected here. For the other I determine with Albertinus Bottonus, a Doctor of Padua, that it is first in *imagination, and afterwards in reason, if the disease be inveterate, or as it is more or less of continuance:* but by accident, as Hercules de Saxonia adds; *faith, opinion, discourse, ratiocination, are all accidentally depraved by the default of imagination.*

To the part affected, I may here add the parties, which shall be more opportunely spoken of elsewhere, now only signified. Such as have the *Moon, Saturn, Mercury,* misaffected in their genitures; such as live in over-cold or over-hot climes: such as are born of *melancholy* parents: such as offend in those six non-natural things, are black, or of an high sanguine complexion, that have little heads, that have a hot heart, moist brain, hot liver and cold stomack, have been long sick: such as are solitary by nature, great students, given to much contemplation, lead a life out of action, are most subject to *melancholy*. Of sexes both, but men more often, yet women misaffected are far more violent, and grievously troubled. Of seasons of the year, the *Autumn* is most melancholy. Of peculiar times; old age, from which natural melancholy is almost an inseparable accident; but this artificial malady is more frequent in such as are of a middle age. Some assign 40 years, Gariopontus 30; Jubertus excepts neither young nor old from this adventitious. Daniel Sennertus involves all of all sorts, out of common experience. Aetius and Aretæus ascribe into the number *not only discontented, passionate, and miserable persons, swarthy, black; but such as are most merry & pleasant, scoffers & high coloured. Generally,* saith Rhasis, *the finest wits, and most generous spirits, are before other obnoxious to it.* I cannot except any complexion, any condition, sex, or age, but fools and Stoicks, which, according to Synesius, are never troubled with any manner of passion, but, as Anacreon's grasshopper, free from pain and flesh and blood, almost a little god. Erasmus vindicates fools from this melancholy catalogue, because they have most part moist brains, and light hearts, *they are free from ambition, envy, shame and fear, they are neither troubled in conscience, nor macerated with cares, to which our whole life is most subject.*

SUBSECTION 3 — *Of the Matter of Melancholy*

OF the Matter of *Melancholy* there is much question betwixt Avicenna & Galen, as you may read in Cardan's Contradictions, Valesius' Controversies, Montanus, Prosper Calenus, Cappivaccius, Bright, Ficinus, that have written either whole tracts, or copiously of it, in their several treatises of this subject. *What this humour is, or whence it proceeds, how it is engendered in the body, neither Galen, nor any old writer, hath sufficiently discussed,* as Jacchinus thinks: the Neotericks cannot agree. Montanus, in his Consultations, holds *melancholy* to be *material* or *immaterial,* & so doth Arculanus. The *material* is one of the four humours before mentioned, and natural; the *immaterial* or adventitious acquisite, redundant, unnatural, artificial: which Hercules de Saxonia will have reside in the spirits alone, and to proceed from an *hot, cold, dry, moist distemperature, which, without matter, alters the brain & functions of it.* Paracelsus wholly rejects and derides this division of four humours and complexions, but our Galenists generally approve of it, subscribing to this opinion of Montanus.

This material *Melancholy* is either *simple* or *mixed;* offending in *quantity* or *quality,* varying according to his place, where it settleth, as brain, spleen, meseraick veins, heart, womb, & stomack: or differing according to the mixture of those natural humours amongst themselves,

or four unnatural adust humours, as they are diversely tempered &
mingled. If natural *melancholy* abound in the body, which is cold & dry,
*so that it be more than the body is well able to bear, it must needs be
distempered,* saith Faventinus, *& diseased:* and so the other, if it be
depraved, whether it arise from that other *melancholy* of *choler* adust,*
or from *blood,* produceth the like effects, & is, as Montaltus contends,
if it come by adustion of humours, most part hot & dry. Some difference I find, whether this *melancholy* matter may be engendered of all
four humours, about the colour and temper of it. Galen holds it may
be engendered of three alone, including *phlegm,* or *pituita,* whose true
assertion Valesius and Menardus stiffly maintain, and so doth Fuchsius,
Montaltus, Montanus. How (say they) can white become black? But
Hercules de Saxonia & Cardan are of the opposite part (it may be engendered of phlegm, though it seldom come to pass) ; so is Guianerius,
& Laurentius, with Melancthon, in his Book, the Soul, & Chapter
of Humours; he calls it asinine, dull, swinish *melancholy,* and saith
that he was an eye-witness of it: so is Wecker. From *melancholy* adust
ariseth one kind, from *choler* another, which is most brutish: another
from *phlegm,* which is dull; and the last from *blood,* which is best. Of
these some are cold and dry, others hot & dry, varying according to
their mixtures, as they are intended, & remitted. And indeed, as Rod.
à Fonseca determines, ichors & those serous matters being thickened
become phlegm, and phlegm degenerates into choler, choler adust becomes troublesome melancholy, as vinegar out of purest wine putrefied,
or by exhalation of purer spirits, is so made, and becomes sour and
sharp; and from the sharpness of this humour proceed much waking,
troublesome thoughts & dreams, &c., so that I conclude as before. If
the humour be cold, it is, saith Faventinus, *a cause of dotage, & produceth milder symptoms: if hot, they are rash, raving mad, or inclining
to it.* If the brain be hot, the animal spirits are hot, much madness
follows with violent actions: if cold, fatuity & sottishness, Capivaccius.
*The colour of this mixture varies likewise according to the mixture, be
it hot or cold; 'tis sometimes black, sometimes not,* Altomarus. The
same Melanelius proves out of Galen; & Hippocrates, in his Book of
Melancholy (if at least it be his), giving instance in a burning coal,
*which when it is hot, shines; when it is cold, looks black; & so doth
the humour.* This diversity of melancholy matter produceth diversity of
effects. If it be within the body, & not putrefied, it causeth black jaundice; if putrefied, a quartan ague; if it break out to the skin, leprosy;

* Burning choler.

if to parts, several maladies, as scurvy, &c. If it trouble the mind, as it is diversely mixed, it produces several kinds of madness and dotage: of which in their place.

SUBSECTION 4 — *Of the species or kinds of Melancholy*

WHEN the matter is diverse and confused, how should it otherwise be, but that the species should be diverse and confused? Many new and old writers have spoken confusedly of it, confounding *melancholy* and *madness,* as Heurnius, Guianerius, Gordonius, Sallustius Salvianus, Jason Pratensis, Savanarola, that will have *madness* no other than *melancholy* in extent, differing (as I have said) in degrees. Some make two distinct species, as Ruffus Ephesius, an old writer, Constantinus Africanus, Aretæus, Aurelianus, Paulus Ægineta: others acknowledge a multitude of kinds, and leave them indefinite, as Aetius in his Tetrabiblos, Avicenna, Arculanus, Montanus. *If natural melancholy be adust, it maketh one kind; if blood, another; if choler, a third, differing from the first; and so many several opinions there are about the kinds, as there be men themselves.* Hercules de Saxonia sets down two kinds, *material and immaterial; one from spirits alone, the other from humours and spirits.* Savanarola will have the kinds to be infinite; one from the *myrach,* called *myrachialis* of the Arabians; another *stomachalis,* from the *stomack;* another from the *liver, heart, womb, hemrods, one beginning, another consummate.* Melancthon seconds him, *as the humour is diversly adust and mixed, so are the species diverse.* But what these men speak of species, I think ought to be understood of symptoms, and so doth Arculanus interpret himself: infinite species, that is, symptoms: and in that sense, as Jo. Gorrhæus acknowledgeth in his medicinal definitions, the species are infinite, but they may be reduced to three kinds, by reason of their seat; *head, body,* and *hypochondries.* This threefold division is approved by Hippocrates in his Book of Melancholy (if it be his, which some suspect); by Galen, by Alexander, Rhasis, Avicenna, & most of our new writers. Th. Erastus makes two kinds; one perpetual, which is *head melancholy;* the other interrupt, which comes and goes by fits, which he subdivides into the other two kinds, so that all comes to the same pass. Some again make four or five kinds, with Rodericus à Castro, and Lod. Mercatus, who in his second book will have that melancholy of nuns, widows, and more ancient maids, to be a peculiar species of melancholy differing from the rest. Some will reduce enthusiasts, exstatical and demoniacal persons, to this rank, adding *love melancholy* to the first, and *lycanthropia.* The most received division is into three kinds. The first proceeds from the sole fault of the *brain,* & is called *head melancholy:* the second sympathetically proceeds from the *whole body,* when the whole temperature is melancholy: the third ariseth from the bowels, liver, spleen, or membrane called *mesenterium,* named *hypochondriacal or windy melancholy,* which Laurentius subdivides into three parts, from those three members, *Hepatick, splenetick, meseraick. Love melancholy,* which Avicenna calls *ilishi,* & *lycanthropia,* which he calls *cucubuth,* are commonly included in head melancholy: but of this last, which Gerardus de Solo calls *amorous,* and most, *Knight melancholy,* with that of *religious melancholy,* of virgins & widows, maintained by Rod. a Castro and Mercatus, and the other kinds of *love melancholy,* I will speak apart by themselves in my third partition. The three precedent species are the subject of my present discourse, which I will anatomize, & treat of, through all their causes, symptoms, cures, together and apart; that every man that is any measure affected with this malady, may know how to examine it in himself, and apply remedies unto it.

It is a hard matter, I confess, to distinguish these three species one from the other, to express their several causes, symptoms, cures, being that they are so often confounded amongst themselves, having such affinity, that they can scarce be discerned by the most accurate Physicians, & so often intermixed with other diseases, that the best experienced have been plunged. Montanus names a patient that had this disease of melancholy & *caninus appetitus* * both together: and with *vertigo ;* Julius Cæsar Claudinus with stone, gout, jaundice; Trincavellius with an ague, jaundice, *caninus appetitus,* &c. Paulus Regoline, a great Doctor in his time, consulted in this case, was so confounded with a confusion of symptoms, that he knew not to what kind of melancholy to refer it. Trincavellius, Fallopius, and Francanzanus, famous Doctors in Italy, all three conferred with about one party at the same time, gave three different opinions. And, in another place, Trincavellius being demanded what he thought of a melancholy young man, to whom he was sent for, ingenuously confessed, that he was indeed melancholy, but he knew not to what kind to reduce it. In his 17th consultation, there is the like disagreement about a melancholy monk. Those symptoms, which others ascribe to misaffected parts and humours, Herc. de Saxonia attributes wholly to distempered spirits, & those immaterial, as I have said. Sometimes they cannot well discern this disease from

---

* Dog-hunger, never knowing when to stop eating.

others. In Reinerus Solenander's counsels, he and Dr. Brande both agreed, that the patient's disease was hypochondriacal melancholy. Dr. Matholdus said it was *asthma,* and nothing else. Solenander and Guarionius, lately sent for to the melancholy Duke of Cleve, with others, could not define what species it was, or agree among themselves. The species are so confounded, as in Cæsar Claudinus his 44th consultation for a Palonian Count ; in his judgment *he laboured of head melancholy, and that which proceeds from the whole temperature, both at once.* I could give instance of some that have had three kinds at one and the same time, and some successively. So that I conclude of our melancholy species, as many Politicians do of their pure forms of Commonwealths, Monarchies, Aristocracies, Democracies, are most famous in contemplation, but in practice they are temperate and usually mixed, (so Polybius informeth us) as the Lacedæmonian, the Roman of old, German now, and many others. What Physicians say of distinct species in their books, it much matters not, since that in their patients' bodies they are commonly mixed. In such obscurity, therefore, variety and confused mixture of symptoms, causes, how difficult a thing it is to treat of several kinds apart ; to make any certainty or distinction among so many casualties, distractions, when seldom two men shall be like affected in every respect. 'Tis hard, I confess, yet nevertheless I will adventure through the midst of these perplexities, & led by the clue or thread of the best writers, extricate myself out of a labyrinth of doubts and errors, and so proceed to the causes.

SECTION 2 MEMBER 1

SUBSECTION 1 — *Causes of Melancholy. God a cause*

IT *is in vain to speak of cures, or think of remedies, until such time as we have considered of the causes ;* so Galen prescribes Glauco : and the common experience of others confirms that those cures must be imperfect, lame, and to no purpose, wherein the causes have not first been searched, as Prosper Calenus well observes in his tract about black bile to Cardinal Cæsius : insomuch that Fernelius *puts a kind of necessity in the knowledge of the causes, and without which it is impossible to cure or prevent any manner of disease.* Empiricks may ease, and sometimes help, but not throughly root out : as the saying is, if the cause be removed, the effect is likewise vanquished. It is a most difficult thing (I confess) to be able to discern these causes whence they are, and in

such variety to say what the beginning was. He is happy that can perform it aright. I will adventure to guess as near as I can, and rip them
all up, from the first to the last, *general* and *particular*, to every *species*,
that so they may the better be descried.

    General causes are either *supernatural* or *natural*. *Supernatural are
from God and his angels*, or, *by God's permission, from the devil* and
his ministers. That God himself is a cause, for the punishment of sin,
and satisfaction of his justice, many examples & testimonies of holy
Scriptures make evident unto us: Foolish men are plagued for their
offence and by reason of their wickedness. Gehazi was strucken with
leprosy; Jehoram with dysentery and flux, and great diseases of the
bowels, David plagued for numbering his people; Sodom and Gomorrah
swallowed up. And this disease is peculiarly specified: He brought
down their heart through heaviness. He stroke them with madness,
blindness and astonishment of heart. An evil spirit was sent by the
Lord upon Saul to vex him. Nebuchadnezzar did eat grass like an ox,
and *his heart was made like the beasts of the field.* Heathen stories are
full of such punishments. Lycurgus, because he cut down the vines in
the country, was by Bacchus driven into madness: so was Pentheus
and his mother Agave for neglecting their sacrifice. Censor Fulvius ran
mad for untiling Juno's Temple, to cover a new one of his own, which he
had dedicated to Fortune, and was confounded to death with grief and
sorrow of heart. When Xerxes would have spoiled Apollo's Temple at
Delphi of those infinite riches it possessed, a terrible thunder came from
Heaven and struck 4,000 men dead, the rest ran mad. A little after, the
like happened to Brennus, lightning, thunder, earthquakes, upon such
a sacrilegious occasion. If we may believe our pontifical writers, they
will relate unto us many strange and prodigious punishments in this
kind, inflicted by their saints: — how Clodoveus, sometime King of
France, the son of Dagobert, lost his wits for uncovering the body of
S. Denis: and how a sacrilegious Frenchman, that would have stolen
away a silver image of S. John, at Birgburge, became frantick on a
sudden, raging, and tyrannising over his own flesh; of a Lord of Rad-
nor, that, coming from hunting late at night, put his dogs into S. Avan's
Church, (Llan Avan they called it), and rising betimes next morning,
as hunters use to do, found all his dogs mad, himself being suddenly
strucken blind; of Tiridates, an Armenian King, for violating some holy
nuns, that was punished in like sort, with loss of his wits. But Poets
and Papists may go together for fabulous tales; let them free their own
credits: howsoever they feign of their Nemesis, and of their Saints, or

by the devil's means may be deluded; we find it true, that He is God the avenger, as David styles him; and that it is our crying sins that pull this and many other maladies on our heads; that he can by his Angels, which are his Ministers, strike and heal (saith Dionysius) whom he will; that he can plague us by his creatures, sun, moon, and stars, which he useth as his instruments, as a husbandman (saith Zanchius) doth an hatchet. Hail, snow, winds, &c. The trumpeter draweth together the winds as in Joshua's time, as in Pharaoh's reign in Egypt; they are but as so many executioners of his justice. He can make the proudest spirits stoop, & cry out with Julian the Apostate, *Thou hast conquered, O Galilean!* or with Apollo's Priest in Chrysostom, O heaven! O earth! what an enemy is this? And pray with David, acknowledging his power, *I am weakened and sore broken, I roar for the grief of mine heart; mine heart panteth, &c., O Lord, rebuke me not in thine anger, neither chastise me in thy wrath. Make me to hear joy and gladness. that the bones which thou hast broken may rejoice. Restore to me the joy of thy salvation, and establish me with thy free spirit.* For these causes belike Hippocrates would have a Physician take special notice whether the disease come not from a divine supernatural cause, or whether it follow the course of nature. But this is farther discussed by Francis Valesius, Fernelius, and J. Cæsar Claudinus, to whom I refer you, how this place of Hippocrates is to be understood. Paracelsus is of opinion, that such spiritual diseases (for so he calls them) are spiritually to be cured, and not otherwise. Ordinary means in such cases will not avail: we must not wrestle with God. When that monster-taming Hercules overcame all in the Olympicks, Jupiter at last in an unknown shape wrestled with him; the victory was uncertain, till at length Jupiter descried himself, and Hercules yielded. No striving with supreme powers, no use to make great offers to the physician. Physicians and Physick can do no good, *we must submit under the mighty hand of God,* acknowledge our offences, call to him for mercy. If he strike us, one and the same hand will bring hurt and help, as it is with them that are wounded with the spear of Achilles, he alone must help; otherwise our diseases are incurable, and we not to be relieved.

SUBSECTION 2 — *A Digression of the nature of Spirits, bad Angels, or Devils, and how they cause Melancholy*

How far the power of Spirits and Devils doth extend, and whether they can cause this, or any other disease, is a serious question, and worthy to be considered: for the better understanding of which, I will make a brief digression of the nature of Spirits. And although the question be very obscure, according to Postellus, *full of controversy and ambiguity,* beyond the reach of human capacity, saith Austin, *I confess I am not able to understand it, the finite cannot deal with the infinite;* we can sooner determine with Tully, what they are not than what they are; our subtle Schoolmen, Cardans, Scaligers, profound Thomists, Fracastorian & Fernelian geniuses are weak, dry, obscure, defective in these mysteries, and all our quickest wits, as an owl's eyes at the sun's light, wax dull, and are not sufficient to apprehend them; yet, as in the rest, I will adventure to say something to this point. In former times, as we read, the Sadducees denied that there were any such Spirits, Devils, or Angels. So did Galen the Physician, the Peripateticks, even Aristotle himself, as Pomponatius stoutly maintains, and Scaliger in some sort grants; though Dandinus the Jesuit stiffly denies it. Separate essences and intelligences are the same which Christians call Angels, and Platonists Devils, for they name all the Spirits daimons, be they good or bad Angels, as Julius Pollux observes. Epicures and Atheists are of the same mind in general, because they never saw them. Plato, Plotinus, Porphyrius, Iamblicus, Proclus, insisting in the steps of Trismegistus, Pythagoras and Socrates, make no doubt of it: nor Stoicks, but that there are such spirits, though much erring from the truth. Concerning the first beginning of them, the Talmudists say that Adam had a wife called Lilis, before he married Eve, & of her he begat nothing but Devils. The Turks' Alcoran is altogether as absurd and ridiculous in this point: but the Scripture informs us Christians, how Lucifer, the chief of them, with his associates, fell from heaven for his pride and ambition; created of God, placed in heaven, and sometimes an Angel of light, now cast down into the lower aerial sublunary parts, or into Hell, and delivered into chains of darkness to be kept unto damnation. There is a foolish opinion, which some hold, that they are the souls of men departed, good and more noble were deified, the baser grovelled on the ground, or in the lower parts, and were devils; the which, with Tertullian, Porphyrius the Philosopher, M. Tyrius maintains. *These spirits,* he saith, *which we call Angels and Devils, are nought but souls of men departed, which, either through love and pity of their friends yet living, help and assist them, or else persecute their enemies, whom they hated,* as Dido threatened to persecute Æneas:

> *I'll haunt you in all places like a ghost:*
> *Wretch, you shall pay full penalty.*

They are (as others suppose) appointed by those higher Powers to keep men from their nativity, and to protect or punish them, as they see cause: and are called good and evil Genii by the Romans; Heroes, Lares, if good, Lemures or Larvæ, if bad, by the Stoicks; governors of countries, men, cities, saith Apuleius: All those mortals are called gods, who, their course of life having been prudently guided and governed, are honoured by men with temples & sacrifices, as Osiris in Egypt, &c. Guardians, Capella calls them, *which protected particular men as well as princes.* Socrates had his saturnine and fiery daimon, which of all spirits is best, raising the mind to sublime thoughts, as the Platonists supposed; Plotinus his; and we Christians our assisting Angel, as Andreas Victorellus, a copious writer of this subject, Lodovicus de La-Cerda, the Jesuit, in his voluminous Tract on Guardian Angels, Zan-chius, and some Divines think. But this absurd Tenent of Tyrius, Proclus confutes at large in his book on the Soul and the Devil.

Psellus, a Christian, and sometime Tutor (saith Cuspinian) to Michael Parapinatius, Emperor of Greece, a great observer of the nature of Devils, holds they are corporeal, and have *aerial bodies, that they are mortal, live and die,* (which Martianus Capella likewise maintains, but our Christian Philosophers explode), *that they are nourished and have excrements, that they feel pain if they be hurt* (which Cardan confirms, and Scaliger justly laughs him to scorn for; if they feed on air, why do they not strive for air more pure? &c.) *or stroken:* &, if their bodies be cut, with admirable celerity they come together again. Austin approves as much, so doth Hierome, Origen, Tertullian, Lactantius, and many ancient Fathers of the Church: that in their fall their bodies were changed into a more aerial and gross substance. Bodine, and David Crusius, by several arguments proves Angels and Spirits to be corporeal: whatever occupies space is corporeal: — spirit occupies space, *therefore,* &c. Bodine goes farther yet, and will have these detached souls, genii, Spirits, Angels, Devils, and so likewise souls of men departed, if corporeal (which he most eagerly contends), to be of some shape, and that absolutely round, like Sun and Moon, because that is the most perfect form, which has no roughness, angles, tortuousness, prominences, but is the most perfect among perfect bodies; therefore all spirits are corporeal, he concludes, & in their proper shapes round. That they can assume other aerial bodies, all manner of shapes at their pleasures, appear in what likeness they will themselves, that they are most swift in motion, can pass many miles in an instant, & so likewise transform bodies of others into what shape they please, and with admirable celerity remove them from place to place; (as the Angel did Habakkuk to Daniel, and as Philip the Deacon was carried away by the Spirit, when he had baptized the Eunuch; so did Pythagoras and Apollonius remove themselves and others, with many such feats); that they can represent castles in the air, palaces, armies, spectrums, prodigies, and such strange objects to mortal men's eyes, cause smells, savours, &c. deceive all the senses, most writers of this subject credibly believe; and that they can foretell future events, and do many strange miracles. Juno's image spake to Camillus, and Fortune's statue to the Roman matrons, with many such. Zanchius, Bodine, Spondanus, and others, are of opinion that they cause a true Metamorphosis, as Nebuchadnezzar was really translated into a beast, Lot's wife into a pillar of salt, Ulysses' companions into hogs and dogs by Circe's charms; turn themselves and others, as they do witches, into cats, dogs, hares, crows, &c. Strozzius Cicogna hath many examples, which he there confutes, as Austin likewise doth. That they can be seen when, and in what shape, and to whom they will, saith Psellus, though he himself never saw them nor desired it; and use sometimes carnal copulation (as elsewhere * I shall prove more at large) with women and men. Many will not believe they can be seen, and if any man shall say, swear, and stiffly maintain, though he be discreet and wise, judicious and learned, that he hath seen them, they account him a timorous fool, a melancholy dizzard, a weak fellow, a dreamer, a sick or a mad man, they contemn him, laugh him to scorn, and yet Marcus of his credit told Psellus that he had often seen them. And Leo Suavius, a Frenchman, (out of some Platonists,) will have the air to be as full of them as snow falling in the skies, and that they may be seen, and withal sets down the means how men may see them; by gazing steadfastly on the sun lighted by its brightest rays, &c., & saith moreover he tried it, proved the dish before eating, & it was true that the Platonists said. Paracelsus confesseth that he saw them divers times, & conferred with them, & so doth Alexander *that he so found it by experience, when as before he doubted of it.* Many deny it, saith Lavater, *because they never saw them themselves;* but as he reports at large all over his book, they are often seen & heard, & familiarly converse with men, as Lod. Vives assureth us, innumerable records, histories, and testimonies evince in all ages, times, places, and all travellers besides; in the West Indies and our Northern climes, nothing is more common than to see spirits in the fields and cities, to hear them bidding or forbidding, &c. Hieronymus, Basil, Nicephorus, Eusebius, Socrates, Sozomenus, Jacobus Bois-

* Part. 3, Sect. 2, Memb. 1, Subs. 1.

sardus, in his Tract on the appearances of spirits, Petrus Loyerus, Wierus, have infinite variety of such examples of apparitions of spirits, for him to read that farther doubts, to his ample satisfaction. One alone I will briefly insert. A nobleman in Germany was sent ambassador to the King of Sweden (for his name, the time, & such circumstances, I refer you to Boissardus, mine Author). After he had done his business, he sailed to Livonia, on set purpose to see those familiar spirits, which are there said to be conversant with men, & do their drudgery works. Amongst other matters, one of them told him where his wife was, in what room, in what clothes, what doing, & brought him a ring from her, which at his return, not without wondering at everything, he found to be true; and so believed that ever after, which before he doubted of. Cardan relates of his father, Facius Cardan, that after the accustomed solemnities, in 1491, 13 August, he conjured up 7 Devils in Greek apparel, about 40 years of age, some ruddy of complexion, & some pale, as he thought; he asked them many questions, & they made ready answer, that they were aerial Devils, that they lived & died as men did, save that they were far longer liv'd, (700 or 800 years); they did as much excel men in dignity, as we do juments, and were as far excelled again of those that were above them; our governors & keepers they are moreover, which Plato in Critias delivered of old, & subordinate to one another, for as man governs man, so devil governs devil; they rule themselves as well as us, & the spirits of the meaner sort had commonly such offices, as we make horse-keepers, neat-herds, & the basest of us overseers of our cattle; & that we can no more apprehend their natures and functions, than an horse a man's. They knew all things, but might not reveal them to men; & ruled & domineered over us, as we do over our horses; the best Kings amongst us, & the most generous spirits, were not comparable to the basest of them. Sometimes they did instruct men, & communicate their skill, reward & cherish, and sometimes again terrify & punish, to keep them in awe, as they thought fit, desiring nothing more (saith Lysius) than the admiration of mankind. The same author, Cardan, in his Hyperchen, out of the doctrine of Stoicks, will have some of these Genii (for so he calls them) to be desirous of men's company, very affable, & familiar with them, as dogs are; others again to abhor as serpents, & care not for them. The same, belike, Trithemius calls fiery and sublunary, which never go to the lower parts, and have scarce any dealings on the earth. *Generally they far excel men in worth, as a man the meanest worm; though some of them are inferior to those of their own rank in worth, as the black guard in a Prince's Court, and*

*to men again, as some degenerate, base, rational creatures, are excelled
of brute beasts.*

That they are mortal, besides these testimonies of Cardan, Martianus,
&c., many other Divines and Philosophers hold, that after a long time
they all die; the Platonists and some Rabbins, Porphyrius and Plutarch,
as appears by that relation of Thamus: The great God Pan is dead:
Apollo Pythius ceased; and so the rest. S. Hierome, in the life of Paul
the Eremite, tells a story how one of them appeared to S. Antony in the
wilderness, and told him as much. Paracelsus, of our late writers, stiffly
maintains that they are mortal, live and die, as other creatures do.
Zozimus farther adds, that religion and policy dies and alters with them.
The Gentiles' gods, he saith, were expelled by Constantine, and together
with them the Fortune and Majesty of the Roman Empire decayed and
vanished, as that heathen in Minucius formerly bragged, when the Jews
were overcome by the Romans, the Jews' God was likewise captivated
by that of Rome: and Rabshakeh to the Israelites, no God should
deliver them out of the hands of the Assyrians. But these paradoxes of
their power, corporeity, mortality, taking of shapes, transposing bodies,
and carnal copulations, are sufficiently confuted by Zanchius, Pererius,
in his comment, and Tostatus, questions on the sixth of Genesis, Th.
Aquinas, S. Austin, Wierus, Th. Erastus, Delrio, Sebastian Michaelis,
Dr. Reinolds. They may deceive the eyes of men, yet not take true
bodies, or make a real metamorphosis: but, as Cicogna proves at large,
they are mere illusions and cozenings, like that tale of the Obol of
Pasetes,* in Suidas, or that of Autolycus, Mercury's son, that dwelt in
Parnassus, who got so much treasure by cozenage and stealth. His
father, Mercury, because he could leave him no wealth, taught him
many fine tricks to get means, for he could drive away men's cattle, and
if any pursued him, turn them into what shapes he would, and so did
mightily enrich himself. This no doubt is as true as the rest; yet thus
much in general, Thomas, Durand, and others, grant that they have
understanding far beyond men, can probably conjecture, and foretell
many things; they can cause and cure most diseases, deceive our senses;
they have excellent skill in all Arts and Sciences: and that the most illiterate Devil is more knowing than any man, as Cicogna maintains out
of others. They know the virtues of herbs, plants, stones, minerals, &c.
of all creatures, birds, beasts, the four elements, stars, planets; can aptly
apply and make use of them as they see good, perceiving the causes of

---

* Pasetes, or Pases, a juggler, had a magical obol which returned to his purse again
after it was spent.

all meteors, and the like. The devils give to themselves (as Austin hath it) any color, shape themselves to any form, blend into any sound, approximate any odor, impart themselves to a flavor; they deceive all our senses, even our understanding itself at once. They can produce miraculous alterations in the air, and most wonderful effects, conquer armies, give victories, help, further, hurt, cross and alter, human at‚ tempts and projects (by the permission of God) as they see good them- selves. When Charles the Great attempted to make a channel betwixt the Rhine and Danube, look what his workmen did in the day, these spirits flung down in the night, so that they made the King desist from his attempt. Such feats can they do. But that which Bodine thinks, (following Tyrius belike and the Platonists), [that] they can tell the secrets of a man's heart, is most false; his reasons are weak, and suffi- ciently confuted by Zanchius, Hierome, Athanasius, and others.

As for those orders of good & bad Devils, which the Platonists hold, [it] is altogether erroneous, & those Ethnicks' good & evil *Genii* are to be exploded. These heathen writers agree not in this point among them- selves, as Dandinus notes, some will have all spirits good or bad to us by a mistake; as if an ox or horse could discourse, he would say the butcher was his enemy because he kill'd him, the grazier his friend be- cause he fed him; an hunter preserves and yet kills his game, and is hated nevertheless of his game; nor can the fish love the fisherman, &c. But Iamblicus, Psellus, Plutarch, & most Platonists acknowledge bad, for they are enemies of man-kind, & this Plato learned in Egypt, that they quarrelled with Jupiter, and were driven by him down to hell. That which Apuleius, Xenophon, & Plato contend of Socrates' Daimon is most absurd: that which Plotinus of his, that he had likewise God as his Daimon: and that which Porphyry concludes of them all in general, if they be neglected in their sacrifice they are angry; nay more, as Cardan in his Hyperchen will, they feed on men's souls, the elements are food to the plants, plants to animals, animals to man, man to other beings, — not the gods, for their nature is far removed from ours, — wherefore to the Dæmonii: and so, belike, that we have so many battles fought in all ages, countries, is to make them a feast, and their sole delight. But to return to that I said before, if displeased, they fret and chafe, (for they feed, belike, on the souls of beasts, as we do on their bodies), & send many plagues amongst us; but, if pleased, they do much good; is as vain as the rest, & confuted by Austin, Eusebius, & others. Yet thus much I find, that our School-men & other Divines make 9 kinds of bad Spirits, as Dionysius hath done of Angels. In the first rank are those false gods of the Gentiles, which were adored heretofore in several Idols, and gave Oracles at Delphi, and elsewhere; whose Prince is Beelzebub. The second rank is of Liars, and Equivocators, as Apollo Pythius, and the like. The third are those vessels of anger, inventors of all mischief; as that Theuth in Plato; Esay calls them vessels of fury; their Prince is Belial. The fourth are malicious revenging Devils; and their Prince is Asmodæus. The fifth kind are cozeners, such as belong to Magicians and Witches; their Prince is Satan. The sixth are those aerial devils that corrupt the air, & cause plagues, thunders, fires, &c., spoken of in the Apocalypse, and Paul to the Ephesians names them the Princes of the air; Meresin is their Prince. The seventh is a destroyer, Captain of the Furies, causing wars, tumults, combustions, uproars, mentioned in the Apocalypse, and called Abaddon. The eighth is that accusing or calumniating Devil, whom the Greeks call Diabolos, that drives men to despair. The ninth are those tempters in several kinds, and their Prince is Mammon. Psellus makes six kinds, yet none above the Moon. Wierus, in his Pseudo-monarchy of Devils, out of an old book, makes many more divisions and subordinations, with their several names, numbers, offices, &c. but Gazæus cited by Lipsius will have all places full of Angels, Spirits, and Devils, above and beneath the Moon, æthereal and aerial, which Austin cites out of Varro. *The celestial Devils above, & aerial beneath,* or as some will, gods above, *Semidei* or half Gods beneath, *Lares, Heroes, Genii,* which climb higher, if they lived well, as the Stoicks held, but grovel on the ground as they were baser in their lives, nearer to the earth: & are *Manes, Lemures, Lamiæ,* &c. They will have no place void but all full of Spirits, Devils, or some other inhabitants, saith Gazæus; though Anthony Rusca in his book on the Inferno, would confine them to the middle Region, yet they will have them everywhere. Not so much as an hair breadth empty in heaven, earth, or waters, above or under the earth. The air is not so full of flies in summer, as it is at all times of invisible devils: this Paracelsus stiffly maintains, and that they have every one their several Chaos; others will have infinite worlds, and each world his peculiar Spirits, Gods, Angels, and Devils, to govern and punish it.

> *Some persons think that every star's a world,*
> *And call this earth of ours an obscure star,*
> *Presided over by the least of gods.* (PALINGENIUS)

Gregorius Tholosanus makes seven kinds of ætherial Spirits or Angels, according to the number of the seven Planets, Saturnine, Jovial, Martial, of which Cardan discourseth; he calls them prime substances, Trithemius calls them Olympian dæmons, who rule over the Zodiac, &c., and will have them to be good Angels above, Devils beneath the Moon, their several names and offices he there sets down, and, which Dionysius of Angels, will have several spirits for several countries, men, offices, &c. which live about them, & as so many assisting powers cause their operations; will have in a word innumerable, as many of them as there be stars in the skies. Marcilius Ficinus seems to second this opinion, out of Plato, or from himself, I know not, (still ruling their inferiors, as they do those under them again, all subordinate, and the nearest to the earth rule us, whom we subdivide into good and bad Angels, call Gods or Devils, as they help or hurt us, and so adore, love or hate), but it is most likely from Plato, for he relying wholly on Socrates, who (he writes) would rather die than tell a lie, out of Socrates' authority alone, made nine kinds of them: which opinion, belike, Socrates took from Pythagoras, & he from Trismegistus, he from Zoroaster, first God, secondly Ideas; 3. Intelligences, 4. Arch-Angels, 5. Angels, 6. Devils, 7. Heroes, 8. Principalities, 9. Princes: of which some were absolutely good, as Gods, some bad, some indifferent between gods and men, as heroes and daimons, which ruled men, and were called *genii,* or, as Proclus and Iamblicus will, the middle betwixt God and men, Principalities and Princes, which commanded & swayed Kings and countries, and had several places in the Spheres perhaps, for as every Sphere is higher, so hath it more excellent inhabitants: which, belike, is that Galileo (and Kepler) aims at in his Sidereal Messenger * when he will have Saturnine and Jovial inhabitants: and which Tycho Brahe doth in some sort touch or insinuate in one of his Epistles: but these things Zanchius justly explodes. So that, according to these men, the number of ætherial Spirits must needs be infinite: for if that be true that some of our Mathematicians say: if a stone could fall from the starry heaven, or eighth sphere, and should pass every hour an hundred miles, it would be 65 years, or more, before it would come to ground, by reason of the great distance of heaven from earth, which contains, as some say, 170 millions 803 miles, besides those other heavens, whether they be crystalline or watery, which Maginus adds, which peradventure hold as much more, how many such spirits may it contain? And yet for all this Thomas, Albertus, and most, hold that there be far more Angels than Devils.

But be they more or less, what is above us does not concern us.

* The Sidereal Messenger was Galileo's treatise announcing celestial novelties; Kepler wrote a friendly Discussion with the Sidereal Messenger.

Howsoever, as Martianus foolishly supposeth, they care not for us, do not attend our actions, or look for us, those ætherial spirits have other worlds to reign in, belike, or business to follow. We are only now to speak in brief of these sublunary Spirits or Devils: for the rest, our Divines determine that the Devil had no power over stars, or heavens. By their charms they can draw down the moon from the heavens, &c. Those are poetical fictions, and that they can stop rivers and turn back the stars in their courses, &c., &c., as Canidia in Horace, 'tis all false. They are confined until the day of judgement to this sublunary world, and can work no farther than the four elements, and as God permits them. Wherefore of these sublunary Devils, though others divide them otherwise according to their several places and offices, Psellus makes six kinds, fiery, aerial, terrestrial, watery, and subterranean Devils, besides those Fairies, Satyrs, Nymphs, &c.

Fiery Spirits or Devils are such as commonly work by blazing stars, firedrakes, or *ignes fatui;* which lead men often into rivers or precipices, saith Bodine, whom, if travellers wish to keep off, they must pronounce the name of God with a clear voice, or adore him with their faces prone on the ground; we owe this amulet to our ancestors, &c. Likewise they counterfeit suns and moons, stars oftentimes, and sit on ship masts; and are called Dioscuri, as Eusebius informeth us, out of the authority of Zenophanes; or little clouds, which fly into motion without the knowing; which never appear, saith Cardan, but they signify some mischief or other to come unto men; though some again will have them to pretend good, and victory to that side they come towards in sea-fights; St. Elmo's fires they commonly call them, & they do likely appear after a sea storm. Radzivilius, the Polonian Duke, calls this apparition the Heavenly Brothers; and saith moreover that he saw the same after, in a storm, as he was sailing, 1582, from Alexandria to Rhodes. Our stories are full of such apparitions in all kinds. Some think they keep their residence in that Hecla, a mountain in Iceland, Ætna in Sicily, Lipari, Vesuvius, &c. These Devils were worshipped heretofore by that superstitious Pyromanteia * and the like.

Aerial Spirits or Devils are such as keep quarter most part in the air, cause many tempests, thunder, and lightnings, tear oaks, fire steeples, houses, strike men and beasts, make it rain stones, as in Livy's time, wool, frogs, &c. counterfeit armies in the air, strange noises, swords, &c. as at Vienna, before the coming of the Turks, & many times in Rome, as Scheretzius, Lavater, Julius Obsequens, an old Roman, in

* Divination by fire.

his book of prodigies, Machiavel hath illustrated by many examples, and Josephus, in his book The Judaic Wars, before the destruction of Jerusalem. All which Guil. Postellus in his first book of the Harmony of the Sphere, useth as an effectual argument (as indeed it is) to persuade them that will not believe there be Spirits or Devils. They cause whirl-winds on a sudden, & tempestuous storms; which though our Meteor-ologists generally refer to natural causes, yet I am of Bodine's mind, they are more often caused by those aerial Devils, in their several quarters; for they show themselves in stormy weather, saith Rich. Ar-gentine; as when a desperate man makes away himself, which by hang-ing or drowning they frequently do, as Kornmannus observes, dancing and rejoicing at the death of a sinner. These can corrupt the air, and cause plagues, sickness, storms, shipwrecks, fires, inundations. At Mons Draconis in Italy, there is a most memorable example in Jovianus Pontanus: and nothing so familiar (if we may believe those rela-tions of Saxo Grammaticus, Olaus Magnus, Damianus a Goes) as for Witches and Sorcerers, in Lapland, Lithuania, and all over Scandia, to sell winds to mariners, and cause tempests, which Marco Polo the Venetian relates likewise of the Tartars. These kind of Devils much delighted in sacrifices, (saith Porphyry), held all the world in awe, and had several names, idols, sacrifices, in Rome, Greece, Egypt, and at this day tyrannize over, and deceive, those Ethnicks, and Indians, being adored and worshipped for Gods. For the Gentile Gods were Devils, (as Trismegistus confesseth in his Asclepius, and he himself could make them come to their images by magic spells) : and are now as much *respected by our Papists* (saith Pictorius) *under the name of Saints.* These are they which, Cardan thinks, desire so much carnal copulation with Witches, (*Incubi* and *Succubi*), transform bodies, and are so very cold, if they be touched; and that serve Magicians. His father had one of them (as he is not ashamed to relate) an aerial Devil, bound to him for twenty and eight years. As Agrippa's dog had a Devil tied to his collar; some think that Paracelsus (or else Erastus belies him) had one confined to his sword pummel; others wear them in rings, &c. Jannes and Jambres did many things of old by their help; Simon Magus, Cinops, Apollonius Tyanæus, Iamblicus & Trithemius of late, that showed Maximilian the Emperor his wife, after she was dead, (saith Godolman) so much as the wart on her neck. Delrio hath divers exam-ples of their feats; Cicogna, and Wierus, in his book on the Deceptions of Devils: Boissardus, on Magicians & Sorcerers.

Water-devils are those *Naiades* or Water-nymphs, which have been heretofore conversant about waters and rivers. The water (as Paracelsus thinks) is their Chaos, wherein they live; some call them Fairies and say that Habundia is their Queen; these cause inundations, many times shipwrecks, and deceive men divers ways, as *Succubae,* or otherwise, appearing most part, (saith Trithemius), in women's shapes. Paracelsus hath several stories of them that have lived and been married to mortal men, & so continued for certain years with them, and after, upon some dislike, have forsaken them. Such a one as Egeria, with whom Numa was so familiar, Diana, Ceres, &c. Olaus Magnus hath a long narration of one Hotherus, a King of Sweden, that, having lost his company, as he was hunting one day, met with these Water-nymphs or Fairies, and was feasted by them; and Hector Boethius of Macbeth and Banquo, two Scottish Lords, that, as they were wandering in the woods, had their fortunes told them by three strange women. To these heretofore they did use to sacrifice, by that hydromanteia, or divination by waters.

Terrestrial devils are those *Lares, Genii, Fauns, Satyrs,* Wood-nymphs, Foliots, Fairies, *Robin Goodfellows, Trolls,* &c. which as they are most conversant with men, so they do them most harm. Some think it was they alone that kept the heathen people in awe of old, and had so many idols and temples erected to them. Of this range was *Dagon* amongst the Philistines, *Bel* amongst the Babylonians, *Astarte* amongst the Sidonians, *Baal* amongst the Samaritans, *Isis* and *Osiris* amongst the Egyptians, &c. Some put our Fairies into this rank, which have been in former times adored with much superstition, with sweeping their houses, and setting of a pail of clean water, good victuals, and the like, and then they should not be pinched, but find money in their shoes, and be fortunate in their enterprizes. These are they that dance on heaths and greens, as Lavater thinks with Trithemius, &, as Olaus Magnus adds, leave that green circle, which we commonly find in plain fields, which others hold to proceed from a meteor falling, or some accidental rankness of the ground; so Nature sports herself. They are sometimes seen by old women and children. Hieronymus Pauli, in his description of the city of Bercino in Spain, relates how they have been familiarly seen near that town, about fountains & hills. At times they lead simple men into their mountain retreats, where they exhibit marvellous sights, saith Trithemius, and astonish their ears by the sound of bells, &c. Giraldus Cambrensis gives instance in a Monk of Wales that was so deluded. Paracelsus reckons up many places in Germany, where they do usually walk in little coats some two foot long. A bigger kind there is of them, called with us *Hobgoblins,* & *Robin Goodfellows,* that would in those superstitious times grind corn for a mess of milk, cut wood, or do any manner of drudgery work. They would mend old irons in those Æolian Isles of Lipari in former ages, and have been often seen and heard. Tholosanus calls them *Trollos* and *Getulos,* and saith that in his days they were common in many places of France. Dithmarus Bleskenius, in his description of Iceland, reports for a certainty, that almost in every family they have yet some such familiar spirits; & Felix Malleolus, in his book affirms as much, that these *Trolli,* or *Telchines,* are very common in Norway, *and seen to do drudgery work;* to draw water, saith Wierus, dress meat, or any such thing. Another sort of these there are, which frequent forlorn houses, which the Italians call *Foliots,* most part innoxious, Cardan holds. *They will make strange noises in the night, howl sometimes pitifully, and then laugh again, cause great flame and sudden lights, fling stones, rattle chains, shave men, open doors and shut them, fling down platters, stools, chests, sometimes appear in the likeness of hares, crows, black dogs, &c.,* of which read Pet. Thyræus the Jesuit, who will have them to be Devils, or the souls of damned men that seek revenge, or else souls out of Purgatory that seek ease. For such examples peruse Sigismundus Scheretzius, which he saith he took out of Luther most part; there be many instances. Pliny the Younger remembers such a house at Athens, which Athenodorus the Philosopher hired, which no man durst inhabit for fear of Devils. Austin relates as much of Hesperius the Tribune's house at Zubeda, near their city of Hippo, vexed with evil spirits, to his great hindrance, together with the affliction of his animals and slaves. Many such instances are to be read in Nider's Formicarius, &c. Whether I may call these *Ziim* and *Ochim,* which Isaiah speaks of, I make a doubt. See more of these in the said Scheretz; he is full of examples. These kind of Devils many times appear to men, and affright them out of their wits, sometimes walking at noon day, sometimes at nights, counterfeiting dead men's ghosts, as that of Caligula, which (saith Suetonius) was seen to walk in Lavinia's garden, where his body was buried, spirits haunted, and the house where he died; every night this happened, there was no quietness, till the house was burned. About Hecla in Iceland Ghosts commonly walk, saith Olaus [& others]. *Such sights are frequently seen,* saith Lavater, in Monasteries, and about church-yards, marshes, great buildings, solitary places, or places notorious because of some murder, &c. Thyræus adds, where some very dreadful crime has been committed, there the impious, and infamous, and grinders of the poor, generally dwell. These spirits often foretell men's deaths by several signs, as knocking, groanings, &c. though Rich. Argentine will ascribe these predictions to good Angels, out of the authority of Ficinus and others; prodigies frequently occur at the deaths of illustrious men, &c., as in the Lateran Church in Rome, the Popes' deaths are foretold by Sylvester's tomb. Near Rupes Nova in Finland, in the Kingdom of Sweden, there is a Lake, in which, before the Governor of the Castle dies, a *spectrum,* in the habit of Arion with his harp, appears, and makes excellent musick, like those blocks in Cheshire, which (they say) presage death to the master of the family; or that oak in Lanthadran Park in Cornwall, which foreshows as much. Many families in Europe are so put in mind of their last by such predictions, and many men are forewarned (if we may believe Paracelsus) by familiar spirits in divers shapes, as cocks, crows, owls, which often hover about sick men's chambers, even bringing torment to the dying, as Baracellus conjectures, & and so croak over the house of the sick because they smell a corse; or for that (as Bernardinus de Bustis thinketh) God permits the devil to appear in the form of crows, and such like creatures, to scare such as live wickedly here on earth. A little before Tully's death (saith Plutarch) the crows made a mighty noise about him, they pulled the pillow from under his head. Rob. Gaguinus telleth such another wonderful story at the death of Johannes de Montefort, a French Lord, in 1345; such a multitude of crows alighted on the house of the dying man, as no one imagined could have existed in all of France. Such prodigies are very frequent in authors. See more of these in the said Lavater, Thyræus, Pictorius, Delrio, Cicogna. Necromancers take upon them to raise and lay them at their pleasures. And so likewise those which Mizaldus calls *Ambulones,* that walk about midnight on great heaths and desert places, which (saith Lavater) *draw men out of the way, and lead them all night a by-way, or quite bar them of their way.* These have several names in several places; we commonly call them Pucks. In the desert of Lop in Asia, such illusions of walking spirits are often perceived, as you may read in Marco Polo the Venetian, his travels. If one lose his company by chance, these devils will call him by his name, and counterfeit voices of his companions to seduce him. Hieronymus Pauli, in his book of the hills of Spain, relates of a great mount in Cantabria, where such *spectrums* are to be seen. Lavater and Cicogna have variety of examples of spirits and walking devils in this kind. Sometimes they sit by the highway side, to give men falls, and make their horses stumble and start as they ride, if you will believe the relation of that holy man Ketellus, in Nubrigensis, that had an especiall grace to see devils, brought together by heavenly influence & talk with them, and mingle with them freely, without offence; & if a man curse or spur his horse for stumbling, they do heartily rejoice at it; with many such pretty feats.

Subterranean devils are as common as the rest, and do as much harm. Olaus Magnus makes six kinds of them, some bigger, some less. These (saith Munster) are commonly seen about mines of metals, and are some of them noxious, some again do no harm. The metal-men in many places count it good luck, a sign of treasure, and rich ore, when they see them. Georgius Agricola, in his book On Spirits of the Underworld, reckons two more notable kinds of them, which he calls *Gœtuli* and *Cobali*; both *are clothed after the manner of metal-men, and will many times imitate their works*. Their office, as Pictorius & Paracelsus think, is to keep treasure in the earth, that it be not all at once revealed; and, besides, Cicogna avers, that they are the frequent causes of those horrible earthquakes, *which often swallow up, not only houses, but whole islands and cities;* in his third book he gives many instances.

The last are conversant about the centre of the earth, to torture the souls of damned men to the Day of Judgement. Their egress and regress some suppose to be about Ætna, Lipari, Mons Hecla in Iceland, Vesuvius, Terra del Fuego, &c., because many shrieks and fearful cries are continually heard thereabouts, and familiar apparitions of dead men, Ghosts and Goblins.

Thus the Devil reigns, and in a thousand several shapes, as a roaring lion still seeks whom he may devour, by earth, sea, land, air, as yet unconfined, though some will have his proper place the air, all that space betwixt us & the Moon for them that transgressed least, & Hell for the wickedest of them; here, as though in prison to the end of the world, afterwards thrust into the place of doom, as Austin holds in The City Of God. But be [he] where he will, he rageth while he may to comfort himself, as Lactantius thinks, with other men's falls, he labours all he can to bring them into the same pit of perdition with him. For *men's miseries, calamities, and ruins, are the Devil's banqueting dishes.* By many temptations, and several engines, he seeks to captivate our souls. The Lord of lies, saith Austin, *as he was deceived himself, he seeks to deceive others,* the ring-leader to all naughtiness, as he did by Eve & Cain, Sodom and Gomorrah, so would he do by all the world. Sometimes he tempts by covetousness, drunkenness, pleasure, pride, &c., errs, dejects, saves, kills, protects, and rides some men, as they do their horses. He studies our overthrow, and generally seeks our destruction; and although he pretend many times human good, and vindicate himself for a God, by curing of several diseases, by restoring health to the sick and sight to the blind, as Austin declares, as Apollo, Æsculapius, Isis, of old have done; divert plagues, assist them in wars, pretend their happiness, yet nothing so impure, nothing so pernicious, as may well appear by their tyrannical and bloody sacrifices of men to Saturn and Moloch, which are still in use amongst those barbarous Indians, their several deceits and cozenings to keep men in obedience, their false oracles, sacrifices, their superstitious impositions of fasts, penury, &c., heresies, superstitious observations of meats, times, &c. by which they crucify the souls of mortal men, as shall be shewed in our Treatise of Religious Melancholy. As Bernard expresseth it, by God's permission he rageth a while, hereafter to be confined to hell and darkness, which is prepared for him and his Angels.

How far their power doth extend, it is hard to determine; what the Ancients held of their effects, force, and operations, I will briefly shew you. Plato in Critias, and after him his followers, gave out that these spirits or devils *were men's governors and keepers, our lords and masters, as we are of our cattle. They govern Provinces and Kingdoms by oracles, auguries,* dreams, rewards and punishments, prophecies, inspirations, sacrifices, and religious superstitions, varied in as many forms as there be diversity of spirits; they send wars, plagues, peace, sickness, health, dearth, plenty, standing near by us, observers & judges, &c., as appears by those histories of Thucydides, Livy, Dionysius Halicarnasseus, with many others that are full of their wonderful stratagems, and were therefore by those Roman and Greek Commonwealths adored and worshipped for gods, with prayers, and sacrifices, &c. In a word, they seek nothing more earnestly than the fear and admiration of mankind; and, as another hath it, It is scarce possible to describe the impotent ardour with which these malign spirits aspire to dominion over men and divine worship. Trithemius, in his book The Lucky Seven, assigns names to such Angels as are Governors of particular Provinces, by what authority I know not, and gives them several jurisdictions. Asclepiades a Grecian, Rabbi Achiba the Jew, Abraham Avenezra, and Rabbi Azariel, Arabians, (as I find them cited by Cicogna) farther add, that they are not our Governors only, but as they agree, so do we and our Princes, or disagree, stand or fall. Juno was a bitter enemy to Troy, Apollo a good friend, Jupiter indifferent, Venus was favorable. Pallas unfavorable; some are for us still, some against us. Religion, policy, publick and private quarrels, wars are procured by them, and they are delighted perhaps to see men fight, as men are with cocks, bulls and dogs, bears, &c. Plagues, dearths, depend on them, our good and evil moods, and almost all our other peculiar actions, (for, as Anthony Rusca contends, every man hath a good and a bad Angel attending of him in particular all his life long, which Iamblicus calls a daimon), preferments, losses, weddings, deaths, rewards, and punishments, and, as Proclus will, all offices whatsoever, motherhood to one, artizanship to another, &c., and several names they give them according to their offices, as *Lares, Indigetes, Præstites, &c.* When the Arcades in that battle at Chæronea, which was fought against King Philip for the liberty of Greece, had deceitfully carried themselves, long after, in the very same place, the gods of Greece being avengers (saith mine Author) they were miserably slain by Metellus the Roman: so likewise, in smaller matters, they will have things fall out, as these good and evil *Genii* favour or dislike us. He that is *Saturnine* shall never likely be preferred. That base fellows are often advanced, undeserving Gnathos,* and vicious parasites, when as discreet, wise, virtuous, and worthy men are neglected, and unrewarded, they refer to those domineering spirits, or subordinate *Genii;* as they are inclined, or favour men, so they thrive, are ruled & overcome, for, as Libanius supposeth, in our ordinary conflicts and contentions, one Genius yields and is overcome by another. All particular events almost they refer to these private spirits; & (as Paracelsus adds) they direct, teach, inspire, and instruct men. Never was any man extraordinarily famous in any art, action, or great commander, that had not a familiar to inform him, as Numa, Socrates, and many such, as Cardan illustrates (Secrets of Statesmanship). The magi say (Boissardus), as a special favour from God, they are instructed and taught by the heavenly spirits. But these are most erroneous paradoxes, stupid and fabulous trifles, rejected by our Divines & Christian Churches. 'Tis true they have, by God's permission, power over us, and we find by experience that they can hurt not our fields only, cattle, goods, but our bodies and minds. At Hammel in Saxony, on the 20th of June, 1484, the Devil, in the likeness of a pied piper, carried away 130 children, that were never after seen. Many times men are affrighted out of their wits, carried away quite, as Scheretzius illustrates, and severally molested by his means. Plotinus the Platonist laughs them to scorn that hold the Devil or Spirits can cause any such diseases. Many think he can work upon the body, but not upon the mind.

---

* Gnatho was a parasite in a play of Terence.

But experience pronounceth otherwise, that he can work both upon body and mind. Tertullian is of this opinion, that he can cause both sickness and health, and that secretly. Taurellus adds, by clancular * poisons he can infect the bodies, & hinder the operations of the bowels, though we perceive it not, closely creeping into them, saith Lipsius, & so crucify our souls, and drive people mad by grievous melancholy. For being a spiritual body, he struggles with our spirits, saith Rogers, and suggests (according to Cardan), words without a voice, apparitions without sight, envy, lust, anger, &c., as he sees men inclined.

The manner how he performs it, Biarmannus, in his Oration against Bodine, sufficiently declares. *He begins first with the phantasy, & moves that so strongly, that no reason is able to resist.* Now he moves the *phantasy* by mediation of humours; although many Physicians are of opinion, that the Devil can alter the mind, and produce this disease of himself. Of the same mind is Psellus, & Rhasis the Arab, *that this disease proceeds especially from the Devil, & from him alone.* Arculanus, Ælianus Montaltus, Daniel Sennertus, confirm as much, that the Devil can cause this disease; by reason many times that the parties affected prophesy, speak strange language, but not without the humour, as he interprets himself; no more doth Avicenna, if contaminated by a dæmon it is enough for us that it tends the whole system towards black bile; the immediate cause is choler adust, which Pomponatius likewise labours to make good: Galgerandus of Mantua, a famous Physician, so cured a dæmoniacal woman in his time, that spake all languages, by purging black choler; and thereupon belike this humour of Melancholy is called the Devil's Bath; the Devil, spying his opportunity of such humours, drives them many times to despair, fury, rage, &c., mingling himself amongst these humours. This is that which Tertullian avers, they inflict shrewd and sudden turns on body and mind, and distort limbs, making their attack by stealth, &c., and which Lemnius goes about to prove, the bad Genii mix themselves with depraved humours and black bile, &c., and Jason Pratensis, *that the Devil, being a slender incomprehensible spirit, can easily insinuate and wind himself into human bodies, and, cunningly couched in our bowels, vitiate our healths, terrify our souls with fearful dreams, and shake our mind with furies.* And in another place, *These unclean spirits settled in our bodies, and now mixed with our melancholy humours, do triumph as it were, and sport themselves as in another heaven.* Thus he argues, and that they go in and out of our bodies, as bees do in a hive, and so

* Secret.

provoke and tempt us, as they perceive our temperature inclined of it-self, and most apt to be deluded. Agrippa and Lavater are persuaded, that this humour invites the Devil to it, wheresoever it is in extremity, and, of all other, melancholy persons are most subject to diabolical temp-tations and illusions, and most apt to entertain them, and the Devil best able to work upon them; but whether by obsession, or possession, or otherwise, I will not determine; 'tis a difficult question. Delrio the Jesuit, Springer and his colleague, Thyreus the Jesuit, Hieronymus Men-gus, and others of that rank of pontifical writers, it seems, by their exor-cisms and conjurations approve of it, having forged many stories to that purpose. A nun did eat a lettuce *without grace, or without signing with the sign of the cross,* and was instantly possessed. Durand relates that he saw a wench possessed in Bononia with two devils, by eating an unhallowed pomegranate, as she did afterwards confess, when she was cured by exorcisms. And therefore our papists do sign themselves so often with the sign of the cross, that the demon dare not enter, and ex-orcise all manner of meats, as being unclean or accursed otherwise, as Bellarmine defends. Many such stories I find amongst pontifical writ-ers, to prove their assertions; let them free their own credits; some few I will recite in this kind out of most approved Physicians. Cornelius Gemma relates of a young maid, called Katherine Gualter, a cooper's daughter, in the year 1571, that had such strange passions and convul-sions, three men could not sometimes hold her; she purged a live eel, which he saw, a foot and a half long, and touched himself, but the eel afterwards vanished; she vomited some 24 pounds of fulsome stuff of all colours twice a day for 14 days; and after that she voided great balls of hair, pieces of wood, pigeons' dung, parchment, goose dung, coals; and after them two pounds of pure blood, and then again coals and stones, of which some had inscriptions, bigger than a walnut, some of them pieces of glass, brass, &c., besides paroxysms of laughing, weep-ing and ecstasies, &c. And this (he says), I saw with horror. They could do no good on her by physick, but left her to the Clergy. Marcellus Donatus hath such another story of a country fellow, that had four knives in his belly, indented like a saw, every one a span long, with a wreath of hair like a globe, with much baggage of like sort, wonderful to behold. How it should come into his guts, he concludes, could only have been through the artifice and craft of a dæmon. Langius hath many relations to this effect, and so hath Christopherus à Vega. Wierus, Sckenkius, Scribonius, all agree that they are done by the subtility and illusion of the Devil. If you shall ask a reason of this, 'tis to exercise our patience; for, as Tertullian holds, virtue is not virtue unless it has a foe by the conquering of which it shows its merit; 'tis to try us and our faith, 'tis for our offences, and for the punishment of our sins, by God's permission they do it, executioners of his will, as Tolosanus styles them; or rather as David, He cast upon them the fierceness of his anger, indignation, wrath, and vexation, by sending out of evil Angels. So did he afflict Job, Saul, the lunaticks and dæmoniacal persons whom Christ cured. This, I say, happeneth for a punishment of sin, for their want of faith, incredulity, weakness, distrust, &c.

SUBSECTION 3 — *Of Witches and Magicians, how they cause Melancholy*

You have heard what the Devil can do of himself, now you shall hear what he can perform by his instruments, who are many times worse (if it be possible) than he himself, and to satisfy their revenge and lust cause more mischief. Much harm had never been done, as Erastus thinks, had he not been provoked by Witches to it. He had not appeared in Samuel's shape, if the Witch of Endor had let him alone; or represented those Serpents in Pharaoh's presence, had not the Magicians urged him unto it: men and cattle might go free (Erastus maintains), if the Witches would let him alone. Many deny Witches at all, or, if there be any, they can do no harm. Of this opinion is Wierus, Austin Lerchemer, a Dutch writer, Biarmannus, Ewichius, Euwaldus, our countryman Scot; with him in Horace,

> *Dreams, magic terrors, miracles, and witches,*
> *And nightly spectres, and Thessalian portents,*
> *All these they laugh at.*

They laugh at all such stories; but on the contrary are most Lawyers, Divines, Physicians, Philosophers, Austin, Hemingius, Danæus, Chytræus, Zanchius, Aretius, &c., Delrio, Springer, Niderius, Cuiatius, Bartolus, Bodine, Godelman, Damhoderius, &c., Paracelsus, Erastus, Scribanius, Camerarius, &c. The parties by whom the Devil deals, may be reduced to these two, such as command him in shew at least, as Conjurers, and Magicians, whose detestable and horrid mysteries are contained in their book called *Arbatell;* for the demons appear when invoked, and suffer themselves to be, as it were, compelled by exorcisms & conjurations, that they may keep the wretched race of magi in their impiety; or such as are commanded, as Witches, that deal on the one part intricately, on the other clearly, as the King * hath well defined.

* James I., in his Daemonologie (1599).

Many subdivisions there are, & many several species of Sorcerers, Witches, Enchanters, Charmers, &c. They have been tolerated heretofore some of them; and Magick hath been publickly professed in former times, in Salamanca, Cracovia, and other places, though after censured by several Universities, and now generally contradicted, though practised by some still, maintained and excused, as a secret thing, so to say, imparted by heavenly favour for the special instruction of great men (I use Boissardus his words): and so far approved by some Princes, that they attempt nothing in politicks, religion, nor indeed in the making of any plan without their counsel; they consult still with them, and dare indeed do nothing without their advice. Nero & Heliogabalus, Maxentius, & Julian the Apostate, were never so much addicted to Magick of old, as some of our modern Princes and Popes themselves are nowadays. Erricus, King of Sweden, had an enchanted Cap, by virtue of which, and some magical murmur or whispering terms, he could command spirits, trouble the air, and make the wind stand which way he would; insomuch that when there was any great wind or storm, the common people were wont to say, the King now had on his conjuring Cap. But such examples are infinite. That which they can do, is as much almost as the Devil himself, who is still ready to satisfy their desires, to oblige them the more unto him. They can cause tempests, storms, which is familiarly practised by Witches in Norway, Iceland, as I have proved. They can make friends enemies, and enemies friends, by philters; enforce love, tell any man where his friends are, about what employed, though in the most remote places; and, if they will, *bring their sweethearts to them by night, upon a goat's back flying in the air,* (Sigismund Scheretzius reports confidently, that he conferred with sundry such, that had been so carried many miles, and that he heard Witches themselves confess as much); hurt, and infect men and beasts, vines, corn, cattle, plants, make women abortive, not to conceive, *barren,* men and women unapt and *unable,* married and unmarried, fifty several ways, saith Bodine, fly in the air, meet when and where they will, as Cicogna proves, and Lavater; *steal young children out of their cradles,* through the aid of demons, *and put deformed in their rooms, which we call changelings,* saith Scheretzius, make men victorious, fortunate, eloquent; and therefore in those ancient monomachies and combats they were searched of old, they had no magical charms; they can make stick-frees,* such as shall endure a rapier's point, musket shot, and never be

* "Stab-frees," persons free from possibility of wound.

wounded: of which read more in Boissardus, the manner of the adjuration, and by whom 'tis made, where and how to be used in warlike expeditions, and in wars, &c., with many peculiar instances and examples; they can walk in fiery furnaces, make men feel no pain on the rack, nor any other tortures; they can stanch blood, represent dead men's shapes, alter and turn themselves and others into several forms at their pleasures. Agaberta, a famous Witch in Lapland, would do as much publickly to all spectators, now young, now old, high, low, like a cow, like a bird, a snake, and what not? She could represent to others what forms they most desired to see, shew them friends absent, reveal secrets, to the greatest wonder of everybody, &c. And yet for all this subtilty of theirs, as Lipsius well observes, neither these Magicians nor Devils themselves can take away gold or letters out of mine or Crassus' chest, and give them to their clients, for they are base, poor, contemptible, fellows most part. As Bodine notes, they can do nothing, they cannot give money to their Clients, alter Judges' decrees, or Councels of Kings, these petty Genii cannot do it; the higher powers reserve these things to themselves. Now and then peradventure there may be some more famous Magicians, like Simon Magus, Apollonius Tyanæus, Pases,* Iamblicus, Eudo de Stellis, that for a time can build castles in the air, represent armies, &c., as they are said to have done, command wealth and treasure, feed thousands with all variety of meats upon a sudden, protect themselves and their followers from all Princes' persecutions, by removing from place to place in an instant, reveal secrets, future events, tell what is done in far countries, make them appear that died long since, &c., and do many such miracles, to the world's terror, admiration, and opinion of Deity to themselves; yet the Devil forsakes them at last, they come to wicked ends, and seldom or never such Impostors are to be found. The vulgar sort of them can work no such feats. But to my purpose, they can, last of all, cure and cause most diseases to such as they love or hate, and this of *Melancholy* amongst the rest. Paracelsus in express words affirms: many are bewitched into melancholy, out of his experience. The same, saith Danæus: I have seen those that have caused melancholy in the most grievous manner, *dried up women's paps, cured gout, palsy, this and apoplexy, falling sickness, which no physick could help,* by touch alone. Ruland gives an instance

* Pases, or Pasetes, in addition to his famous obol which after being spent returned again to his purse, had other magical tricks. Cornelius Agrippa's Vanity of the Arts and Sciences (edition of 1676) says that he " was wont to shew a great Banquet to an abundance of guests sitting thereat, which when he pleas'd he caused to vanish again out of sight, leaving all the Guests adry and hungry."

of one David Helde, a young man, who, by eating cakes which a Witch gave him, began to dote on a sudden, and was instantly mad. F. H. D. in Hildesheim, consulted about a melancholy man, thought his disease was partly magical and partly natural, because he vomited pieces of iron and lead, and spake such languages as he had never been taught; but such examples are common in Scribanius, Hercules de Saxonia, and others. The means by which they work, are usually charms, images, as that in Hector Boethius of King Duff; characters stamped of sundry metals, and at such and such constellations, knots, amulets, words, philters, &c. which generally make the parties affected melancholy; as Monavius discourseth at large in an Epistle of his to Scoltzius, giving instance in a Bohemian Baron that was so troubled by a philter taken. Not that there is any power at all in those spells, charms, characters, and barbarous words; but that the Devil doth use such means to delude them; that he may so keep the faithful magi (saith Libanius) to their duty, and also call them to the aid of malefactors.

SUBSECTION 4 — *Stars a cause. Signs from Physiognomy, Metoposcopy, Chiromancy*

Natural causes are either *primary* and *universal,* or *secondary* and more *particular. Primary* causes are the heavens, planets, stars, &c. by their influence (as our Astrologers hold) producing this and such like effects. I will not here stand to discuss by the way, whether stars be causes, or signs; or to apologize for judicial Astrology. If either Sextus Empiricus, Picus Mirandula, Sextus ab Heminga, Pererius, Erastus, Chambers, &c., have so far prevailed with any man, that he will attribute no virtue at all to the heavens, or to sun or moon, more than he doth to their signs at an inn-keeper's post, or tradesman's shop, or generally condemn all such Astrological Aphorisms approved by experience: I refer him to Bellantius, Pirovanus, Marascallerus, Goclenius, Sir Christopher Heydon, &c. If thou shalt ask me what I think, I must answer, for I too am conversant with these learned errors, they do incline but not compel; no necessity at all, they lead, not drive: and so gently incline, that a wise man may resist them; the wise man will rule his stars: they rule us, but God rules them. All this (methinks) Joh. de Indagine hath comprised in brief. *Wilt thou know how far the stars work upon us? I say they do but incline, & that so gently, that if we will be ruled by reason, they have no power over us; but if we follow our own nature, and be led by sense, they do as much in us as in brute beasts, and we are no better.* So that, I hope, I may justly conclude with

Cajetan that the heaven is God's instrument, by mediation of which he governs and disposeth these elementary bodies; or a great book, whose letters are the stars, (as one calls it) wherein are written many strange things for such as can read, *or an excellent harp, made by an eminent workman, on which he that can but play will make most admirable musick.* But to the purpose.

Paracelsus is of opinion, *that a Physician without the knowledge of stars can neither understand the cause or cure of any disease, either of this, or gout, nor so much as tooth-ache; except he see the peculiar geniture and scheme of the party affected.* And for this proper malady, he will have the principal and primary cause of it proceed from the heaven, ascribing more to stars than humours, *and that the constellation alone many times produceth melancholy, all other causes set apart.* He gives instance in lunatick persons, that are deprived of their wits by the moon's motion, and in another place refers all to the ascendant, and will have the true and chief cause of it to be sought from the stars. Neither is it his opinion only, but of many Galenists and Philosophers, though they not so stiffly and peremptorily maintain as much. *This variety of melancholy symptoms proceeds from the stars,* saith Melancthon: the most generous melancholy, as that of Augustus, comes from the conjunction of Saturn & Jupiter in Libra: the bad, as that of Catiline's, from the meeting of Saturn and the Moon in Scorpio. Jovianus Pontanus discourseth to this purpose at large; *many diseases proceed from black choler, as it shall be hot or cold; & though it be cold in its own nature, yet it is apt to be heated, as water may be made to boil, and burn as bad as fire, or made cold as ice: and thence proceed such variety of symptoms, some mad, some solitary, some laugh, some rage, &c.,* the cause of all which intemperance he will have chiefly and primarily proceed from the heavens: *from the position of Mars, Saturn, and Mercury.* His Aphorisms be these: *Mercury in any geniture, if he shall be found in Virgo, or Pisces his opposite sign, & that in the horoscope, irradiated by those quartile aspects of Saturn or Mars, the child shall be mad or melancholy.* Again, *He that shall have Saturn or Mars, the one culminating, the other in the 4th house, when he shall be born, shall be melancholy, of which he shall be cured in time, if Mercury behold them. If the Moon be in conjunction or opposition at the birth time with the Sun, Saturn or Mars, or in a quartile aspect with them* (from a bad quarter of heaven, Leovitius adds), *many diseases are signified, especially the head and brain is like to be mis-affected with pernicious humours, to be melancholy,* *lunatick, or mad ;* Cardan adds, begotten during the lunar [menstruous] quarter [of the month], [or during] eclipses, [or] earthquakes. Garcæus and Leovitius will have the chief judgement to be taken from the Lord of the geniture, or when there is an aspect betwixt the Moon and Mercury, and neither behold the horoscope, or Saturn and Mars shall be Lord of the present conjunction or opposition in Sagittary or Pisces, of the Sun or Moon, such persons are commonly epileptick, dote, dæmoniacal, melancholy. but see more of these Aphorisms in the above-named Pontanus, Garcæus, Schoner, which he hath gathered out of Ptolemy, Albubater, and some other Arabians, Junctine, Ranzovius, Lindhout, Origan, &c. But these men you will reject peradventure, as Astrologers, and therefore partial judges ; then hear the testimony of Physicians, Galenists themselves. Crato confesseth the influence of stars to have a great hand to this peculiar disease, so doth Jason Pratensis, Lonicerus, Ficinus, Fernelius, &c. P. Cnemander acknowledgeth the stars an universal cause, the particular from parents, and the use of the six non-natural things. Baptista Porta will have them causes to every particular iota. Instances and examples, to evince the truth of those Aphorisms, are common amongst those Astrologian Treatises. Cardan in his 37th geniture, gives instance of Daniel Gare, and others ; but see Garcæus, Gauricus, &c. The time of this melancholy is, when the significators of any geniture are directed according to art, as the horoscope,* moon, hylech, &c., to the hostile beams or terms of ♄ [Saturn] and ♂ [Mars] especially, or any fixed star of their nature, or if ♄ by his revolution or transit, shall offend any of those radical promissors in the geniture.

Other signs there are taken from Physiognomy, Metoposcopy, Chiromancy, which because John de Indagine, and Rotman, the Landgrave of Hesse his Mathematician, not long since in his Chiromancy, Baptista Porta, in his Celestial Physiognomy, have proved to hold great affinity with Astrology, to satisfy the curious, I am the more willing to insert.

The general notions Physiognomers give, be these ; *black colour argues natural melancholy: so doth leanness, hirsuteness, broad veins, much hair on the brows,* saith Gratarolus, and a little head, out of Aristotle ; high, sanguine, red colour, shews head melancholy ; they that stutter and are bald will be soonest melancholy, (as Avicenna supposeth) by reason of the dryness of their brains. But he that will know

* The horoscope, in Astrology, is that sign of the Zodiac which at the instant of nativity is in the ascendant, or at the eastern horizon. Hylach (or hyleg) is the planet ruling that sign.

more of the several signs of humours and wits out of Physiognomy, let him consult with old Adamantus and Polemus, that comment, or rather paraphrase, upon Aristotle's Physiognomy, Baptista Porta's four pleasant books, Michael Scot's The Secrets of Nature, John de Indagine, Montaltus, Antony Zara's Anatomy of Wit and Wisdom.

Chiromancy hath these Aphorisms to foretell melancholy. Taisnier, who hath comprehended the sum of John de Indagine, Tricassus, Corvinus, and others, in this book, thus hath it; *The Saturnine line going from the rascetta through the hand to Saturn's mount, and there intersected by certain little lines, argues melancholy; so if the vital and natural make an acute angle, Aphorism 100. The Saturnine, hepatick and natural lines, making a gross triangle in the hand, argue as much;* which Goclenius repeats *verbatim* out of him. In general they conclude all, that, if Saturn's mount be full of many small lines and intersections, *such men are most part melancholy, miserable, and full of disquietness, care and trouble, continually vexed with anxious and bitter thoughts, alway sorrowful, fearful, suspicious; they delight in husbandry, buildings, pools, marshes, springs, woods, walks, &c.* Thaddæus Haggesius, in his Metoposcopia, hath certain Aphorisms derived from Saturn's lines in the fore-head by which he collects a melancholy disposition; and Baptista Porta makes observations from those other parts of the body, as if a spot be over the spleen; *or in the nails, if it appear black, it signifieth much care, grief, contention, and melancholy;* the reason he refers to the humours, and gives instance in himself, that for seven years' space he had such black spots in his nails, and all that while was in perpetual law-suits, controversies for his inheritance, fears, loss of honour, banishment, grief, care, &c., and when his miseries ended, the black spots vanished. Cardan, in his book on his own books, tells such a story of his own person, that a little before his son's death he had a black spot, which appeared in one of his nails, and dilated itself as he came near to his end. But I am over tedious in these toys, which howsoever, in some men's too severe censures, they may be held absurd and ridiculous, I am the bolder to insert, as not borrowed from circumforanean Rogues and Gipsies, but out of the writings of worthy Philosophers and Physicians, yet living some of them, and religious Professors in famous Universities, who are able to patronize that which they have said, and vindicate themselves from all cavillers and ignorant persons.

SUBSECTION 5 — *Old age a cause*

SECONDARY peculiar causes efficient, so called in respect of the other precedent, are either congenite, as they term them, inward, innate, in-bred; or else outward and adventitious, which happen to us after we are born: congenite, or born with us, are either natural, as old age, or præternatural (as Fernelius calls it) that distemperature which we have from our parents' seed, it being an hereditary disease. The first of these, which is natural to all, and which no man living can avoid, is old age, which being cold and dry, and of the same quality as Melancholy is, must needs cause it, by diminution of spirits and substance, and increasing of adust humours. Therefore Melancthon avers out of Aristotle, as an undoubted truth that old men familiarly dote, because of black choler, which is then superabundant in them: and Rhasis, that Arabian Physician, calls it *a necessary and inseparable accident* to all old & decrepit persons. *After 70 years* (as the Psalmist saith) *all is trouble and sorrow;* and common experience confirms the truth of it in weak and old persons, especially in such as have lived in action all their lives, had great employment, much business, much command, and many servants to oversee, and leave off as Charles the Fifth did to King Philip, resign up all on a sudden. They are overcome with melancholy in an instant: or, if they do continue in such courses, they dote at last, (an old man is twice a boy), and are not able to manage their estates through common infirmities incident in their age; full of ache, sorrow, and grief, children again, dizzards, they carle * many times as they sit, and talk to themselves, they are angry, waspish, displeased with every thing, *suspicious of all, wayward, covetous, hard,* (saith Tully) *self-willed, superstitious, self-conceited, braggers, & admirers of themselves,* as Balthasar Castalio hath truly noted of them. This natural infirmity is most eminent in old women, and such as are poor, solitary, live in most base esteem and beggary, or such as are witches; insomuch that Wierus, Baptista Porta, Ulricus Molitor, Edwicus, do refer all that witches are said to do to imagination alone, and this humour of melancholy. And whereas it is controverted, whether they can bewitch cattle to death, ride in the air upon a coulstaff out of a chimney-top, transform themselves into cats, dogs, &c., translate bodies from place to place, meet in companies, and dance, as they do, or have carnal copulation with the Devil, they ascribe all to this redundant melancholy which domineers in them, to somniferous potions, and natural causes, the

* Act like a churl.

Devil's policy. They do no such wonders at all (saith Wierus), only their brains are crazed. *They think they are Witches and can do hurt, but do not.* But this opinion Bodine, Erastus, Danæus, Scribanius, Sebastian Michaelis, Campanella, & Dandinus the Jesuit, explode; Cicogna confutes at large. That Witches are melancholy they deny not, but not out of corrupt phantasy alone, so to delude themselves and others, or to produce such effects.

SUBSECTION 6 — *Parents a cause by propagation*

THAT other inward inbred cause of Melancholy is our temperature, in whole or part, which we receive from our parents, which Fernelius calls unnatural, it being an hereditary disease; for as he justifies, such as the temperature of the father is, such is the son's, and look what disease the father had when he begot him, his son will have after him, *and is as well inheritor of his infirmities as of his lands. And where the complexion and constitution of the father is corrupt, there* (saith Roger Bacon) *the complexion and constitution of the son must needs be corrupt, and so the corruption is derived from the father to the son.* Now this doth not so much appear in the composition of the body, according to that of Hippocrates, *in habit, proportion, scars, and other lineaments, but in manners and conditions of the mind,* the habits of the fathers go forth with the children. Seleucus had an anchor on his thigh, so had his posterity, as Trogus records, Lepidus in Pliny was purblind, so was his son. That famous family of Ænobarbi were known of old, and so surnamed, from their red beards. The Austrian lip, and those Indians' flat noses are propagated, the Bavarian chin, and goggle eyes amongst the Jews, as Buxtorfius observes. Their voice, pace, gesture, looks, is likewise derived with all the rest of their conditions & infirmities; such a mother, such a daughter; their very affections Lemnius *contends to follow their seed, and the malice and bad conditions of children are many times wholly to be imputed to their parents.* I need not therefore make any doubt of Melancholy, but that it is an hereditary disease. Paracelsus in express words affirms it; so doth Crato in an Epistle of his to Monavius. So doth Bruno Seidelius in his book On Incurable Diseases. Montaltus proves, out of Hippocrates and Plutarch, that such hereditary dispositions are frequent, & he says, (speaking of a patient), I think he became so by participation of Melancholy. Daniel Sennertus will have his melancholy constitution derived not only from the father to the son, but to the whole family sometimes. Forestus, in his medicinal observations, illustrates this point, with an example of a merchant his patient, that had this infirmity by inheritance; so doth Rodericus à Fonseca, by an instance of a young man that was so affected from a melancholy mother, and bad diet together. Lodovicus Mercatus, a Spanish Physician, in that excellent tract which he hath lately written of hereditary diseases, reckons up leprosy, as those Galbots in Gascony, hereditary lepers, pox, stone, gout, epilepsy, &c. Amongst the rest, this and madness after a set time comes to many, which he calls a miraculous thing in nature, and sticks for ever to them as an incurable habit. And that which is more to be wondered at, it skips in some families the father, and goes to the son, *or takes every other, & sometimes every third in a lineal descent, and doth not always produce the same, but some like, and a symbolizing disease.* These secondary causes hence derived are commonly so powerful, that (as Wolfius holds) they do often alter the primary causes, and decrees of the heavens. For these reasons belike the Church and Commonwealth, human and divine laws, have conspired to avoid hereditary diseases, forbidding such marriages as are any whit allied; and as Mercatus adviseth all families to take such, if possible, as are most distant by nature, and to make choice of those that are most differing in complexion from them, if they love their own, and respect the common good. And sure, I think, it hath been ordered by God's especial providence, that in all ages there should be (as usually there is) once in 600 years a transmigration of Nations, to amend and purify their blood, as we alter seed upon our land, and that there should be as it were an inundation of those Northern Goths and Vandals, and many such like people which came out of that continent of Scandia, and Sarmatia (as some suppose) and overran, as a deluge, most part of Europe and Africa, to alter for our good our complexions, which were much defaced with hereditary infirmities, which by our lust and intemperance we had contracted. A sound generation of strong and able men were sent amongst us, as those Northern men usually are, innocuous, free from riot, and free from diseases; to qualify and make us as those poor naked Indians are generally at this day, and those about Brazil (as a late Writer observes) in the Isle of Maragnan, free from all hereditary diseases, or other contagion, whereas without help of physick they live commonly 120 years or more, of temperance and intemperance, but I will descend to particulars, and as in the Orcades and many other places. Such are the common effects shew by what means, and by whom especially, this infirmity is derived unto us.

Old men's children are seldom of a good temperament, as Scoltzius

supposeth, and therefore most apt to this disease; and, as Levinus Lemnius farther adds, old men beget most part wayward, peevish, sad, melancholy sons, and seldom merry. He that begets a child on a full stomack, will either have a sick child or a crazed son (as Cardan thinks), or if the parents be sick, or have any great pain of the head, or megrim, headache, (Hieronymus Wolfius doth instance in a child of Sebastian Castalio's), or if a drunken man get a child, it will never likely have a good brain, as Gellius argues. One drunkard begets another, saith Plutarch, whose sentence Lemnius approves, [so] Alsarius Crutius, Macrobius, Avicenna, and Aristotle himself. Foolish, drunken, or hare-brain women most part bring forth children like unto themselves, morose & languid, and so likewise he that lies with a menstruous woman. Excessive venery, which Lemnius especially condemneth in sailors, who enter in unto their wives without regard to this, and without observing the interlunary period, is a principal cause of great injury (Roderick Castro, the Spaniard, calls such congress pestiferous & deadly, and that it is detested by all medical men), and, moreover, those luckless ones begotten at this period of lunar influence are commonly mad, doting, stupid, ailing, filthy, impotent, plague-ridden, of the lowest vitality, & robbed of all strength of mind and body; born to labour, though lords themselves, saith Eustathius, as were Hercules & others. The Jews bitterly inveigh against this foul and filthy coupling amongst Christians; they abhor it as unlawful, and prohibit it amongst their own people. And because Christians so often are leprous, raving, debilitated, scabby, since there are so many diseases, white spots, itch, skin and facial blotches, so many contagious pestilences, painful and malignant, they charge it to this impure intercourse, and call those men bloody in their pledges, who, when the impurity of the month is discharging, do not abhor coupling. 'Twas once condemned by Divine Law, men of this habit punished by death; the father stoned, if children were deformed, for that he kept not himself from an unclean woman. Gregory the Great, when Augustine of Canterbury asked whether he should tolerate intercourse of this kind among the Britons, strictly forbade his men to copulate with women during their menstrual periods.*
Another cause some give, inordinate diet, as if a man eat garlick, onions,

---

* Burton has a footnote to this long Latin passage which runs: " Good Master Schoolmaster, do not English this," and then, at the end of the passage, " I spare to English this which I have said." The editors, therefore, feel some reluctance in doing what was against Burton's own desire; but they feel that what might have seemed blushworthy to a frocked bachelor of the Seventeenth Century is but a commonplace in this day of psycho-analytic literature.

fast overmuch, study too hard, be over-sorrowful, dull, heavy, dejected in mind, perplexed in his thoughts, fearful, &c., *their children* (saith Cardan) *will be much subject to madness & melancholy; for if the spirits of the brain be fusled or misaffected by such means at such a time, their children will be fusled in the brain; they will be dull, heavy, timorous, discontented, all their lives.* Some are of opinion and maintain that paradox, or problem, that wise men beget commonly fools; Suidas gives instance in Aristarchus the Grammarian, that he left two sons, Aristarchus and Aristachorus, both fools; &, which Erasmus urgeth in his Moria, fools beget wise men. Cardan gives this cause, because their natural spirits are resolved by study, and turned into animal; drawn from the heart, and those other parts to the brain. Lemnius subscribes to that of Cardan, and assigns this reason, they pay their debt (as Paul calls it) to their wives remissly, by which means their children are weaklings, and many times idiots and fools.

Some other causes are given, which properly pertain, and do proceed from the mother. If she be over-dull, heavy, angry, peevish, discontented, and melancholy, not only at the time of conception, but even all the while she carries the child in her womb (saith Fernelius) her son will be so likewise affected, and worse, as Lemnius adds. If she grieve overmuch, be disquieted, or by any casualty be affrighted, & terrified by some fearful object, heard or seen, she endangers her child, and spoils the temperature of it; for the strange imagination of a woman works effectually upon her infant, that, as Baptista Porta proves, she leaves a mark upon it, which is most especially seen in such as prodigiously long for such & such meats; the child will love those meats, saith Fernelius, and be addicted to like humours; *if a great-bellied woman see a hare, her child will often have an harelip,* as we call it. Garcæus hath a memorable example of one Thomas Nickell, born in the City of Brandenburg, 1551, *that went reeling and staggering all the days of his life, as if he would fall to the ground, because his mother being great with child saw a drunken man reeling in the street.* Such another I find in Martin Wenrichius: I saw (saith he) at Wittenberg in Germany, a citizen that looked like a carkass. *I asked him the cause, he replied, his mother, when she bore him in her womb, saw a carkass by chance, and was so sore affrighted with it, that from a ghastly impression the child was like it.*

So many several ways are we plagued and punished for our fathers' defaults: in so much that, as Fernelius truly saith, *it is the greatest part of our felicity to be well born, & it were happy for human kind, if only*

such parents as are sound of body & mind should be suffered to marry.
An husbandman will sow none but the best & choicest seed upon his
land; he will not rear a bull or an horse, except he be right shapen in all
parts, or permit him to cover a mare, except he be well assured of his
breed; we make choice of the best rams for our sheep, rear the neatest
kine, and keep the best dogs. And how careful then should we be in
begetting of our children! In former times some countries have been so
chary in this behalf, so stern, that, if a child were crooked or deformed
in body or mind, they made him away; so did the Indians of old by the
relation of Curtius, & many other well-governed commonwealths, according to the discipline of those times. Heretofore in Scotland, saith
Hect. Boethius, *if any were visited with the falling sickness, madness,
gout, leprosy, or any such dangerous disease, which was likely to be
propagated from the father to the son, he was instantly gelded: a woman
kept from all company of men; and if by chance, having some such
disease, she were found to be with child, she with her brood were buried
alive:* and this was done for the common good, lest the whole nation
should be injured or corrupted. A severe doom, you will say, and not to
be used amongst Christians, yet more to be looked into than it is. For
now by our too much facility in this kind in giving way for all to marry
that will, too much liberty and indulgence in tolerating all sorts, there is
a vast confusion of hereditary diseases, no family secure, no man almost
free from some grievous infirmity or other. When no choice is had, but
still the eldest must marry, as so many stallions of the race; or if rich,
be they fools or dizzards, lame or maimed, unable, intemperate, dissolute, exhaust through riot, as he said, they must be wise and able by
inheritance: it comes to pass that our generation is corrupt, we have
many weak persons, both in body and mind, many feral diseases raging
amongst us, crazed families, fathers the cause of ruin; our fathers bad,
and we are like to be worse.

MEMBER 2

SUBSECTION 1 — *Bad Diet a cause. Substance. Quality of Meats*

ACCORDING to my proposed method, having opened hitherto these secondary causes, which are inbred with us, I must now proceed to the
outward and adventitious, which happen unto us after we are born. And
those are either evident, remote; or inward, antecedent, and the nearest:

continent causes some call them. These outward, remote, precedent causes are subdivided again into *necessary* and *not necessary*. *Necessary* (because we cannot avoid them, but they will alter us, as they are used or abused) are those six non-natural things, so much spoken of amongst Physicians, which are principal causes of this disease. For almost in every consultation, whereas they shall come to speak of the causes, the fault is found, and this most part objected to the patient, — he hath still offended in one of those six. Montanus consulted about a melancholy Jew, gives that sentence, so did Frisemelica in the same place; and in his 244th counsel, censuring a melancholy soldier, assigns that reason of his malady, *he offended in all those six non-natural things, which were the outward causes, from which came those inward obstructions;* and so in the rest.

These six non-natural things are diet, retention, and evacuation, which are more material than the other, because they make new matter, or else are conversant in keeping or expelling of it. The other four are air, exercise, sleeping, waking, and perturbations of the mind, which only alter the matter. The first of these is diet, which consists in meat and drink, and causes melancholy, as it offends in substance, or accidents, that is, quantity, quality, or the like. And well may it be called a material cause, since that, as Fernelius holds, *it hath such a power in begetting of diseases, & yields the matter and sustenance of them; for neither air, nor perturbations, nor any of those other evident causes take place, or work this effect, except the constitution of body & preparation of humours do concur; that a man may say this diet is the mother of diseases, let the father be what he will; and from this alone melancholy and frequent other maladies arise.* Many physicians I confess have written copious volumes of this one subject, of the nature and qualities of all manner of meats; as mainly, Galen, Isaac the Jew; Halyabbas, Avicenna, Mesue, Arabians; Gordonius, Villanovanus, Wecker, Iohannes Bruerinus (Sitology of Foods & Drinks), Michael Savanarola, Anthony Fumanellus, Curio in his Comment on the Salernitan school, Godefridus Stekius, Marsilius Cognatus, Ficinus, Ranzovius, Fonseca, Lessius, Magninus, Frietagius, Hugo Fridevallius, &c., besides many other in English, and almost every peculiar physician discourseth at large of all peculiar meats in his chapter of Melancholy. Yet because these books are not at hand to every man, I will briefly touch what kind of meats engender this humour, through their several species, and which are to be avoided. How they alter and change the matter, spirits first, and after humours, by which we are preserved, and the constitution of our body, Fernelius and others will shew you. I hasten to the thing itself: and first of such diet as offends in substance.

Beef, a strong & hearty meat (cold in the first degree, dry in the second, saith Galen) is condemned by him, and all succeeding authors, to breed gross melancholy blood: good for such as are sound, and of a strong constitution, for labouring men, if ordered aright, corned, young, of an ox (for all gelded meats in every species are held best) or if old, such as have been tired out with labour, are preferred. Aubanus & Sabellicus commend Portugal beef to be the most savoury, best and easiest of digestion; we commend ours: but all is rejected and unfit for such as lead a resty life, any ways inclined to Melancholy, or dry of complexion; such, Galen thinks, are easily seized with melancholy diseases.

Pork of all meats is most nutritive in his own nature, but altogether unfit for such as live at ease, are any ways unsound of body or mind: too moist, full of humours, and therefore saith Savanarola, naught for queasy stomacks, in so much that frequent use of it may breed a quartan ague.

Savanarola discommends goat's flesh, and so doth Bruerinus, calling it a filthy beast, and rammish; and therefore supposeth it will breed rank and filthy substance: yet kid, such as are young and tender, Isaac accepts, Bruerinus, and Galen.

Hart, and red deer, hath an evil name, it yields gross nutriment; a strong and great grained meat, next unto a horse. Which although some countries eat as Tartars, and they of China, yet Galen condemns. Young foals are as commonly eaten in Spain as red deer, and to furnish their navies, about Malaga especially, often used; but such meats ask long baking, or seething, to qualify them, and yet all will not serve.

All venison is melancholy, and begets bad blood; a pleasant meat: in great esteem with us, (for we have more Parks in England than there are in all Europe besides), in our solemn feasts. 'Tis somewhat better hunted than otherwise, and well prepared by cookery; but generally bad, and seldom to be used.

Hare, a black meat, melancholy, and hard of digestion; it breeds *incubus,* often eaten, and causeth fearful dreams; so doth all venison, and is condemned by a jury of Physicians. Mizaldus and some others say that hare is a merry meat, and that it will make one fair, as Martial's Epigram testifies to Gellia, but this is by the way, because of the good sport it makes, merry company, and good discourse, that is commonly at the eating of it, and not otherwise to be understood

Conies are of the nature of hares. Magninus compares them to beef, pig, and goat, yet young rabbits by all men are approved to be good.

Generally, all such meats as are hard of digestion breed melancholy. Aretæus reckons up heads and feet, bowels, brains, entrails, marrow, fat, blood, skins, and those inward parts, as heart, lungs, liver, spleen, &c. They are rejected by Isaac, Magninus, Bruerinus, Savanarola.

Milk, and all that comes of milk, as butter and cheese, curds, &c. increase melancholy (whey only excepted, which is most wholesome): some except asses' milk. The rest, to such as are sound, is nutritive and good, especially for young children, but because soon turned to corruption, not good for those that have unclean stomacks, are subject to headache, or have green wounds, stone, &c. Of all cheeses, I take that kind which we call Banbury cheese to be the best. The older, stronger, and harder, the worst, as Langius discourseth in his Epistle to Melancthon, cited by Mizaldus, Isaac, Galen, &c.

Amongst fowl, peacocks and pigeons, all fenny fowl are forbidden, as ducks, geese, swans, herns, cranes, coots, didappers, waterhens, with all those teals, curs, sheldrakes, and peckled * fowls, that come hither in winter out of Scandia, Muscovy, Greenland, Friezland, which half the year are covered all over with snow, and frozen up. Though these be fair in feathers, pleasant in taste, and have a good out-side, like hypocrites, white in plumes, and soft, their flesh is hard, black, unwholesome, dangerous, melancholy meat; they load & putrefy the stomach, saith Isaac. Their young ones are more tolerable, but young pigeons he quite disproves.

Rhasis and Magninus discommend all fish, and say they breed *viscosities,* slimy nutriment, little and humorous nourishment. Savanarola adds cold, moist; and phlegmatick, Isaac; and therefore unwholesome for all cold and melancholy complexions. Others make a difference, rejecting only, amongst fresh water fish, eel, tench, lamprey, crawfish (which Bright approves) and such as are bred in muddy and standing waters, and have a taste of mud, as Franciscus Bonsuetus poetically defines,

> *All fish, that standing pools, and lakes frequent,*
> *Do ever yield bad juice and nourishment.*

Lampreys Paulus Jovius highly magnifies, and saith, none speak against them, but some foolish and scrupulous persons; but *eels he abhorreth in all places, at all times, all physicians detest them, especially*

* Speckled.

about the solstice. Gomesius doth immoderately extol seafish, which others as much vilify, and, above the rest, dried, soused, indurate fish, as ling, fumadoes, red-herrings, sprats, stockfish, haberdine, poor-John, all shell fish. Tim. Bright excepts lobster and crab. Messarius commends salmon, which Bruerinus contradicts, Magninus rejects conger, sturgeon, turbot, mackerel, skate.

Carp is a fish of which I know not what to determine, Franciscus Bonsuetus accounts it a muddy fish. Hippolytus Salvianus, in his Book On the Nature and Preparation of Fish, which was printed at Rome in Folio, 1554, with most elegant Pictures, esteems carp no better than a slimy watery meat. Paulus Jovius, on the other side, disallowing tench, approves of it; so doth Dubravius in his Books of Fish-ponds. Frietagius extols it for an excellent wholesome meat, and puts it amongst the fishes of the best rank; and so do most of our Country Gentlemen, that store their ponds almost with no other fish. But this controversy is easily decided, in my judgment, by Bruerinus. The difference riseth from the site and nature of pools, sometimes muddy, sometimes sweet; they are in taste as the place is, from whence they be taken. In like manner almost we may conclude of other fresh fish. But see more in Rondoletius, Bellonius, Oribasius, Isaac, especially Hippolytus Salvianus, who is alone equal to all others. Howsoever they may be wholesome and approved, much use of them is not good. P. Forestus, in his Medicinal Observations, relates the Carthusian Friars, whose living is most part fish, are more subject to melancholy than any other order, & that he found by experience, being sometimes their Physician ordinary at Delph in Holland. He exemplifies it with an instance of one Buscodnese, a Carthusian of a ruddy colour, and well liking, that by solitary living, and fish-eating, became so misaffected.

Amongst herbs to be eaten, I find gourds, cowcumbers, coleworts, melons, disallowed, but especially cabbage. It causeth troublesome dreams, and sends up black vapours to the brain. Galen of all herbs condemns cabbage; and Isaac, it brings heaviness to the soul. Some are of opinion that all raw herbs and sallets breed melancholy blood, except bugloss and lettuce. Crato speaks against all herbs and worts, except borage, bugloss, fennel, parsley, dill, balm, succory. Magninus all herbs are simply evil to feed on (as he thinks.) So did that scoffing Cook in Plautus hold.

> *Like other cooks I do not supper dress,*
> *That put whole meadows into a platter,*
> *And make no better of their guests than beeves,*
> *With herbs and grass to feed them fatter.*

Our Italians and Spaniards do make a whole dinner of herbs and sallets, which our said Plautus calls garden suppers, Horace * bloodless suppers, by which means, as he follows it,

> *Their lives, that eat such herbs, must needs be short,*
> *And 'tis a fearful thing for to report,*
> *That men should feed on such a kind of meat,*
> *Which very juments would refuse to eat.*

They are windy, and therefore not fit to be eaten of all men raw, though qualified with oil, but in broths, or otherwise. See more of these in every husbandman and herbalist. Roots, saith Bruerinus, although the wealth of some countries, and sole food, are windy and bad, or troublesome to the head; as onions, garlick, scallions, turnips, carrots, radishes, parsnips. Crato disallows all roots, though some approve of parsnips and potatoes. Magninus is of Crato's opinion, *they trouble the mind, sending gross fumes to the brain, make men mad,* especially garlick, onions, if a man liberally feed on them a year together. Guianerius complains of all manner of roots, and so doth Bruerinus, even parsnips themselves, which are the best.

Crato utterly forbids all manner of fruits, as pears, apples, plums, cherries, strawberries, nuts, medlers, serves, &c. They infect the blood, saith Villanovanus, and putrefy it, Magninus holds, and must not therefore be taken, not to make a meal of, or in any great quantity. Cardan makes that a cause of their continual sickness at Fez in Africa, *because they live so much on fruits, eating them thrice a day.* Laurentius approves of many fruits, in his Tract of Melancholy, which others disallow, and amongst the rest apples, which some likewise commend, sweetings, pearmains, pippins, as good against Melancholy; but to him that is any way inclined or touched with this malady, Nicholas Piso, in his Practicks, forbids all fruits, as windy, or to be sparingly eaten at least, and not raw. Amongst other fruits, Bruerinus, out of Galen, excepts grapes and figs, but I find them likewise rejected.

All pulse are naught, beans, pease, fitches, &c., they fill the brain (saith Isaac) with gross fumes, breed black thick blood, and cause troublesome dreams. And therefore, that which Pythagoras said to his Scholars of old, may be for ever applied to melancholy men, eat no pease, nor beans. Yet, to such as will needs eat them, I would give this counsel, to prepare them according to those rules that Arnoldus Villanovanus and Frietagius prescribe, for eating and dressing fruits, herbs, roots, pulse, &c.

Spices cause hot and head melancholy, and are for that cause for-

* A mistake for Ovid.

bidden by our physicians to such men as are inclined to this malady, as pepper, ginger, cinnamon, cloves, mace, dates, &c., honey, and sugar. Some except honey; to those that are cold it may be tolerable, but sweets turn into bile, they are obstructive. Crato therefore forbids all spice (in a consultation of his, for a melancholy schoolmaster), all aromatics, and whatever dries up the blood; so doth Fernelius, Guianerius, Mercurialis. To these I may add all sharp and sour things, luscious, and oversweet, or fat, as oil, vinegar, verjuice, mustard, salt; as sweet things are obstructive, so these are corrosive. Gomesius, in his books highly commends Salt; so doth Codronchus in his tract. Yet common experience finds salt, & salt-meats, to be great procurers of this disease. And for that cause, belike, those Egyptian Priests abstained from salt, even so much as in their bread, saith mine Author, that their souls might be free from perturbations.

Bread that is made of baser grain, as pease, beans, oats, rye, or over-hard baked, crusty, and black, is often spoken against, as causing melancholy juice and wind. Joh. Mayor, in the first book of his History of Scotland, contends much for the wholesomeness of oaten bread. It was objected to him, then living at Paris in France, that his countrymen fed on oats, and base grain, as a disgrace; but he doth ingenuously confess, Scotland, Wales, and a third part of England, did most part use that kind of bread, that it was as wholesome as any grain, and yielded as good nourishment. And yet Wecker (out of Galen) calls it horsemeat, and fitter for juments than men to feed on. But read Galen himself, more largely discoursing of corn and bread.

All black wines, overhot, compound, strong thick drinks, as Muscadine, Malmsey, Alicant, Rumney, Brown Bastard, Metheglin, and the like, of which they have thirty several kinds in Muscovy, all such made drinks are hurtful in this case, to such as are hot, or of a sanguine cholerick complexion, young, or inclined to head-melancholy. For many times the drinking of wine alone causeth it. Arculanus puts in wine for a great cause, especially if it be immoderately used. Guianerius tells a story of two Dutchmen, to whom he gave entertainment in his house, *that in one month's space were both melancholy by drinking of wine,* one did nought but sing, the other sigh. Galen, Matthiolus on Dioscorides, and above all other Andreas Bachius, have reckoned up those inconveniences that come by wine. Yet, notwithstanding all this, to such as are cold, or sluggish melancholy, a cup of wine is good physick, and so doth Mercurialis grant. In that case, if the temperature be cold, as to most melancholy men it is, wine is much commended, if it be mod-

erately used. Cider and Perry are both cold and windy drinks, and for
that cause to be neglected, and so are all those hot spiced strong drinks.

Beer, if it be over new or over stale, over strong, or not sod, smell of
the cask, sharp, or sour, is most unwholesome, frets, and galls, &c.
Henricus Ayrerus, in a consultation of his, for one that laboured of
hypochondriacal melancholy, discommends beer. So doth Crato, in that
excellent counsel of his, as too windy, because of the hop. But he means
belike that thick black Bohemian beer used in some other parts of
Germany.

> *Nothing comes in so thick,*
> *Nothing goes out so thin,*
> *It must needs follow then*
> *The dregs are left within.*

As that old Poet scoffed, calling it a monstrous drink, like the River
Styx. But let them say as they list, to such as are accustomed unto it,
'tis a most wholesome (so Polydore Virgil calleth it) *and a pleasant
drink,* it is more subtle and better for the hop that rarefies it, hath an
especial virtue against melancholy, as our Herbalists confess, Fuchsius
approves, and many others.

Standing waters, thick and ill coloured, such as come forth of pools
and moats, where hemp hath been steeped, or slimy fishes live, are most
unwholesome, putrefied, and full of mites, creepers, slimy, muddy, unclean, corrupt, impure, by reason of the sun's heat, and still standing.
They cause foul distemperatures in the body and mind of man, are
unfit to make drink of, to dress meat with, or to be used about men
inwardly or outwardly. They are good for many domestical uses, to
wash horses, water cattle, &c., or in time of necessity, but not otherwise. Some are of opinion, that such fat standing waters make the best
beer, and that seething doth defecate it, as Cardan holds, *it mends the
substance and savour of it,* but it is a paradox. Such beer may be stronger
but not so wholesome as the other, as Jobertus truly justifieth out of
Galen, that the seething of such impure waters doth not purge or purify
them. Pliny is of the same tenet, and P. Crescentius. Pamphilius Herila-
chus, [says] such waters are naught, not to be used, and, by the testimony of Galen, *breed agues, dropsies, pleurisies, splenetick and melancholy passions, hurt the eyes, cause a bad temperature and ill disposition
of the whole body, with bad colour.* This Jobertus stiffly maintains,
that it causeth blear eyes, bad colour, and many loathsome diseases, to
such as use it. This which they say stands with good reason; for, as
Geographers relate, the water of Astracan breeds worms in such as drink

it. Axius, or (as now called) Vardar, the fairest River in Macedonia, makes all cattle black that taste of it. Aliacmon, now Peleca, another stream in Thessaly, turns cattle most part white, if you take them there to drink. J. Aubanus Bohemus refers that *struma*, or poke, of the Bavarians and Styrians, to the nature of their waters, as Munster doth that of the Valesians in the Alps, and Bodine supposeth the stuttering of some families in Aquitania, about Labden, to proceed from the same cause, *and that the filth is derived from the water to their bodies.* So that they that use filthy, standing, ill-coloured, thick, muddy water, must needs have muddy, ill-coloured, impure, and infirm bodies. And because the body works upon the mind, they shall have grosser understandings, dull, foggy, melancholy spirits, and be really subject to all manner of infirmities.

To these noxious simples, we may reduce an infinte number of compound, artificial, made dishes, of which our cooks afford us a great variety, as tailors do fashions in our apparel. Such are puddings stuffed with blood, or otherwise composed, baked meats, soused, indurate meats, fried, and broiled, buttered meats, condite, powdered and over-dried, all Cakes, Simnels, Buns, Cracknels, made with butter, spice, &c., Fritters, Pancakes, Pies, Sausages, and those several sauces, sharp or over sweet, of which the cook-shop science, as Seneca calls it, hath served those Apician tricks, and perfumed dishes, which Adrian the Sixth, Pope, so much admired in the accounts of his predecessor Leo the Tenth; and which prodigious riot and prodigality have invented in this age. These do generally ingender gross humours, fill the stomack with crudities, and all those inward parts with obstructions. Montanus gives instance in a melancholy Jew, that, by eating such tart sauces, made dishes, and salt meats, with which he was overmuch delighted, became melancholy, and was evil affected. Such examples are familiar and common.

SUBSECTION 2 — *Quantity of Diet a Cause*

THERE is not so much harm proceeding from the substance itself of meat, and quality of it, in ill dressing and preparing, as there is from the quantity, disorder of time and place, unseasonable use of it, intemperance, overmuch or overlittle taking of it. A true saying it is, this gluttony kills more than the sword, this all-devouring and murdering gut. And that of Pliny is truer, *simple diet is the best ; heaping up of several meats is pernicious, and sauces worse ; many dishes bring many diseases.* Avicenna cries out that *nothing is worse than to feed on many dishes, or to protract the time of meals longer than ordinary; from thence proceed our infirmities, and 'tis the fountain of all diseases, which arise out of the repugnancy of gross humours.* Thence, saith Fernelius, come crudities, wind, oppilations, *cacochymia, plethora, cachexia, bradypepsia,* sudden death, intestate old age, and what not.

As a lamp is choked with a multitude of oil, or a little fire with over-much wood quite extinguished; so is the natural heat with immoderate eating strangled in the body. An insatiable paunch, one saith, is a pernicious sink, and the fountain of all diseases, both of body and mind. Mercurialis will have it a peculiar cause of this private disease; Solenander illustrates this of Mercurialis with an example of one so melancholy by unseasonable feasting. Crato confirms as much, in that often cited Counsel, putting superfluous eating for a main cause. But what need I seek farther for proofs? Hear Hippocrates himself, *Impure bodies, the more they are nourished, the more they are hurt, for the nourishment is putrefied with vicious humours.*

And yet for all this harm, which apparently follows surfeiting and drunkenness, see how we luxuriate and rage in this kind. Read what Johannes Stuckius hath written lately of this subject, in his great volume The Feasts of Olden Times, and of our present age; what prodigious suppers; those who invite us to supper but bring us to our tomb! What *Fagos, Epicures, Apicii, Heliogabali,* our times afford! Lucullus' ghost walks still, and every man desires to sup in *Apollo.** Æsop's † costly dish is ordinarily served up. Those things please most which cost most. The dearest cates are best, and 'tis an ordinary thing to bestow twenty or thirty pound on a dish, some thousand crowns upon a dinner. Muley-Hamet, King of Fez and Morocco, spent three pounds on the sauce of a capon: it is nothing in our times, we scorn all that is cheap. *We loathe the very light* (some of us, as Seneca notes) *because it comes free, and we are offended with the sun's heat, and those cool blasts, because we buy them not.* This air we breathe is so common, *we care not for it;* nothing pleaseth but what is dear. And if we be witty in anything, it is for the gullet's sake: if we study at all, it is the study of debauchery, to please the palate, and to satisfy the gut. *A cook of old was a base knave* (as Livy complains) *but now a great man in request: cookery is become an art, a noble science: cooks are Gentlemen:* Belly is God. They wear *their brains in their bellies, and their guts in their heads;* as Agrippa taxed some parasites of his time, rushing on their own destruc-

* Apollo was a rich chamber so called in Lucullus' house.
† The son of the tragic actor Æsop, friend of Cicero.

tion, as if a man should run upon the point of a sword, they eat till they burst: all day, all night, let the Physician say what he will, imminent danger and feral diseases are now ready to seize upon them, they will eat till they vomit, and vomit to eat again, saith Seneca; (which Dion relates of Vitellius, his meat did pass through, and away;) or till they burst again. They load their belly with the carnage of animals, and rake over all the world, as so many slaves, belly-gods, and land-serpents; the whole world cannot satisfy their appetite. *Sea, Land, Rivers, Lakes, &c., may not give content to their raging guts.* To make up the mess, what immoderate drinking in every place! A drunken old woman drags a drunken old man, how they flock to the Tavern! as if they were born to no other end but to eat and drink, like Offellius Bibulus, that famous Roman Parasite, who while he lived was either taking in wine or pissing it off, as so many casks to hold wine, yea worse than a cask, that mars wines, and itself is not marred by it, yet these are brave men, drunken Silenus was no braver. And what were vices are now considered virtues: 'tis now the fashion of our times, an honour: 'tis now come to that pass, (as Chrysostom comments,) that he is [held] no Gentleman, a very milk-sop, a clown, of no bringing up, that will not drink, fit for no company; he is your only gallant that plays it off finest, no disparagement now to stagger in the streets, reel, rave, &c., but much to his fame and renown; as, in like case, Epidicus told Thesprio his fellow-servant, in the Poet: in good sooth an ill deed, one urged, the other replied, 'tis now no fault, there be so many brave examples to bear one out; 'tis a credit to have a strong brain, and carry his liquor well: the sole contention who can drink most, and fox his fellow soonest. 'Tis the greatest good of our *tradesmen,* their felicity, life and soul, saith Pliny, their chief comfort, to be merry together in an Alehouse or Tavern, as our modern Muscovites do in their Mede-Inns, and Turks in their Coffee-houses, which much resemble our Taverns; they will labour hard all day long to be drunk at night, and spend a whole year's profits, as St. Ambrose adds, in a tippling feast; convert day into night, as Seneca taxeth some in his times, when we rise, they commonly go to bed, like our Antipodes, as we feel the first breath of orient steeds panting up our sky, among them Vesper, all crimson, is lighting its evening torch. So did Petronius in Tacitus, Heliogabalus in Lampridius,

He sat up all the night, and slept all day. (HORACE)
Smindyrides the Sybarite never saw the sun rise or set, so much as once in twenty years. Verres, against whom Tully so much inveighs, in winter he never was out of doors, never almost out of bed, still wenching,

and drinking; so did he spend his time, and so do *myriads* in our days. They have drinking-schools and rendezvous; these *Centaurs* and *Lapithæ* toss pots and bowls as so many balls; invent new tricks, as Sausages, Anchovies, Tobacco, Caviare, pickled Oysters, Herrings, Fumadoes, &c., innumerable salt-meats, to increase their appetite, and study how to hurt themselves by taking antidotes, *to carry their drink the better: and when naught else serves, they will go forth, or be conveyed out, to empty their gorge, that they may return to drink afresh.* They make laws, insane laws against the neglect of drinking, and brag of it when they have done, crowning that man that is soonest gone, as their drunken predecessors have done (What do I see? — Your drunken Pseudolus with a crown,) and, when they are dead, will have a can of wine (with Maron's old woman) to be engraven on their tombs. So they triumph in villany, and justify their wickedness: with Rabelais, that French Lucian, [they say] drunkenness is better for the body than physick, because there be more old drunkards than old Physicians. Many such frothy arguments they have, inviting and encouraging others to do as they do, and love them dearly for it (no glue like to that of good-fellowship). So did Alcibiades in Greece, Nero, Bonosus, Heliogabalus in Rome, or Alegabalus rather, as he was styled of old, (as Ignatius proves out of some old coins.) So do many great men still, as Heresbachius observes. When a Prince drinks till his eyes stare, like Bitias in the Poet, *He eager drained the bowl brimming with wine,* and comes off clearly, sound Trumpets, Fife, and Drums, the spectators will applaud him, *the Bishop himself* (if he belie them not) *with his Chaplain will stand by, and do as much;* O 'twas done like a Prince! *Our Dutchmen invite all comers with a pail and a dish.* They drain inexhaustible noggins even as a funnel, & from monstrous vessels they pour them into their more monstrous selves, *making barrels of their bellies.* 'Tis incredible to say, as one of their own country-men complains, how much liquor that most immoderate race will take, &c. *How they love a man that will be drunk, crown him and honour him for it,* hate him that will not pledge him, stab him, kill him: a most intolerable offense, and not to be forgiven! *He is a mortal enemy that will not drink with him,* as Munster relates of the Saxons. So in Poland, he is the best servitor, and the honestest fellow, saith Alexander Gaguinus, *that drinketh most healths to the honour of his master;* he shall be rewarded as a good servant, and held the bravest fellow, that carries his liquor best, when as a brewer's horse will bear much more than any sturdy drinker; yet for his noble exploits in this kind he shall be accounted a most valiant man, for as much valour is to be found in feasting as in fighting, and some of our City Captains, and Carpet Knights, will make this good, and prove it. Thus they many times wilfully pervert the good temperature of their bodies, stifle their wits, strangle nature, and degenerate into beasts.

Some again are in the other extreme, and draw this mischief on their heads by too ceremonious and strict diet, being over precise, Cockney-like, and curious in their observation of meats, times, as that *Medicina Statica* prescribes, just so many ounces at dinner, which Lessius enjoins, so much at supper, not a little more, nor a little less, of such meat, and at such hours; a diet-drink in the morning, cock-broth, China-broth, at dinner plum-broth, a chicken, a rabbit, rib of a rack of mutton, wing of a capon, the merry-thought of a hen, &c.; to sounder bodies this is too nice and most absurd. Others offend in over-much fasting: pining adays, saith Guianerius, and waking anights, as many Moors and Turks in these our times do. *Anchorites, Monks, and the rest of that superstitious rank* (as the same Guianerius witnesseth, *that he hath often seen to have happened in his time*) *through immoderate fasting have been frequently mad.* Of such men belike Hippocrates speaks, when as he saith, *they more offend in too sparing diet, and are worse damnified, than they that feed liberally, and are ready to surfeit.*

SUBSECTION 3 — *Custom of Diet, Delight, Appetite, Necessity, how they cause or hinder*

No rule is so general, which admits not some exception; to this therefore which hath been hitherto said, (for I shall otherwise put most men out of commons), and those inconveniences which proceed from the substance of meats, and intemperate or unseasonable use of them, custom somewhat detracts and qualifies, according to that of Hippocrates, *Such things as we have been long accustomed to, though they be evil in their own nature, yet they are less offensive.* Otherwise it might well be objected, that it were a mere tyranny to live after those strict rules of physick; for custom doth alter nature itself, and to such as are used to them it makes bad meats wholesome, and unseasonable times to cause no disorder. Cider and Perry are windy drinks, (so are all fruits windy in themselves, cold most part,) yet in some shires of England, Normandy in France, Guipuscoa in Spain, 'tis their common drink, and they are no whit offended with it. In Spain, Italy, and Africa, they live most on roots, raw herbs, camels' milk, and it agrees well with them; which to a stranger will cause much grievance. In Wales they feed themselves on milk-food as Humfrey Lluyd confesseth, a Cambro-Briton himself, in his elegant Epistle to Abraham Ortelius, they live most on white meats: in Holland on fish, roots, butter; and so at this day in Greece, as Bellonius observes, they had much rather feed on fish than flesh. With us, we feed on flesh most part, saith Polydore Virgil, as all Northern countries do; and it would be very offensive to us to live after their diet, or they to live after ours. We drink beer, they wine; they use oil, we butter: we in the North are great eaters, they most sparing in those hotter countries: and yet they and we, following our own customs, are well pleased. An Ethiopian of old, seeing an European eat bread, wondered how we could eat such kind of meats: so much differed his countrymen from ours in diet, that, as mine Author infers, if any man should so feed with us, it would be all one to nourish, as hemlock, aconite, or hellebore itself. At this day in China the common people live in a manner altogether on roots and herbs, and to the wealthiest horse, ass, mule, dogs, cats-flesh, is as delightsome as the rest; so Mat. Riccius the Jesuit relates, who lived many years amongst them. The Tartars eat raw meat, and most commonly horse-flesh, drink milk and blood, as the Nomads of old. They scoff at our Europeans for eating bread, which they call tops of weeds, and horse-meat, not fit for men; and yet Scaliger accounts them a sound and witty nation, living an hundred years; even in the civilest country of them they do thus, as Benedict the Jesuit observed in his travels from the great Mogor's Court by Land to Paquin, which Riccius contends to be the same with Cambalu in Cathay. In Scandia their bread is usually dried fish, and so likewise in the Shetland Isles: and their other fare, as in Iceland, saith Dithmarus Bleskenius, *butter, cheese, and fish; their drink water, their lodging on the ground.* In America in many places their bread is roots, their meat palmitos, pinas, potatoes, &c., and such fruits. There be of them too that familiarly drink salt sea-water all their lives, eat raw meat, grass, and that with delight; with some, fish, serpents, spiders; and in divers places they eat man's flesh raw, and roasted, even the Emperor Montezuma himself. In some coasts again, one tree yields them cocoa-nuts, meat and drink, fire, fuel, apparel with his leaves, oil, vinegar, cover for houses, &c. and yet these men, going naked, feeding coarse, live commonly a hundred years, are seldom or never sick; all which diet our Physicians forbid. In Westphalia they feed most part on fat meats and wourts,* knuckle deep, and call it Jupiter's brain: in the Low Countries with roots, in Italy frogs and snails are used. The Turks, saith Bus-

* Cabbage.

bequius, delight most in fried meats. In Muscovy garlick and onions are ordinary meat and sauce, which would be pernicious to such as are unaccustomed unto them, delightsome to others; and all is because they have been brought up unto it. Husbandmen, and such as labour, can eat fat bacon, salt gross meat, hard cheese, &c., (O what iron digestions mowers have!) coarse bread at all times, go to bed and labour upon a full stomack, which to some idle persons would be present death, and is against the rules of physick; so that custom is all in all. Our travellers find this by common experience; when they come in far Countries, and use their diet, they are suddenly offended; as our Hollanders & Englishmen when they touch upon the coasts of Africa, those Indian capes and islands, are commonly molested with calentures, fluxes, and much distempered by reason of their fruits. Strange meats, though pleasant, cause notable alterations and distempers. On the other side, use or custom mitigates or makes all good again. Mithridates by often use, which Pliny wonders at, was able to drink poison; and a maid, as Curtius records, sent to Alexander from K. Porus, was brought up with poison from her infancy. The Turks, saith Bellonius, eat Opium familiarly, a dram at once, which we dare not take in grains. Garcius ab Horto writes of one whom he saw at Goa in the East Indies, that took ten drams of Opium in three days; and yet spake understandingly; so much can custom do. Theophrastus speaks of a shepherd that could eat hellebore in substance. And therefore Cardan concludes out of Galen, custom is howsoever to be kept, except it be extreme bad: he adviseth all men to keep their old customs, and that by the authority of Hippocrates himself; and therefore to continue as they began, be it diet, bath, exercise, &c., or whatsoever else.

Another exception is delight, or appetite, to such and such meats. Though they be hard of digestion, melancholy, yet, as Fuchsius excepts, *the stomack doth readily digest, and willingly entertain, such meats we love most, and are pleasing to us, abhors on the other side such as we distaste;* which Hippocrates confirms. Some cannot endure cheese, out of a secret antipathy, or to see a roasted duck, which to others is a delightsome meat.

The last exception is necessity, poverty, want, hunger, which drives men many times to do that which otherwise they are loath, cannot endure, and thankfully to accept of it: as beverage in ships, and, in sieges of great cities, to feed on dogs, cats, rats, and men themselves. Three outlaws, in Hector Boethius, being driven to their shifts, did eat raw flesh, and flesh of such fowl as they could catch, in one of the Hebrides, for some few months. These things do mitigate or disannul that which hath been said of melancholy meats, and make it more tolerable; but to such as are wealthy, live plenteously, at ease, may take their choice, and refrain if they will, these viands are to be forborne, if they be inclined to, or suspect, melancholy, as they tender their healths: otherwise, if they be intemperate, or disordered in their diet, at their peril be it.

He who warns you loves you.
Farewell, and be on your guard.

SUBSECTION 4 — *Retention and Evacuation a cause, and how*

OF retention and evacuation there be divers kinds, which are either concomitant, assisting, or sole causes many times of melancholy. Galen reduceth defect and abundance to this head; others, *all that is separated, or remains.*

In the first rank of these, I may well reckon up costiveness, and keeping in of our ordinary excrements, which, as it often causes other diseases, so this of Melancholy in particular. Celsus saith *it produceth inflammation of the head, dulness, cloudiness, headache, &c.* Prosper Calenus will have it distemper not the organ only, *but the mind itself by troubling of it:* and sometimes it is a sole cause of Madness, as you may read in the first Book of Skenkius his Medicinal Observations. A young Merchant, going to Nordeling Fair in Germany, for ten days space never went to stool; at his return he was grievously melancholy, thinking that he was robbed, and would not be persuaded, but that all his money was gone. His friends thought that he [had] had some philter given him, but Cnelinus, a Physician, being sent for, found his costiveness alone to be the cause, and thereupon gave him a clyster, by which he was speedily recovered. Trincavellius saith as much of a melancholy Lawyer, to whom he administered physick, and Rodericus à Fonseca of a Patient of his, that for eight days was bound, and therefore melancholy affected. Other retentions and evacuations there are, not simply necessary, but at some times; as Fernelius accounts them, as suppression of emrods, monthly issues in women, bleeding at nose, immoderate or no use at all of *Venus;* or any other ordinary issues.

Detention of emrods, or monthly issues, Villanovanus, Arculanus, Vittorius Faventinus, Bruel, &c., put for ordinary causes. Fuchsius goes farther and saith that *many men, unseasonably cured of the emrods, have been corrupted with melancholy; seeking to avoid Scylla, they fall into Charybdis.* Galen illustrates this by an example of Lucius Martius, whom he cured of madness, contracted by this means: and Sckenkius has two other instances of two melancholy and mad women, so caused from the suppression of their months. The same may be said of bleeding at the nose, if it be suddenly stopt, and have been formerly used, as Villanovanus urgeth: and Fuchsius stiffly maintains, that *without great danger such an issue may not be stayed.*

Venus omitted produceth like effects. Matthiolus *avoucheth of his knowledge, that some through bashfulness abstained from Venery, and thereupon became very heavy and dull; and some others, that were very timorous, melancholy, and beyond all measure sad.* Oribasius speaks of some, *that, if they do not use carnal copulation, are continually troubled with heaviness and headache; and some in the same case by intermission of it.* Not use of it hurts many; Arculanus and Magninus think, because it *sends up poisoned vapours to the brain and heart.* And so doth Galen himself hold, that, if this *natural seed be over-long kept* (*in some parties*) *it turns to poison.* Hieronymus Mercurialis, in his Chapter of Melancholy, cites it for an especial cause of this malady, Priapismus, Satyriasis, &c. Halyabbas reckons up this and many other diseases. Villanovanus saith he *knew many monks and widows grievously troubled with melancholy, and that from this sole cause.* Lodovicus Mercatus, and Rodericus à Castro treat largely of this subject, and will have it produce a peculiar kind of melancholy in stale maids, nuns, and widows; on account of suppressed menses, & omission of venery they are timid, unhappy, anxious, sheepish, mistrustful, listless, without purpose at the very height of life, & despairing of more favorable circumstances, &c., they are melancholy in the highest degree, and all for want of husbands. Ælianus Montaltus confirms as much out of Galen; so doth Wierus; Christophorus à Vega relates many such examples of men and women, that he had seen so melancholy. Felix Plater, in the first Book of his Observations, *tells a story of an ancient Gentleman in Alsatia, that married a young wife, and was not able to pay his debts in that kind for a long time together, by reason of his several infirmities: but she, because of this inhibition of* Venus, *fell into a horrible fury, and desired every one that came to see her, by words, looks, and gestures, to have to do with her, &c.* Bernardus Paternus, a Physician, saith, he knew *a good honest godly Priest, that, because he would neither willingly marry, nor make use of the stews, fell into grievous melancholy fits.* Hildesheim hath such another example of an Italian melancholy Priest, in a consultation had in the year of 1580. Jason Pratensis gives instance in a married man, that from his wife's death abstaining, *after marriage, became exceeding melancholy;* Rodericus à

Fonseca in a young man so misaffected. To these you may add, if you please, that conceited tale of a Jew, so visited in like sort, and so cured, out of Poggio the Florentine.

Intemperate *Venus* is all out as bad in the other extreme. Galen, reckons up melancholy amongst those diseases which are *exasperated by venery:* so doth Avicenna, Oribasius, Marsilius Cognatus, Montaltus, Guianerius. Magninus gives the reason, because *it infrigidates & dries up the body, consumes the spirits; and would therefore have all such as are cold and dry to take heed of and to avoid it as a mortal enemy.* Jacchinus ascribes the same cause, and instanceth in a Patient of his, that married a young wife in a hot summer, *and so dried himself with chamber-work, that he became in short space from melancholy mad:* he cured him by moistening remedies. The like example I find in Lælius à Fonte Eugubinus of a Gentleman of Venice, that, upon the same occasion, was first melancholy, afterwards mad. Read in him the story at large.

Any other evacuation stopped will cause it, as well as these above named, be it bile, ulcer, issue, &c. Hercules de Saxoniâ, and Gordonius, verify this out of their experience. They saw one wounded in the head, who, as long as the sore was open, was well; but when it was stopped his melancholy fit seized on him again.

Artificial evacuations are much like in effect, as hot-houses, baths, blood-letting, purging, unseasonably and immoderately used. Baths dry too much, if used in excess, be they natural or artificial, and offend extreme hot, or cold: one dries, the other refrigerates, overmuch. Montanus saith, they over-heat the liver. Joh. Struthius contends, *that if one stay longer than ordinary at the bath, go in too oft, or at unseasonable times, he putrefies the humours in his body.* To this purpose writes Magninus; Guianerius utterly disallows all hot baths in melancholy adust. *I saw* (saith he) *a man that laboured of the gout, who, to be freed of his malady, came to the bath, and was instantly cured of his disease, but got another worse, and that was madness.* But this judgment varies, as the humour doth, in hot or cold: baths may be good for one melancholy man, bad for another; that which will cure it in this party, may cause it in a second.

Phlebotomy, many times neglected, may do much harm to the body, when there is a manifest redundance of bad humours, and melancholy blood; and when these humours heat and boil, if this be not used in time, the parties affected, so inflamed, are in great danger to be mad; but if it be unadvisedly, importunely, immoderately used, it doth as much harm by refrigerating the body, dulling the spirits, and consuming them. As Joh. Curio, in his 10th Chapter, well reprehends, such kind of letting blood doth more hurt than good: *the humours rage much more than they did before, and is so far from avoiding melancholy, that it increaseth it, and weakeneth the sight.* Prosper Calenus observes as much of all phlebotomy, except they keep a very good diet after it: yea, and, as Leonartus Jacchinus speaks out of his own experience, *the blood is much blacker to many men after their letting of blood than it was at first.* For this cause belike Salvianus will admit or hear of no blood-letting at all in this disease, except it be manifest it proceed from blood. He was (it appears by his own words in that place,) Master of an Hospital of mad men, *and found by long experience, that this kind of evacuation, either in head, arm or any other part, did more harm than good.* To this opinion of his Felix Plater is quite opposite; *though some wink at, disallow, & quite contradict, all phlebotomy in Melancholy, yet by long experience I have found innumerable so saved, after they had been twenty, nay, sixty times let blood, and to live happily after it. It was an ordinary thing of old, in Galen's time, to take at once from such men six pound of blood, which now we dare scarce take in ounces: but let doctors see to it;* great books are written of this subject.

Purging upward and downward, in abundance of bad humours omitted, may be for the worst; so likewise, as in the precedent, if overmuch, too frequent or violent, it weakeneth their strength, saith Fuchsius, or if they be strong or able to endure physick, yet it brings them to an ill habit, they make their bodies no better than apothecaries' shops, this, and such like infirmities, must needs follow.

SUBSECTION 5 — *Bad Air a Cause of Melancholy*

AIR is a cause of great moment, in producing this or any other disease, being that it is still taken into our bodies by respiration, and our more inner parts. *If it be impure and foggy, it dejects the spirits, and causeth diseases by infection of the heart,* as Paulus hath it, Avicenna, Mercurialis, Montaltus, &c. Fernelius saith, *a thick air thickeneth the blood and humours.* Lemnius reckons up two main things most profitable, and most pernicious to our bodies; air and diet: and this peculiar disease nothing sooner causeth (Jobertus holds) *than the air wherein we breathe and live.* Such is the air, such be our spirits; and as our spirits, such are our humours. It offends commonly, if it be too hot and dry, thick, fuliginous, cloudy, blustering, or a tempestuous air. Bodine in his fifth book On The Republic, and in his Method of History, proves that hot countries are most troubled with melancholy, and that there are therefore in Spain, Africa, and Asia Minor, great numbers of mad men, insomuch, that they are compelled, in all cities of note, to build peculiar Hospitals for them. Leo Afer on The City of Fez, Ortelius, and Zuinger, confirm as much. They are ordinarily so cholerick in their speeches, that scarce two words pass without railing or chiding in common talk, and often quarrelling in their streets. Gordonius will have every man take notice of it: *Note this* (saith he) *that in hot countries it is far more familiar than in cold;* although this we have now said be not continually so, for, as Acosta truly saith, under the Æquator itself is a most temperate habitation, wholesome air, a Paradise of pleasure, the leaves ever green, cooling showers. But it holds in such as are intemperately hot, as Johannes à Meggen found in Cyprus, others in Malta, Apulia, and the Holy Land, where at some seasons of the year is nothing but dust, their rivers dried up, their air scorching hot, and earth inflamed; insomuch that many Pilgrims, going barefoot for devotion sake from Joppa to Jerusalem upon the hot sands, often run mad, or else quite overwhelmed with sand, as in many parts of Africa, Arabia Deserta, Bactriana, now Khorassan, when the West Wind blows, the passers by perish in clouds of sand. Hercules de Saxonia, a Professor in Venice, gives this cause, why so many Venetian women are melancholy, that they tarry too long in the sun. Montanus amongst other causes assigns this, why that Jew his Patient was mad, he exposed himself so much to heat and cold. And for that reason in Venice, there is little stirring in those brick-paved streets in summer about noon, they are most part then asleep: as they are likewise in the great Mogor's Countries, and all over the East Indies. At Aden in Arabia, as Lodovicus Vertomannus relates in his travels, they keep their markets in the night, to avoid extremity of heat; and in Ormus, like cattle in a pasture, people of all sorts lie up to the chin in water all day long. At Braga in Portugal, Burgos in Castile, Messina in Sicily, all over Spain and Italy, their streets are most part narrow, to avoid the sun-beams. The Turks wear great turbans to refract the sun-beams; and much inconvenience that hot air of Bantam in Java yields to our men, that sojourn there for traffick; where it is so hot, *that they that are sick of the pox lie commonly bleaching in the sun, to dry up their sores.* Such a complaint I read of those Isles of Cape Verde, fourteen degrees from the Æquator, they do have a bad name: one calls them the unhealthiest clime of the world, for fluxes, fevers, phrenzies, calentures, which commonly seize on sea-faring men that touch at them, and all by reason of a hot distemperature of the air.

The hardiest men are offended with this heat, and stiffest clowns ca..not resist it, as Constantine affirms. They that are naturally born in such air, may not endure it, as Niger records of some part of Mesopotamia, now called Diarbekr: 'tis so hot there in some places, that men of the country and cattle are killed with it: and Adricomius of Arabia Felix, by reason of myrrh, frankincense, and hot spices there growing, the air is so obnoxious to their brains, that the very inhabitants at some times cannot abide it, much less weaklings and strangers. Amatus Lusitanus reports of a young maid, that was one Vincent a currier's daughter, some thirteen years of age, that would wash her hair in the heat of the day (in July) and so let it dry in the sun, *to make it yellow, but by that means tarrying too long in the heat, she inflamed her head, and made herself mad.*

Cold air, in the other extreme, is almost as bad as hot, and so doth Montaltus esteem of it, if it be dry withal. In those Northern Countries the people are therefore generally dull, heavy, and many witches, which (as I have before quoted) Saxo Grammaticus, Olaus, Baptista Porta, ascribe to melancholy. But these cold climes are more subject to natural melancholy (not this artificial) which is cold and dry: for which cause Mercurius Britannicus, belike, puts melancholy men to inhabit just under the Pole. The worst of the three is a thick, cloudy, misty, foggy air, or such as comes from fens, moorish grounds, lakes, muckhills, draughts, sinks, where any carcasses or carrion lies, or from whence any stinking fulsome smell comes. Galen, Avicenna, Mercurialis, new and old Physicians, hold that such air is unwholesome, and engenders melancholy, plagues, and what not? Alexandretta, an haven town in the Mediterranean Sea, Saint John de Ullua, an haven in Nova-Hispania, are much condemned for a bad air, so as Durazzo in Albania, Lithuania, Ditmarsch, the Pontine Marshes in Italy, the territories about Pisa, Ferrara, &c., Romney Marsh with us, the Hundreds in Essex, the Fens in Lincolnshire. Cardan finds fault with the site of those rich and most populous Cities in the Low Countries, as Bruges, Ghent, Amsterdam, Leyden, Utrecht, &c., the air is bad; and so at Stockholm in Sweden, Rhegium in Italy, Salisbury with us, Hull and Lynn. They may be commodious for navigation, this new kind of fortification, and many other good necessary uses; but are they so wholesome? Old Rome hath descended from the hills to the valley, 'tis the site of most of our new Cities, and held best to build in Plains, to take the opportunity of Rivers. Leander Albertus pleads hard for the air and site of Venice, though the black moorish lands appear at every low water; the sea, fire, and smoke (as he thinks) qualify the air: and some suppose that a thick foggy air helps the memory, as in them of Pisa in Italy; and our Camden, out of Plato, commends the site of Cambridge, because it is so near the Fens. But let the site of such places be as it may, how can they be excused that have a delicious seat, a pleasant air, and all that nature can afford, and yet through their own nastiness and sluttishness, immund and sordid manner of life, suffer their air to putrefy, and themselves to be choked up? Many Cities in Turkey do bear a bad name in this kind, Constantinople itself, where commonly carrion lies in the street. Some find the same fault in Spain, even in Madrid, the King's seat, a most excellent air, a pleasant site; but the inhabitants are slovens, and the streets uncleanly kept.

A troublesome tempestuous air is as bad as impure, rough and foul weather, impetuous winds, cloudy dark days, as it is commonly with us, Polydore calls it a filthy sky, & one in which clouds are quick to take form; as Tully's brother Quintus wrote to him in Rome, being then Quæstor in Britain. *In a thick and cloudy air* (saith Lemnius) *men are tetrick, sad, and peevish: and if the Western Winds blow, and that there be a calm, or a fair sunshine day, there is a kind of alacrity in men's minds; it cheers up men and beasts: but if it be a turbulent, rough, cloudy, stormy weather, men are sad, lumpish, and much dejected, angry, waspish, dull, and melancholy.* This was Virgil's experiment of old,

> *But when the face of heaven changed is*
> *To tempests, rain, from season fair:*
> *Our minds are altered, and in our breasts*
> *Forthwith some new conceits appear.*

And who is not weather-wise against such and such conjunctions of Planets, moved in foul weather, dull and heavy in such tempestuous seasons? Aquarius saddens the now turned year: the time requires, and the Autumn breeds it; Winter is like unto it, ugly, foul, squalid; the air works on all men more or less, but especially on such as are melancholy, or inclined to it, as Lemnius holds; *they are most moved with it, and those which are already mad rave downright, either in or against a tempest. Besides, the devil many times takes his opportunity in such storms, and when the humours by the air be stirred, he goes in with them, exagitates our spirits, and vexeth our souls; as the sea-waves, so are the spirits and humours in our bodies tossed with tempestuous winds and storms.* To such as are melancholy, therefore, Montanus will have tempestuous and rough air to be avoided, and all night air, and would not have them to walk abroad but in a pleasant day. Lemnius discommends the South and Eastern Winds, commends the North. Montanus *will not any windows to be opened in the night,* he discommends especially the South Wind, and nocturnal air: so doth Plutarch; the night and darkness makes men sad; the like do all subterranean vaults, dark houses in caves & rocks; desert places cause melancholy in an instant, especially such as have not been used to it, or otherwise accustomed. Read more of air in Hippocrates, Aetius, Oribasius, &c.

SUBSECTION 6 — *Immoderate Exercise a Cause and how. Solitariness, Idleness*

NOTHING so good, but it may be abused. Nothing better than exercise (if opportunely used) for the preservation of the body: nothing so bad, if it be unseasonable, violent, or overmuch. Fernelius, out of Galen, saith, *that much exercise and weariness consumes the spirits and substance, refrigerates the body; and such humours which Nature would have otherwise concocted and expelled, it stirs up, and makes them rage: which being so enraged, diversely affect and trouble the body and mind.* So doth it, if it be unseasonably used, upon a full stomack, or when the body is full of crudities, which Fuchsius so much inveighs against, giving that for a cause why school-boys in Germany are so often scabbed, because they use exercise presently after meats. Bayerus puts in a caveat against such exercise, because it *corrupts the meat in the stomack, and carries the same juice raw, and as yet undigested, into the veins* (saith Lemnius), *which there putrefies, and confounds the animal spirits.* Crato protests against all such exercise after meat, as being the greatest enemy to concoction that may be, and cause of corruption of humours, which produce this and many other diseases. Not without good reason then doth Sallustius Salvianus, and Leonartus Jacchinus, Mercurialis, Arculanus, and many others, set down immoderate exercise as a most forcible cause of melancholy.

Opposite to exercise is idleness (the badge of gentry), or want of exercise, the bane of body and mind, the nurse of naughtiness, stepmother of discipline, the chief author of all mischief, one of the seven deadly sins, and a sole cause of this and many other maladies, the devil's cushion, as Gualter calls it, his pillow and chief reposal. *For the mind can never rest, but still meditates on one thing or other; except it be occupied about some honest business, of his own accord it rusheth into melancholy. As too much & violent exercise offends on the one side, so doth an idle life on the other,* (saith Crato) *it fills the body full of phlegm, gross humours, & all manner of obstructions, rheums, catarrhs, &c.* Rhasis accounts of it as the greatest cause of melancholy. *I have often seen* (saith he) *that idleness begets this humour more than any thing else.* Montaltus seconds him out of his experience; *they that are idle are far more subject to melancholy than such as are conversant or employed about any office or business.* Plutarch reckons up idleness for a sole cause of the sickness of the soul. *There are they* (saith he) *troubled in mind, that have no other cause but this.* Homer brings in Achilles eating of his own heart in his idleness, because he might not fight. Mercurialis, for a melancholy young man, urgeth it is a chief cause; why was he melancholy? because idle. Nothing begets it sooner, increaseth and continueth it oftener, than idleness; a disease familiar to all idle persons, an inseparable companion to such as live at ease, a life out of action, and have no calling or ordinary employment to busy themselves about, that have small occasions; and, though they have, such is their laziness, dullness, they will not compose themselves to do ought; they cannot abide work, though it be necessary, easy, as to dress themselves, write a letter, or the like; yet, as he that is benumbed with cold sits still shaking, that might relieve himself with a little exercise or stirring, do they complain, but will not use the facile and ready means to do themselves good; and so are still tormented with melancholy. Especially if they have been formerly brought up to business, or to keep much company, and upon a sudden come to lead a sedentary life, it crucifies their souls, and seizeth on them in an instant; for whilst they are any ways employed, in action, discourse, about any business, sport or recreation, or in company to their liking, they are very well; but if alone or idle, tormented instantly again; one day's solitariness, one hour's sometimes, doth them more harm than a week's physick, labour, and company, can do good. Melancholy seizeth on them forthwith being alone, and is such a torture, that, as wise Seneca well saith, I had rather be sick than idle. This idleness is either of body or mind. That of body is nothing but a kind of benumbing laziness, intermitting exercise; which, if we may believe Fernelius, *causeth crudities, obstructions, excremental humours, quencheth the natural heat, dulls the spirits, and makes them unapt to do anything whatsoever.*

As fern grows in untilled grounds, and all manner of weeds, so do gross humours in an idle body. A horse in a stable that never travels, a hawk in a mew that seldom flies, are both subject to diseases; which, left unto themselves, are most free from any such incumbrances. An idle dog will be mangy, and how shall an idle person think to escape? Idleness of the mind is much worse than this of the body; wit without employment, is a disease, the rust of the soul, a plague, a hell itself, the greatest danger to the soul, Galen calls it. *As in a standing pool worms and filthy creepers increase,* (the water itself putrefies, and air likewise, if it be not continually stirred by the wind), *so do evil and corrupt thoughts in an idle person,* the soul is contaminated. In a Commonwealth, where is no publick enemy, there is, likely, civil wars, and they rage upon themselves: this body of ours, when it is idle, and knows not how to bestow itself, macerates and vexeth itself with cares, griefs, false fears, discontents, and suspicions; it tortures and preys upon his own bowels, and is never at rest. Thus much I dare boldly say, he or she that is idle, be they of what condition they will, never so rich, so well allied, fortunate, happy, let them have all things in abundance, and felicity, that heart can wish and desire, all contentment; so long as he or she or they are idle, they shall never be pleased, never well in body and mind, but weary still, sickly still, vexed still, loathing still, weeping, sighing, grieving, suspecting, offended with the world, with every object, wishing themselves gone or dead, or else carried away with some foolish phantasy or other. And this is the true cause that so many great men, Ladies, and Gentlewomen, labour of this disease in Country and City; for idleness is an appendix to nobility, they count it a disgrace to work, and spend all their days in sports, recreations, and pastimes, and will therefore take no pains, be of no vocation: they feed liberally, fare well, want exercise, action, employment, (for to work, I say, they may not abide), and company to their desires, & thence their bodies become full of gross humours, wind, crudities, their minds disquieted, dull, heavy, &c. Care, jealousy, fear of some diseases, sullen fits, weeping fits, seize too familiarly on them. For what will not fear and phantasy work in an idle body? what distempers will they not cause? When the children of Israel murmured against Pharaoh in Egypt, he commanded his officers to double their task, and let them get straw themselves, and yet make their full number of bricks; for the sole cause why they mutiny, and are evil at ease, is, *they are idle.* When you shall hear and see so many discontented persons in all places where you come, so many several grievances, unnecessary complaints, fear, suspicions, the best means to redress it is to set them awork, so to busy their minds; for the truth is, they are idle. Well they may build castles in the air for a time, and soothe up themselves with phantastical and pleasant humours, but in the end they will prove as bitter

as gall, they shall be still I say discontent, suspicious, fearful, jealous, sad, fretting and vexing of themselves; so long as they be idle, it is impossible to please them. As that A. Gellius could observe: he that knows not how to spend his time, hath more business, care, grief, anguish of mind, than he that is most busy in the midst of all his business. An idle person, (as he follows it) knows not when he is well, what he would have, or whither he would go. He is tired out with everything, displeased with all, weary of his life: neither well at home nor abroad, he wanders, and lives beside himself. In a word, what the mischievous effects of laziness and idleness are, I do not find anywhere more accurately expressed, than in these verses of Philolaches in the Comical Poet, which, for their elegancy, I will in part insert [and paraphrase] : —
A young man is like a fair new house, the carpenter leaves it well built, in good repair, of solid stuff; but a bad tenant lets it rain in, and for want of reparation fall to decay, &c. Our Parents, Tutors, Friends, spare no cost to bring us up in our youth in all manner of virtuous education; but when we are left to ourselves, idleness as a tempest drives all virtuous notions out of our minds, &, on a sudden, by sloth and such bad ways, we come to naught.

Cousin-german to idleness, and a concomitant cause, which goes hand in hand with it, is too much solitariness, by the testimony of all Physicians, cause & symptom both; but as it is here put for a cause, it is either coact, enforced, or else voluntary. Enforced solitariness is commonly seen in Students, Monks, Friars, Anchorites, that by their order and course of life must abandon all company, society of other men and betake themselves to a private cell: the seclusion of excessive idleness, as Bale and Hospinian well term it, such as are the Carthusians of our time, that eat no flesh (by their order), keep perpetual silence, never go abroad; such as live in prison, or some desert place, and cannot have company, as many of our Country Gentlemen do in solitary houses, they must either be alone without companions, or live beyond their means, and entertain all comers as so many hosts, or else converse with their servants and hinds, such as are unequal, inferior to them, and of a contrary disposition; or else, as some do to avoid solitariness, spend their time with lewd fellows in taverns, and in ale-houses, and thence addict themselves to some unlawful disports, or dissolute courses. Divers again are cast upon this rock of solitariness for want of means, or out of a strong apprehension of some infirmity, disgrace, or through bashfulness, rudeness, simplicity, they cannot apply themselves to others' company. To the unhappy man nothing is dearer than solitude, where there is none to reproach him for his misery. This enforced solitariness takes place, and produceth his effect soonest, in such as have spent their time jovially, peradventure in all honest recreations, in good company, in some great family or populous City, and are upon a sudden confined to a desert Country Cottage far off, restrained of their liberty, and barred from their ordinary associates: solitariness is very irksome to such, most tedious, and a sudden cause of great inconvenience.

Voluntary solitariness is that which is familiar with Melancholy, and gently brings on like a Siren, a shoeing-horn, or some Sphinx, to this irrevocable gulf, a primary cause Piso calls it; most pleasant it is at first, to such as are melancholy given, to lie in bed whole days, and keep their chambers, to walk alone in some solitary Grove, betwixt Wood and Water, by a Brook side, to meditate upon some delightsome and pleasant subject, which shall affect them most; happy madness and delightful illusion. A most incomparable delight it is so to melancholize, & build castles in the air, to go smiling to themselves, acting an infinite variety of parts, which they suppose and strongly imagine they represent, or that they see acted or done. It is indeed charming, saith Lemnius, to conceive and meditate of such pleasant things sometimes, *present, past, or to come,* as Rhasis speaks. So delightsome these toys are at first, they could spend whole days and nights without sleep, even whole years alone in such contemplations, and phantastical meditations, which are like unto dreams, and they will hardly be drawn from them, or willingly interrupt. So pleasant their vain conceits are, that they hinder their ordinary tasks and necessary business, they cannot address themselves to them, or almost to any study or employment, these phantastical and bewitching thoughts so covertly, so feelingly, so urgently, so continually, set upon, creep in, insinuate, possess, overcome, distract, & detain them, they cannot, I say, go about their more necessary business, stave off or extricate themselves, but are ever musing, melancholizing, and carried along, as he (they say) that is led round about an heath with a *Puck* in the night, they run earnestly on in this labyrinth of anxious and solicitous melancholy meditations, and cannot well or willingly refrain, or easily leave off, winding and unwinding themselves, as so many clocks, and still pleasing their humours, until at last the scene is turned upon a sudden, by some bad object, and they, being now habituated to such vain meditations and solitary places, can endure no company, can ruminate of nothing but harsh and distasteful subjects. Fear, sorrow, suspicion, clownish timidity, discontent, cares, and weariness of life surprise them in a moment, and they can think of nothing else; continually suspecting, no sooner are their eyes open, but this infernal plague of Melancholy seizeth on them, and terrifies their souls, representing some dismal object to their minds, which now by no means, no labour, no persuasions, they can avoid, the deadly arrow yet remains in their side, they may not be rid of it, they cannot resist. I may not deny but that there is some profitable meditation, contemplation, and kind of solitariness to be embraced, which the Fathers so highly commended, Hierom, Chrysostom, Cyprian, Austin, in whole tracts, which Petrarch, Erasmus, Stella, and others, so much magnify in their books; a Paradise, an Heaven on earth, if it be used aright, good for the body, and better for the soul: as many of those old Monks used it, to divine contemplations; as Simulus, a Courtier in Adrian's time, Dioclesian the Emperor, retired themselves, &c. in that sense, Vatia lives alone, which the Romans were wont to say, when they commended a country life; or to the bettering of their knowledge, as Democritus, Cleanthes, and those excellent Philosophers have ever done, to sequester themselves from the tumultuous world, or as in Pliny's Villa Laurentina, Tully's Tusculan, Jovius' study, that they might better serve God & follow their studies. Methinks, therefore, our too zealous innovators were not so well advised, in that general subversion of Abbies and Religious Houses, promiscuously to fling down all. They might have taken away those gross abuses crept in amongst them, rectified such inconveniences, and not so far to have raved and raged against those fair buildings, and everlasting monuments of our forefathers' devotion, consecrated to pious uses. Some Monasteries and Collegiate Cells might have been well spared, and their revenues otherwise employed, here and there one, in good Towns or Cities at least, for men and women of all sorts & conditions to live in, to sequester themselves from the cares and tumults of the world, that were not desirous or fit to marry, or otherwise willing to be troubled with common affairs, and knew not well where to bestow themselves, to live apart in, for more conveniency, good education, better company sake, to follow their studies (I say) to the perfection of arts and sciences, common good, &, as some truly devoted Monks of old had done, freely and truly to serve God. For these men are neither solitary, nor idle, as the Poet made answer to the husbandman in Æsop, that objected idleness to him; he was never so idle as in his company; or that Scipio Africanus in Tully, never less solitary than when he was alone, never more busy than when he seemed to be most idle. It is reported by Plato, in his dialogue on

love, in that prodigious commendation of Socrates, how a deep meditation coming into Socrates' mind by chance, he stood still musing, from
morning to noon, and when as then he had not yet finished his meditation, he so continued till the evening, the soldiers (for he then followed
the camp) observed him with admiration, and on set purpose watched
all night, but he persevered immovable till the sun rose in the morning,
and then, saluting the sun, went his ways. In what humour constant
Socrates did thus, I know not, or how he might be affected, but this
would be pernicious to another man; what intricate business might so
really possess him, I cannot easily guess. But this is serene leisure, it
is far otherwise with these men, according to Seneca, solitude prompts
us to all kinds of evil; this solitude undoeth us, 'tis a destructive solitariness. These men are Devils alone, as the saying is, a man alone is
either a Saint or a Devil; his mind is either dull or devilish; and, in
this sense, woe be to him that is so alone! These wretches do frequently
degenerate from men, and of sociable creatures become beasts, monsters,
inhuman, ugly to behold, *misanthropes,* they do even loath themselves,
and hate the company of men, as so many Timons, Nebuchadnezzars,
by too much indulging to these pleasing humours, and through their
own default. So that which Mercurialis sometimes expostulated with his
melancholy patient, may be justly applied to every solitary and idle
person in particular: *Nature may justly complain of thee, that, whereas
she gave thee a good wholesome temperature, a sound body, and God
hath given thee so divine and excellent a soul, so many good parts and
profitable gifts, thou hast not only contemned and rejected, but hast
corrupted them, polluted them, overthrown their temperature, and perverted those gifts with riot, idleness, solitariness, and many other ways,
thou art a traitor to God and Nature, an enemy to thyself and to the
world.* Thou hast lost thyself wilfully, cast away thyself, *thou thyself
art the efficient cause of thine own misery, by not resisting such vain
cogitations, but giving way unto them.*

SUBSECTION 7 — *Sleeping and Waking, causes*

WHAT I have formerly said of exercise, I may now repeat of sleep.
Nothing better than moderate sleep, nothing worse than it, if it be in
extremes, or unseasonably used. It is a received opinion, that a melancholy man cannot sleep over-much; excessive sleep is good, as an only
antidote, and nothing offends them more, or causeth this malady sooner,
than waking; yet in some cases sleep may do more harm than good
in that phlegmatick, swinish, cold, and sluggish melancholy, which

Melancthon speaks of, that thinks of waters, sighing most part, &c. It dulls the spirits, if overmuch, and senses, fills the head full of gross humours, causeth distillations, rheums, great store of excrements in the brain and all the other parts, as Fuchsius speaks of them, that sleep like so many dormice. Or if it be used in the day time, upon a full stomack, the body ill composed to rest, or after hard meats, it increaseth fearful dreams, nightmare, night walking, crying out, & much unquietness; such sleep prepares the body, as one observes, *to many perilous diseases.* But, as I have said, waking overmuch is both a symptom & an ordinary cause. *It causeth dryness of the brain, phrenzy, dotage, & makes the body dry, lean, hard, and ugly to behold,* as Lemnius hath it. *The temperature of the brain is corrupted by it, the humours adust, the eyes made to sink into the head, choler increased, & the whole body inflamed:* &, as may be added out of Galen, *it overthrows the natural heat, it causeth crudities, hurts concoction,* & what not? Not without good cause therefore Crato, Hildesheim, Jacchinus, Arculanus (on Rhasis,) Guianerius, & Mercurialis, reckon up this over-much waking as a principal cause.

MEMBER 3

SUBSECTION 1 — *Passions and Perturbations of the Mind, how they cause Melancholy*

As that Gymnosophist in Plutarch made answer to Alexander, (demanding which spake best), every one of his fellows did speak better than the other: so may I say of these causes to him that shall require which is the greatest, every one is more grievous than other, and this of passion the greatest of all. A most frequent and ordinary cause of Melancholy, (Piccolomineus calls it), this thunder and lightning of perturbation, which causeth such violence and speedy alterations in this our Microcosm, and many times subverts the good estate and temperature of it. For as the body works upon the mind, by his bad humours, troubling the spirits, sending gross fumes into the brain, and so disturbing the soul, and all the faculties of it,

> *The body, clogged with yesterday's excess,*
> *Drags down the mind as well,* (HORACE)

with fear, sorrow, &c. which are ordinary symptoms of this disease: so, on the other side, the mind most effectually works upon the body, producing by his passions and perturbations miraculous alterations, as

melancholy, despair, cruel diseases, and sometimes death itself, insomuch, that it is most true which Plato saith in his Charmides, all the
mischiefs of the body proceed from the soul : & Democritus in Plutarch
urgeth, — if the body should in this behalf bring an action against the
soul, surely the soul would be cast & convicted, that by her supine negligence had caused such inconveniences, having authority over the body,
and using it for an instrument, as a smith doth his hammer (saith
Cyprian), imputing all those vices & maladies to the mind. Even so
doth Philostratus, the body is not corrupted but by the soul. Lodovicus
Vives will have such turbulent commotions proceed from *Ignorance* &
indiscretion. All Philosophers impute the miseries of the body to the
soul, that should have governed it better by command of reason, and
hath not done it. The Stoicks are altogether of opinion (as Lipsius &
Piccolomineus record) that a wise man should be without all manner
of passions and perturbations whatsoever, as Seneca reports of Cato,
the Greeks of Socrates, and Jo. Aubanus of a nation in Africa, so free
from passion, or rather so stupid, that, if they be wounded with a sword,
they will only look back. Lactantius will exclude *fear from a wise man :*
others except all, some the greatest passions. But let them dispute how
they will, set down in theses, give precepts to the contrary ; we find that
of Lemnius true by common experience ; *no mortal man is free from
these perturbations :* or if he be so, sure he is either a god or a block.
They are born and bred with us, we have them from our parents by
inheritance, saith Pelezius, 'tis born with us, & grows with us, 'tis propagated from Adam ; Cain was melancholy, as Austin hath it, and who
is not ? Good discipline, education, philosophy, divinity, (I cannot
deny), may mitigate and restrain these passions in some few men at
some times, but most part they domineer, and are so violent, that as
a torrent, bears down all before, and overflows his banks, lays bare the
fields, lays waste the crops, they overwhelm reason, judgement, & pervert the temperature of the body. The charioteer is run away with, nor
does the chariot obey the reins. Now such a man (saith Austin) *that
is so led, in a wise man's eye, is no better than he that stands upon his
head.* It is doubted by some whether humours or perturbations cause
the more grievous maladies. But we find that of our Saviour most true,
the spirit is willing, the flesh is weak, we cannot resist : and this of
Philo Judæus, *perturbations often offend the body, & are most frequent
causes of melancholy, turning it out of the hinges of his health.* Vives
compares them to *winds upon the sea, some only move as those great
gales, but others, turbulent, quite overturn the ship.* Those which are

light, easy, and more seldom, to our thinking do us little harm, and are therefore contemned of us: yet, if they be reiterated, *as the rain* (saith Austin) *doth a stone, so do these perturbations penetrate the mind,* and (as one observes) *produce an habit of melancholy at the last,* which, having gotten the mastery in our souls, may well be called diseases.

How these passions produce this effect, Agrippa hath handled at large, Cardan, Lemnius, Suarez, T. Bright, in his Melancholy Treatise, Wright the Jesuit in his book of the Passions of the Mind, &c. Thus in brief, to our imagination cometh, by the outward sense or memory, some object to be known (residing in the foremost part of the brain) which he, misconceiving or amplifying, presently communicates to the heart, the seat of all affections. The pure spirits forthwith flock from the brain to the heart by certain secret channels, and signify what good or bad object was presented; which immediately bends itself to prosecute or avoid it, and, withal, draweth with it other humours to help it. So in pleasure, concur great store of purer spirits; in sadness, much melancholy blood; in ire, choler. If the imagination be very apprehensive, intent, and violent, it sends great store of spirits to or from the heart, and makes a deeper impression, and greater tumult; as the humours in the body be likewise prepared, and the temperature itself ill or well disposed, the passions are longer and stronger: so that the first step and fountain of all our grievances in this kind is a distorted imagination, which, misinforming the heart, causeth all these distemperatures, alteration and confusion, of spirits and humours; by means of which, so disturbed, concoction is hindered, and the principal parts are much debilitated; as Dr. Navarra well declared, being consulted by Montanus about a melancholy Jew. The spirits so confounded, the nourishment must needs be abated, bad humours increased, crudities and thick spirits engendered, with melancholy blood. The other parts cannot perform their functions, having the spirits drawn from them by vehement passion, but fail in sense and motion; so we look upon a thing, and see it not; hear, and observe not; which otherwise would much affect us, had we been free. I may therefore conclude with Arnoldus; great is the force of imagination, and much more ought the cause of melancholy to be ascribed to this alone, than to the distemperature of the body. Of which imagination, because it hath so great a stroke in producing this malady, and is so powerful of itself, it will not be improper to my discourse, to make a brief digression, and speak of the force of it, and how it causeth this alteration. Which manner of digression however some dislike, as frivolous and impertinent, yet I am of Beroaldus his opinion, *Such digressions do mightily delight and refresh a weary reader, they are like sauce to a bad stomack, and I do therefore most willingly use them.*

SUBSECTION 2 — *Of the Force of Imagination*

WHAT Imagination is, I have sufficiently declared in my *digression of the Anatomy of the Soul.* I will only now point at the wonderful effects and power of it; which, as it is eminent in all, so most especially it rageth in melancholy persons, in keeping the species of objects so long, mistaking, amplifying them by continual & strong meditation, until at length it produceth in some parties real effects, causeth this and many other maladies. And although this phantasy of ours be a subordinate faculty to reason, and should be ruled by it, yet in many men, through inward or outward distemperatures, defect of organs, which are unapt or hindered, or otherwise contaminated, it is likewise unapt, hindered, and hurt. This we see verified in sleepers, which, by reason of humours, & concourse of vapours troubling the phantasy, imagine many times absurd & prodigious things, & in such as are troubled with Incubus, or witch-ridden (as we call it); if they lie on their backs, they suppose an old woman rides, & sits so hard upon them, that they are almost stifled for want of breath, when there is nothing offends but a concourse of bad humours, which trouble the phantasy. This is likewise evident in such as walk in the night in their sleep, and do strange feats: these vapours move the phantasy, the phantasy the appetite, which, moving the *animal* spirits, causeth the body to walk up and down, as if they were awake. Fracastorius refers all ecstasies to this force of imagination, such as lie whole days together in a trance: as that priest whom Celsus speaks of, that could separate himself from his senses when he list, & lie like a dead man, void of life and sense. Cardan brags of himself, that he could do as much, and that when he list. Many times such men, when they come to themselves, tell strange things of Heaven & Hell, what visions they have seen; as that St. Owen in Mathew Paris, that went into St. Patrick's Purgatory, and the Monk of Evesham in the same Author. Those common apparitions in Bede and Gregory, St. Bridget's revelations, Wierus, Cæsar Vanninus in his dialogues, &c. reduceth, (as I have formerly said,) with all those tales of Witches' progresses, dancing, riding, transformations, operations, &c. to the force of imagination, and the Devil's illusions. The like effects almost are to be seen in such as are awake: how many chimæras, anticks, golden mountains, and castles in the air, do they build unto themselves! I appeal to painters, mechanicians, mathematicians. Some ascribe all vices to a false and corrupt imagination, anger, revenge, lust, ambition, covetousness, which prefers falsehood before that which is right and good, deluding the soul with false shews and suppositions. Bernardus Penottus will have heresy and superstition to proceed from this fountain; as he falsely imagineth, so he believeth; and as he conceiveth of it, so it must be, and it shall be, all the world notwithstanding, he will have it so. But most especially in passions and affections, it shews strange and evident effects: what will not a fearful man conceive in the dark? what strange forms of Bugbears, Devils, Witches, Goblins? Lavater imputes the greatest cause of spectrums, and the like apparitions, to fear, which, above all other passions, begets the strongest imagination, (saith Wierus), and so likewise love, sorrow, joy, &c. Some die suddenly, as she that saw her son come from the battle at Cannæ, &c. Jacob the Patriarch, by force of imagination, made peckled lambs, laying peckled rods before his sheep. Persina, that Æthiopian Queen in Heliodorus, by seeing the picture of Perseus and Andromeda, instead of a blackamoor, was brought to bed of a fair white child. In imitation of whom, belike, an hard favoured fellow in Greece, because he and his wife were both deformed, to get a good brood of children, hung the fairest pictures he could buy for money in his chamber, *that his wife, by frequent sight of them, might conceive and bear such children.* And if we may believe Bale, one of Pope Nicholas the Third's concubines, by seeing of a bear, was brought to bed of a monster. *If a woman* (saith Lemnius) *at the time of her conception, think of another man present or absent, the child will be like him.* Great-bellied women, when they long, yield us prodigious examples in this kind, as moles, warts, scars, harelips, monsters, especially caused in their children by force of a depraved phantasy in them. She imprints that stamp upon her child, which she conceives unto herself. And therefore Lodovicus Vives gives a special caution to great-bellied women, *that they do not admit such absurd conceits and cogitations, but by all means avoid those horrible objects, heard or seen, or filthy spectacles.* Some will laugh, weep, sigh, groan, blush, tremble, sweat, at such things as are suggested unto them by their imagination. Avicenna speaks of one that could cast himself into a palsy when he list; and some can imitate the tunes of birds and beasts, that they can hardly be discerned. Dagobertus' and Saint Francis' scars and wounds, like to those of Christ's (if at the least any such were), Agrippa supposeth to have happened by force of imagination. That some are turned to wolves, from men to women, and women again to men (which is constantly believed) to the same imagination; or from men to asses, dogs, or any other shapes; Wierus ascribes all those famous transformations to imagination. That in *Hydrophobia* they seem to see the picture of a dog still in their water, that melancholy men and sick men, conceive so many phantastical visions, apparitions to themselves, and have such absurd suppositions, as that they are Kings, Lords, cocks, bears, apes, owls; that they are heavy, light, transparent, great and little, senseless and dead (as shall be shewed more at large in our Section of Symptoms) can be imputed to naught else but to a corrupt, false, and violent imagination. It works not in sick and melancholy men only, but even most forcibly sometimes in such as are sound: it makes them suddenly sick, and alters their temperature, in an instant. And sometimes a strong conceit or apprehension, as Valesius proves, will take away diseases: in both kinds it will produce real effects. Men, if they see but another man tremble, giddy, or sick of some fearful disease, their apprehension and fear is so strong in this kind, that they will have the same disease. Or if by some soothsayer, wiseman, fortune-teller, or physician, they be told they shall have such a disease, they will so seriously apprehend it, that they will instantly labour of it. A thing familiar in China (saith Riccius the Jesuit): *if it be told them they shall be sick on such a day, when that day comes, they will surely be sick, and will be so terribly afflicted, that sometimes they die upon it.* Dr. Cotta, in his Discovery of ignorant Practitioners of Physick, hath two strange stories to this purpose, what fancy is able to do; the one of a Parson's wife in Northamptonshire in the year 1607, that, coming to a Physician, and told by him that she was troubled with the *sciatica,* as he conjectured, (a disease she was free from), the same night after her return, upon his words, fell into a grievous fit of a *sciatica ;* and such another example he hath of another good wife, that was so troubled with the cramp, after the same manner she came by it, because her Physician did but name it. Sometimes death itself is caused by force of phantasy. I have heard of one that, coming by chance in company of him that was thought to be sick of the plague (which was not so), fell down suddenly dead. Another was sick of the plague with conceit. One, seeing his fellow let blood, falls down in a swoon. Another (saith Cardan out of Aristotle) fell down dead (which is familiar to women at any ghastly sight) seeing but a man hanged. A Jew in France (saith Lodovicus Vives) came by chance over a dangerous passage, or plank, that lay over a brook in the dark, without harm, the next day, perceiving what danger he was in, fell down dead. Many will not believe such stories to be true, but laugh commonly, and deride when they hear of them; but let these men consider with themselves, as Peter Byarus illustrates it, if they were set to walk upon a plank on high, they would be giddy, upon which they dare securely walk upon the ground. Many (saith Agrippa) *strong-hearted men otherwise, tremble at such sights, dazzle, and are sick, if they look but down from an high place, and what moves them but conceit?* As some are so molested by phantasy, so some again by fancy alone, and a good conceit, are as easily recovered. We see commonly the tooth-ache, gout, falling-sickness, biting of a mad dog, and many such maladies, cured by spells, words, characters and charms; and many green wounds by that now so much used Weapon Salve * magnetically cured, which Crollius & Goclenius in a book of late hath defended, Libavius in a just tract as stiffly contradicts, and most men controvert. All the world knows there is no virtue in such charms, or cures, but a strong conceit and opinion alone, as Pomponatius holds, *which forceth a motion of the humours, spirits, & blood, which takes away the cause of the malady from the parts affected.* The like we may say of our magical effects, superstitious cures, and such as are done by mountebanks and wizards. *As by wicked incredulity many men are hurt* (so saith Wierus of charms, spells, &c.), *we find in our experience, by the same means many are relieved.* An Empirick oftentimes, and a silly Chirurgeon, doth more strange cures than a rational Physician. Nymannus gives a reason, because the Patient puts his confidence in him, which Avicenna *prefers before art, precepts, and all remedies whatsoever.* 'Tis opinion alone (saith Cardan) that makes or mars Physicians, and he doth the best cures, according to Hippocrates, in whom most trust. So diversely doth this phantasy of ours affect, turn and wind, so imperiously command our bodies, which, as another *Proteus, or a Chameleon, can take all shapes; and is of such force* (as Ficinus adds) *that it can work upon others as well as ourselves.* How can otherwise blear eyes in one man cause the like affection in another? Why doth one man's yawning make another yawn; one man's pissing provoke a second many times to do the like? Why doth scraping of trenchers offend a third, or hacking of files? Why doth a carkass bleed, when the murderer is brought before it, some weeks after the murder hath been done? Why do witches and old women fascinate and bewitch children? but as Wierus, Paracelsus, Cardan, Mizaldus, Valleriola, Cæsar Vanninus, Campanella, and many Philosophers think, the forcible imagination of the one party moves and alters the spirits of the

* The Weapon Salve was applied to the weapon which had caused the wound.

other. Nay more, they can cause and cure not only diseases, maladies, and several infirmities, by this means, as Avicenna supposeth, in parties remote, but move bodies from their places, cause thunder, lightning, tempests, which opinion Alkindus, Paracelsus, and some others, approve of. So that I may certainly conclude this strong conceit or imagination is a man's star, and the rudder of this our ship, which reason should steer, but overborne by phantasy cannot manage, and so suffers itself and this whole vessel of ours to be over-ruled, and often overturned. Read more of this in Wierus, Franciscus Valesius, Marcellus Donatus, Levinus Lemnius, Cardan, Cornelius Agrippa, Camerarius, Nymannus, and him that is worth all of them together, Fienus, a famous Physician of Antwerp, that wrote three books on The Power of Imagination. I have thus far digressed, because this imagination is the common carrier of passions, by whose means they work and produce many times prodigious effects ; and as the phantasy is more or less intended or remitted, and their humours disposed, so do perturbations move, more or less, and take deeper impression.

SUBSECTION 3 — *Division of Perturbations*

PERTURBATIONS and passions, which trouble the phantasy, though they dwell between the confines of sense and reason, yet they rather follow sense than reason, because they are drowned in corporeal organs of sense. They are commonly reduced into two inclinations, *irascible*, and *concupiscible*. The Thomists subdivide them into eleven, six in the *coveting*, and five in the *invading*. Aristotle reduceth all to pleasure and pain, Plato to love and hatred, Vives to good and bad. If good, it is present, and then we absolutely joy and love : or to come, and then we desire and hope for it : if evil, we absolutely hate it : if present, it is sorrow ; if to come, fear. These four passions Bernard compares *to the wheels of a chariot, by which we are carried in this world*. All other passions are subordinate unto these four, or six, as some will : love, joy, desire, hatred, sorrow, fear. The rest, as anger, envy, emulation, pride, jealousy, anxiety, mercy, shame, discontent, despair, ambition, avarice, &c., are reducible unto the first : and if they be immoderate, they consume the spirits, and melancholy is especially caused by them. Some few discreet men there are, that can govern themselves, and curb in these inordinate affections, by religion, philosophy, and such divine precepts, of meekness, patience, and the like ; but most part, for want of government, out of indiscretion, ignorance, they suffer themselves wholly to be led by sense, and are so far from repressing rebellious inclinations, that they give all encouragement unto them, leaving the reins, and using all provocations to further them: bad by nature, worse by art, discipline, custom, education, and a perverse will of their own, they follow on, wheresoever their unbridled affections will transport them, and do more out of custom, self-will, than out of reason. This stubborn will of ours, as Melancthon calls it, perverts judgment, which sees and knows what should and ought to be done, and yet will not do it. Slaves to their several lusts and appetite, they precipitate and plunge themselves into a labyrinth of cares, blinded with lust, blinded with ambition; *they seek that at God's hands which they may give unto themselves, if they could but refrain from those cares and perturbations, wherewith they continually macerate their minds.* But giving way to these violent passions of fear, grief, shame, revenge, hatred, malice, &c., they are torn in pieces, as Actæon was with his dogs, and crucify their own souls.

SUBSECTION 4 — *Sorrow a Cause of Melancholy*

IN this Catalogue of Passions, which so much torment the soul of man, and cause this malady (for I will briefly speak of them all, and in their order) the first place in this irascible appetite may justly be challenged by *sorrow;* an inseparable companion, *the mother and daughter of melancholy, her epitome, symptom, and chief cause.* As Hippocrates hath it, they beget one another, and tread in a ring, for sorrow is both cause and symptom of this disease. How it is a symptom shall be shewed in his place. That it is a cause all the world acknowledgeth. Sorrow, saith Plutarch to Apollonius, is a cause of madness, a cause of many other incurable diseases, a sole cause of this mischief, Lemnius calls it. So doth Rhasis, & Guianerius. And if it take root once, it ends in despair, as Felix Plater observes, and, as in Cebes' Table, may well be coupled with it. Chrysostom, in his seventeenth Epistle to Olympia, describes it to be *a cruel torture of the soul, a most inexplicable grief, a poisoned worm, consuming body and soul, and gnawing the very heart, a perpetual executioner, continual night, profound darkness, a whirlwind, a tempest, an ague not appearing, heating worse than any fire, and a battle that hath no end: it crucifies worse than any Tyrant; no torture, no strappado, no bodily punishment, is like unto it.* 'Tis the eagle without question which the Poets feigned to gnaw Prometheus' heart, and no heaviness is like unto the heaviness of the heart. *Every perturbation is a misery, but grief a cruel torment,* a domineering passion: as in old Rome, when the Dictator was created, all inferior magistracies ceased, when grief appears, all other passions vanish. It dries up the bones, saith Solomon, makes them hollow-ey'd, pale, and lean, furrow-faced, to have dead looks, wrinkled brows, riveled cheeks, dry bodies, and quite perverts their temperature that are mis-affected with it. As Elenora that exil'd mournful Duchess (in our English Ovid) laments to her noble husband Humphrey, Duke of Gloucester,

> *Sawest thou those eyes in whose sweet cheerful look*
> *Duke Humphrey once such joy and pleasure took,*
> *Sorrow hath so despoil'd me of all grace,*
> *Thou couldst not say this was my Elenor's face.*
> *Like a foul Gorgon, &c.*   (DRAYTON)

It hinders concoction, refrigerates the heart, takes away stomack, colour, & sleep; thickens the blood, contaminates the spirits; overthrows the natural heat, perverts the good estate of body and mind, & makes them weary of their lives, cry out, howl and roar, for very anguish of their souls. David confessed as much, *I have roared for the very disquietness of my heart: My soul melteth away for very heaviness; I am like a bottle in the smoke.* Antiochus complained that he could not sleep, and that his heart fainted for grief. Christ himself, a man of sorrows, out of an apprehension of grief did sweat blood; his soul was heavy to the death, and no sorrow was like unto his. Crato gives instance in one that was so melancholy by reason of grief: and Montanus, in a noble Matron, *that had no other cause of this mischief.* I. S. D. (in Hildesheim,) fully cured a patient of his, that was much troubled with melancholy, and for many years, *but afterwards, by a little occasion of sorrow, he fell into his former fits, and was tormented as before.* Examples are common, how it causeth melancholy, desperation, and sometimes death itself; for *of heaviness comes death. Worldly sorrow causeth death, My life is wasted with heaviness, and my years with mourning.* Why was Hecuba said to be turned to a dog? Niobe into a stone? but that for grief she was senseless and stupid. Severus the Emperor died for grief, and how many myriads besides! So great is the fierceness and madness of grief. Melancthon gives a reason of it, *the gathering of much melancholy blood about the heart, which collection extinguisheth the good spirits, or at least dulleth them, sorrow strikes the heart, makes it tremble and pine away, with great pain, and the black blood drawn from the spleen, and diffused under the ribs on the left side, makes those perilous hypocondriacal convulsions, which happen to them that are troubled with sorrow.*

SUBSECTION 5 — *Fear, a Cause*

COUSIN-GERMAN to *sorrow* is *fear*, or rather a sister, a faithful squire, and continual companion, an assistant and a principal agent in procuring of this mischief, a cause and symptom as the other. In a word, as Virgil of the Harpies, I may justly say of them both,

> *A sadder monster, or more cruel plague so fell,*
> *Or vengeance of the Gods, ne'er came from Styx or Hell.*

This foul fiend of Fear was worshipped heretofore as a God by the Lacedæmonians, and most of those other torturing affections, and so was Sorrow, amongst the rest, under the name of *Angerona Dea ;* they stood in such awe of them, as Austin noteth out of Varro. Fear was commonly adored and painted in their Temples with a Lion's head ; and, as Macrobius records (Saturnalia), *in the Calends of January Angerona had her holy day, to whom in the Temple of Volupia,* or Goddess of Pleasure, their Augurs and Bishops did yearly sacrifice ; that, being propitious to them, she might expel all cares, anguish, and vexation of the mind for that year following.* Many lamentable effects this fear causeth in men, as to be red, pale, tremble, sweat, it makes sudden cold and heat to come over all the body, palpitation of the heart, syncope, &c. It amazeth many men that are to speak, or shew themselves in publick assemblies, or before some great personages, as Tully confessed of himself, that he trembled still at the beginning of his speech ; and Demosthenes that great Orator of Greece before Philip. It confounds voice and memory, as Lucian wittily brings in Jupiter Tragœdus so much afraid of his auditory, when he was to make a speech to the rest of the Gods, that he could not utter a ready word, but was compelled to use Mercury's help in prompting. Many men are so amazed and astonished with fear, they know not where they are, what they say, what they do, and that which is worst, it tortures them many days before with continual affrights and suspicion. It hinders most honourable attempts, and makes their hearts ache, sad and heavy. They that live in fear are never free, resolute, secure, never merry, but in continual pain : that, as Vives truly said, no greater misery, no rack, no torture like unto it ; ever suspicious, anxious, solicitous, they are childishly drooping without reason, without judgement, *especially if some terrible object be offered,* as Plutarch hath it. It causeth oftentimes sudden madness, and almost all manner of diseases, as I have sufficiently illustrated in my digression of the Force of

---

* " Ay, in the very temple of Delight
  Veil'd Melancholy has her sovran shrine." — Keats.

Imagination, and shall do more at large in my section of Terrors. Fear makes our imagination conceive what it list, invites the devil to come to us, as Agrippa and Cardan avouch, and tyrannizeth over our phantasy more than all other affections, especially in the dark. We see this verified in most men, as Lavater saith, what they fear they conceive, and feign unto themselves; they think they see Goblins, Hags, Devils, and many times become melancholy thereby. Cardan hath an example of such an one, so caused to be melancholy (by sight of a bugbear) all his life after. Augustus Cæsar durst not sit in the dark, unless some one sat by him, saith Suetonius. And 'tis strange what women and children will conceive unto themselves, if they go over a Church-yard in the night, lie or be alone in a dark room, how they sweat and tremble on a sudden. Many men are troubled with future events, fore-knowledge of their fortunes, destinies, as Severus the Emperor, Adrian, and Domitian, much tortured in mind, saith Suetonius, because he foreknew his end; with many such, of which I shall speak more opportunely in another place. Anxiety, mercy, pity, indignation, &c. and such fearful branches derived from these two stems of fear and sorrow, I voluntarily omit; read more of them in Carolus Pascalius, Dandinus, &c.

SUBSECTION 6 — *Shame and Disgrace, Causes*

SHAME and disgrace cause most violent passions, and bitter pangs. Generous minds are often moved with shame to despair for some pub-lick disgrace. And *he,* saith Philo, *that subjects himself to fear, grief, ambition, shame, is not happy, but altogether miserable, tortured with continual labour, care, and misery.* It is as forcible a batterer as any of the rest. *Many men neglect the tumults of the world, and care not for glory, and yet they are afraid of infamy, repulse, disgrace; they can severely contemn pleasure, bear grief indifferently, but they are quite battered and broken with reproach and obloquy;* and are so dejected many times for some publick injury, disgrace, as a box on the ear by their inferior, to be overcome of their adversary, foiled in the field, to be out in a speech, some foul fact committed or disclosed, &c., that they dare not come abroad all their lives after, but melancholize in corners, and keep in holes. The most generous spirits are most subject to it. Aristotle, because he could not understand the motion of Euripus, for grief and shame drowned himself. Homer was swallowed up with this passion of shame, *because he could not unfold the fisherman's riddle.* Sophocles killed himself, *for that a tragedy of his was hissed off the stage.* Lucretia stabbed herself, and so did Cleopatra, *when she saw that she was reserved for a triumph, to avoid the infamy.* Antonius the

Roman, *after he was overcome of his enemy, for three days' space sat solitary in the fore-part of the ship, abstaining from all company, even of Cleopatra herself, and afterwards for very shame butchered himself. Apollonius Rhodius wilfully banished himself, forsaking his country, and all his dear friends, because he was out in reciting his Poems.* Ajax ran mad, because his arms were adjudged to Ulysses. In China 'tis an ordinary thing for such as are excluded in those famous trials of theirs, or should take degrees, for shame and grief to lose their wits. Hostratus the Friar took that book which Reuchlin had writ against him, under the name of Letters of Obscure Men, so to heart, that for shame and grief he made away himself. A grave and learned Minister, & an ordinary Preacher at Alkmaar in Holland, was (one day as he walked in the fields for his recreation) suddenly taken with a lask or looseness, and thereupon compelled to retire to the next ditch; but being surprised at unawares by some Gentlewomen of his Parish wandering that way, was so abashed, that he did never after shew his head in publick, or come into the Pulpit, but pined away with Melancholy. So shame amongst other passions can play his prize.

I know there be many base, impudent, brazen-faced rogues, that will be moved with nothing, take no infamy or disgrace to heart, laugh at all; let them be proved perjured, stigmatized, convict rogues, thieves, traitors, lose their ears, be whipped, branded, carted, pointed at, hissed, reviled, and derided, with Ballio the Bawd in Plautus, they rejoice at it: Most excellent singer! Wonderful! and Odds bodkins! — what care they? We have too many such in our times. Melicerta says that all modesty has vanished from the world. Yet a modest man, one that hath grace, a generous spirit, tender of his reputation, will be deeply wounded, and so grievously affected with it, that he had rather give myriads of crowns, lose his life, than suffer the least defamation of honour, or blot in his good name. And if so be that he cannot avoid it, as a nightingale (saith Mizaldus), dies for shame, if another bird sing better, he languisheth and pineth away in the anguish of his spirit.

SUBSECTION 7 — *Envy, Malice, Hatred, Causes*

ENVY and Malice are two links of this chain, and both, as Guianerius proves out of Galen, *cause this malady by themselves, especially if their bodies be otherwise disposed to melancholy.* 'Tis Valescus de Taranta and Felix Platerus' observation, *Envy so gnaws many men's hearts, that they become altogether melancholy.* And therefore, belike, Solomon calls it *the rotting of the bones;* Cyprian, an hidden wound; the Sicilian tyrants never invented the like torment. It crucifies their souls, withers their bodies, makes them hollow-ey'd, pale, lean, and ghastly to behold. *As a moth gnaws a garment,* so, saith Chrysostom, *doth envy consume a man :* to be a living anatomy, *a skeleton, to be a lean and pale carcass, quickened with a fiend,* [saith] Hall in " Characters," * for so often as an envious wretch sees another man prosper, to be enriched, to thrive, and be fortunate in the world, to get honours, offices, or the like, he re-pines and grieves :

> *Ill to her the sight of men's content ;*
> *Herself her own worst punishment.*   (OVID)

He tortures himself if his equal, friend, neighbour, be preferred, com-mended, do well, if he understand of it, it galls him afresh, and no greater pain can come to him than to hear of another man's well-doing, 'tis a dagger at his heart every such object. He looks at him, as they that fell down in Lucian's rock of honour, with an envious eye, and will damage himself to do another a mischief. As he did in Æsop, lose one eye willingly, that his fellow might lose both, or that rich man in Quin-tilian, that poisoned the flowers in his garden, because his neighbor's bees should get no more honey from them. His whole life is sorrow, and every word he speaks a *satire,* nothing fats him but other men's ruins. For, to speak in a word, envy is naught else but sorrow for other men's good, be it present, past, or to come : & joy at their harms, opposite to mercy, which grieves at other men's mischances, and mis-affects the body in another kind ; so Damascen defines it, and we find it true. 'Tis a common disease, and almost natural to us, as Tacitus holds, to envy another man's prosperity. And 'tis in most men an incurable disease. *I have read,* saith Marcus Aurelius, *Greek, Hebrew, Chaldee Authors, I have consulted with many wise men, for a remedy for envy, I could find none, but to renounce all happiness, and to be a wretch, and miserable for ever.* 'Tis the beginning of hell in this life, and a passion not to be excused. *Every other sin hath some pleasure annexed to it, or will admit of an excuse ; envy alone wants both. Other sins last but for a while ; the gut may be satisfied, anger remits, hatred hath an end, envy never ceaseth.* Divine and human examples are very familiar, you may run and read them, as that of Saul and David, Cain and Abel, he was not angered because of a wrong, saith Theodoret, it was his brother's good fortune galled him. Rachel envied her sister, being barren ; Joseph's brethren him. David had a touch of this vice, as he confesseth. Jeremy and Habbakuk, they repined at others' good, but in the end they cor-rected themselves. *Fret not thyself, &c.* Domitian spited Agricola for

* Bishop Joseph Hall in " Characters of Virtues and Vices " (1608).

his worth, *that a private man should be so much glorified.* Cæcina was envied of his fellow-citizens, because he was more richly adorned. But of all others, women are most weak, envious against beauty; they love, or hate, no medium amongst them. Wronged women seldom forgive. Agrippina-like, *a woman, if she see her neighbour more neat or elegant, richer in tires, jewels, or apparel, is enraged, & like a lioness sets upon her husband, rails at her, scoffs at her, and cannot abide her;* so the Roman Ladies in Tacitus did at Salonina, Cæcina's wife, *because she had a better horse, and better furniture; as if she had hurt them with it, they were much offended.* In like sort our Gentlewomen do at their usual meetings, one repines or scoffs at another's bravery and happiness. Myrsine, an Attic wench, was murdered of her fellows, *because she did excel the rest in beauty,* [saith] Constantine. Every Village will yield such examples.

SUBSECTION 8 — *Emulation, Hatred, Faction, Desire of revenge,*
Causes

OUT of this root of envy spring those feral branches of faction, hatred, livor, emulation, which cause the like grievances, and are the saws of the soul, affections full of desperate amazement; or, as Cyprian describes emulation, it is *a moth of the soul, a consumption, to make another man's happiness his misery, to torture, crucify, and execute himself, to eat his own heart. Meat and drink can do such men no good, they do always grieve, sigh and groan, day and night; without intermission their breast is torn asunder:* and a little after, *whosoever he is whom thou dost emulate and envy, he may avoid thee, but thou canst neither avoid him, nor thyself; wheresoever thou art, he is with thee, thine enemy is ever in thy breast, thy destruction is within thee, thou art a captive, bound hand and foot, as long as thou art malicious, and envious, and canst not be comforted. It was the devil's overthrow;* and whensoever thou art thoroughly affected with this passion, it will be thine. Yet no perturbation so frequent, no passion so common.

> *A potter emulates a potter;*
> *One smith envies another:*
> *A beggar emulates a beggar;*
> *A singing man his brother.* (HESIOD)

Every society, corporation, and private family, is full of it, it takes hold almost of all sorts of men, from the Prince to the Ploughman, even amongst Gossips it is to be seen; scarce three in a company but there is siding, faction, emulation, between two of them, some dissension, jar, private grudge, heart-burning, in the midst of them. Scarce two Gentlemen dwell together in the Country, (if they be not near kin or linked in marriage), but there is emulation betwixt them and their servants, some quarrel or some grudge betwixt their wives or children, friends and followers, some contention about wealth, gentry, precedency, &c. by means of which, like the frog in Æsop, *that would swell till she was as big as an ox, burst her self at last,* they will stretch beyond their fortunes, callings, and strive so long, that they consume their substance in lawsuits, or otherwise in hospitality, feasting, fine clothes, to get a few bombast titles, for we all vie with one another in our ostentatious poverty; to out-brave one another, they will tire their bodies, macerate their souls, and through contentions or mutual invitations beggar themselves. Scarce two great Scholars in an age, but with bitter invectives they fall foul one on the other, and their adherents; Scotists, Thomists, Realists, Nominalists, Platonists, and Aristotelians, Galenists and Paracelsians, &c. It holds in all professions.

Honest emulation in studies, in all callings, is not to be disliked, 'tis, as one calls it, the whetstone of wit, the nurse of wit and valour, and those noble Romans out of this spirit did brave exploits. There is a modest ambition, as Themistocles was roused up with the glory of Miltiades, Achilles' trophies moved Alexander.

> *'Tis silly impudence to strive ever;*
> *But idle conceit to strive never.*   (GROTIUS)

'Tis a sluggish humour not to emulate or to sue at all, to withdraw himself, neglect, refrain from such places, honours, offices, through sloth, niggardliness, fear, bashfulness, or otherwise to which by his birth, place, fortunes, education, he is called, apt, fit, and well able to undergo; but when it is immoderate, it is a plague and a miserable pain. What a deal of money did Henry the 8, & Francis the First, King of France, spend at that famous interview! and how many vain Courtiers, seeking each to out-brave other, spent themselves, their livelihood and fortunes, and died beggars! Adrian the Emperor was so galled with it, that he killed all his equals; so did Nero. This passion made Dionysius the Tyrant banish Plato and Philoxenus the Poet, because they did excel and eclipse his glory, as he thought; the Romans exile Coriolanus, confine Camillus, murder Scipio; the Greeks by *ostracism* to expel Aristides, Nicias, Alcibiades, imprison Theseus, make away Phocion, &c. When Richard the First, and Philip of France, were fellow-soldiers together at the siege of Acre in the Holy Land, and Richard had approved himself to be the more valiant man, in so much that all men's eyes were upon him, it so galled Philip, saith mine Author, that he cavilled at all his proceedings, and fell at length to open defiance; he could contain no longer, but, hasting home, invaded his territories, and professed open war. Hatred stirs up contention, and they break out at last into immortal enmity, into virulency, and more than *Vatinian* * hate and rage; they persecute each other, their friends, followers, and all their posterity, with bitter taunts, hostile wars, scurrile invectives, libels, calumnies, fire, sword, and the like, and will not be reconciled. Witness that Guelph and Ghibeline faction in Italy; that of the Adurni and Fregosi in Genoa; that of Cnæus Papirius & Quintus Fabius in Rome; Cæsar and Pompey; Orleans and Burgundy in France; York and Lancaster in England. Yea, this passion so rageth many times, that it subverts not men only, and families, but even populous Cities. Carthage and Corinth can witness as much, nay, flourishing Kingdoms are brought into a wilderness by it. This hatred, malice, faction, and desire of revenge, invented first all those racks, and wheels, strappadoes, brazen bulls, feral engines, prisons, inquisitions, severe laws, to macerate and torment one another. How happy might we be, and end our time with blessed days and sweet content, if we could contain ourselves, and, as we ought to do, put up injuries, learn humility, meekness, patience, forget and forgive, as in God's word we are enjoined, compose such small controversies amongst ourselves, moderate our passions in this kind, *and think better of others,* as Paul would have us, *than of ourselves: be of like affection one towards another, and not avenge ourselves, but have peace with all men!* But being that we are so peevish and perverse, insolent and proud, so factious and seditious, so malicious and envious, we do by turns harass, maul and vex one another, torture, disquiet, and precipitate ourselves into that gulf of woes and cares, aggravate our misery and melancholy, heap upon us hell and eternal damnation.

SUBSECTION 9 — *Anger a Cause*

ANGER, a perturbation, which carries the spirits outwards, preparing the body to melancholy, and madness itself: anger is temporary madness; and, as Piccolomineus accounts it, one of the three most violent passions. Aretæus sets it down for an especial cause (so doth Seneca) of this malady. Magninus gives the reason; it over-heats their bodies, and, if it be too frequent, it breaks out into manifest madness, saith S. Ambrose. 'Tis a known saying, the most patient spirit that is, if he be often

---

* Vatinius was a Roman so vehemently attacked in publick by Cicero for his crimes, that " Vatinian crime " and " Vatinian hate " became proverbial expressions.

provoked, will be incensed to madness, it will make a Devil of a Saint. And therefore Basil (belike) in his Homily On Anger, calls it the darkening of our understanding, and a bad Angel. Lucian, in Renunciation, will have this passion to work this effect, especially in old men and women. *Anger and calumny* (saith he) *trouble them at first, and after a while break out into open madness: many things cause fury in women, especially if they love or hate overmuch, or envy, be much grieved or angry; these things by little and little lead them on to this malady.* From a disposition they proceed to an habit, for there is no difference betwixt a mad man and an angry man in the time of his fit. Anger, as Lactantius describes it, is a cruel tempest of the mind, *making his eyes sparkle fire, and stare, teeth gnash in his head, his tongue stutter, his face pale or red, and what more filthy imitation can be of a mad man?*

> *With anger faces swollen show,*
> *The veins turn black with rush of blood,*
> *The eyes with Gorgon fires aglow.*   (OVID)

They are void of reason, inexorable, blind, like beasts & monsters for the time, say and do they know not what, curse, swear, rail, fight, and what not? How can a mad man do more? As he said in the Comedy, I am not mine own man. If these fits be immoderate, continue long, or be frequent, without doubt they provoke madness. Montanus had a melancholy Jew to his patient, he ascribes this for a principal cause: he was easily moved to anger. Ajax had no other beginning of his madness; and Charles the Sixth, that lunatick French King, fell into this misery out of the extremity of his passion, desire of revenge, and malice; incensed against the Duke of Britain, he could neither eat, drink, nor sleep, for some days together, and in the end, about the Calends of July, 1392, he became mad upon his horse-back, drawing his sword, striking such as came near him promiscuously, and so continued all the days of his life. Æmilius hath such a story of Herod, that out of an angry fit became mad; leaping out of his bed, he killed Joseph, and played many such Bedlam pranks, the whole Court could not rule him for a long time after. Sometimes he was sorry and repented, much grieved for that he had done, after his anger had cooled down, by & by outrageous again. In hot cholerick bodies, nothing so soon causeth madness as this passion of anger, besides many other diseases, as Pelesius observes. It diminishes blood, it increases bile: and, as Valesius controverts, many times kills them quite out. If this were the worst of this passion, it were more tolerable, *but it ruins and subverts whole towns, cities, families, and kingdoms.* No plague, saith Seneca, hath done mankind so much harm.

Look into our Histories, and you shall almost meet with no other subject, but what a company of hare-brains have done in their rage! We may do well therefore, to put this in our litany amongst the rest: *From all blindness of heart, from pride, vain-glory, and hypocrisy, from envy, hatred, and malice, anger, and all such pestiferous perturbations, Good Lord, deliver us!*

SUBSECTION 10 — *Discontents, Cares, Miseries, &c., Causes*

DISCONTENTS, cares, crosses, miseries, or whatsoever it is, that shall cause any molestation of spirits, grief, anguish, and perplexity, may well be reduced to this head. Preposterously placed here in some men's judgments they may seem; yet in that Aristotle in his Rhetorick defines these cares, as he doth envy, emulation, &c., still by grief, I think I may well rank them in this irascible row; being that they are, as the rest, both causes and symptoms of this disease, producing the like inconveniences, and are most part accompanied with anguish and pain. The common etymology will evince it, the heart is well nigh consumed with care, — biting, eating, gnawing, cruel, bitter, sick, sad, unquiet, pale, tetrick, miserable, intolerable cares, as the Poets call them, worldly cares, and are as many in number as the sea sands. Galen, Fernelius, Felix Plater, Valescus de Taranta, &c., reckon afflictions, miseries, even all these contentions, and vexations of the mind, as principal causes, in that they take away sleep, hinder concoction, dry up the body, and consume the substance of it. They are not so many in number, but their causes be as diverse, and not one of a thousand free from them, or that can vindicate himself, whom that *Ate Dea,*

> *Over men's heads walking aloft,*
> *With tender feet treading so soft,* (LUCIAN)

Homer's Goddess *Ate,* hath not involved into this discontented rank, or plagued with some misery or other. Hyginus to this purpose hath a pleasant tale. Dame Cura by chance went over a brook, and, taking up some of the dirty slime, made an image of it; Jupiter, eftsoons coming by, put life to it, but Cura and Jupiter could not agree what name to give him, or who should own him. The matter was referred to Saturn as Judge, he gave this arbitrement; his name shall be Earth-Man, Care shall have him whilst he lives; Jupiter his soul, and Tellus his body, when he dies. But to leave tales, a general cause, a continuate cause, an inseparable accident to all men, is discontent, care, misery; were there no other particular affliction (which who is free from?) to molest a man in this life, the very cogitation of that common misery were enough to macerate, and make him weary of his life; to think that he can never be secure, but still in danger, sorrow, grief, and persecution. For to begin at the hour of his birth, as Pliny doth elegantly describe it, *he is born naked, and falls a whining at the very first, he is swaddled and bound up like a prisoner, cannot help himself, and so he continues to his life's end;* the food of every wild beast, saith Seneca, impatient of heat and cold, impatient of labour, impatient of idleness, exposed to Fortune's contumelies. To a naked mariner Lucretius compares him, cast on shore by shipwreck, cold and comfortless in an unknown land: no estate, age, sex, can secure himself from this common misery. *A man that is born of a woman is of short continuance, and full of trouble; and, while his flesh is upon him, he shall be sorrowful, and, while his soul is in him, it shall mourn. All his days are sorrow, and his travail grief, his heart also taketh not rest in the night. All that is in it is sorrow and vexation of spirit.* Ingress, progress, regress, egress, much alike. *Blindness seizeth on us in the beginning, labour in the middle, grief in the end, error in all. What day ariseth to us, without some grief, care, or anguish? Or what so secure and pleasing a morning have we seen, that hath not been overcast before the evening?* One is miserable, another ridiculous, a third odious. One complains of this grievance, another of that: now the head aches, then the feet, now the lungs, then the liver, &c.; he is rich, but base born; he is noble, but poor; a third hath means, but he wants health, peradventure, or wit to manage his estate. Children vex one, wife a second, &c. No man is pleased with his fortune, a pound of sorrow is familiarly mixt with a dram of content, little or no joy, little comfort, but everywhere danger, contention, anxiety in all places. Go where thou wilt, and thou shalt find discontents, cares, woes, complaints, sickness, diseases, incumbrances, exclamations. *If thou look into the Market, there* (saith Chrysostom) *is brawling and contention, if to the Court, there knavery and flattery, &c., if to a private man's house, there's cark & care, heaviness, &c.* As he said of old, No creature so miserable as man, so generally molested, *in miseries of body, in miseries of mind, miseries of heart, in miseries asleep, in miseries awake, in miseries wheresoever he turns,* as Bernard found. A mere temptation is our life, on this earth, ever fettered of sorrow: Who can endure the miseries of it? *In prosperity we are insolent and intolerable, dejected in adversity, in all fortunes foolish & miserable. In adversity I wish for prosperity, & in prosperity I am afraid of adversity. What mediocrity may be found? where is no temptation? what condition of life is free? Wisdom hath labour annexed to it, glory envy; riches & cares, chil-*

dren & incumbrances, pleasure & diseases, rest & beggary, go to-
gether: as if a man were therefore born, (as the Platonists hold),
to be punished in this life for some precedent sins; or that, as Pliny
complains, *Nature may be rather accounted a stepmother than a*
mother unto us, all things considered. No creature's life so brittle, so
full of fear, so mad, so furious; only man is plagued with envy, discon-
tent, griefs, covetousness, ambition, superstition. Our whole life is an
Irish Sea, wherein there is naught to be expected but tempestuous
storms and troublesome waves, and those infinite;

> *So great a sea of troubles do I see,*
> *That to swim out from it does seem impossible;*   (EURIPIDES)

no Halcyonian times, wherein a man can hold himself secure, or agree
with his present estate: but, as Boethius infers, *there is something in*
every one of us, which before trial we seek, & having tried abhor: we
earnestly wish, and eagerly covet, and are eftsoons weary of it. Thus
betwixt hope and fear, suspicions, angers, betwixt falling in, falling out,
&c., we bangle away our best days, befool out our times, we lead a
contentious, discontent, tumultuous, melancholy, miserable life; insomuch, that if we could foretell what was to come, and it put to our
choice, we should rather refuse than accept of this painful life. In a
word, the world itself is a maze, a labyrinth of errors, a desert, a wilderness, a den of thieves, cheaters, &c., full of filthy puddles, horrid rocks,
precipices, an ocean of adversity, an heavy yoke, wherein infirmities
and calamities overtake and follow one another, as the sea waves; and
if we scape Scylla, we fall foul on Charybdis, and so, in perpetual fear,
labour, anguish, we run from one plague, one mischief, one burden, to
another, serving a hard servitude, and you may as soon separate weight
from lead, heat from fire, moistness from water, brightness from the
sun, as misery, discontent, care, calamity, danger, from a man. Our
Towns and Cities are but so many dwellings of human misery; *in which*
grief and sorrow (as he right well observes out of Solon) *innumerable*
troubles, labours of mortal men, and all manner of vices, are included
as in so many pens. Our villages are like mole-hills, and men as so many
emmets, busy, busy still, going to and fro, in and out, and crossing one
another's projects, as the lines of several *sea-cards* cut each other in a
globe or map. *Now light and merry,* but (as one follows it) *by-and-by*
sorrowful and heavy; now hoping, then distrusting; now patient, to-
morrow crying out; now pale, then red; running, sitting, sweating,
trembling, halting, &c. Some few amongst the rest, or perhaps one of a
thousand, may be Jove's favourite, in the World's esteem, the white

hen's chick, an happy and fortunate man, because rich, fair, well allied, in honour and office; yet peradventure ask himself, and he will say that, of all others, he is most miserable and unhappy. A fair shoe, as he said, but thou knowest not where it pincheth. It is not another man's opinion can make me happy; but, as Seneca well hath it, *he is a miserable wretch, that doth not account himself happy; though he be Sovereign Lord of a world, he is not happy, if he think himself not to be so: for what availeth it what thine estate is, or seem to others, if thou thyself dislike it?* A common humour it is of all men to think well of other men's fortunes, and dislike their own: but how comes it to pass, Maecenas? what's the cause of it? Many men are of such a perverse nature, they are well pleased with nothing (saith Theodoret) *neither with riches nor poverty, they complain when they are well and when they are sick, grumble at all fortunes, prosperity and adversity; they are troubled in a cheap year, in a barren, plenty or not plenty, nothing pleaseth them, war nor peace, with children, nor without.* This for the most part is the humour of us all, to be discontent, miserable, and most unhappy, as we think at least; and shew me him that is not so, or that ever was otherwise. Quintus Metellus his felicity is infinitely admired amongst the Romans, insomuch, that as Paterculus mentioneth of him, you can scarce find of any nation, order, age, sex, one for happiness to be compared unto him: he had, in a word, goods of mind, body, and fortune; so had P. Mutianus Crassus. Lampito, that Lacedæmonian Lady, was such another in Pliny's conceit, *a King's wife, a King's mother, a King's daughter.* And all the world esteemed as much of Polycrates of Samos. The Greeks brag of their Socrates, Phocion, Aristides; the Psophidians in particular of their Aglaus, a happy life for all, free from all danger (which by the way Pausanias held impossible) the Romans of their Cato, Curius, Fabricius, for their composed fortunes, and retired estates, government of passions, and contempt of the world: yet none of all these was happy, or free from discontent; neither Metellus, Crassus, nor Polycrates, for he died a violent death, and so did Cato: and how much evil doth Lactantius and Theodoret speak of Socrates, a weak man, and so of the rest. There is no content in this life, but, as he said, all is *vanity and vexation of spirit;* lame and imperfect. Hadst thou Samson's hair, Milo's strength, Scanderberg's arm, Solomon's wisdom, Absalom's beauty, Crœsus his wealth, the obol of Pasetes, Cæsar's valour, Alexander's spirit, Tully's or Demosthenes' eloquence, Gyges' ring, Perseus' Pesagus, and Gorgon's head, Nestor's years to come, all this would not make thee absolute, give thee content, and true happiness, in this life,

or so continue it. Even in the midst of all our mirth, jollity, and laughter, is sorrow and grief: or if there be true happiness amongst us, 'tis
but for a time;

A handsome maid above, a fish below, (HORACE)

a fair morning turns to a lowering afternoon. Brutus and Cassius, once
renowned, both eminently happy, yet you shall scarce find two (saith
Paterculus), whom fortune sooner forsook. Hannibal, a conqueror all
his life, met with his match, and was subdued at last. One is brought in
triumph, as Cæsar into Rome, Alcibiades into Athens, crowned, honoured, admired; by-and-by his statues demolished, he hissed out, massacred, &c. Magnus Gonsalvo, that famous Spaniard, was of the Prince
and people at first honoured, approved; forthwith confined & banished;
'tis Polybius his observation, grievous enmities, and bitter calumnies,
commonly follow renowned actions. One is born rich, dies a beggar:
sound to-day, sick to-morrow: now in most flourishing estate, fortunate
and happy, by-and-by deprived of his goods by foreign enemies, robbed
by thieves, spoiled, captivated, impoverished, as they of Rabbah, *put
under iron saws, and under iron harrows, and under axes of iron, and
cast into the tile-kiln.*

Why, friends, so often did you call me happy?

He that has fallen never was secure. (BOETHIUS)

He that erst marched like Xerxes with innumerable armies, as rich as
Crœsus, now shifts for himself in a poor cock-boat, is bound in iron
chains with Bajazet the Turk, & a foot-stool with Aurelian, for a tyrannizing conqueror to trample on. So many casualties there are, that, as
Seneca said of a City consumed with fire, one day betwixt a great city
and none: so many grievances from outward accidents, and from ourselves, our own indiscretion, inordinate appetite, one day betwixt a man
and no man. And which is worse, as if discontents and miseries would
not come fast enough upon us, man is a devil to his fellow man; we
maul, persecute, and study how to sting, gall, and vex one another with
mutual hatred, abuses, injuries; preying upon, and devouring, as so
many ravenous birds; and, as jugglers, pandars, bawds, cozening one
another; or raging as wolves, tigers, and devils, we take a delight to
torment one another; men are evil, wicked, malicious, treacherous, and
naught, not loving one another, or loving themselves, not hospitable,
charitable, nor sociable, as they ought to be, but counterfeit, dissemblers,
ambidexters, all for their own ends, hard-hearted, merciless, pitiless, and,
to benefit themselves, they care not what mischief they procure to others.
Praxinoe and Gorgo in the Poet, [Theocritus, Idyll XV] when they had

got to see those costly sights, they then cried, We're all right now! and would thrust out all the rest: when they are rich themselves, in honour preferred, full, and have even that they would, they debar others of those pleasures which youth requires, and they formerly have enjoyed. He sits at table in a soft chair at ease, but he doth not remember in the mean time that a tired waiter stands behind him, *an hungry fellow ministers to him full, he is athirst that gives him drink* (saith Epictetus) *& is silent while he speaks his pleasure; pensive, sad, when he laughs.* He drinks from golden goblets; he feasts, revels, and profusely spends, hath variety of robes, sweet musick, ease, and all the pleasure the world can afford, whilst many an hunger-starved poor creature pines in the street, wants clothes to cover him, labours hard all day long, runs, rides, for a trifle, fights peradventure from sun to sun, sick and ill, weary, full of pain and grief, is in great distress and sorrow of heart. He loathes and scorns his inferior, hates or emulates his equal, envies his superior, insults over all such as are under him, as if he were of another *species*, a demi-god, not subject to any fall, or human infirmities. Generally they love not, are not beloved again: they tire out others' bodies with continual labour, they themselves living at ease, caring for none else, born to themselves; and are so far many times from putting to their helping hand, that they seek all means to depress even most worthy and well deserving, better than themselves, those whom they are by the laws of nature bound to relieve and help, as much as in them lies, they will let them cater-waul, starve, beg, and hang, before they will any ways (though it be in their power) assist, or ease: so unnatural are they for the most part, so unregardful, so hard-hearted, so churlish, proud, insolent, so dogged, of so bad a disposition. And being so brutish, so devilishly bent one towards another, how is it possible, but that we should be discontent of all sides, full of cares, woes, and miseries?

If this be not a sufficient proof of their discontent and misery, examine every condition and calling apart. Kings, Princes, Monarchs, and Magistrates, seem to be most happy, but look into their estate, you shall find them to be most encumbered with cares, in perpetual fear, agony, suspicion, jealousy: that, as he said of a Crown, if they knew but the discontents that accompany it, they would not stoop to take it up. What King (saith Chrysostom) canst thou shew me not full of cares? *Look not on his crown, but consider his afflictions: attend not his number of servants, but multitude of crosses.* 'Tis nothing more than the height of responsibility, as Gregory seconds him; sovereignty is a tempest of the soul: Sylla-like they have brave titles, but terrible fits: which made

Demosthenes vow, if to be a Judge, or to be condemned, were put to his choice, he would be condemned. Rich men are in the same predicament: what their pains are they feel, fools perceive not, as I shall prove elsewhere, and their wealth is brittle, like children's rattles: they come and go, there is no certainty in them; those whom they elevate, they do as suddenly depress, and leave in a vale of misery. The middle sort of men are as so many asses to bear burdens; or, if they be free, and live at ease, they spend themselves, and consume their bodies and fortunes with luxury and riot, contention, emulation, &c. The poor I reserve for another place, and their discontents.

For particular professions, I hold, as of the rest, there's no content or security in any. On what course will you pitch, how resolve? To be a Divine? 'tis contemptible in the world's esteem: to be a Lawyer? 'tis to be a wrangler: to be a Physician? a piss-prophet, 'tis loathed: a Philosopher? a mad man: an Alchemist? a beggar: a Poet? an hungry Jack: a Musician? a player: a School-master? a drudge: an Husband-man? an Emmet: a Merchant? his gains are uncertain: a Mechanician? base: a Chirurgeon? fulsome: a Tradesman? a liar: a Tailor? a thief: a Servingman? a slave: a Soldier? a butcher: a Smith, or a Metalman? the pot's never from 's nose: a Courtier? a parasite. As he could find no tree in the wood to hang himself, I can shew no state of life to give content. The like you may say of all ages: children live in a perpetual slavery, still under that tyrannical government of masters: young men, and of riper years, subject to labour, and a thousand cares of the world, to treachery, falsehood, and cozenage,

He treads on smothered fires, scarce extinct,　(HORACE)

old are full of aches in their bones, cramps and convulsions, earthbent, dull of hearing, weak-sighted, hoary, wrinkled, harsh, so much altered as that they cannot know their own face in a glass, a burden to themselves and others; after 70 years, *all is sorrow* (as David hath it), they do not live but linger. If they be sound, they fear diseases; if sick, weary of their lives: Long years are not life; healthy years are life. One complains of want, a second of servitude, another of a secret or incurable disease, of some deformity of body, of some loss, danger, death of friends, shipwreck, persecution, imprisonment, disgrace, repulse, contumely, calumny, abuse, injury, contempt, ingratitude, unkindness, scoffs, flouts, unfortunate marriage, single life, too many children, no children, unhappy children, barrenness, false servants, banishment, oppression, frustrate hopes, and ill success, &c. Cases like these are so many that talking Fabius will be tired before he can tell half of them;

they are the subject of whole volumes, and shall (some of them) be more opportunely dilated elsewhere. In the mean time thus much I may say of them, that generally they crucify the soul of man, attenuate our bodies, dry them, wither them, rivel them up like old apples, make them as so many anatomies (he is all skin and bones, so thin is he with cares), they cause cumbersome days, slow, dull, and heavy times; make us howl, roar, and tear our hairs, as Sorrow did in Cebes' Table, and groan for the very anguish of our souls. Our hearts fail us, as David's did, for innumerable troubles that compassed him; and we are ready to confess with Hezekiah, *behold, for felicity I had bitter grief:* to weep with Heraclitus, to curse the day of our birth with Jeremy, and our stars with Job: to hold that axiom of Silenus, *better never to have been born, and the next best of all to die quickly:* or, if we must live, to abandon the world, as Timon did, creep into caves and holes, as our Anchorites; cast all into the sea, as Crates Thebanus: or, as Cleombrotus Ambraciotes' 400 auditors, precipitate ourselves to be rid of these miseries.

SUBSECTION 11 — *Concupiscible Appetite, as Desires, Ambition, Causes*

THESE concupiscible and irascible appetites are as the two twists of a rope, mutually mixt one with the other, and both twining about the heart: both good, as Austin holds, *if they be moderate: both pernicious if they be exorbitant.* This concupiscible appetite, howsoever it may seem to carry with it a shew of pleasure and delight, and our concupiscences most part affect us with content and a pleasing object, yet, if they be in extremes, they rack & wring us on the other side. A true saying it is, *Desire hath no rest,* is infinite in itself, endless, & as one calls it, a perpetual rack, or horse-mill, according to Austin, still going round as in a ring. They are not so continual, as divers, saith Bernard, you may as well reckon up the motes in the Sun as them. *It extends itself to every thing,* as Guianerius will have it, *that is superfluously sought after:* or to any *fervent desire,* as Fernelius interprets it; be it in what kind soever, it tortures, if immoderate, and is (according to Plater and others) an especial cause of melancholy. Austin confessed that he was torn a pieces with his manifold desires: and so doth Bernard complain, *that he could not rest for them a minute of an hour: this I would have, and that, and then I desire to be such and such.* 'Tis a hard matter therefore to confine them, being they are so various and many, unpossible to apprehend all. I will only insist upon some few of the chief, and most noxious in their kind, as that exorbitant appetite and desire of honour, which we commonly call *ambition:* love of money, which is *covetousness,* and that greedy desire of gain: *self-love,* pride, and inordinate desire of *vain-glory* or applause; *love of study* in excess: *love of women,* (which will require a just volume of itself). Of the other I will briefly speak, and in their order.

Ambition, a proud covetousness, or a dry thirst of honour, a great torture of the mind, composed of envy, pride, and covetousness, a gallant madness, one defines it, a pleasant poison, Ambrose, *a canker of the soul, an hidden plague:* Bernard, *a secret poison, the father of livor,** *and mother of hypocrisy, the moth of holiness, and cause of madness, crucifying and disquieting all that it takes hold of.* Seneca calls it a windy thing, a vain, solicitous, and fearful thing. For commonly they that, like Sisyphus, roll this restless stone of ambition, are in a perpetual agony, still perplexed, always falling back, silently & sadly, (Lucretius) doubtful, timorous, suspicious, loth to offend in word or deed, still cogging and colloguing, embracing, capping, cringing, applauding, flattering, fleering, visiting, waiting at men's doors, with all affability, counterfeit honesty and humility. If that will not serve, if once this humour (as Cyprian describes it) possess his thirsty soul, by hook and by crook he will obtain it, *& from his hole he will climb to all honours & offices, if it be possible for him to get up; flattering one, bribing another, he will leave no means unassay'd to win all.* It is a wonder to see how slavishly these kind of men subject themselves, when they are about a suit, to every inferior person; what pains they will take, run, ride, cast, plot, countermine, protest and swear, vow, promise, what labours undergo, early up, down late; how obsequious and affable they are, how popular and courteous, how they grin and fleer upon every man they meet; with what feasting and inviting, how they spend themselves and their fortunes, in seeking that many times, which they had much better be without, as Cineas the Orator told Pyrrhus: with what waking nights, painful hours, anxious thoughts, and bitterness of mind, betwixt hope and fear, distracted and tired, they consume the *interim* of their time. There can be no greater plague for the present. If they do obtain their suit, which with such cost and solicitude they have sought, they are not so freed, their anxiety is anew to begin, for they are never satisfied; their thoughts, actions, endeavours are all for sovereignty & honour, like Lues Sforza, that huffing Duke of Milan, *a man of singular wisdom, but profound ambition, born to his own, & to the destruction of Italy;* though it be to their own ruin, & friends' undoing, they will contend, they may not cease; but, as a dog in a wheel, a bird in a cage, or a squirrel in a

* Envy.

chain, (so Budæus compares them), they climb and climb still, with
much labour, but never make an end, never at the top. A Knight would
be a Baronet, and then a Lord, and then a Viscount, and then an Earl,
&c., a Doctor a Dean, and then a Bishop: from Tribune to Prætor: from
Bailiff to Mayor: first this office, and then that; as Pyrrhus in Plutarch,
they will first have Greece, then Africa, and then Asia, and swell with
Æsop's frog so long, till in the end they burst, or come down with
Sejanus to the Gemonian steps,* and break their own necks: or as
Evangelus the piper, in Lucian, that blew his pipe so long, till he fell
down dead. If he chance to miss, and have a canvas,† he is in a hell on
the other side; so dejected, that he is ready to hang himself, turn
Heretick, Turk, or Traitor, in an instant. Enraged against his enemies,
he rails, swears, fights, slanders, detracts, envies, murders: and, for his
own part, if he cannot satisfy his desire (as Bodine writes) he runs mad.
So that both ways, hit or miss, he is distracted so long as his ambition
lasts, he can look for no other but anxiety and care, discontent and grief,
in the mean time; madness itself, or violent death, in the end. The event
of this is common to be seen in populous Cities, or in Princes' Courts;
for a Courtier's life (as Budæus describes it) *is a gallimaufry of ambition, lust, fraud, imposture, dissimulation, detraction, envy, pride; the
Court, a common conventicle of flatterers, time-servers, politicians, &c.*
or (as Anthony Perez will) *the suburbs of hell itself.* If you will see such
discontented persons, there you shall likely find them. And, which he
observed of the markets of old Rome,

> *In case you would meet a perjurer, go to the Comitium;*
> *For a liar and a blow-hard, try the temple of Venus Cloacina;*
> *For rich marriage spendthrifts take the Basilica.*   (PLAUTUS)

Perjur'd knaves, Knights of the Post, liars, crackers, bad husbands, &c.
keep their several stations, they do still, and always did, in every commonwealth.

SUBSECTION 12 — *Covetousness, a Cause*

PLUTARCH, in his book whether the diseases of the body be more grievous than those of the soul, is of opinion, *if you will examine all the
causes of our miseries in this life, you shall find them most part to have
had their beginning from stubborn anger, that furious desire of contention, or some unjust or immoderate affection, as covetousness, &c.* From
whence *are wars and contentions amongst you?* S. James asks. I will add
usury, fraud, rapine, Simony, oppression, lying, swearing, bearing false

* Down which, in Rome, the bodies of executed criminals were dragged.
† Be " given the sack," be dismissed.

witness, &c. are they not from this fountain of covetousness, that greediness in getting, tenacity in keeping, sordidity in spending? that they are so wicked, *unjust against God, their neighbour, themselves,* all comes hence. *The desire of money is the root of all evil, and they that lust after it, pierce themselves through with many sorrows.* Hippocrates therefore, in his Epistle to Crateva, an Herbalist, gives him this good counsel, that, if it were possible, *amongst other herbs, he should cut up that weed of covetousness by the roots, that there be no remainder left ; and then know this for a certainty, that together with their bodies, thou mayst quickly cure all diseases of their minds.* For it is indeed the pattern, image, epitome of all Melancholy, the fountain of many miseries, much discontent, care and woe ; this *inordinate or immoderate desire of gain, to get or keep money,* as Bonaventure defines it : or, as Austin describes it, a madness of the soul ; Gregory, a torture ; Chrysostom, an insatiable drunkenness : Cyprian, blindness, a gilded torture, a plague subverting Kingdoms, families, an incurable disease ; Budæus, an ill habit, *yielding to no remedies :* neither Æsculapius nor Plutus can cure them : a continual plague, saith Solomon, and vexation of spirit, another Hell. I know there be some of opinion that covetous men are happy, and worldly wise, that there is more pleasure in getting of wealth than in spending, and no delight in the world like unto it. 'Twas Bias' problem of old, *With what art thou not weary? with getting money. What is most delectable? to gain.* What is it, trow you, that makes a poor man labour all his life time, carry such great burdens, fare so hardly, macerate himself, and endure so much misery, undergo such base offices with so great patience, to rise up early, & lie down late, if there were not an extraordinary delight in getting & keeping of money? What makes a Merchant that hath no need, that hath enough and to spare at home, to range all over the world, through all those intemperate Zones of heat & cold ; voluntarily to venture his life, and be content with such miserable famine, nasty usage, in a stinking ship, if there were not a pleasure & hope to get money, which doth season the rest, and mitigate his indefatigable pains? What makes them go into the bowels of the earth an hundred fathom deep, endangering their dearest lives, enduring damps and filthy smells, when they have enough already, if they could be content, and no such cause to labour, but an extraordinary delight they take in riches? This may seem plausible at first shew, a popular and strong argument ; but let him that so thinks consider better of it, and he shall soon perceive that it is far otherwise than he supposeth ; it may be haply pleasing at the first, as most part all melancholy is. For such men

likely have some lucid intervals, pleasant symptoms intermixt. But you
must note that of Chrysostom, *'Tis one thing to be rich, another to be
covetous;* generally they are all fools, dizzards, mad-men, miserable
wretches, living besides themselves, with no notion of enjoyment, in
perpetual slavery, fear, suspicion, sorrow, and discontent, they have
more gall than honey; and are, indeed, *rather possessed by their money
than possessors,* as Cyprian hath it; bound prentice to their goods, as
Pliny; or as Chrysostom, slaves & drudges to their substance; and we
may conclude of them all, as Valerius doth of Ptolemæus, King of
Cyprus, *he was in title a King of that Island, but in his mind a miserable drudge of money,* wanting his liberty, which is better than gold.
Damasippus the Stoick, in Horace, proves that all mortal men dote by
fits, some one way, some another, but that covetous men are madder
than the rest; and he that shall truly look into their estates, & examine
their symptoms, shall find no better of them, but that they are all fools,
as Nabal was, both in name and thing. For what greater folly can there
be, or madness, than to macerate himself when he need not? and when,
as Cyprian notes, *he may be freed from his burden, and eased of his
pains, will go on still, his wealth increasing, when he hath enough, to get
more, to live besides himself,* to starve his *Genius,* keep back from his
wife and children, neither letting them nor other friends use or enjoy
that which is theirs by right, and which they much need perhaps; like
a hog, or dog in the manger, he doth only keep it, because it shall do
nobody else good, hurting himself and others; and, for a little momentary pelf, damn his own soul? They are commonly sad and tetrick by
nature, as Ahab's spirit was because he could not get Naboth's Vineyard, and if he lay out his money at any time, though it be to necessary
uses, to his own Children's good, he brawls and scolds, his heart is
heavy, much disquieted he is, and loth to part from it: stinting himself,
and fearing to make use of it. He is of a wearish, dry, pale constitution,
and cannot sleep for cares and worldly business, his riches, saith Solomon, will not let him sleep, and unnecessary business which he heapeth
on himself; or, if he do sleep, 'tis a very unquiet, interrupt, unpleasing
sleep, with his bags in his arms. And though he be at a banquet, or at
some merry feast, *he sighs for grief of heart* (as Cyprian hath it) *and
cannot sleep though it be upon a down bed; his wearish body takes no
rest, troubled in his abundance, & sorrowful in plenty, unhappy for the
present, and more unhappy in the life to come,* Basil. He is a perpetual
drudge, restless in his thoughts, & never satisfied, a slave, a wretch, a
dust-worm; still seeking what sacrifice he may offer to his golden god,

by right or wrong, he cares not how; his trouble is endless, his wealth increaseth, and the more he hath, the more he wants: like Pharaoh's lean kine, which devoured the fat, & were not satisfied. Austin therefore defines covetousness, an unhonest & unsatiable desire of gain; & in one of his Epistles compares it to Hell, *which devours all, and yet never hath enough, a bottomless pit,* an endless misery; on which rock of avarice whitened old men are broken, and, that which is their greatest corrosive, they are in continual suspicion, fear, and distrust. He thinks his own wife and children are so many thieves, and go about to cozen him, his servants are all false:

> *If his doors creek, then out he cries anon,*
> *His goods are gone, and he is quite undone.* (PLAUTUS)

Timid Plutus, an old proverb, as fearful as Plutus: so doth Aristophanes, & Lucian, bring him in fearful still, pale, anxious, suspicious, and trusting no man. *They are afraid of tempests for their corn, they are afraid of their friends, lest they should ask something of them, beg or borrow; they are afraid of their enemies, lest they hurt them, thieves lest they rob them; they are afraid of war & afraid of peace, afraid of rich & afraid of poor; afraid of all.* Last of all, they are afraid of want, that they shall die beggars, which makes them lay up still, and dare not use that they have: (what if a dear year come, or dearth, or some loss?) and were it not that they are loth to lay out money on a rope, they would be hanged forthwith, and sometimes die to save charges, & make away themselves, if their corn & cattle miscarry, though they have abundance left, as A. Gellius notes. Valerius makes mention of one that in a famine sold a mouse for 200 pence, and famished himself: such are their cares, griefs and perpetual fears. These symptoms are elegantly expressed by Theophrastus in his character of a covetous man; *lying in bed, he asked his wife whether she shut the trunks and chests fast, the capcase* be sealed, and whether the hall door be bolted; and, though she say all is well, he riseth out of his bed in his shirt, bare foot and barelegged, to see whether it be so, with a dark lanthorn searching every corner,* scarce sleeping a wink all night. Lucian, in that pleasant and witty dialogue called Gallus, brings in Micyllus the cobbler disputing with his cock, sometime Pythagoras; where after much speech, *pro* and *con,* to prove the happiness of a mean estate, and discontents of a rich man, Pythagoras his cock in the end, to illustrate by examples that which he had said, brings him to Gnipho the usurer's house at mid-night, and after that to Eucrates; whom they found both awake, casting up their ac-

* Money-box.

counts, and telling of their money, lean, dry, pale and anxious, still suspecting lest some body should make a hole through the wall, and so get
in; or, if a rat or mouse did but stir, starting upon a sudden, and running to the door to see whether all were fast. Plautus, in his Aulularia,
makes old Euclio commanding Staphyla his wife to shut the doors fast,
and the fire to be put out, lest any body should make that an errand to
come to his house; when he washed his hands, he was loth to fling away
the foul water; complaining that he was undone, because the smoke got
out of his roof. And as he went from home, seeing a crow scrat * upon
the muck-hill, returned in all haste, taking it for an ill sign, his money
was digged up; with many such. He that will but observe their actions,
shall find these and many such passages not feigned for sport, but really
performed, verified indeed by such covetous and miserable wretches, and
that it is a mere madness, to live like a wretch, and die rich.

> *Sheer madness 'tis to live thus poor,*
> *And die with coffers running o'er.*   (JUVENAL)

SUBSECTION 13 — *Love of Gaming, &c. and pleasures immoderate; Causes*

IT is a wonder to see, how many poor, distressed, miserable wretches,
one shall meet almost in every path & street, begging for an alms, that
have been well descended, and sometime in flourishing estate, now
ragged, tattered, & ready to be starved, lingering out a painful life, in
discontent & grief of body and mind, and all through immoderate lust,
gaming, pleasure, & riot. 'Tis the common end of all sensual epicures and
brutish prodigals, that are stupefied & carried away headlong with their
several pleasures and lusts. Cebes in his Table, S. Ambrose in his second
book of Abel & Cain, and amongst the rest Lucian, in his tract, hath
excellent well deciphered such men's proceedings in his picture of
Opulentia, whom he feigns to dwell on the top of a high mount, much
sought after by many suitors; at their first coming they are generally
entertained by *Pleasure* and *Dalliance,* and have all the content that
possibly may be given, so long as their money lasts; but, when their
means fail, they are contemptibly thrust out a backdoor, headlong, and
there left to *Shame, Reproach, Despair.* And he that had at first so many
attendants, parasites, and followers, young and lusty, richly arrayed,
and all the dainty fare that might be had, with all kind of welcome and
good respect, is now upon a sudden stript of all, pale, naked, old, diseased and forsaken, cursing his stars, and ready to strangle himself;
having no other company but *Repentance, Sorrow, Grief, Derision, Beg-*

* Scratch.

gary, and *Contempt*, which are his daily attendants to his life's end. As the prodigal son had exquisite musick, merry company, dainty fare at first, but a sorrowful reckoning in the end; so have all such vain delights and their followers. Whoso will remember his lusts shall remember that the end of pleasure is sadness, as bitter as gall & wormwood is their last; grief of mind, madness itself. The ordinary rocks upon which such men do impinge & precipitate themselves, are Cards, Dice, Hawks & Hounds, the mad desire for hunting, one [Agrippa] calls it, their mad structures, disports, plays, &c. when they are unseasonably used, imprudently handled, and beyond their fortunes. Some men are consumed by mad phantastical buildings, by making Galleries, Cloisters, Terraces, Walks, Orchards, Gardens, Pools, Rillets, Bowers & such like places of pleasure; useless buildings, Xenophon calls them, which, howsoever they be delightsome things in themselves, and acceptable to all beholders, an ornament, and befitting some great men, yet unprofitable to others, & the sole overthrow of their estates. Forestus, in his observations, hath an example of such a one that became melancholy upon the like occasion, having consumed his substance in an unprofitable building, which would afterward yield him no advantage. Others, I say, are overthrown by those mad sports of Hawking and Hunting; honest recreations, and fit for some great men, but not for every base inferior person. Whilst they will maintain their Falconers, Dogs, and Hunting Nags, their wealth, saith Salmuth, *runs away with Hounds, and their fortunes fly away with Hawks:* they persecute beasts so long, till, in the end, they themselves degenerate into beasts, as Agrippa taxeth them, Actæon like, for as he was eaten to death by his own dogs, so do they devour themselves and their patrimonies, in such idle and unnecessary disports, neglecting in the mean time their more necessary business, and to follow their vocations. Over-mad too sometimes are our great men in delighting and doting too much on it: *when they drive poor husbandmen from their tillage,* as Sarisburiensis objects, *fling down country Farms, and whole Towns, to make Parks and Forests, starving men to feed beasts, and punishing in the mean time such a man that shall molest their game, more severely than him that is otherwise a common hacker, or a notorious thief.* But great men are some ways to be excused, the meaner sort have no evasion why they should not be counted mad. Poggio, the Florentine, tells a merry story to this purpose, condemning the folly and impertinent business of such kind of persons. A physician of Milan, said he, that cured mad men, had a pit of water in his house, in which he kept his patients, some up to the knees, some to the girdle, some to the chin, as they were more or less affected. One of them by chance, that was well recovered, stood in the door, and, seeing a gallant ride by with a hawk on his fist, well mounted, with his Spaniels after him, would needs know to what use all this preparation served. He made answer, to kill certain fowl. The patient demanded again, what his fowl might be worth which he killed in a year. He replied, 5 or 10 Crowns; & when he urged him farther what his Dogs, Horse, and Hawks, stood him in, he told him 400 Crowns. With that the patient bade him be gone, as he loved his life and welfare, " for if our master come and find thee here, he will put thee in the pit amongst mad men up to the chin ": taxing the madness and folly of such vain men that spend themselves in those idle sports, neglecting their business and necessary affairs. Leo X, that hunting Pope, is much discommended by Jovius in his life, for his immoderate desire of hawking and hunting, in so much that (as he saith) he would sometimes live about Ostia weeks and months together, leave suitors unrespected, Bulls and Pardons unsigned, to his own prejudice, and many private men's loss; *and if he had been by chance crossed in his sport, or his game not so good, he was so impatient, that he would revile & miscall many times men of great worth with most bitter taunts, look so sour, be so angry and waspish, so grieved & molested, that it is incredible to relate it.* But if he had good sport, had been well pleased on the other side, with unspeakable bounty and munificence he would reward all his fellow-hunters, and deny nothing to any suitor, when he was in that mood. To say truth, 'tis the common humour of all gamesters, as Galatæus observes; if they win, no men living are so jovial and merry, but if they lose, though it be but a trifle, two or three games at Tables, or a dealing at Cards, for two pence a game, they are so cholerick & testy that no man may speak with them, and break many times into violent passions, oaths, imprecations, and unbeseeming speeches, little differing from mad men for the time. Generally of all gamesters and gaming, if it be excessive, thus much we may conclude, that, whether they win or lose for the present, their winnings, as that wise Seneca determines, are not fortune's gifts, but baits, the common catastrophe is beggary. As the plague takes away life, so doth gaming goods, for all gamblers are cleaned out, poor and needy.

> *Chance a greedy Scylla is, the surest kind of theft,*
> *Intent on ill, her passion drowns in ruin, we are bereft;*
> *Filth, thieving, infame, sloth and madness: but these are left.*
>
> (PETRARCH)

For a little pleasure they take, and some small gains and gettings now and then, their wives and children are wringed in the mean time, & they themselves with loss of body and soul rue it in the end. I will say nothing of those prodigious prodigals, born to squander money, as he taxed Anthony, who, without scruple, flung away his whole fortune at the gaming table, saith Cyprian, and mad Sybaritical spendthrifts that eat up all at a breakfast, at a supper, or amongst Bawds, Parasites, and Players, consume themselves in an instant, as if they had flung it into Tybur, with great wagers, vain and idle expences, &c., not themselves only, but even all their friends, as a man desperately swimming drowns him that comes to help him, by suretyship and borrowing they will willingly undo all their associates and allies; as he saith, angry with their money. What with a wanton eye, a liquorish tongue, and a gamesome hand, when they have indiscreetly impoverished themselves, mortgaged their wits together with their lands, and entombed their ancestors' fair possessions in their bowels, they may lead the rest of their days in prison, as many times they do; they repent at leisure; and when all is gone begin to be thrifty; but when they have reached the bottom of the purse, 'tis then too late to look about; their end is misery, sorrow, shame, and discontent. And well they deserve to be infamous and discontent, to be beaten in the Amphitheatre, as by Adrian the Emperor's edict they were of old, wasters of all good, so he calls them, prodigal fools, to be publickly shamed, and hissed out of all societies, rather than to be pitied or relieved. The Tuscans and Bœotians brought their bankrupts into the market place in a bier with an empty purse carried before them, all the boys following, where they sat all day, the people standing round, to be infamous and ridiculous. At Padua in Italy they have a stone called *the stone of turpitude,* near the Senate house, where spendthrifts, and such as disclaim nonpayment of debts, do sit with their hinder parts bare, that by that note of disgrace others may be terrified from all such vain expence, or borrowing more than they can tell how to pay. The *civilians* of old set guardians over such brain-sick prodigals, as they did over mad men, to moderate their expences, that they should not so loosely consume their fortunes, to the utter undoing of their families.

I may not here omit those two main plagues, and common dotages of human kind, Wine and Women, which have infatuated and besotted myriads of people. They go commonly together.

> *He who is fond of wine, whom dice undoes,*
> *Is also prone to Venus.*   (PERSIUS)

To whom is sorrow, saith Solomon, to whom is woe, but to such a one as loves drink? It causeth torture, and bitterness of mind. Jeremy calls it wine of madness, as well he may, for it makes sound men sick and sad, and wise men mad, to say and do they know not what. Hear a miserable accident, (saith St. Austin), — Cyrillus' son, this day, in his drink, struck down his pregnant mother, would have violated his sister, killed his father, and mortally wounded two other sisters, &c. A true saying it was of him, drink causeth mirth, and drink causeth sorrow, drink causeth poverty and want, shame and disgrace. Many men have made shipwrack of their fortunes, and go like rogues and beggars, having turned all their substance into potable gold, that otherwise might have lived in good worship and happy estate, and for a few hours' pleasure, for their *Hilary Term's* but short, or *free madness,* as Seneca calls it, purchase unto themselves eternal tediousness and trouble.

That other madness is on women. It maketh the heart to apostatise, saith the wise man, and impaireth a man's brain. Pleasant at first she is, like Dioscorides' Rhododaphne, that fair plant to the eye, but poison to the taste, the rest as bitter as wormwood in the end and sharp as a two-edged sword. *Her house is the way to Hell, and goes down to the Chambers of Death.* What more sorrowful can be said? They are miserable in this life, mad, beasts, led like oxen to the slaughter: & that which is worse, whoremasters & drunkards shall be judged; saith Austin, they lose grace and glory,

> — *that brief pleasure*
> *Blots out the everlasting joy of heaven.*

They gain Hell and eternal damnation.

SUBSECTION 14 — *Philautia, or Self-love, Vain-glory, Praise, Honour, Immoderate Applause, Pride, over-much Joy, &c. Causes*

SELF-LOVE, Pride and Vain-glory, which Chrysostom calls one of the devil's three great nets; Bernard, *an arrow which pierceth the soul through, & slays it; a sly insensible enemy, not perceived,* are main causes. Where neither anger, lust, covetousness, fear, sorrow, &c. nor any other perturbation can lay hold, this will slily and insensibly pervert us. Those, (saith Cyprian) whom surfeiting could not overtake, self-love hath overcome. *He that hath scorned all money, bribes, gifts, upright otherwise and sincere, hath inserted himself to no fond imagination, and sustained all those tyrannical concupiscences of the body, hath lost all his honour, captivated by vain-glory.* It consumes both mind and heart. A great assault and cause of our present malady, although we do most part neglect, take no notice of it, yet this is a violent batterer of our souls, causeth melancholy and dotage. This pleasing humour, this soft and whispering popular air, this delectable frenzy, most irrefragable passion, this delightful illusion, this acceptable disease, which so sweetly sets upon us, ravisheth our senses, lulls our souls asleep, puffs up our hearts as so many bladders, and that without all feeling, in so much as *those that are misaffected with it, never so much as once perceive it, or think of any cure.* We commonly love him best in this malady, that doth us most harm, and are very willing to be hurt; we gladly listen to flattery, (saith Jerome) we love him, we love him, for it: O Bonciarus, such praise from you! 'twas sweet to hear it. And, as Pliny doth ingenuously confess to his dear friend Augurinus, *all thy writings are most acceptable, but those especially that speak of us.* Again, a little after to Maximus: *I cannot express how pleasing it is to me to hear myself commended.* Though we smile to ourselves, at least ironically, when Parasites bedaub us with false *Encomiums,* as many Princes cannot choose but do, when they know they come as far short, as a mouse to an elephant, of any such virtues; yet it doth us good. Though we seem many times to be angry, *and blush at our own praises, yet our souls inwardly rejoice, it puffs us up;* 'tis beguiling pleasantness, a flattering demon, *makes us swell beyond our bounds, and forget ourselves.* Her two daughters are lightness of mind, immoderate joy and pride, not excluding those other concomitant vices, which Jodocus Lorichius reckons up, bragging, hypocrisy, peevishness, and curiosity.

Now the common cause of this mischief, ariseth from ourselves or others, we are active and passive. It proceeds inwardly from ourselves, as we are active causes, from an over-weening conceit we have of our good parts, own worth, (which indeed is no worth), our bounty, favour, grace, valour, strength, wealth, patience, meekness, hospitality, beauty, temperance, gentry, knowledge, wit, science, art, learning, our excellent gifts and fortunes, for which, Narcissus-like, we admire, flatter, & applaud, ourselves, and think all the world esteems so of us; and, as deformed women easily believe those that tell them they be fair, we are too credulous of our own good parts and praises, too well persuaded of ourselves. We brag and venditate our own works, and scorn all others in respect of us; our knowledge puffeth us (saith Paul), our wisdom, our learning; all our geese are swans; and we as basely esteem and villify other men's, as we do over-highly prize & value our own. We will not suffer them to be in second rank, no not in third; what? Is Ulysses compared to me? they are nits and flies compared to his inexorable and supercilious, eminent and arrogant Worship: though indeed they be far before him. Only wise, only rich, only fortunate, valorous, and fair, puffed up with this tympany of self-conceit; as that proud Pharisee, they are not (as they suppose) *like other men,* of a purer and more precious metal: the only persons able to conduct affairs, which that wise Periander held of such: Their affairs are thought to be of prime importance, &c. (saith Erasmus) I knew one so arrogant, that he thought himself inferior to no man living, like Callisthenes the Philosopher, that neither held Alexander's acts, or any other subject, worthy of his pen, such was his insolency; or Seleucus, King of Syria, who thought none fit to contend with him but the Romans. That which Tully writ to Atticus long since, is still in force, *there was never yet true Poet nor Orator, that thought any other better than himself.* And such for the most part are your Princes, Potentates, great Philosophers, Historiographers, Authors of Sects or Heresies, and all our great Scholars, as Hierom defines; *a natural Philosopher is glory's creature, and a very slave of rumour, fame, & popular opinion;* and, though they write on the contempt of glory, yet, as he observes, they will put their names to their books. Saith Trebellius Pollio, I have wholly consecrated myself to you and fame. *'Tis all my desire, night and day, 'tis all my study, to raise my name.* Proud Pliny seconds him; and that vain-glorious Orator is not ashamed to confess, in an Epistle of his to Marcus Lucceius: *I burn with an incredible desire to have my name registered in thy book.* Out of this fountain proceed all those cracks and brags. —— *We hope to make poems worthy anointing with cedar-oil and preserving in polished cypress.* —— *On no common nor weak wing shall I be borne aloft, nor longer shall I stay on earth.* —— *Nothing little, nothing lowly, nothing of mere mortal commonness will I sing.* —— *I shall be chanted where rough Aufidus roars.* —— *I have builded a monument more durable than brass.* —— *And now my work is done, which neither the wrath of Jove, nor fire, &c., let the day come, &c., Still, in my better part, I shall be borne immortal far beyond the lofty stars, and I shall have an undying name.* This of Ovid I have paraphrased in English:

> *And when I am dead and gone,*
> *My corpse laid under a stone,*
> *My fame shall yet survive,*
> *And I shall be alive;*
> *In these my works for ever,*
> *My glory shall persever, &c.*

and that of Ennius,

> *Let no one grace my grave with tears! For why?*
> *I live upon men's lips eternally;*

with many such proud strains, and foolish flashes, too common with Writers. Not so much as Demochares on the Topicks, but he will be immortal. Typotius, On Fame, shall be famous, and well he deserves, because he writ of Fame; and every trivial Poet must be renowned, and seek celebrity through the plaudits of the mob. This puffing humour it is, that hath produced so many great tomes, built such famous monuments, strong Castles, and *Mausolean* Tombs, to have their acts eternized, to be pointed at with the finger, and have them say, That is he; to see their names inscribed, as Phryne on the walls of Thebes, *Phryne made it.* This causeth so many bloody battles,

And forces us to watch during calm nights, (LUCRETIUS)
long journies,

Great are the heights I must scale, but glory lends me strength,
(PROPERTIUS)

gaining honour, a little applause, pride, self-love, vain-glory. This is it which makes them take such pains, and break out into those ridiculous strains, this high conceit of themselves, to scorn all others; as Palæmon the Grammarian contemned Varro, and brings them to that height of insolency, that they cannot endure to be contradicted, *or hear of anything but their own commendation,* which Hierom notes of such kind of men; and, as Austin well seconds him, *'tis their sole study day and night to be commended and applauded;* when as indeed, in all wise men's judgments, they are mad, empty vessels, funges, beside themselves, derided, & as the camel in the old saw, seeking for horns, it lost even its ears, their works are toys, as an Almanack out of date, they perish through their author's garrulity, they seek fame and immortality, but reap dishonour and infamy, they are a common obloquy, irrationalities, and come far short of that which they suppose or expect.

O boy, I fear thou'rt shortlived! (HORACE)

Of so many myriads of Poets, Rhetoricians, Philosophers, Sophisters, as Eusebius well observes, which have written in former ages, scarce one of a thousand's works remains, their books and bodies are perished together. It is not as they vainly think, they shall surely be admired and immortal, as one told Philip of Macedon insulting after a victory, that his shadow was no longer than before, we may say to them,

We marvel too, not as the vulgar we,

But as we Gorgons, Harpies, or Furies see; (BUCHANAN)

or if we do applaud, honour and admire; how small a part, in respect of the whole world, never so much as hears our names! how few take notice of us! how slender a tract, as scant as Alcibiades his land in a

Map! And yet every man must and will be immortal, as he hopes, and extend his fame to our Antipodes, when as half, no not a quarter, of his own Province or City, neither knows nor hears of him: but say they did, what's a City to a Kingdom, a Kingdom to Europe, Europe to the World, the World itself that must have an end, if compared to the least visible Star in the Firmament, eighteen times bigger than it? And then, if those Stars be infinite, and every Star there be a Sun, as some will, & as this Sun of ours hath his Planets about him, all inhabited, what proportion bear we to them, and where's our glory? As he crackt in Petronius, all the world was under Augustus: and so in Constantine's time, Eusebius brags he governed all the world, so of Alexander it is given out, the 4 Monarchies, &c., when as neither Greeks nor Romans ever had the fifteenth part of the now known world, nor half of that which was then described. What braggadocians are they and we then! as he said, the name of glory should be despised, how short a time, how little a while, doth this fame of ours continue! Every private Province, every small Territory and City, when we have all done, will yield as generous spirits, as brave examples, in all respects as famous as ourselves! Cadwallader in Wales, Rollo in Normandy, Robin Hood and Little John are as much renowned in Sherwood, as Cæsar in Rome, Alexander in Greece, or his Hephæstio. In all ages and among all people, every Town, City, Book, is full of brave Soldiers, Senators, Scholars, and though Brasidas was a worthy Captain, a good man, and, as they thought, not to be matched in Lacedæmon, yet, as his mother truly said, Sparta had many better men than ever he was; and howsoever thou admirest thyself, thy friend, many an obscure fellow the world never took notice of, had he been in place or action, would have done much better than he or he, or thou thyself.

Another kind of mad men there is, opposite to these, that are insensibly mad, and know not of it, such as contemn all praise and glory, think themselves most free, when as indeed they are most mad: they trample upon others, but with a different kind of pride: a company of Cynicks, such as are Monks, Hermits, Anachorites, that contemn the world, contemn themselves, contemn all titles, honours, offices: and yet in that contempt are more proud than any man living whatsoever. They are proud in humility, proud in that they are not proud; with a greater vanity, oftimes, does a man glory of his contempt of vain glory, as Austin hath it, like Diogenes, they brag inwardly, and feed themselves fat with a self-conceit of sanctity, which is no better than hypocrisy. They go in sheep's russet, many great men that might maintain them-

selves in cloth of gold, and seem to be dejected, humble, by their outward carriage, when as inwardly they are swoln full of pride, arrogancy,
and self-conceit. And therefore Seneca adviseth his friend Lucilius, in
*his attire and gesture, outward actions, especially to avoid all such
things as are more notable in themselves: as a rugged attire, hirsute
head, horrid beard, contempt of money, coarse lodging, and whatsoever
leads to fame that opposite way.*

All this madness yet proceeds from ourselves; the main engine which
batters us is from others, we are merely passive in this business, from a
company of parasites & flatterers, that with immoderate praise, & bombast epithets, glozing titles, false elogiums, so bedaub & applaud, gild
over many a silly & undeserving man, that they clap him quite out of his
wits. As Hierome notes, this common applause is a most violent thing,
(a drum, fife, and trumpet cannot so animate), that fattens men, erects
and dejects them in an instant. It makes them fat and lean, as frost
doth conies. *And who is that mortal man that can so contain himself,
that, if he be immoderately commended, and applauded, will not be
moved?* Let him be what he will, those Parasites will overturn him: if
he be a King, he is one of the Nine Worthies, more than a man, a God
forthwith, —— It is the edict of our Lord and God: and they will sacrifice unto him, ——

> *If you will accept divine acclaim,*
> *We'll rear altars in your name.* (STROZA)

If he be a soldier, then Themistocles, Epaminondas, Hector, Achilles,
two thunder-bolts in war, the triumvirate of the world, &c., and the
valour of both Scipios is too little for him, he is most invincible, most
serene, adorned with many trophies, a lord of Nature, although he be a
hare in armour, indeed a very coward, a milk-sop, and as he said of
Xerxes, last in battle, first in flight, & such a one as never durst look his
enemy in the face. If he be a big man, then is he a Sampson, another
Hercules: if he pronounce a speech, another Tully or Demosthenes: (as
of Herod in the Acts, the voice of God and not of man) if he can make
a verse, Homer, Virgil, &c. And then my silly weak patient takes all
these elogiums to himself; if he be a Scholar so commended for his
much reading, excellent style, method, &c. he will eviscerate himself
like a spider, study to death; When praised, Peacock-like, he will display all his feathers. If he be a soldier, and so applauded, his valour
extoll'd, though it be as unequal a contest, as that of Achilles and
Troilus, unhappy lad, he will combat with a Giant, run first upon a
breach; as another Philippus, he will ride into the thickest of his

enemies. Commend his house-keeping, and he will beggar himself : commend his temperance, he will starve himself.

> *Applauded virtue ever thrives,*
> *And glory spurs our jaded lives.*   (OVID)

He is mad, mad, mad, no whoe with him; —— He will brook no rival, he will over the Alps to be talked of, or to maintain his credit. Commend an ambitious man, some proud Prince or Potentate, if he be much praised (saith Erasmus), he sets up his crest, and will be no longer a man, but a God ;

> *Nothing too monstrous for belief is phrased,*
> *When to his face the worthless wretch is prais'd ;*
> *Whom vile court-flatt'ry to a God has rais'd.*   (JUVENAL)

How did this work with Alexander, that would needs be Jupiter's son, and go like Hercules in a lion's skin ! Domitian a God, (*our Lord God* [so Suetonius tells of it] *bids that this be done*), like the Persian Kings, whose Image was adored by all that came into the City of Babylon. Commodus the Emperor was so gulled by his flattering parasites, that he must be called Hercules. Antonius the Roman would be crowned with ivy, carried in a chariot, and adored for Bacchus. Cotys, King of Thrace, was married to Minerva, and sent three several messengers one after another, to see if she were come to his bedchamber. Such a one was Jupiter Menecrates, Maximinus Jovianus, Dioclesianus Hercules, Sapor the Persian King, brother of the Sun and Moon, and our modern Turks, that will be Gods on earth, Kings of Kings, God's shadow, Commanders of all that may be commanded, our Kings of China and Tartary in this present age. Such a one was Xerxes, that would whip the sea, fetter Neptune, in his silly boastfulness, & send a challenge to Mount Athos : and such are many sottish Princes, brought into a fool's Paradise by their parasites. 'Tis a common humour, incident to all men, when they are in great places, or come to the solstice of honour, have done, or deserv'd well, to applaud and flatter themselves. Your very tradesmen, (saith Platerus), if they be excellent, will crack and brag, and shew their folly in excess. They have good parts, and they know it, you need not tell them of it ; out of a conceit of their worth, they go smiling to themselves, and perpetual meditation of their trophies & plaudits ; they run at the last quite mad, and lose their wits. Petrarch confessed as much of himself, & Cardan, in his 5th book of wisdom, gives an instance in a Smith of Milan, a fellow Citizen of his, one Galeus de Rubeis, that, being commended for refining of an instrument of Archimedes, for joy ran mad. Plutarch, in the life of Artaxerxes, hath such a like story of one Chamus, a soldier, that wounded King Cyrus in battle, and *grew thereupon so arrogant, that in a short space after he lost his wits.* So many men, if any new honour, office, preferment, booty, treasure, possession, or patrimony unexpectedly fall unto them, for immoderate joy, and continual meditation of it, cannot sleep, or tell what they say or do; they are so ravished on a sudden, and with vain conceits transported, there is no rule with them. Epaminondas therefore, the next day after his Leuctrian victory, *came abroad all squalid and submiss,* and gave no other reason to his friends of so doing, than that he perceived himself the day before, by reason of his good fortune, to be too insolent, overmuch joyed. That wise and virtuous Lady, Queen Katharine, Dowager of England, in private talk, upon like occasion, said, that *she would not willingly endure the extremity of either fortune; but if it were so that of necessity she must undergo the one, she would be in adversity, because comfort was never wanting in it, but still counsel and government were defective in the other:* they could not moderate themselves.

SUBSECTION 15 — *Love of Learning, or over-much Study. With a Digression of the Misery of Scholars, and why the Muses are Melancholy*

LEONARTUS FUCHSIUS, Felix Plater, Hercules de Saxonia, speak of a peculiar *fury,* which comes by overmuch study. Fernelius puts *study,* contemplation, and continual meditation, as an especial cause of madness: and in his 86th Consultation cites the same words. Jo. Arculanus amongst other causes reckons up overmuch study: so doth Levinus Lemnius. *Many men* (saith he) *come to this malady by continual study, and night-waking, and, of all other men, scholars are most subject to it:* and such, Rhasis adds, *that have commonly the finest wits.* Marsilius Ficinus puts Melancholy amongst one of those five principal plagues of students, 'tis a common maul unto them all, and almost in some measure an inseparable companion. Varro belike for that cause calls philosophers sombre and stern; severe, sad, dry, tetrick, are common epithets to scholars: and Patritius therefore, in the Institution of Princes, would not have them to be great students. For (as Machiavel holds) study weakens their bodies, dulls their spirits, abates their strength and courage; and good scholars are never good soldiers, which a certain Goth well perceived, for when his country-men came into Greece, and would have burned all their books, he cried out against it, by all means they should [not] do it: *leave them that plague, which in*

time will consume all their vigour, and martial spirits. The Turks abdicated Corcutus, the next heir, from the Empire, because he was so
much given to his book: and 'tis the common tenent of the world, that
learning dulls and diminisheth the spirits, and so by consequence, produceth melancholy.

Two main reasons may be given of it, why students should be more
subject to this malady than others. The one is, they live a sedentary,
solitary life, to themselves and letters, free from bodily exercise, and
those ordinary disports which other men use: and many times, if discontent and idleness concur with it, which is too frequent, they are
precipitated into this gulf on a sudden: but the common cause is overmuch study; too much learning (as Festus told Paul) hath made thee
mad; 'tis that other extreme which effects it. So did Trincavellius find
by his experience, in two of his patients, a young Baron, and another,
that contracted this malady by too vehement study. So Forestus found
in a young Divine in Louvain, that was mad, and said *he had a Bible in
his head.* Marsilius Ficinus *gives many reasons why students dote more
often than others.* The first is their negligence: *other men look to their
tools; a painter will wash his pencils; a smith will look to his hammer,
anvil, forge: an husbandman will mend his plough-irons, and grind his
hatchet if it be dull; a falconer or huntsman will have an especial care
of his hawks, hounds, horses, dogs, &c. a musician will string and unstring his lute,* &c., *only scholars neglect that instrument, their brain &
spirits (I mean), which they daily use, and by which they range over all
the world, which by much study is consumed.* See thou (saith Lucian)
twist not the rope so hard, till at length it break. Ficinus in his fourth
Chapter gives some other reasons; Saturn and Mercury, the Patrons of
Learning, are both dry Planets: and Origanus assigns the same cause,
why Mercurialists are so poor, and most part beggars; for that their
President Mercury had no better fortune himself. The Destinies of old
put poverty upon him as a punishment; since when Poetry and Beggary are twin-born brats, inseparable companions:

And to this day is every scholar poor;
Gross gold from them runs headlong to the boor. (MARLOWE)

Mercury can help them to knowledge, but not to money. The second
is contemplation, *which dries the brain and extinguisheth natural heat;
for whilst the spirits are intent to meditation above in the head, the
stomack and liver are left destitute, and thence come black blood and
crudities by defect of concoction, and for want of exercise the superfluous vapours cannot exhale.* &c. The same reasons are repeated by

Gomesius, Nymannus, Jo. Voschius: and something more they add, that hard students are commonly troubled with gouts, catarrhs, rheums, wasting, indigestion, bad eyes, stone, and colick, crudities, oppilations, *vertigo*, winds, consumptions and all such diseases as come by overmuch sitting; they are most part lean, dry, ill coloured, spend their fortunes, lose their wits, and many times their lives, and all through immoderate pains, and extraordinary studies. If you will not believe the truth of this, look upon great Tostatus and Thomas Aquinas' Works, and tell me whether those men took pains? peruse Austin, Hierome, &c., and many thousands besides.

> *He that desires this wished goal to gain,*
> *Must sweat and freeze before he can attain,*   (HORACE)

and labour hard for it. So did Seneca, by his own confession: *not a day that I spend idle, part of the night I keep mine eyes open, tired with waking, and now slumbering, to their continual task.* Hear Tully: *whilst others loitered, & took their pleasures, he was continually at his book.* So they do that will be scholars, and that to the hazard (I say) of their healths, fortunes, wits, & lives. How much did Aristotle and Ptolemy spend, they say, more than a King's ransom; how many crowns a year to perfect arts, the one about his History of Creatures, the other on his Almagest! How much time did Thebet Benchorat employ, to find out the motion of the eighth sphere! forty years and more, some write. How many poor scholars have lost their wits, or become dizzards, neglecting all worldly affairs and their own health, wealth, being & well being, to gain knowledge! for which, after all their pains, in the world's esteem they are accounted ridiculous and silly fools, idiots, asses, and (as oft they are) rejected, contemned, derided, doting, and mad! Look for examples in Hildesheim, read Trincavellius, Montanus, Garceus, Mercurialis, Prosper Calenus, in his Book On Black Bile. Go to Bedlam and ask. Or if they keep their wits, yet they are esteemed scrubs and fools by reason of their carriage: *after seven years' study* ——

> *In general he's more silent than a statue,*
> *And makes the people shake their sides with laughter.*

Because they cannot ride an horse, which every clown can do; salute and court a gentlewoman, carve at table, cringe, and make congies, which every common swasher can do, &c. they are laughed to scorn, and accounted silly fools by our gallants. Yea, many times, such is their misery, they deserve it: a mere scholar, a mere ass.

> —————— *Who do lean awry*
> *Their heads, piercing the earth with a fixt eye;*

When, by themselves, they gnaw their murmuring,
And furious silence, as 'twere balancing
Each word upon their outstretched lip, and when
They meditate the dreams of old sick men,
As, " Out of nothing, nothing can be brought ;
And that which is, can ne'er be turn'd to nought."

(PERSIUS, translated by Mr. B. Holiday)

Thus they go commonly meditating unto themselves, thus they sit, such is their action and gesture. Fulgosus makes mention how Th. Aquinas, supping with King Lewis of France, upon a sudden knocked his fist upon the table, and cried, " The Manichees are wrong! " — his wits were a woolgathering, as they say, and his head busied about other matters; when he perceived his error, he was much abashed. Such a story there is of Archimedes in Vitruvius, that having found out the means to know how much gold was mingled with the silver in King Hiero's crown, ran naked forth of the bath and cried Eureka, I have found: *and was commonly so intent to his studies, that he never perceived what was done about him ; when the city was taken, and the soldiers now ready to rifle his house, he took no notice of it.* S. Bernard rode all day long by Lake Leman, and asked at last where he was. It was Democritus' carriage alone that made the Abderites suppose him to have been mad, and send for Hippocrates to cure him: if he had been in any solemn company, he would upon all occasions fall a laughing. Theophrastus saith as much of Heraclitus, for that he continually wept, and Laertius of Menedemus, [a disciple of Colotes of] Lampsacus, because he ran like a madman, *saying, he came from hell as a spy, to tell the devils what mortal men did.* Your greatest students are commonly no better; silly, soft fellows in their outward behaviour, absurd, ridiculous to others, and no whit experienced in worldly business; they can measure the heavens, range over the world, teach others wisdom, and yet in bargains and contracts they are circumvented by every base tradesman. Are not these men fools? and how should they be otherwise, *but as so many sots in schools, when (as he well observed) they neither hear nor see such things as are commonly practised abroad?* how should they get experience, by what means? *I knew in my time many Scholars,* saith Æneas Sylvius (in an Epistle of his to Kaspar Schlick, Chancellor to the Emperor) *excellent well learned, but so rude, so silly, that they had no common civility, nor knew how to manage their domestick or publick affairs. Paglarensis was amazed, and said his farmer had surely cozened him, when he heard him tell that his sow had eleven pigs, and his ass had but one foal.* To say the best of this Profession, I can give no other testimony of them in general, than that of Pliny of Isæus; *he is yet a scholar, than which kind of men there is nothing so simple,* so sincere, none better; they are most part harmless, honest, *upright, innocent,* plain dealing men.

Now because they are commonly subject to such hazards, and inconveniences, as dotage, madness, simplicity, &c. Jo. Voschius would have good scholars to be highly rewarded, and had in some extraordinary respect above other men, *to have greater privileges than the rest, that adventure themselves and abbreviate their lives for the publick good.* But our Patrons of Learning are so far nowadays from respecting the *Muses,* and giving that honour to scholars, or reward, which they deserve, and are allowed by those indulgent privileges of many noble Princes, that, after all their pains taken in the *Universities,* cost and charge, expences, irksome hours, laborious tasks, wearisome days, dangers, hazards, (barred meanwhile from all pleasures which other men have, mewed up like hawks all their lives), if they chance to wade through them, they shall in the end be rejected, contemned, and, which is their greatest misery, driven to their shifts, exposed to want, poverty, and beggary. Their familiar attendants are,

> *Grief, labour, care, pale sickness, miseries,*
> *Fear, filthy poverty, hunger that cries,*
> *Terrible monsters to be seen with eyes.*   (VIRGIL)

If there were nothing else to trouble them, the conceit of this alone were enough to make them all melancholy. Most other Trades and Professions, after some seven years' Prenticeship, are enabled by their Craft to live of themselves. A Merchant adventures his goods at sea, and, though his hazard be great, yet, if one Ship return of four, he likely makes a saving voyage. An husbandman's gains are almost certain; which Jupiter himself cannot diminish, ('tis Cato's hyperbole, a great husband himself;) only scholars, methinks, are most uncertain, unrespected, subject to all casualties, and hazard. For first, not one of a many proves to be a scholar, all are not capable and docile, a Mercury is not to be made out of every log: we can make Mayors and Officers every year, but not Scholars: Kings can invest Knights and Barons, as Sigismund the Emperor confessed; Universities can give Degrees; and, *What you are any one i' th' world can be;* but he, nor they, nor all the world, can give Learning, make Philosophers, Artists, Orators, Poets. We can soon say, as Seneca well notes, What a good man you are! how rich!, point at a rich man, a good, an happy man, a proper man, richly clad, primped & perfumed; at what great cost of time we win such praise as,

" What a learned man you are! " but 'tis not so easily performed to find
out a learned man. Learning is not so quickly got. Though they may be
willing to take pains, to that end sufficiently informed, and liberally
maintained by their Patrons and Parents, yet few can compass it. Or,
if they be docile, yet all men's wills are not answerable to their wits,
they can apprehend, but will not take pains; they are either seduced by
bad companions, they come to grief with wine or women, and so spend
their time to their friends' grief and their own undoings. Or, put case
they be studious, industrious, of ripe wits, and perhaps good capacities,
then how many diseases of body and mind must they encounter! No
labour in the world like unto study! It may be, their temperature will
not endure it, but, striving to be excellent, to know all, they lose health,
wealth, wit, life, and all. Let him yet happily escape all these hazards,
with a body of brass, and is now consummate and ripe, he hath profited
in his studies, and proceeded with all applause: after many expences,
he is fit for preferment: where shall he have it? he is as far to seek it
(after twenty years' standing) as he was at the first day of his coming
to the University. For what course shall he take, being now capable and
ready? The most parable and easy, and about which many are employed, is to teach a School, turn Lecturer or Curate, and for that he
shall have Falconer's wages, ten pounds a year, and his diet, or some
small stipend, so long as he can please his Patron or the Parish; if they
approve him not (for usually they do but a year or two) as inconstant
as they that cried *Hosanna!* one day, and *Crucify him!* the other; serv-
ing-man-like, he must go and look a new Master: if they do, what is his
reward?

> *This too awaits: your fate may be to teach*
> *In some suburban school the parts of speech.* (HORACE)

Like an ass, he wears out his time for provender, and can shew a
stumpe rod, saith Hædus, an old torn gown, an ensign of his infelicity,
he hath his labour for his pain, a *modicum* to keep him till he be decrepit, and that is all. The scholar is not a happy man. If he be a
trencher Chaplain in a Gentleman's house, as it befel Euphormio, after
some seven years' service, he may perchance have a Living to the halves,
or some small Rectory with the mother of the maids at length, a poor
kinswoman, or a crackt chambermaid, to have and to hold during the
time of his life. But if he offend his good Patron, or displease his Lady
Mistress in the mean time, as Hercules did by Cacus, he shall be dragged
forth of doors by the heels, away with him! If he bend his forces to some
other studies, with an intent to be secretary to some Nobleman, or in

such a place with an Embassador, he shall find that these persons rise like Prentices one under another, as in so many Tradesmen's shops, when the Master is dead, the Foreman of the shop commonly steps in his place. Now for Poets, Rhetoricians, Historians, Philosophers, Mathematicians, Sophisters, &c., they are like Grasshoppers, sing they must in Summer, and pine in the Winter, for there is no preferment for them. Even so they were at first, if you will believe that pleasant Tale of Socrates, which he told fair Phædrus under a Plane-tree, at the banks of the river Ilissus. About noon, when it was hot, and the Grasshoppers made a noise, he took that sweet occasion to tell him a Tale, how Grasshoppers were once Scholars, Musicians, Poets, &c., before the *Muses* were born, and lived without meat and drink, and for that cause were turned by Jupiter into Grasshoppers; and may be turned again into Tithonus' grasshoppers, or frogs of the Lycians, for any reward I see they are like to have: or else, in the mean time, I would they could live, as they did, without any viaticum, like so many *Manucodiatæ*, those Indian Birds of Paradise, as we commonly call them, those I mean that live with the Air, and Dew of Heaven, and need no other food: for, being as they are, their *Rhetorick only serves them to curse their bad fortunes,* & many of them for want of means are driven to hard shifts; from Grasshoppers they turn Humble-Bees and Wasps, plain Parasites, and make the *Muses,* Mules, to satisfy their hunger-starved paunches, and get a meal's meat. To say truth, 'tis the common fortune of most scholars to be servile and poor, to complain pitifully, and lay open their wants to their respectless Patrons, as Cardan doth, as Xylander, and many others; and, which is too common in those Dedicatory Epistles, for hope of gain, to lie, flatter, and with hyperbolical elogiums and commendations to magnify and extol an illiterate unworthy idiot for his excellent virtues, whom they should rather, as Machiavel observes, vilify and rail at downright for his most notorious villanies and vices. So they prostitute themselves, as fiddlers or mercenary tradesmen, to serve great men's turns for a small reward. They are like Indians, they have store of gold, but know not the worth of it: for I am of Synesius' opinion, *King Hiero got more by Simonides' acquaintance, than Simonides did by his:* they have their best education, good institution, sole qualification from us, and, when they have done well, their honour and immortality from us; we are the living tombs, registers, and so many trumpeters of their fames: what was Achilles without Homer? Alexander without Arrian and Curtius? who had known the Cæsars but for Suetonius and Dion?

Many brave persons lived ere Agamemnon:
But are all buried in night's long obscurity,
Unwept, unknown, because they lacked a bard. (HORACE)

They are more beholden to scholars, than scholars to them; but they under-value themselves, and so by those great men are kept down. Let them have that *Encyclopædian,* all the learning in the world; they must keep it to themselves, *live in base esteem, and starve, except they will submit,* as Budæus well hath it, *so many good parts, so many ensigns of arts, virtues, be slavishly obnoxious to some illiterate Potentate, and live under his insolent Worship, or Honour, like Parasites,* who, like mice, devour another man's bread. For, to say truth, as Guido Bonat, that great Astrologer, could foresee, they be not gainful arts these, but poor and hungry.

The rich Physician, honour'd Lawyers ride,
Whilst the poor Scholar foots it by their side. (BUCHANAN)

Poverty is the *Muse's* Patrimony, and, as that Poetical divinity teacheth us, when Jupiter's daughters were each of them married to the Gods, the *Muses* alone were left solitary, Helicon forsaken of all Suitors, and I believe it was, because they had no portion.

Why did Calliope live so long a maid?
Because she had no dowry to be paid. (BUCHANAN)

Ever since all their followers are poor, forsaken, and left unto themselves; in so much that, as Petronius argues, you shall likely know them by their clothes. *There came,* saith he, *by chance into my company, a fellow not very spruce to look on, that I could perceive by that note alone he was a Scholar, whom commonly rich men hate. I asked him what he was; he answered, a Poet. I demanded again why he was so ragged; he told me this kind of learning never made any man rich.*

A merchant's gain is great, that goes to sea;
A soldier embossed all in gold;
A flatterer lies fox'd in brave array;
A scholar only ragged to behold. (PETRONIUS)

All which our ordinary Students, right well perceiving in the Universities how unprofitable these Poetical, Mathematical, and Philosophical Studies are, how little respected, how few Patrons, apply themselves in all haste to those three commodious Professions of Law, Physick, and Divinity, sharing themselves between them, rejecting these Arts in the mean time, History, Philosophy, Philology, or lightly passing them over, as pleasant toys fitting only table talk, and to furnish them with discourse. They are not so behoveful: he that can tell his money hath Arithmetick enough: he is a true Geometrician, can measure out a good fortune to himself; a perfect Astrologer, that can cast the rise and fall of others, and mark their errant motions to his own use. The best Opticks are to reflect the beams of some great men's favour and grace to shine upon him. He is a good Engineer that alone can make an instrument to get preferment. This was the common tenent and practice of Poland, as Cromerus observed not long since in the first Book of his History; their Universities were generally base; not a Philosopher, a Mathematician, an Antiquary, &c., to be found of any note amongst them, because they had no set reward or stipend; but every man betook himself to Divinity, a good Parsonage was their aim. This was the practice of some of our near neighbors, as Lipsius inveighs; *they thrust their children to the study of Law and Divinity, before they be informed aright, or capable of such studies.* In fact the hope of gain stands before all the arts, and a load of gold is more beautiful than all that Greek and Latin dizzards have written. Such monied men come to govern the helm of State, and are present and prominent at King's councils. O my father! O my country! ———— So he complained, and so may others. For even so we find, to serve a great man, to get an Office in some Bishop's Court, to practise in some good Town, or compass a Benefice, is a mark we shoot at, as being so advantageous, the high way to preferment.

Although many times, for ought I can see, these men fail as often as the rest in their projects, and are as usually frustrate of their hopes. For let him be a Doctor of the Law, an excellent Civilian of good worth, where shall he practise and expatiate? Their fields are so scant, the Civil Law with us so contracted with Prohibitions, so few Causes, by reason of those all-devouring municipal Laws, an illiterate and a barbarous study, saith Erasmus, (for though they be never so well learned in it, I can hardly vouchsafe them the name of Scholars, except they be otherwise qualified), and so few Courts are left to that profession, such slender offices, and those commonly to be compassed at such dear rates, that I know not how an ingenious man should thrive amongst them. Now for Physicians, there are in every village so many Mountebanks, Empiricks, Quacksalvers, Paracelsians, as they call themselves, pretenders, and killers of the healthy, so Clenard terms them, Wizards, Alchemists, poor Vicars, cast Apothecaries, Physicians' men, Barbers, and Goodwives, professing great skill, that I make great doubt how they shall be maintained, or who shall be their Patients. Besides, there are so many of both sorts, and some of them such Harpies, so covetous, so clamorous, so impudent; and as he said, litigious idiots,

> *Which have no skill but prating arrogance,*
> *No learning, such a purse-milking nation,*
> *Gown'd vultures, thieves, and a litigious rout*
> *Of cozeners, that haunt this occupation, &c.* (DOUSA)

that they cannot well tell how to live one by another, but, as he jested (in the Comedy) of clocks, they were so many, they are almost starved a great part of them, and ready to devour their fellows, to mislead them by sneaking malice; such a multitude of pettifoggers and Empiricks, such impostors, that an honest man knows not in what sort to compose and behave himself in their society, to carry himself with credit in so vile a rout; among so many who profess the name of science, they are ashamed to confess to their own lucubrations, &c.

Last of all to come to our Divines, the most noble profession and worthy of double honour, but of all others the most distressed and miserable. If you will not believe me, hear a brief of it, as it was not many years since publickly preached at Paul's Cross, by a grave Minister then, and now a Reverend Bishop of this land.* *We that are bred up in learning, & destinated by our Parents to this end, we suffer our childhood in the Grammar-school, which Austin calls a great despotism & most grievous affliction & compares it to the torments of martyrdom; when we come to the University, if we live of the College allowance, as Phalaris objected to the Leontines, needy of all things but hunger & fear; or, if we be maintained but partly by our Parents' cost, do expend in unnecessary maintenance, books, & degrees, before we come to any perfection, five hundred pounds, or a thousand marks. If, by this price of the expence of time, our bodies and spirits, our substance and patrimonies, we cannot purchase those small rewards, which are ours by law, and the right of inheritance, a poor Parsonage, or a Vicarage, of £50 a year, but we must pay to the Patron for the lease of a life (a spent & outworn life) either in annual pension, or above the rate of a copy-hold, & that with the hazard & loss of our souls, by Simony and perjury, and the forfeiture of all our spiritual preferments in being and strength, both present and to come; what father after a while will be so improvident, to bring up his son, to his great charge, to this necessary beggary? What Christian will be so irreligious, to bring up his son in that course of life, which by all probability & necessity enforcing to sin, will entangle him in Simony and perjury, when as the Poet saith, a beg-*

---

* Joh. Howson, 4 Novembris, 1597. The sermon was printed by Arnold Hartfield. — Burton's note.

gar's brat taken from the bridge where he sits a begging, if he knew the inconvenience, had cause to refuse it. ———— This being thus, have not we fished fair all this while, that are initiate Divines, to find no better fruits of our labours? Is it for this that we look pale and lose our stomacks? Do we macerate ourselves for this? Is it for this we rise so early all the year long, *leaping* (as he saith) *out of our beds, when we hear the bell ring, as if we had heard a thunderclap?* If this be all the respect, reward, and honour, we shall have, " Break your trifling pens, Thalia," let us give over our books, and betake ourselves to some other course of life. To what end should we study? Why did my foolish parents teach me letters? What did our parents mean to make us Scholars, to be as far to seek of preferment after twenty years' study, as we were at first? Why do we take such pains? Why the insane desire to turn pallid over mere paper? If there be no more hope of reward, no better encouragement, I say again, Break your trifling pens. Thalia, and destroy your books; let's turn soldiers, sell our books, and buy swords, guns, and pikes, or stop bottles with them, turn our Philosophers' gowns, as Cleanthes once did, unto millers' coats, leave all, and rather betake ourselves to any other course of life, than to continue longer in this misery. It would be better to make toothpicks, than, by literary labours to try to win the favour of the great.

Yea, but methinks I hear some man except at these words, that, though this be true which I have said of the estate of Scholars, and especially of Divines, that it is miserable and distressed at this time, that the Church suffers shipwrack of her goods, and that they have just cause to complain, there is a fault, but whence proceeds it? If the cause were justly examined, it would be retorted upon ourselves; if we were cited at that tribunal of truth, we should be found guilty, and not able to excuse it. That there is a fault among us, I confess, and were there not a buyer, there would not be a seller: but to him that will consider better of it, it will more than manifestly appear, that the fountain of these miseries proceeds from these griping Patrons. In accusing them, I do not altogether excuse us; both are faulty, they and we: yet, in my judgment, theirs is the greater fault, more apparent causes, & more to be condemned. For my part, if it be not with me as I would, or as I should, I do ascribe the cause, as Cardan did in the like case, to mine own infelicity rather than their naughtiness; although I have been baffled in my time by some of them, & have as just cause to complain as another: or rather indeed to mine own negligence; for I was ever like that Alexander in Plutarch, Crassus his tutor in Philosophy, **who,** though he lived many years familiarly with rich Crassus, was even as poor when from, (which many wondered at), as when he came first to him; he never asked, the other never gave him any thing; when he travelled with Crassus, he borrowed an hat of him, at his return restored it again. I have had some such noble friends, acquaintance, and scholars, but most part, (common courtesies and ordinary respects excepted), they and I parted as we met, they gave me as much as I requested, and that was ————.* And as Alexander ab Alexandro made answer to Hieronymus Massainus, that wondered, as he saw slothful and base-born men advanced daily to greatness and preferment, why, when other men rose, still he was in the same state, and why he did not receive the reward of work and study, whom he thought to deserve as well as the rest; he made answer, that he was content with his present estate, was not ambitious; and although he chid him for his backwardness, yet he was still the same: and for my part (though I be not worthy perhaps to carry Alexander's books) yet by some overweening and well wishing friends the like speeches have been used to me; but I replied still with Alexander, that I had had enough, and more peradventure than I deserved; and with Libanius Sophista, that rather chose (when honours and offices by the Emperor were offered unto him) to be Sophist than Prefect. I had as lief be still *Democritus Junior,* and a private person, if I had the choice now, than a Doctor of Divinity, or Lord Bishop. But to what purpose do I say all this? For the rest, 'tis on both sides a dirty deed to buy and sell Livings, to detain from the Church that which God's and men's Laws have bestowed on it; but in them most, and that from the covetousness and ignorance of such as are interested in this business; I name covetousness in the first place, as the root of all these mischiefs, which Achan-like, compels them to commit sacrilege, and to make Simoniacal compacts, (and what not?) to their own ends, that kindles God's wrath, brings a plague, vengeance, and an heavy visitation, upon themselves and others. Some, out of that insatiable desire of filthy lucre, to be enriched, care not how they come by it, by right or wrong, hook or crook, so they have it. And others, when they have with riot and prodigality imbezelled their estates, to recover themselves, make a prey of the Church, robbing it, as Julian the Apostate did, spoil Parsons of their revenues (in *keeping half back,* as a great man amongst us observes,) *and that maintenance on which they should live:* by means whereof barbarism is increased, and a great decay of Chris-

* I had no money, I wanted impudence, I could not scamble, temporize, dissemble. — Burton's note.

tian Professors: for who will apply himself to these divine studies, his son, or friend, when, after great pains taken, they shall have nothing whereupon to live? But with what event do they these things? They toil and moil, but what reap they? They are commonly unfortunate families that use it, accursed in their progeny, &, as common experience evinceth, accursed themselves in all their proceedings. *With what face* (as he quotes out of Austin) *can they expect a blessing or inheritance from Christ in Heaven, that defraud Christ of his inheritance here on earth?* I would all our Simoniacal Patrons, and such as detain Tithes, would read those judicious Tracts of Sʳ Henry Spelman, and Sʳ James Sempil, Knights; those late elaborate and learned Treatises of Dʳ. Tillesley, and Mʳ. Montagu, which they have written of that subject. But though they should read, it would be to small purpose, though you should raise a clamour and confound the sea with high heaven; thunder, lighten, preach hell and damnation, tell them 'tis a sin, they will not believe it; denounce and terrify, they have *cauterized consciences,* they do not attend; as the enchanted adder, they stop their ears. Call them base, irreligious, profane, barbarous, Pagans, Atheists, Epicures, (as some of them surely are), with the Bawd in Plautus, Excellent! Admirable! they cry, and applaud themselves with that Miser, as often as they gaze on the moneys in the chest: say what you will, by any means get wealth: as a dog barks at the Moon, to no purpose are your sayings: take your Heaven, let them have money; — a base, profane, Epicurean, hypocritical rout! For my part, let them pretend what zeal they will, counterfeit religion, blear the world's eyes, bombast themselves, and stuff out their greatness with Church spoils, shine like so many peacocks; so cold is my charity, so defective in this behalf, that I shall never think better of them, than that they are rotten at core, their bones are full of Epicurean hypocrisy, and Atheistical marrow, they are worse than Heathens. For, as Dionysius Halicarnasseus observes, as of prime importance, *Greeks and Barbarians observe all religious rites, and dare not break them for fear of offending their Gods;* but our Simoniacal contractors, our senseless Achans, our stupefied Patrons, fear neither God nor Devil, they have evasions for it, it is no sin, or not due divine law, or, if a sin, no great sin, &c. And though they be daily punished for it, and they do manifestly perceive, that, as he said, frost and fraud come to foul ends; yet, as Chrysostom follows it, they are rather worse than better, — and the more they are corrected, the more they offend: but let them take their course, *Gnaw, goat, the vines,* go on still as they begin, 'tis no sin! let them rejoice secure, God's vengeance will overtake them in the end, and these ill-gotten goods, as an eagle's feathers, will consume the rest of their substance: it is the gold of Tolosa, and will produce no better effects. *Let them lay it up safe, and make their conveyances never so close, lock and shut door,* saith Chrysostom, *yet fraud and covetousness, two most violent thieves, are still included, and a little gain evil-gotten will subvert the rest of their goods.* The eagle in Æsop, seeing a piece of flesh, now ready to be sacrificed, swept it away with her claws, and carried it to her nest; but there was a burning coal stuck to it by chance, which unawares consumed her young ones, nest and all together. Let our Simoniacal Church-chopping Patrons, and sacrilegious Harpies, look for no better success.

A second cause is ignorance, and from thence contempt, which Junius well perceived: this hatred and contempt of learning proceeds out of ignorance; as they are themselves barbarous, idiots, dull, illiterate, & proud, so they esteem of others. Let there be Mæcenases, Flaccus, and the Maros will not fail: let there be bountiful Patrons, and there will be painful Scholars in all Sciences. But when they contemn learning, and think themselves sufficiently qualified, if they can write and read, scamble at a piece of Evidence, or have so much Latin as that Emperor had, *He that knows not how to dissemble knows not how to live;* * they are unfit to do their country service, to perform or undertake any action or employment, which may tend to the good of a Common-wealth, except it be to fight, or to do country Justice, with common sense, which every Yeoman can likewise do. And so they bring up their children. rude as they are themselves, unqualified, untaught, uncivil most part. Which of our youths is sufficiently learned in letters? Who handles well the orators and philosophers? Who reads History, the soul, as it were of actions? Parents are in too great a hurry for their own desires, &c. 'twas Lipsius' complaint to his illiterate country-men, it may be ours. Now shall these men judge of a Scholar's worth, that have no worth, that know not what belongs to a student's labours, that cannot distinguish between a true Scholar and a drone? or him that by reason of a voluble tongue, a strong voice, a pleasing tone, and some trivantly *Polyanthean* helps, steals and gleans a few notes from other men's Harvests, and so makes a fairer show than he that is truly learned indeed: that thinks it no more to preach than to speak, *or to run away with an empty cart,* as a grave man said; and thereupon vilify us and our pains; scorn us and all learning. Because they are rich, and have other means to live, they think it concerns them not to know, or to

* The maxim of the Emperor Frederick Barbarossa.

trouble themselves with it; a fitter task for younger brothers, or poor men's sons, to be Pen and Inkhorn men, pedantical slaves, and no whit beseeming the calling of a Gentleman; as Frenchmen and Germans commonly do, neglect therefore all human learning, what have they to do with it? Let Mariners learn Astronomy; Merchants' Factors study Arithmetick; Surveyors get them Geometry; Spectacle-makers Opticks: Landleapers Geography; Town Clerks Rhetorick; what should he do with a spade, that hath no ground to dig? or they with Learning, that have no use of it? Thus they reason, and are not ashamed to let Mariners, Prentices, and the basest servants, be better qualified than themselves. In former times, Kings, Princes, and Emperors, were the only Scholars, excellent in all faculties.

Julius Cæsar mended the year, and writ his own Commentaries,

> *And, though for ever fighting, yet found time*
> *To study th' heavenly bodies.*   (LUCAN)

Antonius, Adrian, Nero, Severus, Julian, &c., Michael the Emperor, and Isacius, were so much given to their studies, that no base fellow would take so much pains: Orion, Perseus, Alphonsus, Ptolemæus, famous Astronomers: Saber, Mithridates, Lysimachus, admired Physicians: Plato's kings all: Evax, that Arabian Prince, a most expert Jeweller, and an exquisite Philosopher; the Kings of Egypt were Priests of old, chosen and from thence, — the kings of men were Priests of Apollo: but those heroical times are past; the *Muses* are now banished in this bastard age, to meaner persons, and confined alone almost to *Universities*. In those days Scholars were highly beloved, honoured, esteemed; as old Ennius by Scipio Africanus, Virgil by Augustus, Horace by Mæcenas: Princes' companions; dear to them, as Anacreon to Polycrates, Philoxenus to Dionysius, and highly rewarded. Alexander sent Xenocrates the Philosopher fifty talents, because he was poor; men of learning and distinction were frequently brought together at the King's tables, as Philostratus relates of Adrian, and Lampridius of Alexander Severus. Famous Clerks came to these Princes' Courts, even as in the Lyceum, as to an University, and were admitted to their tables, as though on a couch at a banquet of the gods; Archelaus, that Macedonian King, would not willingly sup without Euripides, (amongst the rest he drank to him at supper one night, and gave him a cup of gold for his pains) being delighted by the agreeable conversation of the poet; and it was fit it should be so, because, as Plato in his Protagoras well saith, a good Philosopher as much excels other men, as a great King doth the Commons of his country; and again, seeing that they need nothing, &

are accustomed to wanting but little, & that they alone are able to discipline themselves; they needed not to beg so basely, as they compel Scholars in our times to complain of poverty, or crouch to a rich chuff for a meal's meat, but could vindicate themselves, and those Arts which they professed. Now they would & cannot: for it is held by some of them, as an axiom, that to keep them poor will make them study; they must be dieted, as horses to a race, not pampered; a fat bird will not sing, a fat dog cannot hunt; and so by this depression of theirs, some want means, others will, all want encouragement, as being forsaken almost, & generally contemned. 'Tis an old saying: " Let there be Mæcenases, Flaccus, and Maros will not be wanting," and 'tis a true saying still. Yet oftentimes, I may not deny it, the main fault is in ourselves. Our Academicks too frequently offend in neglecting patrons, as Erasmus well taxeth, or making ill choice of them; or, if we get a good one, we do not ply and follow him as we should. The same happened to me when I was a young man, (saith Erasmus, acknowledging his fault), and so may I say myself, I have offended in this,* and so peradventure have many others. We did not apply ourselves with that readiness we should: idleness, love of liberty, as he confesseth, & bashfulness, melancholy, timorousness, cause many of us to be too backward and remiss. So some offend in one extreme, but too many on the other; we are most part too forward, too solicitous, too ambitious, too impudent; we commonly complain that Mæcenases are wanting, want of encouragement, want of means, when as the true defect is in our own want of worth, our insufficiency. Did Mæcenas take notice of Horace or Virgil till they had showed themselves first? or had Bavius and Mævius any patrons? Let them, saith Erasmus, approve themselves worthy first, sufficiently qualified for learning and manners, before they presume or impudently intrude and put themselves on great men, as too many do; with such base flattery, parasitical colloguing, such hyperbolical elogies they do usually insinuate, that it is a shame to hear and see. Excessive panegyric raises envy rather than praise; and vain commendations derogate from truth; and we think in conclusion, ill of both, the commender and commended. So we offend, but the main fault is in their harshness, defect of patrons. How beloved of old, and how much respected was Plato to Dionysius? How dear to Alexander was Aristotle, Demaratus to Philip, Solon to Crœsus, Anaxarchus to Alexander, and Trebatius to Augustus, Cassius to Vespasian, Plutarch to Trajan, Seneca to Nero, Simonides to Hiero! how honoured! But those days are gone:

* Had I done as others did, put myself forward, I might have haply been as great a man as many of my equals. — Burton's note.

On Cæsar all our studies must depend:
For Cæsar is alone our hope and friend: (JUVENAL)

as he said of old, we may truly say now; he is our Amulet, our Sun, our
sole comfort and refuge, our Ptolemy, our common Mæcenas, James the
munificent, James the pacific, the priest of the Muses, the Platonic
King: our mighty pride and pillar: a famous Scholar himself, and the
sole Patron, Pillar, and sustainer of learning: but his worth in this kind
is so well known, that, as Paterculus of Cato, it would be monstrous to
praise him: and, which Pliny to Trajan, — He pays his homage to you
in a serious poem, the praise of the eternal years, not short and shameful
commendation. But he is now gone, the Sun of ours set, and yet no night
follows. We have such another * in his room, *another branch is there,*
without fail, of gold as pure, a twig blossoming with as fine an ore; and
long may he reign and flourish amongst us!

Let me not be malicious, and lie against my *Genius;* I may not deny
but that we have a sprinkling of our Gentry, here and there one, excellently well learned, like those Fuggers in Germany, Du Bartas, Du
Plessis, Sadael in France; Picus Mirandula, Schottus, Barotius in Italy;

Here and there, in the ocean waste, a swimmer is seen.   (VIRGIL)

But they are but few in respect of the multitude, the major part (& some
again excepted, that are indifferent) are wholly bent for hawks and
hounds, and carried away many times with intemperate lust, gaming,
and drinking. If they read a book at any time (if they have any leisure
from hunting, drinking, dicing, drabbing) 'tis an English Chronicle, Sir
Huon of Bordeaux, Amadis de Gaul, &c., a Play-book, or some pamphlet of News, and that at such seasons only, when they cannot stir
abroad, to drive away time, their sole discourse is dogs, hawks, horses,
and what News? If some one have been a traveller in Italy, or as far as
the Emperor's Court, wintered in Orleans, and can court his Mistress in
broken French, wear his clothes neatly in the newest fashion, sing some
choice out-landish tunes, discourse of Lords, Ladies, Towns, Palaces,
and Cities, he is complete, and to be admired: otherwise he and they are
much at one; no difference betwixt the Master and the Man, but worshipful titles: wink and choose betwixt him that sits down (clothes
excepted) and him that holds the trencher behind him. Yet these men
must be our Patrons, our Governors too sometimes, statesmen, magistrates, noble, great, and wise, by inheritance.

Mistake me not (I say again) O you of Patrician blood, you that are
worthy Senators, Gentlemen, I honour your names and persons, and with
all submissiveness prostrate myself to your censure and service. There

* Charles I.

are amongst you, I do ingenuously confess, many well deserving Patrons, and true patriots, of my knowledge, besides many hundreds which I never saw, no doubt, or heard of, pillars of our commonwealth,* whose worth, bounty, learning, forwardness, true zeal in Religion and good esteem of all Scholars, ought to be consecrated to all posterity; but of your rank there are a debauched, corrupt, covetous, illiterate crew again, no better than stocks, mere cattle, (I call God to witness, that they do not seem to me to deserve the name of free men), barbarous Thracians, (and what Thracian would deny this?) a sordid, profane, pernicious company, irreligious, impudent and stupid, (I know not what epithets to give them,) enemies to learning, confounders of the Church, and the ruin of a common-wealth. Patrons they are by right of inheritance, and put in trust freely to dispose of such Livings to the Church's good; but (hard taskmasters they prove) they take away their straw, and compel them to make their number of brick: they commonly respect their own ends, commodity is the steer[er] of all their actions; and him they present, in conclusion, as a man of greatest gifts, that will give most; no penny, no *Pater Noster,* as the saying is. Cease to dream that heaven's destiny can be swayed by prayer: their attendants and officers must be bribed, feed, and made, as Cerberus is with a sop by him that goes to hell. It was an old saying, *All things are for sale at Rome,* 'tis a rag of Popery, which will never be rooted out, there is no hope, no good to be done, without money. A Clerk may offer himself, approve his worth, learning, honesty, religion, zeal; they will commend him for it, but — virtue is praised, and — starves. If he be a man of extraordinary parts, they will flock afar off to hear him, as they did in Apuleius, to see Psyche: many mortal men came to see fair Psyche, the glory of her age; they did admire her, commend, desire her for her divine beauty, and gaze upon her, but as on a picture; but she perceived that no King nor Prince did repair to woo her; none would marry her, because she was without dowry; fair Psyche had no money. So they do by learning;

> *Your rich men have now learn'd of latter days*
> *T'admire, commend, and come together*
> *To hear and see a worthy Scholar speak,*
> *As children do a Peacock's feather.* (JUVENAL)

He shall have all the good words that may be given, *a proper man, and 'tis pity he hath no preferment,* all good wishes, but inexorable, indurate

---

* I have often met with myself, and conferred with, divers worthy gentlemen in the country, no whit inferior, if not to be preferred for divers kinds of learning, to many of our Academicks. — Burton's note.

as he is, he will not prefer him, though it be in his power, because he hath no money. Or if he do give him entertainment, let him be never so well qualified, plead affinity, consanguinity, sufficiency, he shall serve seven years, as Jacob did for Rachel, before he shall have it. If he will enter at first, he must get in at that Simoniacal gate, come off * soundly, and put in good security to perform all covenants, else he will not deal with, or admit him. But if some poor scholar, some Parson Chuffe will offer himself; some Trencher Chaplain, that will take it to the halves, thirds, or accept of what he will give, he is welcome; be conformable, preach as he will have him, he likes him before a million of others; for the best is always best cheap: and then as Hierom said to Chromatius, 'Tis a cover worthy of the pot; such a Patron, such a Clerk; the Cure is well supplied, and all parties pleased. So that is still verified in our age, which Chrysostom complained of in his time; rich men keep these Lecturers, and fawning Parasites, like so many dogs, at their tables, and filling their hungry guts with the offals of their meat, they abuse them at their pleasure, and make them say what they propose. *As children do by a bird or a butterfly in a string, pull in and let him out as they list, do they by their Trencher Chaplains, prescribe, command their wits, let in and out, as to them it seems best.* If the Patron be precise, so must his Chaplain be, if he be Papistical, his Clerk must be so too, or else be turned out. These are those Clerks which serve the turn, whom they commonly entertain, and present to Church Livings, whilst in the mean time we that are University men, like so many hide-bound calves in a pasture, tarry out our time, wither away as a flower ungathered in a garden, & are never used: or, as too many candles, illuminate ourselves alone, obscuring one another's light, & are not discerned here at all, the least of which, translated to a dark room, or to some Country Benefice, where it might shine apart, would give a fair light, and be seen over all. Whilst we lie waiting here, as those sick men did at the pool of Bethesda, till the Angel stirred the water, expecting a good hour, they step between, and beguile us of our preferment. I have not yet said. If after long expectation, much expence, travail, earnest suit of ourselves and friends, we obtain a small Benefice at last, our misery begins afresh; we are suddenly encountered with the flesh, world, and Devil, with a new onset; we change a quiet life for an ocean of troubles, we come to a ruinous house, which, before it be habitable, must be necessarily (to our great damage) repaired; we are compelled to sue for dilapidations, or else sued ourselves, and, scarce yet settled, we are called

* Pay.

upon for our predecessor's arrearages; first fruits, tenths, subsidies, are instantly to be paid, benevolence, procurations, &c., and, which is most to be feared, we light upon a crackt title, as it befel Clenard of Brabant, for his Rectory and Charge of his Beginæ; he was no sooner inducted, but instantly sued, (saith he) : at length after ten years' suit, as long as Troy's siege, when he had tired himself, and spent his money, he was fain to leave all for quietness' sake, and give it up to his adversary. Or else we are insulted over and trampled on by domineering officers, fleeced by those greedy Harpies to get more fees; we stand in fear of some precedent lapse; we fall amongst refractory, seditious sectaries, peevish Puritans, perverse Papists, a lascivious rout of Atheistical Epicures, that will not be reformed, or some litigious people, (*those wild beasts of Ephesus* must be fought with), that will not pay their dues without much repining, or compelled by long suit; for the generality of laymen despise the clergy, — an old axiom; all they think well gotten that is had from the Church, and by such uncivil harsh dealings they make their poor Minister weary of his place, if not his life : and put case they be quiet honest men, make the best of it, as often it falls out, from a polite and terse Academick he must turn rustick, rude, melancholise alone, learn to forget; or else, as many do, become Malsters, Graziers, Chapmen, &c. (now banished from the Academy, all commerce of the Muses, and confined to a country village, as Ovid was from Rome to Pontus,) and daily converse with a company of idiots and clowns.

Meantime, as regards us (for we are not free from this fault) the same charge remains, the same accusation, if not a much heavier one, may be brought against us; for it is through our fault, our carelessness, our avarice, that there are such frequent and foul traffickings in the Church (the Temple is put up for sale, and even God himself), such corruptions prevalent, such impiety and wickedness rampant, such a mad Euripus of miseries, such an estuary of troubles; all this is, I say, owing to the fault of all of us, but especially us University-bred men. For we are the main cause why the State is oppressed with so many evils; we of our own selves introduce this sad state of affairs, though deserving meantime any scorn and misery for not counteracting it to the best of our abilities. For what do we expect can happen, when every day, pell-mell, poor sons of Alma Mater, sprung from the soil, manikins of no rank whatever, are eagerly admitted to degrees? And if these have learnt by heart one or two definitions and distinctions, and spent the usual number of years in chopping logic, it matters not to what profit, whatever kind of fellows they eventually turn out to be, idiots, triflers, idlers, gamesters, tipplers, worthless, slaves to lust and pleasure,

> *Such as the suitors of Penelope,*
> *Or worthless courtiers of Alcinous,* (HORACE)

provided they have spent so many years at the University, and passed muster as gownsmen, they are presented for lucre's sake and through the interest of their friends: I may add often with splendid testimonials to their morals & learning; and on leaving College they are furnished with these, written most amply in their favour, by those who undoubtedly thereby abandon good faith and lose credit. For Doctors & Professors (as one saith) care for this only, that from their divers professions, irregular more frequently than legitimate ones, they may promote their own interests, and make their gains at the cost of the public. The only thing our annual officials generally desire is that they may squeeze money from the number of those who take degrees, nor do they much care what manner of men they are, whether literate or illiterate, provided they are fat, & sleek, & handsome, and, to sum up in one word, monied. Philosophasters who have no art * become Masters of Arts: and the authorities bid those be wise who are endowed with no wisdom, and bring nothing to their degree but the desire to take it. Theologasters, sufficiently, & more than sufficiently learned if they but pay the fees, emerge full-blown B.D.'s & D.D.'s. And hence it happens that such sorry buffoons everywhere, so many idiots, placed in the twilight of letters, ghosts of pastors, itinerant quacks, stupid, dolts, clods, asses, mere animals, burst with unwashed feet into the sacred precincts of Theology, bringing nothing but a brazen countenance, some vulgar trash, and scholastic trifles hardly worth hearing on the high roads. This is that unworthy & half-starved class of men, indigent, vagabond, slaves to their belly, that ought to be sent back to the plough-tail, fitter for sties than altars, who basely prostitute our Divinity; these are they who fill pulpits, creep into noblemen's houses, and, since they are deprived of other means of livelihood by their feebleness of mind & body, and are very unfitted for any other functions in the State, flee to this sacred refuge, clutching at the Priesthood by hook or by crook, not in sincerity, but, as Paul saith, *making merchandise of the word of God.* Let no one meantime think that I intend any disparagement to the very many in

* Such were satirized not long ago in Philosophaster, a Latin comedy, presented at Christ Church, Oxford, February 16, 1617. — Burton's note. [Philosophaster was Burton's only play, concerning which he took pains (because of its similarity to Ben Jonson's Alchemist, acted 1610) to have it known that it was originally planned in 1606.]

the Church of England, exceptionably learned, eminent, & of spotless
fame, who are more, perhaps, than any other nation in Europe could
produce; let no one think that I intend any disparagement to our most
flourishing Universities, which produce in abundance men most learned
in every branch of learning, and men to be respected for every kind of
virtue; and both Oxford & Cambridge would have many more such, and
be far more famous, did not these blots obscure their splendid lustre, did
not corruption stand in the way, did not some huckstering Harpies &
proletaries envy them this distinction. For no one has so blind a mind
as not to see, no one so dull an intelligence as not to perceive, no one so
obstinate a judgement, as to refuse to realize that sacred Theology is
polluted by these idiots & mountebanks, and the heavenly Muses prostituted as some common thing. Vile souls full of effrontery (to use the
language of Luther), for the sake of gain, as flies to the milk-pails, fly
to the tables of nobles and heroes, in the hope of the Priesthood or any
honour & office, and pour into any Hall or Town, willing to undertake
any duty,

As marionettes dance on the Showman's wires, (HORACE)

following wherever hunger leads them, &, like parrots, in hope of prey
they chatter anything: complaisant Parasites (as Erasmus calls them),
they teach, say, write, urge, prove, anything against their conscience,
not to improve the flock, but to get for themselves a large fortune. They
enunciate any opinions & tenents contrary to the word of God, not to
offend their Patron, and to retain the favour of influential persons, and
the applause of the people, and to heap up riches for themselves. For
the spirit in which they generally approach Theology is not to look after
Divinity, but themselves; not to promote the welfare of the Church, but
to plunder it; seeking, as Paul saith, not the things of Jesus Christ, but
their things, not the Master's treasure, but to store up treasure for
themselves & their families. Nor is this the case only with those of
poorer fortunes and mean lot: this evil has invaded the middle and
highest classes, men of eminence, not to say Bishops.

The part that money plays in sacred things,

Tell us, ye Pontiffs, how it rings. (PERSIUS)

For ofttimes the very highest men are perverted by avarice, and those
who outshine all others in the exemplariness of their character lead the
way to Simony, and, dashing against this rock of corruption, not only
shear but fleece the flock, &, wherever they betake themselves, plunder,
& drain, pillage, making shipwreck of their reputation, if not of their
souls; so that the evil seems to have proceeded not from bottom to top,

but from top to bottom, and that is true which one of old playfully said, *What one first bought, that may one justly sell.*

The Simoniac (to use the words of Leo), has not received a favour, & if he receives it not, he has it not, and if he has it not, he cannot be favoured. So far indeed are some of those at the helm from promoting others, that they stand altogether in their way, being well aware themselves to what arts they owe their own place. For he who thinks they rose on account of their love of letters is a fool: indeed he who supposes promotion is the reward of genius, learning, experience, probity, piety, & devotion to the Muses (as was once actually the case, but now is only an expectation), is very plainly a madman. However or wherever this evil originated I shall not seek further; from these beginnings sprung these dregs of corruptions, every calamity, all the numerous miseries that pester the Church. Hence the so common Simony, hence have arisen complaints, frauds, impostures; from this source has sprung all wickedness. I shall not speak, in passing, of the ambition, the flattery, grosser than that of Courts, to escape from short commons at home, the luxury, the frequent bad example of their lives, by which they offend some, their Sybaritic drinking-parties, &c. Hence that Academic squalor, that sadness of the Muses in these days, since any manikin ignorant of the arts rises by these arts, is promoted & grows rich in this manner, distinguished by ambitious titles, and majestic with many dignities, and attracts the eyes of the vulgar mob, and holds his head high, & exhibits a certain majesty & grandeur, & great solicitude about his personal appearance, being venerable through his beard, neat in his gown, glittering in purple, & especially conspicuous for the splendour of his household arrangements & the number of his servants.

As the statues (one says), which are placed on the columns in sacred buildings, seem as if yielding beneath their load, and as if they sweated, when really they are inanimate, & add nothing to the firmness of the stone; so these wish to seem Atlases, though they are, in reality, stony statues, shadowy manikins, perhaps stupid & dolts, differing in nothing from stone.

Meantime learned men, endowed with the graces of a holy life, & bearing the burden and heat of the day, by some unfair destiny serve these men, perhaps contented with a very small salary, called by plain names, humble, obscure, & needy, though far more worthy, & unhonoured lead a private life, buried in some scanty country Living, or imprisoned all their lives in their Colleges, and languish in obscurity. But

I will not dwell on this sad theme any longer. Hence come our tears, hence it is that the Muses are in mourning, hence it is that Religion itself, to use the words of Sesellius, is brought into ridicule & contempt, and the Priesthood is debased; and, since this is the case, I may venture to say so, and to quote the low saying of a low person about the Clergy, — that they are a base lot, poor, ignorant, sordid, melancholy, wretched, despicable, & deserving of contempt!

MEMBER 4

SUBSECTION 1 — *Non-necessary, Remote, Outward, Adventitious, or Accidental Causes: as First from the Nurse*

Of those remote, outward, ambient, necessary causes, I have sufficiently discoursed in the precedent number. The non-necessary follow; of which, saith Fuchsius, no art can be made, by reason of their uncertainty, casualty, and multitude; so called not necessary, because (according to Fernelius) they may be avoided, *and used without necessity.* Many of these accidental causes, which I shall entreat of here, might have well been reduced to the former, because they cannot be avoided, but fatally happen to us, though accidentally, and unawares, at some time or other: the rest are contingent and evitable, and more properly inserted in this rank of causes. To reckon up all is a thing unpossible; of some therefore most remarkable of these contingent causes which produce Melancholy, I will briefly speak, and in their order.

From a child's nativity, the first ill accident that can likely befall him in this kind is a bad nurse, by whose means alone he may be tainted with this malady from his cradle. Aulus Gellius brings in Favorinus, that eloquent Philosopher, proving this at large, *that there is the same virtue and property in the milk as in the seed, and not in men alone, but in all other creatures. He gives instance in a kid and lamb: if either of them suck of the other's milk, the lamb of the goat's, or the kid of the ewe's, the wool of the one will be hard, and the hair of the other soft.* Giraldus Cambrensis confirms this by a notable example which happened in his time. A sow-pig by chance sucked a brach,* and, when she was grown, *would miraculously hunt all manner of deer, and that as well, or rather better than any ordinary hound.* His conclusion is, *that men and beasts participate of her nature and conditions, by whose milk they are fed.* Favorinus urgeth it farther, and demonstrates it more evidently, that if

* A deer-hound.

a nurse be *misshapen, unchaste, unhonest, impudent, drunk,* cruel or the like, the child that sucks upon her breast will be so too; all other affections of the mind, and diseases, are almost engrafted, as it were, & imprinted into the temperature of the infant, by the nurse's milk, as pox, leprosy, melancholy, &c. Cato for some such reason would make his servants' children suck upon his wife's breast, because by that means they would love him and his the better, & in all likelihood agree with them. A more evident example that the minds are altered by milk, cannot be given, than that of Dion, which he relates of Caligula's cruelty; it could neither be imputed to father nor mother, but to his cruel nurse alone, that anointed her paps with blood still when he sucked, which made him such a murderer, & to express her cruelty to an hair: and that of Tiberius, who was a common drunkard, because his nurse was such a one. And if she be a fool or dolt, the child she nurseth will take after her, or otherwise be misaffected; which Franciscus Barbarus proves at full, & Ant. Guivarra: the child will surely participate. For bodily sickness there is no doubt to be made. Titus, Vespasian's son, was therefore sickly, because the nurse was so, Lampridius. And if we may believe Physicians, many times children catch the pox from a bad nurse. Besides evil attendance, negligence, and many gross inconveniences, which are incident to nurses, much danger may so come to the child. For these causes Aristotle, Favorinus, and Marcus Aurelius, would not have a child put to nurse at all, but every mother to bring up her own of what condition soever she be; for a sound and able mother to put out her child to nurse is an outrage upon Nature, so Guatso calls it, 'tis fit therefore she should be nurse herself; the mother will be more careful, loving, and attendant, than any servile woman, or such hired creatures; this all the world acknowledgeth; it is most fit, (as Rodericus a Castro, in many words, confesseth), that the mother should suckle her own infant, who denies that it should be so? and which some women most curiously observe; amongst the rest, that Queen of France, a Spaniard by birth, that was so precise and zealous in this behalf, that, when in her absence a strange nurse had suckled her child, she was never quiet till she had made the infant vomit it up again. But she was too jealous. If it be so, as many times it is, they must be put forth, the mother be not fit or well able to be a nurse, I would then advise such mothers, (as Plutarch doth in his book,* and S. Hierome, & the said Rodericus) that they make choice of a sound woman, of a good complexion, honest, free from bodily diseases, if it be possible, and all

* On the Education of Children.

passions and perturbations of the mind, as sorrow, fear, grief, folly, melancholy. For such passions corrupt the milk, and alter the temperature of the child, which now being moist & pliable clay, is easily seasoned and perverted. And if such a nurse may be found out, that will be diligent and careful withal, let Favorinus and M. Aurelius plead how they can against it, I had rather accept of her in some cases than the mother herself, and (which Bonacialus, the Physician, Nic. Biesius the politician, approves,) *some nurses are much to be preferred to some mothers.* For why may not the mother be naught, a peevish drunken flirt, a waspish cholerick slut, a crazed piece, a fool, (as many mothers are), unsound, as soon as the nurse? There is more choice of nurses than mothers; and therefore, except the mother be most virtuous, staid, a woman of excellent good parts, and of a sound complexion, I would have all children in such cases committed to discreet strangers. And 'tis the only way (as by marriage they are engrafted to other families) to alter the breed, or, if any thing be amiss in the mother, as Lodovicus Mercatus contends, to prevent diseases and future maladies, to correct and qualify the child's ill-disposed temperature, which he had from his parents. This is an excellent remedy, if good choice be made of such a nurse.

SUBSECTION 2 — *Education a Cause of Melancholy*

EDUCATION, of these accidental causes of Melancholy, may justly challenge the next place, for if a man escape a bad nurse, he may be undone by evil bringing up. Jason Pratensis puts this of *Education* for a principal cause; bad parents, step-mothers, tutors, masters, teachers, too rigorous, too severe, too remiss or indulgent on the other side, are often fountains and furtherers of this disease. Parents, and such as have the tuition and oversight of children, offend many times in that they are too stern, always threatening, chiding, brawling, whipping, or striking; by means of which their poor children are so disheartened and cowed, that they never after have any courage, a merry hour in their lives, or take pleasure in any thing. There is a great moderation to be had in such things, as matters of so great moment to the making or marring of a child. Some fright their children with beggars, bugbears, and hobgoblins, if they cry, or be otherwise unruly: but they are much to blame in it, many times, saith Lavater, for fear they fall into many diseases, and cry out in their sleep, and are much the worse for it all their lives: these things ought not at all, or to be sparingly done, & upon just occasion. Tyrannical, impatient, hare-brain Schoolmasters, dry-as-dusts, so Fabius terms them, flogging Ajaxes, are in this kind as bad as hangmen and executioners, they make many children endure a martyrdom all the while they are at school, with bad diet, if they board in their houses, too much severity and ill usage, they quite pervert their temperature of body and mind: still chiding, railing, frowning, lashing, tasking, keeping, that they are broken in spirit, moped many times, weary of their lives, and think no slavery in the world (as once I did myself) like to that of a Grammar Scholar. The pupil's faculties are perverted by the indiscretion of the master, saith Erasmus, they tremble at his voice, looks, coming in. S. Austin in the first book of his Confessions calls this schooling an awful enforcement, and elsewhere a martyrdom, and confesseth of himself, how cruelly he was tortured in mind for learning Greek: *I knew nothing, and with cruel terrors and punishment I was daily compelled.* Beza complains in like case of a rigorous Schoolmaster in Paris, that made him by his continual thunder and threats once in a mind to drown himself, had he not met by the way with an uncle of his that vindicated him from that misery for the time, by taking him to his house. Trincavellius had a patient nineteen years of age, extremely melancholy by reason of overmuch study, and his Tutor's threats. Many Masters are hard-hearted, and bitter to their servants, and by that means do so deject, with terrible speeches and hard usage so crucify them, that they become desperate, and can never be recalled.

Others again, in that opposite extreme, do as great harm by their too much remissness; they give them no bringing up, no calling to busy themselves about, or to live in, teach them no trade, or set them in any good course; by means of which their servants, children, scholars, are carried away with that stream of drunkenness, idleness, gaming, and many such irregular courses, that in the end they rue it, curse their parents, and mischief themselves. Too much indulgence causeth the like,
———— the father's foolish mildness & wicked easy-going; when as, Micio-like, with too much liberty and too great allowance, they feed their children's humours, let them revel, wench, riot, swagger, and do what they will themselves, and then punish them with a noise of musicians. He feasts & drinks & scents himself at my expense, [saith one in Terence's Comedy of the Brothers]. Doth he love? I supply the money as long as I find it convenient. Has he broken open street-doors? they shall be mended. Has he torn any clothes? they must be sewn up again. Let him do what he will, take, spend, waste; I am resolved to submit.
———— But as Demea told him, your lenity will be his undoing, I seem to see the day when he will flee the country and enlist; I foresee his ruin. So parents often err, many fond mothers especially, dote so

much upon their children, like Æsop's Ape, till in the end they crush them to death. Pampering up their bodies to the undoing of their souls, they will not let them be corrected or controlled, but still soothed up in every thing they do, that in conclusion *they bring sorrow, shame, heaviness to their parents, become wanton, stubborn, wilful, and disobedient ;* rude, untaught, head-strong, incorrigible, and graceless. *They love them so foolishly,* saith Cardan, *that they rather seem to hate them, bringing them not up to virtue but injury, not to learning but to riot, not to sober life and conversation, but to all pleasure and licentious behaviour.* Who is he of so little experience that knows not this of Fabius to be true? *Education is another nature, altering the mind and will, and I would to God* (saith he) *we ourselves did not spoil our children's manners by our overmuch cockering and nice education, and weaken the strength of their bodies and minds. That causeth custom, custom nature, &c.* For these causes Plutarch, in his book on the education of children, and Hierom, gives a most especial charge to all parents, and many good cautions about bringing up of children, that they be not committed to undiscreet, passionate, bedlam Tutors, light, giddy-headed, or covetous persons, & spare for no cost, that they may be well nurtured & taught, it being a matter of so great consequence. For such parents as do otherwise, Plutarch esteems of them *that [they] are more careful of their shoes than of their feet,* that rate their wealth above their children. And he, saith Cardan, *that leaves his son to a covetous Schoolmaster to be informed, or to a close Abbey to fast and learn wisdom together, doth no other, than that he be a learned fool, or a sickly wise man.*

SUBSECTION 3 — *Terrors and Affrights, Causes of Melancholy*

TULLY (in the 4th of his Tusculans) distinguisheth these terrors which arise from the apprehension of some terrible object heard or seen from other fears, and so doth Patritius. Of all fears they are most pernicious and violent, and so suddenly alter the whole temperature of the body, move the soul & spirits, strike such a deep impression, that the parties can never be recovered, causing more grievous and fiercer Melancholy, (as Felix Plater speaks out of his experience,) than any inward cause whatsoever: *and imprints itself so forcibly in the spirits, brain, humours, that, if all the mass of blood were let out of the body, it could hardly be extracted. This horrible kind of Melancholy* (for so he terms it) *had been often brought before him, and troubles and affrights commonly men and women, young and old, of all sorts.* Hercules de Saxonia calls this kind of Melancholy by a peculiar name, it comes from the agitation, motion, contraction, dilatation of spirits, not from any dis-temperature of humours, and produceth strong effects. This terror is most usually caused, as Plutarch will have, *from some imminent danger, when a terrible object is at hand,* heard, seen, or conceived, *truly appearing, or in a dream:* and many times the more sudden the accident, it is the more violent,

> *Their soul's affright, their heart amazed quakes,*
> *The trembling liver pants i' th' veins, and aches.*   (SENECA)

Artemidorus the Grammarian lost his wits by the unexpected sight of a Crocodile. The Massacre at Lyons, 1572, in the reign of Charles the 9th, was so terrible and fearful, that many ran mad, some died, great-bellied women were brought to bed before their time, generally all affrighted and aghast. Many lose their wits *by the sudden sight of some spectrum or devil, a thing very common in all ages,* saith Lavater, as Orestes did at the sight of the Furies, which appeared to him in black (as Pausanias records). The Greeks call them mormoluches,* which so terrify their souls. Or if they be but affrighted by some counterfeit devils in jest, as children in the dark conceive hobgoblins, and are sore afraid, they are the worse for it all their lives; some by sudden fires, earthquakes, inundations, or any such dismal objects. Themison the Physician fell into an *Hydrophobia* by seeing one sick of that disease, or by the sight of a monster, a carcase, they are disquieted many months following, & cannot endure the room where a corse had been, for a world would not be alone with a dead man, or lie in that bed many years after in which a man hath died. At Basil a many little children in the spring time went to gather flowers in a meadow at the town's end, where a malefactor hung in gibbets; all gazing at it, one by chance flung a stone, and made it stir, by which accident the children affrighted ran away; one, slower than the rest, looking back, and seeing the stirred carcase wag towards her, cried out it came after, & was so terribly affrighted, that for many days she could not rest, eat, or sleep, she could not be pacified, but melancholy died. In the same town another child, beyond the Rhine, saw a grave opened, & upon the sight of the carcase was so troubled in mind,

---

* In the text, in Greek letters, mormolykeia, but "mormoluche" appears elsewhere in Burton as a translation of the word. "Mormo" was a Greek she-monster of hideous aspect; "lykeia" refers to Mt. Lykaion, of which gruesome tales were told. There was a Lykaian Zeus, in whose festival the central rite was a human sacrifice, and he who tasted of the entrails of this sacrifice was turned into a wolf. But the word for wolf is "lykos." Perhaps, therefore, "werewolf" best suggests the meaning of the "mormoluche." The word is also seen in English, as in H. G. Wells' "Time Machine," as "Morlock."

that she could not be comforted, but a little after departed, and was buried by it. A Gentlewoman of the same city saw a fat hog cut up; when the entrails were opened, and a noisome savour offended her nose, she much misliked, and would not longer abide: a Physician in presence told her, as that hog, so was she, full of filthy excrements, and aggravated the matter by some other loathsome instances, in so much this nice Gentlewoman apprehended it so deeply, that she fell forthwith a vomiting, was so mightily distempered in mind and body, that, with all his art and persuasions, for some months after, he could not restore her to herself again, she could not forget it, or remove the object out of her sight (F. Plater). Many cannot endure to see a wound opened, but they are offended, a man executed, or labour of any fearful disease, as possession, apoplexies, one bewitched, or if they read by chance of some terrible thing, the symptoms alone of such a disease, or that which they dislike, they are instantly troubled in mind, aghast, ready to apply it to themselves, they are as much disquieted as if they had seen it, or were so affected themselves. They dream and continually think of it. As lamentable effects are caused by such terrible objects heard, read, or seen; as Plutarch holds, no sense makes greater alteration of body & mind: sudden speech sometimes, unexpected news, be they good or bad, will move as much, as a Philosopher observes, will take away our sleep, and appetite, disturb and quite overturn us. Let them bear witness that have heard those tragical alarums, out-cries, hideous noises, which are many times suddenly heard in the dead of the night by irruption of enemies & accidental fires, &c., those panick fears, which often drive men out of their wits, bereave them of sense, understanding and all, some for a time, some for their whole lives, they never recover it. The Midianites were so affrighted by Gideon's soldiers, they breaking but every one a pitcher; and Hannibal's army by such a panick-fear was discomfited at the walls of Rome. Augusta Livia, hearing a few tragical verses recited out of Virgil, fell down dead in a swoon. Edinus, King of Denmark, by a sudden sound which he heard, *was turned into fury, with all his men*. Amatus Lusitanus had a patient, that by reason of bad tidings became *epileptic*. Cardan saw one that lost his wits by mistaking of an *echo*. If one sense alone can cause such violent commotions of the mind, what may we think when hearing, sight & those other senses, are all troubled at once, as by some earth-quakes, thunder, lightning, tempests, &c.? At Bologna in Italy, in the year 1504, there was such a fearful earth-quake about eleven a clock in the night (as Beroaldus, in his book On the Motion of the Earth, hath commended to posterity) that all the city trembled, the people thought the world was at an end; such a fearful noise it made, such a detestable smell, the inhabitants were infinitely affrighted, and some ran mad. Hear a strange story, and worthy to be chronicled (mine author adds), I had a servant at the same time called Fulco Argelanus, a bold proper man, so grievously terrified with it, that he was first melancholy, after doted, at last mad, & made away himself. At Fuscinum in Japan *there was such an earth-quake and darkness on a sudden, that many men were offended with headache, many overwhelmed with sorrow and melancholy.* At Meacum *whole streets & goodly palaces were overturned at the same time, & there was such an hideous noise withal, like thunder, and filthy smell, that their hair stared for fear, and their hearts quaked; men and beasts were incredibly terrified.* In Sacai, another city, *the same earthquake was so terrible unto them, that many were bereft of their senses; and others by that horrible spectacle so much amazed, that they knew not what they did.* Blasius, a Christian, the reporter of the news, was so affrighted for his part that, though it were two months after, he was scarce his own man, neither could he drive the remembrance of it out of his mind. Many times some years following they will tremble afresh at the remembrance or conceit of such a terrible object, even all their lives long, if mention be made of it. Cornelius Agrippa relates out of Gulielmus Parisiensis a story of one, that, after a distasteful purge which a Physician had prescribed unto him, was so much moved, *that at the very sight of physick he would be distempered;* though he never so much as smelled to it, the box of physick long after would give him a purge; nay, the very remembrance of it did effect it; *like travellers and sea-men,* saith Plutarch, *that when they have been stranded, or dashed on a rock, for ever after fear not that mischance only, but all such dangers whatsoever.*

SUBSECTION 4 — *Scoffs, Calumnies, bitter Jests, how they cause Melancholy*

IT is an old saying, *a blow with a word strikes deeper than a blow with a sword:* & many men are as much galled with a calumny, a scurrile & bitter jest, a libel, a pasquil, satire, apologue, epigram, stage-plays, or the like, as with any misfortune whatsoever. Princes & Potentates that are otherwise happy, & have all at command, secure and free, are grievously vexed with these pasquilling libels & satires: they fear a railing Aretine more than an enemy in the field, which made most Princes of his time (as some relate) *allow him a liberal pension, that he should not* *tax them in his satires.* The Gods had their Momus, Homer his Zoilus, Achilles his Thersites, Philip his Demades: the Cæsars themselves in Rome were commonly taunted. There was never wanting a Petronius, a Lucian, in those times, nor will be a Rabelais, an Euphormio, a Boccalini, in ours. Pope Adrian the Sixth was so highly offended and grievously vexed with Pasquillers * at Rome, he gave command that statue should be demolished and burned, the ashes flung into the river Tiber, and had done it forthwith, had not Lodovicus Suessanus, a facete companion, dissuaded him to the contrary, by telling him that Pasquil's ashes would turn to frogs in the bottom of the river, and croak worse and louder than before. — Poets, as a class, are irritable; and therefore Socrates in Plato adviseth all his friends, *that respect their credits, to stand in awe of Poets, for they are terrible fellows, can praise and dispraise as they see cause.* Thus the pen is much worse than the sword. The Prophet David complains, that his soul was full of the mocking of the wealthy, and of the despitefulness of the proud; and *for the voice of the wicked &c., and their hate; his heart trembled within him,* and *the terrors of death came upon him: fear and horrible fear, &c.,* and *Rebuke hath broken my heart, and I am full of heaviness.* Who hath not like cause to complain, and is not so troubled, that shall fall into the mouths of such men? for many are of so petulant a spleen, and have that figure *sarcasmus* so often in their mouths, so bitter, so foolish, as Balthasar Castilio notes of them, that *they cannot speak, but they must bite;* they had rather lose a friend than a jest; and what company soever they come in, they will be scoffing, insulting over their inferiors, especially over such as any way depend upon them, humouring, misusing, or putting gulleries on some or other, till they have made, by their humouring or gulling, a madman out of a mope or a noddy, and all to make themselves merry:

> *Beware! he's vicious: so he gains his end,*
> *A selfish laugh, he will not spare a friend.*   (HORACE)

Friends, neuters, enemies, all are as one; to make a fool a madman is their sport, & they have no greater felicity than to scoff & deride others; they must sacrifice to the god of laughter, with them in Apuleius, once a day, or else they shall be melancholy themselves; they care not how they grind and misuse others, so they may exhilarate their own persons. Their wits indeed serve them to that sole purpose, to make sport, to break a scurrile jest, which is the froth of wit, as Tully holds; and for this they are often applauded. In all other discourse dry, barren, stra-

* See Index for Pasquil.

mineous, dull & heavy, here lies their *Genius ;* in this alone they excel, please themselves & others. Leo the 10th, that scoffing Pope, as Jovius hath registred in the 4th Book of his Life, took an extraordinary delight in humouring of silly fellows, and to put gulleries upon them ; *by commending some, persuading others* to this or that ; he made soft fellows stark noddies, & such as were foolish quite mad before he left them. One memorable example he recites there, of Tarascomus of Parma, a Musician, that was so humoured by Leo the 10th, & Bibiena his second in this business, that he thought himself to be a man of most excellent skill, (who was indeed a ninny) ; they *made him set foolish songs, and invent new ridiculous precepts, which they did highly commend,* as to tie his arm that played on the lute, to make him strike a sweeter stroke, *and to pull down the Arras hangings, because the voice would be clearer, by reason of the reverberation of the wall.* In the like manner they persuaded one Baraballius, of Gaeta, that he was as good a Poet as Petrarch ; would have him to be made a Laureate Poet, and invite all his friends to his instalment ; and had so possessed the poor man with a conceit of his excellent Poetry, that, when some of his more discreet friends told him of his folly, he was very angry with them, and said *they envied his honour and prosperity.* It was strange (saith Jovius) to see an old man of 60 years, a venerable and grave old man, so gulled. But what cannot such scoffers do, especially if they find a soft creature, on whom they may work ? Nay, to say truth, who is so wise, or so discreet, that may not be humoured in this kind, especially if some excellent wits shall set upon him ? He that mads others, if he were so humoured, would be as mad himself, as much grieved and tormented ; he might cry with him in the Comedy, By Jupiter ! You're a man to drive a body crazy. For all is in these things as they are taken ; if he be a silly soul, and do not perceive it, 'tis well, he may haply make others sport, and be no whit troubled himself ; but if he be apprehensive of his folly, and take it to heart, then it torments him worse than any lash. A bitter jest, a slander, a calumny, pierceth deeper than any loss, danger, bodily pain, or injury whatsoever ; it flies swiftly, as Bernard of an arrow, but wounds deeply, especially if it shall proceed from a virulent tongue, it cuts (saith David) *like a two-edged sword. They shoot bitter words as arrows. And they smote with their tongues,* & that so hard, that they leave an incurable wound behind them. Many men are undone by this means, moped, & so dejected, that they are never to be recovered ; and, of all other men living, those which are actually melancholy, or inclined to it, are most sensible (as being suspicious, cholerick, apt to mistake) & impatient of an injury in that kind: they aggravate, and so meditate continually of it, that it is a perpetual corrosive, not to be removed till time wear it out. Although they peradventure that so scoff do it alone in mirth and merriment, and hold it an excellent thing to enjoy another man's madness; yet they must know that it is a mortal sin (as Thomas holds) and, as the Prophet David denounceth, they that use it shall never dwell in God's tabernacle.

Such scurrile jests, flouts, & sarcasms, therefore, ought not at all to be used, especially to our betters, to those that are in misery, or any way distressed; for to such, they multiply grief, and, as he perceived, many are ashamed, many vexed, angered, and there is no greater cause or furtherer of melancholy. Martin Cromerus, in the 6th Book of his History, hath a pretty story to this purpose, of Vladislaus the Second, King of Poland, and Peter Dunnius, Earl of Shrine; they had been hunting late, & were enforced to lodge in a poor cottage. When they went to bed, Vladislaus told the Earl in jest, that his wife lay softer with the Abbot of Shrine; he, not able to contain, replied, & yours with Dobessus, a gallant young Gentleman in the Court, whom Christina the Queen loved. These words of his so galled the Prince, that he was long after very sad and melancholy for many months: but they were the Earl's utter undoing: for when Christina heard of it, she persecuted him to death. Sophia the Empress, Justinian's wife, broke a bitter jest upon Narses the Eunuch, (a famous Captain, then disquieted for an overthrow which he lately had), that he was fitter for a distaff, & to keep women company, than to wield a sword, or to be General of an army: but it cost her dear, for he so far distasted it, that he went forthwith to the adverse part, much troubled in his thoughts, caused the Lombards to rebel, and thence procured many miseries to the Common-wealth. Tiberius the Emperor with-held a Legacy from the people of Rome, which his Predecessor Augustus had lately given, and, perceiving a fellow round * a dead corse in the ear, would needs know wherefore he did so; the fellow replied, that he wished the departed soul to signify to Augustus the commons of Rome were yet unpaid; for this bitter jest the Emperor caused him forthwith to be slain, and carry the news himself. For this reason, all those that otherwise approve of jests in some cases, and facete companions, (as who doth not?) let them laugh and be merrie, & burst Codrus' sides, 'tis laudable and fit; those yet will by no means admit them in their companies, that are in any way inclined to this malady; no jesting with a discontented person. 'Tis Castilio's caveat, Io. Pontanus', and Galateus', and every good man's.

* Whisper to.

Play with me, but hurt me not:
Jest with me, but shame me not.

Comitas * is a virtue betwixt *rusticity and scurrility, two extremes, as affability* is betwixt *flattery* and *contention,* it must not exceed, but be still accompanied with innocency, which hurts no man, abhors all offer of injury. Though a man be liable to such a jest or obloquy, have been overseen,† or committed a foul fact, yet it is no good manners or humanity to upbraid, to hit him in the teeth with his offence, or to scoff at such a one; 'tis an old axiom, All reproach cast upon the unconvicted is unwarrantable. I speak not of such as generally tax vice; Barclay, Gentilis, Erasmus, Agrippa, Fishcart, &c., the Varronists and Lucians of our time, Satirists, Epigrammatists, Comedians, Apologists, &c. but such as personate, rail, scoff, calumniate, perstringe ‡ by name, or in presence offend.

Who jests with swinish impudence,
No Sestius is, but a pack-horse, — hence! (MARTIAL)

'Tis horse-play this, and those jests (as he saith) *are no better than injuries,* biting jests, they are poisoned jests, leave a sting behind them, and ought not to be used.

Set not thy foot to make the blind to fall,
Nor wilfully offend thy weaker brother:
Nor wound the dead with thy tongue's bitter gall,
Neither rejoice thou in the fall of other. (PYBRAC)

If these rules could be kept, we should have much more ease and quietness than we have, less melancholy: whereas, on the contrary, we study to misuse each other, how to sting and gall, like two fighting boars, bending all our force and wit, friends, fortunes, to crucify one another's souls; by means of which there is little content and charity, much virulency, hatred, malice, and disquietness, among us.

SUBSECTION 5 — *Loss of Liberty, Servitude, Imprisonment, how they cause Melancholy*

To this catalogue of causes I may well annex loss of liberty, servitude, or imprisonment, which to some persons is as great a torture as any of the rest. Though they have all things convenient, sumptuous houses to their use, fair walks and gardens, delicious bowers, galleries, good fare & diet, & all things correspondent, yet they are not content, because they are confined, may not come and go at their pleasure, have & do

---

* Pleasantry or good humor, here: ordinarily, courtesy.
† Drawn into error.
‡ Censure.

what they will, but live at another man's table and command. As it is in meats, so is it in all other things, places, societies, sports; let them be never so pleasant, commodious, wholesome, so good; yet there is a loathing satiety of all things; (the children of Israel were tired with *Manna;*) it is irksome to them so to live, as to a bird in a cage, or a dog in his kennel, they are weary of it. They are happy, it is true, and have all things, to another man's judgment, that heart can wish, or that they themselves can desire, had they but a sense of their blessings, yet they loathe it, and are tired with the present. Men's nature is still desirous of news, variety, delights; and our wandering affections are so irregular in this kind, that they must change, though it be to the worst. Bachelors must be married, and married men would be bachelors; they do not love their own wives, though otherwise fair, wise, virtuous, and well qualified, because they are theirs; our present estate is still the worst; we cannot endure one course of life long, (and hate what we have just prayed for) one calling long, to be in office pleases, then, in a twinkling, displeases, one place long, At Rome I long for Tibur, and at Tibur long for Rome; that which we earnestly sought we now contemn. This alone kills many a man, that they are tied to the same still; as a horse in a mill, a dog in a wheel, they run round, without alteration or news; their life groweth odious, the world loathsome, & that which crosseth their furious delights, *What? still the same?* Marcus Aurelius and Solomon, that had experience of all worldly delights and pleasure, confessed as much of themselves; what they most desired was tedious at last, and that their lust could never be satisfied; all was vanity and affliction of mind.

Now if it be death itself, another hell, to be glutted with one kind of sport, dieted with one dish, tied to one place, though they have all things otherwise as they can desire, & are in heaven to another man's opinion, what misery and discontent shall they have, that live in slavery, or in prison itself! How worse than death is bondage, as Hermolaus told Alexander in Curtius. All brave men at arms (Tully holds) are so affected. I am he (saith Boterus) that account servitude the extremity of misery. And what calamity do they endure, that live with those hard taskmasters, in gold-mines (like those 30,000 Indian slaves at Potosi, in Peru), tin-mines, lead-mines, stone-quarries, coalpits, like so many mouldwarps * under ground, condemned to the gallies, to perpetual drudgery, hunger, thirst, and stripes, without all hope of delivery! How are those women in Turkey affected, that most

* Moles.

part of the year come not abroad; those Italian and Spanish Dames, that are mewed up like hawks, and lockt up by their jealous husbands! How tedious is it to them that live in stoves and caves half a year together, as in Iceland, Muscovy, or under the Pole itself, where they have six months perpetual night! Nay, what misery and discontent do they endure, that are in prison! They want all those six non-natural things at once, good air, good diet, exercise, company, sleep, rest, ease, &c., that are bound in chains all day long, suffer hunger, and (as Lucian describes it) *must abide that filthy stink, and rattling of chains, howlings, pitiful out-cries, that prisoners usually make: these things are not only troublesome but intolerable.* They lie nastily amongst toads and frogs in a dark dungeon, in their own dung, in pain of body, in pain of soul, as Joseph did, — *they hurt his feet in the stocks, the iron entered his soul.* They live solitary, alone, sequestered from all company but heart-eating melancholy; and, for want of meat, must eat that bread of affliction, prey upon themselves. Well might Arculanus put long imprisonment for a cause, especially to such as have lived jovially, in all sensuality and lust, upon a sudden are estranged and debarred from all manner of pleasures: as were Huniades, Edward ii., and Richard ii., Valerian the Emperor, Bajazet the Turk. If it be irksome to miss our ordinary companions & repast for once a day, or an hour, what shall it be to lose them for ever? If it be so great a delight to live at liberty, and to enjoy that variety of objects the world affords, what misery and discontent must it needs bring to him, that shall now be cast headlong into that Spanish Inquisition, to fall from Heaven to Hell, to be cubbed up upon a sudden? how shall he be perplexed, what shall become of him? Robert Duke of Normandy, being imprisoned by his youngest brother Henry the First, saith Matthew Paris, from that day forward pined away with grief. Jugurtha, that generous Captain, *brought to Rome in triumph, and after imprisoned, through anguish of his soul and melancholy died.* Roger, Bishop of Salisbury, the second man from King Stephen (he that built that famous Castle of Devizes in Wiltshire) was so tortured in prison with hunger, and all those calamities accompanying such men that he would not live, and could not die, betwixt fear of death and torments of life. Francis, King of France, was taken prisoner by Charles the Fifth, saith Guicciardini, melancholy almost to death, and that in an instant. But this is as clear as the Sun, and needs no further illustration.

SUBSECTION 6. — *Poverty and Want, Causes of Melancholy*

POVERTY and want are so violent oppugners, so unwelcome guests, so much abhorred of all men, that I may not omit to speak of them apart. Poverty, although (if considered aright, to a wise, understanding, truly regenerate, & contented man) it be a blessed estate, the way to Heaven, as Chrysostom calls it, God's gift, the mother of modesty, & much to be preferred before riches (as shall be shewed in his place) yet, as it is esteemed in the world's censure, it is a most odious calling, vile and base, a severe torture, a most intolerable burden. We shun it all, worse than a dog or snake, we abhor the name of it, poverty is shunned & persecuted throughout the world as being the fountain of all other miseries, cares, woes, labours, and grievances whatsoever. To avoid which, we will take any pains, — hasten to India's furthest bounds, we will leave no haven, no coast, no creek of the world unsearched, though it be to the hazard of our lives; we will dive to the bottom of the sea, to the bowels of the earth, five, six, seven, eight, nine hundred fathom deep, through all five Zones, and both extremes of heat and cold: we will turn parasites and slaves, prostitute ourselves, swear and lie, damn our bodies and souls, forsake God, abjure Religion, steal, rob, murder, rather than endure this unsufferable yoke of Poverty, which doth so tyrannize, crucify, and generally depress us.

For look into the world, and you shall see men most part esteemed according to their means, and happy as they are rich: Everywhere they are judged by what they have. If he be likely to thrive, and in the way of preferment, who but he? In the vulgar opinion, if a man be wealthy, no matter how he gets it, of what parentage, how qualified, how virtuously endowed, or villainously inclined; let him be a bawd, a gripe, an usurer, a villain, a Pagan, a Barbarian, a wretch, Lucian's Tyrant, *on whom you may look with less security than on the Sun:* so that he be rich (and liberal withal) he shall be honoured, admired, adored, reverenced & highly magnified. *The rich is had in reputation because of his goods.* He shall be befriended: *for riches gather many friends;* all happiness ebbs and flows with his money. He shall be accounted a gracious Lord, a *Mæcenas,* a benefactor, a wise, discreet, a proper, a valiant, a fortunate man, of a generous spirit, Jupiter's favourite, the white hen's chick, a hopeful, a good man, a virtuous honest man. As Tully said of Octavianus, while he was adopted Cæsar, and an heir apparent of so great a Monarchy, he was a golden child. All honour, offices, applause, grand titles, and turgent epithets, are put upon him; all men's eyes are upon him, God bless his good Worship! his Honour! every man speaks well of him, every man presents him, seeks and sues to him for his love, favour, & protection, to serve him, belong unto him; every man riseth to him, as to Themistocles in the Olympicks; if he speak, as of Herod, it is the voice of God, not of man! All the graces, Veneres, pleasures, elegances attend him, golden Fortune accompanies and lodgeth with him, and, as to those Roman Emperors, is placed in his chamber; he may sail as he will himself, and temper his estate at his pleasure; Jovial days, splendour and magnificence, sweet musick, dainty fare, the good things and fat of the land, fine clothes, rich attires, soft beds, down pillows, are at his command; all the world labours for him; thousands of artificers are his slaves, to drudge for him, run, ride, and post for him: Divines (for Pythia Philippizat), Lawyers, Physicians, Philosophers, Scholars, are his, wholly devote to his service. Every man seeks his acquaintance, his kindred, to match with him; though he be an oaf, a ninny, a monster, a goosecap, he may marry Danae, when and whom he will; some King & Queen may court him to be their son-in-law — he is an excellent match for my son, my daughter, my niece, &c. Whatever he treads upon will be made a rose; let him go whither he will, trumpets sound, bells ring, &c. all happiness attends him, every man is willing to entertain him, he sups in *Apollo* wheresoever he comes; what preparation is made for his entertainment, fish & fowl, spices & perfumes, all that sea and land affords! What cookery, masking, mirth, to exhilarate his person! Give it to Trebius, set it before Trebius! Brother, do have some of these delicacies? What dish will your good Worship eat of?

> *Sweet apples, and whate'er thy fields afford,*
> *Before thy Gods be served, let serve thy Lord.*   (HORACE)

What sport will your Honour have? hawking, hunting, fishing, fowling, bulls, bears, cards, dice, cocks, players, tumblers, fiddlers, jesters, &c., they are at your good Worship's command. Fair houses, gardens, orchards, terraces, galleries, cabinets, pleasant walks, delightsome places, they are at hand; milk in golden goblets, wine in silver, pretty wenches at beck and call, &c., a Turkey Paradise, an Heaven upon earth. Though he be a silly soft fellow, and scarce have common sense, yet if he be born to fortunes, (as I have said), he must have honour and office in his course: none so worthy as himself: he shall have it, vying with Servius or Labeo. Get money enough, and command Kingdoms, Provinces, Armies, hearts, hands, and affections; thou shalt have Popes, Patriarchs, to be thy Chaplains and Parasites; thou shalt have (Tamerlane-like) Kings to draw thy coach, Queens to be thy Laundresses, Emperors thy footstools, build more Towns and Cities than great Alexander, Babel Towers, Pyramids, and Mausolean Tombs, &c., command Heaven and Earth, and tell the World it is thy vassal; a diadem is bought with gold, silver opens the way to heaven, a philosopher may be hired for a penny, money controls justice, an obol feeds a man of letters, money purchases health, wealth attracts friends. And therefore, not without good cause, John de Medici, that rich Florentine, when he lay upon his death-bed, calling his sons Cosmo and Lorenzo before him, amongst other sober sayings, repeated this, — it doth me good to think yet, though I be dying, that I shall leave you my children *sound and rich.* For wealth sways all. It is not with us, as amongst those Lacedæmonian Senators of Lycurgus in Plutarch; *he preferred that deserved best, was most virtuous and worthy of the place; not swiftness, or strength, or wealth, or friends, carried it in those days;* but the most temperate & best. We have no *Aristocracies* but in contemplation, all *Oligarchies,* wherein a few rich men domineer, do what they list, and are privileged by their greatness. They may freely trespass, and do as they please, no man dare accuse them, no not so much as mutter against them, there is no notice taken of it, they may securely do it, live after their own laws, and for their money get Pardons, Indulgences, redeem their souls from Purgatory and Hell itself, — Jove is prisoner in a treasure-chest. Let them be Epicures, or Atheists, Libertines, Machiavelians, (as often they are),

Perjured, of low extraction, stained with blood, (HORACE)

they may go to heaven through the eye of a needle, if they will themselves, they may be canonized for Saints, they shall be honourably interred in Mausolean Tombs, commended by Poets, registered in Histories, have Temples and Statues erected to their names, — and from their ashes shall spring violets. — If he be bountiful in his life, & liberal at his death, he shall have one to swear, as he did by Claudius the Emperor in Tacitus, he saw his soul go to Heaven, and be miserably lamented at his funeral. The girl flute-players mourn, &c., Trimalchio's factotum in Petronius went right to Heaven: (a base quean! *thou wouldst have scorned once in thy misery to take bread from her hand*) and why? she measured her money by the bushel. These prerogatives do not usually belong to rich men, but to such as are most part seeming rich; let him have but a good outside, he carries it, and shall be adored for a God, as Cyrus was amongst the Persians, for his gay tires. Now most men are esteemed according to their clothes. In our gullish times, whom you peradventure in modesty would give place to, as being deceived by his habit, and presuming him some great Worshipful man, believe it, if you shall examine his estate, he will likely be proved a serving man of no great note, my Lady's Tailor, his Lordship's Barber, or some such gull, a Fastidious Brisk, a Sir Petronel Flash, a mere out-side. Only this respect is given him, that, wheresoever he comes, he may call for what he will, and take place by reason of his outward habit.

But on the contrary, if he be poor, all his days are miserable, he is under hatches, dejected, rejected, and forsaken, poor in purse, poor in spirit; as things go with us, so are our spirits affected; money gives life and soul. Though he be honest, wise, learned, well deserving, noble by birth, and of excellent good parts: yet, in that he is poor, unlikely to rise, come to honour, office, or good means, he is contemned, neglected, he is wise in vain, he hungers in spite of his knowledge, he is galling as a friend. If he speak, what babbler is this? his nobility without wealth is more worthless than sea-weed, and he not esteemed. We are a vile brood, hatched from unlucky eggs, if once poor, we are metamorphosed in an instant, base slaves, villains, and vile drudges; for to be poor is to be a knave, a fool, a wretch, a wicked, an odious fellow, a common eye-sore; say poor and say all: they are born to labour, to misery, to carry burdens like juments, to eat trodden dung with Ulysses' companions, and, as Chremylus objected in Aristophanes, to lick salt, to empty jakes, clear channels, carry out dirt and dunghills, sweep chimneys, rub horseheels, &c. I say nothing of Turks' Galley-slaves, which are bought and sold like juments, or those African Negroes, or poor Indian drudges, who daily faint beneath the burdens they carry from place to place, for they draw loads which oxen & asses do with us. Such is all the life of the wretched Indians, &c. They are ugly to behold, and, though erst spruce, now rusty and squalid, because poor, a frowzy fate & dingy dress go well together; it is ordinarily so. *Others eat to live, but they live to drudge,* a servile generation, that dare refuse no task. Here, Dorus, take this fan, sirrah, blow wind upon us while we wash; and bid your fellow get him up betimes in the morning; be it fair or foul, he shall run 50 miles afoot to morrow, to carry me a letter to my mistress; *Sosia* shall tarry at home and grind malt all day long; *Tristan* [shall] thresh. Thus are they commanded, being indeed some of them as so many foot-stools for rich men to tread on, blocks for them to get on horse-back, or as *walls for them to piss on.* They are commonly such people, rude, silly, superstitious, idiots, nasty, unclean, lousy, poor, dejected, slavishly humble: and, as Leo Afer observes of the commonalty of Africa, they are base by nature, and no more esteemed than dogs; no learning, no knowledge, no civility, scarce common sense, nought but barbarism amongst them; like rogues & vagabonds, they go bare-footed & bare-legged, the soles of their feet being as hard as horse hoofs, as Radzivilius observed at Damietta in Egypt, leading a laborious, miserable, wretched, unhappy life, *like beasts and juments, if not worse:* (for a Spaniard in Yucatan sold three Indian boys for a cheese, and an hundred Negro slaves for an horse): their discourse is scurrility, their greatest delight a pot of Ale. There is not any slavery which these villains will not undergo; among them many clean privies, others look after cooking, tend stables, are divers, & other employment of the like, &c., like those people that dwell in the Alps, *chimney-sweepers, jakes-farmers, dirt-daubers, vagrant rogues,* they labour hard some, and yet cannot get clothes to put on, or bread to eat. For what can filthy poverty give else, but beggary, fulsome nastiness, squalor, contempt, drudgery, labour, ugliness, hunger and thirst: any number (as he well followed it in Aristophanes) of fleas & lice? rags for his raiment, and a stone for his pillow, he sits in a broken pitcher, or on a block, for a chair, & he drinks water, and lives on wort leaves, pulse, like a hog, or scraps like a dog; and, (as Chremylus concludes his speech,) as we poor men live nowadays, who will not take our life to be infelicity, misery, and madness? *

If they be of a little better condition than those base villains, hunger-starved beggars, wandering rogues, those ordinary slaves, and day-labouring drudges, yet they are commonly so preyed upon by polling officers for breaking laws, by their tyrannizing land-lords, so flead and fleeced by perpetual exactions, that, though they do drudge, fare hard, and starve their *Genius,* they cannot live in some countries; but what they have is instantly taken from them; the very care they take to live, to be drudges, to maintain their poor families, their trouble and anxiety, *takes away their sleep;* it makes them weary of their lives: when they have taken all pains, done their utmost and honest endeavours, if they be cast behind by sickness, or over-taken with years, no man pities them; hard-hearted and merciless, uncharitable as they are, they leave them so distressed, to beg, steal, murmur, & rebel,† or else starve. The

* I write not this any ways to upbraid, or scoff at, or misuse poor men, but rather to condole and pity them by expressing, &c. — Burton's note.

† Montaigne, in his Essays, speaks of certain Indians in France, that, being asked how they liked the country, wondered how a few rich men could keep so many poor men in subjection, that they did not cut their throats. — Burton's note.

feeling and fear of this misery compelled those old Romans, whom Menenius Agrippa pacified, to resist their governors: outlaws, and rebels,
in most places, to take up seditious arms; and in all ages hath caused
uproars, murmurings, seditions, rebellions, thefts, murders, mutinies,
jars and contentions, in every common-wealth: grudging, repining, complaining, discontent, in each private family, because they want means
to live according to their callings, bring up their children; it breaks
their hearts they cannot do as they would. No greater misery than for
a Lord to have a Knight's living, a Gentleman a Yeoman's, not to be
able to live as his birth and place requires! Poverty and want are generally corrosives to all kinds of men, especially to such as have been in
good and flourishing estate, are suddenly distressed, nobly born, liberally brought up, and by some disaster and casualty miserably dejected. For the rest, as they have base fortunes, so have they base minds
correspondent, like beetles — born and bred in a dung-hill —, as they
were obscurely born and bred, so they delight and live in obscenity;
they are not so thoroughly touched with it.

The puny soul fits well the puny breast.   (VIRGIL)

Yea, that which is no small cause of their torments, if once they come
to be in distress, they are forsaken of their fellows, most part neglected,
and left unto themselves; as poor Terence in Rome was by Scipio,
Lælius, and Furius, his great and noble friends.

> *Publius Scipio, Lælius, Furius, three*
> *Such famous Lords that day did seldom see:*
> *Now surely 'twas strange they couldn't arrange*
> *To lodge their poor friend in his dree.*   (DONATUS)

'Tis generally so, if the times are cloudy, he is left cold and comfortless,
no friend will visit departed wealth, all flee from him as from a rotten
wall, now ready to fall on their heads. Poverty separates them from
their neighbours.

> *Whilst fortune favour'd, friends, you smiled on me,*
> *But when she fled, a friend I could not see.*   (PETRONIUS)

Which is worse yet, if he be poor every man contemns him, insults over
him, oppresseth him, scoffs at, aggravates his misery.

> *When once the tottering house begins to shrink,*
> *Thither comes all the weight by an instinct.*   (OVID)

Nay, they are odious to their own brethren and dearest friends. His
brethren hate him if he be poor; his neighbours hate him, as he complained in the Comedy, friends & strangers, all forsake me. Which is
most grievous, poverty makes men ridiculous, they must endure jests,

taunts, flouts, blows, of their betters, and take all in good part to get a meal's meat: poverty is a great reproach, bids us do and suffer all. He must turn parasite, jester, fool (to play with folly, saith Euripides), slave, villain, drudge, to get a poor living, apply himself to each man's humours, to win and please, &c. and be buffeted, when he hath all done, (as Ulysses was by Melanthius in Homer,) be reviled, baffled, insulted over, for the folly of the powerful must be endured, and may not so much as mutter against it. He must turn rogue and villain, for, as the saying is, poverty alone makes men thieves, rebels, murderers, traitors, assassinates, (because of poverty we have sinned,) swear and forswear, bear false witness, lie, dissemble, any thing, as I say, to advantage themselves, and to relieve their necessities; it instigates to crime, when a man is driven to his shifts, what will he not do?

> *If cruel fortune has made Sinon wretched,*
> *'Twill also make of him a faithless liar;* (VIRGIL)

he will betray his father, Prince, and Country, turn Turk, forsake Religion, abjure God and all; there is no treason so horrible (saith Leo Afer) that they will not commit for gain. Plato therefore calls poverty *thievish, sacrilegious, filthy, wicked, & mischievous,* and well he might; for it makes many an upright man otherwise, had he not been in want, to take bribes, to be corrupt, to do against his conscience, to sell his tongue, heart, hand, &c. to be churlish, hard, unmerciful, uncivil, to use indirect means to help his present estate. It makes Princes to exact upon their subjects, Great men tyrannize, Landlords oppress, Justice mercenary, Lawyers vultures, Physicians Harpies, friends importunate, tradesmen liars, honest men thieves, devout assassinates, great men to prostitute their wives, daughters, and themselves, middle sort to repine, commons to mutiny, all to grudge, murmur, and complain. A great temptation to all mischief, it compels some miserable wretches to counterfeit several diseases, to dismember, make themselves blind, lame, to have a more plausible cause to beg, and lose their limbs to recover their present wants. Jodocus Damhoderius, a Lawyer of Bruges, hath some notable examples of such counterfeit cranks, and every village almost will yield abundant testimonies amongst us; we have dummerers, *Abraham* men; * &c. And, that which is the extent of misery, it enforceth them, through anguish and wearisomeness of their

---

* Dummerers were mendicants who pretended to be afflicted with dumbness. Abraham-men were originally a class of lunatics kept in the Abraham ward of Bedlam (properly, Bethlehem hospital), and allowed to go out begging on certain days. Later the term was applied generally to beggars who pretended to lunacy or sickness.

lives, to make away themselves. They had rather be hanged, drowned, &c. than to live without means.

> *Much better 'tis to break thy neck,*
> *Or drown thyself i' th' sea,*
> *Than suffer irksome poverty:*
> *Go make thyself away.* (THEOGNIS)

A Sybarite of old, as I find it registered in Athenæus, supping meagrely * in Sparta, & observing their hard fare, said it was no marvel if the Lacedæmonians were valiant men; *for his part he would rather run upon a sword point (& so would any man in his wits) than live with such base diet, or lead so wretched a life.* In Japan 'tis a common thing to stifle their children if they be poor, or to make an abort, which Aristotle commends. In that civil commonwealth of China, the mother strangles her child, if she be not able to bring it up, and had rather lose than sell it, or have it endure such misery as poor men do. Arnobius, & Lactantius object as much to those ancient Greeks and Romans, *they did expose their children to wild beasts, strangle, or knock out their brains against a stone,* in such cases. If we may give credit to Munster, amongst us Christians in Lithuania they voluntarily mancipate and sell themselves, their wives and children, to rich men, to avoid hunger & beggary: many make away themselves in this extremity. Apicius the Roman, when he cast up his accounts, and found but 100,000 Crowns left, murdered himself for fear he should be famished to death. P. Forestus, in his medicinal observations, hath a memorable example of two brothers of Louvain, that, being destitute of means, became both melancholy, and in a discontented humour massacred themselves; another of a merchant, learned, wise otherwise and discreet, but, out of a deep apprehension he had of a loss at seas, would not be persuaded but, as Ummidius in the Poet, he should die a beggar. In a word, thus much I may conclude of poor men, that, though they have good parts, they cannot shew or make use of them: the road to virtue is obstructed by poverty, 'tis hard for a poor man to rise, they do not easily rise, whose narrow fortunes stand in the way of their merits; the wisdom of the poor is despised, and his words are not heard, his works are rejected, contemned, for the baseness and obscurity of the author; though laudable and good in themselves, they will not likely take.

> *No poems can please long or live that are*
> *Written by water-drinkers.* (HORACE)

Poor men cannot please, their actions, counsels, consultations, proj-

* At their Phiditias, or parsimonious feasts.

ects, are vilified in the world's esteem, their wits vanish with their property, which Gnatho long since observed. A wise man never cobbled shoes, as he said of old, but how doth he prove it? I am sure we find it otherwise in our days, eloquence shivers in wretched rags. Homer himself must beg if he want means, and, as by report sometimes he did, *go from door to door and sing ballads, with a company of boys about him.* This common misery of theirs must needs distract, make them discontent and melancholy, as ordinarily they are, wayward, peevish, like a weary traveller, (for hunger & delay summon the bile to the nostrils,) still murmuring and repining. The poor are peevish, which is a dangerous thing, as Plutarch quotes out of Euripides, and that comical Poet well seconds,

> *When people are poor they're alert for a slight,*
> *If you laugh, they are sure that you mock their sad plight.*
> (TERENCE)

If they be in adversity, they are more suspicious and apt to mistake; they think themselves scorned by reason of their misery; and therefore many generous spirits in such cases withdraw themselves from all company, as that Comedian Terence is said to have done; when he perceived himself to be forsaken and poor, he voluntarily banished himself to Stymphalus, a base town in Arcadia, and there miserably died:

> *Reduced to desperate poverty, he went*
> *From the sight of men, to the far ends of Greece.*

Neither is it without cause, for we see men commonly respected according to their means, (all enquire whether a man is rich, none whether he is good), & vilified if they be in bad clothes. Philopœmen the Orator was sent to cut wood, because he was so homely attired. Terentius was placed at the lower end of Cæcilius' table, because of his homely outside. Dante, that famous Italian Poet, by reason his clothes were but mean, could not be admitted to sit down at a feast. Gnatho scorned his old familiar friend because of his apparel: " A mass of rags and antiquity; I was full of contempt for him by the side of myself." King Perseus, overcome, sent a letter to Paulus Æmilius the Roman General: *Perseus giveth greetings to Paulus the Consul;* but he scorned him any answer (saith mine author), silently upbraiding him with his present fortune. Charles the Bold, that great Duke of Burgundy, made H. Holland, late Duke of Exeter, exil'd, run after his horse like a lackey, and would take no notice of him: 'tis the common fashion of the world. He that hath £5 per annum coming in more than others, scorns him that hath less and is a better man. So that such men as are poor may justly be discontent, melancholy, and complain of their present misery, and all may pray with Solomon, *Give me, O Lord, neither riches nor poverty, feed me with food convenient for me.*

SUBSECTION 7 — *An heap of other Accidents causing Melancholy, Death of Friends, Losses, &c.*

IN this Labyrinth of accidental causes, the farther I wander, the more intricate I find the passage, & new causes as so many by-paths offer themselves to be discussed. To search out all were an Herculean work, & fitter for Theseus: I will follow mine intended thread; and point only at some few of the chiefest.

Amongst which loss and death of friends may challenge a first place. As Vives well observes, many are melancholy after a feast, holy-day, merry meeting, or some pleasing sport, if they be solitary by chance, left alone to themselves, without employment, sport, or want their ordinary companions; some, at the departure of friends only, whom they shall shortly see again, weep and howl, and look after them as a cow lows after her calf, or a child takes on that goes to school after holidays. Thy coming (which Tully writ to Atticus), was not so welcome to me as thy departure was harsh. Montanus makes mention of a countrywoman that, parting with her friends and native place, became grievously melancholy for many years; and Trallianus of another, so caused for the absence of her husband. Which is an ordinary passion amongst our good wives; if their husband tarry out a day longer than his appointed time, or break his hour, they take on presently with sighs and tears, " he is either robbed or dead, some mischance or other is surely befallen him," they cannot eat, drink, sleep, or be quiet in mind, till they see him again. If parting of friends, absence alone, can work such violent effects, what shall death do, when they must eternally be separated, never in this world to meet again? This is so grievous a torment for the time, that it takes away their appetite, desire of life, extinguisheth all delights, it causeth deep sighs and groans, tears, exclamations,

O mother's sweet child! O my very blood
O tender flower! alas! and art thou gone?

howling, roaring, many bitter pangs, and by frequent meditation extends so far sometimes, *they think they see their dead friends continually in their eyes*, as Conciliator confesseth he saw his mother's ghost presenting herself still before him. What the wretched overmuch desire, they easily believe; still, still, still, that good father, that good son, that good wife, that dear friend runs in their minds; a single thought fills

all their mind all the year long, as Pliny complains to Romanus, methinks I see Virginius, I hear Virginius, I talk with Virginius, &c.

> *Without thee, ah! wretched man am I,*
> *Lilies are black; the roses fade & die,*
> *Hyacinth hath lost her ruddy glow,*
> *Nor laurel nor myrtle have fragrance here below.*
>
> (CALPURNIUS SICULUS)

They that are most staid and patient are so furiously carried headlong
by the passion of sorrow in this case, that brave discreet men otherwise
oftentimes forget themselves, and weep like children many months together, as if that they to water would, and will not be comforted. They
are gone! they are gone! Snatched away by glowering death, and overwhelmed ———— What shall I do?

> *Fountains of tears who gives? who lends me groans,*
> *Deep sighs, sufficient to express my moans?*
> *Mine eyes are dry, my breast in pieces torn,*
> *My loss so great, I cannot enough mourn.*

So Stroza Filius, that elegant Italian Poet, in his Elegy, bewails his
father's death, he could moderate his passions in other matters (as he
confesseth) but not in this, he yields wholly to sorrow; unconquered
once, with strong and steadfast soul; now I, unlucky, grant that my
mind grows faint. How doth Quintilian complain for the loss of his son,
to despair almost! Cardan lament his only child in his book on his
own books & elsewhere in many other of his tracts! S. Ambrose his
brother's death! (Can I ever recall thee without tears? O bitter
days! O nights of woe!) Gregory Nazianzen that noble Pulcheria! (O
beautiful, fresh, young flower, thou art broken!) Alexander, a man of
a most invincible courage, after Hephæstio's death, as Curtius relates,
lay three days together upon the ground, obstinate to die with him, and
would neither eat, drink, nor sleep. The woman that communed with
Esdras when her son fell down dead, fled into the field, & would not
return into the city, but there resolved to remain, neither to eat nor
drink, but mourn & fast until she died. Rachel wept for her children, and
would not be comforted because they were not. So did Adrian the Emperor bewail his Antinous; Hercules, Hylas; Orpheus, Eurydice;
David, Absolom; (*O my dear son Absolom!*) Austin his mother Monica;
Niobe her children, insomuch that the Poets feigned her to be turned
into a stone, as being stupefied through the extremity of grief. Ægeus,
impatient of sorrow for his son's death, drowned himself. Our late Physicians are full of such examples. Montanus had a patient troubled with

this infirmity, by reason of her husband's death, many years together. Trincavellius hath such another, almost in despair after his mother's departure, and ready through distraction to make away himself: and (in his 15th counsel) tells a story of one fifty years of age, *that grew desperate upon his mother's death*, and, cured by Fallopius, fell many years after into a relapse by the sudden death of a daughter which he had, and could never after be recovered. The fury of this passion is so violent sometimes, that it daunts whole kingdoms and cities. Vespasian's * death was pitifully lamented all over the Roman Empire, the whole world mourned, saith Aurelius Victor. Alexander commanded the battlements of houses to be pulled down, mules and horses to have their manes shorn off, and many common soldiers to be slain, to accompany his dear Hephæstio's death. Which is now practised amongst the Tartars, when a great Cham dieth, ten or twelve thousand must be slain, men and horses, all they meet; and, among those Pagan Indians, their wives and servants voluntarily die with them. Leo Decimus was so much bewailed in Rome after his departure, that, as Jovius gives out, the common safety, all good fellowship, peace, mirth, and plenty died with him, they grieved as though they were all interred in the same tomb with Leo; for it was a golden age whilst he lived, but after his decease an iron season succeeded, wars, plagues, vastity, discontent. When Augustus Cæsar died, saith Paterculus, we were all afraid, as if heaven had fallen upon our heads. Budæus records how that at Lewis the 12th his death, they that were erst in heaven, upon a sudden, as if they had been planet-stricken, lay grovelling on the ground; they look't like cropt trees. At Nancy in Lorraine, when Claudia Valesia, Henry the Second French king's sister, and the Duke's wife deceased, the Temples for forty days were all shut up, no Prayers nor Masses but in that room where she was; the Senators all seen in black, *and for a twelve months' space throughout the city they were forbid to sing or dance.*

> *In those days, Daphnis, none there were,*
> *To feed the oxen, none to stir,*
> *And drive them down to the cool stream's brink;*
> *No beast was there to crop the grass or drink.* (VIRGIL)

How were we affected here in England for our Titus, the delight of humankind, Prince Henry's immature death, as if all our dearest friends' lives had exhaled with his! Scanderbeg's death was not so much lamented in Epirus. In a word, as he saith of Edward the First at the news of Edward of Caernarvon his son's birth, he was immortally glad,

* Titus Flavius Vespasianus is meant.

may we say on the contrary of friends' deaths, we are divers of us, as so many turtles, eternally dejected with it.

There is another sorrow, which ariseth from the loss of temporal goods and fortunes, which equally afflicteth, and may go hand in hand with the precedent. Loss of time, loss of honour, office, of good name, of labour, frustrate hopes will much torment; but, in my judgment, there is no torture like unto it, or that sooner procureth this malady and mischief:

> *Lost money is bewept with genuine tears,*   (JUVENAL)

it wrings true tears from our eyes, many sighs, much sorrow from our hearts, and often causeth habitual melancholy itself. Guianerius repeats this for an especial cause. *Loss of friends, and loss of goods, make many men melancholy, as I have often seen by continual meditation of such things.* The same causes Arnoldus Villanovanus inculcates, we are injured by the loss of fortune and the death of friends, &c. Want alone will make a man mad, to be without money will cause a deep and grievous melancholy. Many persons are affected like Irishmen in this behalf, who, if they have a good scimitar, had rather have a blow on their arm than their weapon hurt: they will sooner lose their life than their goods: and the grief that cometh hence continueth long, (saith Plater), *and out of many dispositions procureth an habit.* Montanus and Frisemelica cured a young man of 22 years of age, that so became melancholy, for a sum of money which he had unhappily lost. Sckenkius hath such another story of one melancholy, because he overshot himself, and spent his stock in unnecessary building. Roger, that rich Bishop of Salisbury, spoiled of his goods by King Stephen, through grief ran mad, spake and did he knew not what. Nothing so familiar as for men in such cases, through anguish of mind, to make away themselves. A poor fellow went to hang himself, (which Ausonius hath elegantly expressed in a neat Epigram), but, finding by chance a pot of money, flung away the rope, and went merrily home; but he that hid the gold, when he missed it, hanged himself with that rope which the other man had left, in a discontented humour. Such feral accidents can want and penury produce. Be it suretyship, shipwrack, fire, spoil and pillage of soldiers, or what loss soever, it boots not, it will work the like effect, the same desolation in Provinces and Cities, as well as private persons. The Romans were miserably dejected after the battle of Cannæ, the men amazed for fear, the stupid women tore their hair & cried; the Hungarians, when their King Ladislaus, & bravest soldiers, were slain by the Turks; there was general grief, &c., the Venetians, when their forces were overcome by the French King Louis, the French & Spanish Kings, Pope, Emperor, all conspired against them, at Cambray, the French Herald denounced open war in the Senate: Lauredane, the leader of the Venetians, &c. &c., and they had lost Padua, Brixia, Verona, Forum Julium, their territories in the continent, & had now nothing left but the City of Venice itself, (saith Bembus), and the loss of that was likewise to be feared, they were pitifully plunged, never before in such lamentable distress. In the year 1527, when Rome was sacked by Bourbonius, the common soldiers made such spoil, that fair Churches were turned to stables, old monuments and books made horse-litter, or burned like straw; reliques, costly pictures, defaced; altars demolished; rich hangings, carpets, &c. trampled in the dirt: their wives and loveliest daughters constuprated by every base cullion, as Sejanus' daughter was by the hangman in publick, before their fathers' and husbands' faces; Noblemen's children, and of the wealthiest citizens, reserved for Princes' beds, were prostitute to every common soldier, and kept for concubines; Senators and Cardinals themselves dragg'd along the streets, and put to exquisite torments, to confess where their money was hid; the rest, murdered on heaps, lay stinking in the streets; infants' brains dashed out before their mothers' eyes. A lamentable sight it was to see so goodly a City so suddenly defaced, rich citizens sent a begging to Venice, Naples, Ancona, &c., that erst lived in all manner of delights! *Those proud palaces, that even now vaunted their tops up to Heaven, were dejected as low as Hell in an instant.* Whom will not such misery make discontent? Terence the Poet drowned himself (some say) for the loss of his Comedies, which suffered shipwreck. When a poor man hath made many hungry meals, got together a small sum, which he loseth in an instant; a Scholar spent many an hour's study to no purpose, his labours lost, &c.; how should it otherwise be? I may conclude with Gregory, riches do not so much exhilarate us with their possession, as they torment us with their loss.

Next to Sorrow still I may annex such accidents as procure Fear; for, besides those Terrors which I have before touched, and many other fears (which are infinite), there is a superstitious Fear, one of the three great causes of Fear in Aristotle, commonly caused by prodigies & dismal accidents, which much trouble many of us. (*I have a presentiment of misfortune*). As if a hare cross the way at our going forth, or a mouse gnaw our clothes: if they bleed three drops at nose, the salt falls towards them, a black spot appear in their nails, &c. with many such, which Delrio, Austin Niphus, in his book On Auguries, Polydore Virgil, On

Prodigies, Sarisburiensis in Polycraticus, discuss at large. They are so much affected, that, with the very strength of Imagination, Fear, and the Devil's craft, they pull those misfortunes they suspect upon their own heads, *and that which they fear shall come upon them,* as Solomon foretelleth, and Isay denounceth, which, *if they could neglect and contemn, would not come to pass.* They are intended and remitted, as our opinion is fixed, more or less. He is punished, saith Crato of such an one, would that he had not drawn it upon himself; he is the cause of it himself. Harm watch, harm catch. The thing that I feared, saith Job, is fallen upon me.

As much we may say of them that are troubled with their fortunes, or ill destinies fore-seen; the fore-knowledge of what shall come to pass crucifies many men, fore-told by Astrologers, or Wizards, the heavens being angry, be it ill accident, or death itself: which often falls out by God's permission; because they fear evil spirits, God permits it to happen so, saith Chrysostom. Severus, Adrian, Domitian, can testify as much, of whose fear and suspicion Suetonius, Herodian, and the rest of those writers, tell strange stories in this behalf. Montanus hath one example of a young man, exceeding melancholy upon this occasion. Such fears have still tormented mortal men in all ages, by reason of those lying Oracles, and juggling Priests. There was a fountain in Greece, near Ceres' Temple in Achaia, where the event of such diseases was to be known; *a glass let down by a thread, &c.* Amongst those Cyanean rocks at the springs of Lycia, was the Oracle of Thyrxean Apollo, *where all fortunes were foretold, sickness, health, or what they would besides:* so common people have been always deluded with future events. At this day this foolish fear mightily crucifies them in China, as Matthew Riccius the Jesuit informeth us, in his Commentaries of those countries, of all Nations they are most superstitious, and much tormented in this kind, attributing so much to their Divinators that fear itself and conceit cause it to fall out: if he foretell sickness such a day, that very time they will be sick [from fear,] and many times die as it is fore-told. A true saying, the fear of death is worse than death itself, and the memory of that sad hour, to some fortunate and rich men, is as bitter as gall. The fear of death sadly troubles our life, a worse plague cannot happen to a man than to be so troubled in his mind; 'tis an heavy separation, to leave their goods, with so much labour got, pleasures of the world, which they have so deliciously enjoyed, friends and companions whom they so dearly loved, all at once. Axiochus the Philosopher was bold and courageous all his life, and gave good precepts about indifference to death, and against the vanity of the world, to others; but, being now ready to die himself, he was mightily dejected; Shall I be deprived of this light of day, stripped of these good things I have? he lamented like a child, &c. And though Socrates himself was there to comfort him, Where is your old boast of virtues, Axiochus? ———— yet he was very timorous & impatient of death, much troubled in his mind. *O Clotho*, Megapenthes, the Tyrant in Lucian, exclaims, now ready to depart, *let me live a while longer. I will give thee a thousand talents of gold, and two bowls besides, which I took from Cleocritus, worth an hundred talents apiece! Woe's me!* saith another, *what goodly manors shall I leave! what fertile fields! what a fine house! what pretty children! how many servants! Who shall gather my grapes, my corn? Must I now die, so well settled? leave all, so richly and well provided? Woe's me! what shall I do? Dear, fluttering, fleeting soul of mine, whither wilt thou now be going?*

To these tortures of *Fear & Sorrow* may well be annexed *Curiosity,* that irksome, that tyrannizing care, excessive anxiety, *superfluous industry about unprofitable things and their qualities,* as Thomas defines it: an itching humour or a kind of longing to see that which is not to be seen, to do that which ought not to be done, to know that secret which should not be known, to eat of the forbidden fruit. We commonly molest and tire ourselves about things unfit & unnecessary, as Martha troubled herself to little purpose. Be it in Religion, Humanity, Magick, Philosophy, Policy, any action or study, 'tis a needless trouble, a mere torment. For what else is School Divinity? How many doth it puzzle! what fruitless questions about the Trinity, Resurrection, Election, Predestination, Reprobation, Hell-fire, &c., how many shall be saved, damned! What else is all Superstition, but an endless observation of idle Ceremonies, Traditions? What is most of our Philosophy, but a Labyrinth of opinions, idle questions, propositions, metaphysical terms? Socrates therefore held all Philosophers cavillers & mad men, saith Eusebius, because they commonly sought after such things which could be neither understood nor grasped by us, or, put case they did understand, yet they were altogether unprofitable. For what matter is it for us to know how high the *Pleiades* are, how far distant *Perseus* and *Cassiopea* from us, how deep the sea, &c.? We are neither wiser, as he follows it, nor modester, nor better, nor richer, nor stronger, for the knowledge of it. What is above us does not concern us. I may say the same of those Genethliacal studies. What is Astrology, but vain elections, predictions? all Magick, but a troublesome error, a pernicious

foppery? Physick, but intricate rules and prescriptions? Philology, but
vain criticisms? Logick, [but] needless sophisms? Metaphysicks themselves, but intricate subtilties, & fruitless abstractions? Alchemy, but a
bundle of errors? To what end are such great Tomes? why do we spend
so many years in their studies? Much better to know nothing at all, as
those barbarous Indians are wholly ignorant, than, as some of us, to be
so sore vexed about unprofitable toys, it is foolish to waste labour on
trifles, to build an house without pins, make a rope of sand; to what
end? for whose benefit? He studies on, but, as the boy told S. Austin,
when I have laved the sea dry, thou shalt understand the mystery of
Trinity. He makes observations, keeps times and seasons; and as Con-
radus the Emperor would not touch his new Bride, till an Astrologer
had told him a masculine hour; but with what success? He travels into
Europe, Africa, Asia, searcheth every creek, sea, city, mountain, gulf; to
what end? See one promontory, saith Socrates of old, one mountain, one
sea, one river, & see all. An Alchemist spends his fortunes to find out
the Philosopher's stone forsooth, cure all diseases, make men long-
lived, victorious, fortunate, invisible, and beggars himself, misled by
those seducing impostors (which he shall never attain) to make gold;
an Antiquary consumes his treasure and time to scrape up a company
of old coins, statues, rolls, edicts, manuscripts, &c. he must know what
was done of old in Athens, Rome, what lodging, diet, houses, they had,
& have all the present news at first, though never so remote, before all
others, what projects, counsels, consultations, &c. what Juno whispered
in the ear of Jupiter, what's now decreed in France, what in Italy: who
was he, whence comes he, which way, whither goes he, &c. Aristotle
must find out the motion of Euripus; Pliny must needs see Vesuvius;
but how sped they? One loseth goods, another his life. Pyrrhus will conquer Africa first, and then Asia, he will be a sole Monarch; a second immortal, a third rich, a fourth commands. A great hurricane of hopes stirs
our city; we run, ride, take indefatigable pains, all up early, down late,
striving to get that which we had better be without, (Ardelio's busy-
bodies as we are); it were much fitter for us to be quiet, sit still, and
take our ease. His sole study is for words, that they be a skillfully set
mosaic, not a syllable misplaced, to set out a stramineous * subject; as
thine is about apparel, to follow the fashion, to be terse and polite, 'tis
thy sole business; both with like profit. His only delight is building, he
spends himself to get curious pictures, intricate models & plots; another
is wholly ceremonious about titles, degrees, inscriptions: a third is over-

* Straw-like.

solicitous about his diet, he must have such and such exquisite sauces, meat so dressed, so far fetched, birds from strange countries, so cooked, &c. something to provoke thirst, something anon to quench his thirst. Thus he redeems his appetite with extraordinary charge to his purse, is seldom pleased with any meal, whilst a trivial stomack useth all with delight, and is never offended. Another must have roses in winter, flowers out of season, snow-water in summer, fruits before they can be or are usually ripe, artificial gardens and fish-ponds on the tops of houses, all things opposite to the vulgar sort, intricate and rare, or else they are nothing worth. So busy, nice, curious wits, make that unsupportable in all vocations, trades, actions, employments, which to duller apprehensions is not offensive, earnestly seeking that which others as scornfully neglect. Thus through our foolish curiosity do we macerate ourselves, tire our souls, and run headlong, through our indiscretion, perverse will, & want of government, into many needless cares and troubles, vain expenses, tedious journeys, painful hours; and, when all is done, to what end?

It is wise ignorance not to wish to know
What our great Master does not wish to teach us. (JOS. SCALIGER)

Amongst these passions and irksome accidents, unfortunate marriage may be ranked: a condition of life appointed by God himself in Paradise, an honourable and happy estate, and as great a felicity as can befall a man in this world, if the parties can agree as they ought, and live as Seneca lived with his Paulina : but if they be unequally matched, or at discord, a greater misery cannot be expected, to have a scold, a slut, an harlot, a fool, a fury, or a fiend, there can be no such plague. *He that hath her is as if he held a Scorpion,* and *a wicked wife makes a sorry countenance, and heavy heart ; and he had rather dwell with a Lion, than keep house with such a wife.* Her properties Jovianus Pontanus hath described at large, under the name of Euphorbia. Or if they be not equal in years, the like mischief happens. Cæcilius, in A. Gellius, complains much of an old wife; whilst I gape after her death, I live a dead man amongst the living; or, if they dislike upon any occasion,

Judge, who that are unfortunately wed,
What 'tis to come into a loathèd bed. (DANIEL)

The same inconvenience befalls women.

Hard-hearted parents, both lament my fate,
If self I kill or hang, to ease my state. (CHALONER)

A young Gentlewoman in Basil was married, saith Felix Plater, to an ancient man against her will, whom she could not affect; she was continually melancholy, and pined away for grief; and, though her husband did all he could possibly to give her content, in a discontented humour at length she hanged herself. Many other stories he relates in this kind. Thus men are plagued with women, they again with men, when they are of divers humours and conditions; he a spendthrift, she sparing; one honest, the other dishonest, &c. Parents many times disquiet their children, and they their parents. *A foolish son is an heaviness to his mother.* A step-mother often vexeth a whole family, is matter of repentance, exercise of patience, fuel of dissension, which made Cato's son expostulate with his father, why he should offer to marry his client Salonius' daughter, a young wench: *Why do you bring in a stepmother?* what offence had he done, that he should marry again?

Unkind, unnatural friends, evil neighbours, bad servants, debts and debates, &c. 'twas Chilo's sentence, misery and usury go commonly together; suretyship is the bane of many families, be surety, and harm is at hand; *he shall be sore vexed that is surety for a stranger; and he that hateth suretyship is sure.* Contention, brawling, law-suits, falling out of neighbours & friends, frantic Strife, are equal to the first, grieve many a man, and vex his soul. *Nothing so miserable* (Boter holds), *as such men, full of cares, griefs, anxieties, as if they were stabbed with a sharp sword; fear, suspicion, desperation, sorrow, are their ordinary companions.* Our Welchmen are noted by some of their own writers * to consume one another in this kind; but, whosoever they are that use it, these are their common symptoms, especially if they be convict or overcome, cast in a suit. Arius, put out of a Bishoprick by Eustathius, turned Heretick, and lived after discontented all his life. Every repulse is of like nature; Alas, what a hope to be shattered! Disgrace, infamy, detraction, will almost effect as much, and that a long time after. Hipponax, a Satirical Poet, so vilified and lashed two painters in his Iambicks, that Pliny saith, both hanged themselves. All oppositions, dangers, perplexities, discontents, to live in any suspense, are of the same rank: are you able to sleep in this trouble? Who can be secure in such cases? Ill bestowed benefits, ingratitude, unthankful friends, much disquiet and molest some. Unkind speeches trouble as many, uncivil carriage or dogged answers, weak women above the rest; if they proceed from their surly husbands, [they] are as bitter as gall, and not to be digested. A glass-man's wife in Basil became melancholy, because her husband said he would marry again if she died. *No cut to unkindness,*

* Humphrey Lluyd, epistle to Abraham Ortelius. Mr. Vaughan, in his Golden Fleece. — Burton's note.

as the saying is; a frown and hard speech, ill respect, a brow-beating, or bad look, especially to Courtiers, or such as attend upon great persons, is present death:

> *At the great man's glance, he stands or falls,*   (OVID)

they ebb and flow with their masters' favours. Some persons are at their wits' ends, if by chance they overshoot themselves in their ordinary speeches or actions, which may after turn to their disadvantage or disgrace, or have any secret disclosed. Ronseus reports of a Gentlewoman 25 years old, that, falling foul with one of her Gossips, was upbraided with a secret infirmity (no matter what) in publick, and so much grieved with it, that she did thereupon forsake all company, quite moped, and in a melancholy humour pine away. Others are as much tortured to see themselves rejected, contemned, scorned, disabled, diffamed, detracted, undervalued, or *left behind their fellows*. Lucian brings in Hetœmocles, a Philosopher, in his Lapiths, much discontented that he was not invited amongst the rest, expostulating the matter, in a long Epistle, with Aristænetus their Host. Prætextatus, a robed Gentleman in Plutarch, would not sit down at a Feast, because he might not sit highest, but went his ways all in a chafe. We see the common quarrellings that are ordinary with us, for taking of the wall, precedency, and the like, which though toys in themselves, and things of no moment, yet they cause many distempers, much heart-burning amongst us. Nothing pierceth deeper than a contempt or disgrace, especially if they be generous spirits; scarce anything affects them more than to be despised or vilified. Crato exemplifies it, and common experience confirms it. Of the same nature is oppression, *surely oppression makes a wise man mad;* loss of liberty, which made Brutus venture his life, Cato kill himself, & Tully complain, mine heart's broken, I shall never look up, or be merry again; to some parties 'tis a most intolerable loss. Banishment is a great misery, as Tyrtæus describes it in an Epigram of his,

> *A miserable thing 'tis so to wander,*
> *And like a beggar for to whine at door.*
> *Contemn'd of all the world an exile is,*
> *Hated, rejected, needy still and poor.*

Polynices, in his conference with Jocasta in Euripides, reckons up five miseries of a banished man, the least of which alone were enough to deject some pusillanimous creatures. Oftentimes a too great feeling of our own infirmities or imperfections of body or mind will rivel us up; as, if we be long sick,

Oh blessed health! thou bringest in the Spring
With all its joyous blossoms.

O blessed health! *thou art above all gold and treasure!* the poor man's riches, the rich man's bliss, without thee there can be no happiness: or visited with some loathsome disease, offensive to others, or troublesome to ourselves, as a stinking breath, deformity of our limbs, crookedness, loss of an eye, leg, hand, paleness, leanness, redness, baldness, or want of hair, &c., saith Synesius (he himself troubled not a little by this loss,) the loss of hair alone strikes a cruel stroke to the heart. Acco, an old woman, seeing by chance her face in a true glass, (for she used false flattering glasses belike at other times, as most Gentlewomen do), ran mad. Broteas, the son of Vulcan, because he was ridiculous for his imperfections, flung himself into the fire. Lais, of Corinth, now grown old, gave up her glass to Venus, for she could not abide to look upon it:

Venus, take my votive glass;
Since I am not what I was,
What from this day I shall be,
Venus, let me never see.

Generally to fair nice pieces old age and foul linen are two most odious things, a torment of torments, they may not abide the thought of it.

Ye gods, whoever of you hears me, grant
That I may wander naked among lions,
Ere ugly leanness seize my comely cheeks,
And all my beauty leave my tender frame!
I'd rather in my flower be food for tigers. (HORACE)

To be foul, ugly, and deformed! much better be buried alive! Some are fair but barren, and that galls them. Hannah wept sore, did not eat, and was troubled in spirit, and all for her barrenness, and Rachel said in the anguish of her soul, give me a child, or I shall die: another hath too many: one was never married, and that's his hell; another is, & that's his plague. Some are troubled in that they are obscure; others by being traduced, slandered, abused, disgraced, vilified, or any way injured: I marvel not (as he said), at all if offences make men mad. Seventeen particular causes of anger & offence Aristotle reckons up, which for brevity's sake I must omit. No tidings troubles one; ill reports, rumours, bad tidings or news, hard hap, ill success, cast in a suit, vain hopes, or hope deferred, another: expectation, so grievous is expectation always & in all things, as Polybius observes; one is too eminent, another too base born, and that alone tortures him as much as the rest: one is out of action, company, employment; another overcome & tormented with worldly cares, and onerous business. But what tongue can suffice to speak of all?

Many men catch this malady by eating certain meats, herbs, roots, at unawares; as henbane, nightshade, cicuta, mandrakes, &c. A company of young men at Agrigentum, in Sicily, came into a Tavern; where after they had freely taken their liquor, whether it were the wine itself, or some thing mixt with it, 'tis not yet known, but upon a sudden they began to be so troubled in their brains, and their phantasy so crazed, that they thought they were in a ship at sea, and now ready to be cast away by reason of a tempest. Wherefore, to avoid shipwrack and present drowning, they flung all the goods in the house out at the window into the street, or into the sea, as they supposed. Thus they continued mad a pretty season, and being brought before the Magistrate to give an account of this their fact, they told him (not yet recovered of their madness) that what was done they did for fear of death, and to avoid eminent danger. The spectators were all amazed at this their stupidity, and gazed on them still, whilst one of the ancientest of the company in a grave tone excused himself to the Magistrate upon his knees, O Tritons, I beseech your Deities, &c. for I was in the bottom of the ship all the while: another besought them, as so many Sea-Gods, to be good unto them, and, if ever he and his fellows came to land again, he would build an Altar to their service. The Magistrate could not sufficiently laugh at this their madness, bid them sleep it out, and so went his ways. Many such accidents frequently happen upon these unknown occasions. Some are so caused by philters, wandering in the sun, biting of a mad dog, a blow on the head, stinging with that kind of spider called *tarantula*, an ordinary thing, if we may believe Sckenkius, in Calabria and Apulia in Italy. Their symptoms are merrily described by Jovianus Pontanus, how they dance altogether, and are cured by Musick. Cardan speaks of certain stones, if they be carried about one, which will cause melancholy and madness; he calls them unhappy, as an Adamant, Selenites, &c. *which dry up the body, increase cares, diminish sleep.* Ctesias, in Persicis, makes mention of a well in those parts, of which if any man drink, *he is mad for 24 hours.* Some lose their wits by terrible objects (as elsewhere I have more copiously dilated) and life itself many times, as Hippolytus affrighted by Neptune's sea-horses, Athamas by Juno's Furies: but these relations are common in all Writers.

> *Many such causes, much more could I say,*
> *But that for provender my cattle stay,*
> *The sun declines, and I must needs away.* (JUVENAL)

These causes, if they be considered and come alone, I do easily yield, can do little of themselves, seldom, or apart, (an old oak is not felled at a blow), though many times they are all sufficient every one: yet, if they concur, as often they do, power is strengthened by union; & things which, singly, are of no avail, are together harmful; they may batter a strong constitution; as Austin said, *many grains and small sands sink a ship, many small drops make a flood, &c.,* often reiterated, many dispositions produce an habit.

MEMBER 5

SUBSECTION 1 — *Continent, inward, antecedent, next Causes, and how the Body works on the Mind*

As a purly hunter, I have hitherto beaten about the circuit of the forest of this microcosm, and followed only those outward adventitious causes. I will now break into the inner rooms, and rip up the antecedent immediate causes which are there to be found. For as the distraction of the mind, amongst other outward causes & perturbations, alters the temperature of the body, so the distraction and distemper of the body will cause a distemperature of the soul; & 'tis hard to decide which of these two do more harm to the other. Plato, Cyprian, & some others, as I have formerly said, lay the greatest fault upon the soul, excusing the body; others again, accusing the body, excuse the soul, as a principal agent. Their reasons are, because *the manners do follow the temperature of the body,* as Galen proves in his book of that subject, Prosper Calenius, Jason Pratensis, Lemnius, and many others. And that which Gualter hath commented is most true; concupiscence and original sin, inclinations, and bad humours, are radical in every one of us, causing these perturbations, affections, and several distempers, offering many times violence unto the soul. Every man is tempted by his own concupiscence; the spirit is willing, but the flesh is weak, and rebelleth against the spirit, as our Apostle teacheth us: that methinks the soul hath the better plea against the body, which so forcibly inclines us, that we cannot resist; we are neither able to make head against it nor struggle as we should. How the body, being material, worketh upon the immaterial soul, by mediation of humours & spirits which participate of both, and ill disposed organs, Cornelius Agrippa hath discoursed, Levinus Lemnius, Perkins, & T. Bright, in his Treatise of Melancholy. For as anger, fear, sorrow, obtrectation, emulation, &c. saith Lemnius, cause grievous

diseases in the body, so bodily diseases affect the soul by consent. Now
the chiefest causes proceed from the heart, humours, spirits: as they are
purer, or impurer, so is the mind, & equally suffers, as a lute out of
tune; if one string or one organ be distempered, all the rest miscarry;

The body, by yesterday's excess o'erladen,
Weighs down with it the soul. (HORACE)

The body is the home of the soul, her house, abode, and stay; and as a
torch gives a better light, a sweeter smell, according to the matter it is
made of, so doth our soul perform all her actions better or worse, as
her organs are disposed; or as wine savours of the cask wherein it is
kept, the soul receives a tincture from the body through which it works.
We see this in old men, children, Europeans, Asians, hot and cold climes.
Sanguine are merry, Melancholy sad, Phlegmatick dull, by reason of
abundance of those humours, and they cannot resist such passions which
are inflicted by them. For in this infirmity of human nature, as Melancthon declares, the understanding is so tied to & captivated by his inferior senses, that without their help he cannot exercise his functions,
and the will, being weakened, hath but a small power to restrain those
outward parts, but suffers herself to be overruled by them; that I must
needs conclude with Lemnius, spirits and humours do most harm in
troubling the soul. How should a man choose but be cholerick and
angry, that hath his body so clogged with abundance of gross humours?
or melancholy, that is so inwardly disposed? That thence comes then
this malady, Madness, Apoplexies, Lethargies, &c. it may not be denied.

Now this body of ours is most part distempered by some precedent
diseases, which molest his inward organs & instruments, & so in consequence cause melancholy, according to the consent of the most approved Physicians. *This humour* (as Avicenna, Arnoldus, Jacchinus,
Montaltus, Nicholas Piso, &c., suppose) *is begotten by the distempera-*
ture of some inward part, innate, or left after some inflammation, or
else included in the blood after an ague, or some other malignant
disease. This opinion of theirs concurs with that of Galen. Guianerius
gives an instance in one so caused by a quartan ague; & Montanus,
in a young man of 28 years of age, so distempered after a quartan,
which had molested him 5 years together; Hildesheim relates of a
Dutch Baron, grievously tormented with melancholy after a long ague.
Galen puts the plague a cause; Botaldus, in his book, the French Pox
for a cause; others Phrensy, Epilepsy, Apoplexy, because those diseases
do often degenerate into this. Of suppression of Hæmrods, Hæmorrhagia, or bleeding at nose, menstruous retentions, (although they de-

serve a larger explication, as being the sole cause of a proper kind of melancholy in more ancient maids, nuns, and widows, handled apart by Rodericus à Castro, and Mercatus, as I have elsewhere signified,) or any other evacuation stopped, I have already spoken. Only this I will add, that this melancholy, which shall be caused by such infirmities, deserves to be pitied of all men, and to be respected with a more tender compassion, according to Laurentius, as coming from a more inevitable cause.

SUBSECTION 2 — *Distemperature of particular Parts, Causes*

THERE is almost no part of the body, which, being distempered, doth not cause this malady, as the Brain and his parts, Heart, Liver, Spleen, Stomack, Matrix or Womb, Pylorus, Myrach, Mesentery, Hypochondries, Meseraick veins; and in a word, saith Arculanus, *there is no part which causeth not Melancholy, either because it is adust, or doth not expel the superfluity of the nutriment.* Savanarola is of the same opinion, that Melancholy is engendered in each particular part, and Crato. Gordonius, who is worth them all, confirms as much, putting the *matter of Melancholy sometimes in the Stomack, Liver, Heart, Brain, Spleen, Myrach, Hypochondries, when as the melancholy humour resides there, or the Liver is not well cleansed from melancholy blood.*

The Brain is a familiar and frequent cause, too hot, or too cold, *through adust blood so caused,* as Mercurialis will have it, *within or without the head,* the brain itself being distempered. Those are most apt to this disease, *that have a hot heart and moist brain,* which Montaltus approves out of Halyabbas, Rhasis, and Avicenna. Mercurialis assigns the coldness of the brain a cause, and Sallustius Salvianus will have it *arise from a cold and dry distemperature of the brain.* Piso, Benedictus, Victorius Faventinus, will have it proceed from a *hot distemperature of the brain;* and Montaltus from the brain's heat, scorching the blood. The brain is still distempered by himself, or by consent: by himself or his proper affection, as Faventinus calls it, *or by vapours which arise from the other parts, and fume up into the head, altering the animal faculties.*

Hildesheim thinks it may be caused from a *distemperature of the heart, sometimes hot, sometimes cold.* A hot Liver & a cold Stomack are put for usual causes of Melancholy. Mercurialis assigns a hot Liver and cold Stomack for ordinary causes. Monavius, in an Epistle of his to Crato, in Scoltzius, is of opinion that Hypochondriacal Melancholy may proceed from a cold Liver. The question is there discussed. Most agree that a hot Liver is in fault. *The Liver is the shop of humours, & especially causeth Melancholy by his hot & dry distemperature. The Stomack and Meseraick veins do often concur, by reason of their obstructions, & thence their heat cannot be avoided, & many times the matter is so adust & inflamed in those parts, that it degenerates into Hypochondriacal Melancholy.* Guianerius holds the Meseraick veins to be a sufficient cause alone. The spleen concurs to this malady, (by all their consents,) & suppression of Hæmrods, saith Montaltus, if it be *too cold and dry, and do not purge the other parts as it ought.* Montanus puts the *spleen stopped* for a great cause. Christophorus à Vega reports, of his knowledge, that he hath known Melancholy caused from putrefied blood in those seed-veins and womb: Arculanus, *from that menstruous blood turned into melancholy, and seed too long detained* (as I have already declared) *by putrefaction or adustion.*

The *Mesenterium,* or Midriff, *Diaphragma,* which the Greeks called Phrenes, is a cause, because by his inflammation the mind is much troubled with convulsions and dotage. All these, most part, offend by inflammation, corrupting humours and spirits, in this non-natural melancholy: for from these are engendered fuliginous & black spirits. And for that reason Montaltus will have *the efficient cause of Melancholy to be hot and dry, not a cold and dry distemperature, as some hold, from the heat of the Brain, roasting the blood, immoderate heat of the Liver and Bowels, and inflammation of the Pylorus: and so much the rather because that,* as Galen holds, *all spices inflame the blood, solitariness, waking, agues, study, meditation all which heat: and therefore he concludes that this distemperature causing adventitious Melancholy, is not cold and dry, but hot and dry.* But of this I have sufficiently treated in the matter of Melancholy, and hold that this may be true in non-natural Melancholy, which produceth madness, but not in that natural, which is more cold, and, being immoderate, produceth a gentle dotage. Which opinion Geraldus de Solo maintains in his comment upon Rhasis.

SUBSECTION 3 — *Causes of Head-Melancholy*

AFTER a tedious discourse of the general causes of Melancholy, I am now returned at last to treat in brief of the three particular species, and such causes as properly appertain unto them. Although these causes promiscuously concur to each and every particular kind, and commonly produce their effects in that part which is most weak, ill disposed, and least able to resist, and so cause all three species, yet many of them are proper to some one kind, & seldom found in the rest. As, for example, Head-Melancholy is commonly caused by a cold or hot distemperature of the Brain, according to Laurentius, but, as Hercules de Saxonia contends, from that agitation or distemperature of the animal spirits alone: Sallust. Salvianus, before mentioned, will have it proceed from cold: but that I take of natural melancholy, such as are fools and dote; for, as Galen writes, and Avicenna, *a cold and moist Brain is an inseparable companion of folly.* But this adventitious melancholy, which is here meant, is caused of an hot and dry distemperature, as Damascen the Arabian thinks, and most writers; Altomarus and Piso call it *an innate burning untemperatenesse, turning blood and choler into melancholy.* Both these opinions may stand good, as Bruel maintains, and Capivaccius, *if the brain be hot, the animal spirits will be hot, & thence comes madness: if cold, folly.* David Crusius grants melancholy to be a disease of an inflamed brain, but cold notwithstanding of itself; hot by accident only. I am of Capivaccius' mind for my part. Now this humour, according to Salvianus, is sometimes in the substance of the Brain, sometimes contained in the Membranes and Tunicles that cover the Brain, sometimes in the passages of the Ventricles of the Brain, or veins of those Ventricles. It follows many times *Phrensy, long diseases, agues, long abode in hot places, or under the Sun, a blow on the head,* as *Rhasis* informeth us: Piso adds solitariness, waking, inflammations of the head, proceeding most part from much use of spices, hot wines, hot meats; all which Montanus reckons up for a melancholy Jew; and Heurnius repeats: hot baths, garlic, onions, saith Guianerius, bad, corrupt air, much waking, &c. retention of seed or abundance, stopping of *hæmorrhagia,* the Midriff misaffected; and, according to Traillianus, immoderate cares, troubles, griefs, discontent, study, meditation, and, in a word, the abuse of all those six non-natural things. Hercules de Saxonia will have it caused from a cautery, or boil dried up, or any issue. Amatus Lusitanus gives instance in a fellow that had a boil in his arm, *after that was healed, ran mad, and when the wound was open, he was cured again.* Trincavellius hath an example of a melancholy man, so caused by overmuch continuance in the Sun, frequent use of Venery, and immoderate exercise: and, from an headpiece over-heated, which caused head-melancholy. Prosper Calenus brings in Cardinal Cæsius for a pattern of such as are so melancholy by long study: but examples are infinite.

SUBSECTION 4 — *Causes of Hypochondriacal, or Windy Melancholy*

IN repeating of these causes, I must set warmed-over cabbage before you & say that again which I have formerly said, in applying them to their proper species. *Hypochondriacal* or flatuous Melancholy is that which the Arabians call Myrachial, and is, in my judgement, the most grievous and frequent, though Bruel and Laurentius make it least dangerous, and not so hard to be known or cured. His causes are inward or outward. Inward from divers parts or organs, as Midriff, Spleen, Stomack, Liver, Pylorus, Womb, Diaphragma, Meseraick veins, stopping of issues, &c. Montaltus, out of Galen, recites *heat and obstruction of those Meseraick veins, as an immediate cause, by which means the passage of the Chylus to the Liver is detained, stopped, or corrupted, and turned into rumbling and wind.* Montanus hath an evident demonstration, Trincavellius another, and Plater a third, for a Doctor of the Law visited with this infirmity, from the said obstruction and heat of these Meseraick veins, and bowels: the veins are inflamed about the Liver and Stomack. Sometimes those other parts are together misaffected, and concur to the production of this malady: a hot liver and cold stomack or cold belly. Look for instances in Hollerius, Victor Trincavellius, Hildesheim, Solenander, Montanus, for the Earl of Montfort in Germany, 1549, & Frisimelica in the 233rd consultation of the said Montanus. J. Cæsar Claudinus gives instance of a cold stomack & over-hot liver, almost in every consultation, for a certain Count; & for a Polonian Baron; by reason of heat the blood is inflamed, and gross vapours sent to the heart and brain. Mercurialis subscribes to them, *the Stomack being misaffected,* which he calls the King of the Belly, because, if he be distempered, all the rest suffer with him, as being deprived of their nutriment, or fed with bad nourishment, by means of which come crudities, obstructions, wind, rumbling, griping, &c. Hercules de Saxonia, besides heat, will have the weakness of the liver and his obstruction a cause, which he calls the mineral of melancholy. Laurentius assigns this reason, because the liver over-hot draws the meat undigested out of the stomack, and burneth the humours. Montanus proves that sometimes a cold liver may be a cause. Laurentius, Trincavellius, and Gualter Bruel, seem to lay the greatest fault upon the Spleen, that doth not his duty in purging the Liver as he ought, being too great, or too little, in drawing too much blood sometimes to it, and not expelling it, as P. Cnemiandrus in a consultation of his noted; tumor of the spleen, he names it, and the fountain of melancholy. Diocles supposed the ground of this kind of Melancholy to proceed from the inflammation of the Pylorus, which is the nether mouth of the Ventricle. Others assign the Mesenterium or Midriff distempered by heat, the womb misaffected, stopping of Hæmrods, with many such. All which Laurentius reduceth to three, Mesentery, Liver, and Spleen, from whence he denominates Hepatick, Splenetick, and Meseraick Melancholy. Outward causes are bad diet, care, griefs, discontents, and, in a word, all those six non-natural things, as Montanus found by his experience. Solenander, for a Citizen of Lyons in France, gives his reader to understand, that he knew this mischief procured by a medicine of Cantharides, which an unskilful Physician ministered his patient to drink, to arouse the erotick passions. But most commonly fear, grief, and some sudden commotion or perturbation of the mind, begin it, in such bodies especially as are ill-disposed. Melancthon will have it as common to men, as the mother to women, upon some grievous trouble, dislike, passion, or discontent. For, as Camerarius records in his life, Melancthon himself was much troubled with it, and therefore could speak out of experience. Montanus, for an insane Jew, confirms it, grievous symptoms of the mind brought him to it. Rondoletius relates of himself, that, being one day very intent to write out a Physician's notes, molested by an occasion, he fell into an hypochondriacal fit, to avoid which he drank the decoction of wormwood, and was freed. Melancthon (*being the disease is so troublesome and frequent*) *holds it a most necessary and profitable study for every man to know the accidents of it, and a dangerous thing to be ignorant,* and would therefore have all men in some sort to understand the causes, symptoms, and cures of it.

SUBSECTION 5 — *Causes of Melancholy from the whole Body*

As before, the cause of this kind of Melancholy is inward or outward. Inward *when the liver is apt to engender such an humour, or the spleen weak by nature, and not able to discharge his office.* A melancholy temperature, retention of hæmrods, monthly issues, bleeding at nose, long diseases, agues, and all those six non-natural things, increase it: but especially bad diet, as Piso thinks, pulse, salt meat, shell-fish, cheese, black wine, &c. Mercurialis, out of Averroes and Avicenna, condemns all herbs: Galen, especially cabbage. So likewise fear, sorrow, discontents, &c. but of these before. And thus in brief you have had the general and particular causes of Melancholy.

Now go and brag of thy present happiness, whosoever thou art, brag

of thy temperature, of thy good parts, insult, triumph, & boast; thou
seest in what a brittle state thou art, how soon thou mayest be dejected,
how many several ways, by bad diet, bad air, a small loss, a little sorrow or discontent, an ague, &c. how many sudden accidents may procure thy ruin, what a small tenure of happiness thou hast in this life,
how weak and silly a creature thou art. Humble thyself therefore under
the mighty hand of God, know thyself, acknowledge thy present misery,
and make right use of it. Let him that standeth take heed lest he fall.
Thou dost now flourish, and hast goods of body, mind, and fortune, thou
knowest not what storms and tempests the late evening may bring with
it. Be not secure then, *be sober and watch,* behave with all respect to
fortune, if fortunate and rich; if sick and poor, moderate thyself. I
have said.

Section 3 Member 1

Subsection i — *Symptoms, or Signs of Melancholy in the Body*

Parrhasius, a painter of Athens, amongst those Olynthian captives
Philip of Macedon brought home to sell, bought one very old man; and
when he had him at Athens, put him to extreme torture and torment,
the better by his example to express the pains and passions of his
Prometheus, whom he was then about to paint. I need not be so barbarous, inhumane, curious, or cruel, for this purpose to torture any poor
melancholy man; their symptoms are plain, obvious and familiar, there
needs no such accurate observation or far-fetcht object, they delineate
themselves, they voluntarily bewray themselves, they are too frequent
in all places, I meet them still as I go, they cannot conceal it, their
grievances are too well known, I need not seek far to describe them.

Symptoms therefore are either universal or particular, saith Gordonius, to persons, to species. *Some signs are secret, some manifest, some
in the body, some in the mind; and diversely vary, according to the
inward or outward causes,* Capivaccius: or from stars, according to
Jovianus Pontanus, and celestial influences, or from the humours diversely mixt. As they are hot, cold, natural, unnatural, intended, or remitted, so will Aëtius have diversity of melancholy signs. Laurentius
ascribes them to their several temperatures, delights, natures, inclinations, continuance of time, as they are simple or mixt with other
diseases; as the causes are divers, so must the signs be almost infinite.
And as wine produceth divers effects, or that herb Tortocolla in Laurentius, *which makes some laugh, some weep, some sleep, some dance,*

some sing, some howl, some drink, &c., so doth this our melancholy humour work several signs in several parties.

But to confine them, these general symptoms may be reduced to those of the *Body* or the *Mind*. Those usual signs, appearing in the *bodies* of such as are melancholy, be these, cold and dry, or they are hot and dry, as the humour is more or less adust. From these first qualities arise many other second, as that of colour, black, swarthy, pale, ruddy, &c., some are, as Montaltus observes out of Galen, very red and high coloured. Hippocrates, in his book On Insanity and Melancholy, reckons up these signs, that they are *lean, withered, hollow-eyed, look old, wrinkled, harsh, much troubled with wind, and a griping in their bellies, or belly-ache, belch often, dry bellies and hard, dejected looks, flaggy beards, singing of the ears, vertigo, lightheaded, little or no sleep, & that interrupt, terrible and fearful dreams,* ———— Sister Anne, what dreams be these that confound and appall me! The same symptoms are repeated by Melanelius (in his Book of Melancholy, collected out of Galen, Ruffus, Aëtius,) by Rhasis, Gordonius, & all the Juniors, *continual, sharp, & stinking belchings, as if their meat in their stomack were putrefied, or that they had eaten fish, dry bellies, absurd & interrupt dreams, & many phantastical visions about their eyes, vertiginous, apt to tremble, & prone to Venery*. Some add palpitation of the heart, cold sweat, as usual symptoms, and a leaping in many parts of the body, a kind of itching, saith Laurentius, on the superfices of the skin, like a flea-biting sometimes. Montaltus puts fixed eyes and much twinkling of their eyes for a sign; & so doth Avicenna, they are very red-faced, &c.; they stutter most part, which he took out of Hippocrates' Aphorisms. Rhasis makes *headache and a binding heaviness* for a principal token, *much leaping of wind about the skin, as well as stutting, or tripping in speech, &c., hollow eyes, gross veins, & broad lips*. To some too, if they be far gone, mimical gestures are too familiar, laughing, grinning, fleering, murmuring, talking to themselves, with strange mouths and faces, inarticulate voices, exclamations, &c. And although they be commonly lean, hirsute, uncheerful in countenance, withered, and not so pleasant to behold, by reason of those continual fears, griefs, and vexations, dull, heavy, lazy, restless, unapt to go about any business: yet their memories are most part good, they have happy wits, and excellent apprehensions. Their hot and dry brains make them they cannot sleep, they have mighty and often watchings, sometimes waking for a month, a year, together. Hercules de Saxonia faithfully averreth, that he hath heard his mother swear, she slept not for seven months together: Trincavellius speaks of one that waked 50 days, and Sckenkius hath examples of two years, and all without offence. In natural actions their appetite is greater than their concoction, as Rhasis hath it, they covet to eat, but cannot digest. And although they *do eat much, yet they are lean, ill liking,* saith Aretæus, *withered & hard, much troubled with costiveness,* crudities, oppilations, spitting, belching, &c. Their pulse is rare & slow, except it be of the *carotides,* which is very strong; but that varies according to their intended passions or perturbations, as Struthius hath proved at large. To say truth, in such chronick diseases the pulse is not much to be respected, there being so much superstition in it, as Crato notes, and so many differences in Galen, that he dares say they may not be observed, or understood, of any man.

Their urine is most part pale, & low coloured, (Aretæus), not much in quantity; but this, in my judgement, is all out as uncertain as the other, varying so often according to several persons, habits, & other occasions, not to be respected in chronick diseases. *Their melancholy excrements, in some very much, in others little, as the spleen plays his part;* and thence proceeds wind, palpitation of the heart, short breath, plenty of humidity in the stomack, heaviness of heart & heartache, & intolerable stupidity and dulness of spirits; their excrements or stool hard, black to some, & little. If the heart, brain, liver, spleen, be misaffected, as usually they are, many inconveniences proceed from them, many diseases accompany, as Incubus,* Apoplexy, Epilepsy, Vertigo, those frequent wakings and terrible dreams, intempestive laughing, weeping, sighing, sobbing, bashfulness, blushing, trembling, sweating, swooning, &c. All their senses are troubled, they think they see, hear, smell, and touch, that which they do not, as shall be proved in the following discourse.

SUBSECTION 2 — *Symptoms or Signs in the Mind*

ARCULANUS will have these symptoms to be infinite, as indeed they are, varying according to the parties, *for scarce is there one of a thousand that dotes alike.* Some few of greater note I will point at; and, amongst the rest, *Fear* and *Sorrow,* which, as they are frequent causes, so, if they persevere long, according to Hippocrates' and Galen's Aphorisms, they are most assured signs, inseparable companions, and characters of melancholy; of present melancholy, and habituated, saith Montaltus, and common to them all, as the said Hippocrates, Galen, Avicenna, and all Neotericks, hold. But as hounds many times run away with a false

* Here meaning Nightmare.

cry, never perceiving themselves to be at a fault, so do they. For Diocles of old, (whom Galen confutes), and, amongst the Juniors, Hercules de Saxonia, with Lod. Mercatus, take just exceptions at this Aphorism of Hippocrates, 'tis not always true, or so generally to be understood. *Fear* and *Sorrow* are no common symptoms to all melancholy; *upon more serious consideration, I find some* (saith he) *that are not so at all. Some indeed are sad, and not fearful; some fearful, and not sad; some neither fearful nor sad; some both.* Four kinds he excepts, fanatical persons, such as were Cassandra, Manto, Nicostrata, Mopsus, Proteus, the Sibyls, whom Aristotle confesseth to have been deeply melancholy. Baptista Porta seconds him, they were stirred by black bile. Demoniacal persons, & such as speak strange languages, are of this rank; some Poets; such as laugh always, and think themselves Kings, Cardinals, &c. sanguine they are, pleasantly disposed most part, and so continue. Baptista Porta confines fear and sorrow to them that are cold; but lovers, Sibyls, enthusiasts, he wholly excludes. So that I think I may truly conclude, they are not always sad and fearful, but usually so, and that *without a cause; although not all alike,* (saith Altomarus), *yet all likely fear, some with an extraordinary and a mighty fear,* Aretæus. *Many fear death, and yet, in a contrary humour, make away themselves.* Some are afraid that heaven will fall on their heads: some afraid they are damned, or shall be. *They are troubled with scruples of Conscience, distrusting God's mercies, think they shall go certainly to Hell, the Devil will have them, & make great lamentation,* Jason Pratensis. Fear of Devils, death, that they shall be sick of some such or such disease, ready to tremble at every object, they shall die themselves forthwith, or that some of their dear friends or near allies are certainly dead; imminent danger, loss, disgrace, still torment others, &c. that they are all glass, and therefore they will suffer no man to come near them; that they are all cork, as light as feathers; others as heavy as lead; some are afraid their heads will fall off their shoulders, that they have frogs in their bellies, &c. Montanus speaks of one *that durst not walk alone from home, for fear he should swoon, or die.* A second *fears every man he meets will rob him, quarrel with him, or kill him.* A third dares not venture to walk alone, for fear he should meet the Devil, a thief, be sick, fears all old women as witches, & every black dog or cat he sees he suspecteth to be a Devil, every person comes near him is maleficiated, every creature, all intend to hurt him, seek his ruin. Another dares not go over a bridge, come near a pool, rock, steep hill, lie in a chamber where cross beams are, for fear he be tempted to hang, drown, or precipitate himself. If he be in a silent auditory, as at a sermon, he is afraid he shall speak aloud at unawares, some thing undecent, unfit to be said. If he be locked in a close room, he is afraid of being stifled for want of air, and still carries biscuit, Aquavitæ, or some strong waters about him, for fear of fainting, or being sick; or if he be in a throng, middle of a Church, multitude, where he may not well get out, though he sit at ease, he is so misaffected. He will freely promise, undertake any business beforehand, but, when it comes to be performed, he dare not adventure, but fears an infinite number of dangers, disasters, &c. Some are *afraid to be burned, or that the ground will sink under them, or swallow them quick, or that the King will call them in question for some fact they never did, & that they shall surely be executed.* The terror of such a death troubles them, and they fear as much, & are equally tormented in mind, *as they that have committed a murder, and are pensive without a cause, as if they were now presently to be put to death.* They are afraid of some loss, danger, that they shall surely lose their lives, goods, and all they have, but why they know not. Trincavellius had a patient that would needs make away himself, for fear of being hanged, and could not be persuaded, for three years together, but that he had killed a man. Plater hath two other examples of such as feared to be executed without a cause. If they come in a place where a robbery, theft, or any such offence, hath been done, they presently fear they are suspected, & many times betray themselves without a cause. Louis XI., the French King, suspected every man a traitor that came about him, durst trust no officer. *Some fear all alike, some certain men,* and cannot endure their companies, are sick in them, or if they be from home. Some suspect treason still, others *are afraid of their dearest and nearest friends* (Melanelius out of Galen, Ruffus &c.), & dare not be alone in the dark, for fear of Hobgoblins and Devils: he suspects everything he hears or sees to be a Devil, or enchanted; and imagineth a thousand chimeras and visions, which to his thinking he certainly sees, bugbears, talks with black men, ghosts, goblins, &c.

> *The very breezes fright him, every sound*
> *Excites him.*   (VIRGIL)

Another through bashfulness, suspicion, & timorousness, will not be seen abroad, *loves darkness as life, & cannot endure the light,* or to sit in lightsome places; his hat still in his eyes, he will neither see nor be seen by his good will, Hippocrates, On Insanity & Melancholy. He dare not come in company for fear he should be misused, disgraced, overshoot himself in gesture or speeches, or be sick: he thinks every man observes him, aims at him, derides him, owes him malice. Most part *they are afraid they are bewitched, possessed, or poisoned by their enemies,* and sometimes they suspect their nearest friends: *he thinks something speaks or talks within him, or to him, & he belcheth of the poison.* Christophorus à Vega had a patient so troubled, that by no persuasion or physick could he be reclaimed. Some are afraid that they shall have every fearful disease they see others have, hear or read of, and dare not therefore hear or read of any such subject, no not of melancholy itself, lest, by applying to themselves that which they hear or read, they should aggravate and increase it. If they see one possessed, bewitched, an epileptick paroxysm, a man shaking with the palsy, or giddy headed, reeling, or standing in a dangerous place, &c. for many days after it runs in their minds, they are afraid they shall be so too, they are in like danger, as Perkins well observes in his Cases of Conscience, and many times by violence of imagination they produce it. They cannot endure to see any terrible object, as a Monster, a man executed, a carcase, hear the Devil named, or any tragical relation seen, but they quake for fear, Hecate will appear to them in their sleep, (Lucian), they dream of Hobgoblins, and may not get it out of their minds a long time after: they apply (as I have said) all they hear, see, read, to themselves; as Felix Plater notes of some young Physicians, that studying to cure diseases catch them themselves, will be sick, and appropriate all symptoms they find related of others to their own persons. And therefore (as I again advise, even though I may inspire disgust in the reader, for I had rather repeat words ten times than omit anything) I would advise him, that is actually melancholy, not to read this tract of symptoms, lest he disquiet or make himself for a time worse, and more melancholy than he was before. Generally of them all take this, saith Aretæus; they complain of toys, & fear without a cause, and still think their melancholy to be most grievous, none so bad as they are, though it be nothing in respect, yet never any man sure was so troubled, or in this sort: as really tormented and perplexed, in as great an agony for toys & trifles, (such things as they will after laugh at themselves), as if they were most material & essential matters indeed, worthy to be feared, & will not be satisfied. Pacify them for one, they are instantly troubled with some other fear; always afraid of something, which they foolishly imagine or conceive to themselves, which never peradventure was, never can be, never likely will be; troubled in mind upon every small occasion, unquiet, still complaining, grieving, vexing, suspecting, grudging, discontent, and cannot be freed so long as their melancholy continues.

Or if their minds be more quiet for the present, and they free from foreign fears, outward accidents, yet their bodies are out of tune, they suspect some part or other to be amiss, now their head aches, heart, stomack, spleen, &c. is misaffected, they shall surely have this or that disease; still troubled in body, mind, or both, & through wind, corrupt phantasy, some accidental distemper, continually molested. Yet for all this, as Jacchinus notes, *in all other things they are wise, staid, discreet, & do nothing unbeseeming their dignity, person, or place, this foolish, ridiculous, and childish fear excepted,* which so much, so continually, tortures and crucifies their souls; like a barking dog that alwayes bawls, but seldom bites, this fear ever molesteth, and, so long as their melancholy lasteth, cannot be avoided.

Sorrow is that other character, & inseparable companion, as individual as Saint Cosmo and Damian, a faithful attendant, as all writers witness, a common symptom, a continual; and still, without any evident cause; grieving still, but why they cannot tell: never laughing, sad, thoughtful, they look as if they had newly come forth of Trophonius' den. And though they laugh many times, & seem to be extraordinary merry (as they will by fits) yet extreme lumpish again in an instant, dull, & heavy, simultaneously merry & sad, but most part sad: pleasant thoughts depart soon, sorrow sticks by them still continually, gnawing as the vulture did Tityus' bowels, & they cannot avoid it. No sooner are their eyes open but, after terrible and troublesome dreams, their heavy hearts begin to sigh: they are still fretting, chafing, sighing, grieving, complaining, finding faults, repining, grudging, weeping, *Heautontimorumenoi,** vexing themselves, disquieted in mind, with restless, unquiet thoughts, discontent, either for their own, other men's, or publick affairs, such as concern them not, things past, present, or to come; the remembrance of some disgrace, loss, injury, abuse, &c. troubles them now, being idle, afresh, as if it were new done; they are afflicted otherwise for some danger, loss, want, shame, misery, that will certainly come, as they suspect and mistrust. Mournful Ate frowns upon them, insomuch that Aretæus well calls it a vexation of the mind, a perpetual agony. They can hardly be pleased, or eased, though in other men's opinion most happy. Go, tarry, run, ride,

Behind the horseman sits livid Care: (HORACE)

they cannot avoid this feral plague; let them come in what company they will, the fatal shaft remains fixt in their side; as to a deer that is struck, whether he run, go, rest, with the herd, or alone, this grief re-

* An allusion to The Self-Tormentor, a play of Terence's.

mains: irresolution, inconstancy, vanity of mind, their fear, torture, care, jealousy, suspicion, &c. continues, and they cannot be relieved. So he complained in the Poet: — He came home sorrowful, and troubled in his mind; his servants did all they possibly could to please him; one pulled off his socks, another made ready his bed, a third his supper, all did their utmost endeavours to ease his grief, and exhilarate his person, he was profoundly melancholy, he had lost his son, that was his torture, that was his heart-sorrow, his pain, his agony, which could not be removed.

Hence it proceeds many times that they are weary of their lives, and feral thoughts to offer violence to their own persons come into their minds; being bored with life is a common symptom, their days pass wearily by, they are soon tired with all things; they will now tarry, now be gone; now in bed they will rise, now up, then go to bed; now pleased, then again displeased; now they like, by and by dislike all, weary of all; now they desire to live, and now to die, saith Aurelianus, but most part they hate life; discontent, disquieted, perplexed, upon every light or no occasion, object: often tempted, I say, to make away themselves: they cannot die, they will not live: they complain, weep, lament, and think they lead a most miserable life; never was any man so bad, or so before, every poor man they see is most fortunate in respect of them, every beggar that comes to the door is happier than they are, they could be contented to change lives with them, especially if they be alone, idle, & parted from their ordinary company, molested, displeased, or provoked: grief, fear, agony, discontent, wearisomeness, laziness, suspicion, or some such passion, forcibly seizeth on them. Yet by and by, when they come in company again which they like, or be pleased, as Octavius Horatianus observes, they condemn their former mislike, and are well pleased to live. And so they continue, till with some fresh discontent they be molested again, and then they are weary of their lives, weary of all, they will die, and shew rather a necessity to live than a desire. Claudius the Emperor, as Suetonius describes him, had a spice of this disease, for, when he was tormented with the pain of his stomack, he had a conceit to make away himself. Jul. Cæsar Claudinus had a Polonian to his patient so affected, that through fear and sorrow, with which he was still disquieted, hated his own life, wished for death every moment, and to be freed of his misery; Mercurialis another, and another that was often minded to despatch himself, and so continued for many years.

Suspicion and *jealousy* are general symptoms: they are commonly distrustful, timorous, apt to mistake, and amplify, testy, pettish, peevish, and ready to snarl upon every small occasion, with their greatest friends, and without a cause, given or not given, it will be to their offense. If they speak in jest, he takes it in good earnest. If they be not saluted, invited, consulted with, called to counsel, &c. or that any respect, small compliment, or ceremony be omitted, they think themselves neglected and contemned: for a time that tortures them. If two talk together, discourse, whisper, jest, or tell a tale in general, he thinks presently they mean him, applies all to himself. Or if they talk with him, he is ready to misconstrue every word they speak, and interpret it to the worst; he cannot endure any man to look steadily on him, speak to him almost, laugh, jest, or be familiar, or hem, or point, cough, or spit, or make a noise sometimes, &c. He thinks they laugh or point at him, or do it in disgrace of him, circumvent him, contemn him; every man looks at him, he is pale, red, sweats for fear and anger, lest some body should observe him. He works upon it, and long after this false conceit of an abuse troubles him. Montanus gives instance in a melancholy Jew, that was stormier than the Adriatic Sea, so waspish and suspicious, so prone to wrath, that no man could tell how to carry himself in his company.

Inconstant they are in all their actions, vertiginous, restless, unapt to resolve of any business, they will and will not, persuaded to and fro upon every small occasion, or word spoken; and yet, if once they be resolved, obstinate, hard to be reconciled; if they abhor, dislike, or distaste, once settled, though to the better, by no odds, counsel or persuasion to be removed; yet in most things wavering, irresolute, unable to deliberate, through fear. Now prodigal, and then covetous, they do, and by-and-by repent them of that which they have done, so that both ways they are troubled, whether they do or do not, want or have, hit or miss, disquieted of all hands, soon weary, and still seeking change, restless, I say, fickle, fugitive, they may not abide to tarry in one place long,

At Rome you hanker for your country home;
Once in the country, there's no place like Rome, (HORACE)
no company long, or to persevere in any action or business:
Like scions of the great, he calls for victuals ready-chewed,
When nurse would rock his cradle, becometh loud & rude, (PERSIUS)
eftsoons pleased, and anon displeased; as a man that's bitten with fleas, or that cannot sleep, turns to and fro in his bed, their restless minds are tossed & vary, they have no patience to read out a book, to play out a game or two, walk a mile, sit an hour, &c. erected and dejected in an instant; animated to undertake, and upon a word spoken again discouraged.

Extreme passionate, and what they desire, they do most furiously seek: anxious ever & very solicitous, distrustful and timorous, envious, malicious, profuse one while, sparing another, but most part covetous, muttering, repining, discontent, and still complaining, grudging, peevish, prone to revenge, soon troubled, and most violent in all their imaginations, not affable in speech, or apt to vulgar compliment, but surly, dull, sad, austere, brooding still, very intent, and, as Albertus Durer paints Melancholy, like a sad woman leaning on her arm with fixed looks, neglect habit, &c. held therefore by some proud, soft, sottish, or half-mad, as the Abderites esteemed of Democritus: and yet of a deep reach, excellent apprehension, judicious, wise, & witty: for I am of that Nobleman's mind, *Melancholy advanceth men's conceits more than any humour whatsoever,* improves their meditations more than any strong drink or sack. They are of profound judgement in some things, although in others they judge not well because of their unease, saith Fracastorius. And, as Arculanus terms it, their judgement is generally perverse, and corrupt, since they count honesty dishonesty, friends as enemies, they will abuse their best friends, and dare not offend their enemies. Cowards most part, saith Cardan, loth to offend; and if they chance to overshoot themselves in word or deed, or any small business or circumstance be omitted, forgotten, they are miserably tormented, and frame a thousand dangers & inconveniences to themselves, make an elephant out of a fly, if once they conceit it: overjoyed with every good rumour, tale, or prosperous event, transported beyond themselves: with every small cross again, bad news, misconceived injury, loss, danger, afflicted beyond measure, in great agony, perplexed, dejected, astonished, impatient, utterly undone: fearful, suspicious of all: yet again, many of them desperate harebrains, rash, careless, fit to be assassinates, as being void of all fear and sorrow, according to Hercules de Saxonia, *most audacious, and such as dare walk alone in the night through deserts and dangerous places, fearing none.*

They are prone to love, and easy to be taken: quickly enamoured, and dote upon all, love one dearly, till they see another, and then dote on her, first this one, and this one, then that one & all the rest; the present moves most, and the last commonly they love best. Yet some again (Anterotes *) cannot endure the sight of a woman, abhor the sex, as that same melancholy Duke of Muscovy, that was instantly sick if he came but in sight of them: and that Anchorite, that fell into a cold palsy, when a woman was brought before him.

* From Anteros, the anti-Eros, avenger of slighted love.

Humorous they are beyond all measure, sometimes profusely laughing, extraordinary merry, and then again weeping without a cause, (which is familiar with many Gentlewomen), groaning, sighing, pensive, sad, almost distracted; they feign many absurdities (saith Frambesarius), vain, void of reason: one supposeth himself to be a dog, cock, bear, horse, glass, butter, &c. He is a Giant, a Dwarf, as strong as an hundred men, a Lord, Duke, Prince, &c. And if he be told he hath a stinking breath, a great nose, that he is sick, or inclined to such or such a disease, he believes it eftsoons, and peradventure, by force of imagination, will work it out. Many of them are immovable, and fixed in their conceits; others vary upon every object, heard or seen. If they see a stage-play, they run upon that a week after; if they hear music, or see dancing, they have naught but bag-pipes in their brain; if they see a combat, they are all for arms; if abused, an abuse troubles them long after; if crossed, that cross, &c. Restless in their thoughts and actions, continually meditating, more like dreams than men awake, they feign a company of antick, phantastical conceits, they have most frivolous thoughts, impossible to be effected; and sometimes think verily they hear and see present before their eyes such phantasms or goblins, they fear, suspect, or conceive, they still talk with, and follow them. In fine, their thoughts are like to dreams; still, saith Avicenna, they wake as others dream, and such for the most part are their imaginations and conceits, absurd, vain, foolish toys, yet they are most curious and solicitous; continually beyond all bounds & preoccupied with something or other; as serious in a toy, as if it were a most necessary business, of great moment, importance, and still, still, still, thinking of it, macerating themselves. Though they do talk with you, and seem to be otherwise employed, and to your thinking very intent and busy, still that toy runs in their mind, that fear, that suspicion, that abuse, that jealousy, that agony, that vexation, that cross, that castle in the air, that crotchet, that whimsy, that fiction, that pleasant waking dream, whatsoever it is. They neither ask questions nor respond to them, (saith Fracastorius); they do not much heed what you say, their mind is on another matter; ask what you will, they do not attend, or much intend that business they are about, but forget themselves what they are saying, doing, or should otherwise say or do, whither they are going, distracted with their own melancholy thoughts. One laughs upon a sudden, another smiles to himself, a third frowns, calls, his lips go still, he acts with his hand, as he walks, &c. 'Tis proper to all melancholy men, saith Mercurialis, *what conceit they have once entertained, to be most intent, violent, and continually about it.* It happens, willy-nilly, do what they may, they cannot be rid of it, against their wills they must think of it a thousand times over, they are continually troubled with it, in company, out of company; at meat, at exercise, at all times and places, they do not cease to think about what they least wish to remember; if it be offensive especially, they cannot forget it, they may not rest or sleep for it, but, still tormenting themselves, they roll upon themselves the stone of Sisyphus, as Brunner observes. It is a perpetual calamity, and terrible scourge.

Crato, Laurentius, & Fernelius, put bashfulness for an ordinary symptom; clumsy manners, or some breach of propriety, is a thing which much haunts & torments them. If they have been misused, derided, disgraced, chidden, &c. or by any perturbation of mind misaffected, it so far troubles them, that they become quite moped many times, and so disheartened, dejected, they dare not come abroad, into strange companies especially, or manage their ordinary affairs, so childish, timorous, and bashful, they can look no man in the face; some are more disquieted in this kind, some less, longer some, others shorter, by fits, &c. though some on the other side, (according to Fracastorius), be impudent and peevish. But most part they are very shamefac'd, and that makes them with Pet. Blesensis, Christopher Urswick, & many such, to refuse Honours, Offices, and Preferments, which sometimes fall into their mouths, they cannot speak, or put forth themselves, as others can, timorousness & bashfulness hinder their proceedings, they are contented with their present estate, unwilling to undertake any office, & therefore never likely to rise. For that cause they seldom visit their friends, except some familiars: of few words, and oftentimes wholly silent. Frambesarius, a Frenchman, had two such patients, wholly taciturn, their friends could not get them to speak: Rodericus à Fonseca gives instance in a young man, of 27 years of age, that was frequently silent, bashful, moped, solitary, that would not eat his meat, or sleep, and yet again by fits apt to be angry, &c.

Most part they are, as Plater notes, slothful, and taciturn; they will scarce be compelled to do that which concerns them, though it be for their good, so diffident, so dull, of small or no compliment, unsociable, hard to be acquainted with, especially of strangers; they had rather write their minds than speak, & above all things love *solitariness*. Are they so solitary for pleasure (one asks) or pain? for both: yet I rather think for fear and sorrow, &c.

Hence 'tis they grieve and fear, avoiding light,
And shut themselves in prison dark from sight.   (VIRGIL)

As Bellerophon in Homer,

That wandered in the woods sad all alone,
Forsaking men's society, making great moan,

they delight in floods & waters, desert places, to walk alone in orchards, gardens, private walks, back-lanes, averse from company, as Diogenes in his tub, or Timon the Misanthrope, they abhor all companions at last, even their nearest acquaintance, & most familiar friends, for they have a conceit (I say) every man observes them, will deride, laugh to scorn, or misuse them; confining themselves therefore wholly to their private houses or chambers, they flee from mankind without cause (saith Rhasis) & hate them, will diet themselves, feed, and live alone. It was one of the chiefest reasons why the Citizens of Abdera suspected Democritus to be melancholy and mad, because that, as Hippocrates related in his Epistle to Philopœmen, *he forsook the City, lived in groves & hollow trees, upon a green bank by a brook side, or confluence of waters, all day long, & all night.* It often happens (saith he) that those who are vexed of black bile & melancholy desert their fellows and are averse to society; which is an ordinary thing with melancholy men. The Egyptians therefore in their Hieroglyphicks expressed a melancholy man by an hare sitting in her form, as being a most timorous and solitary creature.* But this & all precedent symptoms are more or less apparent, as the humour is intended or remitted, hardly perceived in some, or not at all, most manifest in others; childish in some, terrible in others; to be derided in one, pitied or admired in another; to him by fits, to a second continuate: and, howsoever these symptoms be common and incident to all persons, yet they are the more remarkable, frequent, furious, and violent, in melancholy men. To speak in a word, there is nothing so vain, absurd, ridiculous, extravagant, impossible, incredible, so monstrous a chimæra, so prodigious and strange, such as Painters and Poets durst not attempt, which they will not really fear, feign, suspect, & imagine unto themselves: and that which Ludovicus Vives said in jest of a silly country fellow, that killed his ass for drinking up the Moon, that he might restore the moon to the world, you may truly say of them in earnest; they will act, conceive all extremes, contrarieties, and contradictions, & that in infinite varieties; scarce two of 2000 that concur in the same symptoms. The Tower of *Babel* never

* Pierius in Hieroglyphica.

yielded such confusion of tongues, as this Chaos of Melancholy doth variety of symptoms. There is in all melancholy, like men's faces, a disagreeing likeness still; and as, in a river, we swim in the same place, though not in the same numerical water; as the same instrument affords several lessons, so the same disease yields diversity of symptoms; which howsoever they be diverse, intricate, and hard to be confined, 1 will adventure yet, in such a vast confusion and generality, to bring them into some order; and so descend to particulars.

SUBSECTION 3 — *Particular Symptoms from the influence of Stars, parts of the body, and humours*

SOME men have peculiar symptoms, according to their temperament and *crisis,* which they had from the Stars and those Celestial influences, variety of wits and dispositions, as Anthony Zara contends. One saith diverse diseases of the body and mind proceed from their influences, as I have already proved out of Ptolemy, Pontanus, Lemnius, Cardan, and others, as they are principal significators of manners, diseases, mutually irradiated, or Lords of the geniture, &c. Ptolemæus in his Centiloquy, Hermes, or whosoever else the author of that Tract, attributes all these symptoms, which are in melancholy men, to celestial influences: which opinion Mercurialis rejects; but, as I say, Jovianus Pontanus & others stiffly defend. That some are solitary, dull, heavy, churlish; some again blithe, buxom, light, and merry, they ascribe wholly to the Stars. As if *Saturn* be predominant in his Nativity, and cause Melancholy in his temperature, then he shall be very austere, sullen, churlish, black of colour, profound in his cogitations, full of cares, miseries, and discontents, sad and fearful, always silent, solitary, still delighting in husbandry, in Woods, Orchards, Gardens, Rivers, Ponds, Pools, dark Walks and close: their ideas are wishing to build, wishing to plant, to till the fields, etc. to catch Birds, Fishes, &c. still contriving and musing of such matters. If *Jupiter* domineers, they are more ambitious, still meditating of Kingdoms, Magistracies, Offices, Honours, or that they are Princes, Potentates, and how they would carry themselves, &c. If *Mars,* they are all for wars, brave combats, monomachies, testy, cholerick, harebrain, rash, furious, and violent in their actions. They will feign themselves Victors, Commanders, are passionate and satirical in their speeches, great braggers, ruddy of colour. And though they be poor in shew, vile and base, yet, like Telephus and Peleus in the Poet,

     Toss off their bombast and their yard-long words,   (HORACE)
their mouths are full of myriads, and Tetrarchs at their tongues' end.

If the *Sun,* they will be Lords, Emperors, in conceit at least, and Monarchs, give Offices, Honours, &c. If *Venus,* they are still courting of their mistresses, and most apt to love, amorously given; they seem to hear music, plays, see fine pictures, dancers, merriments, and the like; ever in love, and dote on all they see. *Mercurialists* are solitary, much in contemplation, subtile, Poets, Philosophers, and musing most part about such matters. If the *Moon* have a hand, they are all for peregrinations, sea-voyages, much affected with travels, to discourse, read, meditate of such things; wandering in their thoughts, divers, much delighting in waters, to fish, fowl, &c.

But the most immediate symptoms proceed from the Temperature itself, and the Organical parts, as Head, Liver, Spleen, Meseraick veins, Heart, Womb, Stomack, &c. and most especially from distemperature of spirits (which, as Hercules de Saxonia contends, are wholly immaterial), or from the four humours in those seats, whether they be hot or cold, natural, unnatural, innate or adventitious, intended or remitted, simple or mixt, their diverse mixtures, and several adustions, combinations, which may be as diversely varied as those four first qualities in Clavius, and produce as many several symptoms and monstrous fictions as wine doth effects, which, as Andreas Bachius observes, are infinite. Of greater note be these.

If it be natural Melancholy, as Lod. Mercatus, T. Bright, hath largely described, either of the Spleen, or of the veins, faulty by excess of quantity, or thickness of substance, it is a cold and dry humour, as Montanus affirms, the parties are sad, timorous, & fearful. Prosper Calenus, in his book, will have them to be more stupid than ordinary, cold, heavy, dull, solitary, sluggish, if they have much black & cold bile. Hercules de Saxonia *holds these that are naturally melancholy to be of a leaden colour or black,* and so doth Guianerius, and such as think themselves dead many times, or that they see, talk with, black men, dead men, Spirits and Goblins frequently, if it be in excess. These symptoms vary according to the mixture of those four humours adust, which is unnatural melancholy. For, as Trallianus hath written, *there is not one cause of this melancholy, nor one humour which begets it, but divers diversely intermixt, from whence proceeds this variety of symptoms:* and those varying again as they are hot or cold. *Cold melancholy* (saith Benedic. Vittorius Faventinus), *is a cause of dotage, & more mild symptoms; if hot or more adust, of more violent passions and furies.* Fracastorius will have us to consider well of it, *with what kind of Melancholy every one is troubled, for it much avails to know it; one is enraged by fervent heat, another is possessed by sad and cold; one is fearful, shamefast, the other impudent and bold,* as *Ajax,* who furiously snatched up arms and demanded battle, — quite mad or tending to madness: attacking now this, now that. Bellerophon, on the other side, wanders alone in the woods; one despairs, weeps, and is weary of his life, another laughs, &c. All which variety is produced from the several degrees of heat and cold, which Hercules de Saxonia will have wholly proceed from the distemperature of spirits alone, animal especially, and those immaterial, the next, and immediate causes of Melancholy, as they are hot, cold, dry, moist, and from their agitation proceeds that diversity of symptoms, which he reckons up in the 13th chap. of his Tract of Melancholy, and that largely through every part. Others will have them come from the diverse adustion of the four humours, which, in this unnatural melancholy, by corruption of blood, adust choler, or melancholy natural, *by excessive distemper of heat turned, in comparison of the natural, into a sharp lye by force of adustion, cause, according to the diversity of their matter, diverse and strange symptoms,* which T. Bright reckons up in his following chapter. So doth Arculanus, according to the four principal humours adust, and many others.

For example, if it proceed from phlegm, (which is seldom and not so frequent as the rest), it stirs up dull symptoms, and a kind of stupidity, or impassionate hurt: they are sleepy, saith Savanarola, dull, slow, cold, blockish, ass-like; asinine melancholy, Melancthon calls it; *they are much given to weeping, and delight in waters, ponds, pools, rivers, fishing, fowling, &c.* they are pale of colour, slothful, apt to sleep, heavy; *much troubled with head-ache,* continual meditation, and muttering to themselves; they dream of waters, that they are in danger of drowning, and fear such things, Rhasis. They are fatter than others that are melancholy, of a muddy complexion, apter to spit, sleep, more troubled with rheum than the rest, and have their eyes still fixed on the ground. Such a patient had Hercules de Saxonia, a widow in Venice, that was fat and very sleepy still; Christophorus à Vega another affected in the same sort. If it be inveterate or violent, the symptoms are more evident, they plainly dote, and are ridiculous to others, in all their gestures, actions, speeches: imagining impossibilities, as he in Christophorus à Vega, that thought he was a Tun of Wine, and that Siennois, that resolved with himself not to piss, for fear he should drown all the town.

If it proceed from blood adust, or that there be a mixture of blood in it, *such are commonly ruddy of complexion, & high-coloured,* according to Sallustius Salvianus, and Hercules de Saxonia; and, as Savanarola, Vittorius Faventinus, farther add, *the veins of their eyes be red, as well as their faces.* They are much inclined to laughter, witty and merry, conceited in discourse, pleasant, if they be not far gone, much given to musick, dancing, and to be in women's company. They meditate wholly on such things, and think *they see or hear plays, dancing, and such like sports* (free from all fear and sorrow, as Hercules de Saxonia supposeth,) if they be more strongly possessed with this kind of melancholy, Arnoldus adds, like him of Argos in the Poet, that sat laughing all day long, as if he had been at a Theatre. Such another is mentioned by Aristotle, living at Abydos, a town of Asia Minor, that would sit after the same fashion, as if he had been upon a Stage, and sometimes act himself; now clap his hands, and laugh, as if he had been well pleased with the sight. Wolfius relates of a country fellow called Brunsellius, subject to this humour, *that, being by chance at a sermon, saw a woman fall off from a form half asleep, at which object most of the company laughed, but he, for his part, was so much moved, that for three whole days after he did nothing but laugh, by which means he was much weakened, & worse a long time following.* Such a one was old Sophocles, and Democritus himself had a merry kind of madness, much in this vein. Laurentius thinks this kind of melancholy, which is a little adust with some mixture of blood, to be that which Aristotle meant, when he said melancholy men of all others are most witty, which causeth many times divine ravishment, and a kind of divine inspiration, which stirreth them up to be excellent Philosophers, Poets, Prophets, &c. Mercurialis gives instance in a young man his patient, sanguine melancholy, *of a great wit, and excellently learned.*

If it arise from choler adust, they are bold and impudent, and of a more harebrain disposition, apt to quarrel and think of such things, battles, combats, and their manhood; furious, impatient in discourse, stiff, irrefragable, and prodigious in their tenents; and, if they be moved, most violent, outrageous, ready to disgrace, provoke any, to kill themselves & others; Arnoldus adds, stark mad by fits, *they sleep little, their urine is subtile and fiery;* (Guianerius) *in their fits you shall hear them speak all manner of languages, Hebrew, Greek and Latin, that never were taught or knew them before.* Apponensis speaks of a mad woman that spake excellent good Latin; and Rhasis knew another, that could prophesy in her fit, and foretell things truly to come. Guianerius had a patient could make Latin verses when the Moon was combust, otherwise illiterate. Avicenna and some of his adherents will have these symptoms, when they happen, to proceed from the Devil, and that they are rather possessed, than mad or melancholy, or both together, as Jason Pratensis thinks, but most ascribe it to the humour; which opinion Montaltus stiffly maintains, confuting Avicenna and the rest, referring it wholly to the quality and disposition of the humour & subject. Cardan holds these men of all others fit to be assassinates, bold, hardy, fierce, and adventurous, to undertake any thing by reason of their choler adust. *This humour,* saith he, *prepares them to endure death itself, and all manner of torments, with invincible courage, and 'tis a wonder to see with what alacrity they will undergo such tortures,* that it seems preternatural: he ascribes this generosity, fury, or rather stupidity, to this adustion of choler and melancholy: but I take these rather to be mad or desperate, than properly melancholy: for commonly this humour, so adust and hot, degenerates into madness.

If it come from melancholy itself adust, those men, saith *Avicenna, are usually sad and solitary, and that continually, and in excess, more than ordinary suspicious, more fearful, and have long, sore, and most corrupt imaginations;* cold and black, bashful, and so solitary, that, as Arnoldus writes, *they will endure no company, they dream of graves still, and dead men, and think themselves bewitched or dead:* if it be extreme, they think they hear hideous noises, see and talk *with black men, and converse familiarly with Devils, and such strange chimaeras and visions,* (Gordonius), or that they are possessed by them, that somebody talks to them, or within them. Such melancholy folk are generally possessed. Valescus de Taranta had such a woman in cure, *that thought she had to do with the Devil:* and Gentilis Fulgosus writes that he had a melancholy friend, that *had a black man in the likeness of a soldier,* still following him wheresoever he was. Laurentius hath many stories of such as have thought themselves bewitched by their enemies; and some that would eat no meat as being dead. In the year 1550, an Advocate of Paris fell into such a melancholy fit, that he believed verily he was dead; he could not be persuaded otherwise, or to eat or drink, till a kinsman of his, a Scholar of Bourges, did eat before him, dressed like a corse. The story, saith Serres, was acted in a Comedy before Charles the Ninth. Some think they are beasts, wolves, hogs, and cry like dogs, foxes, bray like asses, and low like kine, as King Prœtus' daughters. Hildesheim hath an example of a Dutch Baron so affected, and Trincavellius another of a nobleman in his country, *that thought he was certainly a beast, and would imitate most of their voices,* with many such symptoms, which may properly be reduced to this kind.

If it proceed from the severall combinations of these four humours, or spirits, (Herc. de Saxon. adds hot, cold, dry, moist, dark, confused, settled, constringed, as it participates of matter, or is without matter), the symptoms are likewise mixt. One thinks himself a Giant, another a Dwarf; one is heavy as lead, another is as light as a feather. Marcellus Donatus makes mention out of Seneca, of one Senecio, a rich man, *that thought himself and every thing else he had great, great wife, great horses; could not abide little things, but would have great pots to drink in, great hose, and great shoes bigger than his feet.* Like her in Trallianus, *that supposed she could shake all the world with her finger,* and was afraid to clench her hand together, lest she should crush the world like an apple in pieces: or him in Galen, that thought he was Atlas, and sustained heaven with his shoulders. Another thinks himself so little, that he can creep into a mousehole: one fears heaven will fall on his head; a second is a cock; and such a one Guianerius saith he saw at Padua, that would clap his hands together and crow. Another thinks he is a nightingale, and therefore sings all the night long: another he is all glass, a pitcher, and will therefore let nobody come near him, and such a one Laurentius gives out, upon his credit, that he knew in France. Christophorus à Vega, Sckenkius, and Marcellus Donatus have many such examples, and one amongst the rest of a Baker in Ferrara, that thought he was composed of butter, & durst not sit in the sun, or come near the fire, for fear of being melted: of another that thought he was a case of leather, stuffed with wind. Some laugh, weep; some are mad, some dejected, moped, in much agony, some by fits, others continuate, &c. Some have a corrupt ear, (they think they hear musick, or some hideous noise as their phantasy conceives,) some corrupt eyes, some smelling, some one sense, some another. Louis XI. had a conceit every thing did stink about him; all the odoriferous perfumes they could get would not ease him, but still he smelled a filthy stink. A melancholy French Poet in Laurentius, being sick of a fever, and troubled with waking, was by his Physicians appointed to use an ointment made of poplar to anoint his temples; but he so distasted the smell of it, that, for many years after, he imagined all that came near him to scent of it, and would let no man talk with him but aloof off, or wear any new clothes, because he thought still they smelled of it; in all other things wise and discreet, he would talk sensibly save only in this. A Gentleman in Limousin, saith Anthony de Verdeur, was persuaded he had but one leg, affrighted by a wild boar, that by chance stroke him on the leg: he could not be satisfied his leg was sound (in all other things well) untill two

Franciscans, by chance coming that way, fully removed him from the conceit. But we have heard enough tales.

SUBSECTION 4 — *Symptoms from Education, Custom, Continuance of Time, or Condition, mixt with other Diseases, by Fits, Inclination, &c.*

ANOTHER great occasion of the variety of these symptoms proceeds from custom, discipline, education, and several inclinations. *This humour will imprint in melancholy men the objects most answerable to their condition of life, and ordinary actions, and dispose men according to their several studies and callings.* If an ambitious man become melancholy, he forthwith thinks he is a King, an Emperor, a Monarch, and walks alone, pleasing himself with a vain hope of some future preferment, or present as he supposeth, and withal acts a Lord's part, takes upon him to be some Statesman or Magnifico, makes congies, gives entertainment, looks big, &c. Francisco Sansovino records of a melancholy man in Cremona, that he would not be induced to believe but that he was Pope, gave pardons, made Cardinals, &c. Christophorus à Vega makes mention of another of his acquaintance, that thought he was a King driven from his Kingdom, and was very anxious to recover his estate. A covetous person is still conversant about purchasing of lands and tenements, plotting in his mind how to compass such and such Manors, as if he were already Lord of, and able to go through with it; all he sees is his property or that for which he yearns, he hath devoured it in hope, or else in conceit esteems it his own; like him in *Athenœus,* that thought all the ships in the haven to be his own. A lascivious *inamorato* plots all the day long to please his mistress, acts and struts, and carries himself, as if she were in presence, still dreaming of her, as Pamphilus of his Glycerium, or as some do in their morning sleep. Marcellus Donatus knew such a Gentlewoman in Mantua, called Elionora Meliorina, that constantly believed she was married to a King, and *would kneel down and talk with him, as if he had been there present with his associates; and if she had found by chance a piece of glass in a muck-hill, or in the street, she would say that it was a jewel sent from her Lord and husband.* If devout and religious, he is all for fasting, prayer, ceremonies, alms, interpretations, visions, prophecies, revelations, he is inspired by the Holy Ghost, full of the spirit: one while he is saved, another while damned, or still troubled in mind for his sins, the Devil will surely have him, &c. More of these in the third Partition, of Love-Melancholy. A Scholar's mind is busied about his studies, he ap-

plauds himself for that he hath done, or hopes to do, one while fearing
to be out in his next exercise, another while contemning all censures;
envies one, emulates another; or else with indefatigable pains and
meditation consumes himself. So of the rest, all which vary according
to the more remiss or violent impression of the object, or as the humour
itself is intended or remitted. For some are so gently melancholy, that
in all their carriage, and to the outward apprehension of others, it can
hardly be discerned, yet to them an intolerable burden, and not to be
endured. Some signs are manifest and obvious to all at all times, some
to few, or seldom, or hardly perceived; let them keep their own counsel,
none will take notice or suspect them. *They do not express in outward
shew their depraved imaginations,* as Hercules de Saxonia observes, *but
conceal them wholly to themselves, and are very wise men, as I have
often seen: some fear, some do not fear at all, as such as think themselves kings or dead; some have more signs, some fewer, some great,
some less;* some vex, fret, still fear, grieve, lament, suspect, laugh, sing,
weep, chafe, &c. by fits (as I have said), or more during and permanent.
Some dote in one thing, are most childish, and ridiculous, and to be
wondered at, in that, and yet for all other matters most discreet and
wise. To some it is in disposition, to another in habit; and, as they
write of heat and cold, we may say of this humour, one is melancholy
eight degrees, a second two degrees less, a third half-way. 'Tis super-
particular, whether melancholy one-and-a-half, one-and-a-third, or more
than two parts, &c., all those geometrical proportions are too little to
express it. *It comes to many by fits, & goes; to others it is continuate:*
many (saith Faventinus) *in Spring & Fall only are molested,* some once
a year, as that Roman Galen speaks of: one at the conjunction of the
Moon alone, or some unfortunate aspects, at such and such set hours &
times, like the sea-tides; to some women when they be with child, as
Plater notes, never otherwise: to others 'tis settled and fixed: to one, led
about and variable still by that *ignis fatuus* of phantasy, like an *arthritis*
or running gout, 'tis here and there, and in every joint, always molesting
some part or other; or if the body be free, in a myriad of forms exer-
cising the mind. A second, once peradventure in his life, hath a most
grievous fit, once in seven years, once in five years, even to the extremity of madness, death, or dotage, and that upon some feral accident or perturbation, terrible object, and that for a time, never perhaps so before, never after. A third is moved upon all such troublesome
objects, cross fortune, disaster, and violent passions, otherwise free,
once troubled in three or four years. A fourth, if things be to his mind,

or he in action, well pleased, in good company, is most jocund, and of a good complexion: if idle, or alone, very dispirited, or carried away wholly with pleasant dreams and phantasies, but if once crossed and displeased, his countenance is altered on a sudden, his heart heavy, irksome thoughts crucify his soul, and in an instant he is moped, or weary of his life, he will kill himself. A fifth complains in his youth, a sixth in his middle age, the last in his old age.

Generally thus much we may conclude of melancholy: that it is most pleasant at first, I say, a most charming illusion, a most delightsome humour, to be alone, dwell alone, walk alone, meditate, lie in bed whole days, dreaming awake as it were, and frame a thousand phantastical imaginations unto themselves. They are never better pleased than when they are so doing, they are in Paradise for the time, and cannot well endure to be interrupt; with him in the Poet,

By Pollux, friends, quoth he,
You've slain, and not befriended me!   (HORACE)

you have undone him, he complains, if you trouble him: tell him what inconvenience will follow, what will be the event, all is one, the dog returneth to his vomit, 'tis so pleasant, he cannot refrain. He may thus continue peradventure many years by reason of a strong temperature, or some mixture of business, which may divert his cogitations: but at the last a wrecked imagination, his phantasy is crazed, & now habituated to such toys, cannot but work still like a fate; the Scene alters upon a sudden, Fear and Sorrow supplant those pleasing thoughts, suspicion, discontent, and perpetual anxiety succeed in their places; so by little and little, by that shoeing-horn of idleness, and voluntary solitariness, Melancholy, this feral fiend, is drawn on, & as far as it reaches its branches towards the heavens, so far does it plunge its roots to the depths beneath; it was not so delicious at first, as now it is bitter and harsh: a cankered soul macerated with cares and discontents, a being tired of life, impatience, agony, inconstancy, irresolution, precipitate them unto unspeakable miseries. They cannot endure company, light, or life itself, some; unfit for action, and the like. Their bodies are lean and dried up, withered, ugly, their looks harsh, very dull, and their souls tormented, as they are more or less intangled, as the humour hath been intended, or according to the continuance of time they have been troubled.

To discern all which symptoms the better, Rhasis the Arabian makes three degrees of them. The first is false conceits and idle thoughts: to misconstrue and amplify, aggravating every thing they conceive or fear:

the second is to talk to themselves, or to use inarticulate, incondite voices, speeches, obsolete gestures, and plainly to utter their minds and conceits of their hearts by their words and actions, as to laugh, weep, to be silent, not to sleep, eat their meat, &c.: the third is to put in practice that which they think or speak. Savanarola confirms as much: *when he begins to express that in words which he conceives in his heart, or talks idly, or goes from one thing to another,* which Gordonius calls having neither head nor tail, he is in the middle way: *but when he begins to act it likewise, and to put his fopperies in execution, he is then in the extent of melancholy or madness itself.* This progress of melancholy you shall easily observe in them that have been so affected, they go smiling to themselves at first, at length they laugh out; at first solitary, at last they can endure no company: or, if they do, they are now dizzards, past sense and shame, quite moped, they care not what they say or do, all their actions, words, gestures, are furious or ridiculous. At first his mind is troubled, he doth not attend what is said, if you tell him a tale, he cries at last, what said you? but in the end he mutters to himself, as old women do many times, or old men when they sit alone, upon a sudden they laugh, whoop, halloo, or run away, and swear they see or hear Players, Devils, Hobgoblins, Ghosts, strike, or strut, &c. grow humorous in the end: like him in the Poet, he often keeps two hundred slaves, often only ten, he will dress himself, and undress, careless at last, grows insensible, stupid, or mad. He howls like a wolf, barks like a dog, and raves like Ajax and Orestes, hears Musick and outcries which no man else hears. As he did whom Amatus Lusitanus mentioneth, or that woman in Springer, that spake many languages, and said she was possessed: that farmer in Prosper Calenus, that disputed and discoursed learnedly in Philosophy and Astronomy with Alexander Achilles, his master, at Bologna in Italy. But of these I have already spoken.

Who can sufficiently speak of these symptoms, or prescribe rules to comprehend them? As Echo to the Painter in Ausonius, foolish fellow, what wilt? if you must needs paint me, paint a voice, if you will describe melancholy, describe a phantastical conceit, a corrupt imagination, vain thoughts and different; which who can do? The four and twenty letters make no more variety of words in divers languages, than melancholy conceits produce diversity of symptoms in several persons. They are irregular, obscure, various, so infinite, Proteus himself is not so diverse; you may as well make the Moon a new coat, as a true character of a melancholy man; as soon find the motion of a bird in the air, as the heart of man, a melancholy man. They are so confused, I say, diverse, intermixt with other diseases. As the species be confounded (which I have shewed) so are the symptoms; sometimes with headache, wasting away, dropsy, stone, (as you may perceive by those several examples and illustrations, collected by Hildesheim, Mercurialis,) with headache, epilepsy, priapisms (Trincavellius), with gout, abnormal appetite, (Montanus), with falling sickness, headache, vertigo, lycanthropia, (Julius Cæsar Claudinus), with gout, agues, hæmrods, stone, &c. Who can distinguish these melancholy symptoms so intermixt with others, or apply them to their several kinds, confine them into method? 'Tis hard, I confess; yet I have disposed of them as I could, and will descend to particularize them according to their species. For hitherto I have expatiated in more general lists or terms, speaking promiscuously of such ordinary signs, which occur amongst writers. Not that they are all to be found in one man, for that were to paint a Monster or Chimæra, not a man; but some in one, some in another, and that successively or at several times.

Which I have been the more curious to express and report, not to upbraid any miserable man, or by way of derision (I rather pity them), but the better to discern, to apply remedies unto them; and to shew that the best and soundest of us all is in great danger, how much we ought to fear our own fickle estates, remember our miseries and vanities, examine and humiliate ourselves, seek to God, and call to him for mercy, that needs not look for any rods to scourge ourselves, since we carry them in our bowels, and that our souls are in a miserable captivity, if the light of grace and heavenly truth doth not shine continually upon us: and by our discretion to moderate ourselves, to be more circumspect and wary in the midst of these dangers.

MEMBER 2

SUBSECTION 1 — *Symptoms of Head-Melancholy*

IF *no symptoms appear about the stomack, nor the blood be misaffected, and fear and sorrow continue, it is to be thought the brain itself is troubled, by reason of a melancholy juice bred in it, or otherways conveyed into it, and that evil juice is from the distemperature of the part, or left after some inflammation.* Thus far Piso. But this is not always true, for blood and hypochondries both are often affected even in head-melancholy. Hercules de Saxonia differs here from the common current of Writers, putting peculiar signs of head-melancholy from the sole distemperature of spirits in the brain, as they are hot, cold, dry, moist, *all without matter, from the motion alone and tenebrosity of spirits.* Of melancholy which proceeds from humours by adustion he treats apart, with their several symptoms and cures. The common signs, if it be by essence in the head, *are ruddiness of face, high sanguine complexion, most part* with a flushed red colour, one calls it bluish, and sometimes full of pimples, with red eyes. (Avicenna, Duretus and others out of Galen.) Hercules de Saxonia to this of redness of face adds *heaviness of the head, fixed and hollow eyes. If it proceed from dryness of the brain, then their heads will be light, vertiginous, and they most apt to wake, & to continue whole months together without sleep. Few excrements in their eyes and nostrils, & often bald by reason of excess of dryness,* Montaltus adds. If it proceed from moisture, dullness, drowsiness, headache follows; and, as Sallust. Salvianus, out of his own experience found, they are epileptical, with a multitude of humours in the head. They are very bashful if ruddy, apt to blush, and to be red upon all occasions, especially if any fear troubles them. But the chiefest symptom to discern this species, as I have said, is this, that there be no notable signs in the stomach, hypochondries, or elsewhere, *digna,* as Montaltus terms them, or of greater note, because oftentimes the passions of the stomack concur with them. Wind is common to all three species, and is not excluded, only that of the *hypochondries is more windy* than the rest, saith Hollerius. Aetius maintains the same, if there be more signs, and more evident in the head than elsewhere, the brain is primarily affected, and prescribes head-melancholy to be cured by meats (amongst the rest) void of wind, and good juice, not excluding wind, or corrupt blood, even in head-melancholy itself: but these species are often confounded, and so are their symptoms, as I have already proved. The symptoms of the mind are superfluous and continual cogitations: *for, when the head is heated, it scorcheth the blood, and from thence proceed melancholy fumes, which trouble the mind, Avicenna.* They are very cholerick, and soon hot, solitary, sad, often silent, watchful, discontent, *Montaltus.* If any thing trouble them, they cannot sleep, but fret themselves still, till another object mitigate, or time wear it out. They have grievous passions, and immoderate perturbations of the mind, fear, sorrow, &c. yet not so continuate but that they are sometimes merry, apt to profuse laughter, which is more to be wondered at, and that by the authority of Galen himself, by reason of mixture of blood; if they be ruddy, they are delighted in jests, and oftentimes scoffers themselves, conceited, and, as Rodericus à Vega comments on that place of Galen, merry, witty, of a pleasant disposition, and yet grievously melancholy anon after. They learn everything without a teacher, saith Aretæus: and, as Laurentius supposeth, those feral passions and symptoms of such as think themselves glass, pitchers, feathers, &c. speak strange languages, proceed (if it be in excess), from the brain's distempered heat.

SUBSECTION 2 — *Symptoms of Windy Hypochondriacal Melancholy*

IN *this hypochondriacal or flatuous melancholy the symptoms are so ambiguous,* saith Crato in a counsel of his for a Noblewoman, *that the most exquisite physicians cannot determine of the part affected.* Matthew Flaccius, consulted about a Noble matron, confessed as much, that in this malady he with Hollerius, Fracastorius, Fallopius, and others, being to give their sentence of a party labouring of hypochondriacal melancholy, could not find out by the symptoms which part was most especially affected; some said the womb, some heart, some stomack, &c. and therefore Crato boldly avers that, in this diversity of symptoms which commonly accompany this disease, *no physician can truly say what part is affected.* Galen reckons up these ordinary symptoms, which all the Neotericks repeat, out of Diocles; only this fault he finds with him, that he puts not *fear* and *sorrow* amongst the other signs. Trincavellius excuseth Diocles, because that oftentimes in a strong head and constitution, a generous spirit, and a valiant, these symptoms appear not, by reason of his valour and courage. Hercules de Saxonia (to whom I subscribe) is of the same mind (which I have before touched) that *fear* and *sorrow* are not general symptoms; some fear and are not sad; some are sad and fear not; some neither fear nor grieve. The rest are these, beside fear and sorrow, *sharp belchings, fulsome crudities, heat in the bowels, wind and rumbling in the guts, vehement gripings, pain in the belly and stomack sometimes, after meat that is hard of concoction, much watering of the stomack, and moist spittle, cold sweat, unseasonable sweat all over the body,* as Octavius Horatianus calls it: *cold joints, indigestion, they cannot endure their own fulsome belchings, continual wind about their hypochondries, heat & griping in their bowels, midriff and bowels are pulled up, the veins about their eyes look red, and swell from vapours & wind.* Their ears sing now & then, *vertigo* & giddiness come by fits, turbulent dreams, dryness, leanness; apt they are to sweat upon all occasions, of all colours and complexions. Many of them are high-coloured, especially after meals, which symptom Cardinal Cæsius was much troubled with, & of which he complained to Prosper Calenus his Physician, he could not eat, or drink a cup of wine, but he was as red in the face as if he had been at a Mayor's Feast. That symptom alone vexeth many. Some again are black, pale, ruddy, sometimes their shoulders and shoulder-blades ache, there is a leaping all over their bodies, sudden trembling, a palpitation of the heart, and that grief in the mouth of the stomack, which maketh the patient think his heart itself acheth, and sometimes suffocation, short breath, hard wind, strong pulse, swooning. Montanus, Trincavellius, Fernelius, Frambesarius, Hildesheim, Claudinus, &c. give instance of every particular. The peculiar symptoms, which properly belong to each part, be these. If it proceed from the stomack, saith Savanarola, 'tis full of pain, wind. Guianerius adds *vertigo, nausea,* much spitting, &c. If from the myrach,* a swelling and wind in the hypochondries, a loathing, and appetite to vomit, pulling upward. If from the heart, aching and trembling of it, much heaviness. If from the liver, there is usually a pain in the right hypochondry. If from the spleen, hardness and grief in the left hypochondry, a rumbling, much appetite and small digestion, Avicenna. If from the meseraick veins and liver on the other side, little or no appetite, Herc. de Saxonia. If from the hypochondries, a rumbling inflation, concoction is hindered, often belching, &c. And from these crudities windy vapours ascend up to the brain, which trouble the imagination, and cause fear, sorrow, dullness, heaviness, many terrible conceits and chimæras, as Lemnius well observes; *as a black and thick Cloud covers the Sun, and intercepts his beams and light, so doth this melancholy vapour obnubilate the mind, enforce it to many absurd thoughts and imaginations,* and compel good, wise, honest, discreet men (arising to the brain from the lower parts, *as smoke out of a chimney*) to dote, speak and do that which becomes not them, their persons, callings, wisdoms. One, by reason of those ascending vapours and gripings rumbling beneath, will not be persuaded but that he hath a serpent in his guts, a viper; another frogs. Trallianus relates a story of a woman, that imagined she had swallowed an eel or a serpent: and Felix Platerus hath a most memorable example of a countryman of his, that, by chance falling into a pit where frogs and frogs' spawn was, and a little of that water swallowed, began to suspect that he had likewise swallowed frogs' spawn, and with that conceit and fear his phantasy wrought so far, that he verily thought he had young live frogs in his belly, that lived by his nourishment, and was so certainly

* The Arabian medical term for the epigastrium or pit of the stomach.

persuaded of it, that for many years following he could not be rectified
in his conceit: he studied Physick seven years together to cure himself,
travelled into Italy, France, and Germany, to confer with the best Physicians about it, and, in the year 1609, asked his counsel amongst the
rest; he told him it was wind, his conceit, &c. but he pertinaciously contradicted, and strove to prove his case by words and writings: no saying
would serve: it was no wind, but real frogs: *and do you not hear them
croak?* Platerus would have deceived him by putting live frogs into
his excrements: but he, being a Physician himself, would not be deceived, a wise and learned man otherwise, a Doctor of Physick, and
after seven years' dotage in this kind, he was cured of his phantasy.
Laurentius and Goulart have many such examples, if you be desirous
to read them. One commodity, above the rest which are melancholy,
these windy flatuous have, lucid intervals, their symptoms and pains
are not usually so continuate as the rest, but come by fits, fear and
sorrow and the rest: yet in another they exceed all others; and that is,
they are luxurious, incontinent, and prone to Venery, by reason of wind,
& fall easily in love, & are generally not very particular who the woman
is, (Jason Pratensis). Rhasis is of opinion, that Venus doth many of
them much good; the other symptoms of the mind be common with
the rest.

SUBSECTION 3 — *Symptoms of Melancholy abounding in the Whole
Body*

THEIR bodies, that are affected with this universal melancholy, are most
part black, *the melancholy juice is redundant all over,* hirsute they are,
and lean, they have broad veins, their blood is gross and thick. *Their
spleen is weak,* and liver apt to engender the humour; they have kept
bad diet, or have had some evacuation stopped, as hæmrods, or months
in women, which Trallianus, in the cure, would have carefully to be in-
quired, and withal to observe of what complexion the party is of, black
or red. For, as Forestus and Hollerius contend, if they be black, it proceeds from abundance of natural melancholy; if it proceeds from cares,
agony, discontents, diet, exercise, &c. they may be as well of any other
colour, red, yellow, pale, as black, & yet their whole body corrupt, (saith
Montaltus). The best way to discern this species is to let them bleed;
if the blood be corrupt, thick and black, and they withal free from those
hypochondriacal symptoms, & not so grievously troubled with them or
those of the head, it argues they are melancholy from the whole body.
The fumes which arise from this corrupt blood disturb the mind, and

make them fearful and sorrowful, heavy-hearted, as the rest, rejected, discontented, solitary, silent, weary of their lives, dull and heavy, or merry, &c. and, if far gone, that which Apuleius wished to his enemy, by way of imprecation, is true in them; *dead men's bones, hobgoblins, ghosts, are ever in their minds, and meet them still in every turn: all the bugbears of the night and terrors, fairybabes of tombs and graves are before their eyes and in their thoughts, as to women and children, if they be in the dark alone.* If they hear, or read, or see, any tragical object, it sticks by them; they are afraid of death, and yet weary of their lives; in their discontented humours they quarrel with all the world, bitterly inveigh, tax satirically, and because they cannot otherwise vent their passions, or redress what is amiss, as they mean, they will by violent death at last be revenged on themselves.

SUBSECTION 4 — *Symptoms of Maids', Nuns', and Widows' Melancholy*

BECAUSE Lodovicus Mercatus, in his second book, and Rodericus à Castro, two famous Physicians in Spain (Daniel Sennertus of Wittenberg, with others,) have vouchsafed, in their works not long since published, to write two just treatises on the Melancholy of Maids, Nuns, and Widows, as a peculiar species of Melancholy (which I have already specified) distinct from the rest, (for it much differs from that which commonly befalls men and other women, as having only one cause proper to women alone), I may not omit, in this general survey of melancholy symptoms, to set down the particular signs of such parties so misaffected.

The causes are assigned out of Hippocrates, Cleopatra, Moschion, and those old gynecological writers, of this feral malady, in more ancient Maids, Widows, and barren Women, saith Mercatus, by reason of the midriff or *diaphragma,* heart and brain offended with those vicious vapours which come from menstruous blood; Rodericus adds an inflammation of the back, which with the rest is offended by that fuliginous exhalation of corrupt seed, troubling the brain, heart, and mind; the brain I say, not in essence, but by consent; a fallen uterus & spoilt menstrual blood are general causes, for, in a word, the whole malady proceeds from that inflammation, putridity, black smoky vapours, &c., from thence comes care, sorrow, and anxiety, obfuscation of spirits, agony, desperation, and the like, which are intended or remitted, from any amatory propensity, or any other violent object or perturbation of mind. This melancholy may happen to Widows, with much care and sorrow, as frequently it doth, by reason of a sudden alteration of their accustomed course of life, &c. To such as lie in childbed, by lack of stooling; but to Nuns and more ancient Maids, and some barren women, for the causes abovesaid, 'tis more familiar, it happens to these more frequently than to the rest, saith Rodericus, the rest are not altogether excluded.

Out of these causes Rodericus defines it, with Aretæus, to be a vexation of the mind, a sudden sorrow from a small, light, or no occasion, with a kind of still dotage and grief of some part or other, head, heart, breasts, sides, back, belly, &c. with much solitariness, weeping, distraction, &c. from which they are sometimes suddenly delivered, because it comes and goes by fits, and is not so permanent as other melancholy.

But, to leave this brief description, the most ordinary symptoms be these, a beating about the back, which is almost perpetual, the skin is many times rough, squalid, especially, as Aretæus observes, about the arms, knees, and knuckles. The midriff and heartstrings do burn and beat fearfully, and when this vapour or fume is stirred, flieth upward, the heart itself beats, is sore grieved, & faints, the gullet is dry and stopped up, so that it is difficult to distinguish between this & uterine suffocation, like fits of the mother; scant stools, for the most, & bilous, yellow, acid urine. They complain many times, saith Mercatus, of a great pain in their heads, about their hearts, and hypochondries, and so likewise in their breasts, which are often sore; sometimes ready to swoon, their faces are inflamed, and red, they are dry, thirsty, suddenly hot, much troubled with wind, cannot sleep, &c. And from hence proceed a brutish kind of dotage, troublesome sleep, terrible dreams in the night, a foolish kind of bashfulness to some, perverse conceits and opinions, dejection of mind, much discontent, preposterous judgement. They are apt to loath, dislike, disdain, to be weary of every object, &c. each thing almost is tedious to them, they pine away, void of counsel, apt to weep and tremble, timorous, fearful, sad, and out of all hope of better fortunes. They take delight in nothing for the time, but love to be alone and solitary, though that do them more harm. And thus they are affected so long as this vapour lasteth; but by and by as pleasant and merry as ever they were in their lives, they sing, discourse, and laugh, in any good company, upon all occasions; and so by fits it takes them now and then, except the malady be inveterate, and then 'tis more frequent, vehement, and continuate. Many of them cannot tell how to express themselves in words, or how it holds them, what ails them, you cannot understand them, or well tell what to make of their sayings; so far gone sometimes, so stupefied and distracted, they think themselves bewitched, they are in despair, & ready to weep. Mercatus therefore adds. now their breasts, how their hypochondries, belly and sides, then their heart and head aches; now heat, then wind, now this, now that offends, they are weary of all; and yet will not, cannot again tell how, where, or what offends them, though they be in great pain, agony, and frequently complain, grieving, sighing, weeping and discontented still, without any manifest cause, most part; yet, I say, they will complain, grudge, lament, and not be persuaded but that they are troubled with an evil spirit, which is frequent in Germany, saith Rodericus amongst the common sort, and to such as are most grievously affected; (for he makes three degrees of this disease in women); they are in despair, surely forespoken or bewitched, and in extremity of their dotage, weary of their lives, some of them will attempt to make away themselves. Some think they see visions, confer with spirits and devils, they shall surely be damned, are afraid of some treachery, imminent danger, & the like, they will not speak, make answer to any question, but are almost distracted, mad, or stupid for the time, and by fits: and thus it holds them, as they are more or less affected, and as the inner humour is intended or remitted, or by outward objects and perturbations aggravated, solitariness, idleness, &c.

Many other maladies there are incident to young women, out of that one and only cause above specified, many feral diseases. I will not so much as mention their names, melancholy alone is the subject of my present discourse, from which I will not swerve. The several cures of this infirmity, concerning diet, which must be very sparing, phlebotomy, physick, internal, external remedies, are at large in great variety in Rodericus à Castro, Sennertus, and Mercatus, which whoso will, as occasion serves, may make use of. But the best and surest remedy of all is to see them well placed, & married to good husbands in due time; hence these tears, that's the primary cause, and this the ready cure, to give them content to their desires. I write not this to patronize any wanton, idle flirt, lascivious or light housewives, which are too forward many times, unruly, and apt to cast away themselves on him that comes next, without all care, counsel, circumspection, and judgement. If religion, good discipline, honest education, wholesome exhortation, fair promises, fame, and loss of good name, cannot inhibit and deter such, (which to chaste and sober maids cannot choose but avail much), labour and exercise, strict diet, rigour, and threats, may more opportunely be used, and are able of themselves to qualify & divert an ill-disposed temperament. For seldom shall you see an hired servant, a poor handmaid, though ancient, that is kept hard to her work and bodily labour, a coarse country wench, troubled in this kind, but Noble Virgins, nice

Gentlewomen, such as are solitary and idle, live at ease, lead a life out of action and employment, that fare well, in great houses and jovial companies, ill-disposed peradventure of themselves, and not willing to make any resistance, discontented otherwise, of weak judgement, able bodies, and subject to passions; noble maids, saith Mercatus, barren women, and widows, are generally melancholy, such for the most part are misaffected, & prone to this disease. I do not so much pity them that may otherwise be eased, but those alone that out of a strong temperament, innate constitution, are violently carried away with this torrent of inward humours, and though very modest of themselves, sober, religious, virtuous, and well given, (as many so distressed maids are), yet cannot make resistance; these grievances will appear, this malady will take place, and now manifestly shews itself, and may not otherwise be helped. But where am I? Into what subject have I rushed? What have I to do with Nuns, Maids, Virgins, Widows? I am a Bachelor myself, and lead a Monastick life in a College. I am truly a very unfit person to talk about these subjects, I confess 'tis an *indecorum* and as Pallas, a Virgin, blushed, when Jupiter by chance spake of Love matters in her presence, and turned away her face, I will check myself; though my subject necessarily require it, I will say no more.

And yet I must and will say something more, add a word or two on behalf of Maids and Widows, in favour of all such distressed parties, in commiseration of their present estate. And as I cannot choose but condole their mishap that labour of this infirmity, and are destitute of help in this case, so must I needs inveigh against them that are in fault, more than manifest causes, and as bitterly tax those tyrannizing pseudo-politicians' superstitious orders, rash vows, hard-hearted parents, guardians, unnatural friends, allies, (call them how you will), those careless and stupid overseers, that, out of worldly respects, covetousness, supine negligence, their own private ends, (because, meanwhile, it is well for him), can so severely reject, stubbornly neglect, and impiously contemn, without all remorse and pity, the tears, sighs, groans, and grievous miseries, of such poor souls committed to their charge. How odious and abominable are those superstitious and rash vows of Popish Monasteries, so to bind and enforce men and women to vow virginity, to lead a single life against the laws of nature, opposite to religion, policy, and humanity, so to starve, to offer violence to, to suppress the vigour of youth! by rigorous statutes, severe laws, vain persuasions, to debar them of that to which by their innate temperature they are so furiously inclined, urgently carried, and sometimes precipitated, even irresistibly led, to the prejudice of their souls' health, and good estate of body and mind! and all for base and private respects, to maintain their gross superstition, to enrich themselves and their territories, as they falsely suppose, by hindering some marriages, that the world be not full of beggars, and their parishes pestered with orphans! Stupid politicians! ought these things so to be carried? Better marry than burn, saith the Apostle, but they are otherwise persuaded. They will by all means quench their neighbour's house, if it be on fire, but that fire of lust, which breaks out into such lamentable flames, they will not take notice of, their own bowels oftentimes, flesh and blood, shall so rage and burn, and they will not see it: it is pitiable, saith Austin, and they are miserable in the mean time, that cannot pity themselves, the common good of all, and consequently, their own estates. For let them but consider what fearful maladies, feral diseases, gross inconveniences, come to both sexes by this enforced temperance. It troubles me to think of, much more to relate, those frequent aborts & murdering of infants in their Nunneries, (read Kemnitius and others), their notorious fornications, those male-prostitutes, masturbators, strumpets, &c., those rapes, incests, adulteries, mastuprations, sodomies, buggeries, of Monks and Friars. See Bale's Visitation of Abbies, Mercurialis, Rodericus à Castro, Peter Forestus, and divers physicians. I know their ordinary apologies and excuses for these things, but let the Politicians, the Doctors, and Theologians look out: I shall more opportunely meet with them elsewhere.

Lest you should think that I do plead
Some certain maid's or widow's need,
I'll say no more.

MEMBER 3

Immediate Cause of these precedent Symptoms

To give some satisfaction to melancholy men that are troubled with these symptoms, a better means in my judgement cannot be taken than to shew them the causes whence they proceed; not from Devils, as they suppose, or that they are bewitched or forsaken of God, hear or see, &c. as many of them think, but from natural and inward causes; that so, knowing them, they may better avoid the effects, or at least endure them with more patience. The most grievous and common symptoms are fear and sorrow, and that without a cause, to the wisest and discreetest men, in this malady not to be avoided. The reason why they are so Aetius discusseth at large, in his first problem out of Galen. For Galen imputeth all to the cold that is black, and thinks that, the spirits being darkened, and the substance of the brain cloudy and dark, all the objects thereof appear terrible, and the *mind* itself, by those dark, obscure, gross fumes, ascending from black humours, is in continual darkness, fear and sorrow; divers terrible monstrous fictions in a thousand shapes & apparitions occur, with violent passions, by which the brain and phantasy are troubled and eclipsed. Fracastorius *will have cold to be the cause of fear & sorrow; for such as are cold are indisposed to mirth, dull and heavy, by nature solitary, silent; & not for any inward darkness (as Physicians think), for many melancholy men dare boldly be, continue, and walk in the dark, and delight in it:* only the cold are timid: if they be hot, they are merry, and the more hot, the more furious, and void of fear, as we see in madmen: but this reason holds not, for then no melancholy, proceeding from choler adust, should fear. Averroes scoffs at Galen for his reasons, and brings five arguments to refell them: so doth Herc. de Saxonia, assigning other causes, which are copiously censured and confuted by Ælianus Montaltus, Lod. Mercatus, Altomarus, Guianerius, Bright, Laurentius, Valesius. *Distemperature,* they conclude, *makes black juice, blackness obscures the spirits, the spirits obscured cause fear and sorrow. Laurentius* supposeth these black fumes offend especially the *diaphragma* or midriff, and so consequently, the mind, which is obscured as the Sun by a cloud. To this opinion of Galen almost all the Greeks and Arabians subscribe, the Latins new and old, as children are affrighted in the dark, so are melancholy men at all times, as having the inward cause with them, & still carrying it about. Which black vapours, whether they proceed from the black blood about the heart, as T. W. Jes.* thinks, in his Treatise of the passions of the mind, or stomack, spleen, midriff, or all the misaffected parts together, it boots not; they keep the mind in a perpetual dungeon, and oppress it with continual fears, anxieties, sorrows, &c. It is an ordinary thing for such as are sound to laugh at this dejected pusillanimity, and those other symptoms of melancholy, to make themselves merry with them, and to wonder at such, as toys and trifles, which may be resisted and withstood, if they will themselves: but let him that so wonders consider with himself that, if a man should tell him on a sudden some of his especial friends were dead, could he choose but grieve? or set him upon a steep rock, where he should be in danger to be precipitated, could he be secure? his heart would tremble for fear, and his head be giddy.

* Thomas Wright, Jesuit. See Index.

Peter Byarus gives instance (as I have said [elsewhere]) : *and put case* (saith he) *in one that walks upon a plank ; if it lie on the ground, he can safely do it, but if the same plank be laid over some deep water, instead of a bridge, he is vehemently moved, & 'tis nothing but his imagination,* the idea of falling being impressed upon him, *to which his other members and faculties obey.* Yea, but you infer that such men have a just cause to fear, a true object of fear ; so have melancholy men an inward cause, a perpetual fume and darkness, causing fear, grief, suspicion, which they carry with them ; an object which cannot be removed, but sticks as close, and is as inseparable, as a shadow to a body, and who can expel, or over-run his shadow? remove heat of the liver, a cold stomack, weak spleen : remove those adust humours and vapours arising from them, black blood from the heart, all outward perturbations ; take away the cause, and then bid them not grieve nor fear, or be heavy, dull, lumpish ; otherwise counsel can do little good ; you may as well bid him that is sick of an ague not to be adry, or him that is wounded not to feel pain.

Suspicion follows fear and sorrow at heels, arising out of the same fountain, so thinks Fracastorius, *that fear is the cause of suspicion, and still they suspect some treachery or some secret machination to be framed against them,* still they distrust. Restlessness proceeds from the same spring, variety of fumes makes them like and dislike. Solitariness, avoiding of light, that they are weary of their lives, hate the world, arise from the same causes, for their spirits and humours are opposite to light, fear makes them avoid company, and absent themselves, lest they should be misused, hissed at, or overshoot themselves, which still they suspect. They are prone to Venery by reason of wind. Angry, waspish, and fretting still, out of abundance of choler, which causeth fearful dreams, and violent perturbations to them both sleeping and waking. That they suppose they have no heads, fly, sink, they are pots, glasses, &c. is wind in their heads. Herc. de Saxonia doth ascribe this to the several motions in the animal spirits, *their dilatation, contraction, confusion, alteration, tenebrosity, hot or cold distemperature,* excluding all material humours. Fracastorius accounts it *a thing worthy of inquisition why they should entertain such false conceits, as that they have horns, great noses, that they are birds, beasts, &c.,* why they should think themselves Kings, Lords, Cardinals. For the first Fracastorius gives two reasons : *one is the disposition of the body : the other the occasion of the phantasy,* as if their eyes be purblind, their ears sing, by reason of some cold and rheum, &c. To the second Laurentius answers, the imagination, inwardly or outwardly moved, represents to the understanding, not enticements only, to favour the passion, or dislike, but a very intensive pleasure follows the passion, or displeasure, and the will and reason are captivated by delighting in it.

Why students and lovers are so often melancholy & mad, the Philosophers of Coimbra * assign this reason, *because, by a vehement & continual meditation of that wherewith they are affected, they fetch up the spirits into the brain, and with the heat brought with them they incend † it beyond measure: and the cells of the inward senses dissolve their temperature, which being dissolved, they cannot perform their offices as they ought.*

Why melancholy men are witty, which Aristotle hath long since maintained in his Problems, and why all learned men, famous Philosophers, and Law-givers, have still been melancholy, is a problem much controverted. Jason Pratensis will have it understood of natural melancholy, which opinion Melancthon inclines to, in his book On the Mind, and Marcilius Ficinus, but not simple, for that makes men stupid, heavy, dull, being cold and dry, fearful, fools, and solitary, but mixt with the other humours, phlegm only excepted; and they not adust, but so mixt, as that blood be half, with little or no adustion, that they be neither too hot nor too cold. Apponensis, cited by Melancthon, thinks it proceeds from melancholy adust, excluding all natural melancholy as too cold. Laurentius condemns his *tenent,* because adustion of humours makes men mad, as lime burns when water is cast on it. It must be mixt with blood, & somewhat adust, and so that old Aphorism of Aristotle may be verified, no excellent wit without a mixture of madness. Fracastorius shall decide the controversy; *Phlegmatick are dull: Sanguine lively, pleasant, acceptable & merry, but not witty: Cholerick are too swift in motion & furious, impatient of contemplation, deceitful wits: Melancholy men have most excellent wits, but not all; this humour may be hot or cold, thick or thin; if too hot, they are furious and mad; if too cold, dull, stupid, timorous, and sad: if temperate, excellent, rather inclining to the extreme of heat than cold.* This sentence of his will agree with that of Heraclitus, a dry light makes a wise mind; temperate heat & dryness are the chief causes of a good wit; therefore, saith Ælian, an elephant is the wisest of all brute beasts, because his brain is dryest, and because of his plentiful supply of black bile: this reason Cardan approves, Jo. Baptista Silvaticus, a Physician of Milan, in his first con-

* See Index.
† To inflame.

troversy, hath copiously handled this question, Rulandus in his Problems, Cælius Rhodiginus, Valleriola, Herc. de Saxonia, Lodovicus Mercatus, Baptista Porta, and many others.

Weeping, sighing, laughing, itching, trembling, sweating, blushing, hearing and seeing strange noises, visions, wind, crudity, are motions of the body, depending upon these precedent motions of the mind. Neither are tears affections, but actions (as Scaliger holds) : *the voice of such as are afraid trembles, because the heart is shaken.* Why they stut or falter in their speech, Mercurialis and Montaltus give like reasons out of Hippocrates, *dryness, which makes the nerves of the tongue torpid.* Fast speaking (which is a symptom of some few), Aetius will have caused *from abundance of wind, and swiftness of imagination: baldness comes from excess of dryness,* hirsuteness from a dry temperature. The cause of much waking is a dry brain, continual meditation, discontent, fears, & cares, that suffer not the mind to be at rest ; incontinency is from wind, and an hot liver. Rumbling in the guts is caused from wind, and wind from ill concoction, weakness of natural heat, or a distempered heat and cold ; palpitation of the heart from vapours ; heaviness & aching from the same cause. That the belly is hard, wind is a cause, and of that leaping in many parts. Redness of the face, & itching, as if they were flea-bitten, or stung with pismires, from a sharp subtile wind : cold sweat from vapours arising from the hypochondries, which pitch upon the skin ; leanness for want of good nourishment. Why their appetite is so great Aetius answers : cold in those inward parts, cold belly & hot liver causeth crudity ; and intention proceeds from perturbations, our soul for want of spirits cannot attend exactly to so many intentive operations ; being exhaust, & overswayed by passion, she cannot consider the reasons which may dissuade her from such affections.

Bashfulness and blushing is a passion proper to men alone, and is not only caused for some shame and ignominy, or that they are guilty unto themselves of some foul fact committed but, as Fracastorius well determines, *from fear and a conceit of our defects. The face labours and is troubled at his presence that sees our defects, & nature, willing to help, sends thither heat, heat draws the subtilest blood, & so we blush. They that are bold, arrogant, and careless, seldom or never blush, but such as are fearful.* Anthonius Lodovicus, in his book on bashfulness, will have this subtle blood to arise in the face, not so much for the reverence of our betters in presence, *but for joy and pleasure, or if anything at unawares shall pass from us, a sudden accident, occurse, or meeting,* (which Disarius in Macrobius confirms) any object heard or seen, for blind men never blush, as Dandinus observes, the night & darkness make men impudent. Or by being staid before our betters, or in company we like not, or if any thing molest and offend us, blushing turns to a continuate redness. Sometimes the extremity of the ears tingle, and are red, sometimes the whole face, even though one has done nothing wrong, as Lodovicus holds: though Aristotle is of opinion, all shame for some offence. But we find otherwise; it may as well proceed from fear, from force and inexperience, (so Dandinus holds), as vice; a hot liver, saith Duretus, *from a hot brain, from wind, the lungs heated, or after drinking of wine, strong drink, perturbations, &c.*

Laughter, what it is, saith Tully, *how caused, where, & so suddenly breaks out that, desirous to stay it, we cannot, how it comes to possess & stir our face, veins, eyes, countenance, mouth, sides, let Democritus determine.* The cause that it often affects melancholy men so much is given by Gomesius, abundance of pleasant vapours, which, in sanguine melancholy especially, break from the heart, *and tickle the midriff, because it is transverse and full of nerves: by which titillation the sense being moved, and the arteries distended, or pulled, the spirits from thence move and possess the sides, veins, countenance, eyes.* See more in Jossius, On Laughter and Weeping. Tears, as Scaliger defines, proceed from grief & pity, *or from the heating of a moist brain, for a dry cannot weep.*

That they see and hear so many phantasms, chimæras, noises, visions, &c., as Fienus hath discoursed at large in his book of imagination, & Lavater, On Spectres, their corrupt phantasy makes them see & hear that which indeed is neither heard nor seen. They that much fast, or want sleep, as melancholy or sick men commonly do, see visions, or such as are weak-sighted, very timorous by nature, mad, distracted, or earnestly seek. As the saying is, they dream of that they desire. Like Sarmiento the Spaniard, who, when he was sent to discover the Straits of Magellan, and confine places, by the Prorex * of Peru, standing on the top of an Hill, thought he looked down upon a most pleasant open country, magnificent buildings, numerous Hamlets, lofty Towers, splendid Temples, and brave Cities, built like ours in Europe, not, saith mine Author, that there was any such thing, but that he was very imaginative and too credulous, and would fain have had it so. Or, as Lod. Mercatus proves, by reason of inward vapours, and humours from blood, choler, &c. diversely mixt, they apprehend and see outwardly, as they suppose, divers images, which indeed are not. As they that drink wine think all

* Viceroy.

runs round, when it is in their own brain, so is it with these men, the fault and cause is inward, as Galen affirms, mad men and such as are near death, have in their eyes images of what they think they see, 'tis in their brain, which seems to be before them; the brain, as a concave glass, reflects solid bodies. For the aged often have such hollow & dry brains that they fancy themselves to see that which is not, (saith Bois-sardus) ; old men are too frequently mistaken & dote in like case: or as he that looketh through a piece of red glass, judgeth every thing he sees to be red; corrupt vapours mounting from the body to the head, and distilling again from thence to the eyes, when they have mingled them-selves with the watery crystal which receiveth the shadows of things to be seen, make all things appear of the same colour, which remains in the humour that overspreads our sight, as to melancholy men all is black, to phlegmatick all white, &c. Or else, as before, the organs, corrupt by a corrupt phantasy, as Lemnius well quotes, *cause a great agitation of spirits and humours, which wander to and fro in all the creeks of the brain, and cause such apparitions before their eyes.* One thinks he reads something written in the Moon, as Pythagoras is said to have done of old, another smells brimstone, hears Cerberus bark: Orestes, now mad, supposed he saw the Furies tormenting him, and his mother still ready to run upon him.

O Mother! I beg you pursue me no more
With serpentine furies that thirst for my gore.
See! see! they attack me, they compass me sore!　(EURIPIDES)

but Electra told him, thus raving in his mad fit, he saw no such sights at all, it was but his crazed imagination.

Rest, rest unhappy one; rest on thy bed;
You see but the fancies of a too-fevered head.　(EURIPIDES)

So Pentheus (in Euripides' Bacchæ) saw two Suns, two Thebes, his brain alone was troubled. Sickness is an ordinary cause of such sights. Cardan saith that diseased minds, enfeebled by distress & hunger, cause themselves to see, to hear, &c. Andrew Osiander beheld strange visions, and Alexander ab Alexandro, both in their sickness, which he relates. Albategnius, that noble Arabian, on his death bed saw a ship ascending and descending, which Fracastorius records of his friend Baptista Turrianus. Weak sight, and a vain persuasion withal, may effect as much, and second causes concurring, as an oar in water makes a refraction, and seems bigger, bended double, &c. The thickness of the air may cause such effects, or any object not well discerned in the dark, fear and phantasy will suspect to be a Ghost, a Devil, &c. What the wretched overmuch desire, they easily believe; we are apt to believe and mistake in such cases. Marcellus Donatus brings in a story out of Aristotle of one Antipheron, which likely saw, wheresoever he was, his own image in the air, as in a glass. Vitellio hath such another instance of a familiar acquaintance of his, that, after the want of three or four nights' sleep, as he was riding by a river side, saw another riding with him, and using all such gestures as he did, but when more light appeared, it vanished. Eremites and Anachorites have frequently such absurd Visions, Revelations, by reason of much fasting and bad diet, many are deceived by Legerdemain, as [Reginald] Scot hath well shewed in his Book of the Discovery of Witchcraft, and Cardan. Suffites,* perfumes, suffumigations, mixt candles, perspective glasses, and such natural causes, make men look as if they were dead, or with horse-heads, bull's-horns, and such like brutish shapes, the room full of snakes, adders, dark, light, green, red, of all colours, as you may perceive in Baptista Porta, Alexis, Albertus, and others; glow-worms, firedrakes, meteors, *Ignis fatuus,* which Plinius calls Castor and Pollux, with many such that appear in moorish grounds, about Church-yards, moist valleys, or where battles have been fought, the causes of which read in Goclenius, Velcurius, Finkius, &c. Such feats are often done to frighten children with squibs, rotten wood, &c., to make folks look as if they were dead, bigger than usual, lesser, fairer, fouler, or to appear as if standing on their heads or all on fire, or in the form of demons. Take the hairs of a black dog, &c., saith Albertus; and so 'tis ordinary to see strange uncouth sights by Catoptricks †; who knows not that, if in a dark room the light be admitted at one only little hole, and a paper or glass put upon it, the Sun shining will represent on the opposite wall all such objects as are illuminated by his rays? With concave and cylinder glasses we may reflect any shape of men, Devils, Anticks, (as Magicians most part do, to gull a silly spectator in a dark room), we will [see] ourselves, & that hanging in the air, when 'tis nothing but such an horrible image as Agrippa demonstrates, placed in another room. Roger Bacon of old is said to have represented his own image walking in the air by this art, though no such thing appear in his perspectives. But most part is in the brain that deceives them, although I may not deny but that oftentimes the Devil deludes them, takes his opportunity to suggest, and represent vain objects to melancholy men, and such as are ill affected. To these you may add the knavish impostures of Jugglers, Exorcists,

* Incense-burnings.
† Use of reflected lights, by mirrors, &c.

Mass-Priests, and Mountebanks, of whom Roger Bacon speaks, &c. They can counterfeit the voices of all birds and brute beasts almost, all tones and tunes of men, and speak within their throats, as if they spoke afar off, that they make their auditors believe they hear Spirits, and are thence much astonished and affrighted with it. Besides, those artificial devices to over-hear their confessions, like that whispering place of Gloucester with us, or like the Duke's place at Mantua in Italy, where the sound is reverberated by a concave wall; a reason of which Blancanus in his Echometria gives, and mathematically demonstrates.

So that the hearing is as frequently deluded as the sight, from the same causes almost, as he that hears bells, will make them sound what he list. *As the fool thinketh, so the bell clinketh.* Theophilus, in Galen, thought he heard musick from vapours which made his ears sound, &c. Some are deceived by Echoes, some by roaring of waters, or concaves & reverberation of air in the ground, hollow places and walls. At Cadur-cum, in Aquitaine, words & sentences are repeated by a strange Echo to the full, or whatsoever you shall play upon a musical instrument, more distinctly & louder than they are spoken at first. Some Echoes repeat a thing spoken seven times, as at Olympus in Macedonia, as Pliny relates, some twelve times, as at Charenton, a village near Paris, in France. At Delphi in Greece heretofore was a miraculous Echo, and so in many other places. Cardan hath wonderful stories of such as have been de-luded by these Echoes. Blancanus the Jesuit in his Echometria hath variety of examples, & gives his readers full satisfaction of all such sounds by way of demonstration. At Barry, an Isle in the Severn Mouth, they seem to hear a smith's forge: so at Lipari, & those sulphureous Isles, and many such like which Olaus speaks of in the Continent of Scandia, & those Northern Countries. Cardan mentioneth a woman, that still supposed she heard the Devil call her, & speaking to her, she was a painter's wife in Milan: & many such illusions & voices, which proceed most part from a corrupt imagination.

Whence it comes to pass that they prophesy, speak several languages, talk of Astronomy, & other unknown sciences to them, (of which they have been ever ignorant), I have in brief touched, only this I will here add, that Arculanus, Bodine, & some others, hold as a manifest token that such persons are possessed with the devil: so doth Hercules de Saxonia, and Apponensis, and fit only to be cured by a Priest. But Guia-nerius, Montaltus, Pomponatius of Padua, & Lemnius refer it wholly to the ill disposition of the humour, & that out of the authority of Aristotle, because such symptoms are cured by purging; & as by the striking of a flint fire is enforced, so, by the vehement motions of spirits, they do compel strange speeches to be spoken: another argument he hath from Plato's recollections, which is all out as likely as that which Marsilius Ficinus speaks of his friend Pierleonus; by a divine kind of infusion he understood the secrets of nature, & tenents of Grecian and Barbarian Philosophers, before ever he heard of, saw, or read their works: but in this I should rather hold with Avicenna and his associates, that such symptoms proceed from evil Spirits, which take all opportunities of humours decayed, or otherwise, to pervert the soul of man; and besides, the humour itself is the Devil's Bath, and, as Agrippa proves, doth entice him to seize upon them.

SECTION 4   MEMBER 1

Prognosticks of Melancholy

PROGNOSTICKS, or signs of things to come, are either good or bad. If this malady be not hereditary, and taken at the beginning, there is good hope of cure, saith Avicenna. That which is with laughter of all others is most secure, gentle, and remiss, Hercules de Saxonia. *If that evacuation of hæmrods, or varices which they call the water between the skin, shall happen to a melancholy man, his misery is ended* (Hippocrates). Galen confirms the same; and to this Aphorism of Hippocrates all the Arabians, new and old Latins, subscribe; Montaltus, Hercules de Saxonia, Mercurialis, Vittorius, Faventinus, &c. Sckenkius illustrates this Aphorism with an example of one Daniel Federer, a Coppersmith, that was long melancholy, and in the end mad about the 27th year of his age; these *varices* or water began to arise in his thighs, and he was freed from his madness. Marius the Roman was so cured, some say, though with great pain. Sckenkius hath some other instances of women that have been helped by flowing of their months, which before were stopped. That the opening of hæmrods will do as much for men, all Physicians jointly signify, so they be voluntary, some say, and not by compulsion. All melancholy men are better after a quartan; Jobertus saith, scarce any man hath that ague twice: but whether it free him from this malady, 'tis a question; for many Physicians ascribe all along agues for especial causes, and a quartan ague amongst the rest. *When melancholy gets out at the superficies of the skin, or settles, breaking out in scabs, leprosy, morphew, or is purged by stools, or by the urine, or that the spleen is enlarged, and those varices appear, the disease is dissolved.* Guianerius adds dropsy, jaundice, dysentery, leprosy, as good signs, to these scabs, morphews, and breaking out, and proves it, out of the 6th of Hippocrates' Aphorisms.

Evil prognosticks on the other part. If melancholy be inveterate, it is incurable, a common axiom, or, as they say that make the best, hardly cured. This Galen witnesseth: *be it in whom it will, or from what cause soever, it is ever long, wayward, tedious, and hard to be cured, if once it be habituated.* As Lucian said of the gout, she was *the Queen of diseases, and inexorable,* may we say of melancholy. Yet Paracelsus will have all diseases whatsoever curable, & laughs at them which think otherwise, as T. Erastus objects to him; although in another place he accounts hereditary diseases incurable, & by no art to be removed. Hildesheim holds it less dangerous if only *imagination be hurt, and not reason; the gentlest is from blood, worse from choler adust, but the worst of all from melancholy putrefied.* Bruel esteems hypochondriacal least dangerous, and the other two species (opposite to Galen) hardest to be cured. The cure is hard in man, but much more difficult in women. And both men and women must take notice of that saying of Montanus: *this malady doth commonly accompany them to their grave; Physicians may ease, & it may lie hid for a time, but they cannot quite cure it, but it will return again more violent & sharp than at first, and that upon every small occasion or error:* as in Mercury's weather-beaten statue, that was once all over gilt, the open parts were clean, yet there was in the chinks a remnant of gold: there will be some reliques of melancholy left in the purest bodies (if once tainted) not so easily to be rooted out. Oftentimes it degenerates into Epilepsy, Apoplexy, Convulsions, and Blindness; by the authority of Hippocrates and Galen, all aver, if once it possess the ventricles of the brain; Frambesarius, & Sallust. Salvianus adds, if it get into the optick nerves, blindness. Mercurialis had a woman to his patient, that from melancholy became epileptick and blind. If it come from a cold cause, or so continue cold, or increase, Epilepsy, Convulsions follow, and Blindness, or else in the end they are moped, sottish, and in all their actions, speeches, gestures, ridiculous. If it come from an hot cause, they are more furious, & boisterous, and in conclusion often mad. If it heat and increase, that is the common event, he is mad by fits, or altogether. For, as Sennertus contends out of Crato, there is in this humour, the very seeds of fire. If it come from melancholy natural adust, and in excess, they are often dæmoniacal, Montanus.

Seldom this malady procures death, except (which is the greatest, most grievous calamity, and the misery of all miseries) they make away themselves, which is a frequent thing, & familiar amongst them. 'Tis Hippocrates' observation, Galen's sentence, — although they fear death, yet they generally commit suicide, the doom of all Physicians. 'Tis Rabbi Moses' Aphorism, the prognosticon of Avicenna, Rhasis, Aetius, Gordonius, Valescus, Altomarus, Sallust. Salvianus, Capivaccius, Mercatus, Hercules de Saxonia, Piso, Bruel, Fuchsius, all, &c.

> *And so far forth death's terror doth affright,*
> *He makes away himself, and hates the light:*
> *To make an end of fear and grief of heart,*
> *He voluntary dies to ease his smart.*   (LUCRETIUS)

In such sort doth the torture and extremity of his misery torment him, that he can take no pleasure in his life, but is in a manner enforced to offer violence unto himself, to be freed from his present insufferable pains. So some (saith Fracastorius) *in fury, but most in despair, sorrow, fear, and out of the anguish and vexation of their souls, offer violence to themselves: for their life is unhappy and miserable. They can take no rest in the night, nor sleep, or, if they do slumber, fearful dreams astonish them.* In the day time they are affrighted still by some terrible object, and torn in pieces with suspicion, fear, sorrow, discontents, cares, shame, anguish, &c. as so many wild horses, that they cannot be quiet an hour, a minute of time, but even against their wills they are intent, and still thinking of it, they cannot forget it, it grinds their souls day and night, they are perpetually tormented, a burden to themselves, as Job was, they can neither eat, drink or sleep. Their soul abhorreth all meat, and they are brought to death's door, being bound in misery and iron: they curse their stars with Job, and day of their birth, and wish for death: for, as Pineda and most interpreters hold, Job was even melancholy to despair, and almost madness itself; they murmur many times against the world, friends, allies, all mankind, even against God himself in the bitterness of their passion, live they will not, die they cannot. And in the midst of these squalid, ugly, and such irksome days, they seek at last, finding no comfort, no remedy, in this wretched life, to be eased of all by death. All creatures seek the best, and for their good as they hope, in shew at least, either because they think it fine to die (saith Hippocrates), or to be freed as they wish. Though many times, as Æsop's fishes, they leap from the frying-pan into the fire itself, yet they hope to be eased by this means; and therefore, saith Felix Platerus, *after many tedious days, at last, either by drowning, hanging, or some such fearful end*, they precipitate or make away themselves: *many lamentable examples are daily seen amongst us:* One hung himself before his

mistress' door, (as Seneca notes), another threw himself from the house-
top, to avoid his master's anger; a third, to escape return to exile
plunged a dagger into his heart, so many causes there are — love, grief,
anger, madness, and shame, &c. 'Tis a common calamity, a fatal end to
this disease, they are condemned to a violent death by a Jury of Physicians, furiously disposed, carried head-long by their tyrannizing wills,
enforced by miseries, and there remains no more to such persons, if that
heavenly Physician, by his assisting grace and mercy alone, do not prevent, (for no human persuasion or art can help), but to be their own
butchers, and execute themselves. Socrates his hemlock, Lucretia's dagger, Timon's halter, are yet to be had; Cato's knife and Nero's sword are
left behind them, as so many fatal engines, bequeathed to posterity, and
will be used to the world's end by such distressed souls: so intolerable,
unsufferable, grievous, and violent, is their pain, so unspeakable, and
continuate. One day of grief is an hundred years, as Cardan observes:
'tis man's torment, as well saith Aretæus, a plague of the soul, the cramp
and convulsion of the soul, an epitome of hell; and if there be an hell
upon earth, it is to be found in a melancholy man's heart.

> For that deep torture may be call'd an hell,
> When more is felt than one hath power to tell.

Yea, that which scoffing Lucian said of the gout in jest, I may truly
affirm of melancholy in earnest.

> O sad and odious name! a name so fell,
> Is this of melancholy, brat of hell,
> There born in hellish darkness doth it dwell.
> The Furies brought it up, Megœra's teat,
> Alecto gave it bitter milk to eat.
> And all conspired a bane to mortal men,
> To bring this devil out of that black den.
> Jupiter's thunderbolt, nor storm at sea,
> Nor whirl-wind, doth our hearts so much dismay.
> What? am I bit by that fierce Cerberus?
> Or stung by serpent so pestiferous?
> Or put on shirt that's dipt in Nessus' blood?
> My pain's past cure; Physick can do no good.

No torture of body like unto it! The tyrants of Sicily have contrived no
greater torture, no strappadoes, hot irons, Phalaris' bulls,*

> Jove's wrath nor Devil's can
> Do so much harm to th' soul of man.   (SILIUS ITALICUS)

* Phalaris of Sicily burnt men alive in a brazen bull.

All fears, griefs, suspicions, discontents, imbonities, insuavities, are swallowed up & drowned in this Euripus, this Irish Sea, this Ocean of misery, as so many small brooks; 'tis a collection of all griefs: which Ammianus applied to his distressed Palladius. I say of our melancholy man, he is the cream of human adversity, the quintessence, & upshot; all other diseases whatsoever are but flea-bitings to melancholy in extent: 'tis the pith of them all,

> *What need more words? 'tis calamity's Inn,*
> *Where seek for any mischief, 'tis within;*   (PLAUTUS)

and a melancholy man is that true Prometheus, which is bound to Caucasus; the true Tityus, whose bowels are still by a vulture devoured, (as Poets feign), for so doth Lilius Geraldus interpret it, of anxieties, and those griping cares, and so ought it to be understood. In all other maladies we seek for help; if a leg or an arm ache, through any distemperature or wound, or that we have an ordinary disease, above all things whatsoever we desire help & health, a present recovery, if by any means possible it may be procured: we will freely part with all our other fortunes, substance, endure any misery, drink bitter potions, swallow those distasteful pills, suffer our joints to be seared, to be cut off, any thing for future health; so sweet, so dear, so precious above all other things in this world is life: 'tis that we chiefly desire, long and happy days, *Grant us many years, O Jupiter!* increase of years all men wish; but to a melancholy man nothing so tedious, nothing so odious; that which they so carefully seek to preserve he abhors, he alone. So intolerable are his pains, some make a question whether the diseases of the body or mind be more grievous, but there is no comparison, no doubt to be made of it, the diseases of the mind are far more grievous. — Body and soul is misaffected here, but the soul especially. So Cardan testifies; Maximus Tyrius, a Platonist, and Plutarch have made just volumes to prove it. Time removeth grief from men; in other diseases there is some hope likely, but these unhappy men are born to misery, past all hope of recovery, incurably sick, the longer they live the worse they are, and death alone must ease them.

Another doubt is made by some Philosophers, whether it be lawful for a man, in such extremity of pain & grief, to make away with himself, and how these men that so do are to be censured. The Platonists approve of it, that it is lawful in such cases, & upon a necessity. Plotinus, and Socrates himself defends it, in Plato's Phædo; if any man labour of an incurable disease, he may despatch himself, if it be to his good. Epicurus & his followers, the Cynicks & Stoicks, in general affirm it, Epictetus &

Seneca among the rest, any way is allowable that leads to liberty, let us give God thanks, that no man is compelled to live against his will: what terrors have prisons and bonds and bars for him? His way out is clear, death is always ready and at hand. Dost thou see that steep place, that river, that pit, that tree? there's liberty at hand, means of escape from slavery and sorrow, as that Laconian lad cast himself headlong (*I'll be no slave,* said he), to be freed of his misery. Every vein in thy body, if these be too difficult ends, will set thee free; what is to your best advantage, to make or to accept the end? there's no necessity for a man to live in misery. It is wrong to live under constraint; but no man is compelled to live under constraint. He is a coward who dies without due cause, & a fool who lives merely to brave out this pain. Wherefore hath our Mother the Earth brought forth poisons, saith Pliny, in so great a quantity, but that men in distress might make away themselves? which Kings of old had ever in readiness, against uncertainties of fortune, Livy writes, and executioners always at hand. Speusippus being sick was met by Diogenes, and carried on his slave's shoulders, he made his moan to the Philosopher: *But I pity thee not,* quoth Diogenes, *thou mayest be freed when thou wilt,* — meaning by death. Seneca therefore commends Cato, Dido, and Lucretia, for their generous courage in so doing, & others that voluntarily die, to avoid a greater mischief, to free themselves from misery, to save their honour, or vindicate their good name, as Cleopatra did, as Sophonisba, Syphax' wife did, Hannibal did, as Junius Brutus, as Vibius Virius, & those Campanian Senators in Livy that poisoned themselves to escape the Roman tyranny. Themistocles drank bull's blood, rather than he would fight against his country, and Demosthenes chose rather to drink poison, Publius Crassus, Censorius, and Plancus, those heroical Romans, to make away themselves, than to fall into their enemies' hands. How many myriads besides in all ages might I remember, who, though guiltless, took death in their own hands, &c. Razis in the Maccabees is magnified for it, Samson's death approved. So did Saul and Jonas sin, and many worthy men and women, whose memory is famous in the Church, saith Leminchus, for killing themselves to save their Chastity and Honour, when Rome was taken, as Austin instances. Jerome vindicateth the same, and Ambrose commendeth Pelagia for so doing. Eusebius admires a Roman Matron for the same fact to save herself from the lust of Maxentius the Tyrant. Adelhelmus, Abbot of Malmesbury, calls them blessed Virgins who died so. Titus Pomponius Atticus, that wise, discreet, renowned Roman Senator, Tully's dear friend, when he had been long sick, as he supposed of an incurable disease, hopeless, was resolved voluntarily by famine to despatch himself, to be rid of his pain, and when as Agrippa, and the rest of his weeping friends, earnestly besought him, not to offer violence to himself, *with a settled resolution he desired again they would approve of his good intent, & not seek to dehort him from it:* and so constantly died. Even so did Corellius Rufus, another grave Senator, by the relation of Pliny the Younger, famish himself to death; for that he suffered the most incredible & cruel tortures from gout, he refused all nourishment; neither he nor Hispulla his wife could divert him, but grew more and more inflexible in his resolve, die he would, and die he did. So did Lycurgus, Aristotle, Zeno, Chrysippus, Empedocles, with myriads, &c. In wars for a man to run rashly upon imminent danger, and present death, is accounted valour & magnanimity, to be the cause of his own, & many a thousand's ruin besides, to commit wilful murder in a manner of himself & others, is a glorious thing, and he shall be crowned for it. The Massagetæ in former times, Derbiccians, and I know not what nations besides, did stifle their old men after 70 years, to free them from grievances incident to that age. So did the inhabitants of the Island of Choa; because their air was pure and good, and the people generally long lived, before they became infirm and imbecile, with poppy or hemlock they prevented * death. Sir Thomas More in his Utopia commends voluntary death, if he be troublesome to himself or others, (*especially if to live be a torment to him*), *let him free himself with his own hands from this tedious life, as from a prison, or suffer himself to be freed by others.* And 'tis the same tenent which Laertius relates of Zeno of old, the wise man is right to put an end to himself, if so be he is twisted by violent pain, or is mutilated, or have incurable disease, & which Plato approves, if old age, poverty, ignominy, &c. oppress, and which Fabius expresseth in effect, no one need long be miserable except through his own fault. It is an ordinary thing in China, (saith Matt. Riccius, the Jesuit), *if they be in despair of better fortunes, or tired & tortured with misery, to bereave themselves of life, & many times, to spite their enemies the more, to hang at their door.* Tacitus the Historian, Plutarch the Philosopher, much approve a voluntary departure, and Austin defends a violent death, so that it be undertaken in a good cause: no man thus afflicted but has at some time desired to die, &c, no man so voluntarily dies, but will he, nill he, he must die at last, & our life is subject to innumerable casualties, who knows when they may happen? rather suffer one death than fear all. *Death is better than a bitter life,* and a harder choice to

* Anticipated.

live in fear than by once dying to be freed from all. Cleombrotus Ambraciotes persuaded I know not how many hundreds of his auditors, by
a luculent oration he made of the miseries of this & happiness of that
other life, to precipitate themselves: and, having read Plato's divine
tract On the Soul, for example's sake led the way first. That neat Epigram of Callimachus will tell you as much;

> *Farewell, O Sun! the Ambracian cried,*
> *Then cast him in the Stygian pool and died;*
> *Tho' free from crime, with naught to hide,* —
> *He'd followed Plato's book as guide.*

Calenus and his Indians hated of old to die a natural death: the Circum-
cellions and Donatists, loathing life, compelled others to make them
away, with many such: but these are false and Pagan positions, profane
Stoical Paradoxes, wicked examples, it boots not what Heathen Philosophers determine in this kind, they are impious, abominable, and
upon a wrong ground. *No evil is to be done that good may come of it;*
God and all good men are against it. He that stabs another can kill his
body, but he that stabs himself kills his own soul. He that gives a beggar
an alms (as that Comical Poet said) doth ill, because he doth but prolong his miseries. But Lactantius calls it a detestable opinion, and fully
confutes it, and S. Austin: so doth Hierome to Marcella of Blæsilla's
death, I admit none such, &c., he calls such men martyrs to a foolish
philosophy, so doth Cyprian, false martyrs, those who thus would die,
either weaklings, or vain, or madness drives them: 'tis mere madness
so to do, dying to escape death, is folly. To this effect writes Aristotle,
Lipsius, but it needs no confutation. This only let me add that in some
cases those hard censures of such as offer violence to their own persons,
or in some desperate fit to others, which sometimes they do, by stabbing,
slashing, &c. are to be mitigated, as in such as are mad, beside themselves
for the time, or found to have been long melancholy, and that in extremity; they know not what they do, deprived of reason, judgement, all,
as a ship that is void of a pilot must needs impinge upon the next rock
or sands, and suffer shipwreck. P. Forestus hath a story of two melancholy brethren, that made away themselves, and for so foul a fact were
accordingly censured to be infamously buried, as in such cases they use,
to terrify others, as it did the Milesian Virgins of old; but, upon farther
examination of their misery and madness, the censure was revoked, and
they were solemnly interred, as Saul was by David. And Seneca well
adviseth, be justly offended with him as he was a murderer, but pity him
now as a dead man. Thus of their goods and bodies we can dispose; but

what shall become of their souls, God alone can tell; His mercy may come betwixt the bridge and the brook, the knife and the throat. What happens to one may happen to any. Who knows how he may be tempted? It is his case, it may be thine. That which is his lot this day, tomorrow may be thine. We ought not to be so rash and rigorous in our censures as some are; charity will judge & hope the best; God be merciful unto us all!

THE SECOND PARTITION

Cure of melancholy is

Sect. 1. General to all, which contains
{ *or* }

Unlawful means forbidden.

Mem.
1. From the Devil, Magicians, Witches, &c., by charms, spells, incantations, images, &c.
   Quest. 1. Whether they can cure this, or other such like diseases?
   Quest. 2. Whether, if they can so cure, it be lawful to seek to them for help?
2. Immediately from God, *a Jove principium*, by prayer, &c.
3. *Quest.* 1. Whether Saints and their Reliques can help this infirmity?
   Quest. 2. Whether that be lawful in this case to sue to them for aid?

Lawful means which are
{ *or* }

4. Mediately by Nature which concerns and works by

Subsect.
1. *Physician*, in whom is required science, confidence, honesty, &c.
2. *Patient*, in whom is required obedience, constancy, willingness, patience, confidence, bounty, &c., not to practise on himself.
3. *Physick*, which consists of
   { Diætetical ♈
   Pharmaceutical ♉
   Chirurgical ♊ }

Particular to the three distinct species ♋ ♌ ♍

♈ Sect. 2. Diætetical, which consists in reforming those six non-natural things, as in

Diet rectified. 1. Memb.

Matter and quality. 1. Subs.
{ *or* }

Such meats as are easy of digestion, well-dressed, hot, sod, &c., young, moist, of good nourishment, &c.
Bread of pure wheat, well-baked.
Water clear from the fountain.
Wine and drink not too strong, &c.

Flesh — Mountain birds, partridge, pheasant, quails, &c. Hen, capon, mutton, veal, kid, rabbit, &c.

Fish — That live in gravelly waters, as pike, perch, trout, sea-fish, solid, white, &c.

Herbs — Borage, bugloss, balm, succory, endive, violets, in broth, not raw, &c.

Fruits — Raisins of the sun, apples corrected for wind, oranges, &c.; parsnips, potatoes, &c.

2. Quantity. — At seasonable and usual times of repast, in good order, not before the first be concocted, sparing, not overmuch of one dish.

2. Rectification of Retention and Evacuation, as costiveness, Venery, bleeding at nose, months stopped, baths, &c.

3. Air rectified, with a digression of the air. — Naturally in the choice and site of our country, dwelling-place to be hot and moist, light, wholesome, pleasant, &c. Artificially, by often change of air, avoiding winds, fogs, tempests, opening windows, perfumes, &c.

4. Exercise. — Of body and mind, but moderate, as hawking, hunting, riding, shooting, bowling, fishing, fowling, walking in fair fields, galleries, tennis, bar. Of mind, as chess, cards, tables, &c., to see plays, masques, &c.; serious studies, business, all honest recreations.

5. Rectification of waking and terrible dreams, &c.
6. Rectifications of passions and perturbations of the mind.

Memb. 6.
Passions and perturbations of the mind rectified.

From himself

Subsect.
1. By using all good means of help, confessing to a friend, &c.
   Avoiding all occasions of his infirmity.
   Not giving way to passions, but resisting to his utmost.
2. By fair and foul means, counsel, comfort, good persuasion, witty
   devices, fictions, and, if it be possible, to satisfy his mind.
3. Musick of all sorts aptly applied.
4. Mirth, and merry company.

or

from his friends.

Sect. 3.
A consolatory digression, containing remedies to all discontents and passions of the mind.

Memb.
1. General discontents and grievances satisfied.
2. Particular discontents, as deformity of body, sickness, baseness of birth, &c.
3. Poverty and want, such calamities and adversities.
4. Against servitude, loss of liberty, imprisonment, banishment, &c.
5. Against vain fears, sorrows for death of friends, or otherwise.
6. Against envy, livor, hatred, malice, emulation, ambition, and self-love, &c.
7. Against repulses, abuses, injuries, contempts, disgraces, contumelies, slanders, and scoffs, &c.
8. Against all other grievous and ordinary symptoms of this disease of melancholy.

8
Sect. 4.
Pharmaceutics, or Physick which cureth with medicines, with a digression of this kind of Physick, is either
Memb. 1.
Subsect. 1.

General to all

Alterative

Simples altering melancholy, with a digression of exotick simples.
2. Subs.

Herbs
3. Subs.

To the heart; borage, bugloss, scorzonera, &c.
To the head; balm, hops, nenuphar, &c.
Liver; eupatory, artemisia, &c.
Stomack; wormwood, centaury, penny-royal.
Spleen; ceterach, ash, tamarisk.
To purify the blood; endive, succory, &c.
Against wind; origan, fennel, aniseed, &c.

4. Precious stones, as smaragdes, chelidonies, &c. Minerals, as gold, &c.

or

or

Compounds altering melancholy, with a digression of compounds.
1. Subs.

Inwardly taken

Liquid

Fluid

Wines; as of hellebore, bugloss, tamarisk, &c.
Syrups of borage, bugloss, hops, epithyme, endive, succory, &c.

or

consisting.

Conserves of violets, maidenhair, borage, bugloss, roses, &c.
Confections; Treacle, Mithridate Eclegms or Linctures.

or

solid, as those aromatical confections.

hot

Diambra, dianthos.
Diamargaritum calidum
Diamoschum dulce.
Electuarium de gemmis.
Lætificans Galeni et Rhasis.

or

cold

Diamargaritum frigidum.
Diarrhodon Abbatis.
Diacorotlli, diacodium, with their tables.

Condites of all sorts, &c.

Outwardly used, as

Oils of Camomile, Violets, Roses, &c.
Ointments, alabastritum, populeum, &c.
Liniments, plasters, cerotes, cataplasms, frontals, fomentations, epithymes, sacks, bags, odoraments, posies, &c.

or

Purging ☽
Particular to the three distinct Species, ♋ ♌ ♍.

℃
Medicines
purging
melancholy,
are either
Memb. 2

Simples
purging
melancholy.

1. *Subs.*
Upward,
as vomits.

Asarabacca, Laurel, white Hellebore, Scylla, or
Sea-onion, Antimony, Tobacco.

or

Down-
ward.

More gentle; as Senna, Epithyme, Polypody,
Myrobalanes, Fumitory, &c.

2. *Subs.*

Stronger; Aloes, lapis Armenus, lapis Lazuli,
black Hellebore.

or

3. *Subs.*
Com-
pounds
purging
melancholy.

Superior
parts.

Mouth

Swallowed.

Liquid; as Potions, Julips, Syrups
wine of Hellebore, bugloss, &c.
Solid; as lapis Armenus, & Lazuli,
pills of Indy, pills of Fumitory,
&c.

or

or

Electuaries, Diasena, confection
of Hamech, Hierologladium, &c.
Not swallowed; as gargarisms, masticatories, &c.

or

Nostrils, sneezing powders, odoraments, perfumes, &c.

Inferior parts, as clysters strong and weak, and suppositories of
Castilian soap, honey boiled, &c.

II. Chirurgical Physick, which
consists of *Memb.* 3.

Phlebotomy, to all parts almost, and all the distinct species.
With knife, horseleeches.
Cupping-glasses.
Cauteries, and searing with hot irons, boring.
Dropax and Sinapismus.
Issues to several parts, and upon several occasions.

♋ *Sect.* 5
Cure of head-
melancholy.
Memb. 1.

1. *Subsect.*
Moderate diet, meat of good juice, moistening, easy of digestion.
Good air.
Sleep more than ordinary.
Excrements daily to be voided by Art or Nature.
Exercise of body and mind, not too violent or too remiss, passions of the mind,
and perturbations to be avoided.

2. Blood-letting, if there be need, or that the blood be corrupt, in the arm, forehead, &c. or with cupping-glasses.

3. Prepara-
tives and
purgers.

Preparatives; as Syrup of borage, bugloss, epithyme, hops,
with their distilled waters, &c.
Purgers; as Montanus, and Matthiolus, Helleborismus, Quer-
cetanus, Syrup of Hellebore, Extract of Hellebore, Pulvis
Hali, Antimony prepared, *Rulandi aqua mirabilis;* which
are used, if gentler medicines will not take place, with
Arnoldus, *vinum buglossatum,* senna, cassia myrobalanes,
aurum potabile, or before Hamech, pil. Indæ, hiera. pil.
de lap. Armeno, Lazuli.

4. Averters.

Cardan's nettles, frictions, clysters, suppositories, sneezings,
masticatories, nasals, cupping-glasses.
To open the Hæmrods with Horseleeches, to apply Horse-
leeches to the forehead without scarification, to the shoulders, thighs.
Issues, boring, cauteries, hot irons in the suture of the crown.

5. Cordials,
resolvers,
hinderers.

A cup of wine or strong drink.
Bezoar's stone, amber, spice.
Conserves of Borage, Bugloss, Roses, Fumitory.
Confection of Alchermes.
Electuarium lætificans Galeni & Rhasis, &c.
Diamargaritum frig. Diaboraginatum, &c.

6. Correctors of accidents, as,

To procure sleep, and are

Inwardly taken,
Simples, Poppy, nymphea, lettuce, roses, purslane, henbane, mandrake, night-shade, opium, &c.
or
Com-pounds.
Liquid, as Syrups of Poppy, Verbasco, Violets, Roses.
Solid, as *requies Nicholai, Philonium Romanum, Laudanum Paracelsi.*

or

Odoraments of Roses, Violets.
Irrigations of the head, with the decoctions of nymphea, lettuce, mallows, &c.
Epithymes, ointments, bags to the heart.
Fomentations of oil for the Belly.
Baths of sweet water, in which were sod mallows, violets, roses, water-lilies, borage flowers, ramsheads, &c.

Outwardly used, as,
Oils of Nymphea, Poppy, Violets, Roses, Mandrake, Nutmegs.
Odoraments of vinegar, rose-water, opium.
Frontals of rose-cake, rose-vinegar, nutmeg.
Ointments, alabastritum, unguentum, populeum, simple, or mixt with opium.
Irrigations of the head, feet, sponges, musick, murmur and noise of waters.
Frictions of the head, and outward parts, sacculi of henbane, wormwood at his pillow, &c.

Against terrible dreams; not to sup late, or eat pease, cabbage, venison, meats heavy of digestion, use balm, hart's-tongue, &c.
Against ruddiness and blushing, inward and outward remedies.

Ω 2. *Mem.*
Cure of melancholy over the body.

Diet, preparatives, purges, averters, cordials, correctors, as before.
Phlebotomy in this kind more necessary, and more frequent.
To correct and cleanse the blood with Fumitory, Senna, Succory, Dandelion, Endive, &c.

Subsect. 1.
Phlebotomy if need require.
Diet, preparatives, averters, cordials, purgers, as before, saving that they must not be so vehement.
Use of penny-royal, wormwood, centaury sod, which alone hath cured many.
To provoke urine with aniseed, daucus, asarum, &c., and stools, if need be, by clysters and suppositories.
To respect the spleen, stomach, liver, hypochondries.
To use Treacle now and then in winter.
To vomit after meals sometimes, if it be inveterate.

℔ Cure of Hypochondriacal or windy melancholy.
3. *Mem.*

2. To expel wind.

Inwardly taken.

Simples,
Roots, Galanga, gentian, enula, angelica, calamus aromaticus, zedoary, china, condite ginger, &c.
Herbs, Penny-royal, rue, calamint, bay-leaves, and berries, scordium, bettany, lavender, camomile, centaury, wormwood, cummin, broom, orange pills.
Spices, Saffron, cinnamon, mace, nutmeg, pepper, musk, zedoary with wine, &c.
Seeds, Aniseed, fennelseed, ammi, cari, cummin, nettle, bays, parsley, grana paradisi.

or

Compounds, as
Dianisum, diagalanga, diaciminum, diacalaminthes, Electuarium de baccis lauri, benedicta laxativa, &c., pulvis carminativus, & pulvis descrip. Antidotario Florentino, aromaticum, rosatum, Mithridate.

Outwardly used, as cupping-glasses to the Hypochondries, without scarification, oil of camomile, rue, aniseed, their decoctions, &c.

THE SECOND PARTITION

The Cure of Melancholy

THE FIRST { SECTION, MEMBER, SUBSECTION

Unlawful Cures rejected

INVETERATE Melancholy, howsoever it may seem to be a continuate, inexorable disease, hard to be cured, accompanying them to their graves most part, as Montanus observes, yet many times it may be helped, even that which is most violent, or at least, according to the same Author, it may be mitigated and much eased. Never despair. It may be hard to cure, but not impossible, for him that is most grievously affected, if he be but willing to be helped.

Upon this good hope I will proceed, using the same method in the cure, which I have formerly used in the rehearsing of the causes; first *general*, then *particular*; and those according to their several species. Of these cures some be *lawful*, some again *unlawful*, which, though frequent, familiar, and often used, yet justly censured, and to be controverted. As first, whether by these diabolical means, which are commonly practised by the Devil and his Ministers, Sorcerers, Witches, Magicians, &c., by Spells, Cabalistical words, Charms, Characters, Images, Amulets, Ligatures, Philters, Incantations, &c., this disease and the like may be cured? and, if they may, whether it be lawful to make use of them, those magnetical cures, or for our good to seek after such means in any case? The first, whether they can do any such cures, is questioned amongst many writers, some affirming, some denying. Valesius, Heurnius, Cælius, Delrio, Wierus, Libanius, Lavater, Holbrenner the Lutheran, Polydore Virgil, Tandlerus, Lemnius, (Hippocrates, and Avicenna amongst the rest), deny that Spirits or Devils have any power over us, and refer all (with Pomponatius of Padua) to natural causes and humours. Of the other opinion are Bodinus, Arnoldus, Marcellus Empiricus, J. Pistorius, Paracelsus, Agrippa, Marcilius Ficinus, Galeottus, Jovianus Pontanus, Pliny, Strabo, Leo Suavius; Goclenius, Oswoldus Crollius, Ernestus Burgravius, Dr. Flud, &c.; Cardan brings many proofs out of Ars Notoria, and Solomon's decayed works, old Hermes, Artesius, Costaben Luca, Picatrix, &c., that such cures may be done. They can make fire it shall not burn, fetch back thieves or stolen goods, shew their absent faces in a glass, make serpents lie still, stanch blood, salve gouts, epilepsies, biting of mad dogs, tooth-ache, melancholy, & all the ills of the world, make men immortal, young again, as the Spanish Marquess is said to have done by one of his slaves, and some which jugglers in China maintain still (as Tragaltius writes) that they can do by their extraordinary skill in Physick, & some of our modern Chemists by their strange limbecks, by their spells, Philosopher's stones, and charms. Many doubt, saith Nicholas Taurellus, whether the Devil can cure such diseases he hath not made, and some flatly deny it: howsoever, common experience confirms to our astonishment that Magicians can work such feats, and that the Devil without impediment can penetrate through all the parts of our bodies, and cure such maladies by means to us unknown. Daneus, in his tract On Divination, subscribes to this of Taurellus; Erastus maintaineth as much, and so do most Divines, that out of their excellent knowledge and long experience they can commit wonders for the suffering, hinder the causes of things, and reach their source, they can work stupend and admirable conclusions; we see the effects only, but not the causes of them. Nothing so familiar as to hear of such cures. Sorcerers are too common; cunning men, wizards, and white-witches, as they call them, in every village, which, if they be sought unto, will help almost all infirmities of body and mind, [saviours] *servatores* in Latin, & they have commonly St. Catherine's Wheel printed in the roof of their mouth, or in some other part about them; they drive off disease by enchantment, (Boissardus writes), &c.; that to doubt of it any longer, or not to believe, were to run into that other sceptical extreme of incredulity, saith Taurellus. Leo Suavius, in his Comment upon Paracelsus, seems to make it an art, which ought to be approved: Pistorius and others stiffly maintain the use of charms, words, characters, &c. The art is true, but there be but a few that have skill in it. Marcellus Donatus proves out of Josephus' Eighth Book of Antiquities that Solomon so cured all the diseases of the mind by spells, charms, and drove away Devils, and that Eleazar did as much before Vespasian. Langius holds Jupiter Menecrates, that did so many stupend cures in his time, to have used this art, and that he was no other than a Magician. Many famous cures are daily done in this kind, the Devil is an expert Physician, as Godelman calls him, and God permits oftentimes these Witches and Magicians to produce such effects, as Lavater, Polydore Virgil, Delrio, and others, admit. Such cures may be done, and, as Paracelsus stiffly maintains, they cannot otherwise be cured but by spells, seals, and spiritual Physick. Arnoldus sets down the making of them, so doth Rulandus, and many others.

It being assumed that they can effect such cures, the main question is whether it be lawful in a desperate case to crave their help, or ask a Wizard's advice. 'Tis a common practice of some men to go first to a Witch, and then to a Physician; if one cannot, the other shall; if they cannot bend Heaven, they will try Hell. It matters not, saith Paracelsus, whether it be God or the Devil, Angels or unclean Spirits cure him, so that he be eased. If a man fall into a ditch, as he prosecutes it, what matter is it whether a friend or an enemy help him out? and if I be troubled with such a malady, what care I whether the Devil himself, or any of his Ministers, by God's permission, redeem me? He calls a Magician God's Minister and his Vicar, applying that of " Ye are Gods " profanely to them, for which he is lashed by T. Erastus; and elsewhere he encourageth his patients to have a good faith, a strong imagination, and they shall find the effects; let Divines say to the contrary what they will. He proves and contends that many diseases cannot otherwise be cured; if they be caused by incantation, they must be cured by incantation. Constantinus approves of such remedies: Bartolus the Lawyer, Peter Ærodius, Salicetus, Godefridus, with others of that sect, allow of them; so they be for the parties' good, or not at all. But these men are confuted by Remigius, Bodinus, Godelmannus, Wierus, Delrio, Erastus; all our Divines, Schoolmen, and such as write Cases of Conscience, are against it, the Scripture itself absolutely forbids it as a mortal sin; *Evil is not to be done that good may come of it.* Much better it were for such patients, that are so troubled, to endure a little misery in this life than to hazard their souls' health for ever, and, as Delrio counselleth, much better die than be so cured. Some take upon them to expel Devils by natural remedies, and magical exorcisms, which they seem to approve out of the practice of the primitive Church, as that above cited of Josephus, Eleazar, Iræneus, Tertullian, Austin. Eusebius makes mention of such, and Magick itself hath been publickly professed in some Universities, as of old in Salamanca in Spain, and Cracovia in Poland: but condemned, in 1318, by the Chancellor and

University of Paris. Our Pontifical writers retain many of these adjurations and forms of exorcisms still in the Church; besides those in Baptism used, they exorcise meats, and such as are possessed, as they hold, in Christ's name. Read Hieronymus Mengus, & Peter Tyreus, what exorcisms they prescribe, besides those ordinary means of fire, suffumigations, lights, cutting the air with swords, herbs, odours: of which Tostatus treats. You shall find many vain and frivolous superstitious forms of exorcisms among them, not to be tolerated or endured.

MEMBER 2

Lawful Cures, first from God

BEING so clearly evinced, as it is, all unlawful cures are to be refused, it remains to treat of such as are to be admitted, and those are commonly such which God hath appointed, by virtue of stones, herbs, plants, meats, &c. and the like, which are prepared and applied to our use by art and industry of Physicians, who are the dispensers of such treasures for our good, and to be honoured for necessities' sake, God's intermediate Ministers, to whom in our infirmities we are to seek for help. Yet not so that we rely too much, or wholly upon them: *From Jove is our origin;* we must first begin with prayer, and then use physick; not one without the other, but both together. To pray alone, and reject ordinary means, is to do like him in Æsop, that, when his cart was stalled, lay flat on his back, and cried aloud, Help, Hercules! but that was to little purpose, except, as his friend advised him, he make an effort himself; he whipt his horses withal, and put his shoulder to the wheel. God works by means, as Christ cured the blind man with clay and spittle. As we must pray for health of body and mind, so we must use our utmost endeavours to preserve & continue it. Some kind of Devils are not cast out but by fasting & prayer, & both necessarily required, not one without the other. For all the physick we can use, art, excellent industry, is to no purpose without calling upon God; it avails nought to promise Craterus mountains of gold to cure us: it is in vain to seek for help, run, ride, except God bless us.

> *Nor dainties force his pall'd desire,*
> *Nor chaunt of birds, nor vocal Lyre,*
>   *To him can sleep afford.*   (HORACE)
> *With house, with land, with money, and with gold,*
> *The master's fever will not be controll'd.*   (HORACE)

We must use prayer and physick both together: and so no doubt but our prayers will be available, and our physick take effect. 'Tis that Hezekiah practised, Luke the Evangelist; and which we are enjoined, not the patient only, but the Physician himself. Hippocrates, an heathen, required this in a good practitioner, and so did Galen, and in that tract of his, regarding Times and Manners, 'tis a thing which he doth inculcate, and many others. Hyperius, speaking of that happiness and good success which all Physicians desire and hope for in their cures, tells them that it is not to be expected, except with a true faith they call upon God, and teach their patients to do the like. The council of Lateran decreed they should do so; the Fathers of the Church have still advised as much. Whatsoever thou takest in hand (saith Gregory) let God be of thy counsel, consult with Him, that healeth those that are broken in heart, and bindeth up their sores. Otherwise, as the Prophet Jeremy denounced to Egypt, *In vain shalt thou use many medicines, for thou shalt have no health.* It is the same counsel which Commines, that politick Historiographer, gives to all Christian Princes, upon occasion of that unhappy overthrow of Charles, Duke of Burgundy, by means of which he was extremely melancholy, and sick to death, in so much that neither physick nor persuasion could do him any good, perceiving his preposterous error belike, adviseth all great men in such cases to pray first to God with all submission and penitency, to confess their sins, & then to use physick. The very same fault it was which the Prophet reprehends in Asa, King of Judah, that he relied more on physick than on God, and by all means would have him to amend it. And 'tis a fit caution to be observed of all other sorts of men. The Prophet David was so observant of this precept, that in his greatest misery and vexation of mind he put this rule first in practice: *When I am in heaviness, I will think on God: Comfort the soul of thy servant, for unto thee I lift up my soul:* and, *In the day of trouble will I call upon thee, for thou hearest me. Save me, O God, by thy name, &c.* And 'tis the common practice of all good men. *When their heart was humbled with heaviness, they cried to the Lord in their trouble, and he delivered them from their distress.* And they have found good success in so doing, as David confesseth, *Thou hast turned my mourning into joy, thou hast loosed my sackcloth, and girded me with gladness.* Therefore he adviseth all others to do the like, *All ye that trust in the Lord, be strong, & He shall establish your heart.* It is reported by Suidas, speaking of Hezekiah, that there was a great Book of old of King Solomon's writing, which contained medicines for all manner of diseases, and lay open still as they came into the Temple: but Hezekiah, King of Jerusalem, caused it to be taken away, because it made the people secure, to neglect their duty in calling and relying upon God, out of a confidence on those remedies. Minucius, that worthy Consul of Rome, in an oration he made to his soldiers, was much offended with them, and taxed their ignorance that in their misery called more on him than upon God. A general fault it is all over the world, and Minucius his speech concerns us all, we rely more on physick, and seek oftener to Physicians than to God himself. As much faulty are they that prescribe as they that ask, respecting wholly their gain, and trusting more to their ordinary receipts and medicines many times than to him that made them. I would wish all patients in this behalf, in the midst of their melancholy, to remember that of Siracides,* *Who feareth the Lord, it shall go well with him at the last, &c.* And: *The fear of the Lord is glory, and gladness, and rejoicing. The fear of the Lord maketh a merry heart, and giveth gladness, and joy, and long life:* and all such as prescribe physick, to begin in the name of God, as Mesue did, to imitate Lælius à Fonte Eugubinus, that in all his consultations still concludes with a prayer for the good success of his business; and to remember that of Crato, one of their predecessors, avoid covetousness, and do nothing without invocation upon God.

MEMBER 3

Whether it be lawful to seek to Saints for Aid in this Disease

THAT we must pray to God no man doubts; but whether we should pray to Saints in such cases, or whether they can do us any good, it may be lawfully controverted; whether their Images, Shrines, Reliques, consecrated things, holy water, medals, benedictions, those divine amulets, holy exorcisms, and the sign of the Cross, be available in this disease. The Papists on the one side stiffly maintain, how many melancholy, mad, dæmoniacal persons are daily cured at St. Anthony's Church in Padua, at St. Vitus' in Germany, by our Lady of Loretto in Italy, our Lady of Sichem in the Low Countries; she cures halt, lame, blind, all diseases of body and mind, and commands the Devil himself, saith Lipsius: 25,000 in a day come thither; who brought them? new news lately done, our eyes and ears are full of her cures, and who can relate

---

* The reference is to the Wisdom of Jesus the Son of Sirach, or Ecclesiasticus.

them all? They have a proper Saint almost for every peculiar infirmity; for poison, gouts, agues, Petronella: St. Romanus for such as are possessed: Valentine for the falling sickness; St. Vitus for mad men, &c. And as of old Pliny reckons up gods for all diseases, (a Sanctuary was appointed for Febris), Lilius Giraldus repeats many of her ceremonies: all affections of the mind were heretofore accounted gods; Love, & Sorrow, Virtue, Honour, Liberty, Contumely, Impudency, had their Temples; Tempests, Seasons, Crepitus Ventris, Dea Vacuna, Dea Cloacina, there was a Goddess of idleness, a Goddess of the draught, or jakes, Prema, Premunda, Priapus, bawdy Gods, and Gods for all offices. Varro reckons up 30,000 gods; Lucian makes Podagra (the Gout) a Goddess, and assigns her Priests & Ministers: and Melancholy comes not behind; for, as Austin mentioneth, there was of old Angerona Dea,* and she had her Chapel and Feasts, to whom (saith Macrobius) they did offer sacrifice yearly, that she might be pacified as well as the rest. 'Tis no new thing, you see, this of Papists; and in my judgement that old doting Lipsius might have fitter dedicated his pen, after all his labours, to this our goddess of Melancholy than to his Virgin of Hal,† and been her Chaplain, it would have becomed him better. But he, poor man, thought no harm in that which he did, and will not be persuaded but that he doth well; he hath so many patrons, and honourable precedents in the like kind, that justify as much, as eagerly, and more than he there saith of his Lady and Mistress: read but superstitious Coster and Gretser's Tract, Arcturus Fanteus, Bellarmine, Delrio, Gregorius Tolosanus, Strozius Cicogna, Tyreus, Hieronymus Mengus, and you shall find infinite examples of cures done in this kind, by holy waters, reliques, crosses, exorcisms, amulets, images, consecrated beads, &c. Barradius the Jesuit boldly gives it out, that Christ's countenance, and the Virgin Mary's would cure melancholy, if one had looked stedfastly on them. P. Morales the Spaniard, in his book confirms the same out of Carthusianus, and I know not whom, that it was a common proverb in those days for such as were troubled in mind to say, let us go to see the son of Mary, as they do now post to St. Anthony's in

---

* The goddess who releases from anguish and secret grief. Of the gods mentioned above, Crepitus Ventris would appear to be the god, if such there was outside of the pages of the comic writers, of Belly Rumblings; Dea Vacuna was the goddess of rural leisure; Dea Cloacina, of the Sewer; Prema presided over the coition of newly married pairs; and Premundia would be the goddess of the arts of the toilet, or the cleansing and beautifying of the person.

† Hal, in Brabant, near Brussels, and close to the birthplace of Lipsius, was a place of pious pilgrimage, celebrated for its miraculous image of the Virgin.

Padua, or to St. Hilary's at Poictiers in France. In a closet of that Church there is at this day St. Hilary's bed to be seen, to which they bring all the mad men in the country, and after some prayers and other ceremonies they lay them down there to sleep, and so they recover. It is an ordinary thing in those parts to send all their mad men to St. Hilary's cradle. They say the like of S. Tubery in another place. Giraldus Cambrensis tells strange stories of S. Ciricius' staff, that would cure this and all other diseases. Others say as much (as Hospinian observes) of the three Kings of Cologne; their names written in parchment, and hung about a patient's neck, with the sign of the cross, will produce like effects. Read Lipomannus, or that Golden Legend of Jacobus de Voragine, you shall have infinite stories, or those new relations of our Jesuits in Japan and China, of Mat. Riccius, Acosta, Loyola, Xaverius' life, &c. Jasper Belga, a Jesuit, cured a mad woman by hanging St. John's Gospel about her neck, and many such. Holy water did as much in Japan, &c. Nothing so familiar in their works, as such examples.

But we, on the other side, seek to God alone. We say with David, *God is our hope and strength, and help in trouble, ready to be found.* For their catalogue of examples, we make no other answer but that they are false fictions, or diabolical illusions, counterfeit miracles. We cannot deny but that it is an ordinary thing, on St. Anthony's day in Padua, to bring divers mad men and dæmoniacal persons to be cured: yet we make a doubt whether such parties be so affected indeed, but prepared by their Priests by certain ointments and drams, to cozen the commonalty, as Hildesheim well saith. The like is commonly practised in Bohemia, as Mathiolus gives us to understand in his preface to his comment upon Dioscorides. But we need not run so far for examples in this kind, we have a just volume published at home to this purpose: A Declaration of egregious Popish Impostures, to withdraw the hearts of religious men under pretence of casting out of Devils, practised by Father Edmunds, alias Weston, a Jesuit, and divers Romish Priests, his wicked associates, with the several parties' names, confessions, examinations, &c. which were pretended to be possessed. But these are ordinary tricks only to get opinion and money, mere impostures. Æsculapius of old, that counterfeit God, did as many famous cures; his temple (as Strabo relates) was daily full of patients, and as many several tables, inscriptions, pendants, donaries, &c. to be seen in his Church, as at this day at our Lady of Loretto's in Italy. It was a custom long since,

> *To hang up mariners' drenched garments in*
> *Great Neptune's temple.* (HORACE)

To do the like, in former times, they were seduced and deluded as they are now. 'Tis the same Devil still, called heretofore Apollo, Mars, Neptune, Venus, Æsculapius, &c. as Lactantius observes. The same Jupiter and those bad Angels are now worshipped and adored by the name of S. Sebastian, Barbara, &c., Christopher and George are come in their places. Our Lady succeeds Venus, as they use her in many offices; the rest are otherwise supplied, as Lavater writes, and so they are deluded. And God often winks at these impostures, because they forsake His Word, & betake themselves to the Devil, as they do that seek after Holy Water, Crosses, &c., saith Wierus. What can these men plead for themselves more than those heathen Gods? the same cures done by both, the same spirit that seduceth: but read more of the Pagan Gods' effects in Austin, and of Æsculapius especially in Cicogna; or put case they could help, why should we rather seek to them than to Christ himself, since that he so kindly invites us unto him, *Come unto me all ye that are heavy laden, & I will ease you,* and we know that there is one God, *one Mediator betwixt God and man, Jesus Christ, who gave himself a ransom for all men. We know that we have an Advocate with the Father, Jesus Christ,* that there is *no other name under heaven, by which we can be saved, but by his,* who is always ready to hear us, and sits at the right hand of God, and from whom we can have no repulse; we are all as one to him, he cares for us all as one, and why should we then seek to any other but to him?

MEMBER 4

SUBSECTION 1 — *Physician, Patient, Physick*

OF those diverse gifts which, our Apostle Paul saith, God hath bestowed on man, this of Physick is not the least, but most necessary, and especially conducing to the good of mankind. Next therefore to God in all our extremities, (*for of the Most High cometh healing,*) we must seek to, and rely upon the Physician, who is the Hand of God, saith Hierophilus, and to whom he hath given knowledge, that he might be glorified in his wondrous works. *With such doth he heal men, and taketh away their pains. When thou hast need of him, let him not go from thee. The hour may come that their enterprises may have good success.* It is not therefore to be doubted that, if we seek a Physician as we ought, we may be eased of our infirmities, such a one I mean as is sufficient, and worthily so called; for there be many Mountebanks, Quacksalvers, Empiricks, in every street almost, and in every village, that take upon them this name, make this noble and profitable Art to be evil spoken of, and contemned, by reason of these base and illiterate Artificers: but such a Physician I speak of as is approved, learned, skilful, honest, &c. of whose duty Wecker, Crato, Julius Alexandrinus, Heurnius, &c., treat at large. For this particular disease, him that shall take upon him to cure it, Paracelsus will have to be a Magician, a Chemist, a Philosopher, an Astrologer; Thurnesserus, Severinus the Dane, and some other of his followers, require as much: many of them cannot be cured but by Magick. Paracelsus is so stiff for those chemical medicines that in his cures he will admit almost of no other Physick, deriding in the mean time Hippocrates, Galen, and all their followers. But Magick, and all such remedies, I have already censured, & shall speak of Chemistry elsewhere. Astrology is required by many famous Physicians, by Ficinus, Crato, Fernelius, doubted of and exploded by others. I will not take upon me to decide the controversy myself; Johannes Hossurtus, Thomas Boderius, and Maginus in the Preface to his Mathematical Physick, shall determine for me. Many Physicians explode Astrology in Physick, (saith he), there is no use of it, an ill-advised art followed by those ignorant ones who are on the look-out for fame, but I will reprove Physicians by Physicians that defend and profess it, Hippocrates, Galen, Avicenna, &c., that count them butchers without it. Paracelsus goes farther, and will have his Physician predestinated to this man's cure, this man's malady, and time of cure, the scheme of each geniture inspected, gathering of herbs, of administering, Astrologically observed; in which Thurnesserus and some iatromathematical * professors are too superstitious in my judgment: Hellebore will help, but not always, not given by every Physician, &c. But these men are too peremptory and self-conceited, as I think. But what do I do, interposing in that which is beyond my reach? A blind man cannot judge of colours, nor I peradventure of these things. Only thus much I would require, honesty in every Physician, that he be not over-careless or covetous, Harpy-like to make a prey of his patient; to extract their fees (as Wecker notes) these scoundrels resort to horrible tortures, as an hungry Chirurgeon often produces and wire-draws his cure, so long as there is any hope of pay:

> *The leech will hang on still,*
> *Till he hath sucked his fill.* (HORACE)

* Medical-mathematical

Many of them, to get a fee, will give Physick to every one that comes, when there is no cause, and they do so, as Heurnius complains, stir up a silent disease, as it often falleth out, which by good counsel, good advice alone, might have been happily composed, or by rectification of those six non-natural things otherwise cured. This is to oppugn nature, & to make a strong body weak. Arnoldus, in his 8th & 11th Aphorisms, gives cautions against, and expressly forbiddeth it: A wise Physician will not give Physick but upon necessity, & first try medicinal diet, before he proceed to medicinal cure. In another place he laughs those men to scorn, that think they can purge phantastical imaginations & the Devil by Physick. Another caution is, that they proceed upon good grounds, if so be there be need of Physick, & not mistake the disease. They are often deceived by the similitude of symptoms, saith Heurnius; and I could give instance in many consultations, wherein they have prescribed opposite Physick. Sometimes they go too perfunctorily to work, in not prescribing a just course of Physick. To stir up the humour, and not to purge it, doth often more harm than good. Montanus, inveighs against such perturbations, that purge to the halves, tire nature, and molest the body to no purpose. 'Tis a crabbed humour to purge, and, as Laurentius calls this disease, the reproach of Physicians; Bessardus, their lash; and for that cause more carefully to be respected. Though the patient be averse, saith Laurentius, desire help, and refuse it again, though he neglect his own health, it behoves a good Physician not to leave him helpless. But most part they offend in that other extreme, they prescribe too much Physick, and tire out their bodies with continual potions, to no purpose. Aëtius will have them by all means therefore to give some respite to nature, to leave off now and then; and Lælius à Fonte Eugubinus, in his consultations, found it (as he there witnesseth) often verified by experience, that, after a deal of Physick to no purpose, left to themselves, they have recovered. 'Tis that which Nic. Piso, Donatus Altomarus, still inculcate, to give nature rest.

SUBSECTION 2 — *Concerning the Patient*

WHEN these precedent cautions are accurately kept, and that we have now got a skilful, an honest Physician to our mind, if his patient will not be conformable, and content to be ruled by him, all his endeavours will come to no good end. Many things are necessarily to be observed and continued on the patient's behalf. First that he be not too niggardly miserable of his purse, or think it too much he bestows upon himself, and to save charges endanger his health. The Abderites, when they sent for Hippocrates, promised him what reward he would, all the gold they had; if all the City were gold, he should have it. Naaman the Syrian, when he went into Israel to Elisha to be cured of his leprosy, took with him ten talents of silver, six thousand pieces of gold, and ten changes of raiments. Another thing is, that he do not out of bashfulness conceal his grief; if ought trouble his mind, let him freely disclose it.

False shame makes fools their uncured sores to hide. (HORACE)

By that means he procures to himself much mischief, and runs into a greater inconvenience: he must be willing to be cured, and earnestly desire it. 'Tis a part of his cure to wish his own health, and not to defer it too long.

He that by cherishing a mischief doth provoke,
Too late at last refuseth to cast off his yoke. (SENECA)
When the skin swells, to seek it to appease
With hellebore is vain; meet your disease. (PERSIUS)

By this means many times, or through their ignorance in not taking notice of their grievance and danger of it, contempt, supine negligence, extenuation, wretchedness, and peevishness, they undo themselves. The Citizens, I know not of what City now, when rumour was brought their enemies were coming, could not abide to hear it; and when the plague begins in many places, and they certainly know it, they command silence and hush it up, but after they see their foes now marching to their gates, and ready to surprise them, they begin to fortify, and resist when 'tis too late; when the sickness breaks out, and can be no longer concealed, then they lament their supine negligence: 'tis no otherwise with these men. And often out of prejudice, a loathing, and distaste of Physick, they had rather die, or do worse, than take any of it. Barbarous immanity (Melancthon terms it) & folly to be deplored, so to contemn the precepts of health, good remedies, & voluntarily to pull death, & many maladies, upon their own heads. Though many again are in that other extreme, too profuse, suspicious, and jealous of their health, too apt to take Physick on every small occasion, to aggravate every slender passion, imperfection, impediment: if their finger do but ache, run, ride, send for a Physician, as many Gentlewomen do, that are sick without a cause, even when they will themselves, upon every toy or small discontent, and when he comes, they make it worse than it is, by amplifying that which is not. Hieronymus Capivaccius sets it down as a common fault of all melancholy persons, to say their symptoms are greater than they are, to help themselves; and, which Mercurialis notes, to be more troublesome to their Physicians than other ordinary patients, that they may have change of Physick.

A third thing to be required in a patient is confidence, to be of good cheer, and have sure hope that his Physician can help him. Damascen, the Arabian, requires likewise in the Physician himself, that he be confident he can cure him, otherwise his Physick will not be effectual, and promise withal that he will certainly help him, make him believe so at least. Galeottus gives this reason, because the form of health is contained in the Physician's mind, and, as Galen holds, confidence and hope do more good than Physick; he cures most in whom most are confident. Axiochus, sick almost to death, at the very sight of Socrates recovered his former health. Paracelsus assigned it for an only cause why Hippocrates was so fortunate in his cures, not for any extraordinary skill he had, but because the common people had a most strong conceit of his worth. To this of confidence we may add perseverance, obedience, and constancy, not to change his Physician, or dislike him upon every toy; for he that so doth, (saith Janus Damascen), or consults with many, falls into many errors; or that useth many medicines. It was a chief caveat of Seneca to his friend Lucilius, that he should not alter his Physician, or prescribed Physick: nothing hinders health more; a wound can never be cured that hath several plasters. Crato taxeth all melancholy persons of this fault: 'tis proper to them, if things fall not out to their mind, and that they have not present ease, to seek another and another, (as they do commonly that have sore eyes), twenty, one after another, and they still promise all to cure them, try a thousand remedies; and by this means they increase their malady, make it most dangerous and difficile to be cured. They try many (saith Montanus) and profit by none; & for this cause he enjoins his patient, before he take him in hand: perseverance & sufferance, for in such a small time no great matter can be effected, & upon that condition he will administer Physick, otherwise all his endeavour & counsel would be to small purpose. And, in his 31st counsel for a notable Matron, he tells her, if she will be cured, she must be of a most abiding patience, faithful obedience, and singular perseverance; if she remit or despair, she can expect or hope for no good success. Counsel 230, for an Italian Abbot, he makes it one of the greatest reasons why this disease is so incurable, because the parties are so restless and impatient, and will therefore have him that intends to be eased to take Physick not for a month, a year, but to apply himself to their prescriptions all the days of his life. Last of all, it is required that the patient be not too bold to practise upon himself, without an approved Physician's consent, or to try conclusions, if he read a receipt in a book; for so many grossly mistake, and do them-

selves more harm than good. That which is conducing to one man, in
one case, the same time is opposite to another. An Ass and a Mule went
over a brook, the one laden with salt, the other with wool: the Mule's
pack was wet by chance, the salt melted, his burden the lighter, and
he thereby much eased: he told the Ass, who, thinking to speed as well,
wet his pack likewise at the next water, but it was much the heavier,
he quite tired. So one thing may be good and bad to several parties,
upon diverse occasions. Many things (saith Penottus) are written in
our Books, which seem to the Reader to be excellent remedies, but they
that make use of them are often deceived, and take for Physick
poison. I remember, in Valleriola's observations, a story of one John
Baptist, a Neapolitan, that, finding by chance a pamphlet in Italian
written in praise of hellebore, would needs adventure on himself, and
took one dram for one scruple, and, had not he been sent for, the poor
fellow had poisoned himself. From whence he concludes, out of Da-
mascenus, that, without exquisite knowledge, to work out of books is
most dangerous: how unsavoury a thing it is to believe writers, and
take upon trust, as this patient perceived by his own peril. I could recite
such another example of mine own knowledge of a friend of mine, that,
finding a receipt in Brassivola, would needs take hellebore in substance,
and try it on his own person; but, had not some of his familiars come
to visit him by chance, he had by his indiscretion hazarded himself.
Many such I have observed. These are those ordinary cautions, which
I should think fit to be noted, and he that shall keep them, as Montanus
saith, shall surely be much eased, if not thoroughly cured.

Subsection 3 — *Concerning Physick*

Physick itself in the last place is to be considered; " for the Lord hath
created medicines of the earth, and he that is wise will not abhor them;
of such doth the Apothecary make a confection," &c. Of these medicines
there be divers and infinite kinds, Plants, Metals, Animals, &c., and
those of several natures; some good for one, hurtful to another, some
noxious in themselves, corrected by art, very wholesome and good,
simples, mixt, &c. and therefore left to be managed by discreet and
skillful Physicians, and thence applied to man's use. To this purpose
they have invented method, and several rules of art, to put these remedies in order, for their particular ends. Physick (as Hippocrates defines
it) is naught else but addition and subtraction; and, as it is required in
all other diseases, so in this of melancholy it ought to be most accurate,
it being (as Mercurialis acknowledgeth) so common an affection in these

our times, and therefore fit to be understood. Several prescripts and methods I find in several men; some take upon them to cure all maladies with one Medicine severally applyed, as that Panacea, Potable Gold,* so much controverted in these days, the Sun-dew, &c. Paracelsus reduceth all diseases to four principal heads, to whom Severinus, Ravelascus, Leo Suavius, and others, adhere and imitate: those are Leprosy, Gout, Dropsy, Falling-sickness: to which they reduce the rest; as to *Leprosy*, Ulcers, Itches, Furfurs, Scabs, &c., to *Gout*, Stone, Cholick, Tooth-ache, Head-ache, &c., to *Dropsy*, Agues, Jaundice, Cachexia, &c. To the *Falling-sickness* belong Palsy, Vertigo, Cramps, Convulsions, Incubus, Apoplexy, &c. If any of these four principal be cured (saith Ravelascus) all the inferior are cured, and the same remedies commonly serve: but this is too general, and by some contradicted. For this peculiar disease of Melancholy, of which I am now to speak, I find several cures, several methods and prescripts. They that intend the practick cure of Melancholy, saith Duretus in his notes to Hollerius, set down nine peculiar scopes or ends; Savanarola prescribes seven especial canons. Ælianus Montaltus, Faventinus in his Empiricks, Hercules de Saxonia, &c., have their several injunctions & rules, all tending to one end. The ordinary is threefold, which I mean to follow, *Diatetica*, *Pharmaceutica*, and *Chirurgica*, Diet or Living, Apothecary, Chirurgery [Surgery], which Wecker, Crato, Guianerius, &c. and most prescribe; of which I will insist, and speak in their order.

SECTION 2 MEMBER 1

SUBSECTION I — *Diet rectified in Substance*

DIET, Diatetica, Victus, or Living, according to Fuchsius and others, comprehend those six non-natural things, which I have before specified, are especial causes, and, being rectified, a sole or chief part of the cure. Johannes Arculanus, on Rhasis, accounts the rectifying of these six a sufficient cure. Guianerius calls them the principal cure: so doth Montanus, Crato, Mercurialis, Altomarus, &c., first to be tried; Lemnius names them the hinges of our health, no hope of recovery without them. Reinerus Solenander, in his seventh consultation for a Spanish young

---

* *Aurum potabile*, drinkable gold, which the alchemists pretended to be able to make, and much esteemed as a medicine. Sometimes it was a rich cordial with pieces of gold-leaf floating in it; again it is described by seventeenth century writers as a blood-red, gummy, or honey-like substance.

Gentlewoman, that was so melancholy she abhorred all company, and would not sit at table with her familiar friends, prescribes this Physick above the rest, no good to be done without it. Aretæus, an old Physician, is of opinion, that this is enough of itself, if the party be not too far gone in sickness. Crato, in a consultation of his for a Noble patient, tells him plainly, that, if his Highness will keep but a good diet, he will warrant him his former health. Montanus, for a Noble-man of France, admonisheth his Lordship to be most circumspect in his diet, or else all his other Physick will be to small purpose. The same injunction I find verbatim in J. Cæsar Claudinus, Scoltzius, & Trallianus, Lælius à Fonte Eugubinus often brags that he hath done more cures in this kind by rectification of Diet than all other Physick besides. So that, in a word, I may say to most melancholy men, as the Fox said to the Weasel that could not get out of the garner, When you are lank again, seek the narrow chink where, when lank, you entered; the six non-natural things caused it, and they must cure it. Which, howsoever I treat of, as proper to the Meridian of Melancholy, yet nevertheless that which is here said with him in Tully, though writ especially for the good of his friends at Tarentus & Sicily, yet it will generally serve most other diseases, and help them likewise, if it be observed.

Of these six non-natural things the first is Diet, properly so called, which consists in meat and drink, in which we must consider substance, quantity, quality, and that opposite to the precedent. In substance, such meats are generally commended which are moist, easy of digestion, and not apt to engender wind, not fried, not roasted, but sod, (saith Valescus, Altomarus, Piso, &c.) hot and moist, and of good nourishment; Crato admits roast meat, if the burned and scorched outside, the brown we call it, be pared off. Salvianus cries out on cold and dry meats; young flesh and tender is approved, as of Kid, Rabbits, Chickens, Veal, Mutton, Capons, Hens, Partridge, Pheasant, Quails, and all mountain birds, which are so familiar in some parts of Africa, and in Italy, and, as Dublinius reports, the common food of Boors and Clowns in Palestine. Galen takes exception at Mutton, but without question he means that rammy Mutton which is in Turkey and Asia Minor, which have those great fleshy tails of 48 pound weight, as Vertomannus witnesseth. The lean of fat meat is best, and all manner of broths, and pottage, with borage, lettuce, and such wholesome herbs, are excellent good, specially of a Cock boiled; all spoon meat. Arabians commend brains, but Laurentius excepts against them, and so do many others. Eggs are justified as a nutritive wholesome meat, Butter and Oil may pass, but with some limitation; so Crato confines it, and to some men sparingly at set times, or in sauce, & so sugar & honey are approved. All sharp and sour sauces must be avoided, and spices, or at least seldom used: and so saffron sometimes in broth may be tolerated; but these things may be more freely used, as the temperature of the party is hot or cold, or as he shall find inconvenience by them. The thinnest, whitest, smallest Wine is best, not thick, nor strong; and so of Beer, the middling is the fittest. Bread of good wheat, pure, well purged from the bran, is preferred; Laurentius would have it kneaded with rain water, if it may be gotten.

Pure, thin, light water by all means use, of good smell and taste, like to the air in sight, such as is soon hot, soon cold, and which Hippocrates so much approves, if at least it may be had. Rain water is purest, so that it fall not down in great drops, and be used forthwith, for it quickly putrefies. Next to it fountain water that riseth in the East, and runneth Eastward, from a quick running spring, from flinty, chalky, gravelly grounds: & the longer a river runneth, it is commonly the purest, though many springs do yield the best water at their fountains. The waters in hotter Countries, as in Turkey, Persia, India, within the Tropicks, are frequently purer than ours in the North, more subtile, thin, and lighter (as our Merchants observe) by four ounces in a pound, pleasanter to drink, as good as our Beer, and some of them, as Choaspes in Persia, preferred by the Persian Kings before Wine itself.

Those who at Clitor's fountain thirst remove,
Loathe wine, and abstinent, mere water love. (OVID)

Many rivers, I deny not, are muddy still, white, thick. like those in China, Nile in Egypt, Tiber at Rome, but after they be settled two or three days, defecate and clear, very commodious, useful and good. Many make use of deep wells, as of old in the Holy Land, lakes, cisterns, when they cannot be better provided; to fetch it in carts or gondolas, as in Venice, or Camels' backs, as at Cairo in Egypt; Radzivilius observed 8,000 Camels daily there, employed about that business. Some keep it in Trunks, as in the East Indies, made four-square with descending steps, and 'tis not amiss: for I would not have any one so nice as that Grecian Calis, sister to Nicephorus, Emperor of Constantinople, and married to Dominicus Silvius, Duke of Venice, that, out of incredible wantonness, would use no vulgar water; but she died (saith mine author) of so fulsome a disease, that no water could wash her clean. Plato would not have a traveller lodge in a City, that is not governed by laws, or hath not a quick stream running by it; one corrupts the body. the other the mind. But this is more than needs, too much curiosity is naught, in time of necessity any water is allowed. Howsoever pure water is best, and which (as Pindar holds) is better than gold; an especial ornament it is, and very commodious to a City (according to Vegetius) when fresh springs are included within the walls, as at Corinth, in the midst of the town almost, there was a goodly mount full of freshwater springs: if nature afford them not, they must be had by art. It is a wonder to read of those stupend Aqueducts; and infinite cost hath been bestowed in Rome of old, Constantinople, Carthage, Alexandria, and such populous Cities, to convey good and wholesome waters: read Frontinus, Lipsius, Plinius, Strabo in his Geography. That Aqueduct of Claudius was most eminent, fetched upon arches 15 miles, every arch 109 foot high: they had 14 such other Aqueducts, besides lakes and cisterns, 700, as I take it; every house had private pipes & channels to serve them for their use. Peter Gillius, in his accurate description of Constantinople, speaks of an old cistern which he went down to see, 336 foot long, 180 foot broad, built of marble, covered over with archwork, and sustained by 336 pillars, twelve foot asunder, and in 11 rows, to contain sweet water. Infinite cost in channels and cisterns, from the Nile to Alexandria, hath been formerly bestowed, to the admiration of these times; their cisterns so curiously cemented and composed, that a beholder would take them to be all of one stone: when the foundation is laid, and cistern made, their house is half built. That Segovian Aqueduct in Spain is much wondered at in these days, upon three rows of pillars, one above another, conveying sweet water to every house: but each City almost is full of such Aqueducts. Amongst the rest [Sir Hugh Middleton,] he is eternally to be commended, that brought that new stream to the North side of London at his own charge: and Mr. Otho Nicholson, founder of our Water-works and elegant Conduit in Oxford. So much have all times attributed to this element, to be conveniently provided of it. Although Galen hath taken exceptions at such waters which run through leaden pipes, for that unctuous ceruse [white lead], which causeth dysenteries and fluxes; yet, as Alsarius Crucius of Genoa well answers, it is opposite to common experience. If that were true, most of our Italian cities, Montpelier in France, with infinite others, would find this inconvenience, but there is no such matter. For private families, in what sort they should furnish themselves, let them consult with P. Crescentius, Pamphilus Hirelacus, and the rest.

Amongst fishes, those are most allowed of that live in gravelly or sandy waters, Pikes, Perch, Trout, Gudgeon, Smelts, Flounders, &c. Hippolytus Salvianus takes exception at Carp, but I dare boldly say, with Dubravius, it is an excellent meat, if it come not from muddy pools, that it retain not an unsavoury taste. The Sea-hedgehog is much commended by Oribasius, Aëtius, and most of our late writers.

Crato censures all manner of fruits, as subject to putrefaction, yet tolerable at some times; after meals, at second course, they keep down vapours, & have their use. Sweet fruits are best, as sweet Cherries, Plums, sweet Apples, Pear-mains, and Pippins, which Laurentius extols, as having a peculiar property against this disease, and Plater magnifies; they are agreeable to all, but they must be corrected for their windiness; ripe Grapes are good, and Raisins of the Sun, Musk-melons well corrected, and sparingly used. Figs are allowed, and Almonds blanched. Trallianus discommends Figs, Salvianus Olives and Capers, which others especially like of, and so of pistick [pistachio] nuts. Montanus and Mercurialis, out of Avenzoar, admit Peaches, Pears, and Apples baked, after meals, only corrected with sugar and aniseed or fennel-seed, and so they may be profitably taken, because they strengthen the stomack, and keep down vapours. The like may be said of preserved Cherries, Plums, Marmelade of Plums, Quinces, &c. but not to drink after them. Pomegranates, Lemons, Oranges, are tolerated, if they be not too sharp.

Crato will admit of no herbs, but Borage, Bugloss, Endive, Fennel, Aniseed, Balm; Calenus and Arnoldus tolerate Lettuce, Spinage, Beets, &c. The same Crato will allow no roots at all to be eaten. Some approve of Potatoes, Parsnips, but all corrected for wind. No raw sallets *; but, as Laurentius prescribes, in broths; and so Crato commends many of them: or to use Borage, Hops, Balm, steeped in their ordinary drink. Avenzoar magnifies the juice of a Pomegranate, if it be sweet, and especially Rose-water, which he would have to be used in every dish, which they put in practice in those hot countries about Damascus, where (if we may believe the relations of Vertomannus) many hogsheads of Rose-water are to be sold in the market at once, it is in so great request with them.

Subsection 2 — *Diet rectified in Quantity*

MAN alone, saith Cardan, eats and drinks without appetite, and useth all his pleasure without necessity, owing to his vicious mind, and thence come many inconveniences unto him. For there is no meat whatsoever, though otherwise wholesome and good, but, if unseasonably taken, or immoderately used, more than the stomack can well bear, it will in-

* Salads.

gender crudity, and do much harm. Therefore Crato adviseth his patient
to eat but twice a day, and that at his set meals, by no means to eat
without an appetite, or upon a full stomack, and to put seven hours difference betwixt dinner and supper. Which rule if we did observe in our
Colleges, it would be much better for our healths. But custom, that
tyrant, so prevails, that, contrary to all good order and rules of Physick,
we scarce admit of five. If, after seven hours' tarrying, he shall have no
stomack, let him defer his meal, or eat very little at his ordinary time
of repast. This very counsel was given by Prosper Calenus to Cardinal
Cæsius, labouring of this disease; and Platerus prescribes it to a patient
of his, to be most severely kept. Guianerius admits of three meals a day,
but Montanus ties him precisely to two. And, as he must not eat overmuch, so he may not absolutely fast; for, as Celsus contends, repletion
and inanition may both do harm in two contrary extremes. Moreover
that which he doth eat must be well chewed, and not hastily gobbled,
for that causeth crudity and wind; and by all means to eat no more than
he can well digest. Some think (saith Trincavellius) the more they eat
the more they nourish themselves: eat and live, as the proverb is; not
knowing that only repairs man which is well concocted,* not that which
is devoured. Melancholy men most part have good appetites, but ill
digestion, and for that cause they must be sure to rise with an appetite:
and that which Socrates and Disarius, the Physicians in Macrobius, so
much require, S. Hierome enjoins Rusticus, to eat and drink no more
than will satisfy hunger and thirst. Lessius the Jesuit holds 12, 13, or
14 ounces, or in our Northern Countries 16 at most, (for all students,
weaklings, and such as lead an idle sedentary life), of meat, bread, &c.
a fit proportion for a whole day, and as much or little more of drink.
Nothing pesters the body and mind sooner than to be still fed, to eat
and ingurgitate beyond all measure, as many do: By overmuch eating
and continual feasts they stifle nature, and choke up themselves; which,
had they lived coarsely, or like galley-slaves been tied to an oar, might
have happily prolonged many fair years.

A great inconvenience comes by variety of dishes, which causeth the
precedent distemperature, than which (saith Avicenna) nothing is
worse; to feed on diversity of meats, or overmuch, Sertorius-like to
sup till daylight, and, as commonly they do in Muscovy and Iceland,
to prolong their meals all day long, or all night. Our Northern Countries
offend especially in this, and we in this Island, (as Polydore notes),
are most liberal feeders, but to our own hurt. " My boy, I hate this Per-

* Digested.

sian luxury." *Excess of meat breedeth sickness, & gluttony causeth cholerick diseases: by surfeiting many perish, but he that dieteth himself prolongeth his life.* We account it a great glory for a man to have his table daily furnished with variety of meats: but hear the Physician, he pulls thee by the ear as thou sittest, & telleth thee, that nothing can be more noxious to thy health than such variety & plenty. Temperance is a bridle of gold, & he that can use it aright is liker a God than a man: for as it will transform a beast to a man again, so it will make a man a God. To preserve thine honour, health, and to avoid therefore all those inflations, torments, obstructions, crudities, and diseases, that come by a full diet, the best way is to feed sparingly of one or two dishes at most, to have a well-governed belly, as Seneca calls it; to choose one of many, & to feed on that alone, as Crato adviseth his patient. The same counsel Prosper Calenus gives to Cardinal Cæsius, to use a moderate & simple diet: and, though his table be Jovially furnished by reason of his state & guests, yet for his own part to single out some one savoury dish and feed on it. The same is inculcated by Crato to a Noble Personage affected with this grievance, he would have his Highness to dine or sup alone, without all his honourable attendance & courtly company, with a private friend or so, a dish or two, a cup of Rhenish wine, &c. Montanus, for a Noble Matron, enjoins her one dish, and by no means to drink betwixt meals; the like, in another counsel, or not to eat till he be an hungry; which rule Berengarius * did most strictly observe, as Hilbertus, Bishop of Mans, writes in his life:

> *Until his throat was parch'd a cup he never drain'd;*
> *Unless his belly yearned, from eating he abstain'd:*

and which all temperate men do constantly keep. It is a frequent solemnity still used with us, when friends meet, to go to the ale-house or tavern, they are not sociable otherwise: and, if they visit one another's houses, they must both eat and drink. I reprehend it not moderately used, but to some men nothing can be more offensive; they had better, I speak it with Saint Ambrose, pour so much water in their shoes.

It much avails likewise to keep good order in our diet, to eat liquid things first, broths, fish, and such meats as are sooner corrupted in the stomack; harder meats of digestion must come last. Crato would have the supper less than dinner, which Cardan disallows, and that by the authority of Galen, and for four reasons he will have the supper biggest. I have read many Treatises to this purpose, I know not how it may concern some few sick men, but for my part, generally for all, I should

* A medieval theologian.

subscribe to that custom of the Romans, to make a sparing dinner, and a liberal supper; all their preparation and invitation was still at supper, no mention of dinner. Many reasons I could give, but, when all is said pro and con, Cardan's rule is best, to keep that we are accustomed unto, though it be naught; and to follow our disposition and appetite in some things is not amiss, to eat sometimes of a dish which is hurtful, if we have an extraordinary liking to it. Alexander Severus loved Hares and Apples above all other meats, as Lampridius relates in his life: one Pope Pork, another Peacock, &c. what harm came of it? I conclude, our own experience is the best Physician; that diet which is most propitious to one is often pernicious to another; such is the variety of palates, humours, and temperatures, let every man observe, and be a law unto himself. Tiberius in Tacitus did laugh at all such, that after 30 years of age would ask counsel of others concerning matters of diet; I say the same.

These few rules of diet he that keeps shall surely find great ease and speedy remedy by it. It is a wonder to relate that prodigious temperance of some Hermits, Anachorites, and Fathers of the Church. He that shall but read their lives, written by Hierom, Athanasius, &c., how abstemious Heathens have been in this kind, those Curii and Fabricii, those old Philosophers, as Pliny records, Emperors and Kings, as Nicephorus relates, of Mauritius, Louis the Pious, &c., and that admirable example of Lodovicus Cornarus, a Patrician of Venice, cannot but admire them. This have they done voluntarily, and in health; what shall these private men do that are visited with sickness, and necessarily enjoined to recover and continue their health? It is a hard thing to observe a strict diet, and he who lives by rule lives miserably, as the saying is, as good be buried, as so much debarred of his appetite; the physick is more troublesome than the disease, so he complained in the Poet, so thou thinkest: yet he that loves himself will easily endure this little misery, to avoid a greater inconvenience; choose the lesser evil, better do this than do worse. And, as Tully holds, better be a temperate old man, than a lascivious youth. 'Tis the only sweet thing, (which he adviseth), so to moderate ourselves, that we may be youthful in our old age, staid in our youth, discreet and temperate in both.

MEMBER 2

Retention and Evacuation rectified

I HAVE declared in the causes what harm costiveness hath done in procuring this disease; if it be so noxious, the opposite must needs be good, or mean at least, as indeed it is, and to this cure necessarily required; it is of the greatest possible benefit, saith Montaltus; it very much avails. Altomarus commends walking in a morning into some fair green pleasant fields, but by all means first, by art or nature, he will have these ordinary excrements evacuated. Piso calls it the benefit, help, or pleasure of the belly, for it doth much ease it. Laurentius prescribes it once a day at least: where nature is defective, art must supply, by those lenitive electuaries,* suppositories, condite prunes, turpentine, Clysters, as shall be shewed. Prosper Calenus commends Clysters in hypochondriachal melancholy, still to be used as occasion serves. Peter Cnemander, in a consultation of his for a hypochondriac, will have his patient continually loose, and to that end sets down there many forms of Potions and Clysters. Mercurialis, if this benefit come not of its own accord, prescribes Clysters in the first place: so doth Montanus, he commends turpentine to that purpose: the same he ingeminates, counsel 230, for an Italian Abbot. 'Tis very good to wash his hands & face often, to shift his clothes, to have fair linen about him, to be decently and comely attired, for nastiness defiles, and dejects any man that is so voluntarily, or compelled by want, it dulleth the spirits.

Baths are either artificial or natural, both have their special uses in this malady, and, as Alexander supposeth, yield as speedy a remedy as any other Physick whatsoever. Aëtius would have them daily used. Galen cracks how many several cures he hath performed in this kind by use of baths alone, and Rufus pills, moistening them which are otherwise dry. Rhasis makes it a principal cure to bathe and afterwards anoint with oil. Jason Pratensis, Laurentius and Montanus, set down their peculiar forms of artificial baths. Crato commends Mallows, Camomile, Violets, Borage, to be boiled in it, and sometimes fair water alone, as in his following counsel: We have good authority for bathing frequently in an abundance of soft water. So doth Fuchsius, Frisimelica.

---

* Electuaries are medicines in which the medicinal ingredients are mixt with conserve, honey or syrop; they are also called eclegms, and the word in both forms keeps the significance of something to be "licked" by the patient's tongue. Lenitive medicines are such as ease pain. Condite means candied cr preserved. Clysters are now called enemas.

Some, beside herbs, prescribe a ram's head and other things to be boiled. Fernelius will have them used 10 or 12 days together; to which he must enter fasting, and so continue in a temperate heat, & after that frictions all over the body. Lælius à Fonte Eugubinus, and Christoph. Ærerus, in a consultation of his, hold once or twice a week sufficient to bathe, the water to be warm, not hot, for fear of sweating. Felix Plater, for a melancholy Lawyer, will have lotions of the head still joined to these baths, with a lee wherein capital herbs have been boiled. Laurentius speaks of baths of milk, which I find approved by many others. And still, after bath, the body to be anointed with oil of bitter Almonds, of violets, new or fresh butter, Capon's grease, especially the back bone, and then lotions of the head, embrocations, &c. These kind of baths have been in former times much frequented, and diversely varied, & are still in general use in those Eastern Countries. The Romans had their publick Baths very sumptuous and stupend, as those of Antoninus and Dioclesian. Pliny saith there were an infinite number of them in Rome, and mightily frequented. Some bathed seven times a day, as Commodus the Emperor is reported to have done, usually twice a day, and they were after anointed with most costly ointments: rich women bathed themselves in milk, some in the milk of 500 she-asses at once. We have many ruins of such Baths found in this Island, amongst those parietines [ruins] and rubbish of old Roman Towns. Lipsius, Rosinus, Scot of Antwerp, and other Antiquaries, tell strange stories of their Baths. Gillius reckons up 155 publick Baths in Constantinople, of fair building; they are still frequented in that City by the Turks of all sorts, men and women, and all over Greece and those hot countries; to absterge [clean] belike that fulsomeness of sweat, to which they are there subject. Busbequius, in his Epistles, is very copious in describing the manner of them, how their women go covered, a maid following with a box of ointment to rub them. The richer sort have private Baths in their houses, the poorer go to the common, and are generally so curious in this behalf, that they will not eat nor drink until they have bathed, before and after meals some, and will not make water or go to stool, but they will wash their hands. Leo Afer makes mention of 100 several Baths at Fez in Africa, most sumptuous, and such as have great revenues belonging to them. Buxtorf speaks of many ceremonies amongst the Jews in this kind; they are very superstitious in their Baths, especially women.

Natural Baths are praised by some, discommended by others; but it is in a diverse respect. Marcus de Oddis, consulted about Baths, condemns them for the heat of the liver, because they dry too fast; and yet by and by, in another counsel for the same disease, he approves them, because they cleanse by reason of the sulphur, and would have their water to be drunk. Aretæus commends Alum Baths above the rest; and Mercurialis those of Lucca in that hypochondriacal passion. He would have his patient tarry there 15 days together, and drink the water of them, and to be bucketed, or have the water poured on his head. John Baptista Silvaticus commends all the Baths in Italy, and drinking of their water, whether they be Iron, Alum, Sulphur; so doth Hercules de Saxoniâ. But, in that they cause sweat, and dry so much, he confines himself to hypochondriacal melancholy alone, excepting that of the head, and the other. Trincavellius prefers those Porrectan Baths before the rest, because of the mixture of Brass, Iron, Alum; and, for a melancholy Lawyer, and in that hypochondriacal passion, the Baths of Aquaria, and the drinking of them. Frisimelica, consulted among the rest, prefers the Waters of Apona before all artificial Baths whatsoever in this disease, and would have one nine years affected with hypochondriacal passions, fly to them, as to an holy anchor. Of the same mind is Trincavellius himself there, and yet both put a hot liver in the same party for a cause, and send him to the waters of S. Helen, which are much hotter. Montanus magnifies the Chalderinian Baths, and he exhorteth to the same, but with this caution, that the liver be outwardly anointed with some coolers, that it be not overheated. But these Baths must be warily frequented by melancholy persons, or if used to such as are very cold of themselves, for as Gabelius concludes of all Dutch Baths, and especially of those of Baden, they are good for all cold diseases, naught for cholerick, hot & dry, and all infirmities proceeding of choler, inflammations of the spleen and liver. Our English Baths, as they are hot, must needs incur the same censure: but Dʳ. Turner of old, and Dʳ. Jones, have written at large of them. Of cold Baths I find little or no mention in any Physician; some speak against them. Cardan alone, out of Agathinus, commends bathing in fresh rivers, & cold waters, and adviseth all such as mean to live long to use it, for it agrees with all ages & complexions, and is most profitable for hot temperatures. As for sweating, urine, blood-letting by hæmrods, or otherwise, I shall elsewhere more opportunely speak of them.

Immoderate Venus in excess, as it is a cause, or in defect; so, moderately used, to some parties an only help, a present remedy. Peter Forestus calls it a most apposite remedy, remitting anger, and reason, that was otherwise bound. Avicenna, & Oribasius contend, out of Ruffus

& others, that many mad-men, melancholy, & labouring of the falling-sickness, have been cured by this alone. Montaltus will have it drive away sorrow, and all illusions of the brain, to purge the heart and brain from ill smokes and vapours that offend them, & if it be omitted, as Valescus supposeth, it makes the mind sad, the body dull and heavy. Many other inconveniences are reckoned up by Mercatus, and by Rodericus à Castro, in their tracts On the Melancholy of Maids & Virgins; they frequently go mad through the retention of their seed, but, as Platerus adds, when wedded they are healed; they rave single, and pine away, much discontent, but marriage mends all. Marcellus Donatus tells a story to confirm this out of Alexander Benedictus, of a maid that was mad, by reason of delayed menses; now it fell out that she, by mischance, got into a bawdy-house, where she lay with fifteen men in the course of a single night, following which was an abundant monthly flow that for many years before had entirely stopped: she departed, whenas morning had come, with a restored mind, but not without exceeding shame. But this must be warily understood, for, as Arnoldus objects: Of what benefit is coitus to Melancholy? What affinity have these two? except it be manifest that super-abundance of seed, or fulness of blood be a cause, or that Love, or an extraordinary desire of Venus, have gone before, or that, as Lod. Mercatus excepts, they be very flatuous, & have been otherwise accustomed unto it. Montaltus will not allow of moderate Venus to such as have the Gout, Palsy, Epilepsy, Melancholy, except they be very lusty, and full of blood. Lodovicus Antonius, in his chapter of Venus, forbids it utterly to all wrestlers, ditchers, labouring men, &c. Ficinus and Marsilius Cognatus put Venus one of the five mortal enemies of a student: it consumes the spirits, and weakeneth the brain. Halyabbas the Arabian, and Jason Pratensis make it the fountain of most diseases, but most pernicious to them who are cold and dry; a melancholy man must not meddle with it but in some cases. Plutarch, in his book, The Preservation of Health, accounts of it as one of the three principal signs and preservers of health, temperance in this kind; to rise with an appetite, to be ready to work, and abstain from Venery, are three most healthful things. We see their opposites how pernicious they are to mankind, as to all other creatures, they bring death, and many feral diseases: The immoderate are short-lived and seldom attain old age. Aristotle gives instance in sparrows, which are short lived because of their salacity, which is very frequent, as Scioppius, in Priapia, will better inform you. The extremes being both bad, the *medium* is to be kept, which cannot easily be determined.

Some are better able to sustain, such as are hot and moist, phlegmatick, as Hippocrates insinuateth, some strong and lusty, well fed like Hercules, Proculus the Emperor, lusty Laurence,* that woman's fancy-man, Messalina the Empress, that by Philters, and such kind of lascivious meats, use all means to enable themselves, and brag of it in the end; in truth you have seen many injured through the belly, but few slain that way, as that Spanish Caelestina merrily said: others impotent, of a cold and dry constitution, cannot sustain those gymnicks without great hurt done to their own bodies, of which number (though they be very prone to it) are melancholy men for the most part.

MEMBER 3

Air rectified. With a digression of the Air

As a long-winged Hawk, when he is first whistled off the fist, mounts aloft, and for his pleasure fetcheth many a circuit in the Air, still soaring higher and higher, till he be come to his full pitch, and in the end, when the game is sprung, comes down amain, and stoops upon a sudden: so will I, having now come at last into these ample fields of Air, wherein I may freely expatiate and exercise myself for my recreation, a while rove, wander round about the world, mount aloft to those ethereal orbs and celestial spheres, and so descend to my former elements again. In which progress I will first see whether that relation of the Friar of Oxford † be true, concerning those Northern parts under the Pole, (if I meet on the way with the Wandering Jew, Elias Artifex, or Lucian's Icaromenippus, they shall be my guides), whether there be such 4 Euripuses [straits], and a great rock of Loadstones, which may cause the needle in the Compass still to bend that way, and what should be the true cause of the variation of the Compass. Is it a magnetical rock, or the Pole-star, as Cardan will; or some other star in the Bear, as Marsilius Ficinus; or a magnetical meridian, as Maurolicus; or situated in a vein of the earth, as Agricola; or the nearness of the next Continent, as Cabeus will; or some other cause, as Scaliger, Cortesius, the Coimbrians, Peregrinus, contend; why at the Azores it looks directly North, otherwise not? In the Mediterranean or Levant (as some observe) it varies 7 degrees; by and by 12, and then 22. In the Baltick Seas, near

* Lusty Laurence was not a definite personage, but a proverbial expression for a good wencher.
† Nich. de Lynna, cited by Mercator in his map. — Burton's note.

Rasceburg in Finland, the needle runs round, if any ships come that way, though Martin Ridley write otherwise, that the needle near the Pole will hardly be forced from his direction. 'Tis fit to be enquired whether certain rules may be made of it, as 11 degrees at London; at another place 36, &c., and, that which is more prodigious, the variation varies in the same place, now taken accurately, 'tis so much after a few years quite altered from that it was: till we have better intelligence, let our Dr Gilbert, and Nicholas Cabeus the Jesuit, that have both written great volumes of this subject, satisfy these inquisitors. Whether the sea be open and navigable by the Pole Arctic, and which is the likeliest way, that of Bartison the Hollander, under the Pole itself, which for some reasons I hold best, or by Davis Strait, or Nova Zembla. Whether Hudson's discovery be true of a new found Ocean, any likelihood of Button's Bay in 50 degrees, Hubberd's Hope in 60, that of the most extreme near Sir Thomas Roe's welcome in North-west Fox, being that the sea ebbs and flows constantly there 15 foot in 12 hours, as our new Cards inform us, that California is not a Cape, but an Island, and the West-winds make the Nepe tides equal to the Spring, or that there be any probability to pass by the straits of Anian to China, by the Promontory of Tabin. If there be, I shall soon perceive whether Marco Polo the Venetian's narration be true or false, of that great City of Quinsay and Cambalu; whether there be any such places, or that, as Matth. Riccius the Jesuit hath written, China and Cathay be all one, the great Cham of Tartary and the King of China be the same: Xuntain and Quinsay, and the City of Cambalu be that new Peking, or such a wall 400 leagues long to part China from Tartary: whether Prester John be in Asia or Africa; Polo the Venetian puts him in Asia, the most received opinion is, that he is Emperor of the Abyssines, which of old was Ethiopia, now Nubia, under the Æquator in Africa. Whether Guinea be an Island or part of the Continent, or that hungry Spaniard's discovery of the Unknown Land of Australia, or Magellanica, be as true as that of Mercurius Britannicus, or his of Utopia, or his of Lusinia.* And yet in likelihood it may be so, for without all question it being extended from the Tropick of Capricorn to the circle Antarctick, and lying as it doth in the temperate Zone, cannot choose but yield in time some flourishing Kingdoms to succeeding ages, as America did unto the Spaniards. Shouten and Le Meir have done well in the discovery of the Straits of Magellan, in finding a more convenient passage to the Pacific

* Lusinia was the imaginary country in John Barclay's Euphormionis Satyricon (1605), a satire on the Jesuits, modelled on Petronius.

Ocean: methinks some of our modern Argonauts should prosecute the rest. As I go by Madagascar, I would see that great Bird Ruck [Roc], that can carry a Man and Horse or an Elephant, with that Arabian Phoenix described by Adricomius; see the Pelicans of Egypt, those Scythian Gryphes in Asia: and afterwards in Africa examine the fountains of the Nile, whether Herodotus, Seneca, Pliny, or Strabo give a true cause of his annual flowing, Pagaphetta discourse rightly of it, or of Niger and Senega; examine Cardan, Scaliger's reasons, and the rest. Is it from those Etesian winds, or melting of snow in the Mountains under the Æquator, (for Jordan yearly overflows when the snow melts in Mount Libanus), or from those great dropping perpetual showers, which are so frequent to the inhabitants within the Tropicks, when the Sun is vertical, and cause such vast inundations in Senega, Maragnan, Orinoco, and the rest of those great rivers in the Torrid Zone, which have all commonly the same passions at set times: and by good husbandry and policy hereafter no doubt may come to be as populous, as well tilled, as fruitful, as Egypt itself, or Cochin China? I would observe all those motions of the sea, and from what cause they proceed, from the Moon (as the Vulgar hold) or Earth's motion, which Galileo, in the fourth dialogue of his System of the World, so eagerly proves, and firmly demonstrates, or winds, as some will. Why in that quiet Ocean of the South, in the Pacifick, it is scarce perceived, in our British Seas most violent, in the Mediterranean and Red Sea so vehement, irregular, & diverse? Why the current in that Atlantick Ocean should still be in some places from, in some again towards the North, and why they come sooner than go? and so from Moabar to Madagascar in that Indian Ocean the Merchants come in three weeks, as Scaliger discusseth, they return scarce in three months, with the same or like winds: the continual current is from East to West. Whether Mount Athos, Pelion, Olympus, Ossa, Caucasus, Atlas, be so high as Pliny, Solinus, Mela relate, above Clouds, Meteors, where there was neither air nor any breeze that they could breathe, (insomuch that they that ascend die suddenly very often, the air is so subtile), 1250 paces high, according to that measure of Dicæarchus, or 78 miles perpendicularly high, as Jacobus Mazonius, expounding that place of Aristotle about Mount Caucasus; and as Blancanus the Jesuit contends out of Clavius & Nonius' demonstrations On Twilight: or rather 32 stadiums, as the most received opinion is, or 4 miles, which the height of no Mountain doth perpendicularly exceed, & is equal to the greatest depths of the Sea, which is, as Scaliger holds, 1580 paces, others 100 paces. I would see those inner parts of America, whether there be any such great City of Manoa or Eldorado in that golden Empire, where the high ways are as much beaten (one reports) as between Madrid & Valladolid in Spain; or any such Amazones as he relates, or gigantical Patagones in Chica; with that miraculous Mountain Ybouyapab in the Northern Brazil, the top of which forms a most pleasant table-land, &c., or that of Periacacca, so high elevated in Peru. The pike of Teneriffe how high is it? 70 miles, or 52, as Patricius holds, or 9, as Snellius demonstrates in his Eratosthenes: see that strange Cirknickzerksey lake in Carniola, whose waters gush so fast out of the ground, that they will overtake a swift horseman, and by and by with as incredible celerity are supped up: which Lazius & Warnerus make an argument of the Argonauts sailing under ground. And that vast den or hole called Esmellen in Muscovia, which, if any thing casually fall in, makes such a roaring noise, that no thunder, or ord- nance, or warlike engine can make the like; such another is Gilber's Cave in Lapland, with many the like. I would examine the Caspian Sea, and see where and how it exonerates itself, after it hath taken in Volga, Jaxares, Oxus, and those great rivers; at the mouth of Oby, or where? What vent the Mexican lake hath, the Titicacan in Peru, or that cir- cular pool in the vale of Terapeia, of which Acosta saith, hot in a cold country, the spring of which boils up in the middle twenty foot square, and hath no vent but exhalation: and that of the Dead Sea in Palestine, of Thrasymene, at Perusium in Italy: the Mediterranean itself. For from the Ocean, at the Straits of Gibraltar, there is a perpetual current into the Levant, and so likewise by the Thracian Bosphorus out of the Euxine or Black Sea, besides all those great rivers of the Nile, the Po, the Rhone, &c., how is this water consumed? by the Sun, or otherwise? I would find out with Trajan the Fountains of the Danube, of Ganges, Oxus, see those Egyptian Pyramids, Trajan's Bridge, the Grotto of the Sibyls, Lucullus' Fish-ponds, the Temple of Nidrose, &c. and, if I could, observe what becomes of swallows, storks, cranes, cuckoos, nightingales, redstarts, & many other kind of singing birds, water-fowls, hawks, &c. some of them are only seen in summer, some in winter; some are ob- served in the snow, and at no other times, each have their seasons. In winter not a bird is in Muscovy to be found, but at the spring in an instant the woods and hedges are full of them, saith Herbastein: how comes it to pass? Do they sleep in winter, like Gesner's Alpine mice; or do they lie hid (as Olaus affirms) in the bottom of lakes and rivers, holding their breath? often so found by fishermen in Poland and Scandia, two together, mouth to mouth, wing to wing; & when the spring comes they revive again, or if they be brought into a stove, or to the fire side. Or do they follow the Sun, as Peter Martyr manifestly convicts, out of his own knowledge? for, when he was Embassador in Egypt, he saw swallows, Spanish kites, and many such other European birds, in December and January, very familiarly flying, and in great abundance, about Alexandria, where, at that season, the flowers were in bloom and the trees green; or lie they hid in caves, rocks, & hollow trees, as most think, in deep Tin-mines or Sea-cliffs, as Mr. Carew gives out? I conclude of them all, for my part, as Munster doth of cranes and storks: whence they come, whither they go, as yet we know not. We see them here, some in summer, some in winter: their coming and going is sure in the night: in the plains of Asia (saith he) the storks meet on such a set day, he that comes last is torn in pieces, and so they get them gone. Many strange places, Isthmuses, Euripuses, Chersoneses, [Peninsulas], creeks, havens, promontories, straits, lakes, baths, rocks, mountains, places, and fields, where Cities have been ruined or swallowed, battles fought, creatures, Sea-monsters, remora,* &c., minerals, vegetals. Zoophytes were fit to be considered in such an expedition, and, amongst the rest, that of Herbastein his Tartar lamb, Hector Boethius' goose-bearing tree in the Orcades, to which Cardan subscribes: Vertomannus' wonderful palm †; that fly in Hispaniola, that shines like a torch in the night, that one may well see to write; those spherical stones in Cuba which nature hath so made, and those like birds, beasts, fishes, crowns, swords, saws, pots, &c. usually found in the metal-mines in Saxony about Mansfield, and in Poland near Nokow and Pallukie, as Munster and others relate. Many rare creatures and novelties each part of the world affords: amongst the rest, I would know for a certain whether there be any such men, as Leo Suavius, in his comment on Paracelsus, and Gaguinus records in his description of Muscovy, that in Lucomoria, a Province in Russia, lie fast asleep as dead all winter from the 27th of November, like frogs and swallows, benumbed with cold, but about the 24th of April in the spring they revive again, and go about their business. I would examine that demonstration of Alexander Piccolomineus, whether the earth's surface be bigger than the Sea's; or that of Archimedes be true, the surface of all water is even. Search the depth, and see that variety of Sea-monsters and fishes, Mermaids, Sea-men, Horses,

---

* A sucking fish that delayed ships.

† Vertomannus mentioneth a tree that bears fruits to eat, wood to burn, bark to make ropes, wine and water to drink, oil and sugar, and leaves as tiles to cover houses, flowers for clothes, &c. — Burton's note.

&c. which it affords. Or whether that be true which Jordanus Brunus scoffs at, that, if God did not detain it, the Sea would overflow the earth by reason of his higher site, and which Josephus Blancanus the Jesuit, in his interpretation on those mathematical places of Aristotle, foolishly fears, and in a just tract proves by many circumstances that in time the Sea will waste away the land, all the globe of the earth shall be covered with water; and, could you but laugh, my friends? what the Sea takes away in one place it adds in another. Methinks he might rather suspect the Sea should in time be filled by land, trees grow up, carcasses, &c. that all-devouring fire will sooner cover and dry up the vast Ocean with sand and ashes. I would examine the true seat of that terrestrial Paradise, and where Ophir was, whence Solomon did fetch his gold; from Peruana, which some suppose, or that Aurea Chersonnesus, as Dominicus Niger, Arias Montanus, Goropius, and others, will. I would censure all Pliny's, Solinus', Strabo's, Sir John Mandeville's, Olaus Magnus', Marco Polo's lies, correct those errors in navigation, reform Cosmographical Charts, and rectify longitudes, if it were possible; not by the Compass, as some dream, with Mark Ridley in his treatise of magnetical bodies; for as Cabeus fully resolves, there is no hope thence, yet I would observe some better means to find them out.

I would have a convenient place to go down with Orpheus, Ulysses, Hercules, Lucian's Menippus, at St. Patrick's Purgatory, at Trophonius' den, Hecla in Iceland, Ætna in Sicily, to descend & see what is done in the bowels of the earth; do stones and metals grow there still? how come fir trees to be digged out from tops of hills, as in our mosses & marshes all over Europe? How come they to dig up fish bones, shells, beams, iron-works, many fathoms under ground, & anchors in mountains far remote from all seas? In the year 1460, at Berne in Switzerland, 50 fathom deep, a ship was digged out of a mountain, where they got metal ore, in which were 48 carcasses of men, with other merchandise. That such things are ordinarily found in tops of hills, Aristotle insinuates in his meteors, Pomponius Mela in his first book, on Numidia, & familiarly in the Alps, saith Blancanus the Jesuit, the like is to be seen. Came this from earth-quakes, or from Noah's flood, as Christians suppose? or is there a vicissitude of Sea & land? as Anaximenes held of old the Mountains of Thessaly would become Seas, and Seas again Mountains. The whole world belike should be new moulded, when it seemed good to those all-commanding Powers, & turned inside out, as we do hay-cocks in Harvest, top to bottom, or bottom to top: or as we turn apples to the fire, move the world upon his Center; that which is under the Poles now, should be translated to the Æquinoctial, and that which is under the Torrid Zone to the Circle Arctick and Antarctick another while, & so be reciprocally warmed by the Sun: or, if the worlds be infinite, & every fixed star a Sun, with his compassing Planets, (as Brunus and Campanella conclude), cast three or four worlds into one; or else of one old world make three or four new, as it shall seem to them best. To proceed, if the earth be 21,500 miles in compass, its Diameter is 7,000 from us to our Antipodes, and what shall be comprehended in all that space? What is the Center of the earth? is it pure element only, as Aristotle decrees, inhabited (as Paracelsus thinks) with creatures, whose Chaos is the earth, or with Fairies, as the woods and waters (according to him) are with Nymphs, or as the Air with Spirits? Dionysiodorus, a Mathematician in Pliny, that sent a letter to the world above after he was dead, from the Center of the earth, to signify what distance the same Center was from the superficies of the same, viz., 42,000 stadiums, might have done well to have satisfied all these doubts. Or is it the place of Hell, as Virgil in his Æneid, Plato, Lucian, Dante, and others, poetically describe it, and as many of our Divines think? In good earnest, Anthony Rusca, one of the society of that Ambrosian College in Milan, in his great volume on Inferno, is stiff in this tenent, 'tis a corporeal fire tow, as he there disputes. Whatsoever Philosophers write, (saith Surius), there be certain mouths of Hell, and places appointed for the punishment of men's souls, as at Hecla in Iceland, where the ghosts of dead men are familiarly seen, & sometimes talk with the living: God would have such visible places, that mortal men might be certainly informed, that there be such punishments after death, & learn hence to fear God. Kranzius subscribes to this opinion of Surius, so doth Colerus, (out of the authority belike of St. Gregory, Durand, and the rest of the Schoolmen, who derive as much from Ætna in Sicily, Lipari, Hiera, and those sulphureous Vulcanian Islands) making Terra del Fuego, and those frequent Volcanoes in America, of which Acosta, that fearful Mount Hecklebirg in Norway, an especial argument to prove it, where lamentable screeches & howlings are continually heard, which strike a terror to the auditors; fiery chariots are commonly seen to bring in the souls of men in the likeness of crows, and Devils ordinarily go in and out. Such another proof is that place near the Pyramids in Egypt, by Cairo, as well to confirm this as the resurrection, mentioned by Kornmannus, Camerarius, Bredenbachius, and some others, where once a year dead bodies arise about March, and walk, & after a while hide themselves again: thousands of people come yearly to see them. But these and such like testimonies others reject, as Fables, illusions of spirits, and they will have no such local known place, more than Styx or Phlegethon, Pluto's Court, or that poetical Infernus, where Homer's soul was seen hanging on a tree, &c. to which they ferried over in Charon's boat, or went down at Hermione in Greece, which is the shortest cut, (saith Gerbelius) and besides there were no fees to be paid. Well then, is it Hell, or Purgatory, as Bellarmine, or the Limbo of the Fathers, as Gallucius will, & as Rusca will (for they have made Maps of it) or Ignatius' Parlour? * Virgil, sometime Bishop of Saltburg (as Aventinus relates), by Bonifacius Bishop of Mentz was therefore called in question, because he held Antipodes (which they made a doubt whether Christ died for) and so by that means took away the seat of Hell, or so contracted it, that it could bear no proportion to Heaven, & contradicted that opinion of Austin, Basil, Lactantius, that held the earth round as a trencher (whom Acosta and common experience more largely confute) but not as a ball; and Jerusalem, where Christ died, the middle of it; or Delos, as the fabulous Greeks feigned, because, when Jupiter let two Eagles loose, to fly from the world's ends East & West, they met at Delos. But that scruple of Bonifacius is now quite taken away by our latter Divines: Franciscus Ribera will have Hell a material & local fire in the Center of the earth, 200 Italian miles in diameter, as he defines it out of those words, They go forth to a lake of blood, &c. But Lessius will have this local Hell far less, one Dutch mile in Diameter, all filled with fire and brimstone: because, as he there demonstrates, that space cubically multiplied will make a Sphere able to hold eight hundred thousand millions of damned bodies (allowing each body six foot square) which will abundantly suffice. But if it be no material fire (as Scotus, Thomas, Bonaventure, Soncinas, Vossius, and others argue) it may be there or elsewhere, as Keckerman disputes, for sure somewhere it is, albeit its boundaries are not definitely assigned. I will end the controversy in Austin's words: Better doubt of things concealed than to contend about uncertainties. Where Abraham's bosom is, and Hell fire, scarce the meek, the contentious shall never find. If it be solid earth, 'tis the fountain of metals, waters, which by his innate temper turns air into water, which springs

---

* Referring to "Ignatius his Conclave, or Inthronisation in Hell," by Donne, according to A. R. Shilleto. The Limbo of the Fathers (*limbus patrum*), mentioned just before, also called the Limbo of the Patriarchs, was the borderland or outermost circle of hell, where the spirits of the righteous who had died before the birth of Christ (sometimes called the pre-Christian saints) were confined till his descent into hell. These were sometimes held to include not only Old Testament patriarchs but also such well-loved classical personages as Virgil and Seneca.

up in several chinks, to moisten the earth's surface, & that in a tenfold proportion (as Aristotle holds) ; or else these fountains come directly from the sea by secret passages, and so made fresh again, by running through the bowels of the earth; and are either thick, thin, hot, cold, as the matter or minerals are by which they pass; or, as Peter Martyr and some others hold, from abundance of rain that falls, or from that ambient heat and cold, which alters that inward heat, and so consequently the generation of waters. Or else it may be full of wind, or a sulphureous innate fire, as our Meteorologists inform us, which, sometimes breaking out, causeth those horrible Earth-quakes, which are so frequent in these days in Japan, China, and oftentimes swallow up whole Cities. Let Lucian's Mennipus consult with or ask of Tiresias, if you will not believe Philosophers; he shall clear all your doubts when he makes a second voyage.

In the mean time let us consider of that which is under Heaven, and find out a true case, if it be possible, of such accidents, meteors, alterations, as happen above ground. Whence proceed that variety of manners, and a distinct character (as it were) to several nations? Some are wise, subtile, witty; others dull, sad, and heavy; some big, some little, as Tully, Plato, Vegetius, and Bodine proves at large; some soft, and some hardy, barbarous, civil, black, dun, white; is it from the air, from the soil, influence of stars, or some other secret cause? Why doth Africa breed so many venomous beasts, Ireland none? Athens owls, Crete none? Why hath Daulis and Thebes no swallows (so Pausanias informeth us) as well as the rest of Greece, Ithaca no hares, Pontus no asses, Scythia no swine? Whence come this variety of complexions, colours, plants, birds, beasts, metals, peculiar almost to every place? Why so many thousand strange birds and beasts proper to America alone, as Acosta demands? Were they created in the six days, or ever in Noah's Ark? If there, why are they not dispersed & found in other countries? It is a thing (saith he) hath long held me in suspense; no Greek, Latin, Hebrew, ever heard of them before, and yet as differing from our European animals, as an egg and a chestnut: and, which is more, kine, horses, sheep, &c. till the Spaniards brought them, were never heard of in those parts. How comes it to pass that in the same site, in one latitude, to such as are Neighbours there should be such difference of soil, complexion, colour, metal, air, &c. The Spaniards are white, and so are Italians, when as the Inhabitants about the Cape of Good Hope are Blackamores, and yet both alike distant from the Æquator: nay, they that dwell in the same parallel line with these Negroes, as about the Straits of Magellan, are white coloured, and yet some in Presbyter John's country in Æthiopia are dun; they in Zeilan and Malabar, parallel with them, again black: Manamotapa in Africa, and St. Thomas' Isle are extreme hot, both under the line, coal black their Inhabitants, whereas in Peru they are quite opposite in colour, very temperate, or rather cold, & yet both alike elevated. Moscow in 53 degrees of latitude extreme cold, as those Northern Countries usually are, having one perpetual hard frost all winter long: and in 52. deg. lat. sometimes hard frost and snow all summer, as in Button's Bay, &c. or by fits; and yet England near the same latitude, and Ireland, very moist, warm, and more temperate in winter than Spain, Italy, or France. Is it the Sea that causeth this difference, and the Air that comes from it? Why then is Ister so cold near the Euxine, Pontus, Bithynia, & all Thrace? Cold regions, Maginus calls them, and yet their latitude is but 42, which should be hot. Quevira, or Nova Albion in America, bordering on the sea, was so cold in July, that our Englishmen could hardly endure it. At Noremberga, in 45. lat., all the sea is frozen Ice, and yet in a more Southern latitude than ours. New England, and the Island of Cambrial Colchos, which that noble Gentleman Mr. Vaughan, or Orpheus Junior, describes in his Golden Fleece, is in the same latitude with little Britain in France, and yet their winter begins not till January, their spring till May; which search he accounts worthy of an Astrologer; is this from the Easterly winds, or melting of ice and snow dissolved within the circle Arctick; or that the air being thick, is longer before it be warm by the Sun beams, and once heated like an oven will keep itself from cold? Our Climes breed lice, Hungary and Ireland have a bad name in this kind; come to the Azores, by a secret virtue of that air they are instantly consumed, & all our European vermin almost, saith Ortelius. Egypt is watered with Nilus not far from the sea, and yet there it seldom or never rains: Rhodes, an Island of the same nature, yields not a cloud, and yet our Islands ever dropping and inclining to rain. The Atlantick Ocean is still subject to storms, but in the South Sea, or Pacifick, seldom or never any. Is it from Tropick stars, the opening of the gates [Aries and Cancer were the Gates of the Sun], in the Dodecatemories or Constellations, the Moon's mansions, such aspects of Planets, such winds, or dissolving air, or thick air, which causeth this and the like differences of heat and cold? Bodine relates of a Portugal Embassador, that, coming from Lisbon to Dantzick in Spruce, found greater heat there than at any time at home. Don Garcia de Sylva, Legate to Philip 3, King of Spain, residing at Spahan in Persia, 1619, in his letter to the Marquess of Bedmar, makes mention of greater cold in

Spahan, whose lat. is 31 degrees than ever he felt in Spain, or any part of Europe. The Torrid Zone was by our predecessors held to be uninhabitable, but by our modern travellers found to be most temperate, bedewed with frequent rains, and moistening showers, the brise and cooling blasts in some parts, as Acosta describes, most pleasant and fertile. Arica in Chili is by report one of the sweetest places that ever the Sun shined on, an heaven on earth: how incomparably do some extol Mexico in Nova Hispania, Peru, Brazil, &c. in some again hard, dry, sandy, barren, a very Desert, and still in the same latitude. Many times we find great diversity of air in the same country, by reason of the site to seas, hills, or dales, want of water, nature of soil, and the like: as in Spain Arragon is harsh and evil inhabited, Estremadura is dry, sandy, barren most part, extreme hot by reason of his plains, Andalusia another Paradise, Valencia a most pleasant air, and continually green; so is it about Granada, on the one side fertile plains, on the other continual snow to be seen all Summer long on the hill tops. That their houses in the Alps are three quarters of the year covered with snow, who knows not? That Teneriffe is so cold at the top, extreme hot at the bottom; Mount Atlas in Africa, Lebanon in Palestine; from burning heat to shade & snow, Tacitus calls it, with many such, and Radzivilius yields it to be far hotter there than in any part of Italy: 'tis true; but they are highly elevated, near the middle region, & therefore cold, because of the slight refraction of the Sun's rays, as Serrarius answers. In the heat of Summer, in the King's Palace in Escurial, the air is most temperate, by reason of a cold blast which comes from the snowy mountains of Sierra de Gudarrama hard by, when as in Toledo it is very hot: so in all other countries. The causes of these alterations are commonly by reason of their nearness (I say) to the middle region: but this diversity of air, in places equally site, elevated, and distant from the Pole, can hardly be satisfied with that diversity of Plants, Birds, Beasts, which is so familiar with us. With Indians, every where, the Sun is equally distant, the same vertical stars, the same irradiations of Planets, Aspects alike, the same nearness of seas, the same superficies, the same soil, or not much different. Under the Æquator itself, amongst the Sierras, Andes, Lanes, as Herrera, Laetus and Acosta, contend, there is such variety of weather, that no Philosophy can yet find out the true cause of it. When I consider how temperate it is in one place, saith Acosta, within the Tropick of Capricorn, as about La Plata, and yet hard by at Potosi, in that same altitude, mountainous alike, extreme cold; extreme hot in Brazil, &c.: hereupon, saith Acosta, I loudly laughed at the meteorological philosophy of Aristotle, since, when the Sun comes nearest to them, they have great tempests, storms, thunder and lightning, great store of rain, snow, and the foulest weather ; when the Sun is vertical, their rivers overflow, the morning fair and hot, noon-day cold and moist : all which is opposite to us. How comes it to pass ? Scaliger discourseth thus of this subject. How comes, or wherefore is this rash placing of Stars, or as Epicurus will, accidental ? Why are some big, some little ? Why are they so confusedly, unequally, site in the heavens, and set so much out of order ? In all other things Nature is equal, proportionable, and constant ; there be just dimensions and wise proportions of parts, as in the fabrick of man, his eyes, ears, nose, face, members, are correspondent ; why not the same of the Sky, the loveliest of all her works ? Why are the heavens so irregular, neither equal in mass, nor in spaces ? Whence is this difference ? To make diversity, (he concludes), of countries, soils, manners, customs, characters & constitutions among us ; and so by this means the same places almost shall be distinguished in manners. But this reason is weak & most unsufficient. The fixed stars are removed since Ptolemy's time 26 degrees from the first of Aries, and if the earth be immoveable, as their site varies, so should countries vary, and divers alterations would follow. But this we perceive not ; as in Tully's time with us in Britain, the sky is overcast and soon cloudy, &c. 'tis so still. Wherefore Bodine, and some others, will have all these alterations and effects immediately to proceed from those Genii, Spirits, Angels, which rule and domineer in several places ; they cause storms, thunder, lightning, earthquakes, ruins, tempests, great winds, floods, &c. The Philosophers of Coimbra will refer this diversity to the influence of that Empyrean Heaven : for some say the eccentricity of the Sun is come nearer to the earth than in Ptolemy's time ; the virtue therefore of all the vegetals is decayed, men grow less, &c.

There are that observe new motions of the Heavens, new stars, wandering stars, comets, clouds, call them what you will, like those Medicean, Bourbonian, Austrian Planets lately detected, which do not decay, but come and go, rise higher and lower, hide and shew themselves amongst the fixed stars, amongst the Planets, above & beneath the Moon, at set times, now nearer, now farther off, together, asunder ; as he that plays upon a Sackbut by pulling it up and down alters his tones and tunes, do they their stations and places, though to us undiscerned ; and from those motions proceed (as they conceive) divers alterations. Clavius conjectures otherwise, but they be but conjectures. About Damascus in Cæle-Syria is a Paradise, by reason of the plenty of waters, the reason is obvious, & the Deserts of Arabia barren, because of rocks, rolling seas of sands, and dry mountains, (saith Adricomius), uninhabitable therefore of men, birds, beasts, void of all green trees, plants and fruits, a vast rocky horrid wilderness, which by no art can be manured, 'tis evident. Bohemia is cold, for that it lies all along to the North. But why should it be so hot in Egypt, or there never rain? Why should those Etesian & North-Eastern winds blow continually and constantly so long together, in some places, at set times, one way still, in the dog-days only: here perpetual drought, there dropping showers; here foggy mists, there a pleasant air; here terrible thunder and lightning, at such set seasons, here frozen seas all the year, there open in the same latitude, to the rest no such thing, nay quite opposite is to be found? Sometimes (as in Peru) on the one side of the mountains it is hot, on the other cold, here snow, there wind, with infinite such. Fromundus, in his Meteors, will excuse or solve all this by the Sun's motion, but when there is such diversity to such as are neighbours, or very near site, how can that position hold?

Who can give a reason of this diversity of Meteors, that it should rain Stones, Frogs, Mice, &c., Rats, which they call Lemmer in Norway, and are manifestly observed (as Munster writes) by the Inhabitants to descend and fall with some fæculent showers, and, like so many Locusts, consume all that is green. Leo Afer speaks as much of Locusts, about Fez in Barbary there be infinite swarms in their fields upon a sudden: so at Arles in France, 1553, the like happened by the same mischief, all their grass & fruits were devoured, to the great wonder and consternation of the inhabitants, (as Valleriola relates), they all of a sudden darkened the sky, &c.; he concludes it could not be from natural causes, they cannot imagine whence they come but from heaven. Are these and such creatures, corn, wood, stones, worms, wool, blood, &c. lifted up into the middle region by the Sun beams, as Baracellus the Physician disputes, and thence let fall with showers, or there engendered? Cornelius Gemma is of that opinion, they are there conceived by celestial influences: others suppose they are immediately from God, or prodigies raised by art and illusions of Spirits, which are Princes of the Air; to whom Bodine subscribes. In fine, of Meteors in general, Aristotle's reasons are exploded by Bernardinus Telesius, by Paracelsus, his principles confuted, & other causes assigned, salt, sulphur, mercury, in which his Disciples are so expert, that they can alter Elements, and separate at their pleasure, make perpetual motions, not as Cardan, Taisneir, Peregrinus, by some magnetical virtue, but by mixture of elements; imitate thunder, like Salmoneus, snow, hail, the sea's ebbing & flowing, give life to creatures (as they say) without generation, and what not? P. Nonius Saluciensis & Kepler take upon them to demonstrate that no Meteors, Clouds, Fogs, Vapours, arise higher than 50 or 80 miles, and all the rest to be purer air or element of fire: which Cardan, Tycho, and John Pena, manifestly confute by refractions, and many other arguments, there is no such element of fire at all. If, as Tycho proves, the Moon be distant from us 50 and 60 semidiameters of the earth: and, as Peter Nonius will have it, the air be so angust,* what proportion is there betwixt the other three Elements and it? to what use serves it? is it full of Spirits which inhabit it, as the Paracelsians and Platonists hold, the higher the more noble, full of birds, or a mere vacuum to no purpose? It is much controverted betwixt Tycho Brahe and Christopher Rotman, the Landgrave of Hesse's Mathematician, in their Astronomical Epistles, whether it be the same clearness, matter of air and heavens, or two distinct essences? Christopher Rotman, John Pena, Jordanus Brunus, with many other late Mathematicians, contend it is the same and one matter throughout, saving that the higher the purer it is, and more subtile; as they find by experience in the top of some hills in America; if a man ascend, he faints instantly for want of thicker air to refrigerate the heart. Acosta calls this mountain Periacacca in Peru, it makes men cast and vomit, he saith, that climb it, as some other of those Andes do in the deserts of Chile for 500 miles together, and for extremity of cold to lose their fingers and toes. Tycho will have two distinct matters of Heaven and Air; but to say truth, with some small qualification, they have one & the self same opinion about the essence and matter of Heavens; that it is not hard and impenetrable, as Peripateticks hold, transparent, of a quintessence, but that it is penetrable & soft as the air itself is, & that the Planets move in it, as Birds in the Air, Fishes in the Sea. This they prove by motion of Comets, and otherwise (though Claremontius in his Antitycho stiffly oppose) which are not generated, as Aristotle teacheth, in the aerial Region, of a hot and dry exhalation, and so consumed: but, as Anaxagoras and Democritus held of old, of a celestial matter: and as Tycho, Helisæus Rœslin, Thaddeus Haggesius, Pena, Rotman, Fracastorius, demonstrate by their progress, parallaxes, refractions, motions of the Planets, which interfere and cut one another's orbs, now higher, and then lower, as ♂ [Mars] amongst the rest, which sometimes, as Kepler confirms by his own and Tycho's accurate observations, comes nearer to the earth than the ⊙ [Sun], and is again eftsoons aloft in Jupiter's

* Scant, or thin.

orb; and other sufficient reasons, far above the Moon: exploding in the mean time that element of fire, those fictitious first watery movers, those Heavens I mean above the Firmament, which Delrio, Lodovicus Imola, Patricius, & many of the Fathers, affirm; those monstrous orbs of Eccentricks, and those wandering in eccentric epicycles; which howsoever Ptolemy, Alhasen, Vitellio, Purbachius, Maginus, Clavius, & many of their associates, stiffly maintain to be real orbs, eccentrick, concentrick, circles æquant, &c. are absurd and ridiculous. For who is so mad to think that there should be so many circles, like subordinate wheels in a clock, all impenetrable and hard, as they feign, add & subtract at their pleasure. Maginus makes eleven Heavens, subdivided into their orbs & circles, and all too little to serve those particular appearances: Fracastorius 72 homocentricks; Tycho Brahe, Nicholas Ramerus, Helisæus Rœslin, have peculiar hypotheses of their own inventions; and they be but inventions, as most of them acknowledge, as we admit of Æquators, Tropicks, Colures, Circles, Arctick and Antarctick, for doctrine's sake (though Ramus thinks them all unnecessary) they will have them supposed only for method and order. Tycho hath feigned I know not how many subdivisions of Epicycles in Epicycles, &c. to calculate and express the Moon's motion: but when all is done, as a supposition, and no otherwise; not (as he holds) hard, impenetrable, subtile, transparent, &c. or making musick, as Pythagoras maintained of old, and Robert Constantine of late, but still quiet, liquid, open, &c.

If the Heavens then be penetrable, as these men deliver, and no lets, it were not amiss in this aerial progress to make wings, and fly up, which that Turk in Busbequius made his fellow-citizens in Constantinople believe he would perform: & some new-fangled wits, methinks, should some time or other find out: or if that may not be, yet with a Galileo's glass, or Icaromenippus' wings in Lucian, command the Spheres and Heavens, and see what is done amongst them. Whether there be generation and corruption, as some think, by reason of æthereal Comets, that in Cassiopea 1572, that in Cygno 1600, that in Sagittarius 1604, and many like, which by no means Julius Cæsar la Galla, that Italian Philosopher, in his physical disputation with Galileo, will admit: or that they were created from the beginning, and shew themselves at set times: and, as Helisæus Rœslin contends, have Poles, Axletrees, Circles of their own, and regular motions. For they do not vanish utterly, Blancanus holds, they come & go by fits, casting their tails still from the Sun: some of them, as a burning glass projects the Sun beams from it; though not always neither: for sometimes a Comet casts his tail from Venus, as

Tycho observes; and, as Helisæus Rœslin of some others, from the Moon, with little Stars about them, to the marvel of Astronomers, with many other wonders in the heavens, all which argue, with those Medicean, Austrian, & Bourbonian Stars, that the Heaven of the Planets is indistinct, pure, and open, in which the Planets move by fixed laws and in certain limits. Examine likewise, whether the heavens be coloured? Whether the Stars be of that bigness, distance, as Astronomers relate, so many in number, 1026, or 1725, as J. Bayerus; or, as some Rabbins, 29,000 myriads; or, as Galileo discovers by his glasses, infinite, & that Milky Way, a confused light of small Stars, like so many nails in a door: or all in a row, like those 12,000 Isles of the Maldives in the Indian Ocean? Whether the least visible Star in the eighth Sphere be 18 times bigger than the earth, and, as Tycho calculates, 14,000 semi-diameters distant from it? Whether they be thicker parts of the orbs, as Aristotle delivers: or so many habitable Worlds, as Democritus? Whether they have light of their own, or from the Sun, or give light round, as Patricius discourseth? Whether they are equidistant from the world's centre? Whether light be of their essence; & that light be a sub-stance or an accident? whether they be hot by themselves, or by accident cause heat? whether there be such a precession of the Æquinoxes, as Copernicus holds, or that the eighth Sphere move? Whether Roger Bacon philosophized aright in his tract Concerning the Multiplication of Appearances, and John Dee in his Aphorisms? Whether there be any such Images ascending with each degree of the Zodiack in the East, as Aliacensis feigns? Whether there be a water above the sky? as Patricius & the Schoolmen will, a crystalline watery heaven, which is certainly to be understood of that in the middle region? for otherwise, if at Noah's flood the water came from thence, it must be above an hundred years falling down to us, as some calculate. Besides, whether the earth is animated? which some so confidently believe, with Orpheus, Hermes, Averroes, from which all other souls of men, beasts, devils, plants, fishes, &c., are derived, and into which again, after some revolutions, as Plato in his Timæus, Plotinus in his Enneades, more largely discuss, they return (see Chalcidius & Bennius, Plato's Commentators) as all philosophical matter, to primal substance. Kepler, Patricius, and some other Neotericks, have in part revived this opinion. And that every star in heaven hath a soul, angel, or intelligence, to animate or move it, &c. Or, to omit all smaller controversies, as matters of less moment, and examine that main paradox, of the Earth's motion, now so much in question: Aristarchus Samius, Pythagoras, maintained it of old, Democritus, and many of their Scholars. Didacus Astunica, Anthony Fascarinus, a Carmelite, & some other Commentators, will have Job to insinuate as much, — "Which shaketh the earth out of her place," &c. — , and that this one place of Scripture makes more for the Earth's motion, than all the other prove against it; whom Pineda confutes, most contradict. Howsoever, it is revived since by Copernicus, not as a truth, but a supposition,* as he confesseth himself in the Preface to Pope Nicholas, but now maintained in good earnest by Calcagninus, Telesius, Kepler, Rotman, Gilbert, Digges, Galileo, Campanella & especially by Lansbergius, as agreeing with nature, truth, and reason, by Origanus. and some others of his followers. For if the Earth be the Center of the World, stand still, and the Heavens move, as the most received opinion is, which they call the disordered disposition of the heavens, though stiffly maintained by Tycho, Ptolemy, and their adherents, what fury is that, saith Dr. Gilbert, sufficient force, as Cabeus notes, that shall drive the Heavens about with such incomprehensible celerity in 24 hours, when as every point of the Firmament, and in the Æquator, must needs move (so Clavius calculates) 176,660 in one 246th part of an hour: and an arrow out of a bow must go seven times about the earth whilst a man can say an Ave Maria, if it keep the same pace, or compass the earth 1,884 times in an hour, which is beyond human conceit: fleeter than a dart and a wind-swift arrow. A man could not ride so much ground, going 40 miles a day, in 2,904 years, as the Firmament goes in 24 hours; or so much in 203 years, as the said Firmament in one minute; which seems incredible: and the Pole star, which to our thinking scarce moveth out of his place, goeth a bigger circuit than the Sun, whose Diameter is much larger than the Diameter of the Heaven of the Sun, and 20,000 Semidiameters of the Earth from us, with the rest of the fixed stars, as Tycho proves. To avoid therefore these impossibilities, they ascribe a triple motion of the Earth, the Sun immovable in the Center of the whole World, the Earth Center of the Moon, alone, above ♀ [Venus] and ☿ [Mercury], beneath ♄ [Saturn], ♃ [Jupiter], ♂ [Mars], (or, as Origanus and others will, one single motion to the Earth, still placed in the Center of the World, which is more probable) a single motion to the Firmament, which moves in 30 or 26 thousand years; and so the Planets, Saturn in 30 years absolves his sole and proper motion, Jupiter in 12, Mars in 3, &c. and so solve all ap-

* Copernicus received on his death-bed the first printed copy of the treatise in which he had set forth his astronomical theory; it contained a dedicatory epistle to Pope Paul III., which unknown to him had been prefaced by an anonymous editorial statement to the effect that these views were merely hypothetical.

pearances better than any way whatsoever: calculate all motions, be they in length or breadth, direct, stationary, retrograde, ascent or descent, without Epicycles, intricate Eccentricks, &c. through the single motion of the earth, saith Lansbergius, much more certain than by those Alphonsine or any such Tables, which are grounded from those other suppositions. And 'tis true they say according to optick principles, the visible appearances of the Planets do so indeed answer to their magnitudes & orbs, & come nearest to mathematical observations, & precedent calculations; there is no repugnancy to physical axioms, because no penetration of orbs: but then, between the sphere of Saturn and the Firmament, there is such an incredible and vast space or distance (7,000,000 semi-diameters of the earth, as Tycho calculates) void of stars: and besides they do so enhance the bigness of the stars, enlarge their circuit, to solve those ordinary objections of Parallaxes & Retrogradations of the fixed stars, that alteration of the Poles, elevation in several places or latitude of Cities here on earth (for, say they, if a man's eye were in the Firmament, he should not at all discern that great annual motion of the earth, but it would still appear an indivisible point, & seem to be fixed in one place, of the same bigness) that it is quite opposite to reason, to natural philosophy, and all out as absurd as disproportional (so some will) as prodigious, as that of the Sun's swift motion of Heavens. But this being assumed, to grant this their tenent of the earth's motion: if the earth move, it is a Planet, & shines to them in the Moon, & to the other Planetary Inhabitants, as the Moon and they to us upon the earth: but shine she doth, as Galileo, Kepler, and others prove, and then, by consequence, the rest of the Planets are inhabited, as well as the Moon, which he grants in his dissertation with Galileo's Sidereal Messenger, that there be Jovial & Saturnine Inhabitants, &c., & those several Planets have their several Moons about them, as the earth hath her's, as Galileo hath already evinced by his glasses: four about Jupiter,* two about Saturn (though Sitius the Florentine, Fortunius Licetus, and Julius Cæsar la Galla cavil at it): yet Kepler, the Emperor's Mathematician, confirms out of his experience that he saw as much by the same help, & more about Mars, Venus; and the rest they hope to find out, peradventure even amongst the fixed stars, which Brunus & Brutius have already averred. Then (I say) the earth and they be Planets alike, inhabited alike, moved about the Sun, the common Center of the World alike, and

---

* Some of those above Jupiter I have seen myself by the help of a glass eight feet long. — Burton's note.

it may be those two green children which Nubrigensis speaks of in his time that fell from Heaven, came from thence; and that famous stone that fell from heaven in Aristotle's time, in the 84th Olympiad, the third year, at Capua, recorded by Laertius, and others, or Ancile or buckler in Numa's time, recorded by Festus. We may likewise insert with Campanella and Brunus that which Pythagoras, Aristarchus Samius, Heraclitus, Epicurus, Melissus, Democritus, Leucippus, maintained in their ages, there be infinite Worlds, and infinite earths or systems, in infinite æther, which Eusebius collects out of their tenents, because infinite stars and planets like unto this of ours, which some stick not still to maintain and publickly defend: I look for innumerable worlds wandering in eternity, &c. (Nic. Hill). For if the Firmament be of such an incomparable bigness, as these Copernical Giants will have it, infinite, or nearly so, so vast and full of innumerable stars, as being infinite in extent, one above another, some higher, some lower, some nearer, some farther off, and so far asunder, and those so huge and great: insomuch that, if the whole sphere of Saturn, and all that is included in it, the aggregate, (as Fromundus of Louvain, in his Tract on The Immobility of the Earth, argues), were moved out among the stars we should not be able to see more than the likeness of a point, so vast is the distance between the earth and the fixed stars. If our world be small in respect, why may we not suppose a plurality of worlds, those infinite stars visible in the Firmament to be so many Suns, with particular fixt Centers; to have likewise their subordinate Planets, as the Sun hath his dancing still round him? which Cardinal Cusanus, Walkarinus, Brunus, and some others, have held, and some still maintain. Minds fed on the teachings of Aristotle, & accustomed to minute speculations, &c. Though they seem close to us, they are infinitely distant, and so, by consequence, there are infinite habitable worlds: what hinders? Why should not an infinite cause (as God is) produce infinite effects? as Nic. Hill disputes. Kepler (I confess) will by no means admit of Brunus' infinite worlds, or that the fixed stars should be so many Suns, with their compassing Planets, yet the said Kepler, betwixt jest and earnest in his Perspectives, Lunar Geography, and his Dream, besides his Dissertation with the Sidereal Messenger [of Galileo], seems in part to agree with this, and partly to contradict. For the Planets, he yields them to be inhabited, he doubts of the Stars: and so doth Tycho in his Astronomical Epistles, out of a consideration of their vastity and greatness, break out into some such like speeches, that he will never believe those great and huge bodies were made to no other use than this that we perceive, to illuminate the earth, a point insensible, in respect of the whole. But who shall dwell in these vast bodies, Earths, Worlds, if they be inhabited? rational creatures? as Kepler demands, or have they souls to be saved? or do they inhabit a better part of the World than we do? Are we or they Lords of the World? And how are all things made for man? It is a difficult knot to untie: 'tis hard to determine; this only he proves, that we are in the best place, best World, nearest the heart of the Sun. Thomas Campanella, a Calabrian Monk, in his second book * subscribes to this of Kepler; that they are inhabited he certainly supposeth, but with what kind of creatures he cannot say, he labours to prove it by all means, and that there are infinite Worlds, having made apology for Galileo, and dedicates this tenent of his to Cardinal Cajetan. Others freely speak, mutter, and would persuade the world (as Marinus Marcennus complains) that our modern Divines are too severe and rigid against Mathematicians, ignorant and peevish in not admitting their true demonstrations and certain observations, that they tyrannize over art, science, and all philosophy, in suppressing their labours (saith Pomponatius) forbidding them to write, to speak a truth, all to maintain their superstition, and for their profit's sake. As for those places of Scripture which oppugn it, they will have them spoken in the vulgar sense, and if rightly understood, and favourably interpreted, not at all against it: and as Otho Casman notes, many great Divines, besides Porphyry, Proclus, Simplicius, and those Heathen Philosophers, famous for their age and learning, argue that the Genesis of Moses is written in a popular sense, seeing that it is far out from true philosophical learning. For Moses makes mention but of two Planets, ⊙ [Sun] and ☾ [Moon], no 4 elements, &c. Read more in him, in Grossius and Junius. But to proceed, these and such like insolent and bold attempts, prodigious paradoxes, inferences must needs follow, if it once be granted, which Rotman, Kepler, Gilbert, Diggeus, Origanus, Galileo, and others, maintain of the Earth's motion, that 'tis a Planet, and shines as the Moon doth, which contains in it both land and sea as the Moon doth: for so they find by their glasses those spots on the face of the moon, the brighter parts are Earth, the dusky Sea, which Thales, Plutarch, and Pythagoras formerly taught: and manifestly discern Hills and Dales, and such like concavities, if we may subscribe to and believe Galileo's observations. But to avoid these paradoxes of the Earth's motion (which the Church of Rome hath lately condemned as heretical, as appears by Blancanus'

* Of De sensu rerum.

and Fromundus' writings) our latter Mathematicians have rolled all
the stones that may be stirred: and, to solve all appearances and objections, have invented new hypotheses, and fabricated new systems
of the World, out of their own Dædalean heads. Fracastorius will have
the Earth stand still, as before; and, to avoid that supposition of Eccentricks & Epicycles, he hath coined 72 Homocentricks, to solve all appearances. Nicholas Ramerus will have the Earth the Center of the
World, but moveable, and the eighth sphere immoveable, the five upper
Planets to move above the Sun, the Sun and Moon about the Earth. Of
which Orbs, Tycho Brahe puts the Earth the Center immoveable, the
stars immoveable, the rest with Ramerus, the Planets without Orbs to
wander in the Air, keep time and distance, true motion, according to
that virtue which God hath given them. Helisæus Rœslin censureth
both, with Copernicus (whose Hypothesis concerning the motion of the
earth Philippus Lansbergius hath lately vindicated, and demonstrated
with solid arguments in a just volume, Jansonius Cæsius hath illustrated in a sphere). The said Johannes Lansbergius, 1633, hath since
defended his assertion against all the cavils and calumnies of Fromundus his Anti-Aristarchus, Baptista Morinus, and Petrus Bartholinus:
Fromundus, 1634, hath written against him again, J. Rosseus of Aber-
deen, &c., (sound Drums and Trumpets), whilst Rœslin (I say) censures all, and Ptolemy himself as unsufficient: one offends against
natural Philosophy, another against Optick principles, a third against
Mathematical, as not answering to Astronomical observations: one puts
a great space betwixt Saturn's Orb and the eighth sphere, another too
narrow. In his own hypothesis he makes the Earth as before the universal Center, the Sun to the five upper Planets, to the eighth sphere he
ascribes diurnal motion, Eccentricks and Epicycles to the seven Planets,
which had been formerly exploded; and so,

When fools avoid one fault they run to the opposite, (HORACE)
as a tinker stops one hole and makes two, he corrects them, and doth
worse himself, reforms some, and mars all. In the mean time the World
is tossed in a blanket amongst them, they hoist the Earth up and down
like a ball, make it stand and go at their pleasures. One saith the Sun
stands, another he moves; a third comes in, taking them all at rebound,
and, lest there should any paradox be wanting, he finds certain spots
and clouds in the Sun by the help of glasses, which multiply (saith
Kepler) a thing seen a thousand times bigger in plane, and makes it
come 32 times nearer to the eye of the beholder: but see the demonstration of this glass in Tarde, by means of which the Sun must turn

round upon his Center, or they about the Sun. Fabricius puts only three, and those in the Sun: Apelles 15, and those without the Sun, floating like the Cyanean Isles in the Euxine Sea. Tarde the Frenchman hath observed 33, and those neither spots nor clouds, as Galileo supposeth, but Planets concentrick with the Sun, and not far from him, with regular motions. Christopher Scheiner, a German Suisser Jesuit, Ursica Rosa, divides them into Spots and Torchlets, and will have them to be fixed on the Sun's surface, and to absolve their periodical and regular motion in 27 or 28 days, holding withal the rotation of the Sun upon his Center; and are all so confident, that they have made schemes and tables of their motions. The Hollander, in his controversy with Apelles, censures all; and thus they disagree amongst themselves, old and new, irreconcileable in their opinions; thus Aristarchus, thus Hipparchus, thus Ptolemy, thus Albateginus, thus Alfraganus, thus Tycho, thus Ramerus, thus Rœslinus, thus Fracastorius, thus Copernicus and his adherents, thus Clavius and Maginus, &c. with their followers, vary and determine of these celestial orbs and bodies; and so, whilst these men contend about the Sun and Moon, like the Philosophers in Lucian, it is to be feared the Sun and Moon will hide themselves, and be as much offended as she was with those, and send another message to Jupiter, by some new fangled Icaromenippus, to make an end of all those curious controversies, and scatter them abroad.*

But why should the Sun and Moon be angry, or take exceptions at Mathematicians and Philosophers, when as the like measure is offered unto God himself by a company of Theologasters? They are not contented to see the Sun and Moon, measure their site and biggest distance in a glass, calculate their motions, or visit the Moon in a Poetical fiction, or a dream, as he † saith: I shall now venture upon a bold and memorable exploit, one never before attempted in this age. I shall explain this night's transactions in the Kingdom of the Moon, a place where no one has yet arrived, save in his dreams — [none] but he and Menippus. Or as Peter Cuneus ‡; I will act in good faith. Know that none of the things which I am going to write are true, I am going to speak of what never took place, nor ever will take place, just out of ingenuity, § to keep my

---

* Icaromenippus, Lucian's satire already referred to, represented the Cynic Philosopher Menippus as returning from a journey made with Dædalian wings among the stars and to Heaven itself. It is believed to be in some sort a parody of a similar satirical work by Menippus, whose writings are lost.

† According to Burton's footnote, the author of Menippean Satires, 1608.

‡ The author of Sardi Venales (Sardinians for Sale), Menippean Satires, 1612.

§ Burton's footnote refers here to Lipsius' Satire in a dream.

hand in; ———— not in jest, but in good earnest, these Gigantical Cyclopes will transcend spheres, heaven, stars, into that Empyrean Heaven; soar higher yet, and see what God himself doth. The Jewish Talmudists take upon them to determine how God spends his whole time, sometimes playing with Leviathan, sometimes overseeing the world, &c. like Lucian's Jupiter, that spent much of the year in painting butter-flies' wings, and seeing who offered sacrifice; telling the hours when it should rain, how much snow should fall in such a place, which way the wind should stand in Greece, which way in Africa. In the Turks' Alcoran Mahomet is taken up to Heaven upon a Pegasus sent a purpose for him, as he lay in bed with his wife, and after some conference with God is set on ground again. The Pagans paint him and mangle him after a thousand fashions; our Hereticks, Schismaticks, and some School-men, come not far behind: some paint him in the habit of an old man, and make Maps of Heaven, number the Angels, tell their several names, offices: some deny God and his providence; some take his office out of his hand, will bind and loose in Heaven, release, pardon, forgive, and be quartermaster with him; some call his Godhead in question, his power, and attributes, his mercy, justice, providence; they will know with Cæcilius, why good and bad are punished together, why war, fires, plagues infest all alike, why wicked men flourish, good are poor, in prison, sick, and ill at ease. Why doth he suffer so much mischief and evil to be done, if he be able to help? why doth he not assist good, or resist bad, reform our wills, if he be not the author of sin, and let such enor-mities be committed, unworthy of his knowledge, wisdom, government, mercy, and providence? why lets he all things be done by fortune and chance? Others as prodigiously enquire after his omnipotency, whether he is able to create more gods like unto himself? whether he can make a god out of a dung-beetle? &c. (*Whither, O priests, are you rushing so fast?*) Some, by visions and revelations, take upon them to be familiar with God, and to be of privy counsel with him; they will tell how many, and who, shall be saved, when the World shall come to an end, what year, what month, and whatsoever else God hath reserved unto himself, and to his Angels. Some again, curious phantasticks, will know more than this, and enquire with Epicurus, what God did before the World was made? was he idle? Where did he bide? What did he make the World of? Why did he then make it, and not before? If he made it new, or to have an end, how is he unchangeable, infinite? &c. Some will dispute, cavil, and object, as Julian did of old, whom Cyril confutes, as Simon Magus is feigned to do, in that dialogue betwixt him and Peter:

and Ammonius the Philosopher, in that dialogical disputation with Zacharias the Christian. If God be infinitely and only good, why should he alter or destroy the World? if he confound that which is good, how shall himself continue good? if he pull it down because evil, how shall he be free from the evil that made it evil? &c., with many such absurd and brainsick questions, intricacies, froth of human wit, and excrements of curiosity, &c., which, as our Saviour told his inquisitive Disciples, are not fit for them to know. But hoo! I am now gone quite out of sight, I am almost giddy with roving about: I could have ranged farther yet, but I am an infant, and not able to dive into these profundities, or sound these depths, not able to understand, much less to discuss. I leave the contemplation of these things to stronger wits, that have better ability, and happier leisure, to wade into such Philosophical mysteries: for put case I were as able as willing, yet what can one man do? I will conclude with Scaliger: We are by no means men, — rather fractions of men; through the agency of all it is possible to accomplish something, though nothing very great: from a single person — absolutely nothing. — Besides (as Nazianzen hath it) God desireth us to be inconspicuous; and with Seneca (on Comets): How much should we marvel at those rare spectacles of the world, not to be set in bounds by fixed laws, not yet to be understood? Many races there are that are familiar with the face of the sky: the time hasteneth when that which is now hid shall, by the diligence of longer ages, be brought forth to the light of day; one age sufficeth not, — the future, &c. ———— When God sees his time, he will reveal these mysteries to mortal men, and shew that to some few at last, which he hath concealed so long. For I am of his mind, that Columbus did not find out America by chance, but God directed him at that time to discover it: it was contingent to him, but necessary to God; he reveals and conceals, to whom and when he will. And which one said of Histories and Records of former times, God in his providence, to check our presumptuous inquisition, wraps up all things in uncertainty, bars us from long antiquity, and bounds our search within the compass of some few ages. Many good things are lost, which our predecessors made use of, as Panciroli will better inform you; many new things are daily invented, to the publick good; so Kingdoms, men, and knowledge, ebb and flow, are hid and revealed, and when you have all done, as the Preacher concluded, *There is nothing new under the sun.* But my melancholy spaniel's quest, my game is sprung, and I must suddenly come down & follow.

Jason Pratensis, in his book on diseases of the head, and chapter of

Melancholy, hath these words out of Galen: Let them come to me to know what meat and drink they shall use; and, besides that, I will teach them what temper of ambient Air they shall make choice of, what wind, what countries they shall choose, and what avoid. Out of which lines of his thus much we may gather, that to this cure of melancholy, amongst other things, the rectification of Air is necessarily required. This is performed, either in reforming Natural or Artificial Air. Natural is that which is in our election to choose or avoid: and 'tis either general, to Countries, Provinces; or particular, to Cities, Towns, Villages, or private houses. What harm those extremities of heat or cold do in this malady, I have formerly shewed: the medium must needs be good, where the Air is temperate, serene, quiet, free from bogs, fens, mists, all manner of putrefaction, contagious and filthy noisome smells. The Egyptians by all Geographers are commended to be jocund, a conceited and merry Nation: which I can ascribe to no other cause than the serenity of their Air. They that live in the Orcades are registered by Hector Boethius and Cardan to be fair of complexion, long-lived, most healthful, free from all manner of infirmities of body and mind, by reason of a sharp purifying Air, which comes from the Sea. The Bœotians in Greece were dull and heavy, fat Bœotians, by reason of a foggy Air in which they lived, —

Born and nurtured in heavy Bœotian air, (HORACE)

— Attica most acute, pleasant, and refined. The Clime changeth not so much customs, manners, wits (as Aristotle hath proved at large) as constitutions of their bodies, temperature itself. In all particular Provinces we see it confirmed by experience; as the Air is, so are the Inhabitants, dull, heavy, witty, subtile, neat, cleanly, clownish, sick, and sound. In Périgord in France the Air is subtile, healthful, seldom any plague or contagious disease, but hilly and barren: the men sound, nimble, and lusty; but in some parts of Guienne full of Moors and Marshes, the people dull, heavy, and subject to many infirmities. Who sees not a great difference betwixt Surrey, Sussex, and Romney Marsh, the Wolds in Lincolnshire, and the Fens? He therefore that loves his health, if his ability will give him leave, must often shift places, and make choice of such as are wholesome, pleasant, and convenient: there is nothing better than change of Air in this Malady, and generally for health to wander up and down, as those Tartars that live in hordes, and take opportunity of times, places, seasons. The Kings of Persia had their Summer and Winter Houses, in Winter at Sardis, in Summer at Susa, now at Persepolis, then at Pasargada. Cyrus lived seven cold months at Baby-

lon, three at Susa, two at Ecbatana, saith Xenophon, and had by that
means a perpetual Spring. The great Turk sojourns sometimes at Constantinople, sometimes at Adrianople, &c. The Kings of Spain have
their Escurial in heat of Summer, Madrid for an wholesome seat, Valladolid a pleasant site, &c., variety of retreats, as all Princes and great
men have, and their several progresses to this purpose. Lucullus the
Roman had his house at Rome, at Baiæ, &c. When Cn. Pompeius, Marcus Cicero (saith Plutarch) and many Noble men in the Summer came
to see him, at supper Pompeius jested with him, that it was an elegant
and pleasant Village [Villa], full of windows, galleries, and all offices fit
for a Summer-House, but in his judgement very unfit for Winter:
Lucullus made answer that the Lord of the House had wit like a Crane,
that changeth her country with the season; he had other houses furnished and built for that purpose, all out as commodious as this. So
Tully had his Tusculanum, Pliny his Larian Village, and every Gentleman of any fashion in our times hath the like. The Bishop of Exeter
had 14 several Houses all furnished, in times past. In Italy, though they
bide in Cities in Winter, which is more Gentleman-like, all the Summer
they come abroad to their Country-Houses, to recreate themselves. Our
Gentry in England live most part in the Country (except it be some
few Castles) building still in bottoms (saith Jovius) or near woods,
a crown of verdant trees; you shall know a Village by a tuft of trees
at or about it, to avoid those strong winds wherewith the Island is
infested, and cold Winter blasts. Some discommend moated houses, as
unwholesome, (so Camden saith of Ew-elme, that it was therefore un-
frequented, by reason of the vapours from stagnant waters near-by),
and all such places as be near lakes or rivers. But I am of opinion that
these inconveniences will be mitigated, or easily corrected, by good
fires, as one reports of Venice, that noisome smell and fog of the moors
is sufficiently qualified by those innumerable smokes. Nay more,
Thomas Philol. Ravennas, a great Physician, contends that the Venetians are generally longer lived than any City in Europe, & live many
of them 120 years. But it is not water simply that so much offends as
the slime and noisome smells that accompany such overflowed places,
which is but at some few seasons after a flood, and is sufficiently recompensed with sweet smells and aspects in Summer; Spring will variegate
the fields with countless hues, and many other commodities of pleasure
and profit; or else may be corrected by the site, if it be somewhat remote from the water, as Lindley, Orton-on-the-Hill, Drayton, or a little
more elevated, though nearer, as Caucut, as Amington, Polesworth,

Weddington (to insist in such places best to me known, upon the river of Anker in Warwickshire, Swarston, and Drakesly upon Trent). Or howsoever they be unseasonable in Winter, or at some times, they have their good use in Summer. If so be that their means be so slender, as they may not admit of any such variety, but must determine once for all, and make one house serve each season, I know no men that have given better rules in this behalf than our husbandry writers. Cato and Columella prescribe a good house to stand by a navigable river, good high-ways, near some City and in a good soil, but that is more for commodity than health.

The best soil commonly yields the worst Air, a dry sandy plat is fittest to build upon, and such as is rather hilly than plain, full of Downs, a Cotswold country, as being most commodious for hawking, hunting, wood, waters, and all manner of pleasures. Périgord in France is barren, yet by reason of the excellency of the air, and such pleasures that it affords, much inhabited by the Nobility; as Nuremberg in Germany, Toledo in Spain. Our countryman Tusser will tell us so much, that the fieldone [field-land] is for profit, the woodland for pleasure and health, the one commonly a deep clay, therefore noisome in Winter, and subject to bad high-ways, the other a dry sand. Provision may be had elsewhere, and our Towns are generally bigger in the woodland than the fieldone, more frequent and populous, and Gentlemen more delight to dwell in such places. Sutton Coldfield in Warwickshire (where I was once a Grammar Scholar) may be a sufficient witness, which stands, as Camden notes, in a bad and barren situation, but in an excellent air, and full of all manner of pleasures. Wadley in Berkshire is situate in a vale, though not so fertile, a soil as some vales afford, yet a most commodious site, wholesome, in a delicious air, a rich and pleasant seat. So Segrave in Leicestershire (which Town I am now bound to remember)* is sited in a Champaign, at the edge of the Wolds, and more barren than the villages about it, yet no place likely yields a better air. And he that built that fair house Wollerton in Nottinghamshire is much to be commended, (though the tract be sandy and barren about it), for making choice of such a place. Constantine praiseth mountains, hilly, steep places, above the rest by the Sea side, and such as look toward the North upon some great river, as Farmack in Derbyshire on the Trent, environed with hills, open only to the North, like Mount Edgemond in Cornwall, which Mr. Carew so much admires for an excellent seat : such

* For I am now Incumbent of that Rectory, presented thereto by my Right Honorable Patron the Lord Berkley. — Burton's note.

as is the general site of Bohemia: the North wind clarifies; but near lakes or marshes, in holes, obscure places, or to the South and West, he utterly disapproves; those winds are unwholesome, putrefying, and make men subject to diseases. The best building for health, according to him, is in high places, and in an excellent prospect, like that of Cuddesdon in Oxfordshire (which place I must in honour mention) is lately and fairly built * in a good air, good prospect, good soil, both for profit and pleasure, not so easily to be matched. P. Crescentius is very copious in this subject, how a house should be wholesomely sited, in a good coast, good air, wind, &c. Varro forbids lakes and rivers, marish [marshy] and manured grounds; they cause a bad air, gross diseases, hard to be cured: if it be so that he cannot help it, better, as he adviseth, sell thy house and land, than lose thine health. He that respects not this in choosing of his seat, or building his house, is mad, Cato saith, and his dwelling next to Hell itself, according to Columella: he commends in conclusion the middle of an hill, upon a descent. Baptista Porta censures Varro, Cato, Columella, and those ancient Rusticks, approving many things, disallowing some, and will by all means have the front of an house stand to the South, which how it may be good in Italy and hotter Climes, I know not, in our Northern Countries I am sure it is best. Stephanus, a Frenchman, subscribes to this, approving especially the descent of an hill South or South-East, with trees to the North, so that it be well watered; a condition in all sites which must not be omitted, as Herbastein inculcates. Julius Cæsar Claudinus, a Physician, for a Nobleman in Poland, melancholy given, adviseth him to dwell in a house inclining to the East, and by all means to provide the air be clear and sweet; which Montanus counselleth the Earl of Montfort his patient, to inhabit a pleasant house, and in a good air. If it be so the natural site may not be altered of our City, Town, Village, yet by artificial means it may be helped. In hot countries therefore they make the streets of their Cities very narrow, all over Spain, Africa, Italy, Greece, and many cities of France, in Languedoc especially, and Provence, those Southern parts: Montpelier, the habitation and University of Physicians, is so built, with high houses, narrow streets, to divert the Sun's scalding rays, which Tacitus commends, as most agreeing to their health, because the height of buildings and narrowness of streets keep away the Sunbeams. Some Cities use Galleries, or arched

---

* By John Bancroft, Dr. of Divinity, my quondam tutor in Christ-church, Oxon, now the Right Reverend Lord Bishop of Oxon, who built this house for himself and his successors. — Burton's note.

Cloisters, towards the street, as Damascus, Bologna, Padua, Berne in Switzerland, Westchester, with us, as well to avoid tempests as the Sun's scorching heat. They build on high hills in hot countries for more air; or to the Sea side, as Baiæ, Naples, &c. In our Northern coasts we are opposite; we commend straight, broad, open, fair streets, as most befitting and agreeing to our clime. We build in bottoms for warmth: and that site of Mitylene in the Island of Lesbos, in the Ægean Sea, (which Vitruvius so much discommends, magnificently built with fair houses, but unadvisedly sited, because it lay along to the South, and when the South wind blew, the people were all sick,) would make an excellent site in our Northern climes.

Of that artificial site of houses I have sufficiently discoursed: if the air of the dwelling may not be altered, yet there is much in choice of such a chamber or room, in opportune opening and shutting of windows, excluding foreign air and winds, and walking abroad at convenient times. Crato, a German, commends East and South site (disallowing cold air and Northern winds in this case, rainy weather and misty days) free from putrefaction, fens, bogs, and muck-hills. If the air be such, open no windows, come not abroad. Montanus will have his patient not to stir at all, if the wind be big or tempestuous, as most part in March it is with us; or in cloudy, lowering, dark days, as in November, which we commonly call the black month; or stormy, let the wind stand how it will, he must not open a casement in bad weather, or in a boisterous season; he especially forbids us to open windows to a South wind. The best site for chamber windows in my judgement are North, East, South, and which is the worst, West. Levinus Lemnius attributes so much to air, and rectifying of wind and windows, that he holds it alone sufficient to make a man sick or well, to alter body and mind. A clear air cheers up the spirits, exhilarates the mind; a thick, black, misty, tempestuous, contracts, overthrows. Great heed is therefore to be taken at what times we walk, how we place our windows, lights, and houses, how we let in or exclude this ambient air. The Egyptians, to avoid immoderate heat, make their windows on the top of the house like chimneys, with two tunnels to draw a through air. In Spain they commonly make great opposite windows without glass, still shutting those which are next to the Sun. So likewise in Turkey and Italy (Venice excepted, which brags of her stately glazed Palaces) they use paper windows to like purpose: and lie beneath the sky, in the top of their flat-roofed houses, so sleeping under the canopy of Heaven. In some parts of Italy they have Windmills, to draw a cooling air out of hollow caves, and disperse the same through all the chambers of their Palaces, to refresh them; as at Custoza the house of Cæsareo Trento, a Gentleman of Vicenza, and elsewhere. Many excellent means are invented to correct nature by art. If none of these courses help, the best way is to make artificial air, which howsoever is profitable and good, still to be made hot and moist, and to be seasoned with sweet perfumes, pleasant and lightsome as may be; to have Roses, Violets, and sweet smelling flowers ever in their windows, Posies in their hand. Laurentius commends Water-Lilies, a vessel of warm water to evaporate in the room, which will make a more delightsome perfume, if there be added Orange flowers, pills of Citrons, Rosemary, Cloves, Bays, Rose-Water, Rose-Vinegar, Benzoin, Ladanum, Styrax, and such like Gums, which make a pleasant & acceptable perfume. Bessardus Bisantinus prefers the smoke of Juniper to melancholy persons, which is in great request with us at Oxford, to sweeten our chambers. Guianerius prescribes the air to be moistened with water, and sweet herbs boiled in it, vine and sallow leaves, &c., to besprinkle the ground and posts with Rose-Water, Rose-Vinegar, which Avicenna much approves. Of colours it is good to behold green, red, yellow, and white, and by all means to have light enough with windows in the day, wax candles in the night, neat chambers, good fires in winter, merry companions; for though melancholy persons love to be dark and alone, yet darkness is a great increaser of the humour.

Although our ordinary air be good by nature or art, yet it is not amiss, as I have said, still to alter it; no better Physick for a melancholy man than change of air and variety of places, to travel abroad and see fashions. Leo Afer speaks of many of his countrymen so cured, without all other Physick: amongst the Negroes there is such an excellent air, that, if any of them be sick elsewhere, and brought thither, he is instantly recovered, of which he was often an eye-witness. Lipsius, Zuinger, and some other, add as much of ordinary travel. No man, saith Lipsius in an Epistle to Philip Lanoius, a Noble friend of his, now ready to make a voyage, can be such a stock or stone, whom that pleasant speculation of countries, cities, towns, rivers, will not affect. Seneca the Philosopher was infinitely taken with the sight of Scipio Africanus' house, near Linternum, to view those old buildings, Cisterns, Baths, Tombs, &c. And how was Tully pleased with the sight of Athens, to behold those ancient and fair buildings, with a remembrance of their worthy inhabitants! Paulus Æmilius, that renowned Roman Captain, after he had conquered Perseus, the last King of Macedonia, and now

made an end of his tedious wars, though he had been long absent from
Rome, and much there desired, about the beginning of Autumn, (as
Livy describes it), made a pleasant peregrination all over Greece, accompanied with his son Scipio, and Athenæus the brother of king
Eumenes, leaving the charge of his army with Sulpicius Gallus. By
Thessaly he went to Delphi, thence to Megaris, Aulis, Athens, Argos,
Lacedæmon, Megalopolis, &c. He took great content, exceeding delight,
in that his voyage, as who doth not that shall attempt the like, though
his travel be, (as one well observes), to crack, gaze, see fine sights and
fashions, spend time, rather than for his own or publick good? (as it
is to many gallants that travel out their best days, together with their
means, manners, honesty, religion), yet it availeth howsoever. For
peregrination charms our senses with such unspeakable and sweet
variety, that some count him unhappy that never travelled, a kind of
prisoner, and pity his case that from his cradle to his old age beholds
the same still; still, still the same, the same: insomuch that Rhasis
doth not only commend but enjoin travel, and such variety of objects
to a melancholy man, and to lie in diverse Inns, to be drawn into several companies. Montaltus and many Neotericks are of the same mind.
Celsus adviseth him therefore that will continue his health to have
diversity of callings, occupations, to be busied about, sometimes to live
in the city, sometimes in the country; now to study or work, to be intent, then again to hawk, or hunt, swim, run, ride, or exercise himself.
A good prospect alone will ease melancholy, as Gomesius contends.
The citizens of Barcelona, saith he, otherwise penned in, melancholy,
and stirring little abroad, are much delighted with that pleasant prospect their city hath into the sea, which, like that of old Athens, besides Ægina, Salamis, and many pleasant Islands, had all the variety
of delicious objects: so are those Neapolitans, and inhabitants of
Genoa, to see the ships, boats, and passengers go by, out of their
windows, their whole cities being sited on the side of an hill, like Pera
by Constantinople, so that each house almost hath a free prospect to
the sea, as some part of London to the Thames: or to have a free prospect all over the city at once, as at Granada in Spain, and Fez in Africa,
the river running betwixt two declining hills, the steepness causeth each
house almost as well to oversee as to be overseen of the rest. Every
country is full of such delightsome prospects, as well within land as by
sea, as Hermon and Ramah in Palestine, Collalto in Italy, the top of
Taygetus or Acrocorinthus, that old decayed castle in Corinth, from
which Peloponnesus, Greece, the Ionian and Ægean Seas, were at one

view to be taken. In Egypt the square top of the great Pyramid, 300 yards in height, and so the Sultan's Palace in Grand Cairo, the country being plain, hath a marvellous fair prospect, as well over Nilus as that great city, five Italian miles long and two broad, by the river side: from Mount Sion in Jerusalem the Holy Land is of all sides to be seen: such high places are infinite: with us those of the best note are Glastonbury Tower, Bever castle, Rodway Grange, Walsby in Lincolnshire, where I lately received a real kindness, by the munificence of the Right Honourable my noble Lady and Patroness, the Lady Frances, Countess Dowager of Exeter: and two amongst the rest, which I may not omit for vicinity's sake, Oldbury in the confines of Warwickshire, where I have often looked about me with great delight, at the foot of which hill I was born *: & Hanbury in Staffordshire, contiguous to which is Falde, a pleasant Village, and an ancient patrimony belonging to our family, now in the possession of mine elder brother William Burton Esquire. Barclay the Scot commends that of Greenwich Tower for one of the best prospects in Europe, to see London on the one side, the Thames, ships, and pleasant meadows, on the other. There be those that say as much and more of S. Mark's Steeple in Venice. Yet these are at too great distance; some are especially affected with such objects as be near, to see passengers go by in some great roadway, or boats in a river, to oversee a Fair, a Market place, or out of a pleasant window into some thorough-fare street, to behold a continual concourse, a promiscuous rout, coming and going, or a multitude of spectators at a Theatre, a Mask, or some such like shew. But I rove: the sum is this, that variety of actions, objects, air, places, are excellent good in this infirmity and all others, good for man, good for beast. Constantine the Emperor holds it an only cure for rotten sheep, and any manner of sick cattle. Lælius à Fonte Eugubinus, that great Doctor, at the latter end of many of his consultations (as commonly he doth set down what success his Physick had) in melancholy most especially approves of this above all other remedies whatsoever: Many other things helped, but change of air was that which wrought the cure, and did most good.

---

* At Lindley in Leicestershire, the possession and dwelling-place of Ralph Burton, Esquire, my late deceased father. — Burton's note.

MEMBER 4

Exercise rectified of Body and Mind

To that great inconvenience, which comes on the one side by immoderate and unseasonable exercise, too much solitariness and idleness on the other, must be opposed, as an Antidote, a moderate and seasonable use of it, and that both of body and mind as a most material circumstance, much conducing to this cure, and to the general preservation of our health. The Heavens themselves run continually round, the Sun riseth and sets, the Moon increaseth and decreaseth, Stars and Planets keep their constant motions, the air is still tossed by the winds, the waters ebb and flow, to their conservation no doubt, to teach us that we should ever be in action. For which cause Hierom prescribes Rusticus the Monk, that he be always occupied about some business or other, that the Devil do not find him idle. Seneca would have a man do something, though it be to no purpose. Xenophon wisheth one rather to play at tables, dice, or make a jester of himself (though he might be far better employed) than do nothing. The Egyptians of old, and many flourishing Commonwealths since, have enjoined labour and exercise to all sorts of men, to be of some vocation and calling, and to give an account of their time, to prevent those grievous mischiefs that come by idleness; *for as fodder, whip, and burden belong to the ass, so meat, correction and work unto the servant.* The Turks enjoin all men whatsoever, of what degree, to be of some trade or other, the grand Seignior himself is not excused. In our memory (saith Sabellicus) Mahomet the Turk, he that conquered Greece, at that very time when he heard Embassadors of other Princes, did either carve or cut wooden spoons, or frame something upon a table. This present Sultan makes notches for bows. The Jews are most severe in this examination of time. All well-governed Places, Towns, Families, and every discreet person will be a law unto himself. But amongst us the Badge of Gentry is idleness, to be of no calling, not to labour, for that's derogatory to their birth, to be a mere spectator, a drone, born only to consume the fruits of the earth, to have no necessary employment to busy himself about in Church and Commonwealth (some few Governors exempted) but to rise to eat, &c., to spend his days in hawking, hunting, &c. and such-like disports and recreations (which our casuists tax) are the sole exercise almost & ordinary actions of our Nobility, and in which they are too immoderate. And thence it comes to pass that in City and Country so many grievances of body and mind, and this feral disease of Melancholy so frequently rageth, and now domineers almost all over Europe amongst our great ones. They know not how to spend their time (disports excepted, which are all their business), what to do, or otherwise how to bestow themselves: like our modern Frenchmen, that had rather lose a pound of blood in a single combat than a drop of sweat in any honest labour. Every man almost hath something or other to employ himself about, some vocation, some trade, but they do all by ministers and servants; they consider themselves born for ease, when truly it is often to their own and others' detriment, as one freely taxeth such kind of men; they are all for pastimes, 'tis all their study; all their invention tends to this alone, to drive away time, as if they were born some of them to no other ends. Therefore to correct and avoid these errors and inconveniences, our Divines, Physicians, and Politicians, so much labour, and so seriously exhort; and for this disease in particular there can be no better cure than continual business, as Rhasis holds, to have some employment or other, which may set their mind awork, and distract their cogitations. Riches may not easily be had without labour and industry, nor learning without study, neither can our health be preserved without bodily exercise. If it be of the body, Guianerius allows that exercise which is gentle, and still after those ordinary frications, which must be used every morning. Montaltus and Jason Pratensis use almost the same words, highly commending exercise, if it be moderate; a wonderful help so used, Crato calls it, and a great means to preserve our health, as adding strength to the whole body, increasing natural heat, by means of which the nutriment is well concocted in the stomack, liver, and veins, few or no crudities left, is happily distributed over all the body. Besides, it expels excrements by sweat, and other insensible vapours, in so much that Galen prefers Exercise before all Physick, Rectification of Diet, or any Regiment in what kind soever; 'tis Nature's Physician. Fulgentius, out of Gordonius, terms exercise a spur of a dull sleepy nature, the comforter of the members, cure of infirmity, death of diseases, destruction of all mischiefs and vices. The fittest time for exercise is a little before dinner, a little before supper, or at any time when the body is empty. Montanus prescribes it every morning to his patient, and that, as Calenus adds, after he hath done his ordinary needs, rubbed his body, washed his hands and face, combed his head, and gargarized. What kind of exercise he should use Galen tells us, and in what measure, till the body be ready to sweat, and roused up; to a ruddy glow, some say, but not to sweat, lest it should dry the body too much; others enjoin those wholesome businesses, as to dig so long in his garden, to hold the plough, and the like. Some prescribe frequent and violent labour and exercises, as sawing every day, so long together, (Hippocrates confounds them), but that is in some cases, to some peculiar men; the most forbid, and by no means will have it go farther than a beginning sweat, as being perilous if it exceed.

Of these labours, exercises, and recreations, which are likewise included, some properly belong to the body, some to the mind, some more easy, some hard, some with delight, some without, some within doors, some natural, some are artificial. Amongst bodily exercises Galen commends to play at ball, be it with the hand or racket, in Tennis-courts or otherwise, it exerciseth each part of the body, and doth much good, so that they sweat not too much. It was in great request of old amongst the Greeks, Romans, Barbarians, mentioned by Homer, Herodotus, and Pliny. Some write, that Aganella, a fair maid of Corcyra, was the inventor of it, for she presented the first ball that ever was made to Nausicaa, the daughter of King Alcinous, and taught her how to use it.

The ordinary sports which are used abroad are Hawking, Hunting, the cheerful toils of hunting, one calls them, because they recreate body and mind; another, the best exercise that is, by which alone many have been freed from all feral diseases. Hegesippus relates of Herod, that he was eased of a grievous melancholy by that means. Plato highly magnifies it, dividing it into three parts, by Land, Water, Air. Xenophon graces it with a great name, the gift of the Gods, a Princely sport, which they have ever used, saith Langius, as well for health as pleasure, and do at this day, it being the sole almost and ordinary sport of our Noblemen in Europe, and elsewhere all over the world. Bohemus styles it therefore a noble employ; 'tis all their study, their exercise, ordinary business, all their talk: and indeed some dote too much after it, they can do nothing else, discourse of naught else. Paulus Jovius doth in some sort tax our English Nobility for it, for living in the country so much, and too frequent use of it, as if they had no other means but Hawking and Hunting to approve themselves Gentlemen with.

Hawking comes near to Hunting, the one in the Air, as the other on the Earth, a sport as much affected as the other, by some preferred. It was never heard of amongst the Romans, invented some 1200 years since, and first mentioned by Firmicus. The Greek Emperors began it, and now nothing so frequent: he is no body that in the season hath not a Hawk on his fist. A great Art, and many books written of it. It is a wonder to hear what is related of the Turks' Officers in this behalf, how many thousand men are employed about it, how many Hawks of all sorts, how much revenues consumed on that only disport, how much time is spent at Adrianople alone every year to that purpose. The Persian Kings hawk after Butterflies with sparrows, made to that use, and starlings; lesser Hawks for lesser games they have, and bigger for the rest, that they may produce their sport to all seasons. The Muscovian Emperors reclaim Eagles to fly at Hinds, Foxes, &c. and such a one was sent for a present to Queen Elizabeth: some reclaim Ravens, Castrils, Pies, [Magpies], &c. and man them for their pleasures.

Fowling is more troublesome, but all out as delightsome to some sorts of men, be it with guns, lime, nets, glades, gins, strings, baits, pitfalls, pipes, calls, stalking-horses, setting-dogs, coy-ducks, &c. or otherwise. Some much delight to take Larks with day-nets, small birds with chaff-nets, plovers, partridges, herons, snite [snipe], &c. Henry iii, King of Castile (as Mariana the Jesuit reports of him) was much affected with catching of Quails, and many Gentlemen take a singular pleasure at morning and evening to go abroad with their Quail-pipes, and will take any pains to satisfy their delight in that kind. The Italians have gardens fitted to such use, with nets, bushes, glades, sparing no cost or industry, and are very much affected with the sport. Tycho Brahe, that great Astronomer, in the Chorography of his Isle of Huena, & Castle of Uraniburge, puts down his nets, and manner of catching small birds, as an ornament, and a recreation, wherein he himself was sometimes employed.

Fishing is a kind of hunting by water, be it with nets, weels, baits, angling or otherwise, and yields all out as much pleasure to some men as dogs or hawks, when they draw their fish upon the bank, saith Nic. Henselius, speaking of that extraordinary delight his Countrymen took in fishing, and in making of pools. James Dubravius, that Moravian, in his book on fish, telleth how, travelling by the highway side in Silesia, he found a Nobleman booted up to the groins, wading himself, pulling the nets, and labouring as much as any fisherman of them all: and when some belike objected to him the baseness of his office, he excused himself, that if other men might hunt Hares, why should not he hunt Carps? Many Gentlemen in like sort with us will wade up to the Arm-holes upon such occasions, and voluntarily undertake that, to satisfy their pleasure, which a poor man for a good stipend would scarce be hired to undergo. Plutarch, in his book On the Cleverness of Animals, speaks against all fishing, as a filthy, base, illiberal employment, having neither wit nor perspicacity in it, nor worth the labour. But he that shall consider the variety of Baits, for all seasons, & pretty devices which our Anglers have invented, peculiar lines, false flies, several sleights, &c., will say that it deserves like commendation, requires as much study and perspicacity as the rest, and is to be preferred before many of them. Because hawking and hunting are very laborious, much riding and many dangers accompany them; but this is still and quiet: and if so be the angler catch no Fish, yet he hath a wholesome walk to the Brook side, pleasant shade by the sweet silver streams; he hath good air, and sweet smells of fine fresh meadow flowers, he hears the melodious harmony of Birds, he sees the Swans, Herons, Ducks, Water-hens, Coots, &c., and many other Fowl, with their brood, which he thinketh better than the noise of Hounds, or blast of Horns, and all the sport that they can make.

Many other sports and recreations there be, much in use, as ringing, bowling, shooting, which Ascham commends in a just volume, and hath in former times been enjoined by statute as a defensive exercise, and an honour to our Land, as well may witness our victories in France. Keelpins, trunks, quoits, pitching bars, hurling, wrestling, leaping, running, fencing, mustering, swimming, wasters, foils, foot-ball, balloon, quintain, &c. and many such, which are the common recreations of the country folks; riding of great horses, running at rings, tilts and tournaments, horse-races, wild-goose chases, which are the disports of greater men, and good in themselves, though many Gentlemen, by that means, gallop quite out of their fortunes.

But the most pleasant of all outward pastimes is that of Aretæus, to make a petty progress, a merry journey now and then with some good companions, to visit friends, see Cities, Castles, Towns,

To see the pleasant fields, the crystal fountains,

And take the gentle air amongst the mountains,　(ꜰʀᴀᴄᴀꜱᴛᴏʀɪᴜꜱ)

to walk amongst Orchards, Gardens, Bowers, Mounts, and Arbours, artificial wildernesses, green thickets, Arches, Groves, Lawns, Rivulets, Fountains, and such like pleasant places, like that Antiochian Daphne, Brooks, Pools, Fishponds, betwixt wood and water, in a fair meadow, by a river side, where are the ever-changing songs of little birds, bright colours, and the meadow-shrubbery, &c., to disport in some pleasant plain, park, run up a steep hill sometimes, or sit in a shady seat, must needs be a delectable recreation. The Prince's garden at Ferrara Schottus highly magnifies, with the groves, mountains, ponds, for a delectable prospect, he was much affected with it; a Persian Paradise, or pleasant park, could not be more delectable in his sight. S. Bernard, in the description of his Monastery, is almost ravished with the pleasures of it. A sick man (saith he) sits upon a green bank, and when the Dog-star parcheth the plains, and dries up rivers, he lies in a shady bower, and feeds his eyes with variety of objects, herbs, trees; to comfort his misery, he receives many delightsome smells, and fills his ears with that sweet and various harmony of Birds. Good God! (saith he) what a company of pleasures hast thou made for man! He that should be admitted on a sudden to the sight of such a Palace as that of Escurial in Spain or to that which the Moors built at Granada, Fontainebleau in France, the Turk's gardens in his Seraglio, wherein all manner of birds and beasts are kept for pleasure, Wolves, Bears, Lynxes, Tigers, Lions, Elephants, &c., or upon the banks of that Thracian Bosphorus: the Pope's Belvedere in Rome, as pleasing as those hanging gardens in Babylon, or that Indian King's delightsome garden in Ælian; or those famous gardens of the Lord Cantelow in France, could not choose, though he were never so ill apaid, but be much recreated for the time; or many of our Noblemen's gardens at home. To take a boat in a pleasant evening, and with musick to row upon the waters, which Plutarch so much applauds, Ælian admires upon the river Peneus, in those Thessalian fields beset with green bays, where birds so sweetly sing that passengers, enchanted as it were with their heavenly musick, forget forthwith all labours, care, and grief: or in a Gondola through the Grand Canal in Venice, to see those goodly Palaces, must needs refresh and give content to a melancholy dull spirit. Or to see the inner rooms of a fair-built and sumptuous edifice, as that of the Persian Kings so much renowned by Diodorus and Curtius, in which all was almost beaten gold, chairs, stools, thrones, tabernacles, and pillars, of gold, plane trees and vines of gold, grapes of precious stones, all the other ornaments of pure gold,

> *Gems on the couches gleam, the yellow jasper*
> *Sets off the furniture, the coverlets*
> *Are Tyrian purple,* (LUCAN)

with sweet odours and perfumes, generous vines, opiparous [sumptuous] fare, &c. besides the gallantest young men, the fairest virgins, the rarest beauties the world could afford, and those set out with costly and curious attires, to the everlasting wonder of all beholders, with exquisite musick, as in Trimalchio's house, in every chamber, sweet voices ever sounding day and night, incomparable splendour, all delights and pleasures in each kind which to please the senses could possibly be devised or had, the guests to crown. Telemachus in Homer is

brought in as one ravished almost, at the sight of that magnificent
Palace and rich furniture of Menelaus, when he beheld

> *Such glittering of gold and brightest brass to shine,*
> *Clear amber, silver pure, and ivory so fine:*
> *Jupiter's lofty Palace, where the Gods do dwell,*
> *Was even such a one, and did it not excel.*

It will refresh the soul of man, to see fair-built Cities, Streets, Theatres,
Temples, Obelisks, &c. The Temple of Jerusalem was so fairly built of
white marble, with so many Pyramids covered with gold; was so
glorious and so glistered afar off, that the spectators might not well
abide the sight of it. But the inner parts were all so curiously set out
with Cedar, Gold, Jewels, &c. as he said of Cleopatra's Palace in Egypt,

> *The woodwork hid by solid gold,*　(LUCAN)

that the beholders were amazed. What so pleasant as to see some Pageant or Sight go by, as at Coronations, Weddings, and such like Solemnities, to see an Embassador or a Prince met, received, entertained,
with Masks, Shews, Fireworks, &c. To see two Kings fight in single
combat, as Porus and Alexander, Canutus and Edmund Ironside, Scanderbeg and Ferat Bassa the Turk, when not honour alone but life itself
is at stake, as the Poet of Hector,

> *The contest was not for some ox or oxhide,*
> *The usual prizes of a race, the stake*
> *Was nothing less than mighty Hector's life.*

To behold a battle fought, like that of Cressy, or Agincourt, or Poictiers,
I do not know (saith Froissart), whether any age can produce such
like. To see one of Cæsar's triumphs in old Rome revived, or the like.
To be present at an Interview, as that famous [one] of Henry VIII. and
Francis I. so much renowned all over Europe; where, with so much
splendour (saith Hubertus Vellius), and so much triumphant display,
both these Kings and their wives met together; no age ever saw the
like. So infinitely pleasant are such Shews, to the sight of which often
times they will come hundreds of miles, give any money for a place, and
remember many years after with singular delight. Bodine, when he
was Embassador in England, said he saw the Noblemen go in their
Robes to the Parliament-House, beheld the spectacle with the greatest
pleasure, he was much affected with the sight of it. Pomponius Columna,
saith Jovius in his Life, saw 13 Frenchmen and so many Italians once
fight for a whole Army: the pleasantest sight that ever he saw in his
life. Who would not have been affected with such a spectacle? Or that
single combat of Breaute the Frenchman and Anthony Schets a Dutch-

man, before the walls of Sylvaducis in Brabant, in the year 1600. They were 22 Horse on the one side, as many on the other, which like Livy's Horatii, Torquati, and Corvini, fought for their own glory and Country's honour, in the sight and view of their whole City and Army. When Julius Cæsar warred about the bankes of Rhone, there came a Barbarian Prince to see him and the Roman Army, and when he had beheld Cæsar a good while, I see the Gods now (saith he) which before I heard of; it was the happiest day that ever he had in his life. Such a sight alone were able of itself to drive away melancholy, if not for ever, yet it must needs expel it for a time. Radzivilius was much taken with the Bassa's Palace in Cairo, and, amongst many other objects which that place afforded, with that solemnity of cutting the banks of Nilus, by Imbram Bassa, when it overflowed; besides two or three hundred gilded Gallies on the water, he saw two millions of men gathered together on the land with Turbans as white as snow, and 'twas a goodly sight. The very reading of feasts, triumphs, interviews, nuptials, tilts, tournaments, combats, and monomachies, is most acceptable and pleasant. Franciscus Modius hath made a large collection of such solemnities in two great Tomes, which whoso will may peruse. The inspection alone of those curious Iconographies of Temples and Palaces, as that of the Lateran Church in Albert Durer, that of the Temple of Jerusalem in Josephus, Adricomius, and Villalpandus: that of the Escurial in Guadas, of Diana at Ephesus in Pliny, Nero's golden Palace in Rome, Justinian's in Constantinople, that Peruvian Incas' in Cuzco, that seemed to have been built by devils rather than men; S. Mark's in Venice by Ignatius, with many such: antiques (saith that interpreter of Pausanias), the rare workmanship of those ancient Greeks, in Theatres, Obelisks, Temples, Statues, gold, silver, ivory, marble images, affect one as much by reading almost as by sight.

The Country hath his recreations, the City his several Gymnicks and Exercises. May-games, Feasts, Wakes, and Merry Meetings, to solace themselves, the very being in the Country; that life itself is a sufficient recreation to some men, to enjoy such pleasures as those old Patriarchs did. Diocletian, the Emperor, was so much affected with it, that he gave over his Sceptre, and turned gardener. Constantine wrote 20 books of Husbandry. Lysander, when Embassadors came to see him, bragged of nothing more than of his orchard, " These are my own planting." What shall I say of Cincinnatus, Cato, Tully, and many such? how have they been pleased with it, to prune, plant, inoculate, and graft, to shew so many several kinds of Pears, Apples, Plums, Peaches, &c.

Sometimes with traps deceive, with line and string
To catch wild birds and beasts, encompassing
The grove with dogs, and out of bushes firing. (VIRGIL)
To seek the nests of birds, their eggs admiring. (MANTUAN)

Jucundus, in his preface to Cato, Varro, Columella, &c., put out by him, confesseth of himself, that he was mightily delighted with these Husbandry studies, and took extraordinary pleasure in them. If the theorick or speculation can so much affect, what shall the place and exercise itself, the practick part, do? The same confession I find in Herbastein, Porta, Camerarius, and many others, which have written of that subject. If my testimony were ought worth, I could say as much of myself; I am a veritable Saturn; no man ever took more delight in Springs, Woods, Groves, Gardens, Walks, Fishponds, Rivers, &c. But

So Tantalus catches at the waves that fly
His thirsty palate. (HORACE)

And so do I; I may wish, but not enjoy.

Every Palace, every City almost, hath his peculiar Walks, Cloisters, Terraces, Groves, Theatres, Pageants, Games, and several Recreations; every Country some professed Gymnicks, to exhilarate their minds, & exercise their bodies. The Greeks had their Olympian, Pythian, Isthmian, Nemean Games, in honour of Neptune, Jupiter, Apollo; Athens hers: some for Honour, Garlands, Crowns; some for beauty, dancing, running, leaping, like our silver games. The Romans had their Feasts, as the Athenians and Lacedæmonians held their publick Banquets, in the Prytaneum, the Panathanæan festivals, the Thesmophorian festivals, the Pheiditia or Common Festivals, Plays, Naumachies, places for [mock] Sea-fights, Theatres, Amphitheatres able to contain 70,000 men, wherein they had several delightsome Shews to exhilarate the people; Gladiators, combats of men with themselves, with wild beasts, and wild beasts one with another, like our Bull-baitings, or Bear-baitings (in which many countrymen and Citizens amongst us so much delight and so frequently use), Dancers on Ropes, Jugglers, Wrestlers, Comedies, Tragedies, publickly exhibited at the Emperor's and Cities' charge, and that with incredible cost & magnificence. In the Low Countries (as Meteran relates) before these wars, they had many solemn Feasts, Plays, Challenges, Artillery Gardens, Colleges of Rhymers, Rhetoricians, Poets: and to this day such places are curiously maintained in Amsterdam, as appears by that description of Isaacus Pontanus. So likewise not long since at Freiburg in Germany, as is evident by that relation of Neander, they had solemn Plays every seven years, which Bocerus, one of their own Poets, hath elegantiy described:

But what shall I tell of their wonderful plays,
That rival old Rome's, in her palmiest days?

In Italy they have solemn Declamations of certain select young Gentlemen in Florence, (like those Reciters in old Rome), and publick
Theatres in most of their Cities, for Stage-players and others, to exercise and recreate themselves. All seasons almost, all places, have
their several pastimes, some in Summer, some in Winter, some abroad,
some within, some of the body, some of the mind, and divers men have
divers recreations and exercises. Domitian the Emperor was much delighted with catching flies, Augustus to play with nuts amongst children, Alexander Severus was often pleased to play with whelps and
young pigs, Adrian was so wholly enamoured with dogs and horses, that
he bestowed monuments and tombs on them, and buried them in graves.
In foul weather, or when they can use no other convenient sports, by
reason of the time, as we do Cock-fighting to avoid idleness, I think,
(though some be seriously taken with it, spend much time, cost and
charges, and are too solicitous about it), Severus used Partridges and
Quails, as many Frenchmen do still, and to keep Birds in Cages, with
which he was much pleased, when at any time he had leisure from
publick cares and businesses. He had (saith Lampridius) tame Pheasants, Ducks, Partridges, Peacocks, and some 20,000 Ringdoves and
Pigeons. Busbequius, the Emperor's Orator, when he lay in Constantinople, & could not stir much abroad, kept for his recreation, busying
himself to see them fed, almost all manner of strange birds and beasts;
this was something, though not to exercise his body, yet to refresh his
mind. Conrad Gesner, at Zurich in Switzerland, kept so likewise, for his
pleasure, a great company of wild beasts, and (as he saith) took great
delight to see them eat their meat. Turkey Gentlewomen, that are perpetual prisoners, still mewed up according to the custom of the place,
have little else besides their household business, or to play with their
children, to drive away time, but to dally with their cats, which they
have as pets, as many of our Ladies and Gentlewomen use Monkeys and
little Dogs. The ordinary recreations which we have in Winter, and in
most solitary times busy our minds with, are Cards, Tables and Dice,
Shovel-board, Chess-play, the Philosopher's game,* small trunks,†
shuttle-cock, billiards, musick, masks, singing, dancing, Yulegames,
frolicks, jests, riddles, catches, purposes, questions and commands,
merry tales of Errant Knights, Queens, Lovers, Lords, Ladies, Giants,

* A kind of chess.
† A game like bagatelle, also called troll-madam, & pigeon-holes.

Dwarfs, Thieves, Cheaters, Witches, Fairies, Goblins, Friars, &c., such as the old woman told [of] Psyche in Apuleius, Boccacio, Novels, and the rest, which some delight to hear, some to tell, all are well pleased with. Amaranthus, the Philosopher, met Hermocles, Diophantus, and Philolaus, his companions, one day busily discoursing about Epicurus' and Democritus' tenents, very solicitous which was most probable and came nearest to truth. To put them out of that surly controversy, and to refresh their spirits, he told them a pleasant tale of Stratocles the Physician's wedding, and of all the particulars, the company, the cheer, the musick, &c., for he was new come from it, with which relation they were so much delighted, that Philolaus wished a blessing to his heart, and many a good wedding, many such merry meetings might he be at, to please himself with the sight, and others with the narration of it. News are generally welcome to all our ears, the mob drinks it in with greedy ears, (as Pliny observes) ; we long after rumour to hear and listen to it. We are most part too inquisitive and apt to hearken after news, which Cæsar in his Commentaries observes of the old Gauls, they would be enquiring of every Carrier and Passenger what they had heard or seen, what news abroad? —

> *What the whole world is doing, what the Thracians,*
> *What the Chinese ; the stepmother's intrigue*
> *With her young stepson, and the latest scandal,*　(JUVENAL)

— as at an ordinary with us, bakehouse, or barber's shop. When that great Gonsalvo was upon some displeasure confined by king Ferdinand to the City of Loja in Andalusia, the only comfort (saith Jovius) he had to ease his melancholy thoughts was to hear news, and to listen after those ordinary occurrents, which were brought him at first by letters or otherwise, out of the remotest parts of Europe. Some men's whole delight is to take Tobacco, and drink all day long in a Tavern or Alehouse, to discourse, sing, jest, roar, talk of a Cock and Bull over a pot, &c. Or when three or four good companions meet, tell old stories by the fireside, or in the Sun, as old folks usually do, remembering afresh and with pleasure ancient matters, and such like accidents, which happened in their younger years. Others' best pastime is to game, nothing to them so pleasant.

> *This man yields to woman's vice,*
> *That man wastes at cards and dice.*　(PERSIUS)

Many too nicely take exceptions at Cards, Tables, and Dice, and such mixt lusorious * lots, whom Gataker well confutes ; which, though they be honest recreations in themselves, yet may justly be otherwise ex-

* Playful.

cepted at, as they are often abused, and forbidden as things most pernicious, a mad and damnable thing, Lemnius calls it. For most part in
these kind of disports, 'tis not art or skill, but subtilty, cunny-catching,
knavery, chance and fortune carries all away, 'tis money that flies, —

In a short fleeting hour it changes masters. (HORACE)

They labour most part not to pass their time in honest disport, but for
filthy lucre, and covetousness of money. Avarice and love of gain most
horribly transform them, as Daneus observes. 'Tis the fountain of
cosenage and villainy; a thing so common all over Europe at this day, &
so generally abused, that many men are utterly undone by it, their
means spent, patrimonies consumed, they and their posterity beggared;
besides swearing, wrangling, drinking, loss of time, and such inconveniences, which are ordinary concomitants: for when once they have
got a haunt of such companies, and habit of gaming, they can hardly
be drawn from it, but as an itch it will tickle them, and as it is with
whoremasters, once entered, they cannot easily leave it off; they are
mad upon their sport. And in conclusion (which Charles the Seventh,
that good French King, published in an Edict against gamesters), that
which was once their livelihood, should have maintained wife, children,
family, is now spent and gone; sorrow and beggary succeeds. So good
things may be abused, and that which was first invented to refresh
men's weary spirits, when they come from other labours and studies, to
exhilarate the mind, to entertain time and company, tedious otherwise
in those long solitary Winter nights, and keep them from worse matters,
an honest exercise, is contrarily perverted.

Chess-play is a good and witty exercise of the mind for some kind of
men, and fit for such melancholy ones, Rhasis holds, as are idle, and
have extravagant impertinent thoughts, or are troubled with cares,
nothing better to distract their mind, and alter their meditations, invented (some say) by the general of an army in a famine, to keep
soldiers from mutiny: but if it proceed from overmuch study, in such
a case it may do more harm than good; it is a game too troublesome for
some men's brains, too full of anxiety, all out as bad as study; besides,
it is a testy cholerick game, and very offensive to him that loseth the
Mate. William the Conqueror in his younger years, playing at chess
with the Prince of France, (Dauphiné was not annexed to that Crown
in those days), losing a mate, knocked the Chess-board about his pate,
which was a cause afterwards of much enmity betwixt them. For some
such reason it is, belike, that Patricius, in his Schooling of Princes, forbids his Prince to play at Chess: hawking and hunting, riding, &c. he

will allow; and this to other men, but by no means to him. In Muscovy, where they live in stoves and hot-houses all Winter long, come seldom or little abroad, it is again very necessary, and therefore in those parts (saith Herbastein) much used. At Fez in Africa, where the like inconvenience of keeping within doors is through heat, it is very laudable, and (as Leo Afer relates) as much frequented. A sport fit for idle Gentlewomen, Soldiers in Garrison, and Courtiers that have nought but Love matters to busy themselves about, but not altogether so convenient for such as are Students. The like I may say of Claude Boissiere's Philosophy Game, D. Fulke's Metromachia and his Ouranomachia, with the rest of those intricate Astrological and Geometrical fictions, for such especially as are Mathematically given; and the rest of those curious games.

Dancing, Singing, Masking, Mumming, Stage-plays, howsoever they be heavily censured by some severe Catos, yet, if opportunely and soberly used, may justly be approved. 'Tis better to dig than to dance, saith Austin: but what is that if they delight in it? " No sober person dances." But in what kind of dance? I know these sports have many oppugners, whole volumes writ against them, when as all they say (if duly considered) is but an Index of Ignorance; and some again, because they are now cold and wayward, past themselves, cavil at all such youthful sports in others, as he did in the Comedy; they think them born gray-beards, &c. Some out of preposterous zeal object many times trivial arguments, and because of some abuse will quite take away the good use, as if they should forbid wine, because it makes men drunk; but in my judgement they are too stern: *there is a time for all things, a time to mourn, a time to dance; a time to embrace, a time not to embrace, and nothing better than that a man should rejoice in his own works.* For my part, I will subscribe to the King's Declaration, and was ever of that mind, those May-games, Wakes, and Whitsun-Ales, &c., if they be not at unseasonable hours, may justly be permitted. Let them freely feast, sing and dance, have their Puppet-plays, Hobby-horses, Tabers, Crowds, Bag-pipes, &c., play at Ball, and Barley-breaks, and what sports and recreations they like best. In Franconia, a province of Germany, (saith Aubanus Bohemus), the old folks, after Evening Prayer, went to the Ale-house, the younger sort to dance: and to say truth with Sarisburiensis, better do so than worse, as without question otherwise (such is the corruption of man's Nature) many of them will do. For that cause Plays, Masks, Jesters, Gladiators, Tumblers, Jugglers, &c. and all that crew is admitted & winked at: that they might be busied about such toys, that would otherwise more perniciously be idle. So that, as Tacitus said of the Astrologers in Rome, we may say of them: they are a debauched company most part, still spoken against, as well they deserve, some of them (for I so relish and distinguish them as Fiddlers, and Musicians) and yet ever retained. Evil is not to be done (I confess) that good may come of it: but this is evil by accident, and in a qualified sense, to avoid a greater inconvenience, may justly be tolerated. Sir Thomas More, in his Utopian Common-wealth, as he will have none idle, so will he have no man labour over-hard, to be toiled out like a horse; 'tis more than slavish infelicity, the life of most of our hired servants and tradesmen elsewhere (excepting his Uto-pians): but half the day allotted to work, and half for honest recreation, or whatsoever employment they shall think fit themselves. If one half-day in the week were allowed to our household servants for their Merry Meetings by their hard masters, or in a year some Feasts, like those Roman Saturnalia, I think they would labour harder all the rest of their time, and both parties be better pleased: but this needs not (you will say), for some of them do nought but loiter all the week long.

This which I aim at is for such as are troubled in mind, to ease them, over-toiled on the one part, to refresh: over-idle on the other, to keep themselves busied. And to this purpose, as any labour or employment will serve to the one, any honest recreation will conduce to the other, so that it be moderate and sparing, as the use of meat and drink; not to spend all their life in Gaming, Playing, and Pastimes, as too many Gen-tlemen do, but to revive our bodies and recreate our souls with honest sports: of which, as there be divers sorts, and peculiar to several callings, ages, sexes, conditions, so there be proper for several seasons, and those of distinct natures, to fit that variety of humours which is amongst them, that if one will not, another may: some in Summer, some in Winter, some gentle, some more violent, some for the mind alone, some for the body and mind: (as to some it is both business and a pleasant recreation to oversee workmen of all sorts, Husbandry, Cattle, Horses, &c. to build, plot, project, to make models, cast up accounts, &c.) some without, some within doors: new, old, &c. as the season serveth, and as men are inclined. It is reported of Philippus Bonus, that Good Duke of Burgundy (by Lodovicus Vives in his letters, and Pont. Heuter in his history) that the said Duke, at the marriage of Eleonora, sister to the King of Portugal, at Bruges in Flanders, which was solemnized in the deep of Winter, when as by reason of unseasonable weather, he could neither hawk nor hunt, and was now tired with cards, dice, &c. and such other domestical sports, or to see Ladies dance, with some of his Court-iers he would in the evening walk disguised all about the Town. It so fortuned, as he was walking late one night, he found a country-fellow dead drunk, snorting on a bulk *; he caused his followers to bring him to his Palace, and there stripped him of his old clothes, and attiring him after the Court fashion, when he waked, he and they were ready to at-tend upon his Excellency, persuading him he was some great Duke. The poor fellow, admiring how he came there, was served in state all the day long; after supper he saw them dance, heard Musick, and the rest of those Court-like pleasures: but late at night, when he was well tippled, & again fast asleep, they put on his old robes, and so conveyed him to the place where they first found him. Now the fellow had not made them so good sport the day before, as he did when he returned to himself, all the jest was to see how he looked upon it. In conclusion, after some little admiration, the poor man told his friends he had seen a Vision, constantly believed it, would not otherwise be persuaded, and so the jest ended. Antiochus Epiphanes would often disguise himself, steal from his Court, and go into Merchants', Goldsmiths', and other Tradesmen's shops, sit and talk with them, and sometimes ride, or walk alone, and fall aboard with any Tinker, Clown, Serving-man, Carrier, or whomsoever he met first. Sometimes he did unexpectedly give a poor fellow money, to see how he would look, or on set purpose lose his purse as he went, to watch who found it, and withal how he would be affected, and with such objects he was much delighted. Many such tricks are ordinarily put in practice by great men, to exhilarate them-selves and others, all which are harmless jests, and have their good uses.

But amongst those exercises, or recreations of the mind within doors, there is none so general, so aptly to be applied to all sorts of men, so fit and proper to expell Idleness and Melancholy, as that of Study. Study delighteth age, informeth youth, adorneth prosperity, charmeth us at home, and is the solace and refuge of adversity, &c., find the rest in Tully. What so full of content, as to read, walk, and see Maps, Pic-tures, Statues, Jewels, Marbles, which some so much magnify, as those that Phidias made of old, so exquisite and pleasing to be beheld, that, as Chrysostom thinketh, if any man be sickly, troubled in mind, or that cannot sleep for grief, and shall but stand over against one of Phidias' Images, he will forget all care, or whatsoever else may molest him, in an instant? There be those so much taken with Michael Angelo's, Raphael de Urbino's, Francesco Francia's Pieces, and many of those Italian and

_____

* Snoring on a bench?

Dutch Painters, which were excellent in their ages; and esteem of it as a most pleasing sight to view those neat Architectures, Devices, Scutcheons, Coats of Arms, read such Books, to peruse old Coins, of several sorts in a fair Gallery, Artificial Works, Perspective Glasses, Old Reliques, Roman Antiquities, variety of colours. A good Picture is an image of reality and a muted poem: and though (as Vives saith), artificial toys please but for a time, yet who is he that will not be moved with them for the present? When Achilles was tormented and sad for the loss of his dear friend Patroclus, his mother Thetis brought him a most elaborate and curious Buckler made by Vulcan, in which were engraven Sun, Moon, Stars, Planets, Sea, Land, men fighting, running, riding, women scolding, hills, dales, towns, castles, brooks, rivers, trees, &c., with many pretty landskips, and perspective pieces, with sight of which he was infinitely delighted, and much eased of his grief.

> *Unmov'd, the hero kindles at the show,*
> *And feels with rage divine his bosom glow;*
> *He turns the radiant gift and feeds his mind*
> *On all the Godly artist had design'd.*

Who will not be affected so in like case, or to see those well furnished Cloisters and Galleries of the Roman Cardinals, so richly stored with all modern Pictures, old Statues and Antiquities? To see their Pictures alone, and read the description, as Boissardus well adds, whom will it not affect? which Bozius, Pomponius Lætus, Marlianus, Schottus, Cavelerius, Ligorius, &c. and he himself hath well performed of late. Or in some Princes' Cabinets, like that of the great Duke's in Florence, of Felix Platerus in Basil, or Noblemen's Houses, to see such variety of attires, faces, so many, so rare, and such exquisite pieces, of men, birds, beasts, &c., to see those excellent landskips, Dutch-works, and curious Cuts of Sadler of Prague, Albert Durer, Goltzius, Urintes, &c., such pleasant Pieces of Perspective, Indian Pictures made of feathers, China works, frames, thaumaturgical motions, exotick toys, &c. Who is he that is now wholly overcome with idleness, or otherwise involved in a labyrinth of worldly cares, troubles, and discontents, that will not be much lightened in his mind by reading of some enticing story, true or feigned, where (as in a glass) he shall observe what our fore-fathers have done, the beginnings, ruins, falls, periods of Common-wealths, private men's actions displayed to the life, &c.? Plutarch therefore calls them the second course and junkets, because they were usually read at Noblemen's Feasts. Who is not earnestly affected with a passionate speech, well penned, an elegant Poem, or some pleasant bewitching discourse, like that of Heliodorus, where quiet pleasure blends with mirth? Julian the Apostate was so taken with an Oration of Libanius the Sophister, that, as he confesseth, he could not be quiet till he had read it all out : *I read a great part of your speech before dinner, but afterward I finished it completely. O what arguments! what style!* ———— I may say the same of this or that pleasing Tract, which will draw his attention along with it. To most kind of men it is an extraordinary delight to study. For what a world of Books offers itself, in all subjects, arts, and sciences, to the sweet content and capacity of the Reader! In Arithmetick, Geometry, Perspective, Opticks, Astronomy, Architecture, Sculpture, Painting, of which so many and such elaborate Treatises are of late written : in Mechanicks & their mysteries, Military Matters, Navigation, Riding of Horses, Fencing, Swimming, Gardening, Planting, great Tomes of Husbandry, Cookery, Falconry, Hunting, Fishing, Fowling, &c. with exquisite Pictures of all sports, games, & what not? In Musick, Metaphysicks, Natural and Moral Philosophy, Philology, in Policy, Heraldry, Genealogy, Chronology, &c., they afford great Tomes, or those Studies of Antiquity, &c.: *What* (saith Cardan), *is more subtle than arithmetical conclusions? what more agreeable than musical harmonies? what more divine than astronomical? what more certain than geometric demonstration?* What so sure, what so pleasant? He that shall but see that Geometrical Tower of Garisenda at Bologna in Italy, the Steeple and Clock at Strasburg, will admire the effects of art, or that Engine of Archimedes to remove the earth itself, if he had but a place to fasten his instrument, Archimedes' water-screw, and rare devices to corrivate waters, musick instruments, & trisyllable Echoes again, again, & again repeated, with myriads of such. What vast Tomes are extant in Law, Physick, & Divinity, for profit, pleasure, practice, speculation, in verse or prose, &c.! Their names alone are the subject of whole Volumes, we have thousands of Authors of all sorts, many great Libraries full well furnished, like so many dishes of meat, served out for several palates ; & he is a very block that is affected with none of them. Some take an infinite delight to study the very Languages wherein these Books are written, Hebrew, Greek, Syriack, Chaldee, Arabick, &c. Methinks it would well please any man to look upon a Geographical Map, on account of the incredible variety and pleasantness of the subject, and would excite to further steps in knowledge ; Chorographical, Topographical Delineations, to behold, as it were, all the remote Provinces, Towns, Cities of the World, and never to go forth of the limits of his study, to measure by the scale and compass their extent, distance, examine their site. Charles the Great, as Platina writes, had three fair silver tables, in one of which superficies was a large Map of Constantinople, in the second Rome neatly engraved, in the third an exquisite Description of the whole World, and much delight he took in them. What greater pleasure can there now be than to view those elaborate Maps of Ortelius, Mercator, Hondius, &c. To peruse those books of Cities, put out by Braunus and Hogenbergius? To read those exquisite descriptions of Maginus, Munster, Herrera, Laetus, Merula, Boterus, Leander, Albertus, Camden, Leo Afer, Adricomius, Nic. Gerbelius, &c? Those famous expeditions of Christopher Columbus, Amerigo Vespucci, Marco Polo the Venetian, Lod. Vertomannus, Aloysius Cadamustus, &c.? those accurate diaries of Portuguese, Hollanders, of Bartison, Oliver à Nort, &c., Hakluyt's Voyages, Peter Martyr's Decades, Benzo, Lerius, Linschoten's Relations, those Travels of Jod. a Meggen, Brocard the Monk, Bredenbachius, Jo. Dublinius, Sands, &c., to Jerusalem, Egypt, and other remote places of the world? those pleasant Itineraries of Paulus Hentznerus, Jodocus Sincerus, Dux Polonus, &c., to read Bellonius' Observations, P. Gillius his Surveys; those parts of America set out, and curiously cut in Pictures, by Fratres a Bry. To see a well cut Herbal, Herbs, Trees, Flowers, Plants, all Vegetals, expressed in their proper colours to the life, as that of Matthiolus upon Dioscorides, Delacampius, Lobel, Bauhinus, and that last voluminous and mighty Herbal of Besler of Nuremburg, wherein almost every Plant is to his own bigness. To see Birds, Beasts, and Fishes of the Sea, Spiders, Gnats, Serpents, Flies, &c., all Creatures set out by the same Art & truly expressed in lively colours, with an exact description of their natures, virtues, qualities, &c., as hath been accurately performed by Ælian, Gesner, Ulysses Aldrovandus, Bellonius, Rondoletius, Hippolytus Salvianus, &c. To know the secrets of the Heavens and of Nature, and the order of the Universe, is a greater happiness and pleasure than any mortal can think or expect to obtain. What more pleasing Studies can there be than the Mathematicks, Theorick, or Practick parts? as to survey land, make Maps, Models, Dials, &c. with which I was ever much delighted myself. Such is the excellency of these studies, (saith Plutarch), that all those ornaments and childish bubbles of wealth are not worthy to be compared to them: Believe me, (saith one), I could even live and die with such meditations, and take more delight, true content of mind, in them than thou hast in all thy wealth and sport, how rich soever thou art. And, as Cardan well seconds me, 'tis a greater honour and glory to understand these truths than to be young or to govern provinces. The like pleasure there is in all other Studies to such as are truly addicted to them. The like sweetness, (one holds), which, as Circe's Cup, bewitcheth a student, he cannot leave off, as well may witness those many laborious hours, days, and nights, spent in the voluminous Treatises written by them; the same content. Julius Scaliger was so much affected with Poetry, that he brake out into a pathetical protestation, he had rather be the Author of 12 verses in Lucan, or such an ode in Horace, than Emperor of Germany. Nicholas Gerbelius, that good old man, was so much ravished with a few Greek Authors restored to light, with hope and desire of enjoying the rest, that he exclaims forthwith: We shall be richer than all the Arabick or Indian Princes; of such esteem they were with him, incomparable worth and value. Seneca prefers Zeno and Chrysippus, two doting Stoicks, (he was so much enamoured on their works), before any Prince or General of an Army; and Orontius the Mathematician so far admires Archimedes, that he calls him a petty God, more than a man; and well he might, for ought I see, if you respect fame or worth, Pindar of Thebes is as much renowned for his Poems, as Epaminondas, Pelopidas, Hercules, or Bacchus, his fellow citizens, for their warlike actions; and, (as Cardan notes), Aristotle is more known than Alexander; for we have a bare relation of Alexander's deeds, but Aristotle is whole in his works: yet I stand not upon this; the delight is it which I aim at; so great pleasure, such sweet content, there is in study. King James, 1605, when he came to our University of Oxford, and, amongst other edifices, now went to view that famous Library, renewed by Sir Thomas Bodley, in imitation of Alexander, at his departure brake out into that noble speech: If I were not a King, I would be an University man; and if it were so that I must be a prisoner, if I might have my wish, I would desire to have no other prison than that Library, and to be chained together with so many good Authors and dead Masters. — So sweet is the delight of study, the more learning they have, (as he that hath a Dropsy, the more he drinks the thirstier he is), the more they covet to learn, and the last day is the pupil of the former; harsh at first learning is, — " bitter the roots," — but " the fruits are sweet," according to that of Isocrates, pleasant at last; the longer they live, the more they are enamoured with the Muses. Heinsius, the keeper of the Library at Leyden in Holland, was mewed up in it all the year long; and that which to thy thinking should have bred a loathing caused in him a greater liking. I no sooner (saith he) come into the Library, but I bolt the door to me, excluding lust, ambition, avarice, and all such vices, whose nurse is idleness, the mother of ignorance, and Melancholy herself, and in the very lap of eternity, amongst so many divine souls, I take my seat, with so lofty a spirit and sweet content, that I pity all our great ones, and rich men that know not this happiness.——— I am not ignorant in the mean time (notwithstanding this which I have said) how barbarously and basely for the most part our ruder Gentry esteem of Libraries & Books, how they neglect & contemn so great a treasure, so inestimable a benefit, as Æsop's Cock did the Jewel he found in the dunghill, and all through error, ignorance, and want of education. And 'tis a wonder withal to observe how much they will vainly cast away in unnecessary expences, (saith Erasmus), what in hawks, hounds, law-suits, vain building, gourmandizing, drinking, sports, plays, pastimes, &c. If a well minded man to the Muses would sue to some of them for an Exhibition, to the farther maintenance or enlargement of such a work, be it College, Lecture, Library, or whatsoever else may tend to the Advancement of Learning, they are so unwilling, so averse, they had rather see these which are already with such cost and care erected, utterly ruined, demolished, or otherwise employed; for they repine many and grudge at such gifts and revenues so bestowed: and therefore it were in vain, as Erasmus well notes, to solicit or ask any thing of such men, that are likely damn'd to riches, to this purpose. For my part I pity these men, I let them go as they are, in the catalogue of Ignoramus. How much, on the other side, are all we bound, that are Scholars, to those munificent Ptolemies, bountiful Mæcenases, heroical Patrons, divine spirits,—

Who gave me all this comfort, in my eyes
Will ever be a God, (VIRGIL)

that have provided for us so many well furnished Libraries as well in our publick Academies in most Cities, as in our private Colleges! How shall I remember Sir Thomas Bodley, amongst the rest, Otho Nicholson, and the Right Reverend John Williams, Lord Bishop of Lincoln, (with many other pious acts), who besides that at S. John's College in Cambridge, that in Westminster, is now likewise engaged with a Library at Lincoln, (a noble precedent for all Corporate Towns and Cities to imitate!) O, how can I sufficiently eulogize you, most illustrious man? But to my task again.

Whosoever he is, therefore, that is overrun with solitariness, or carried away with pleasing melancholy and vain conceits, and for want of employment knows not how to spend his time, or crucified with worldly care, I can prescribe him no better remedy than this of study, to compose himself to the learning of some art or science. Provided always that his malady proceed not from overmuch study, for in such cases he adds fuel to the fire, and nothing can be more pernicious; let him take heed he do not overstretch his wits, and make a skeleton of himself; or such In-amoratoes as read nothing but Play-books, idle Poems, Jests, Amadis de Gaul, the Knight of the Sun, the Seven Champions, Palmerin de Oliva, Huon of Bordeaux, &c. Such many times prove in the end as mad as Don Quixote. Study is only prescribed to those that are otherwise idle, troubled in mind, or carried headlong with vain thoughts and imagina-tions, to distract their cogitations, (although variety of study, or some serious subject, would do the former no harm), and divert their con-tinual meditations another way. Nothing in this case better than study; ever, saith Piso, let them learn something without book, transcribe, translate, &c. read the Scriptures, which Hyperius holds available of it-self; the mind is erected thereby from all worldly cares, and hath much quiet and tranquillity. For, as Austin well hath it, 'tis the acme of all knowledge, 'tis the best nepenthe, surest cordial, sweetest alternative, presentest diverter. For neither, as Chrysostom well adds, those boughs and leaves of trees which are plashed for cattle to stand under, in the heat of the day, in Summer, so much refresh them with their acceptable shade, as the reading of the Scripture doth recreate and comfort a dis-tressed soul in sorrow and affliction. Paul bids pray continually; for, saith Seneca, as meat is to the body, such is reading to the soul. To be at leisure without books is another Hell, & to be buried alive. Cardan calls a Library the physick of the soul; divine authors fortify the mind, make men bold and constant; and (as Hyperius adds) godly conference will not permit the mind to be tortured with absurd cogitations. Rhasis en-joins continual conference to such melancholy men, perpetual discourse of some history, tale, poem, news, &c., which feeds the mind as meat and drink doth the body, and pleaseth as much: and therefore the said Rhasis not without good cause would have somebody still talk seriously, or dispute with them, and sometimes to cavil and wrangle, (so that it break not out to a violent perturbation), for such altercation is like stirring of a dead fire to make it burn afresh, it whets a dull spirit, and will not suffer the mind to be drowned in those profound cogitations which melancholy men are commonly troubled with. Ferdinand and Alphonso, Kings of Arragon and Sicily, were both cured by reading the History, one of Curtius, the other of Livy, when no prescribed Physick would take place. Camerarius relates as much of Lorenzo de Medici. Heathen Philosophers are so full of divine precepts in this kind, that, as some think, they alone are able to settle a distressed mind. There are words and spells by which you can allay that pain, &c. How should he, facing every misfortune of the soul, (saith Lipsius), yea death itself, use these weapons: even as he frees himself from weakness & stimulates courage. When I read Seneca, methinks I am beyond all human fortunes, on the top of an hill above mortality. Plutarch saith as much of Homer, for which cause belike Niceratus, in Xenophon, was made by his parents to con Homer's Iliad and Odyssey without book, as well to make him a good and honest man as to avoid idleness. If this comfort may be got by Philosophy, what shall be had from Divinity? What shall Austin, Cyprian, Gregory, Bernard's divine meditations afford us?

The fair, the foul; what's chaff, what's grain,

Than Chrysippus or Crantor who can better explain?   (HORACE)

Nay, what shall the Scripture itself, which is like an Apothecary's Shop, wherein are all remedies for all infirmities of mind, purgatives, cordials, alteratives, corroboratives, lenitives, &c. Every disease of the soul, saith Austin, hath a peculiar medicine in the Scripture; this only is required that the sick man take the potion which God hath already tempered. Gregory calls it a glass wherein we may see all our infirmities, the Psalms a shining discourse; Origen a Charm. And therefore Hierome prescribes Rusticus the Monk, continually to read the Scripture, and to meditate on that which he hath read; for as mastication is to meat, so is meditation on that which we read. I would for these causes wish him that is melancholy to use both human and divine Authors, voluntarily to impose some task upon himself, to divert his melancholy thoughts: to study the art of memory, Cosmus Rosselius, Pet. Ravennas, Scenkelius' Detectus, or practise Brachygraphy [shorthand], &c., that will ask a great deal of attention: or let him demonstrate a Proposition in Euclid in his last five Books, extract a square root, or study Algebra: than which, as Clavius holds, in all humane disciplines nothing can be more excellent & pleasant, so abstruse and recondite, so bewitching, so miraculous, so ravishing, so easy withal & full of delight. By this means you may define a lion by his claw, as the diverb is, by his thumb alone the bigness of Hercules, or the true dimensions of the great Collossus, Solomon's Temple, and Domitian's Amphitheatre, out of a little part. By this art you may contemplate the variation of the 23 letters, which may be so infinitely varied, that the words complicated and deduced thence will not be contained within the compass of the firmament; ten words may be varied 40,320 several ways: by this art you may examine how many men may stand one by another in the whole superficies of the Earth, some say 148,456,800,000,000. Assigning 5 square feet to each, how many men, supposing all the World as habitable as France, as fruitful and so long lived, may be born in 60,000 years? and so may you demonstrate, with Archimedes, how many sands the mass of the whole World might contain if all sandy, if you did but first know how much a small cube as big as a mustard-seed might hold, with infinite such. But in all Nature what is there so stupend as to examine and calculate the motion of the Planets, their Magnitudes, Apogeums, Perigeums, Eccentricities, how far distant from the Earth, the bigness, thickness, compass of the Firmament, each Star, with their diameters and circumference, apparent area, surface, by those curious helps of Glasses, Astrolabes, Sextants, Quadrants, of which Tycho Brahe in his Mechanicks, Opticks (divine Opticks!) Arithmetick, Geometry, and such like arts and instruments? What so intricate, and pleasing withal, as to peruse and practise Hero Alexandrinus' works, on the air-engine, the war-engine, the engine that moveth itself, Jordanus Nemorarius' on weights, that pleasant Tract of Machometes Bragdedinus on the divisions of surfaces, Apollonius' Conicks, or Commandinus' labours in that kind, on the centre of gravity, with many such Geometrical Theorems and Problems? Those rare instruments and mechanical inventions of Jac. Bessonus and Cardan to this purpose, with many such experiments intimated long since by Roger Bacon, in his Tract, The Secrets of Nature and Art, as to make a chariot to move without an animal, diving boats, to walk on the water by art and to fly in the air, to make several cranes and pullies, by means of which one man can pull a thousand, lift up & remove great weights, mills to move themselves, Archytas' Dove, Albertus' brasen head,* and such thaumaturgical works. But especially to do strange miracles by glasses, of which Proclus and Bacon writ of old, burning glasses, multiplying glasses, perspectives, so that one man appears an army, to see afar off, to represent solid bodies by cylinders and concaves, to walk in the air, so that they really see gold and silver, and whatever else they will, which glasses are much perfected of late by Baptista Porta & Galileo, & much more is promised by Maginus & Midorgius, to be performed in this kind. Otacousticons some speak of, to intend hearing, as the others do sight; Marcellus Vrencken, an Hollander, in his Epistle to Burgravius, makes mention of a friend of his that is about an

---

* " It is related of Albertus that he made an entire man of brass, putting together its limbs under various constellations, and occupying no less than thirty years in its formation. This man would answer all sorts of questions, and was even employed as a domestic. But at length it is said to have become so garrulous that Thomas Aquinas, a pupil of Albertus, finding himself disturbed perpetually by its uncontrollable loquacity, caught up a hammer and beat it to pieces." — William Godwin's Lives of the Necromancers.

instrument, by which one will be able to see what is beyond the horizon. But our Alchemists, methinks, and Rosy-Cross men afford most rarities, and are fuller of experiments: they can make gold, separate and alter metals, extract oils, salts, lees, and do more strange works than Geber, Lullius, Bacon, or any of those Ancients. Crollius hath made, after his master Paracelsus, fulminate of gold, or volatile gold, which shall imitate thunder and lightning, and crack louder than any gunpowder; Cornelius Drible a perpetual motion, inextinguible lights, incombustible cloth, with many such feats; see his book On the Nature of the Elements, besides hail, wind, snow, thunder, lightning, &c. those strange fire-works, devilish petards, and such like warlike machinations, derived hence, of which read Tartalea and others. Ernestus Burgravius, a disciple of Paracelsus, hath published a discourse, in which he specifies a lamp to be made of man's blood, the Lamp of Life and Index of Death, so he terms it, which chemically prepared 40 days, and afterwards kept in a glass, shall shew all the accidents of this life; if this lamp burneth brightly, then the man is cheerful, and healthy in mind and body; if, on the other hand, it be smoky or dim, he is sore afflicted; so it varies with his own state; and, which is most wonderful, it dies with the party, the lamp and the man whence the blood was taken are extinguished together. The same author hath another Tract of Mumia, (all out as vain and prodigious as the first), by which he will cure most diseases, and transfer them from a man to a beast, by drawing blood from one, and applying it to the other, or even to transfer them to plants, and an alexipharmacum, of which Roger Bacon of old, in his Tract On Delaying Old Age, to make a man young again, live 3 or 4 hundred years; besides Panaceas, Martial [or Martian] Amulets, Weapon Salve, [Universal] Balsams, strange Extracts, Elixirs [of Life], and such like magico-magnetical cures. Now what so pleasing can there be as the speculation of these things, to read and examine such experiments, or, if a man be more mathematically given, to calculate or peruse Napier's Logarithms, or those tables of artificial Sines and Tangents, not long since set out by mine old Collegiate, good friend, and late Fellow-Student, of Christ-Church in Oxford, Mr Edmund Gunter, which will perform that by addition and subtraction only, which heretofore Regiomontanus' Tables did by multiplication and division, or those elaborate conclusions of his Sector, Quadrant, and Cross-staff. Or let him that is melancholy calculate Spherical Triangles, square a circle, cast a Nativity, which howsoever some tax, I say with Garcæus, we will in some cases allow: or let him make an Ephemerides, read Suisset the Calculator's works, Scaliger on the correction of Time, and Petavius, his adversary, till he understood them, peruse subtle Scotus' and Saurez' Metaphysicks, or School Divinity, Occam, Th. Aquinas, Entisberus, Durand. If those other do not affect him, and his means be great, to employ his purse & fill his head, he may go find the Philosopher's Stone; he may apply his mind, I say, to Heraldry, Antiquity, invent Impresses, Emblems; make Epithalamiums, Epitaphs, Elegies, Epigrams, Palindromes, Anagrams, Chronograms, Acrosticks upon his friends' names; or write a Comment on Martianus Capella, Tertullian's Cloak, the Nubian Geography, or upon Ælia Lælia Crispis, as many idle fellows have assayed; and rather than do nothing, vary a verse a thousand ways with Putean, so torturing his wits, or as Rainnerus of Luneberg, 2,150 times in his Proteus Poeticus, or Scaliger, Chrysolithus, Cleppisius, and others, have in like sort done. If such voluntary tasks, pleasure and delight, or crabbedness of these Studies, will not yet divert their idle thoughts, and alienate their imaginations, they must be compelled, saith Christophorus à Vega, upon some mulct, if they perform it not, which is incumbent upon them by way of duty, loss of credit or disgrace, such as our Publick University exercises. For as he that plays for nothing will not heed his game, no more will voluntary imployment so freely affect a Student, except he be very intent of himself, and take an extraordinary delight in the study about which he is conversant. It should be of that nature his business, which willy nilly he must necessarily undergo, and without great loss, mulct, shame or hindrance, he may not omit.

Now for women, instead of laborious studies, they have curious needleworks, cut-works, spinning, bone-lace, and many pretty devices of their own making, to adorn their houses, Cushions, Carpets, Chairs, Stools, (" for she eats not the bread of idleness, — she seeketh her wool and flax "), confections, conserves, distillations, &c. which they shew to strangers.

> *Which to her guests she shows, with all her pelf,*
> *Thus far my maids, but this I did myself.* (CHALONER)

This they have to busy themselves about, household offices, &c. neat gardens, full of exotick, versicolour, diversely varied, sweet smelling flowers, and plants in all kinds, which they are most ambitious to get, curious to preserve and keep, proud to possess, and much many times brag of. Their merry meetings and frequent visitations, mutual invitations in good Towns, I voluntarily omit, which are so much in use. gossiping among the meaner sort, &c. Old folks have their beads, an

excellent invention to keep them from idleness that are by nature melancholy, and past all affairs, to say so many Pater Nosters, Ave Marias,
Creeds, if it were not profane and superstitious. In a word, body and
mind must be exercised, not one, but both, and that in a mediocrity,
otherwise it will cause a great inconvenience. If the body be overtired,
it tires the mind. The mind oppresseth the body, as with Students it
oftentimes falls out, who (as Plutarch observes) have no care of the
body, but compel that which is mortal to do as much as that which is
immortal, that which is earthly, as that which is ethereal: But as the
Ox tired told the Camel, (both serving one Master), that refused to
carry some part of his burden, before it were long he should be compelled to carry all his pack, and skin to boot, (which by and by, the Ox
being dead, fell out) the body may say to the soul that will give him no
respite, or remission: a little after an Ague, Vertigo, Consumption,
seizeth on them both; all his study is omitted, and they must be compelled to be sick together. He that tenders his own good estate and
health must let them draw with equal yoke both alike, that so they may
happily enjoy their wished health.

MEMBER 5

Waking and terrible Dreams rectified

As waking, that hurts, by all means must be avoided, so sleep, which so
much helps, by like ways must be procured, by nature or art, inward or
outward medicines, and be protracted longer than ordinary, if it may be,
as being an especial help. It moistens and fattens the body, concocts,
and helps digestion, (as we see in dormice, and those Alpine mice that
sleep all Winter), which Gesner speaks of, when they are so found sleeping under the snow in the dead of Winter, as fat as butter. It expels
cares, pacifies the mind, refresheth the weary limbs after long work.

> *Sleep, rest of things, O pleasing Deity,*
> *Peace of the soul, which cares dost crucify,*
> *Weary bodies refresh and mollify.*   (OVID)

The chiefest thing in all Physick, Paracelsus calls it, above every
secret of precious stones and metals. The fittest time is two or three
hours after supper, when as the meat is now settled at the bottom of the
stomack, and 'tis good to lie on the right side first, because at that site
the liver doth rest under the stomack, not molesting any way, but
heating him as a fire doth a kettle, that is put to it. After the first sleep

'tis not amiss to lie on the left side, that the meat may the better descend, and sometimes again on the belly, but never on the back. Seven or eight hours is a competent time for a melancholy man to rest, as Crato thinks; but, as some do, to lie in bed and not sleep, a day, or half a day together, to give assent to pleasing conceits and vain imaginations, is many ways pernicious. To procure this sweet moistening sleep, it's best to take away the occasions (if it be possible) that hinder it, and then to use such inward or outward remedies, which may cause it. It is well known, even at this day, (saith Boissardus, in his Tract on magic), that many cannot sleep for Witches and Fascinations, which are too familiar in some places; they call it, giving a person a bad night. But the ordinary causes are heat and dryness, which must first be removed; a hot and dry brain never sleeps well: grief, fears, cares, expectations, anxieties, great businesses, and all violent perturbations of the mind must in some sort be qualified, that you may sleep soundly on either ear, before we can hope for any good repose. He that sleeps in the day time, or is in suspense, fear, any way troubled in mind, or goes to bed upon a full stomack, may never hope for quiet rest in the night; hired lodgings, as the Poet saith, Inns and such like troublesome places are not for sleep; one calls Ostler, another Tapster, one cries and shouts, another sings, whoops, halloos —

Whilst passenger and sailor sing the praise
Of absent loves in drunken lays. (HORACE)

Who, not accustomed to such noises, can sleep amongst them? He that will intend to take his rest must go to bed with a secure and composed mind, in a quiet place: At night all the world will be lulled to rest: & if that will not serve, or may not be obtained, to seek then such means as are requisite. To lie in clean linen & sweet; before he goes to bed, or in bed, to hear sweet Musick, which Ficinus commends, or as Jobertus, to read some pleasant Author till he be asleep, to have a bason of water still dropping by his bed side, or to lie near that pleasant murmur, of water gliding by with gentle music, some flood-gates, arches, falls of water, like London Bridge, or some continuate noise which may benumb the senses. As a gentle noise to some procures sleep, so, which Bernardinus Tilesius well observes, silence, in a dark room, and the will itself, is most available to others. Piso commends frications, Andrew Borde a good draught of strong drink before one goes to bed; I say, a nutmeg and ale, or a good draught of muscadine, with a toast and nutmeg, or a posset of the same, which many use in a morning, but, methinks, for such as have dry brains, are much more proper at night; some prescribe a sup of vinegar as they go to bed, a spoonful, saith Aëtius; Piso, a little after meat, because it rarifies melancholy, and procures an appetite to sleep. Donatus Altomarus & Mercurialis approve of it, if the malady proceed from the spleen. Sallust. Salvian, Hercules de Saxoniâ, Ælianus Montaltus, are altogether against it. Lod. Mercatus, in some cases, doth allow it. Rhasis seems to deliberate of it, though Simeon commend it (in sauce peradventure) he makes a question of it: as for baths, fomentations, oils, potions, simples or compounds, inwardly taken to this purpose, I shall speak of them elsewhere. If in the midst of the night when they lie awake, which is usual to toss and tumble, and not sleep, Ranzovius would have them, if it be in warm weather, to rise and walk three or four turns (till they be cold) about the chamber, and then go to bed again.

Against fearful and troublesome dreams, nightmare, and such inconveniences, wherewith melancholy men are molested, the best remedy is to eat a light supper, and of such meats as are easy of digestion; no Hare, Venison, Beef, &c. not to lie on his back, not to meditate or think in the day time of any terrible objects, or especially talk of them before he goes to bed. For, as he said in Lucian after such conference, I seem to dream of Hecate, I can think of nothing but Hobgoblins: and, as Tully notes, for the most part our speeches in the day time cause our phantasy to work upon the like in our sleep, which Ennius writes of Homer: as a dog dreams of an hare, so do men on such subjects they thought on last.

The Gods send not our dreams, we make our own.

For that cause, when Ptolemy, King of Egypt, had posed the 70 interpreters in order, and asked the nineteenth man, what would make one sleep quietly in the night, he told him the best way was to have divine and celestial meditations, and to use honest actions in the day time. Lod. Vives wonders how Schoolmen could sleep quietly, and were not terrified in the night, or walk in the dark, they had such monstrous questions, and thought of such terrible matters all day long. They had need amongst the rest to sacrifice to God Morpheus, whom Philostratus paints in a white and black coat, with a horn and ivory box full of dreams, of the same colours, to signify good and bad. If you will know how to interpret them, read Artemidorus, Sambucus, and Cardan; but how to help them, I must refer you to a more convenient place.

MEMBER 6

SUBSECTION I — *Perturbations of the mind rectified. From himself, by resisting to the utmost, confessing his grief to a friend, &c.*

WHOSOEVER he is that shall hope to cure this malady in himself or any other, must first rectify these passions and perturbations of the mind; the chiefest cure consists in them. A quiet mind is that pleasure, or highest good, of Epicurus; not to grieve, but to want cares, and have a quiet soul, is the only pleasure of the World, as Seneca truly recites his opinion, not that of eating and drinking, which injurious Aristotle * maliciously puts upon him, and for which he is still mistaken, slandered without a cause, and lashed by all posterity. Fear and sorrow therefore are especially to be avoided, and the mind to be mitigated with mirth, constancy, good hope; vain terror, bad objects, are to be removed, and all such persons in whose companies they be not well pleased. Gualter Bruel, Fernelius, Mercurialis, Piso, Jacchinus on Rhasis, Capivaccius, Hildesheim, &c., all inculcate this as an especial means of their cure, that their minds be quietly pacified, vain conceits diverted, if it be possible, with terrors, cares, fixed studies, cogitations, and whatsoever it is that shall any way molest or trouble the soul, because that otherwise there is no good to be done. The body's mischiefs, as Plato proves, proceed from the soul: and if the mind be not first satisfied, the body can never be cured. Alcibiades raves (saith Maximus Tyrius) and is sick, his furious desires carry him from the Lyceum to the pleading-place, thence to the Sea, so into Sicily, thence to Lacedæmon, thence to Persia, thence to Samos, then again to Athens; Critias tyrannizeth over all the city; Sardanapalus is love-sick; these men are ill-affected all, and can never be cured, till their minds be otherwise qualified. Crato therefore, in that often cited Counsel of his for a Nobleman his Patient, when he had sufficiently informed him in diet, air, exercise, Venus, sleep, concludes with these as matters of greatest moment: for the rest, let everything be corrected that touches the mind, from which alone proceeds Melancholy; they are the fountain, the subject, the hinges whereon it turns, and must necessarily be reformed. For anger stirs choler, heats the blood and vital spirits; sorrow on the other side refrigerates the body, and extinguisheth natural heat, overthrows appetite, hinders concoction, dries up the temperature, and perverts the understanding: fear

* Possibly a slip for Athenæus, suggests A. R. Shilleto; Aristotle died when Epicurus was a youth of twenty.

dissolves the spirits, infects the heart, attenuates the soul : and for these causes all passions and perturbations must, to the uttermost of our power, and most seriously, be removed. Ælianus Montaltus attributes so much to them, that he holds the rectification of them alone to be sufficient to the cure of Melancholy in most Patients. Many are fully cured when they have seen or heard, &c. enjoy their desires, or be secured and satisfied in their minds. Galen, the common Master of them all, from whose fountain they all fetch water, brags that he for his part hath cured divers of this infirmity by right settling alone of their minds.

Yea, but you will here infer, that this is excellent good indeed if it could be done; but how shall it be effected, by whom, what art, what means? this is the labour, this the task. 'Tis a natural infirmity, a most powerful adversary: all men are subject to passions, and melancholy above all others, as being distempered by their innate humours, abundance of choler adust, weakness of parts, outward occurrences; and how shall they be avoided? The wisest men, greatest Philosophers, of most excellent wit, reason, judgement, divine spirits, cannot moderate themselves in this behalf; such as are sound in body and mind, Stoicks, Heroes, Homer's Gods, all are passionate, and furiously carried sometimes; and how shall we that are already crazed, sick in body, sick in mind, resist? We cannot perform it. You may advise and give good precepts, as who cannot? But how shall they be put in practice? I may not deny but our passions are violent, and tyrannize of us, yet there be means to curb them; though they be head-strong, they may be tamed, they may be qualified, if he himself or his friends will but use their honest endeavours, or make use of such ordinary helps as are commonly prescribed.

He himself (I say) ; from the Patient himself the first and chiefest remedy must be had; for if he be averse, peevish, waspish, give way wholly to his passions, will not seek to be helped, or be ruled by his friends, how is it possible he should be cured? But if he be willing at least, gentle, tractable, & desire his own good, no doubt but he may be rid of the greater part of his ills, be eased at least, if not cured. He himself must do his utmost endeavour to resist & withstand the beginnings. Resist the first advances. *Give not water passage, no not a little.* If they open a little, they will make a greater breach at length. Whatsoever it is that runneth in his mind, vain conceit, be it pleasing or displeasing, which so much affects or troubleth him, by all possible means he must withstand it, expel those vain, false, frivolous imaginations, absurd conceits, feigned fears and sorrows; from which, saith Piso, this disease primarily proceeds, and takes his first occasion or beginning, by doing something or other that shall be opposite unto them, thinking of something else, persuading by reason, or howsoever, to make a sudden alteration of them. — Though he have hitherto run in a full career, and precipitated himself, following his passions, giving reins to his appetite, let him now stop upon a sudden, curb himself in; and, as Lemnius adviseth, strive against with all his power, to the utmost of his endeavour, and not cherish those fond imaginations, which so covertly creep into his mind, most pleasing and amiable at first, but bitter as gall at last, and so head-strong, that by no reason, art, counsel, or persuasion they may be shaken off. Though he be far gone, and habituated unto such phantastical imaginations, yet, as Tully, and Plutarch advise, let him oppose, fortify, or prepare himself against them, by premeditation, reason, or, as we do by a crooked staff, bend himself another way.

> *In the mean time expel them from thy mind,*
> *Pale fears, sad cares, and griefs which do it grind,*
> *Revengeful anger, pain and discontent;*
> *Let all thy soul be set on merriment!*   (FRACASTORIUS)
> *If thou to health and vigor wouldst attain,*
> *Shun weighty cares, all anger deem profane.**

If it be idleness hath caused this infirmity, or that he perceive himself given to solitariness, to walk alone, and please his mind with fond imaginations, let him by all means avoid it; 'tis a bosom enemy, 'tis delightsome melancholy, a friend in shew, but a secret devil; a sweet poison, it will in the end be his undoing; let him go presently, task or set himself a work, get some good company. If he proceed, as a gnat flies about a candle so long, till at length he burn his body, so in the end he will undo himself: if it be any harsh object, ill company, let him presently go from it. If by his own default, through ill diet, bad air, want of exercise, &c. let him now begin to reform himself. It would be a perfect remedy against all corruption, if, as Roger Bacon hath it, we could but moderate ourselves in those six non-natural things. If it be any disgrace, abuse, temporal loss, calumny, death of friends, imprisonment, banishment, be not troubled with it, do not fear, be not angry, grieve not at it, but with all courage sustain it (Gordonius). Do you more boldly cope with difficulties. If it be sickness, ill success, or any adversity that hath caused it, oppose an invincible courage, fortify thyself by God's word, or otherwise, persuade evil for good, set prosperity against adversity, as we refresh our eyes by seeing some pleasant meadow, fountain, picture,

* From the Salernitan Regimen of Health.

or the like; recreate thy mind by some contrary object, with some more pleasing meditation divert thy thoughts.

Yea, but you infer again, we can easily give counsel to others; every man, as the saying is, can tame a shrew but he that hath her; if you were in our misery, you would find it otherwise, 'tis not so easily performed. We know this to be true, we should moderate ourselves, but we are furiously carried, we cannot make use of such precepts, we are overcome, sick, distempered and habituated in these courses, we can make no resistance; you may as well bid him that is diseased not to feel pain, as a melancholy man not to fear, not to be sad: 'tis within his blood, his brains, his whole temperature; it cannot be removed. But he may choose whether he will give way too far unto it, he may in some sort correct himself. A Philosopher was bitten with a mad dog, and as the nature of that disease is to abhor all waters, and liquid things, and to think still they see the picture of a dog before them: he went for all this, reluctantly, to the Bath, and seeing there (as he thought) in the water the picture of a dog, with reason overcame this conceit: what should a dog do in a Bath? a mere conceit. Thou thinkest thou hearest and seest Devils, black men, &c. 'tis not so, 'tis thy corrupt phantasy, settle thine imagination, thou art well. Thou thinkest thou hast a great nose, thou art sick, every man observes thee, laughs thee to scorn; persuade thyself 'tis no such matter: this is fear only, and vain suspicion. Thou art discontent, thou art sad and heavy: but why? upon what ground? consider of it: thou art jealous, timorous, suspicious; for what cause? examine it thoroughly, thou shalt find none at all, or such as is to be contemned, such as thou wilt surely deride, and contemn in thyself, when it is past. Rule thyself then with reason, satisfy thyself, accustom thyself, wean thyself from such fond conceits, vain fears, strong imaginations, restless thoughts. Thou mayest do it; as Plutarch saith, we may frame ourselves as we will. As he that useth an upright shoe may correct the obliquity or crookedness, by wearing it on the other side, so we may overcome passions if we will. Whatsoever the will desires, (as Seneca saith), she may command: no such cruel affections, but by discipline they may be tamed; voluntarily thou wilt not do this or that, which thou oughtest to do, or refrain, &c. but when thou art lashed like a dull jade, thou wilt reform it; fear of a whip will make thee do, or not do. Do that voluntarily then which thou canst do, and must do by compulsion: thou mayst refrain, if thou wilt, and master thine affections. As in a City (saith Melancthon) they do by stubborn rebellious rogues, that will not submit themselves to political judgement, compel them by force, so must we do by our affections. If the heart will not lay aside those vicious motions, and the phantasy those fond imaginations, we have another form of government to enforce and refrain our outward members, that they be not led by our passions. — If appetite will not obey, let the moving faculty over-rule her, let her resist and compel her to do otherwise. In an ague the appetite would drink, sore eyes that itch would be rubbed, but reason saith no, and therefore the moving faculty will not do it. Our phantasy would intrude a thousand fears, suspicions, chimæras upon us, but we have reason to resist, yet we let it be overborne by our appetite; imagination enforceth spirits which by an admirable league of nature compel the nerves to obey, and they our several limbs: we give too much way to our passions. And as to him that is sick of an ague all things are distasteful and unpleasant, saith Plutarch, not in the meat, but in our taste, so many things are offensive to us, not of themselves, but out of our corrupt judgement, jealousy, suspicion, and the like; we pull these mischiefs upon our own heads.

If then our judgement be so depraved, our reason over-ruled, will precipitated, that we cannot seek our own good, or moderate ourselves, as in this disease commonly it is, the best way for ease is to impart our misery to some friend, not to smother it up in our own breast; canker thrives and flourishes by concealment, &c., and that which was most offensive to us, a cause of fear and grief, another hell; for grief concealed strangles the soul; but when as we shall but impart it to some discreet, trusty, loving friend, it is instantly removed, by his counsel haply, wisdom, persuasion, advice, his good means, which we could not otherwise apply unto ourselves. A friend's counsel is a charm, like mandrake wine, it allayeth our cares; and as a bull that is tied to a fig-tree becomes gentle on a sudden (which some, saith Plutarch, interpret of good words) so is a savage obdurate heart mollified by fair speeches. All adversity finds ease in complaining, (as Isidore holds), and 'tis a solace to relate it,

> *'Tis well to attend*
> *The advice of a friend.*

Friends' confabulations are comfortable at all times, as fire in Winter, shade in Summer, as sleep on the grass to them that are weary, meat and drink to him that is hungry or athirst; Democritus' Collyrium is not so sovereign to the eyes as this is to the heart; good words are cheerful & powerful of themselves, but much more from friends, as so many props, mutually sustaining each other like ivy and a wall, which Camerarius hath well illustrated in an Emblem. The simple narration many times easeth our distressed mind, & in the midst of greatest extremities; so divers have been relieved, by exonerating themselves to a faithful friend: he sees that which we cannot see for passion and discontent, he pacifies our minds, he will ease our pain, assuage our anger; Chrysostom adds what pleasure! what security by that means! Nothing so available, or that so much refresheth the soul of man. Tully, as I remember, in an Epistle to his dear friend Atticus, much condoles the defect of such a friend. *I live here* (saith he) *in a great City, where I have a multitude of acquaintance, but not a man of all that company with whom I dare familiarly breathe, or freely jest. Wherefore I expect thee, I desire thee, I send for thee; for there be many things which trouble and molest me, which, had I but thee in presence, I could quickly disburden myself of in a walking discourse.* The like peradventure may he and he say with that old man in the Comedy,

> *I've not one dear companion whom*
> *I dare to make my secrets' tomb,* (TERENCE)

and much inconvenience may both he and he suffer in the mean time by it. He or he, or whosoever then labours of this malady, by all means let him get some trusty friend, (always have a Pylades to console his Orestes), a Pylades, to whom freely and securely he may open himself. For, as in all other occurrences, so it is in this, as he said in Tully, If a man had gone to heaven, seen the beauty of the skies, stars errant, fixed, &c., it will do him no pleasure, except he have somebody to impart what he hath seen. It is the best thing in the world, as Seneca therefore adviseth in such a case, to get a trusty friend, to whom we may freely and sincerely pour out our secrets; nothing so delighteth and easeth the mind, as when we have a prepared bosom, to which our secrets may descend, of whose conscience we are assured as our own, whose speech may ease our succourless estate, counsel relieve, mirth expel our mourning, and whose very sight may be acceptable unto us. It was the counsel which that politick Comines gave to all Princes, and others distressed in mind, by occasion of Charles, Duke of Burgundy, that was much perplexed: first to pray to God, and lay himself open to him, and then to some special friend, whom we hold most dear, to tell all our grievances to him; nothing so forcible to strengthen, recreate, and heal, the wounded soul of a miserable man.

SUBSECTION 2 — *Help from friends by Counsel, Comfort, fair and foul Means, witty Devices, Satisfaction, Alteration of his Course of Life, removing Objects, &c.*

WHEN the Patient of himself is not able to resist or overcome these heart-eating passions, his friends or Physician must be ready to supply that which is wanting. It will be in accord with their kindness and wisdom to be solicitous about any infirmity whatsoever, (which Tully enjoineth in like case), or by their care to set aright an unexpected lapse. They must all join; it is not enough, saith Hippocrates, for the Physician to do his duty, the Patient and friends must do theirs, &c. First they must especially beware, a melancholy discontented person (be it in what kind of melancholy soever) never be left alone or idle: but, as Physicians prescribe physick, under proper supervision, let them not be left unto themselves, but with some company or other, lest by that means they aggravate and increase their disease; it is not proper for such sick persons to be alone, or to be among strangers, or among those they love or disregard, as Rodericus à Fonseca prescribes. We watch a sorrowful person, (saith Seneca), lest he abuse his solitariness, and so should we do a melancholy man; set him about some business, exercise, or recreation, which may divert his thoughts, and still keep him otherwise intent; for his phantasy is so restless, operative, and quick, that if it be not in perpetual action, ever employed, it will work upon itself, melancholize, and be carried away instantly, with some fear, jealousy, discontent, suspicion, some vain conceit or other. If his weakness be such, that he cannot discern what is amiss, correct or satisfy, it behoves them by counsel, comfort, or persuasion, by fair or foul means, to alienate his mind, by some artificial invention, or some contrary persuasion, to remove all objects, causes, companies, occasions, as may anyways molest him, to humour him, please him, divert him, and, if it be possible, by altering his course of life, to give him security and satisfaction. If he conceal his grievances, and will not be known of them, they must observe by his looks, gestures, motions, phantasy, what it is that offends, and then to apply remedies unto him. Many are instantly cured, when their minds are satisfied. Alexander makes mention of a woman that, by reason of her husband's long absence in travel, was exceedingly peevish and melancholy, but, when she heard her husband was returned, beyond all expectation, at the first sight of him, she was freed from all fear, without help of any other physick restored to her former health. Trincavellius hath such a story of a Venetian, that, being much troubled with melancholy, and ready to die for grief, when he heard his wife was brought to bed of a son, instantly recovered. As Alexander concludes, if our imaginations be not inveterate, by this art they may be cured, especially if they proceed from such a cause. No better way to satisfy than to remove the object, cause, occasion, if by any art or means possible we may find it out. If he grieve, stand in fear, be in suspicion suspense, or any way molested, secure him, free him from his misfortune, give him satisfaction, the cure is ended; alter his course of life, there needs no other Physick. If the party be sad, or otherwise affected, consider (saith Trallianus) the manner of it, all circumstances, and forthwith make a sudden alteration, by removing the occasions, avoid all terrible objects, heard or seen, monstrous and prodigious aspects, tales of Devils, Spirits, Ghosts, tragical stories; to such as are in fear, they strike a great impression, renew many times, and recall such Chimæras and terrible fictions into their minds. Make not so much as mention of them in private talk, or a dumb shew tending to that purpose: such things (saith Galateus) are offensive to their imaginations. And to those that are now in sorrow Seneca forbids all sad companions, and such as lament; a groaning companion is an enemy to quietness. Or if there be any such party, at whose presence the Patient is not well pleased, he must be removed: gentle speeches, and fair means must first be tried; no harsh language used, or uncomfortable words; and not expel, as some do, one madness with another; he that so doth is madder than the Patient himself: all things must be quietly composed; things down must not be dejected, but reared, as Crato counselleth; he must be quietly and gently used, and we should not do any thing against his mind, but by little and little effect it. As an horse that starts at a drum or trumpet, and will not endure the shooting of a piece, may be so manned by art, and animated, that he can not only endure, but is much more generous at the hearing of such things, much more courageous than before, and much delighteth in it: they must not be reformed abruptly, but by all art and insinuation, made to such companies, aspects, objects, they could not formerly away with. Many at first cannot endure the sight of a green wound, a sick man, which afterwards become good chirurgeons, bold empiricks. A horse starts at a rotten post afar off, which coming near, he quietly passeth. 'Tis much in the manner of making such kind of persons, be they never so averse from company, bashful, solitary, timorous, they may be made at last, with those Roman Matrons, to desire nothing more than, in a Publick Shew, to see a full company of Gladiators breathe out their last.

If they may not otherwise be accustomed to brook such distasteful and displeasing objects, the best way then is generally to avoid them. Montanus, to the Earl of Montfort, a Courtier, and his Melancholy Patient, adviseth him to leave the Court, by reason of those continual discontents, crosses, abuses, cares, suspicions, emulations, ambition, anger, jealousy, which that place afforded, and which surely caused him to be so melancholy at the first. Every great house is full of insolent servants ; a company of scoffers and proud Jacks are commonly conversant and attendant in such places, & able to make any man that is of a soft quiet disposition, (as many times they do), if once they humour him, a very Idiot, or stark mad. A thing too much practised in all common societies, and they have no better sport than to make themselves merry by abusing some silly fellow, or to take advantage of another man's weakness. In such cases as in a plague, the best remedy is (for to such a party, especially if he be apprehensive, there can be no greater misery), to get him quickly gone far enough off, and not to be over-hasty in his return. If he be so stupid, that he do not apprehend it, his friends should take some order, & by their discretion supply that which is wanting in him, as in all other cases they ought to do. If they see a man melancholy given, solitary, averse from company, please himself with such private and vain meditations, though he delight in it, they ought by all means to seek to divert him, to dehort him, to tell him of the event and danger that may come of it. If they see a man idle that, by reason of his means otherwise, will betake himself to no course of life, they ought seriously to admonish him he makes a noose to entangle himself, his want of employment will be his undoing. If he have sustained any great loss, suffered a repulse, disgrace, &c. if it be possible, relieve him. If he desire ought, let him be satisfied ; if in suspense, fear, suspicion, let him be secured : and, if it may conveniently be, give him his heart's content ; for the body cannot be cured till the mind be satisfied. Socrates, in Plato, would prescribe no Physick for Charmides' head-ache till first he had eased his troublesome mind ; body and soul must be cured together, as head and eyes.

> *Folly to cure the eye unless the head be sound,*
> *To patch the ailing head until the body's whole ;*
> *To drug the feeble frame were not profound*
> *Unless a tonic's given to the soul.* (PLATO)

If that may not be hoped or expected, yet ease him with comfort, cheerful speeches, fair promises, and good words ; persuade him, advise him. Many, saith Galen, have been cured by good counsel and persuasion alone. *Heaviness of the heart of man doth bring it down, but a good word rejoiceth it. And there is he that speaketh words like the pricking of a sword, but the tongue of a wise man is health ;* a gentle speech is the true cure of a wounded soul, as Plutarch contends out of Æschylus and Euripides : if it be wisely administered, it easeth grief and pain, as divers remedies do many other diseases ; 'tis a charm, soothing to tor-

mented souls, that true Nepenthes of Homer, which was no Indian plant
or feigned medicine, which Polydamna, Thon's wife, sent Helen for a
token, as Macrobius, Goropius, Greg. Nazianzen, and others, suppose,
but opportunity of speech: for Helen's bowl, Medea's unction, Venus'
Girdle, Circe's Cup, cannot so enchant, so forcibly move or alter, as it
doth. A letter sent or read will do as much; *I am much eased,* as Tully
writ to Pomponius Atticus, *when I read thy letters;* and as Julian the
Apostate once signified to Maximus the Philosopher, *as Alexander slept
with Homer's works, so do I with thine Epistles, as with healing drugs,
and I do continually read them again and yet again as new and fresh;
write therefore frequently,* or else come thyself; as a friend you will
come to a friend. Assuredly a wise and well spoken man may do what
he will in such a case; a good Orator alone, as Tully holds, can alter
affections by power of his eloquence, comfort such as are afflicted, erect
such as are depressed, expel and mitigate fear, lust, anger, &c. And how
powerful is the charm of a discreet and dear friend! He rules their
angry passions with his words. What may not he effect? As Chremes
told Menedemus, *Fear not, conceal it not, O friend, but tell me what it is
that troubles thee, and I shall surely help thee by comfort, counsel, or
in the matter itself.* Arnoldus speaks of an Usurer in his time, that upon
a loss, much melancholy and discontent, was so cured. As imagination,
fear, grief, cause such passions, so conceits alone, rectified by good hope,
counsel, &c. are able again to help: and 'tis incredible how much they
can do in such a case, as Trincavellius illustrates by an example of a
Patient of his. Porphyrius, the Philosopher, (in Plotinus' life, written
by him), relates that, being in a discontented humour through unsufferable anguish of mind, he was going to make away himself: but meeting
by chance his Master Plotinus, who, perceiving by his distracted looks
all was not well, urged him to confess his grief: which when he had
heard, he used such comfortable speeches, that he redeemed him from
the jaws of Erebus, pacified his unquiet mind, insomuch that he was
easily reconciled to himself, and much abashed to think afterwards that
he should ever entertain so vile a motion. By all means, therefore, fair
promises, good words, gentle persuasions are to be used, not to be too
rigorous at first, or to insult over them, not to deride, neglect, or contemn, but rather, as Lemnius exhorteth, to pity, and by all plausible
means to seek to reduce them: but if satisfaction may not be had, mild
courses, promises, comfortable speeches, and good counsel, will not take
place; then, as Christopherus à Vega determines, to handle them more
roughly, to threaten and chide, saith Altomarus, terrify sometimes, or,

as Salvianus will have them, to be lashed and whipped, as we do by a starting horse that is affrighted without a cause, or, as Rhasis adviseth, one while to speak fair and flatter, another while to terrify and chide, as they shall see cause.

When none of these precedent remedies will avail, it will not be amiss, which Savanarola and Ælian Montaltus so much commend, to force out one nail with another, to drive out one passion with another, or by some contrary passion, as they do bleeding at nose by letting blood in the arm, to expel one fear with another, one grief with another. Christophorus à Vega accounts it rational Physick, and Lemnius much approves it, to use an hard wedge to an hard knot, to drive out one disease with another, to pull out a tooth, or wound him, to geld him, saith Platerus, as they did Epileptical Patients of old, because it quite alters the temperature, that the pain of the one may mitigate the grief of the other; and " I knew one that was so cured of a quartan ague, by the sudden coming of his enemies upon him." If we may believe Pliny, whom Scaliger calls the father of lies, Q. Fabius Maximus, that renowned Consul of Rome, in a battle fought with the King of the Allobroges at the river Isaurus, was so rid of a quartan ague. Valesius, in his controversies, holds this an excellent remedy, and, if it be discreetly used in this malady, better than any Physick.

Sometimes again by some feigned lie, strange news, witty device, artificial invention, it is not amiss to deceive them. As they hate those, saith Alexander, that neglect or deride, so they will give ear to such as will sooth them up. If they say they have swallowed frogs, or a snake, by all means grant it, and tell them you can easily cure it, 'tis an ordinary thing. Philodotus the Physician cured a melancholy King, that thought his head was off, by putting a leaden cap thereon; the weight made him perceive it, and freed him of his fond imagination. A woman, in the said Alexander, swallowed a serpent as she thought; he gave her a vomit, and conveyed a serpent, such as she conceived, into the bason; upon the sight of it she was amended. The pleasantest dotage that ever I read, saith Laurentius, was of a Gentleman at Senes in Italy, who was afraid to piss, lest all the Town should be drowned; the Physicians caused the bells to be rung backward, and told him the Town was on fire, whereupon he made water, and was immediately cured. Another supposed his nose so big that he should dash it against the wall if he stirred; his Physician took a great piece of flesh, and, holding it in his hand, pinched him by the nose, making him believe that flesh was cut from it. Forestus had a melancholy Patient, who thought he was dead;

he put a fellow in a chest, like a dead man, by his bed's side, and made him rear himself a little, and eat: the melancholy man asked the counterfeit, whether dead men used to eat meat? he told him yea; whereupon he did eat likewise and was cured. Lemnius hath many such instances, and Jovianus Pontanus of the like: but amongst the rest I find one most memorable, registered in the French Chronicles, of an Advocate of Paris before mentioned, who believed verily he was dead, &c. I read a multitude of examples of melancholy men cured by such artificial inventions.

SUBSECTION 3 — Musick a remedy

MANY and sundry are the means which Philosophers and Physicians have prescribed to exhilarate a sorrowful heart, to divert those fixed and intent cares and meditations, which in this malady so much offend; but in my judgement none so present, none so powerful, none so apposite, as a cup of strong drink, mirth, musick, and merry company. *Wine and Musick rejoice the heart.* Rhasis, Altomarus, Ælianus Montaltus, Ficinus, Bened. Victor. Faventinus, are almost immoderate in the commendation of it; a most forcible medicine Jacchinus calls it; Jason Pratensis, a most admirable thing, and worthy of consideration, that can so mollify the mind, and stay those tempestuous affections of it. Musick is a tonick to the saddened soul, a Roaring Meg * against Melancholy, to rear and revive the languishing soul, affecting not only the ears, but the very arteries, the vital and animal spirits; it erects the mind, and makes it nimble. This it will effect in the most dull, severe, and sorrowful souls, expel grief with mirth, and if there be any clouds, dust, or dregs of cares yet lurking in our thoughts, most powerfully it wipes them all away, and that which is more, it will perform all this in an instant: cheer up the countenance, expel austerity, bring in hilarity, inform our manners, mitigate anger. Athenæus calleth it an infinite treasure to such as are endowed with it. Sweet melody repaireth sad hearts, saith Eobanus Hessus. Many other properties Cassiodorus reckons up of this our divine Musick, not only to expel the greatest griefs, but it doth extenuate fears and furies, appeaseth cruelty, abateth heaviness, and to such as are watchful it causeth quiet rest; it takes away spleen and hatred, be it instrumental, vocal, with strings, wind; it leadeth us by the spirit, it cures all irksomeness and heaviness of the soul. Labouring men, that sing to their work, can tell as much, and so can soldiers when they go to fight, whom terror of death cannot so much affright, as the sound of trumpet, drum, fife, and such like musick, an-

---

* Roaring Meg was a powerful cannon.

imates; the fear of death, as Censorinus informeth us, musick driveth away. It makes a child quiet, the nurse's song; and many times the sound of a trumpet on a sudden, bells ringing, a carman's whistle, a boy singing some Ballad tune early in the street, alters, revives, recreates, a restless patient that cannot sleep in the night, &c. In a word, it is so powerful a thing that it ravisheth the soul, the Queen of the senses, by sweet pleasure (which is an happy cure) and corporal tunes, pacifies our incorporeal soul, and rules it without words, and carries it beyond itself, helps, elevates, extends it. Scaliger gives a reason for these effects, because the spirits about the heart take in that trembling and dancing air into the body, are moved together, and stirred up with it, or else the mind, as some suppose, harmonically composed, is roused up at the tunes of musick. And 'tis not only men that are so affected, but almost all other creatures. You know the Tales of Hercules, Gallus, Orpheus, and Amphion, happy spirits, Ovid calls them, that could make stocks and stones, as well as beasts, and other animals, dance after their pipes: the dog and hare, wolf and lamb; the noisy jackdaw, the croaking crow, and Jupiter's eagle, as Philostratus describes it in his Images, stood all gaping upon Orpheus; and trees, pulled up by the roots, came to hear him, and the pine brought her friend the oak.

Arion made fishes follow him, which, as common experience evinceth, are much affected with musick. All singing birds are much pleased with it, especially Nightingales, if we may believe Calcagninus; and bees amongst the rest, though they be flying away, when they hear any tingling sound, will tarry behind. Harts, Hinds, Horses, Dogs, Bears, are exceedingly delighted with it. Elephants, Agrippa adds, and in Lydia in the midst of a lake there be certain floating Islands, (if ye will believe it), that after musick will dance.*

But to leave all declamatory speeches in praise of divine Musick, I will confine myself to my proper subject: besides that excellent power it hath to expel many other diseases, it is a sovereign remedy against Despair and Melancholy, and will drive away the Devil himself. Canus, a Rhodian Fiddler in Philostratus, when Apollonius was inquisitive to know what he could do with his pipe, told him, that he would make a melancholy man merry, and him that was merry much merrier than before, a lover more enamoured, a religious man more devout. Ismenias the Theban, Chiron the Centaur, is said to have cured this and many

---

* Mr. Carew of Anthony, in [his] Descript[ion of] Cornwall, saith of whales, that they will come and shew themselves dancing at the sound of a trumpet. — Burton's note.

other diseases by Musick alone: as now they do those, saith Bodine, that are troubled with S. Vitus' Bedlam dance. Timotheus, the Musician, compelled Alexander to skip up and down, and leave his dinner, (like the tale of the Friar and the Boy), whom Austin so much commends for it. Who hath not heard how David's harmony drove away the evil Spirits from King Saul; and Elisha, when he was much troubled by importunate Kings, called for a Minstrel, *and, when he played, the hand of the Lord came upon him.* Censorinus reports how Asclepiades the Physician helped many frantick persons by this means. Jason Pratensis hath many examples, how Clinias and Empedocles cured some desperately melancholy, and some mad, by this our Musick: which, because it hath such excellent virtues, belike Homer brings in Phemius playing & the Muses singing at the Banquet of the Gods. Aristotle & Plato highly approve of it, & so do all Politicians. The Greeks, Romans, have graced Musick, and made it one of the liberal sciences, though it be now become mercenary. All civil Common-wealths allow it: Cneius Manlius, (as Livy relates), brought first out of Asia to Rome singing wenches, players, jesters, and all kind of Musick to their feasts. Your Princes, Emperors, and persons of any quality maintain it in their Courts; no mirth without Musick. Sir Thomas More, in his absolute Utopian Common-wealth, allows Musick as an appendix to every meal, and that throughout, to all sorts. Epictetus calls a table without musick a manger; *for the consent of Musicians at a banquet is a carbuncle set in gold; and as the signet of an Emerald well trimmed with gold, so is the melody of Musick in a pleasant banquet.* Lewis the Eleventh, when he invited Edward the Fourth to come to Paris, told him that, as a principal part of his entertainment, he should hear sweet voices of children, Ionick and Lydian tunes, exquisite Musick, he should have a ----- and the Cardinal of Bourbon to be his Confessor, which he used as a most plausible argument, as to a sensual man indeed it is. Lucian, in his book On Dancing, is not ashamed to confess that he took infinite delight in singing, dancing, musick, women's company, and such like pleasures; and if thou (saith he) didst but hear them play and dance, I know thou wouldst be so well pleased with the object, that thou wouldst dance for company thyself, without doubt thou wilt be taken with it. So Scaliger ingenuously confesseth: I am beyond all measure affected with musick, I do most willingly behold them dance, I am mightily detained and allured with that grace and comeliness of fair women, I am well pleased to be idle amongst them. — And what young man is not? As it is acceptable and conducing to most, so especially to a melancholy man; provided always, his disease proceed not originally from it, that he be not some light Inamorato, some idle phantastick, who capers in conceit all the day long, and thinks of nothing else but how to make Jigs, Sonnets, Madrigals, in commendation of his Mistress. In such cases Musick is most pernicious, as a spur to a free horse will make him run himself blind, or break his wind; for Musick enchants, as Menander holds, it will make such melancholy persons mad, and the sound of those Jigs and Horn-pipes will not be removed out of the ears a week after. Plato for this reason forbids Musick and wine to all young men, because they are most part amorous, lest one fire increase another. Many men are melancholy by hearing Musick, but it is a pleasing melancholy that it causeth; and therefore to such as are discontent, in woe, fear, sorrow, or dejected, it is a most present remedy; it expels cares, alters their grieved minds, and easeth in an instant. Otherwise, saith Plutarch; musick makes some men mad as a tiger; like Astolpho's horn in Ariosto, or Mercury's golden wand in Homer, that made some wake, others sleep, it hath divers effects: and Theophrastus right well prophesied that diseases were either procured by Musick or mitigated.

SUBSECTION 4 — *Mirth and merry company, fair objects, remedies*

MIRTH and merry company may not be separated from Musick, both concerning and necessarily required in this business. Mirth (saith Vives) purgeth the blood, confirms health, causeth a fresh, pleasing, and fine colour, prorogues life, whets the wit, makes the body young, lively, and fit for any manner of employment. The merrier heart, the longer life; *a merry heart is the life of the flesh. Gladness prolongs his days*, and this is one of the three Salernitan Doctors, Dr Merryman, Dr Diet, Dr Quiet, which cure all diseases * —— a cheerful mind, repose, and a temperate fare. Gomesius is a great magnifier of honest mirth, by which (saith he) we cure many passions of the mind in ourselves and in our friends: which Galateus assigns for a cause why we love merry companions: and well they deserve it, being that, as Magninus holds, a merry companion is better than any musick, and, as the saying is, a pleasant companion is as a waggon to him that is wearied on the way. Pleasant discourse, jests, conceits, merry tales, honeyed words, as Petronius, Pliny, Spondanus, Cælius, and many good Authors plead, are that sole Nepenthes of Homer, Helen's bowl, Venus' girdle, so renowned of old to expel grief and care, to cause mirth and gladness of heart, if they be rightly understood, or seasonably applied. In a word, —

* See Merryman in Index.

Love, pleasure, Venus, graces, joy, and merriment,
Kisses and pleasant conversation, (PLAUTUS)

these are the true Nepenthes. For these causes our Physicians generally prescribe this, as a principal engine to batter the walls of melancholy, a chief antidote, and a sufficient cure of itself. By all means
(saith Mesue) procure mirth to these men in such things as are heard,
seen, tasted, or smelled, or any way perceived, and let them have all
enticements, and fair promises, the sight of excellent beauties, attires,
ornaments, delightsome passages, to distract their minds from fear and
sorrow, and such things on which they are so fixed and intent. Let them
use hunting, sports, plays, jests, merry company, as Rhasis prescribes,
which will not let the mind be molested, a cup of good drink now and
then, hear musick, and have such companions with whom they are especially delighted; merry tales or toys, drinking, singing, dancing, and
whatsoever else may procure mirth: and by no means, saith Guianerius,
suffer them to be alone. Benedictus Victorius Faventinus, in his Empiricks, accounts it an especial remedy against melancholy to hear and
see singing, dancing, maskers, mummers, to converse with such merry
fellows, and fair maids. For the beauty of a woman cheereth the countenance. Beauty alone is a sovereign remedy against fear, grief, and all
melancholy fits; a charm, as Peter de la Seine and many other writers
affirm, a banquet itself; he gives instance in discontented Menelaus that
was so often freed by Helen's fair face: and Tully cites Epicurus as a
chief patron of this tenent. To expel grief, and procure pleasance, sweet
smells, good diet, touch, taste, embracing, singing, dancing, sports,
plays, and, above the rest, exquisite beauties, whose every move gives
pleasure to both eye and mind, are most powerful means, to meet, or
see a fair maid pass by, or to be in company with her. He found it by
experience, and made good use of it in his own person, if Plutarch bely
him not; for he reckons up the names of some more elegant pieces,
Leontium, Boedina, Hedeia, Nicidium, that were frequently seen in
Epicurus' garden, and very familiar in his house. Neither did he try it
himself alone, but if we may give credit to Athenæus, he practised it
upon others. For when a sad and sick Patient was brought unto him to
be cured, he laid him on a down-bed, crowned him with a garland of
sweet-smelling flowers, in a fair perfumed closet delicately set out, and,
after a potion or two of good drink, which he administered, he brought
in a beautiful young wench that could play upon a Lute, sing and dance,
&c. Tully scoffs at Epicurus for this his profane physick (as well he
deserved) and yet Favorinus and Stobæus highly approve of it. Most of

our looser Physicians in some cases, to such parties especially, allow of this, and all of them will have a melancholy, sad, and discontented person, make frequent use of honest sports, companies, and recreations; stimulants to venery, as Rodericus à Fonseca will, the sight and touch of the most beautiful women, to be drawn to such consorts, whether they will or no. Not to be an auditor only, or a spectator, but sometimes an actor himself. To play the fool now and then is not amiss, there is a time for all things. Grave Socrates would be merry by fits, sing, dance, and take his liquor too, or else Theodoret belies him: so would old Cato, Tully by his own confession, and the rest. Xenophon, in his Symposium brings in Socrates as a principal Actor, no man merrier than himself, and sometimes he would ride a cock-horse with his children,

To ride on a long stick,   (HORACE)

(though Alcibiades scoffed at him for it), and well he might; for now and then (saith Plutarch) the most virtuous, honest, and gravest men will use feasts, jests, and toys, as we do sauce to our meats. So did Scipio and Lælius.

Valorous Scipio and gentle Lælius,
Removed from the scene and rout so clamorous,
Were wont to recreate themselves, their robes laid by,
Whilst supper by the cook was making ready.   (HORACE)

Machiavel, in the 8th Book of his Florentine History, gives this note of Cosmo de Medici, the wisest and gravest man of his time in Italy, that he would now and then play the most egregious fool in his carriage, and was so much given to jesters, players, and childish sports, to make himself merry, that he that should but consider his gravity on the one part, his folly and lightness on the other, would surely say, there were two distinct persons in him. Now methinks he did well in it, though Sarisburiensis be of opinion that Magistrates, Senators, & grave men, should not descend to lighter sports, lest the State should seem to be a trifler: but, as Themistocles, still keep a stern and constant carriage. I commend Cosmo de Medici, and Castruccius Castrucanus, than whom Italy never knew a worthier Captain, another Alexander, if Machiavel do not deceive us in his life: when a friend of his reprehended him for dancing beside his dignity (belike at some cushion dance), he told him again: he that is wise in the day may dote a little in the night. Paulus Jovius relates as much of Pope Leo Xth, that he was a grave discreet staid man, yet sometimes most free, and too open in his sports. And 'tis not altogether unfit or mis-beseeming the gravity of such a man, if that decorum of time, place, and such circumstances, be observed. Mix a little mirth with business, and, as he [Sir John Harington] said in an Epigram to his wife, I would have every man say to himself, or to his friend,

Moll, once in pleasant company by chance
I wished that you for company would dance:
Which you refused, and said, your years require,
Now, matron-like, both manners and attire.
Well, Moll, if needs you will be matron-like,
Then trust to this, I will thee matron like:
Yet so to you my love may never lessen,
As you for church, house, bed, observe this lesson.
Sit in the church as solemn as a saint,
No deed, word, thought, your due devotion taint.
Veil, if you will, your head, your soul reveal
To him that only wounded souls can heal:
Be in my house as busy as a bee,
Having a sting for every one but me;
Buzzing in every corner, gath'ring honey:
Let nothing waste that costs or yieldeth money.
And when thou seest my heart to mirth incline,
Thy tongue, wit, blood, warm with good cheer and wine:
Then of sweet sports let no occasion 'scape,
But be as wanton, toying, as an ape.

Those old Greeks had their Goddess of Pleasance, and the Lacedæ-monians, instructed from Lycurgus, did sacrifice to the God of Laugh-ter, after their wars especially, and in times of peace, which was used in Thessaly, as it appears by that of Apuleius, who was made an instru-ment of their laughter himself: because laughter and merriment was to season their labours and modester life. Laughter is the eternal pleasure of gods and men. Princes use jesters, players, and have those masters of revels in their Courts. The Romans at every supper (for they had no solemn dinner) used Musick, Gladiators, Jesters, &c. as Suetonius relates of Tiberius, Dion of Commodus, and so did the Greeks. Besides Musick, in Xenophon's Symposium, Philip, a Jester, was brought to make sport. Paulus Jovius, in the Eleventh Book of his History, hath a pretty digression of our English customs, which, howsoever some may misconster, I, for my part, will interpret to the best. The whole nation beyond all other mortal men is most given to banquetting and feasts; for they prolong them many hours together, with dainty cheer, ex-quisite Musick, and facete jesters, and afterwards they fall a dancing and courting their mistresses, till it be late in the night. Volaterran gives the same testimony of this Island, commending our Jovial manner of entertainment, and good mirth, and methinks he saith well, there is no harm in it, long may they use it, and all such modest sports! Ctesias reports of a Persian king, that had 150 maids attending at his table, to play, sing, and dance by turns; and Lil. Geraldus of an Egyptian Prince, that kept nine Virgins still to wait upon him, and those of the most excellent feature, and sweet voices, which afterwards gave occasion to the Greeks of that fiction of the nine Muses. The King of Ethiopia in Africa, most of our Asiatick Princes have done so and do; those Sophies, Mogors, Turks, &c. solace themselves after supper amongst their Queens and Concubines, taking great pleasure, (saith mine author *), to see and hear them sing and dance. This and many such means, to exhilarate the heart of men, have still been practised in all ages, as knowing there is no better thing to the preservation of man's life. What shall I say then, but to every melancholy man,

> *Feast often, and use friends not still so sad,*
> *Whose jests and merriments may make thee glad.*
>
> (EOBANUS HESSUS)

Use honest and chaste sports, scenical shews, plays, games;

> *Let bands of youths and girls together dance!* (FRACASTORIUS)

And, as Marsilius Ficinus concludes an Epistle to Bernard Canisianus and some other of his friends, will I this Tract to all good Students, *Live merrily, O my friends, free from cares, perplexity, anguish, grief of mind, live merrily, heaven made you for mirth: again and again I request you to be merry; if anything trouble your hearts, or vex your souls, neglect and contemn it, let it pass. And this I enjoin you, not as a Divine alone, but as a Physician, for without this mirth, which is the life and quintessence of Physick, medicines, and whatsoever is used and applied to prolong the life of man, is dull, dead, and of no force.* With Seneca I say, be merry while the Fates allow.

> *Rob us not of lively play,*
> *Youth is short and flies away.* (ANACREON)

It was Tiresias the Prophet's counsel to Menippus, that travelled all the world over, even down to Hell itself, to seek content, and his last farewell to Menippus, to be merry. Contemn the world (saith he) and count that is in it vanity and toys, this only covet all thy life long; be not curious, or over-solicitous, in any thing, but with a well composed and contented estate to enjoy thyself, and above all things to be merry.

* Athenæus.

If, as Mimnermus thinks, sans love and fun
Life's not worth living, live for love and fun.   (HORACE)

Nothing better, (to conclude with Solomon), than *that a man should rejoice in his affairs.* 'Tis the same advice which every Physician in this case rings to his Patient, as Capivaccius to his; avoid over-much study and perturbations of the mind, and, as much as in thee lies, live at heart's ease; Prosper Calenus to that melancholy Cardinal Cæsius, amidst thy serious studies and business, use jests and conceits, plays and toys, and whatsoever else may recreate thy mind. Nothing better than mirth and merry company in this malady. It begins with sorrow, (saith Montanus,) it must be expelled with hilarity.

But see the mischief; many men, knowing that merry company is the only medicine against Melancholy, will therefore neglect their business, and, in another extreme, spend all their days among good fellows in a Tavern or an Ale-house, and know not otherwise how to bestow their time but in drinking; malt-worms, men-fishes, or water-snakes, like so many frogs in a puddle. 'Tis their sole exercise to eat and drink; to sacrifice to Volupia, Rumina, Edulica, Potina, Mellona,* is all their religion. They wish for Philoxenus' neck, Jupiter's three nights,† and that the Sun would stand still as in Joshua's time, to satisfy their lust, that they might play the merry Greeks and play night and day. Flourishing wits, and men of good parts, good fashion, and good worth, basely prostitute themselves to every rogue's company, to take tobacco and drink, to roar and sing scurrile songs in base places.

Cheek by jowl you're sure to find
Him mixed with rogues of ev'ry kind:
Cut-throats, thieves and dirty sailors,
Runaways and lousy tailors.   (JUVENAL)

Which Thomas Erastus objects to Paracelsus, that he would lie drinking all day long with Car-men and Tapsters in a Brothel-house, is too frequent amongst us, with men of better note: like Timocreon of Rhodes, guzzling and gormandizing ever, &c. They drown their wits, seethe their brains, in Ale, consume their fortunes, lose their time, weaken their temperatures, contract filthy diseases, rheums, dropsies, calentures, tremor, get swollen jugulars, pimpled red faces, sore eyes, &c., heat their livers, alter their complexions, spoil their stomacks, over-

---

* Volupia was the goddess of Pleasure, Rumina was the Nourisher, Edulica and Potina presided respectively over children's food and drinking, Mellona was the goddess of bees and honey.

† That is, the three continuous nights on which Jupiter begat Hercules on Alcmena.

throw their bodies; for drink drowns more than the Sea and all the rivers that fall into it, (mere Funges and Casks) confound their souls, suppress reason, go from Scylla to Charybdis, and use that which is an help to their undoing.

> ———— *What matters it if 1*
> *Die by sword or sickness, still I die.* (HORACE)

When the Black Prince went to set the exil'd king of Castile into his kingdom, there was a terrible battle fought betwixt the English and the Spanish: at last the Spanish fled, the English followed them to the river side, where some drowned themselves to avoid their enemies, the rest were killed. Now tell me what difference is between drowning and killing? As good be melancholy still, as drunken beasts and beggars. Company, a sole comfort, and an only remedy to all kinds of discontent, is their sole misery and cause of perdition. As Hermione lamented in Euripides, evil company marr'd her, may they justly complain, bad companions have been their bane. For, as a bad man wishes another to be bad, that there may be one like unto himself, one drunkard in a company, one thief, one whoremaster, will by his good will make all the rest as bad as himself;

> *Although you may swear*
> *That you dread the night air,* (HORACE)

be of what complexion you will, inclination, love or hate, be it good or bad, if you come amongst them, you must do as they do; yea, though it be to the prejudice of your health, you must drink poison for wine. And so, like Grass-hoppers, whilst they sing over their cups all Summer, they starve in Winter; and for a little vain merriment shall find a sorrowful reckoning in the end.

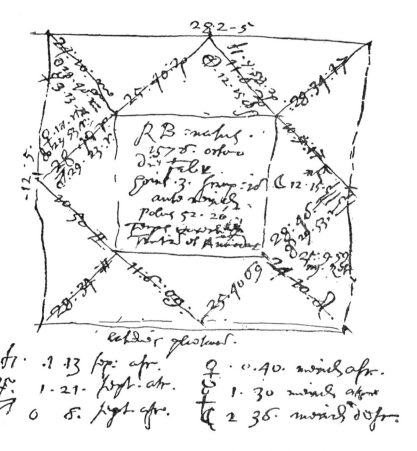

ROBERT BURTON'S NATIVITY (OR HOROSCOPE) IN HIS OWN HANDWRITING

His death was supposed to have been predicted by this nativity, and it was even rumoured that he had " sent up his soul to heaven through a noose about his neck " that the prediction might not be falsified. His epitaph in Christ Church, Oxford, says that he " lived and died by Melancholy. "

THE SECOND PARTITION (*continued*)

SECTION 3 MEMBER 1

A Consolatory Digression containing the Remedies of all manner of Discontents

ECAUSE, in the precedent Section, I have made mention of good counsel, comfortable speeches, persuasion, how necessarily they are required to the cure of a discontented or troubled mind, how present a remedy they yield, and many times a sole sufficient cure of themselves; I have thought fit, in this following Section, a little to digress, (if at least it be to digress in this subject), to collect and glean a few remedies, and comfortable speeches out of our best Orators, Philosophers, Divines, and Fathers of the Church, tending to this purpose. I confess, many have copiously written of this subject, Plato, Seneca, Plutarch, Xenophon, Epictetus, Theophrastus, Xenocrates, Crantor, Lucian, Boethius: and some of late, Sadoletus, Cardan, Budæus, Stella, Petrarch, Erasmus, besides Austin, Cyprian, Bernard, &c., and they so well, that, as Hierome in like case said, if our barren wits were dried up, they might be copiously irrigated from those well-springs: and I shall but repeat what has been done; yet, because these Tracts are not so obvious and common, I will epitomize, and briefly insert some of their divine precepts, reducing their voluminous and vast Treatises to my small scale; for it were otherwise impossible to bring so great vessels into so little a creek. And although (as Cardan said of his book): I know beforehand, this tract of mine many will contemn and reject; they that are fortunate, happy, and in flourishing estate, have no need of such consolatory speeches; they that are miserable and unhappy, think them unsufficient to ease their grieved minds, and comfort their misery: ————— yet I will go on; for this must needs do some good to such as are happy to bring them to a moderation, and make them reflect and know themselves, by seeing the unconstancy of human felicity, others' misery, and to such as are distressed, if they will but attend and consider of this, it cannot choose but give some content and comfort. 'Tis true, no medicine

491

can cure all diseases; some affections of the mind are altogether incur-able; yet these helps of Art, Physick, and Philosophy, must not be con-temned. Arrianus and Plotinus are stiff in the contrary opinion, that such precepts can do little good. Boethius himself cannot comfort in some cases, they will reject such speeches like bread of stones: these are the mad consolations of a doting mind.

Words add no courage, (which Catiline once said to his soldiers), a Captain's Oration doth not make a coward a valiant man: and, as Job feelingly said to his friends, you are but miserable comforters all. 'Tis to no purpose, in that vulgar phrase, to use a company of obsolete sen-tences, and familiar sayings: as Plinius Secundus, being now sorrowful and heavy for the departure of his dear friend, Cornelius Rufus, a Roman Senator, wrote to his fellow Tiro in like case: Comfort me, but supply me with new arguments that are resistless, that neither the writings nor the speeches of the philosophers can teach me; all these are by far too weak to support me under so heavy an affliction; — either say something that I never read nor heard of before, or else hold thy peace. Most men will here except trivial consolations, ordinary speeches, and known persuasions in this behalf will be of small force; what can any man say that hath not been said? To what end are such parænetical discourses? You may as soon remove mount Caucasus as alter some men's affections. Yet sure I think they cannot choose but do some good, comfort and ease a little: though it be the same again, I will say it, and upon that hope I will adventure. 'Tis not my speech this, but of Seneca, Plutarch, Epictetus, Austin, Bernard, Christ, and His Apostles. If I make nothing, as Montaigne said in like case, I will mar nothing; 'tis not my doctrine but by study, I hope I shall do no body wrong to speak what I think, and deserve not blame in imparting my mind. If it be not for thy ease, it may for mine own; so Tully, Car-dan, and Boethius wrote their Consolations as well to help themselves as others. Be it as it may, I will essay.

Discontents and grievances are either general or particular; general are wars, plagues, dearths, famine, fires, inundations, unseasonable weather, epidemical diseases, which afflict whole Kingdoms, Territories, Cities: or peculiar to private men, as cares, crosses, losses, death of friends, poverty, want, sickness, orbities,* injuries, abuses, &c., gen-erally all discontent; we men are battered by fortune's blasts; no condition free; each undergoes his own suffering. Even in the midst of our mirth and jollity, there is some grudging, some complaint; as he

* Bereavements.

saith, our whole life is a *glucupicron,* a bitter sweet passion, honey and gall mixt together, we are all miserable and discontent; who can deny it? If all, and that it be a common calamity, an inevitable necessity, all distressed, then as Cardan infers, who art thou that hopest to go free? Why dost thou not grieve thou art a mortal man, and not governor of the world? To bear the lot which all endure none can refuse! If it be common to all, why should one man be more disquieted than another? If thou alone wert distressed, it were indeed more irksome, and less to be endured; but, when the calamity is common, comfort thyself with this, thou hast more fellows, partners in woe, 'tis not thy sole case, & why shouldst thou be so impatient? " Ay, but, alas! we are more miserable than others: what shall we do? Besides private miseries, we live in perpetual fear, and danger of common enemies; we have Bellona's whips, and pitiful outcries, for Epithalamiums; for pleasant Musick, that fearful noise of Ordnance, Drums, and warlike Trumpets, still sounding in our ears; instead of nuptial Torches, we have firing ot Towns & Cities; for triumphs, lamentations; for joy, tears." * *So it is, & so it was, and ever will be. He that refuseth to see and hear, to suffer this, is not fit to live in this world, and knows not the common condition of all men, to whom, so long as they live, with a reciprocal course, joys and sorrows are annexed, and succeed one another.* It is inevitable, it may not be avoided, and why then should'st thou be so much troubled? As Tully deems out of an old Poet, that which is necessary cannot be grievous. If it be so, then comfort thyself in this, that, whether thou wilt or no, it must be endured: make a virtue of necessity, and conform thyself to undergo it. If it be long, 'tis light; if grievous, it cannot last; it will away, and if nought else, yet time will wear it out, custom will ease it; oblivion is a common medicine for all losses, injuries, griefs, and detriments whatsoever, and when they are once past, this commodity comes of infelicity, it makes the rest of our life sweeter unto us: and one day it will be pleasant to remember these sufferings; the privation and want of a thing many times makes it more pleasant and delightsome than before it was. We must not think, the happiest of us all, to escape here without some misfortunes,

> *So true it is no pleasure is complete,*
>
> *Grief twines with joy; bitter is mix't with sweet.*   (OVID)

Heaven and earth are much unlike; those heavenly bodies indeed are freely carried in their orbs without any impediment or interruption, to continue their course for innumerable ages, and make their conversions:

---

* Lorchan: Gallobelgicus: 1598, of the Low Countries.

but men are urged with many difficulties, and have divers hindrances, oppositions, still crossing, interrupting their endeavours and desires; and no mortal man is free from this law of nature. We must not therefore hope to have all things answer our own expectation, to have a continuance of good success and fortunes. And as Minucius Felix, the Roman Consul, told that insulting Coriolanus, drunk with his good fortunes, " look not for that success thou hast hitherto had "; it never yet happened to any man since the beginning of the world, nor ever will, to have all things according to his desire, or to whom fortune was never opposite and adverse. Even so it fell out to him as he foretold. And so to others, even to that happiness of Augustus; though he were Jupiter's Almoner, Pluto's Treasurer, Neptune's Admiral, it could not secure him. Such was Alcibiades' fortune, Narses', that great Gonsalvo's, and most famous men's, that, as Jovius concludes, it is almost fatal to great Princes, through their own default, or otherwise circumvented with envy and malice, to lose their honours, and die contumeliously. 'Tis so, still hath been, and ever will be, there's nothing happy on its every side,

> *There's no perfection is so absolute,*
> *That some impurity doth not pollute.*

Whatsoever is under the Moon is subject to corruption, alteration; and, so long as thou livest upon the earth, look not for other. Thou shalt not here find peaceable and cheerful days, quiet times, but rather clouds, storms, calumnies; such is our fate. And as those errant planets, in their distinct orbs, have their several motions, sometimes direct, stationary, retrograde, in Apogee, Perigee. oriental, occidental, combust, feral, free, and, as our Astrologers will, have their fortitudes and debilities, by reason of those good and bad irradiations, conferred to each other's site in the heavens, in their terms, houses, case, detriments, &c., so we rise and fall in this world, ebb and flow, in and out, reared and dejected, lead a troublesome life, subject to many accidents and casualties of fortunes, variety of passions, infirmities, as well from ourselves as others.

Yea, but thou thinkest thou art more miserable than the rest, other men are happy in respect of thee, their miseries are but flea-bitings to thine, thou alone art unhappy, none so bad as thyself. Yet if, as Socrates said: all the men in the world should come and bring their grievances together, of body, mind, fortune, sores, ulcers, madness, epilepsies, agues, and all those common calamities of beggary, want, servitude, imprisonment, and lay them on a heap to be equally divided, wouldst thou share alike, and take thy portion, or be as thou art? Without question thou wouldst be as thou art. —————— If some Jupiter should say, to give us all content,

> *Well, be't so then: you, master soldier,*
> *Shall be a merchant ; you, sir lawyer,*
> *A country gentleman ; go you to this,*
> *That side you ; why stand ye? It's well as 'tis.*   (HORACE)

Every man knows his own, but not others' defects and miseries; and 'tis the nature of all men still to reflect upon themselves, their own misfortunes, not to examine or consider other men's, not to confer themselves with others: to recount their miseries, but not their good gifts, fortunes, benefits, which they have, to ruminate on their adversity, but not once to think on their prosperity, not what they have, but what they want: to look still on them that go before, but not on those infinite numbers that come after. Whereas many a man would think himself in heaven, a petty Prince, if he had but the lest part of that fortune which thou so much repinest at, abhorrest, and accountest a most vile and wretched estate. How many thousands want that which thou hast! how many myriads of poor slaves, captives, of such as work day and night in coal-pits, tin-mines, with sore toil to maintain a poor living, of such as labour in body and mind, live in extreme anguish, and pain, all which thou art free from! Thou art most happy if thou couldst be content, and acknowledge thy happiness. We know the value of a thing from the wanting more than from the enjoying; when thou shalt hereafter come to want, that which thou now loathest, abhorrest, and art weary of, and tired with, when 'tis past, thou wilt say thou werest most happy: and, after a little miss, wish with all thine heart thou hadst the same content again, might'st lead but such a life, a world for such a life: the remembrance of it is pleasant. Be silent then, rest satisfied, comfort thyself with other men's misfortunes, and, as the mouldwarp [mole] in Æsop told the fox, complaining for want of a tail, and the rest of his companions: " You complain of toys, but I am blind, be quiet "; I say to thee be thou satisfied. It is recorded of the hares, that, with a general consent, they went to drown themselves, out of a feeling of their misery; but when they saw a company of frogs more fearful than they were, they began to take courage and comfort again. Confer thine estate with others. Consider the like calamities of other men; thou wilt then bear thine own the better. Be content and rest satisfied, for thou art well in respect of others; be thankful for that thou hast, that God hath done for thee; he hath not made thee a monster, a beast, a base creature, as he might, but a man, a Christian, such a man; consider aright of it, thou art full well as thou art. No man can have what he will, he may choose whether he will desire that which he hath not: thy lot is fallen, make the best of it. If we should all sleep at all times, (as Endymion is said to have done), who then were happier than his fellow? Our life is but short, a very dream, and, while we look about, eternity is at hand: our life is a pilgrimage on earth, which wise men pass with great alacrity. If thou be in woe, sorrow, want, distress, in pain, or sickness, think of that of our Apostle, *God chastiseth them whom he loveth. They that sow in teares shall reap in joy. As the furnace proveth the potter's vessel, so doth temptation try men's thoughts;* 'tis for thy good; hadst thou not been so visited, thou hadst been utterly undone; as gold in the fire, so men are tried in adversity. Tribulation maketh rich: and, which Camerarius hath well shadowed in an Emblem of a thresher and corn,

> *As threshing separates from straw the corn,*
> *By crosses from the world's chaff are we born.*

'Tis the very same which Chrysostom comments: Corn is not separated but by threshing, nor men from worldly impediments but by tribulation. 'Tis that which Cyprian ingeminates. 'Tis that which Hierom, which all the Fathers, inculcate; so we are catechised for eternity. 'Tis that which the proverb insinuates: Harming's warning, — What hurteth teacheth; 'tis that which all the world rings into our ears. God, saith Austin, hath one son without sin, none without correction. An expert sea-man is tried in a tempest, a runner in a race, a Captain in a battle, a valiant man in adversity, a Christian in tentation and misery. We are sent as so many soldiers into this world, to strive with it, the flesh, the devil; our life is a warfare, and who knows it not? There is no easy path from earth to stars: and therefore, peradventure, this world here is made troublesome unto us, that, as Gregory notes, we should not be delighted by the way, and forget whither we are going.

> *Go now, brave men, pursue the path of high renown,*
> *Turn not your backs as dolts that fly;*
> *O'ercome the earth, as she the sky,*
> *Then you the stars shall crown.* (BOETHIUS)

Go on then merrily to heaven. If the way be troublesome, and you in misery, in many grievances, on the other side you have many pleasant sports, objects, sweet smells, delightsome tastes, musick, meats, herbs, flowers, &c., to recreate your senses. Or put case thou art now forsaken of the world, dejected, contemned, yet comfort thyself, as it was said to Hagar in the wilderness, *God sees thee, he takes notice of thee:*

there is a God above that can vindicate thy cause, that can relieve thee. And surely, Seneca thinks, he takes delight in seeing thee. The gods are well pleased when they see great men contending with adversity, as we are to see men fight, or a man with a beast. But these are toys in respect. Behold, saith he, a spectacle worthy of God: a good man contented with his estate. A tyrant is the best sacrifice to Jupiter, as the ancients held, and his best object a contented mind. For thy part then rest satisfied, *cast all thy care on him, thy burden on him, rely on him, trust on him, and he shall nourish thee, care for thee, give thee thine heart's desire;* say with David, *God is our hope and strength, in troubles ready to be found. For they that trust in the Lord shall be as mount Sion, which cannot be removed. As the mountains are about Jerusalem, so is the Lord about his people, from henceforth and for ever.*

MEMBER 2

Deformity of Body, Sickness, Baseness of Birth, Peculiar Discontents

PARTICULAR discontents and grievances are either of body, mind, or fortune, which, as they wound the soul of man, produce this melancholy, and many great inconveniences, by that antidote of good counsel and persuasion may be eased or expelled. Deformities & imperfections of our bodies, as lameness, crookedness, deafness, blindness, be they innate or accidental, torture many men: yet this may comfort them, that those imperfections of the body do not a whit blemish the soul, or hinder the operations of it, but rather help and much increase it. Thou art lame of body, deformed to the eye; yet this hinders not but that thou mayst be a good, a wise, upright, honest man. Seldom, saith Plutarch, honesty and beauty dwell together; and oftentimes under a threadbare coat lies an excellent understanding. Cornelius Mussus, that famous Preacher in Italy, when he came first into the Pulpit in Venice, was so much contemned by reason of his outside, a little, lean, poor, dejected person, they were all ready to leave the Church; but when they heard his voice they did admire him, and happy was that Senator could enjoy his company, or invite him first to his house. A silly fellow to look to may have more wit, learning, honesty, than he that struts it out, talks bombast, and is admired in the world's opinion. The best wine comes out of an old vessel. How many deformed Princes, Kings, Emperors, could I reckon up, Philosophers, Orators! Hannibal had but one eye, Appius Claudius, Timoleon, blind, Muley Hassan, King of Tunis, John, King of Bohemia, and Tiresias the Prophet. The night hath his pleasure; and for the loss of that one sense such men are commonly recompensed in the rest; they have excellent memories, other good parts, musick, and many recreations; much happiness, great wisdom, as Tully well discourseth in his Tusculan Questions. Homer was blind, yet who (saith he) made more accurate, lively, or better descriptions, with both his eyes? Democritus was blind, yet, as Laertius writes of him, he saw more than all Greece besides; as Plato concludes, when our bodily eyes are at worst, generally the eyes of our soul see best. Some Philosophers and Divines have evirated [or castrated] themselves, and cut out their eyes voluntarily, the better to contemplate. Angelus Politianus had a tetter in his nose continually running, fulsome in company, yet no man so eloquent and pleasing in his works. Aesop was crooked, Socrates pur-blind, long-legged, hairy, Democritus withered, Seneca lean and harsh, ugly to behold; yet shew me so many flourishing wits, such divine spirits! Horace a little blear-eyed contemptible fellow, yet who so sententious and wise? Marcilius Ficinus, Faber Stapulensis, a couple of dwarfs, Melancthon a short hard-favored man (little was he, yet great), yet of incomparable parts all three. Ignatius Loyola, the founder of the Jesuits, by reason of an hurt he received in his leg at the siege of Pampeluna, the chief town of Navarre in Spain, unfit for wars, and less serviceable at court, upon that accident betook himself to his beads, and by those means got more honour than ever he should have done with the use of his limbs, and properness of person: a wound hurts not the soul. Galba the Emperor was crook-backed, Epictetus lame; that great Alexander a little man of stature, Augustus Caesar of the same pitch; Agesilaus of despicable figure; Boccharis a most deformed Prince as ever Egypt had, yet, as Diodorus Siculus records of him, in wisdom and knowledge far beyond his predecessors. In the year of our Lord 1306, Uladeslaus Cubitalis, that pigmy King of Poland, reigned and fought more victorious battles than any of his long-shanked predecessors. Virtue refuseth no stature; and commonly your great vast bodies, and fine features, are sottish, dull, and leaden spirits. What's in them?

> *What, save sluggish weight, that's join'd*
> *With dull ferocity of mind?* (OVID)

What in Otus and Ephialtes (Neptune's sons in Homer) nine acres long?

> *Like tall Orion stalking o'er the flood,*
> *When with his brawny breast he cuts the waves,*
> *His shoulder scarce the topmost billow laves.* (VIRGIL)

What in Maximinus, Ajax, Caligula, and the rest of those great Zan-
zummins, or gigantical Anakims, heavy, vast, barbarous lubbers?

> *If the Fates give thee a giant body,*
> *Wits they withhold, and thou'rt a noddy.*

Their body, saith Lemnius, is a burden to them, and their spirits not
so lively, nor they so erect and merry. In a big body there's not a grain
of wit. A little diamond is more worth than a rocky mountain; which
made Alexander of Aphrodisias positively conclude, the lesser the
wiser, because the soul was more contracted in such a body. Let Bodine
in the fifth chapter of his Way to the Easy Understanding of History
plead the rest: the lesser they are, as in Asia, Greece, they have generally the finest wits. And for bódily stature, which some so much admire, and goodly presence, 'tis true, to say the best of them, great men
are proper and tall, I grant that they hide their heads in the clouds;
but little men are pretty.

> *The best men of all men,*
> *Cotta, are the small men.*   (MARTIAL)

Sickness, diseases, trouble many, but without a cause. It may be 'tis
for the good of their souls: 'tis parcel of their destiny: the flesh rebels
against the spirit; that which hurts the one must needs help the other.
Sickness is the mother of modesty, putteth us in mind of our mortality;
and when we are in the full career of worldly pomp and jollity, she pull-
eth us by the ear, and maketh us know ourselves. Pliny calls it the
sum of philosophy, if we could but perform that in our health, which we
promise in our sickness. 'Tis when we are sick that we are most virtuous; for what sick man (as Secundus expostulates with Maximus)
was ever lascivious, covetous, or ambitious? he envies no man, admires
no man, flatters no man, despiseth no man, listens not after lies and
tales, &c. And were it not for such gentle remembrances, men would
have no moderation of themselves; they would be worse than tigers,
wolves, and lions: who should keep them in awe? Princes, Masters,
Parents, Magistrates, Judges, friends, enemies, fair or foul means, cannot contain us, but a little sickness (as Chrysostom observes) will correct and amend us. And therefore, with good discretion, Jovianus Pontanus caused this short sentence to be engraven on his tomb in Naples:
Labor, sorrow, grief, sickness, want and woe, to serve proud masters,
bear that superstitious yoke, and bury your dearest friends, &c., are
the sauces of our life. ——————— If thy disease be continuate and painful to thee, it will not surely last: *and a light affliction, which is but for*
a moment, causeth unto us a far more excellent and eternal weight

of glory. Bear it with patience: women endure much sorrow in child-bed, and yet they will not contain [or restrain themselves from it] ; and those that are barren, wish for this pain: be courageous, there is as much valour to be shewed in thy bed, as in an army, or at a sea-fight: thou shalt conquer or be conquered, thou shalt be rid at last. In the mean time, let it take his course, thy mind is not any way disabled. Bilibaldus Pirckheemerus, Senator to Charles V. ruled all Germany, lying most part of his days sick of the gout upon his bed. The more violent thy torture is, the less it will continue: and, though it be severe and hideous for the time, comfort thyself, as martyrs do, with honour and immortality. That famous philosopher, Epicurus, being in as miserable pain of stone and colick as a man might endure, solaced himself with a conceit of immortality; the joy of his soul for his rare inventions repelled the pain of his bodily torments.

Baseness of birth is a great disparagement to some men, especially if they be wealthy, bear office, and come to promotion in a Common-wealth; then (as Boethius observes) if their birth be not answerable to their calling, and to their fellows, they are much abashed and ashamed of themselves. Some scorn their own father and mother, deny brothers and sisters, with the rest of their kindred and friends, and will not suffer them to come near them, when they are in their pomp, accounting it a scandal to their greatness to have such beggarly beginnings. Simon in Lucian, having now got a little wealth, changed his name from Simon to Simonides, for that there were so many beggars of his kin, and set the house on fire where he was born, because no body should point at it. Others buy titles, coats of arms, and by all means screw themselves into ancient families, falsifying pedigrees, usurping scutcheons, and all because they would not seem to be base. The reason is, for that this gentility is so much admired by a company of outsides, and such honour attributed to it, as amongst Germans, Frenchmen, and Venetians, the Gentry scorn the commonalty, and will not suffer them to match with them; they depress, and make them as so many asses to carry burdens. In our ordinary talk and fallings out, the most opprobrious and scur-rile name we can fasten upon a man, or first give, is to call him base rogue, beggarly rascal, and the like: whereas, in my judgement, this ought of all other grievances to trouble men least. Of all vanities and fopperies, to brag of Gentility is the greatest; for what is it they crack so much of, and challenge such superiority, as if they were demi-gods? Birth?

Didst thou so much rely upon thy birth? (VIRGIL)

It is a nonentity, a mere flash, a ceremony, a toy, a thing of nought. Consider the beginning, present estate, progress, ending, of Gentry, and then tell me what it is. Oppression, fraud, cozening, usury, knavery, bawdry, murder, and tyranny, are the beginning of many ancient families. One hath been a blood-sucker, a parricide, the death of many a silly soul in some unjust quarrels, seditions, made many an orphan and poor widow; and for that he is made a Lord or an Earl, and his posterity Gentlemen for ever after. Another hath been a bawd, a pander to some great man, a parasite, a slave, prostituted himself, his wife, daughter, to some lascivious Prince, and for that he is exalted. Tiberius preferred many to honours in his time, because they were famous whore-masters and sturdy drinkers; many come into this parchment-row (so Varro calls it) by flattery or cozening; search your old families, and you shall scarce find of a multitude (as Æneas Sylvius [Pope Pius II., in his Boccacian novel] observes) any that have not had a wicked beginning; as that Plebeian in Machiavel in a set oration proved to his fellows, that do not rise by knavery, force, foolery, villainy, or such indirect means. They are commonly able that are wealthy; virtue and riches seldom settle on one man: who then sees not the base beginning of nobility? spoils enrich one, usury another, treason a third, witchcraft a fourth, flattery a fifth, lying, stealing, bearing false witness a sixth, adultery the seventh, &c. One makes a fool of himself to make his Lord merry, another dandles my young Master, bestows a little nag on him, a third marries a crackt piece, &c. Now may it please your good Worship, your Lordship, who was the first founder of your family? The poet answers,

> *Herding sheep, his humble lot;*
> *Or else, I'd rather not say what!*   (JUVENAL)

Are he or you the better Gentleman? If he, then we have traced him to his form [or lair]. If you, what is it of which thou boastest so much? That thou art his son. It may be his heir, his reputed son, and yet indeed a Priest or a serving-man may be the true father of him; but we will not controvert that now; married women are all honest; thou art his son's son's son, begotten & born within the four seas,* &c. Thy great great great grandfather was a rich citizen, and then in all likelihood a usurer, a lawyer, and then a ————— a courtier, & then a ————— a Country

---

* The presumption in English Law is in favour of the legitimacy of any child of a married woman, and it was in Burton's time held by Sir Edward Coke that " if the husband be within the four seas, *i.e.*, within the jurisdiction of the king of England, and the wife hath issue, no proof shall be admitted to prove the child a bastard unless the husband hath an apparent impossibility of procreation."

Gentleman, and then he scraped it out of sheep, &c. And you are the heir of all his virtues, fortunes, titles; so then, what is your Gentry, but, as Hierom saith, riches grown old, ancient wealth? that is the definition of Gentility. The father goes often to the Devil to make his son a Gentleman. For the present, what is it? It began (saith Agrippa) with strong impiety, with tyranny, oppression, &c.; and so it is maintained: wealth began it (no matter how got), wealth continueth and increaseth it. Those Roman knights were so called, if they could dispend annually so much. In the kingdom of Naples and France, he that buys such lands buys the honour, title, Barony, together with it; and they that can dispend so much amongst us must be called to bear office, to be knights, or fine for it; as one observes, our nobles are measured by their means. And what now is the object of honour? What maintains our Gentry but wealth? Without means, Gentry is naught worth; nothing so contemptible and base: cheaper than seaweed. Saith Nevisanus the lawyer, to dispute of Gentry without wealth, is (saving your reverence) to discuss the original of a mard. So that it is wealth alone that denominates, money which maintains it, gives being to it, for which every man may have it. And what is their ordinary exercise? *sit to eat, drink, lie down to sleep, and rise to play:* wherein lies their worth and sufficiency? in a few coats of arms, eagles, lions, serpents, bears, tigers, dogs, crosses, bends, fesses and such like baubles, which they commonly set up in their galleries, porches, windows, on bowls, platters, coaches, in tombs, churches, men's sleeves, &c. If he can hawk and hunt, ride an horse, play at cards and dice, swagger, drink, swear, take tobacco with a grace, sing, dance, wear his clothes in fashion, court and please his mistress, talk big fustian, insult, scorn, strut, contemn others, and use a little mimical and apish compliment above the rest, he is a complete, (O illustrious praise!) a well-qualified gentleman; these are most of their employments, this their greatest commendation. What is Gentry, this parchment Nobility then, but, as Agrippa defines it, a sanctuary of knavery and naughtiness, a cloke for wickedness and execrable vices, of pride, fraud, contempt, boasting, oppression, dissimulation, lust, gluttony, malice, fornication, adultery, ignorance, impiety? A nobleman therefore, in some likelihood, as he concludes, is an atheist, an oppressor, an epicure, a gull, a dizzard, an illiterate idiot, an outside, a glow-worm, a proud fool, an arrant ass: a slave to his lust & belly, strong only in wantonness. And, as Salvianus observed of his countrymen the Aquitaines in France, first in high places, first too in the vices; and Cabinet du Roy, their own writer, distinctly of the rest: the Nobles of Berry are most part lechers, they of Touraine thieves, they of Narbonne covetous, they of Guienne coiners, they of Provence atheists, they of Rheims superstitious, they of Lyons treacherous, of Normandy proud, of Picardy insolent, &c. We may generally conclude, the greater men, the more vicious. In fine, as Æneas Sylvius adds, they are most part miserable, sottish and filthy fellows, like the walls of their houses, fair without, foul within. What dost thou vaunt of now? What dost thou gape and wonder at? admire him for his brave apparel, horses, dogs, fine houses, manors, orchards, gardens, walks? Why, a fool may be possessor of this as well as he; and he that accounts him a better man, a Nobleman, for having of it, he is a fool himself. Now go and brag of thy Gentility. This is it belike, which makes the Turks at this day scorn Nobility, and all those huffing bombast titles, which so much elevate their poles: except it be such as have got it at first, maintain it by some supereminent quality, or excellent worth. And for this cause, the Ragusian Commonwealth, Switzers, and the United Provinces, in all their Aristocracies, or Democratical Monarchies (if I may so call them), exclude all these degrees of hereditary honours, and will admit of none to bear office but such as are learned, like those Athenian Areopagites, wise, discreet, and well brought up. The Chinenses observe the same custom, no man amongst them Noble by birth; out of their Philosophers and Doctors they choose Magistrates; their politick Nobles are taken from such as be virtuous noble: nobility is from office, not from birth, as in Israel of old, and their office was to defend and govern their Country, in war and peace, not to hawk, hunt, eat, drink, game alone, as too many do. Their Lau-sie,* Mandarins, Literates [or Scholars], Licentiates, and such as have raised themselves by their worth, are their noblemen only, thought fit to govern a state; and why then should any that is otherwise of worth be ashamed of his birth? why should not he be as much respected that leaves a noble posterity, as he that hath had noble ancestors? nay, why not more? for we adore the rising sun most part; and how much better is it to say, I have outshone my ancestors in goodness, to boast himself of his virtues, than of his birth? Cathesbius, Sultan of Egypt and Syria, was by his condition a slave, but for worth, valour, and manhood, second to no King, and for that cause (as Jovius writes) elected Emperor of the Mamelukes. That

* Lau-ye, or Lau-sie, signifying Sir or Father, an honorific title given to Chinese magistrates, their official title in Chinese being Quon-fu, according to the Jesuit missionary Matteo Ricci, whose history of the Christian Campaign in China in the 16th century was the source of Burton's information. Ricci adds: " The Portuguese call these magistrates Mandarins, perchance because they give mandates."

poor Spanish Pizarro, for his valour made by Charles the Fifth Marquess of Anatillo; the Turkey Pashas are all such. Pertinax, Phillipus Arabs, Maximinus, Probus, Aurelius, &c., from common soldiers became Emperors; Cato, Cincinnatus, &c., Consuls; Pius Secundus, Sixtus Quintus, Johannes Secundus, Nicholas Quintus, &c., Popes. Socrates, Virgil, Horace, born of a freedman father. The Kings of Denmark fetch their pedigree, as some say, from one Ulfo, that was the son of a bear. Many a worthy man comes out of a poor cottage. Hercules, Romulus, Alexander, (by Olympia's confession), Themistocles, Jugurtha, King Arthur, William the Conqueror, Homer, Demosthenes, P. Lombard, Peter Comestor, Bartholus, Pope Adrian the Fourth, &c., bastards; and almost in every Kingdom the most ancient families have been at first Princes' bastards; their worthiest captains, best wits, greatest scholars, bravest spirits, in all our Annals, have been base. Cardan, in his Subtilties, gives a reason why they are most part better able than others in body and mind, and so consequently more fortunate. Castruccius Castracanus, a poor child, found in the field, exposed to misery, became Prince of Lucca and Senes in Italy, a most complete soldier, and worthy captain; Machiavel compares him to Scipio or Alexander. And 'tis a wonderful thing (saith he) to him that shall consider of it, that all those, or the greatest part of them, that have done the bravest exploits here upon earth, and excelled the rest of the nobles of their time, have been still born in some abject, obscure place, or of base and obscure abject parents. A most memorable observation, Scaliger accounts it, and not to be overlooked, that most great men came of unknown fathers, and unchaste mothers. I could recite a great catalogue of them, every Kingdom, every Province, will yield innumerable examples: and why then should baseness of birth be objected to any man? Who thinks worse of Tully for being a provincial, an upstart, or Agathocles, that Sicilian King, for being a potter's son? Iphicrates and Marius were meanly born.

What wise man thinks better of any person for his nobility? As he said in Machiavel, we are all born from one ancestor, Adam's sons, conceived all and born in sin, &c. We are by nature all as one, all alike, if you see us naked; let us wear theirs and they our clothes, and what's the difference? To speak truth, as Bale did of P. Schalichius, I more esteem thy worth, learning, honesty, than thy nobility; honour thee more that thou art a writer, a Doctor of Divinity, than Earl of the Huns, Baron of Skradine, or hast title to such and such provinces, &c. Thou art more fortunate and great (so Jovius writes to Cosmo de

Medici, then Duke of Florence) for thy virtues than for thy lovely wife, and happy children, friends, fortunes, or great Duchy of Tuscany. ———— So I account thee, and who doth not so indeed? Abdolonymus was a gardener, and yet by Alexander for his virtues made King of Syria. How much better is it to be born of mean parentage, and to excel in worth, to be morally noble (which is preferred before that natural nobility, by divines, philosophers and politicians), to be learned, honest, discreet, well qualified, to be fit for any manner of employment, in country and commonwealth, war and peace, than to be degenerate Neoptolemuses, as many brave nobles are, only wise because rich, otherwise idiots, illiterate, unfit for any manner of service! Udalricus, Earl of Cilia, upbraided John Huniades with the baseness of his birth; but he replied, Thine Earldom is consumed with riot, mine begins with honor and renown. ———— Thou hast had so many noble ancestors; what is that to thee? Call not these thine own, when thou art a dizzard thyself:

> *Why, tell me, Ponticus, are we assessed*
> *As to whose genealogy's longest and best?* (JUVENAL)

I conclude, hast thou a sound body, and a good soul, good bringing up? art thou virtuous, honest, learned, well qualified, religious, are thy conditions good? thou art a true Nobleman, perfectly noble, although born of Thersites — (*if only thou be like Achilles*); not born but made noble, supereminent: for neither sword, nor fire, nor water, nor sickness, nor outward violence, nor the Devil himself, can take thy good parts from thee. Be not ashamed of thy birth then, thou art a Gentleman all the world over, and shalt be honored; whenas he, strip him of his fine clothes, dispossess him of his wealth, is a funge [or dolt] (which Polynices in his banishment found true by experience, Gentry was not esteemed), like a piece of coin in another country, that no man will take, and shall be contemned. Once more, though thou be a Barbarian, born at Tontonteac, a villain, a slave, a Saldanian Negro, or a rude Virginian in Dasamonquepeuc, he a French Monsieur, a Spanish Don, a Seignior of Italy, I care not how descended, of what family, of what order, Baron, Count, Prince, if thou be well qualified, and he not, but a degenerate Neoptolemus, I tell thee in a word, thou art a man, and he is a beast.

Let no son of the earth, or upstart, insult at this which I have said, no worthy Gentleman take offence. I speak it not to detract from such as are well deserving, truly virtuous and noble: I do much respect and honor true Gentry and Nobility; I was born of worshipful parents my-

self, in an ancient family, but I am a younger brother, it concerns me
not : or had I been some great heir, richly endowed, so minded as I am,
I should not have been elevated at all, but so esteemed of it, as of all
other human happiness, honours, &c., they have their period, are brittle
and unconstant. As Stuckius said of that great river Danube, it riseth
from a small fountain, a little brook at first, sometimes broad, sometimes narrow, now slow, then swift, increased at last to an incredible
greatness by the confluence of 60 navigable rivers, it vanisheth in conclusion, loseth his name, and is suddenly swallowed up of the Euxine Sea :
I may say of our greatest families, they were mean at first, augmented
by rich marriages, purchases, offices, they continue for some ages, with
some little alteration of circumstances, fortunes, places, &c., by some
prodigal son, for some default, or for want of issue, they are defaced in
an instant, and their memory blotted out.

So much in the mean time I do attribute to Gentility, that, if he be
well descended, of worshipful or noble parentage, he will express it in
his conditions :

> *Nor, indeed are doves*
> *Begot from the fierce loves*
> *Of eagles.* (HORACE)

And although the nobility of our times be much like our coins, more in
number and value, but less in weight and goodness, with finer stamps,
cuts, or outsides, than of old : yet if he retain those ancient characters
of true Gentry, he will be more affable, courteous, gently disposed, of
fairer carriage, better temper, of a more magnanimous, heroical, and
generous spirit than that common man, those ordinary boors and peasants, who are, as one observes of them, a rude, brutish, uncivil, wild, a
currish generation, cruel, and malicious, uncapable of discipline and
such as have scarce common sense. And it may be generally spoken of
all, which Lemnius the Physician said of his travel into England, the
common people were silly, sullen, dogged clowns, but the Gentlemen
were courteous and civil. If it so fall out (as often it doth) that such
peasants are preferred by reason of their wealth, chance, error, or otherwise, yet as the cat in the fable, when she was turned to a fair maid,
would play with mice ; a cur will be a cur, a clown will be a clown, he
will likely favour of the stock whence he came, and that innate rusticity
can hardly be shaken off.

> *Purse-proud, he struts as though he owned the earth,*
> *But still betrays the record of his birth.* (HORACE)

And though by their education such men may be better qualified, & more

refined, yet there be many symptoms, by which they may likely be
descried, an affected phantastical carriage, a tailor-like spruceness, a
peculiar garb in all their proceedings, choicer than ordinary in his diet,
and, as Hierome well describes such a one to his Nepotian: an upstart
born in a base cottage, that scarce at first had coarse bread to fill his
hungry guts, must now feed on kickshaws and made dishes, will have
all variety of flesh and fish, the best oysters, &c. A beggar's brat will
be commonly more scornful, imperious, insulting, insolent, than another
man of his rank: nothing so intolerable as a fortunate fool, as Tully
found long since out of his experience. Nothing ruder than a base-born
one climbed above his station: set a beggar on horseback, and he will
ride a-gallop, a-gallop, &c.

> *Who is this doth rage and rave?*
> *One that lately was a slave.*
> *Ah, the wild beasts gentler be*
> *Than a slave at length set free!* (CLAUDIAN)

He forgets what he was, domineers, and many such other symptoms he
hath, by which you may know him from a true Gentleman. Many errors
& obliquities are on both sides, noble, ignoble, made, born: yet still
in all callings, as some degenerate, some are well deserving, and most
worthy of their honours. And as Busbequius said of Solyman the Magnificent, he was worthy of that great Empire: many meanly descended
are most worthy of their honour, politick nobles, and well deserve it.
Many of our Nobility so born (which one said of Hephaestion, Ptole-
maeus, Seleucus, Antigonus, and the rest of Alexander's followers, they
were all worthy to be Monarchs and Generals of Armies) deserve to be
Princes. And I am so far forth of Sesellius his mind, that they ought to
be preferred (if capable) before others, as being nobly born, ingeniously
brought up, and from their infancy trained to all manner of civility.
For learning & virtue in a Nobleman is more eminent, and, as a jewel
set in gold is more precious, and much to be respected, such a man deserves better than others, and is as great an honour to his family as his
Noble family to him. In a word, many Noblemen are an ornament to
their order; many poor men's sons are singularly well endowed, most
eminent and well deserving for their worth, wisdom, learning, virtue,
valour, integrity; excellent members and pillars of a Commonwealth.
And, therefore, to conclude that which I first intended, to be base by
birth, meanly born, is no such disparagement. And thus have I proved
what I had to prove.

Member 3

Against Poverty and Want, with such other Adversities

ONE of the greatest miseries that can befal a man, in the world's esteem, is poverty or want, which makes men steal, bear false witness, swear, forswear, contend, murder and rebel, which breaketh sleep, and causeth death itself. No burden (saith Menander) so intolerable as poverty : it makes men desperate, it erects and dejects : wealth gives honours, and friendships too ; money makes, but poverty mars, &c., and all this in the world's esteem : yet, if considered aright, it is a great blessing in itself, an happy estate, and yields no such cause of discontent, or that men should therefore account themselves vile, hated of God, forsaken, miserable, unfortunate. Christ himself was poor, born in a manger, and had not a house to hide his head in all his life, lest any man should make poverty a judgement of God, or an odious estate. And as he was himself, so he informed his Apostles and Disciples, they were all poor, Prophets poor, Apostles poor (*Silver and gold have I none*). *As sorrowing* (saith Paul) *and yet always rejoicing ; as having nothing, and yet possessing all things.* Your great Philosophers have been voluntarily poor, not only Christians, but many others. Crates Thebanus was adored for a god in Athens : a nobleman by birth, many servants he had, an honorable attendance, much wealth, many Manors, fine apparel ; but when he saw this, that all the wealth of the world was but brittle, uncertain, and no whit availing to live well, he flung his burden into the sea, and renounced his estate. Those Curiuses and Fabriciuses will be ever renowned for contempt of these fopperies, wherewith the world is so much affected. Among Christians I could reckon up many Kings and Queens, that have forsaken their Crowns and fortunes, and wilfully abdicated themselves from these so much esteemed toys ; many that have refused honours, titles, and all this vain pomp and happiness, which others so ambitiously seek, and carefully study to compass and attain. Riches, I deny not, are God's good gifts, and blessings ; and honour is in being honoured, honours are from God ; both rewards of virtue, and fit to be sought after, sued for, and may well be possessed : yet no such great happiness in having, or misery in wanting of them. Saith Austin, good men have wealth that we should not think it evil ; and bad men that we * should not rely on or hold it so good ; as the rain falls on both sorts, so are riches given to good and bad, but they are good only to the godly. But confer both estates, for natural parts they

---

* An emendation for the " they " of the text.

are not unlike; and a beggar's child, as Cardan well observes, is no whit inferior to a Prince's, most part better; and for those accidents of fortune, it will easily appear there is no such odds, no such extraordinary happiness in the one, or misery in the other. He is rich, wealthy, fat; what gets he by it: pride, insolency, lust, ambition, cares, fears, suspicion, trouble, anger, emulation and many filthy diseases of body and mind. He hath indeed variety of dishes, better fare, sweet wine, pleasant sauce, dainty musick, gay clothes, lords it bravely out, &c., and all that which Micyllus admired in Lucian, but with them he hath the gout, dropsies, apoplexies, palsies, stone, pox, rheums, catarrhes, crudities, oppilations, Melancholy, &c. Lust enters in, anger, ambition. According to Chrysostom, the sequel of riches is pride, riot, intemperance, arrogancy, fury, and all irrational courses.

> *Soft riches and luxurious ways*
> *Bring scandal to our present days,*   (JUVENAL)

with their variety of dishes, many such maladies of body and mind get in, which the poor man knows not of. As Saturn, in Lucian, answered the discontented commonalty, (which because of their neglected Saturnal Feasts in Rome made a grievous complaint and exclamation against rich men), that they were much mistaken in supposing such happiness in riches; you see the best, (said he), but you know not their several gripings and discontents: they are like painted walls, fair without, rotten within: diseased, filthy, crazy, full of intemperate effects; and who can reckon half? if you but knew their fears, cares, anguish of mind, and vexation, to which they are subject, you would hereafter renounce all riches.

> *O that their breasts were but conspicuous,*
> *How full of fear within, how furious!*
> *The narrow seas are not so boisterous.*   (SENECA)

Yea, but he hath the world at will that is rich, the good things of the earth; it is pleasant to draw from a great heap: he is a happy man, adored like a God, a Prince, every man seeks to him, applauds, honours, admires him. He hath honours indeed, abundance of all things: but (as I said) withal, pride, lust, anger, faction, emulation, fears, cares, suspicion, enter with his wealth; for his intemperance he hath aches, crudities, gouts, & as fruits of his idleness & fulness, lust, surfeiting, drunkenness, all manner of diseases: the wealthier, the more dishonest. He is exposed to hatred, envy, peril, and treason, fear of death, of degradation, &c.: 'tis a slippery position and close to a precipice, and the higher he climbs, the greater is his fall. The lightning commonly sets on fire the highest towers; in the more eminent place he is, the more sub-

ject to fall. As a tree that is heavy laden with fruit breaks her own
boughs, with their own greatness they ruin themselves: which Joachi-
mus Camerarius hath elegantly expressed. Plenty hath made me poor.
Their means is their misery: though they do apply themselves to the
times, to lie, dissemble, collogue, and flatter their lieges, obey, second
his will and commands, as much as may be, yet too frequently they
miscarry, they fat themselves like so many hogs, as Æneas Sylvius observes, that, when they are full fed, they may be devoured by their
Princes, as Seneca by Nero was served, Sejanus by Tiberius, and Haman by Ahasuerus. I resolve with Gregory, honour is a tempest, the
higher they are elevated, the more grievously depressed. For the rest
of his prerogatives which wealth affords, as he hath more, his expenses
are the greater. " When goods increase, they are increased that eat
them; and what good cometh to the owners, but the beholding thereof
with the eyes? "

You may thresh a hundred thousand bushels of grain,

But more than mine your belly will not contain. (HORACE)

An evil sickness, Solomon calls it, *and reserved to them for an evil. They
that will be rich fall into many fears and temptations, into many foolish
and noisome lusts, which drown men in perdition. Gold and silver hath
destroyed many.* Worldly wealth is the devil's bait: so writes Bernard;
and as the Moon, when she is fuller of light, is still farthest from the
Sun, the more wealth they have, the farther they are commonly from
God. (If I had said this of myself, rich men would have pulled me
a-pieces, but hear who saith, & who seconds it, an Apostle) therefore St.
James bids them *weep and howl for the miseries that shall come upon
them, their gold shall rust and canker, and eat their flesh as fire.* I may
then boldly conclude with Theodoret, as often as you see a man abounding in wealth, who drinks from golden cups and sleeps on down, and
naught withal, I beseech you call him not happy, but esteem him unfortunate, because he hath many occasions offered to live unjustly: on
the other side, a poor man is not miserable, if he be good, but therefore
happy, that those evil occasions are taken from him.

He is not happy that is rich,
And hath the world at will,
But he that wisely can God's gifts
Possess and use them still:
That suffers and with patience
Abides hard poverty,
And chooseth rather for to die
Than do such villainy. (HORACE)

Wherein now consists his happiness? What privileges hath he more than other men? Or rather what miseries, what cares and discontents, hath he not more than other men?

Nor treasures, nor mayors' officers remove
The miserable tumults of the mind:
Or cares that lie about, or fly above
Their high-roofed houses, with huge beams combined. (HORACE)

'Tis not his wealth that can vindicate him, let him have Job's inventory; let who will be Crœsus or Crassus, the golden waves of Pactolus will not wash away a single one of their miseries: Crœsus or rich Crassus cannot now command health, or get himself a stomack. His Worship, as Apuleius describes him, in all his plenty and great provision, is forbidden to eat, or else hath no appetite (sick in bed, can take no rest, sore grieved with some chronick disease, contracted with full diet and ease, or troubled in mind) when as, in the mean time, all his household are merry, and the poorest servant that he keeps doth continually feast. 'Tis gilt happiness, as Seneca terms it, tin-foil'd happiness, an unhappy kind of happiness, if it be happiness at all. His gold, guard, clattering of harness, and fortifications against outward enemies, cannot free him from inward fears and cares.

Indeed, men's * still attending fears and cares,
Nor armours clashing, nor fierce weapons fears:
With kings converse they boldly, and king's peers,
Fearing no flashing that from gold appears. (LUCRETIUS)

Look how many servants he hath, and so many enemies he suspects; for liberty, he entertains ambition; his pleasures are no pleasures; and that which is worst, he cannot be private or enjoy himself as other men do, his state is a servitude. A countryman may travel from kingdom to kingdom, province to province, city to city, and glut his eyes with delightful objects, hawk, hunt, and use those ordinary disports, without any notice taken, all which a Prince or a great man cannot do. He keeps in for state, not to cheapen the dignity of majesty, as our China Kings, of Borneo, and Tartarian Chams, those golden slaves, are said to do, seldom or never seen abroad, that men may note him the more when he does, which the Persian Kings so precisely observed of old. A poor man takes more delight in an ordinary meal's meat, which he hath but seldom, than they do with all their exotick dainties, and continual viands:

Our very sports by repetition tire,
But rare delight breeds ever new desire. (JUVENAL)

'Tis the rarity and necessity that makes a thing acceptable and pleasant.

* An emendation for the " men " in Burton's text.

Darius, put to flight by Alexander, drank puddle water to quench his thirst, and it was pleasanter, he swore, than any wine or mead. All excess, as Epictetus argues, will cause a dislike; sweet will be sour, which made that temperate Epicurus sometimes voluntarily fast. But they, being always accustomed to the same dishes (which [as Tully hath said in his Tusculan Questions] are nastily dressed by slovenly cooks, that after their obscenities never wash their bawdy hands), be they fish, flesh, compounded, made dishes, or whatsoever else, are therefore cloyed: nectar's self grows loathsome to them, they are weary of all their fine palaces, they are to them as so many prisons. A poor man drinks in a wooden dish, and eats his meat in wooden spoons, wooden platters, earthen vessels, and such homely stuff; the other in gold, silver, and precious stones; but with what success? Fear of poison in the one, security in the other. A poor man is able to write, to speak his mind, to do his own business himself; saith Philostratus, a rich man employs a parasite, and, as the Mayor of a City, speaks by the Town-clerk, or by Mr. Recorder, when he cannot express himself. Nonius the Senator hath a purple coat as stiff with Jewels, as his mind is full of vices, rings on his fingers worth 20,000 sesterces, and as Perozes, the Persian King, an union [or pearl] in his ear worth 100 pound weight of gold: Cleopatra hath whole boars and sheep served up to her table at once, drinks jewels dissolved, 40,000 sesterces in value; but to what end? Doth a man that is a-dry, desire to drink in gold? Doth not a cloth suit become him as well, and keep him as warm, as all their silks, satins, damasks, taffeties and tissues? Is not home-spun cloth as great a preservative against cold, as a coat of Tartar Lambs' wool, dyed in grain, or a gown of Giants' beards? Nero, saith Suetonius, never put on one garment twice, and thou hast scarce one to put on; what's the difference? one's sick, the other sound: such is the whole tenor of their lives, and that which is the consummation and upshot of all, death itself, makes the greatest difference. One like an hen feeds on the dunghill all his days, but is served up at last to his Lord's table; the other as a Falcon is fed with Partridge and Pigeons, and carried on his master's fist, but when he dies, is flung to the muckhill, and there lies. The rich man lives, like Dives, jovially here on earth, drunk with money, makes the best of it; and *boasts himself in the multitude of his riches, he thinks his house, called after his own name, shall continue for ever; but he perisheth like a beast, his way utters his folly:* evilly got, evilly spent: *like sheep they lie in the grave. They spend their days in wealth, and go suddenly down to Hell.* For all Physicians and medicines enforcing nature, a swooning wife, family's complaints, friends' tears, Dirges, Masses, funeral-songs, funerals, for all Orations, counterfeit hired acclamations, Elogiums, Epitaphs, hearses, heralds, black mourners, solemnities, obelisks, and Mausolean tombs, if he have them at least, he like a hog goes to Hell with a guilty conscience (*Hell opens its mouth for them*) and a poor man's curse : his memory stinks like the snuff of a candle when it is put out ; scurrile libels, and infamous obloquies accompany him ; when as poor Lazarus is the Temple of God, lives and dies in true devotion, hath no more attendants but his own innocency, the Heaven a tomb, desires to be dissolved, buried in his Mother's lap, and hath a company of Angels ready to convey his soul into Abraham's bosom, he leaves an everlasting and a sweet memory behind him. Crassus and Sulla are indeed still recorded, but not so much for their wealth, as for their victories : Crœsus for his end, Solomon for his wisdom. In a word, to get wealth is a great trouble, anxiety to keep, grief to lose it.

> *I pray for those of doltish mind :*
> *To wealth and place let them aspire ;*
> *What the true blessings are, they'll find*
> *When they of these false burdens tire.*   (BOETHIUS)

But consider all those other unknown, concealed happinesses, which a poor man hath, (I call them unknown, because they be not acknowledged in the world's esteem, or so taken) : happy are they in the mean time, if they would take notice of it, make use or apply it to themselves. *A poor man wise is better than a foolish King.* Poverty is the way to heaven, the mistress of philosophy, the mother of religion, virtue, sobriety, sister of innocency, and an upright mind. How many such encomiums might I add out of the Fathers, Philosophers, Orators ! It troubles many that they are poor, they account of it as a great plague, curse, a sign of God's hatred, damn'd villainy itself, a disgrace, shame and reproach ; but to whom, or why ? If fortune hath envied me wealth, thieves have robbed me, my father have not left me such revenues as others have, that I am a younger brother, basely born, of mean parentage, a dirt-dauber's son, am I therefore to be blamed ? an Eagle, a Bull, a Lion, is not rejected for his poverty, and why should a man ? 'tis fortune's fault, not mine. Good Sir, I am a servant, (to use Seneca's words), howsoever your poor friend ; a servant, and yet your chamberfellow, and if you consider better of it, your fellow-servant. ————— I am thy drudge in the world's eyes, yet in God's sight peradventure thy better, my soul is more precious, and I dearer unto him. As Evangelus at large proves in Macrobius, the meanest servant is most precious in his sight. Thou art an Epicure, I am a good Christian; thou art many parasangs before me in means, favour, wealth, honour, Claudius his Narcissus, Nero's Massa, Domitian's Parthenius, a favourite, a golden slave; thou coverest thy floors with marble, thy roofs with gold, thy walls with statues, fine pictures, curious hangings, &c., thou dost tread upon riches, &c., what of all this? what's all this to true happiness? I live and breathe under that glorious Heaven, that august Capitol of nature, enjoy the brightness of Stars, that clear light of Sun and Moon, those infinite creatures, plants, birds, beasts, fishes, herbs, all that sea and land affords, far surpassing all that art and opulence can give. I am free, and, which Seneca said of Rome, a thatched roof sheltered free men, but slavery afterward dwelt amidst marble and gold: thou hast Amalthea's horn [of nectar and ambrosia], plenty, pleasure, the world at will, I am despicable and poor; but a word over-shot, a blow in choler, a game at tables, a loss at Sea, a sudden fire, the Prince's dislike, a little sickness, &c., may make us equal in an instant; howsoever, take thy time, triumph and insult a while: as Alphonsus said, death will equalize us all at last. I live sparingly in the mean time, am clad homely, fare hardly; is this a reproach? am I the worse for it? am I contemptible for it? am I to be reprehended? A learned man in Nevisanus [the Lawyer, his book of The Nuptial Grove] was taken down for sitting amongst Gentlemen, but he replied, " my nobility is about the head, yours declines to the tail," & they were silent. Let them mock, scoff and revile, 'tis not thy scorn, but his that made thee so; *he that mocketh the poor reproacheth him that made him,* and *he that rejoiceth at affliction, shall not be unpunished.* For the rest, the poorer thou art, the happier thou art: saith Epictetus, he is richer, not better, than thou art, not so free from lust, envy, hatred, ambition.

Happy the man who, far from worldly moil,
With his own oxen tills the paternal soil. (HORACE)

Happy he, in that he is freed from the tumults of the world, he seeks no honours, gapes after no preferment, flatters not, envies not, temporizeth not, but lives privately, and well contented with his estate;

Not hungry with untimely wishes,
Nor fed upon care's empty dishes,
Heeding little or not at all
What in the great world may befal.

He is not troubled with state matters, whether Kingdoms thrive better by succession or election; whether Monarchies should be mixt, temperate, or absolute; the house of Ottomon's and Austria is all one to him; he enquires not after Colonies or new discoveries; whether Peter were at Rome, or Constantine's donation be of force; what comets or new stars signify, whether the earth stand or move, there be a new world in the Moon, or infinite worlds, &c. He is not touched with fear of invasions, factions or emulations.

A happy soul, and like to God himself,
Whom not vain glory macerates or strife,
Or wicked joys of that proud swelling pelf,
But leads a still, poor, and contented life. (POLITIANUS)

A secure, quiet, blissful state he hath, if he could acknowledge it. But here is the misery, that he will not take notice of it; he repines at rich men's wealth, brave hangings, dainty fare, as Simonides objecteth to Hiero: he hath all the pleasures of the world; *he knows not the affliction of Joseph, stretching himself on ivory beds, and singing to the sound of the viol.* And it troubles him that hath not the like; there is a difference (he grumbles) between Laplolly [or Loblolly] and Pheasants, to tumble i'th'straw and lie in a down-bed, betwixt wine and water, a cottage and a palace. He hates nature (as Pliny characterizeth him) that she hath made him lower than a God, and is angry with the Gods that any man goes before him; and although he hath received much, yet (as Seneca follows it) he thinks it an injury that he hath no more, and is so far from giving thanks for his Tribuneship, that he complains he is not Praetor; neither doth that please him, except he may be Consul. Why is he not a Prince, why not a Monarch, why not an Emperor? Why should one man have so much more than his fellows, one have all, another nothing? Why should one man be a drudge or slave to another? one surfeit, another starve, one live at ease, another labour, without any hope of better fortune? Thus they grumble, mutter, and repine: not considering that inconstancy of human affairs, judicially conferring one condition with another, or well weighing their own present estate. What they are now, thou mayest shortly be; and what thou art, they shall likely be. Expect a little, confer future and times past with the present, see the event, and comfort thyself with it. It is as well to be discerned in Commonwealths, Cities, Families, as in private men's estates. Italy was once Lord of the world, Rome, the Queen of Cities, vaunted herself of two myriads of Inhabitants; now that all-commanding Country is possessed by petty Princes, Rome, a small village in respect. Greece, of old the seat of civility, mother of sciences and humanity; now forlorn, the nurse of barbarism, a den of thieves. Germany then, saith Tacitus, was incult and horrid; now full of magnificent Cities. Athens, Corinth,

Carthage, how flourishing Cities! now buried in their own ruins: the haunt of ravens and wild hogs, like so many wildernesses, a receptacle of wild beasts. Venice, a poor fisher-town, Paris, London, small Cottages in Cæsar's time; now most noble Emporiums. Valois, Plantagenet, and Scaliger, how fortunate families! how likely to continue! now quite extinguished and rooted out. He stands aloft to-day, full of favour, wealth, honour, and prosperity, in the top of fortune's wheel: to-morrow in prison, worse than nothing, his son's a beggar. Thou art a poor servile drudge, the dregs of the people, a very slave, thy son may come to be a Prince, with Maximinus, Agathocles, &c., a Senator, a General of an Army. Thou standest bare to him now, workest for him, drudgest for him and his, takest an alms of him: stay but a little, and his next heir peradventure shall consume all with riot, be degraded, thou exalted, and he shall beg of thee. Thou shalt be his most honourable Patron, he thy devout servant, his posterity shall run, ride, and do as much for thine, as it was with Frescobald and Cromwell, it may be for thee. Citizens devour country Gentlemen, and settle in their seats; after two or three descents, they consume all in riot, it returns to the City again.

> Comes a new dweller now; for Nature planned
> None as perpetual owner of the land,
> Not he nor me; but he who me expels
> Must in his turn yet yield to some one else.   (HORACE)

A Lawyer buys out his poor Client, after a while his Client's posterity buy out him and his; so things go round, ebb and flow.

> Umbrenus calls this land his own,
> As once Ofellus; be it known,
> No man can own it: we or they
> Use and enjoy it while we may.   (HORACE)

As he said then, Whose field are you, that have so many masters? so say I of land, houses, movables & money, mine to-day, his anon, whose to-morrow? In fine, (as Machiavel observes), virtue and prosperity beget rest, rest idleness, idleness riot, riot destruction, from which we come again to good Laws; good Laws engender virtuous actions, virtue glory, and prosperity; and it is no dishonour then (as Guicciardine adds) for a flourishing man, City, or State, to come to ruin, nor infelicity to be subject to the Law of nature. Therefore (I say) scorn this transitory state, look up to Heaven, think not what others are, but what thou art: what's thy place in the world: and what thou shalt be, what thou mayest be. Do (I say) as Christ himself did, when he lived here on earth, imitate him as much as in thee lies. How many great Cæsars, mighty Monarchs, Tetrarchs, Dynasts, Princes, lived in his days, in what plenty, what delicacy, how bravely attended, what a deal of gold and silver, what treasure, how many sumptuous palaces had they, what Provinces and Cities, ample territories, fields, rivers, fountains, parks, forests, lawns, woods, cells, &c.!

Yet Christ had none of all this, he would have none of this, he voluntarily rejected all this, he could not be ignorant, he could not err in his choice, he contemned all this, he chose that which was safer, better, & more certain, and less to be repented, a mean estate, even poverty itself; and why dost thou then doubt to follow him, to imitate him, and his Apostles, to imitate all good men? So do thou tread in his divine steps, and thou shalt not err eternally, as too many worldlings do, that run on in their own dissolute courses, to their confusion and ruin, thou shalt not do amiss. Whatsoever thy fortune is, be contented with it, trust in him, rely on him, refer thyself wholly to him. For know this, in conclusion, *it is not as men, but as God will. The Lord maketh poor, and maketh rich, bringeth low, and exalteth, he lifteth the poor from the dust, and raiseth the beggar from the dunghill, to set them amongst Princes, and make them inherit the seat of glory;* 'tis all as he pleaseth, how, and when, and whom; he that appoints the end (though to us unknown) appoints the means likewise subordinate to the end.

Yea, but their present estate crucifies and torments most mortal men, they have no such forecast to see what may be, what shall likely be, but what is, though not wherefore, or from whom: thus it hurts, their present misfortunes grind their souls, and an envious eye which they cast upon other men's prosperities: their neighbor's flock is fatter: how rich, how fortunate, how happy is he! But in the mean time he doth not consider the other's miseries, his infirmities of body and mind, that accompany his estate, but still reflects upon his own false conceived woes and wants, whereas, if the matter were duly examined, he is in no distress at all, he hath no cause to complain.

> *Cease to complain; not poor, indeed,*
> *Is he who hath what fills his need.* (HORACE)

He is not poor, he is not in need. Nature is content with bread and water; and he that can rest satisfied with that, may contend with Jupiter himself for happiness. In that golden age, the trees gave wholesome shade to sleep under, and the clear rivers drink. The Israelites drank water in the wilderness; Sampson, David, Saul, Abraham's servant when he went for Isaac's wife, the Samaritan woman, and how many besides might I reckon up, Egypt, Palestine, whole countries in the

Indies, that drink pure water all their lives. The Persian Kings themselves drank no other drink than the water of Choaspes that runs by
Susa, which was carried in bottles after them, whithersoever they went.
Jacob desired no more of God, but bread to eat, and clothes to put on
in his journey. Happy is he to whom with sparing hand God hath given
sufficiency; bread is enough to strengthen the heart. And if you study
philosophy aright, saith Madaurensis, whatever is beyond this moderation, is not useful, but troublesome. A. Gellius, out of Euripides, accounts bread and water enough to satisfy nature: of which there is no
surfeit; the rest is not a feast, but riot. S. Hierome esteems him rich
that hath bread to eat, and a potent man that is not compelled to be a
slave: hunger is not ambitious, so that it have to eat, and thirst doth
not prefer a cup of gold. It was no Epicurean speech of an Epicure, He
that is not satisfied with a little will never have enough; and very good
counsel of him in the Poet, O my son, mediocrity of means agrees best
with men; too much is pernicious.

> *He who with a mind content*
> *Lives on little, is opulent.* (LUCRETIUS)

And if thou canst be content, thou hast abundance: thou hast little, thou
wantest nothing. 'Tis all one to be hanged in a chain of gold, or in a
rope; to be filled with dainties, or coarser meat.

> *If belly, sides, and feet be well at ease,*
> *A Prince's pleasure can thee no more please.* (HORACE)

Socrates in a Fair, seeing so many things bought and sold, such a multitude of people convened to that purpose, exclaimed forthwith, O ye
Gods, what a sight of things do not I want! It is thy want alone that
keeps thee in health of body and mind, and that which thou persecutest
and abhorrest as a feral plague is thy Physician and chiefest friend,
which makes thee a good man, an healthful, a sound, a virtuous, an
honest, and happy man. For when Virtue came from Heaven, (as the
Poet feigns), rich men kicked her up, wicked men abhorred her, Courtiers scoffed at her, Citizens hated her, and that she was thrust out of
doors in every place, she came at last to her sister Poverty, where she
had found good entertainment. Poverty and Virtue dwell together.

> *Ah, safe the poor man's narrow hearth:*
> *God's gift, not taken at its worth!* (LUCAN)

How happy art thou if thou couldst be content! " Godliness is great
gain, if a man can be content with that which he hath "; and all true
happiness is in a mean estate. I have little wealth, as he [Lipsius] said,
but what the mind makes great, a Kingdom in conceit: —

I ask no more, O son of Maia, save
That I may keep these gifts that now I have. (HORACE)
I have enough, and desire no more.
——— *The Gods were kind*
In giving me a meek and modest mind. (HORACE)
'Tis very well, and to my content. Let my fortune and my garments be
both alike fit for me. And which Sebastian Foscarinus, sometime Duke
of Venice, caused to be engraven on his Tomb in St. Mark's Church,
Hear, O ye Venetians, and I will tell you which is the best thing in the
world: to contemn it. ——— I will engrave it in my heart, it shall be
my whole study to contemn it. Let them take wealth, let the mard love
mards, so that I may have security; who has been well hidden has lived
well; though I live obscure, yet I live clean and honest; and when as
the lofty oak is blown down, the silly reed may stand. Let them take
glory, for that's their misery; let them take honour, so that I may have
heart's ease. Lead me, O God, whither thou wilt, I am ready to follow;
command, I will obey. I do not envy at their wealth, titles, offices;
Let who will, in his might,
Stand on power's slippery height,
let me live quiet and at ease. Peradventure we shall be, (as Puteanus
comforted himself), when they are not; when they are dead and gone,
and all their pomp vanished, our memory may flourish:
The immortal Muses to a name
Give imperishable fame. (MARULLUS)
Let him be my Lord, Patron, Baron, Earl, and possess so many goodly
Castles, it is well for me that I have a poor house, and a little wood, and
a well by it, &c.
With which I feel myself more truly blest
Than if my sires the quaestor's power possess'd. (HORACE)
I live, thank God, as merrily as he, and triumph as much in this my
mean estate, as if my Father and Uncle had been Lord Treasurer, or my
Lord Mayor. He feeds of many dishes, I of one; I care for Christ [saith
S. Hierome], what care I of what stuff my excrements be made?———
He that lives according to nature cannot be poor, and he that exceeds can
never have enough: the whole world cannot give him content. A small
thing that the righteous hath, is better than the riches of the ungodly.
And better is a poor morsel with quietness than abundance with strife.

Be content then, enjoy thyself, and, as Chrysostom adviseth, be not
angry for what thou hast not, but give God hearty thanks for what thou
hast received.

If scanty herbs thou canst with peace enjoy,
Seek not for richer cates mixed with annoy.

But what wantest thou, to expostulate the matter? or what hast thou not better than a rich man? Health, competent wealth, children, security, sleep, friends, liberty, diet, apparel, and what not, or at least mayest have (the means being so obvious, easy and well known) for as he inculcated to himself,

Merry Martial, make thy state
By these means more fortunate,
Toil no more to lay up treasure,
Banish strife and welcome pleasure.

I say again thou hast, or at least mayest have it, if thou wilt thyself, and that which I am sure he wants, a merry heart. Passing by a village in the territory of Milan, (saith S. Austin), I saw a poor beggar that had got, belike, his belly full of meat, jesting and merry; I sighed, and said to some of my friends that were then with me, What a deal of trouble, madness, pain and grief do we sustain and exaggerate unto ourselves, to get that secure happiness, which this poor beggar hath prevented us of, and which we peradventure shall never have! For that which he hath now attained with the begging of some small pieces of silver, a temporal happiness, and present heart's ease, I cannot compass with all my careful windings, and running in and out. And surely the beggar was very merry, but I was heavy: he was secure, but I was timorous. And if any man should ask me now, whether I had rather be merry, or still so solicitous and sad, I should say, Merry. If he should ask me again, Whether I had rather be as I am, or as this beggar was, I should sure choose to be as I am, tortured still with cares and fears; but out of peevishness, and not out of truth. ——— That which S. Austin said of himself here in this place, I may truly say to thee; thou discontented wretch, thou covetous niggard, thou churl, thou ambitious and swelling toad, 'tis not want, but peevishness, which is the cause of thy woes; settle thine affection, thou hast enough.

What thou didst covet, thou hast got;
Rest, then, from thine laborious lot.   (HORACE)

Make an end of scraping, purchasing this Manor, this field, that house, for this and that child; thou hast enough for thyself and them:

Far from Ulubræ thou needst not to roam,
All thou desirest can be found at home.   (HORACE)

'Tis at hand, at home already, which thou so earnestly seekest. But O that I had but one nook of ground, that field there, that pasture! O that

I could but find a poet of money now, to purchase, &c., to build me a new house, to marry my daughter, place my son, &c. O if I might but live a while longer to see all things settled, some two or three years, I would pay my debts, make all my reckonings even; but they are come and past, and thou hast more business than before. O madness! to think [as Cardan saith in his Book on Diversities] to settle that in thine old age when thou hast more, which in thy youth thou canst not now compose, having but a little. Pyrrhus [in Plutarch] would first conquer Africa, and then Asia, and then live merrily, and take his ease: but when Cineas the Orator told him he might do that already, rested satisfied, contemning his own folly. Comparing little things to great, thou mayest do the like, and therefore be composed in thy fortune. Thou hast enough; he that is wet in a bath can be no more wet if he be flung into Tiber, or into the Ocean itself; and if thou hadst all the world, or a solid mass of gold, as big as the world, thou canst not have more than enough; enjoy thyself at length, and that which thou hast; the mind is all; be content, thou art not poor, but rich, and so much the richer, as Censorinus well writ to Cerellius, in wishing less, not having more. I say then, ('tis Epicurus' advice), add no more wealth, but diminish thy desires; and, as Chrysostom well seconds him, if virtue is to be enriched, spurn wealth; that's true plenty, not to have, but not to want riches; 'tis more glory to contemn, than to possess; and to desire nothing is godlike. How many deaf, dumb, halt, lame, blind, miserable persons, could I reckon up that are poor, and withal distressed, in imprisonment, banishment, galley slaves, condemned to the mines, quarries, to gyves, in dungeons, perpetual thraldom, than all which thou art richer, thou art more happy, to whom thou art able to give an alms, a Lord, in respect, a petty Prince! Be contented then, I say, repine and mutter no more, for thou art not poor indeed, but in opinion.

Yea, but this is very good counsel, and rightly applied to such as have it, and will not use it, that have a competency, that are able to work and get their living by the sweat of their brows, by their trade, that have something yet; he that hath birds may catch birds; but what shall we do that are slaves by nature, impotent, and unable to help ourselves, mere beggars, than languish and pine away, that have no means at all, no hope of means, no trust of delivery, or of better success? as those old Britons complained to their Lords and Masters the Romans, oppressed by the Picts, the Barbarians drove them to the sea, the sea drove them back to the Barbarians; our present misery compels us to cry out and howl, to make our moan to rich men; they turn us back with a scornful answer to our misfortune again, and will take no pity of us; they commonly overlook their poor friends in adversity; if they chance to meet them, they voluntarily forget, and will take no notice of them; they will not, they cannot help us. Instead of comfort, they threaten us, miscall, scoff at us, to aggravate our misery, give us bad language, or, if they do give good words, what's that to relieve us? According to that of Thales, easy it is to advise others; who cannot give good counsel? 'tis cheap, it costs them nothing. It is an easy matter when one's belly is full to declaim against feasting. *Doth the wild Ass bray when he hath grass, or loweth the Ox when he hath fodder?* No men living so jocund, so merry, as the people of Rome when they had plenty; but when they came to want, to be hunger-starved, neither shame, nor laws, nor arms, nor Magistrates could keep them in obedience. Seneca pleaded hard for poverty, and so did those lazy Philosophers: but in the mean time he was rich, they had wherewithal to maintain themselves; but doth any poor man extol it? There are those (saith Bernard) that approve of a mean estate, but on that condition they never want themselves; and some again are meek, so long as they may say or do what they list; but if occasion be offered, how far are they from all patience! I would to God (as he said) no man should commend poverty, but he that is poor; or he that so much admires it, would relieve, help, or ease others.

> *Now if thou hear'st us, and art a good man,*
> *Tell him that wants, to get means, if you can.*   (PETRONIUS)

But no man hears us, we are most miserably dejected, the scum of the world,

> *On our hides there's scarce at all*
> *Room for another blow to fall.*   (OVID)

We can get no relief, no comfort, no succour. We have tried all means, yet find no remedy: no man living can express the anguish and bitterness of our souls, but we that endure it; we are distressed, forsaken, in torture of body and mind, in another Hell: and what shall we do? When Crassus, the Roman Consul, warred against the Parthians, after an unlucky battle fought, he fled away in the night, and left four thousand men, sore sick and wounded in his tents, to the fury of the enemy, which when the poor men perceived, they made lamentable moan, and roared down-right, as loud as Homer's Mars when he was hurt, which the noise of 10,000 men could not drown, and all for fear of present death. But our estate is far more tragical and miserable, much more to be deplored, and far greater cause have we to lament; the Devil and the world persecute us, all good fortune hath forsaken us, we are left to the rage of beggary, cold, hunger, thirst, nastiness, sickness, irksomeness, to continual torment, labour and pain, to derision and contempt, bitter enemies all, and far worse than any death; death alone we desire, death we seek, yet cannot have it, and what shall we do?

> ——— *What's bad, 'tis sure*
> *Thou canst by custom well endure.*   (OVID)

Accustom thyself to it, and it will be tolerable at last. Yea, but I may not, I cannot, I am in the extremity of human adversity; and, as a shadow leaves the body when the Sun is gone, I am now left and lost, and quite forsaken of the world. Who's stretched on earth need fear no fall; comfort thyself with this yet, thou art at the worst, and, before it be long, it will either overcome thee, or thou it. If it be violent, it cannot endure, 'twill end, or make an end: let the Devil himself and all the plagues of Egypt come upon thee at once,

> *Yield not thou to any woe,*
> *Against it the more boldly go.*   (VIRGIL)

Be of good courage; misery is virtue's whetstone. As Cato told his soldiers marching in the deserts of Libya, thirst, heat, sands, serpents, were pleasant to a valiant man; honorable enterprises are accompanied with dangers and damages, as experience evinceth; they will make the rest of thy life relish the better. But put case they continue, thou art not so poor as thou wast born, and, as some hold, ['tis] much better to be pitied than envied. But be it so thou hast lost all, poor thou art, dejected, in pain of body, grief of mind, thine enemies insult over thee, thou art as bad as Job; yet tell me (saith Chrysostom) was Job or the Devil the greater conqueror? surely Job. The Devil had his goods, he sate on the muck-hill, and kept his good name; he lost his children, health, friends, but he kept his innocency; he lost his money, but he kept his confidence in God, which was better than any treasure. Do thou then, as Job did, triumph as Job did, and be not molested as every fool is. But how shall this be done? Chrysostom answers, with great facility, if thou shalt but meditate on Heaven. Hannah wept sore, and, troubled in mind, could not eat; *but, why weepest thou?* said Elkanah her husband, *and why eatest thou not? why is thine heart troubled? am not I better to thee than ten sons?* and she was quiet. Thou art here vexed in this world; but say to thyself, Why art thou troubled, O my soul? Is not God better to thee than all temporalities, and momentary pleasures of the world? be then pacified. And though thou beest now peradventure in extreme want, it may be 'tis for thy further good, to try thy patience, as it did Job's, and exercise thee in this life: trust in God, and rely upon Him, and thou

shalt be crowned in the end. What's this life to eternity? The world hath
forsaken thee, thy friends and fortunes all are gone: yet know this, that
the very hairs of thine head are numbered, that God is a spectator of all
thy miseries, He sees thy wrongs, woes and wants. 'Tis His good will
and pleasure it should be so, and He knows better what is for thy good
than thou thyself. His providence is over all, at all times; *he hath
set a guard of Angels over us, and keeps us as the apple of his eye.* Some
he doth exalt, prefer, bless with worldly riches, honours, offices and
preferments, as so many glistering stars he makes to shine above the
rest: some he doth miraculously protect from thieves, incursions, sword,
fire, and all violent mischances, and, as the Poet feigns of that Lycian
Pandarus, Lycaon's son, when he shot at Menelaus the Grecian with a
strong arm, and deadly arrow, Pallas, as a good mother keeps flies from
her child's face asleep, turned by the shaft, and made it hit on the buckle
of his girdle; so some he solicitously defends, others he exposeth to
danger, poverty, sickness, want, misery, he chastiseth and corrects, as
to him seems best, in his deep, unsearchable and secret judgement, and
all for our good. The Tyrant took the City, (saith Chrysostom), God did
not hinder it; led them away captives, so God would have it; he bound
them, God yielded to it; flung them into the furnace, God permitted it;
heated the Oven hotter, it was granted: and when the Tyrant had done
his worst, God shewed his power, and the children's patience, ————
he freed them: so can he thee, and can help in an instant, when it seems
to him good. Rejoice not against me, O my enemy; for though I fall, I
shall rise: when I sit in darkness, the Lord shall lighten me. Remember
all those Martyrs, what they have endured, the utmost that human rage
and fury could invent, with what patience they have borne, with what
willingness embraced it. Though he kill me, saith Job, I will trust in
him. As Chrysostom holds, a just man is impregnable, and not to be
overcome. The gout may hurt his hands, lameness his feet, convulsions
may torture his joints, but not his upright mind, his soul is free.

> *Take then my flock, my gold, my goods, my land,*
> *Put me in prison, bind me foot and hand.* (HORACE)

Take away his money, his treasure is in Heaven; banish him his Country, he is an inhabitant of that heavenly Jerusalem; cast him into bonds,
his conscience is free; kill his body, it shall rise again; he fights with a
shadow, that contends with an upright man: he will not be moved.
Though Heaven itself should fall on his head, he will not be offended.
He is impenetrable, as an anvil hard, as constant as Job.

> *God can deliver me when he will, I ween.* (HORACE)

Be thou such a one; let thy misery be what it will, what it can, with patience endure it, thou mayest be restored as he was. When the earth is forbidden thee, Heaven is thine; when deserted by men, flee to God. *The poor shall not always be forgotten, the patient abiding of the meek shall not perish for ever. The Lord will be a refuge of the oppressed, and a defence in the time of trouble.*

> *Lame was Epictetus, and poor Irus,*
> *Yet to them both God was propitious.*

Lodovicus Vertomannus, that famous traveller, endured much misery, yet surely, saith Scaliger, he was a favourite of God, in that he did escape so many dangers, God especially protected him, he was dear unto him. Thou art now in the vale of misery, in poverty, in agony, in temptation; rest, eternity, happiness, immortality, shall be thy reward, as Chrysostom pleads, if thou trust in God, and keep thine innocency. Though 'tis ill with thee now, 'twill not be always so; a good hour may come upon a sudden; expect a little.

Yea, but this expectation is it which tortures me in the mean time; future hope makes present hunger; whilst the grass grows, the horse starves; despair not, but hope well:

> *Think, Battus, that to-morrow may bring scope*
> *For better things; while there is life there's hope.* (THEOCRITUS)

Cheer up, I say, be not dismayed; the farmer lives on hope: he that sows in tears shall reap in joy.

> *When fortune torments me,*
> *Then hope contents me.*

Hope refresheth, as much as misery depresseth; hard beginnings have many times prosperous events, and that may happen at last, which never was yet. A desire accomplished delights the soul.

> *Which makes m' enjoy my joys long wished at last,*
> *Welcome that hour shall come when hope is past.* (HORACE)

A lowering morning may turn to a fair afternoon. *The hope that is deferred is the fainting of the heart, but when the desire cometh it is a tree of life.* Many men are both wretched and miserable at first, but afterwards most happy; and oftentimes it so falls out, as Machiavel relates of Cosimo de Medici, that fortunate and renowned Citizen of Europe, that all his youth was full of perplexity, danger and misery, till forty years were past, and then upon a sudden the Sun of his honour brake out as through a cloud. Hunniades was fetched out of prison, and Henry the Third of Portugal out of a poor Monastery, to be crowned Kings.

There's many a slip
'Twixt cup and lip.   (ERASMUS)

Beyond all hope and expectation many things fall out, and who knows what may happen? As Phillippus said, all the Suns are not yet set, a day may come to make amends for all. *Though my father and mother forsake me, yet the Lord will gather me up. Wait patiently on the Lord and hope in him. Be strong, hope and trust in the Lord, and he will comfort thee and give thee thine heart's desire.*

Hope, and reserve thyself for better days.   (VIRGIL)

Fret not thyself because thou art poor, contemned, or not so well for the present as thou wouldst be, not respected as thou oughtest to be, by birth, place, worth; or that which is a double corrosive, thou hast been happy, honourable and rich, art now distressed and poor, a scorn of men, a burden to the world, irksome to thyself and others, thou hast lost all. Misery it is to have once been happy, and, as Boethius calls it, the worst kind of ill fortune; this made Timon half mad with melancholy, to think of his former fortunes and present misfortunes; this alone makes many miserable wretches discontent. I confess it is a great misery to have been happy, the quintessence of infelicity, to have been honourable and rich, but yet easily to be endured; security succeeds, and to a judicious man a far better estate. The loss of thy goods and money is no loss; thou hast lost them, they would otherwise have lost thee. If thy money be gone, thou art so much the lighter; and, as Saint Hierome persuades Rusticus the Monk to forsake all and follow Christ: gold and silver are too heavy metals for him to carry that seeks Heaven.

There in the sea now let us cast
The gems and gold we have amassed, —
If truly we repent our sins;
For in these all vice begins.   (HORACE)

Zeno the Philosopher lost all his goods by shipwreck, he made light of it, fortune had done him a good turn: she can take away my means, but not my mind. He set her at defiance ever after, for she could not rob him that had nought to lose: for he was able to contemn more than they could possess or desire. Alexander sent an hundred talents of gold to Phocion of Athens for a present, because he heard he was a good man: but Phocion returned his talents back again with a " Permit me to be a good man still; let me be as I am. I ask not gold, nor any reward." That Theban Crates flung of his own accord his money into the Sea, " I had rather drown you, than you should drown me." Can

Stoicks and Epicures thus contemn wealth, and shall not we that are Christians? It was a generous speech of Cotta in Sallust, *Many miseries have happened unto me at home, and in the wars abroad, of which, by the help of God, some I have endured, some I have repelled and by mine own valour overcome: courage was never wanting to my designs, nor industry to my intents: prosperity or adversity could never alter my disposition.* A wise man's mind, as Seneca holds, is like the state of the world above the Moon, ever serene. Come then what can come, befall what may befall, meet it with an unbroken and unconquerable courage: 'tis in adversity that one should be bold. Hope and patience are two sovereign remedies for all, the surest reposals, the softest cushions to lean on in adversity. What can't be cured must be endured. If it cannot be helped, or amended, make the best of it; he is wise that suits himself to the time. As at a game at tables, so do by all such inevitable accidents. If thou canst not fling what thou wouldest, play thy cast as well as thou canst. Every thing, saith Epictetus, hath two handles, the one to be held by, the other not: 'tis in our choice to take and leave whether we will (all which Simplicius, his Commentator, hath illustrated by many examples) ; and 'tis in our own power, as they say, to make or mar ourselves. Conform thyself then to thy present fortune, and cut thy coat according to thy cloth: be contented with thy lot, state, and calling, whatsoever it is, and rest as well satisfied with thy present condition in this life.

> *Be as thou art; and as they are, so let*
> *Others be still; what is and may be, covet.*

And as he that is invited to a feast eats what is set before him and looks for no other, enjoy that thou hast, and ask no more of God than what he thinks fit to bestow upon thee.

> *Not all of us such fortune gain*
> *As that Corinth we attain.* (HORACE)

We may not be all Gentlemen, all Catos, or Læliuses, as Tully telleth us, all honourable, illustrious and serene, all rich; but because mortal men want many things, therefore, saith Theodoret, hath God diversely distributed his gifts, wealth to one, skill to another, that rich men might encourage and set poor men a-work, poor men might learn several trades to the common good. As a piece of arras is composed of several parcels, some wrought of silk, some of gold, silver, crewel of divers colours, all to serve for the exornation [or embellishment] of the whole; [as] Musick is made of divers discords and keys, a total sum of many small numbers: so is a Commonwealth of several inequal trades and callings. If all should be Crœsuses and Dariuses, all idle, all in fortunes equal, who should till the land? as Menenius Agrippa well satisfied the tumultuous rout of Rome in his elegant Apologue of the belly and the rest of the members. Who should build houses, make our several stuffs for raiments? We should all be starved for company, as Poverty declared at large in Aristophanes' Plutus, and sue at last to be as we were at first. And therefore God hath appointed this inequality of States, orders and degrees, a subordination, as in all other things. The earth yields nourishment to vegetals, sensible creatures feed on vegetals, both are substitutes to reasonable souls, and men are subject amongst themselves, and all to higher powers: so God would have it.

All things then being rightly examined, and duly considered as they ought, there is no such cause of so general discontent, 'tis not in the matter itself, but in our mind, as we moderate our passions, and esteem of things. Saith Cardan, Let thy fortune be what it will, 'tis thy mind alone that makes thee poor or rich, miserable or happy. Saith divine Seneca, I have seen men miserably dejected in a pleasant village, and some again well occupied and at good ease in a solitary desert; 'tis the mind, not the place, causeth tranquillity, and that gives true content. I will yet add a word or two for a corollary. Many rich men, I dare boldly say it, that lie on down-beds, with delicacies pampered every day, in their well furnished houses, live at less heart's ease, with more anguish, more bodily pain, and through their intemperance more bitter hours, than many a prisoner or galley-slave. Mæcenas sleeps no better on down than Regulus in his barrel. Those poor starved Hollanders, whom Bartison their Captain left in Nova Zembla in the year 1596, or those eight miserable Englishmen that were lately left behind to winter in a stove in Greenland in 77 degrees of latitude, 1630, so pitifully forsaken and forced to shift for themselves in a vast dark and desert place, to strive and struggle with hunger, cold, desperation, and death itself. 'Tis a patient and quiet mind (I say it again and again) gives true peace and content. So for all other things, they are, as old Chremes told us, as we use them. Parents, friends, fortunes, country, birth, alliance, &c., ebb and flow with our conceit; please or displease, as we accept and construe them, or apply them to ourselves. Everyone is the builder of his own fortune, and in some sort I may truly say prosperity and adversity are in our own hands. No one is hurt except by himself; and, which Seneca confirms out of his judgment and experience, every man's mind is stronger than fortune, and leads him to what side he will; a cause to himself each one is of his good or bad life. But, will we, or nill we, make the worst of it, and suppose a

man in the greatest extremity, 'tis a fortune which some infinitely * prefer before prosperity; of two extremes, it is the best. Pride runs riot in
prosperity; men in prosperity forget God and themselves, they are
besotted with their wealth, as birds with henbane: miserable, if fortune forsake them, but more miserable if she tarry and overwhelm
them: for when they come to be in great place, rich, they that were most
temperate, sober and discreet, in their private fortunes, as Nero, Otho,
Vitellius, Heliogabalus (excellent rulers, had they never ruled) degenerate on a sudden into brute beasts, so prodigious in lust, such tyrannical oppressors, &c., they cannot moderate themselves, they become
Monsters, odious, Harpies, what not? When they have achieved triumphs, riches, honours, then they give themselves up to revelling and
indolence; 'twas Cato's note, they cannot contain. For that cause belike,

> *Eutrapelus, when he would hurt a knave,*
> *Gave him gay clothes and wealth to make him brave:*
> *Because now rich he would quite change his mind,*
> *Keep whores, fly out, set honesty behind.* (HORACE)

On the other side, in adversity many mutter and repine, despair, &c.,
both bad I confess, as a shoe too big, or too little, one pincheth, the
other sets the foot awry; but of evils choose the least. If adversity hath
killed his thousand, prosperity hath killed his ten thousand: therefore
adversity is to be preferred; the one deceives, the other instructs: the
one miserably happy, the other happily miserable: and therefore many
Philosophers have voluntarily sought adversity, and so much commend
it in their precepts. Demetrius, in Seneca, esteemed it a great infelicity,
that in his lifetime he had no misfortune. Adversity then is not so
heavily to be taken, and we ought not in such cases so much to macerate
ourselves: there is no such odds in poverty and riches. To conclude in
Hierom's words, I will ask our Magnificoes that build with Marble, and
bestow a whole Manor on a thread, what difference betwixt them and
Paul the Eremite, that bare old man? they drink in jewels, he in [or
out of] his hand: he is poor and goes to Heaven, they are rich and go
to Hell.

MEMBER 4

Against Servitude, Loss of Liberty, Imprisonment, Banishment

SERVITUDE, loss of liberty, imprisonment, are no such miseries as they
are held to be: we are slaves & servants, the best of us all: as we do reverence our masters, so do our masters their superiors: Gentlemen serve

* "Indefinitely," in the text.

Nobles, & Nobles subordinate to Kings, every ruler under a harder ruler, Princes themselves are God's servants. They are subject to their own Laws, and, as the Kings of China, endure more than slavish imprisonment, to maintain their state and greatness, they never come abroad. Alexander was a slave to fear, Cæsar of pride, Vespasian to his money (it matters little whether we be enslaved by men or things), Heliogabalus to his gut, and so of the rest. Lovers are slaves to their Mistresses, rich men to their Gold, Courtiers generally to lust and ambition, and all slaves to our affections, as Evangelus well discourseth in Macrobius, and Seneca the Philosopher, an extreme and inescapable servitude, he calls it, a continual slavery, to be so captivated by vices, and who is free? Why then dost thou repine? He is master enough, Hierom saith, who is not forced to serve. Thou carriest no burdens, thou art no prisoner, no drudge, and thousands want that liberty, those pleasures, which thou hast. Thou art not sick, and what wouldest thou have? But we must all eat of the forbidden fruit. Were we enjoined to go to such and such places, we would not willingly go: but being barred of our liberty, this alone torments our wandering soul that we may not go. A Citizen of ours, saith Cardan, was sixty years of age, and had never been forth of the walls of the City Milan; the Prince hearing of it, commanded him not to stir out: being now forbidden that which all his life he had neglected, he earnestly desired, and being denied, he died for grief.

What I have said of servitude, I say again of imprisonment. We are all prisoners. What's our life but a prison? We are all imprisoned in an Island. The world itself to some men is a prison, our narrow seas as so many ditches, and when they have compassed the Globe of the earth, they would fain go see what is done in the Moon. In Muscovy, and many other Northern parts, all over Scandia, they are imprisoned half the year in stoves,* they dare not peep out for cold. At Aden in Arabia they are penned in all day long with that other extreme of heat, and keep their markets in the night. What is a ship but a prison? and so many Cities are but as so many hives of Bees, Ant-hills. But that which thou abhorrest, many seek: women keep in all the Winter, and most part of Summer, to preserve their beauties; some for love of study: Demosthenes shaved his beard, because he would cut off all occasion from going abroad: how many Monks and Friars, Anchorites, abandon the world! A monk in town is a fish out of water. Art in prison? Make right use of it, and mortify thyself. Where may a man contemplate

* Herbastein. See Index.

better than in solitariness, or study more than in quietness? Many worthy men have been imprisoned all their lives, and it hath been occasion of great honour and glory to them, much publick good by their excellent meditation. Ptolemæus, King of Egypt, now being taken with a grievous infirmity of body, that he could not stir abroad, became Strato's scholar, fell hard to his book, and gave himself wholly to contemplation, and upon that occasion (as mine Author adds) to his great honour built that renowned Library at Alexandria, wherein were 40,-000 volumes. Severinus Boethius never writ so elegantly as in prison, Paul so devoutly, for most of his Epistles were dictated in his bonds: Joseph, saith Austin, got more credit in prison than when he distributed corn and was Lord of Pharaoh's house. It brings many a lewd riotous fellow home, many wandering rogues it settles, that would otherwise have been like raving Tigers, ruined themselves and others.

Banishment is no grievance at all, every land is the brave man's land, and that's a man's country where he is well at ease. Many travel for pleasure to that city, saith Seneca, to which thou art banished, and what a great part of the citizens are strangers born in other places! 'Tis their country that are born in it, and they would think themselves banished to go to the place which thou leavest, and from which thou art so loth to depart. 'Tis no disparagement to be a stranger, or so irksome to be an exile. The rain is a stranger to the earth, rivers to the Sea, Jupiter in Egypt, the Sun to us all. The Soul is an alien to the Body, a Nightingale to the air, a Swallow in an house, and Ganymede in Heaven, an Elephant at Rome, a Phœnix in India; and such things commonly please us best which are most strange, and come farthest off. Those old Hebrews esteemed the whole world Gentiles; the Greeks held all Barbarians but themselves; our modern Italians account of us as dull Transalpines by way of reproach, they scorn thee and thy country, which thou so much admirest. 'Tis a childish humour to hone * after home, to be discontent at that which others seek; to prefer, as base Icelanders and Norwegians do, their own ragged Island before Italy or Greece, the Gardens of the world. There is a base Nation in the north, saith Pliny, called Chauci, that live amongst rocks and sands by the sea side, feed on fish, drink water: and yet these base people account themselves slaves in respect, when they come to Rome; (as he concludes), so it is, Fortune favours some to live at home to their further punishment: 'tis want of judgement. All places are distant from Heaven alike, the Sun shines happily as warm in one city as in another, and to a

* Yearn.

wise man there is no difference of climes; friends are every where to him that behaves himself well, and a Prophet is not esteemed in his own Country. Alexander, Cæsar, Trajan, Adrian, were as so many land-leapers [or vagrants], now in the East, now in the West, little at home, and Paulus Venetus, Lodovicus Vertomannus, Pinzonus, Cadamustus, Columbus, Americus Vespuccius, Vascus Gama, Drake, Candish, Oliver á Nort, Schouten, got all their honour by voluntary expeditions. But you say such men's travel is voluntary; we are compelled, and as malefactors must depart: yet know this of Plato to be true, God hath an especial care of strangers, and when he wants friends and allies, he shall deserve better and find more favour with God and men. Besides the pleasure of peregrination, variety of objects will make amends; and so many nobles, Tully, Aristides, Themistocles, Theseus, Codrus, &c., as have been banished, will give sufficient credit unto it. Read Peter Alcionius his two books of this subject.

MEMBER 5

Against Sorrow for Death of Friends or otherwise, vain Fear, &c.

DEATH and departure of friends are things generally grievous; the most austere and bitter accidents that can happen to a man in this life, to part for ever, to forsake the world and all our friends, 'tis the last and the greatest terror, most irksome and troublesome unto us; a man dies as often as he loses his friends. And though we hope for a better life, eternal happiness, after these painful and miserable days, yet we cannot compose ourselves willingly to die; the remembrance of it is most grievous unto us, especially to such who are fortunate and rich: they start at the name of death, as an horse at a rotten post. Say what you can of that other world, with Metezuma that Indian prince, they had rather be here. Nay, many generous spirits, and grave staid men otherwise, are so tender in this, that at the loss of a dear friend, they will cry out, roar, and tear their hair, lamenting some months after, howling O Hone, as those Irish women and Greeks at their graves, commit many undecent actions, and almost go beside themselves. My dear father, my sweet husband, mine only brother's dead, to whom shall I make my moan? O miserable me! What fountains of tears shall I shed, &c. What shall I do?

> *My brother's death my study hath undone,*
> *Woe's me! alas! my brother he is gone!*   (CATULLUS)

Mezentius would not live after his son:

> *Now mid my kind I linger still,*
> *And live: but leave the light I will.*   (VIRGIL)

And Pompey's wife cried out at the news of her husband's death,

> *Ah, 'twould be too base of me*
> *Not to die for love of thee,*   (LUCAN)

as Tacitus of Agrippina, not able to moderate her passions. So, when she heard her son was slain, she abruptly broke off her work, changed countenance and colour, tore her hair, and fell a roaring downright.

> *Her cheek at once the colour fled,*
> *She dropped the distaff and the thread,*
> *And with dishevelled locks she sped,*
> *Loud wailing in her womanhead.*   (VIRGIL)

Another would needs run upon the sword's point after Euryalus' departure:

> *O Rutules, your mercy shew,*
> *And pierce me with your arrows too!*   (VIRGIL)

O let me die, some good man or other make an end of me! How did Achilles take on for Patroclus' departure! A black cloud of sorrows overshadowed him, saith Homer. Jacob rent his clothes, put sack-cloth about his loins, sorrowed for his son a long season, and could not be comforted, but would needs go down into the grave unto his son. Many years after, the remembrance of such friends, of such accidents, is most grievous unto us, to see or hear of it, though it concern not ourselves, but others. Scaliger saith of himself, that he never read Socrates' death, in Plato's Phædo, but he wept. Austin shed tears when he read the destruction of Troy. But howsoever this passion of sorrow be violent, bitter, and seizeth familiarly on wise, valiant, discreet men, yet it may surely be withstood, it may be diverted. For what is there in this life, that it should be so dear unto us? or that we should so much deplore the departure of a friend? The greatest pleasures are common society, to enjoy one another's presence, feasting, hawking, hunting, brooks, woods, hills, musick, dancing, &c., all this is but vanity and loss of time, as I have sufficiently declared.

> *Whilst we drink, prank ourselves, with wenches dally,*
> *Old age upon 's at unawares doth sally.*   (JUVENAL)

As Alchemists spend that small modicum they have to get gold, and never find it, we lose and neglect eternity, for a little momentary pleasure which we cannot enjoy; nor shall ever attain to in this life. We abhor death, pain, & grief, all, & yet we will do nothing of that which should vindicate us from, but rather voluntarily thrust ourselves upon it. The lascivious prefers his whore before his life, or good estate; an angry man his revenge: a parasite his gut; ambitious, honours; covetous, wealth; a thief his booty; a soldier his spoil; we abhor diseases, and yet we pull them upon us. We are never better or freer from cares than when we sleep, and yet, which we so much avoid and lament, death is but a perpetual sleep; and why should it, as Epicurus argues, so much affright us? When we are, death is not: but when death is, then we are not: our life is tedious and troublesome unto him that lives best; 'tis a misery to be born, a pain to live, a trouble to die; death makes an end to our miseries, and yet we cannot consider of it. A little before Socrates drank his potion of hemlock, he bid the Citizens of Athens cheerfully farewell, and concluded his speech with this short sentence, My time is now come to be gone, I to my death, you to live on; but which of these is best, God alone knows. ————— For there is no pleasure here but sorrow is annexed to it, repentance follows it. If I feed liberally, I am likely sick or surfeit; if I live sparingly, my hunger and thirst is not allayed; I am well neither full nor fasting; if I live honest, I burn in lust; if I take my pleasure, I tire and starve myself, and do injury to my body and soul. Of so small a quantity of mirth, how much sorrow! after so little pleasure, how great misery! 'Tis both ways troublesome to me, to rise and go to bed, to eat and provide my meat; cares and contentions attend me all day long, fears and suspicions all my life. I am discontented, and why should I desire so much to live? But an happy death will make an end of all our woes and miseries; 'tis the certain cure for all our troubles; why shouldst not thou then say with old Simeon, since thou art so well affected, *Lord now let thy servant depart in peace:* or with Paul, *I desire to be dissolved, and to be with Christ?* 'Tis a blessed hour that leads us to a blessed life, and blessed are they that die in the Lord. But life is sweet, and death is not so terrible in itself as the concomitants of it, a loathsome disease, pain, horror, &c., and many times the manner of it, to be hanged, to be broken on the wheel, to be burned alive. Servetus the heretick, that suffered in Geneva, when he was brought to the stake, and saw the executioner come with fire in his hand, roared so loud that he terrified the people. An old Stoick would have scorned this. It troubles some to be unburied, or so:

> *Thy gentle parents shall not bury thee,*
> *Amongst thine ancestors entomb'd to be,*
> *But feral fowl thy carcass shall devour,*
> *Or drowned corpse hungry fish-maws shall scour.*   (VIRGIL)

As Socrates told Crito, it concerns me not what is done with me when I am dead; easy is the loss of burial: I care not so long as I feel it not; let them set mine head on the pike of Teneriffe, and my quarters in the four parts of the world; you shall, on a cross, feed crows; let wolves or bears devour me; the canopy of heaven covers him that hath no tomb. So likewise for our friends, why should their departure so much trouble us? They are better, as we hope, and for what then dost thou lament, as those do whom Paul taxed in his time, *that have no hope.* 'Tis fit there should be some solemnity.

> *After one day for grief we ought*
> *To bury our dead with steadfast thought.* (HOMER)

Job's friends said not a word to him the first seven days, but let sorrow and discontent take their course, themselves sitting sad and silent by him. When Jupiter himself wept for Sarpedon, what else did the Poet insinuate, but that some sorrow is good? Who can blame a tender mother, if she weep for her children? Beside, as Plutarch holds, 'tis not in our power not to lament, it takes away mercy and pity, not to be sad; 'tis a natural passion to weep for our friends, an irresistible passion to lament and grieve. I know not how (saith Seneca), but sometimes 'tis good to be miserable in misery: and for the most part all grief evacuates itself by tears.

> *'Tis a kind of pleasure so*
> *To glut thyself upon thy woe,*
> *Raining out thy grief in tears.* (OVID)

Yet after a day's mourning or two, comfort thyself for thy heaviness. 'Tis unbecoming idly to mourn the dead; 'twas Germanicus's advice of old, that we should not dwell too long upon our passions, to be desperately sad, immoderate grievers, to let them tyrannize, there's an art of not being too unhappy, a medium to be kept: we do not (saith Austin) forbid men to grieve, but to grieve overmuch: I forbid not a man to be angry, but I ask for what cause he is so? not to be sad, but why is he sad? not to fear, but wherefore is he afraid? ——— I require a moderation as well as a just reason. The Romans and most civil Commonwealths have set a time to such solemnities, they must not mourn after a set day, or if in a family a child be born, a daughter or son married, some state or honour be conferred, a brother be redeemed from his bands [or chains], a friend from his enemies, or the like, they must lament no more. And 'tis fit it should be so; to what end is all their funeral pomp, complaints, and tears? When Socrates was dying, his friends Apollodorus and Crito, with some others, were weeping by him, which he perceiving, asked them what they meant: for that very cause he put all the women out of the room; upon which words of his they were abashed, and ceased from their tears. Lodovicus Cortesius, a rich lawyer of Padua (as Bernardinus Scardeonius relates) commanded by his last will, and a great mulct if otherwise to his heir, that no funeral should be kept for him, no man should lament: but as at a wedding, music and minstrels to be provided; and instead of black mourners, he took order, that twelve virgins clad in green should carry him to the Church. His will and testament was accordingly performed, and he buried in S. Sophia's Church. Tully was much grieved for his daughter Tulliola's death at first, until such time that he had confirmed his mind with some Philosophical precepts, then he began to triumph over fortune and grief, and for her reception into Heaven to be much more joyed than before he was troubled for her loss. If an Heathen man could so fortify himself from Philosophy, what shall a Christian from Divinity? Why dost thou so macerate thyself? 'Tis an inevitable chance, the first statute in Magna Charta, an everlasting Act of Parliament, all must die. It cannot be revoked, we are all mortal, and these all commanding Gods and Princes die like men: the proud as well as the lowly head is hidden, the last is equalled with the first. O weak condition of human estate! Sylvius exclaims: Ladislaus, King of Bohemia, 18 years of age, in the flower of his youth, so potent, rich, fortunate and happy, in the midst of all his friends, amongst so many Physicians, now ready to be married, in 36 hours sickened and died. We must so be gone sooner or later all, and as Calliopius in the Comedy took his leave of his spectators and auditors, must we bid the world farewell (Exit Calliopius), and having now played our parts, for ever be gone. Tombs and monuments have the like fate, since even to sepulchres themselves are dooms assigned; Kingdoms, Provinces, Towns and cities, have their periods, and are consumed. In those flourishing times of Troy, Mycenæ was the fairest city in Greece, ruled all Greece, but it, alas, and that Assyrian Nineveh are quite overthrown. The like fate hath that Egyptian and Bœotian Thebes, Delos, the common council-house of Greece, and Babylon, the greatest city that ever the sun shone on, hath now nothing but walls and rubbish left.

What of old Athens but the name remains?   (OVID)

Thus Pausanias complained in his times. And where is Troy itself now, Persepolis, Carthage, Cyzicum, Sparta, Argos, and all those Grecian cities? Syracuse and Agrigentum, the fairest towns in Sicily, which had sometime 700,000 inhabitants, are now decayed: the names of Hiero, Empedocles, &c., of those mighty numbers of people, only left. One

Anacharsis is remembered amongst the Scythians; the world itself must have an end, and every part of it. All other towns are mortal, as Peter Gillius concludes of Constantinople, this city alone shall last as long as the world; but 'tis not so: nor site, nor strength, nor sea, nor land, can vindicate a city, but it and all must vanish at last. And as to a traveller, great mountains seem plains afar off, at last are not discerned at all, cities, men, monuments decay, nor can its fabrick preserve the solid globe; the names are only left, those at length forgotten, and are involved in perpetual night.

Returning out of Asia, when I sailed from Ægina towards Megara, I began (saith Servius Sulpicius, in a consolatory epistle of his to Tully) to view the country round about. Ægina was behind me, Megara before, Piræus on the right hand, Corinth on the left, what flourishing towns heretofore, now prostrate and overwhelmed before mine eyes! I began to think with myself, alas, why are we men so much disquieted with the departure of a friend, whose life is much shorter, when so many goodly cities lie buried before us? Remember, O Servius, thou art a man; and with that I was much confirmed, and corrected myself. ——— Correct then likewise, and comfort thyself in this, that we must necessarily die, and all die, that we shall rise again: as Tully held, our second meeting shall be much more pleasant than our departure was grievous.

Ay, but he was my most dear and loving friend, my sole friend,

> *And who can blame my woe?* (HORACE)

Thou mayest be ashamed, I say with Seneca, to confess it, in such a tempest as this to have but one anchor, go seek another; and for his part thou dost him great injury to desire his longer life. Wilt thou have him crazed and sickly still (like a tired traveller that comes weary to his Inn, begin his journey afresh), or to be freed from his miseries? thou hadst more need rejoice that he is gone. Another complains of a most sweet young wife,

> *Not yet had Proserpine cut her golden hair,* (VIRGIL)

such a wife as no mortal man ever had, so good a wife, but she is now dead and gone, and lies low in the tomb. I reply to him in Seneca's words, if such a woman at least ever was to be had, he did either so find or make her; if he found her, he may as happily find another; if he made her, as Critobulus in Xenophon did by his, he may as good cheap inform another, and the second will be as good as the first; he need not despair, so long as the same Master is to be had. But was she good? Had she been so tried peradventure, as that Ephesian widow in

Petronius, by some swaggering soldier, she might not have held out.
Many a man would have been willingly rid of his: before thou wast
bound, now thou art free; and 'tis but a folly to love thy fetters, though
they be of gold. Come into a third place, you shall have an aged Father
sighing for a Son, a pretty Child;

—— He now lies asleep,
Would make an impious Thracian weep,   (HORACE)

or some fine daughter that died young, not having ever yet known the
joys of the bridal bed; or a forlorn Son for his deceased Father. But
why? He came first, and he must go first. Vainly pious, alas, &c. What,
wouldst thou have the Laws of Nature altered, and him to live always?
Julius Cæsar, Augustus, Alcibiades, Galen, Aristotle, lost their Fathers
young. And why on the other side shouldst thou so heavily take the
death of thy little Son?

Neither by destiny nor desert, but pitifully too soon,   (VIRGIL)

he died before his time, perhaps, not yet come to the solstice of his age,
yet was he not mortal? Hear that divine Epictetus, If thou covet thy
wife, friends, children should live always, thou art a fool. He was a
fine Child indeed, worthy of Apollonian tears, a sweet, a loving, a fair,
a witty Child, of great hope, another Eteoneus, whom Pindar the
Poet, and Aristides the Rhetorician, so much lament; but who can tell
whether he would have been an honest man? He might have proved a
thief, a rogue, a spendthrift, a disobedient son, vexed and galled thee
more than all the world beside, he might have wrangled with thee and
disagreed, or with his brothers, as Eteocles and Polynices, and broke thy
heart; he is now gone to eternity, as another Ganymede, in the flower of
his youth, as if he had risen, saith Plutarch, from the midst of a feast
before he was drunk; the longer he had lived, the worse he would have
been (Ambrose thinks) more sinful, more to answer he would have had.
If he was naught [or bad], thou mayest be glad he is gone; if good, be
glad thou hadst such a son. Or art thou sure he was good? It may be he
was an hypocrite, as many are, and howsoever he spake thee fair, peradventure he prayed, amongst the rest that Icaromenippus heard at
Jupiter's whispering place in Lucian, for his Father's death, because
he now kept him short, he was to inherit much goods, and many fair
Manors after his decease. Or put case he was very good, suppose the
best, may not thy dead son expostulate with thee, as he did in the same
Lucian, Why dost thou lament my death, or call me miserable that am
much more happy than thyself? what misfortune is befallen me? is it
because I am not bald, crooked, old, rotten, as thou art? what have I

lost? some of your good cheer, gay clothes, musick, singing, dancing, kissing, merry meetings, happy beddings, &c., is that it? is it not much better not to hunger at all than to eat? not to thirst than to drink to satisfy thirst? not to be cold than to put on clothes to drive away cold? You had more need rejoice that I am freed from diseases, agues, cares, anxieties, livor [or spite], love, covetousness, hatred, envy, malice, that I fear no more thieves, tyrants, enemies, as you do. ————

> *Dost think for these things passing fair*
> *The ashes or the shades do care?* (VIRGIL)

Do they concern us at all, think you, when we are once dead? Condole not others then overmuch, wish not or fear their death: 'tis to no purpose.

> *I left this irksome life with all mine heart,*
> *Lest worse than death should happen to my part.*

Cardinal Brundusinus caused this Epitaph in Rome to be inscribed on his tomb, to show his willingness to die, and tax those that were so loth to depart. Weep and howl no more then, 'tis to small purpose; and as Tully adviseth us in the like case, think what we do, not whom we have lost. So David did, *While the child was yet alive, I fasted and wept; but being now dead, why should I fast? Can I bring him again? I shall go to him, but he cannot return to me.* He that doth otherwise is an intemperate, a weak, a silly, and undiscreet man. Though Aristotle deny any part of intemperance to be conversant about sorrow, I am of Seneca's mind, he that is wise is temperate, and he that is temperate is constant, free from passion, and he that is such a one, is without sorrow: as all wise men should be. The Thracians wept still when a child was born, feasted and made mirth when any man was buried: and so should we rather be glad for such as die well, that they are so happily freed from the miseries of this life. When Eteoneus, that noble young Greek, was so generally lamented by his friends, Pindar the Poet feigns some God saying, be quiet, good folks, this young man is not so miserable as you think; he is neither gone to Styx nor Acheron, but he lives for ever in the Elysian Fields. He now enjoys that happiness which your great Kings so earnestly seek, and wears that garland for which ye contend. If our present weakness is such, we cannot moderate our passions in this behalf, we must divert them by all means, by doing something else, thinking of another subject. The Italians most part sleep away care and grief, if it unseasonably seize upon them; Danes, Dutchmen, Polanders and Bohemians drink it down, our countrymen go to Plays. Do something or other, let it not transpose thee; or by premeditation make such accidents familiar, as Ulysses that wept for his dog, but not for his wife, being prepared with steadfast mind: accustom thyself, and harden beforehand, by seeing other men's calamities, and applying them to thy present estate. The evil is lighter which we anticipate. I will conclude with Epictetus, If thou lovest a pot, remember 'tis but a pot thou lovest, and thou wilt not be troubled when 'tis broken: if thou lovest a son or wife, remember they were mortal, and thou wilt not be so impatient. ———— And for false fears and all other fortuitous inconveniences, mischances, calamities, to resist and prepare ourselves, not to faint is best: 'tis a folly to fear that which cannot be avoided, or to be discouraged at all. For he that so faints or fears, and yields to his passion, flings away his own weapons, makes a cord to bind himself, and pulls a beam upon his own head.

MEMBER 6

Against Envy, Livor, Emulation, Hatred, Ambition, Self-love, and all other Affections

AGAINST those other passions and affections, there is no better remedy than as Mariners when they go to Sea provide all things necessary to resist a tempest: to furnish ourselves with Philosophical and Divine Precepts, other men's examples, from the dangers of others take benefits for ourselves: to balance our hearts with love, charity, meekness, patience, and counterpoise those irregular motions of envy, livor, spleen, hatred, with their opposite virtues, as we bend a crooked staff another way, to oppose sufferance to labour, patience to reproach, bounty to covetousness, fortitude to pusillanimity, meekness to anger, humility to pride, to examine ourselves for what cause we are so much disquieted, on what ground, what occasion, is it just or feigned? And then either to pacify ourselves by reason, to divert by some other object, contrary passion, or premeditation. 'Tis fitting to meditate, like an exile returning home, what manner of misfortune may befall thee, as a son in mischief, a wife dead, a daughter afflicted, and such like, so as not to be anyways surprised; to make them familiar, even all kind of calamities, that when they happen they may be less troublesome unto us; or out of mature judgement to avoid the effect, or disannul the cause, as they do that are troubled with toothache, pull them quite out.

> *The beaver bites off's stones to save the rest:*
> *Do thou the like with that thou art opprest.*   (ALCIATI)

Or as they that play at wasters [or fencing], exercise themselves by a few cudgels how to avoid an enemy's blows: let us arm ourselves against all such violent incursions, which may invade our minds. A little experience and practice will inure us to it; as the Proverb saith, an old fox is not so easily taken in a snare; an old soldier in the world methinks should not be disquieted, but ready to receive all fortunes, encounters, and with that resolute Captain, come what may come, to make answer,

> *No labour comes at unawares to me,*
> *For I have long before cast what may be.* (VIRGIL)
> *'Tis not the first, this wound so sore;*
> *I have suffered worse before!* (SENECA)

The Commonwealth of Venice in their Armoury have this inscription, *Happy is that city which in time of peace thinks of war*; a fit Motto for every man's private house, happy is the man that provides for a future assault. But many times we complain, repine and mutter, without a cause, we give way to passions we may resist, and will not. Socrates was bad by nature, envious, as he confessed to Zopirus the Physiognomer, accusing him of it, froward and lascivious: but as he was Socrates, he did correct and amend himself. Thou art malicious, envious, covetous, impatient, no doubt, and lascivious, yet as thou art a Christian, correct and moderate thyself. 'Tis something, I confess, and able to move any man, to see himself contemned, obscure, neglected, disgraced, undervalued, left behind; some cannot endure it, no, not constant Lipsius, a man discreet otherwise, yet too weak and passionate in this, as his words express, *Not without indignation can I see my old colleagues, nobodies then, now Mæcenases and Agrippas, at the top of the tree.* But he was much to blame for it: to a wise staid man this is nothing, we cannot all be honoured and rich, all Cæsars; if we will be content, our present state is good, and in some men's opinion to be preferred. Let them go on, get wealth, offices, titles, honours, preferments, and what they will themselves, by chance, fraud, imposture, Simony, and indirect means, as too many do, by bribery, flattery, and parasitical insinuation, by impudence and time-serving, let them climb up to advancement in despite of virtue, let them go before, cross me on every side; as he said, correcting his former error, they do not offend me so long as they run not into mine eyes. I am inglorious and poor, but I live secure and quiet: they are dignified, have great means, pomp, and state, they are glorious; but what have they with it? Envy, trouble, anxiety, as much labour to maintain their place with credit, as to get it at first. I am contented with my fortunes, a looker-on from a distance, and love to see the raging ocean from safe land: he is ambitious, and not satisfied with his: but what gets he by it? to have all his life laid open, his reproaches seen: not one of a thousand but he hath done more worthy of dispraise and animadversion than commendation; no better means to help this than to be private. Let them run, ride, strive as so many fishes for a crumb, scrape, climb, catch, snatch, cozen, collogue, temporize and fleer, take all amongst them, wealth, honour, and get what they can, it offends me not: my plot of land affords me a safe and sheltered home. I am well pleased with my fortunes; I reign a king without the things you praise.

I have learned in what state soever I am, therewith to be contented. Come what can come, I am prepared. Be it in a great ship or a tiny boat, nevertheless I sail on. I am the same. I was once so mad to bustle abroad, and seek about for preferment, tire myself, and trouble all my friends, but all my labour was unprofitable; for while death took off some of my friends, to others I remain unknown, or little liked, and these deceive me with false promises. Whilst I am canvassing one party, captivating another, making myself known to a third, my age increases, years glide away, I am put off, and now, tired of the world, and surfeited with human worthlessness, I rest content. And so I say still; although I may not deny but that I have had some bountiful patrons and noble benefactors; let me not now be ungrateful, and I do thankfully acknowledge it, I have received some kindness (which may God repay, if not by their wishes, yet according to their merits), more peradventure than I deserve, though not to my desire, more of them than I did expect, yet not of others to my desert; neither am I ambitious or covetous, all this while, or a Suffenus to myself; what I have said, without prejudice or alteration shall stand. And now as a mired horse that struggles at first with all his might and main to get out, but when he sees no remedy, that his beating will not serve, lies still, I have laboured in vain, rest satisfied, and if I may usurp that of Prudentius,

Mine haven's found, fortune and hope adieu,
Mock others now, for I have done with you.

MEMBER 7

*Against Repulse, Abuses, Injuries, Contempts, Disgraces, Contumelies,
Slanders, Scoffs, &c.*

I MAY not yet conclude, think to appease passions, or quiet the mind,
till such time as I have likewise removed some other of their more
eminent and ordinary causes, which produce so grievous tortures and
discontents: to divert all, I cannot hope; to point alone at some few of
the chiefest, is that which I aim at.

Repulse and *disgrace* are two main causes of discontent, but to an
understanding man not so hardly to be taken. Cæsar himself hath been
denied, and when two stand equal in fortune, birth, and all other qualities alike, one of necessity must lose. Why shouldest thou take it so
grievously? It hath been a familiar thing for thee thyself to deny others.
If every man might have what he would, we should all be Deified, Emperors, Kings, Princes; if whatsoever vain hope suggests, insatiable
appetite affects, our preposterous judgment thinks fit were granted, we
should have another Chaos in an instant, a mere confusion. It is some
satisfaction to him that is repelled, that dignities, honours, offices, are
not always given by desert or worth, but for love, affinity, friendship,
affection, great men's letters, or as commonly they are bought and sold.
Honours in Court are bestowed not according to men's virtues and good
conditions (as an old Courtier observes), but as every man hath means,
or more potent friends, so he is preferred. With us in France (for so
their own Countryman relates) most part the matter is carried by
favour and grace; he that can get a great man to be his mediator, runs
away with all the preferment. The most unworthy is oftenest preferred,
a Vatinius to a Cato, a nobody to a somebody. Slaves govern; asses are
decked with trappings, horses have none. An illiterate fool sits in a
man's seat, and the common people hold him learned, grave and wise.
One professeth (Cardan well notes) for a thousand Crowns, but he deserves not ten, when as he that deserves a thousand cannot get ten. His
salary will scarce pay for his salt. As good horses draw in carts, as
coaches. And oftentimes, which Machiavel seconds, those are not
Princes who for eminence of virtue deserve to be such; he that is most
worthy wants employment; he that hath skill to be a Pilot wants a
Ship, and he that could govern a Commonwealth, a world itself, a King
in conceit, wants means to exercise his worth, hath not a poor office to
manage, and yet all this while he is a better man that is fit to reign,

though he want a kingdom, than he that hath one, and knows not how to rule it. A Lion serves not always his Keeper, but oftentimes the Keeper the Lion, and as Polydore Virgil hath it: Kings a many, wards through ignorance, rule not but are ruled. Hiero of Syracuse was a brave King, but wanted a Kingdom; Perseus of Macedon had nothing of a King, but the bare name and title, for he could not govern it: so great places are often ill bestowed, worthy persons unrespected. Many times, too, the servants have more means than the masters whom they serve, which Epictetus counts an eye-sore and inconvenient. But who can help it? It is an ordinary thing in these days to see a base impudent ass, illiterate, unworthy, insufficient, to be preferred before his betters, because he can put himself forward, because he looks big, can bustle in the world, hath a fair outside, can temporise, collogue, insinuate, or hath good store of friends and money, whereas a more discreet, modest, and better-deserving man shall lie hid or have a repulse. 'Twas so of old, and ever will be, and which Tiresias advised Ulysses in the poet, how to grow rich, &c., is still in use; lie, flatter, and dissemble: if not, as he concludes, then go like a beggar as thou art. Erasmus, Melancthon, Lipsius, Budæus, Cardan, lived and died poor. Gesner was a silly old man, plodding with 's staff, amongst all those huffing Cardinals, swelling Bishops, that flourished in his time, & rode on foot-clothes [trappings]. It is not honesty, learning, worth, wisdom, that prefers men. The race is not to the swift, nor the battle to the strong, but as the wise man said, chance, and sometimes a ridiculous chance. 'Tis fortune's doings, as they say, which made Brutus now dying exclaim: O wretched virtue, you are nothing but a name, and while I have all this time looked upon you as a reality, you are yourself but the slave of fortune! ———— Believe it hereafter, O my friends! virtue serves fortune. Yet be not discouraged (O my well deserving spirits) with this which I have said, it may be otherwise, though seldom I confess, yet sometimes it is. But to your further content, I'll tell you a tale. In Moronia Pia, or Moronia Felix, I know not whether, nor how long since, nor in what Cathedral Church, a fat Prebend fell void. The carcass scarce cold, many suitors were up in an instant. The first had rich friends, a good purse, and he was resolved to outbid any man before he would lose it, every man supposed he should carry it. The second was my Lord Bishop's Chaplain (in whose gift it was), and he thought it his due to have it. The third was nobly born, and he meant to get it by his great parents, patrons, and allies. The fourth stood upon his worth, he had newly found out strange mysteries in Chemistry, and other rare inventions, which he would detect to the publick good. The fifth was a painful Preacher, and he was commended by the whole parish where he dwelt, he had all their hands to his certificate. The sixth was the Prebendary's son lately deceased, his Father died in debt (for it, as they say), left a wife and many poor children. The seventh stood upon fair promises, which to him and his noble friends had been formerly made for the next place in his Lordship's gift. The eighth pretended [that is, asserted as his reason] great losses, and what he had suffered for the Church, what pains he had taken at home and abroad, and besides he brought Noblemen's letters. The ninth had married a kinswoman, and he sent his wife to sue for him. The tenth was a foreign Doctor, a late convert, and wanted means. The eleventh would exchange for another, he did not like the former's site, could not agree with his neighbours and fellows upon any terms, he would be gone. The twelfth and last was (a suitor in conceit) a right honest, civil, sober man, an excellent scholar, and such a one as lived private in the University, but he had neither means nor money to compass it; besides he hated all such courses, he could not speak for himself, neither had he any friends to solicit his cause, and therefore made no suit, could not expect, neither did he hope for, or look after it. The good Bishop, amongst a jury of competitors thus perplexed, and not yet resolved what to do, or on whom to bestow it, at the last, of his own accord, mere motion and bountiful nature, gave it freely to the University student, altogether unknown to him but by fame; and to be brief, the Academical Scholar had the Prebend sent him for a present. The news was no sooner published abroad, but all good students rejoiced, and were much cheered up with it, though some would not believe it; others, as men amazed, said it was a miracle; but one amongst the rest thanked God for it, and said, at last there is some advantage in being studious, and in serving God with integrity! You have heard my tale: but alas! it is but a tale, a mere fiction, 'twas never so, never like to be, and so let it rest. Well, be it so then, they have wealth and honour, fortune and preferment, every man (there's no remedy) must scramble as he may, and shift as he can; yet Cardan comforted himself with this, the star Fomalhaut would make him immortal, and that after his decease his books should be found in Ladies' studies:

> *The Muse forbids the name to die*
> *That's worthy immortality.* (HORACE)

But why shouldest thou take thy neglect, thy canvas, so to heart? It may be thou art not fit, but, as a child that puts on his father's shoes, hat, headpiece, breastplate, breeches, or holds his spear, but is neither able to wield the one, or wear the other, so wouldest thou do by such an office, place, or Magistracy: thou art unfit. And what is dignity to an unworthy man but (as Salvianus holds) a gold ring in a swine's snout? Thou art a brute. Like a bad actor (so Plutarch compares such men) in a Tragedy, that wears a crown, yet cannot be heard: thou wouldest play a King's part, but actest a Clown, speakest like an ass. You ask too much, Phaeton, and for things beyond your powers, &c.; as James and John, the sons of Zebedee, did ask they knew not what; thou dost, as another Suffenus, overween thyself; thou art wise in thine own conceit, but in other more mature judgments altogether unfit to manage such a business. Or be it thou art more deserving than any of thy rank, God in his providence hath reserved thee for some other fortunes, thus divinely foreseen. Thou art humble as thou art, it may be; hadst thou been pre-ferred, thou wouldest have forgotten God and thyself, insulted over others, contemned thy friends, been a block, a tyrant, or a demi-god; pride goeth with beauty. Therefore, saith Chrysostom, good men do not always find grace and favour, lest they should be puffed up with turgent titles, grow insolent and proud.

Injuries, abuses, are very offensive, and so much the more in that they think by taking one they provoke another; but it is an erroneous opinion: for if that were true, there would be no end of abusing each other; strife breeds strife; 'tis much better with patience to bear, or quietly put it up. " If an ass kick me," saith Socrates, " shall I strike him again? " & when his wife Xanthippe struck & misused him, to some friends that would have had him strike her again, he replied, that he would not make them sport, or that they should stand by and say " Go it, Socrates! Go it, Xanthippe! " as we do when dogs fight, animate them the more by clapping of hands. Many men spend them-selves, their goods, friends, fortunes, upon small quarrels, and sometimes at other men's procurements, with much vexation of spirit and anguish of mind, all which with good advice, or mediation of friends, might have been happily composed, or if patience had taken place. Patience in such cases is a most sovereign remedy, to put up, conceal, or dissemble it, to forget and forgive, *not seven, but seventy-seven times, as often as he repents forgive him;* as our Saviour enjoins us, stricken, *to turn the other side:* as our Apostle persuades us, *to recompence no man evil for evil, but as much as is possible to have peace with all men: not to avenge ourselves, and we shall heap burning coals upon our adversary's head.* For if you put up wrong (as Chrysostom comments), you get the victory; he that loseth his money, loseth not the conquest in this our philosophy. If he contend with thee, submit thyself unto him first, yield to him. *Pull and haul build no wall,* as the diverb is, two refractory spirits will never agree, the only means to overcome is to relent, conquer by yielding. Euclid in Plutarch, when his brother had angered him, swore he would be revenged; but he gently replied, Let me not live if I do not make thee to love me again, upon which meek answer he was pacified.

> *A branch if easily bended yields to thee,*
> *Pull hard it breaks: the difference you see.*   (CAMERARIUS)

The noble family of the Colonnas in Rome, when they were expelled the city by that furious Alexander the Sixth, gave the bending branch therefore as an impress, with this motto, Bend it may, break it cannot, to signify that he might break them by force, but so never make them stoop, for they fled in the midst of their hard usage to the Kingdom of Naples, and were honourably entertained by Frederick the King, according to their callings. Gentleness in this case might have done much more, and let thine adversary be never so perverse, it may be by that means thou mayest win him; soft words pacify wrath, and the fiercest spirits are so soonest overcome; a generous Lion will not hurt a beast that lies prostrate, nor an Elephant an innocuous creature, but is a terror and scourge alone to such as are stubborn, and make resistance. It was the symbol of Emanuel Philibert, Duke of Savoy, and he was not mistaken in it, for

> *A greater man is soonest pacified,*
> *A noble spirit quickly satisfied.*   (OVID)

It is reported by Gualter Mapes, an old Historiographer of ours (who lived 400 years since), that King Edward Senior, and Leolin, Prince of Wales, being at an interview near Aust upon Severn, in Gloucestershire, and the Prince sent for, refused to come to the King; he would needs go over to him; which Leolin perceiving, went up to the arms in water, and embracing his boat, would have carried him out upon his shoulders, adding that his humility and wisdom had triumphed over his pride and folly, and thereupon he was reconciled unto him and did his homage. If thou canst not so win him, put it up, if thou beest a true Christian, a good Divine, an Imitator of Christ, (for he was reviled and put it up, whipped and sought no revenge,) thou wilt pray for thine enemies, *and bless them that persecute thee;* be patient, meek, humble, &c. An honest man will not offer thee injury, if he were a brangling knave, 'tis his fashion so to do; where is least heart is most tongue; the more sottish he is, still the more insolent: *Do not answer a fool according to his folly.* If he be thy superior, bear it by all means, grieve not at it, let him take his course; Anytus and Meletus may kill me, they cannot hurt me, as that generous Socrates made answer in like case. The mind remains steadfast; though the body be torn in pieces with wild horses, broken on the wheel, pinched with fiery tongs, the soul cannot be distracted. 'Tis an ordinary thing for great men to vilify and insult, oppress, injure, tyrannise, to take what liberty they list, and who dare speak against? A miserable thing 'tis to be injured of him, from whom is no appeal: and not safe to write against him that can proscribe and punish a man at his pleasure, which Asinius Pollio was aware of, when Octavianus provoked him. 'Tis hard, I confess, to be so injured; one of Chilo's three difficult things: to keep counsel; spend his time well; put up injuries; but be thou patient, and leave revenge unto the Lord. *Vengeance is mine and I will repay,* saith the Lord. *I know the Lord,* saith David, *will avenge the afflicted and judge the poor.* No man (as Plato farther adds) can so severely punish his adversary, as God will such as oppress miserable men. He gives a new judgement and a worse punishment. If there be any Religion, any God, and that God be just, it shall be so; if thou believest the one, believe the other: it shall be so. Nemesis comes after, late but terrible; stay but a little and thou shalt see God's just judgement overtake him.

> *Yet with sure steps, though lame and slow,*
> *Vengeance o'ertakes the trembling villain's speed.* (HORACE)

Thou shalt perceive that verified of Samuel to Agag: *Thy sword hath made many women childless, so shall thy mother be childless amongst other women.* It shall be done to them, as they have done to others. Conradinus, that brave Suevian Prince, came with a well prepared army into the Kingdom of Naples, was taken prisoner by King Charles, and put to death in the flower of his youth; a little after (Nemesis for the death of Conrad, Pandulphus Collinutius, in his Neapolitan History, calls it) King Charles his own son, with 200 Nobles, was so taken prisoner, and beheaded in like sort. Not in this only, but in all other offences, they shall be punished in the same kind, in the same part, like nature, eye with or in the eye, head with or in the head, persecution with persecution, lust with effects of lust; let them march on with ensigns displayed, let drums beat on, trumpets sound taratantara, let them sack Cities, take the spoil of Countries, murder infants, deflower Virgins, destroy, burn, persecute, and tyrannize, they shall be fully rewarded at last in the same measure, they and theirs, and that to their desert.

> *Few tyrants in their beds do die,*
> *But stabb'd or maim'd to hell they hie.* (JUVENAL)

Oftentimes too a base contemptible fellow is the instrument of God's justice to punish, to torture, to vex them, as an ichneumon doth a crocodile. They shall be recompenced according to the works of their hands, as Haman was hanged on the gallows he provided for Mordecai. *They shall have sorrow of heart, and be destroyed from under the Heaven.* Only be thou patient; who endures, conquers; and in the end thou shalt be crowned. Yea, but 'tis a hard matter to do this, flesh and blood may not abide it; 'tis hard, hard! No, (Chrysostom replies) 'tis not hard, man! 'tis not so grievous; neither had God commanded it, if it had been so difficult. But how shall it be done? Easily, as he follows it, if thou shalt look to Heaven, behold the beauty of it, and what God hath promised to such as put up injuries. But if thou resist, and go about to meet force with force, as the custom of the world is, to right thyself, or hast given just cause of offence, 'tis no injury then, but a condign punishment, thou hast deserved as much: 'tis thy fault, be silent, as Ambrose expostulates with Cain. Dionysius of Syracuse, in his exile, was made stand without door, he wisely put it up, and laid the fault where it was, on his own pride and scorn, which in his prosperity he had formerly shewed others. 'Tis Tully's axiom, men ought not to be vexed with what they have brought upon themselves; self do, self have, as the saying is, they may thank themselves. For he that doth wrong, must look to be wronged again; the least fly hath a spleen, and a little bee a sting. An ass overwhelmed a thisselwarp's nest, the little bird pecked his gall'd back in revenge; and the humble-bee in the fable flung down the eagle's eggs out of Jupiter's lap. Brasidas, in Plutarch, put his hand into a mouse-nest, and hurt her young ones, she bit him by the finger: I see now (saith he), there is no creature so contemptible, that will not be revenged. 'Tis the law of like for like, and the nature of all things so to do. If thou wilt live quietly thyself, do no wrong to others; if any be done thee, put it up, with patience endure it. For *this is thankworthy,* saith our Apostle, *if a man for conscience towards God endure grief, and suffer wrong undeserved: for what praise is it, if, when ye be buffeted for your faults, ye take it patiently? but if when ye do well, ye suffer wrong, and take it patiently, there is thanks with God; for hereunto verily we are called.* He that cannot bear injuries witnesseth against himself that he is no good man, as Gregory holds. 'Tis the nature of wicked men to do injuries, as it is the property of all honest men patiently to bear them. Wickedness is never turned aside by indulgence. The wolf in the Emblem sucked the goat, (so the shepherd would have it), but he kept nevertheless a wolf's nature; a knave will be a knave. Injury is on the other side a good man's foot-boy, his faithful Achates, and as a lackey follows him wheresoever he goes. Besides, he is in a miserable estate that wants enemies: it is a thing not to be avoided, and therefore with more patience to be endured. Cato Censorius, that upright Cato, of whom Paterculus gives that honourable elogium, he did well because he could not do otherwise, was 50 times indicted and accused by his fellow-citizens, and, as Ammianus well hath it, if it be sufficient to accuse a man openly or in private, who shall be free? If there were no other respect than that of Christianity, Religion, and the like, to induce men to be long-suffering and patient, yet methinks the nature of injury itself is sufficient to keep them quiet, the tumults, uproars, miseries, discontents, anguish, loss, dangers, that attend upon it, might restrain the calamities of contention: for, as it is with ordinary gamesters, the gains go to the box, so falls it out to such as contend, the Lawyers get all; and therefore, if they would consider of it, other men's misfortunes in this kind, and common experience, might detain them. The more they contend, the more they are involved in a Labyrinth of woes, and the Catastrophe is to consume one another, like the elephant and dragon's conflict in Pliny; the dragon got under the elephant's belly, and sucked his blood so long, till he fell down dead upon the dragon, and killed him with the fall; so both were ruin'd. 'Tis an Hydra's head, contention; the more they strive, the more they may: and, as Praxiteles did by his glass, when he saw a scurvy face in it, break it in pieces: but for that one, he saw many more as bad in a moment: for one injury done, they provoke another with interest, and twenty enemies for one. Do not stir up hornets, oppose not thyself to a multitude: but if thou hast received a wrong, wisely consider of it, and if thou canst possibly, compose thyself with patience to bear it. This is the safest course, and thou shalt find greatest ease to be quiet.

I say the same of scoffs, slanders, contumelies, obloquies, defamations, detractions, pasquilling libels, and the like, which may tend any way to our disgrace: 'tis but opinion: if we could neglect, contemn, or with patience digest them, they would reflect on them that offered them at first. A wise Citizen, I know not whence, had a scold to his wife: when she brawled, he played on his drum, and by that means madded her more, because she saw that he would not be moved. Diogenes in a crowd, when one called him back, and told him how the boys laughed him to scorn: I, he said, am not laughed at, took no notice of it. Socrates was brought upon the stage by Aristophanes, and misused to his face, but he laughed, as if it concerned him not: and, as Ælian relates of him, whatsoever good or bad accident or fortune befell him, going in, or coming out, Socrates still kept the same countenance. Even so should a Christian soldier do, as Hierom describes him, march on through good and bad reports to immortality, not to be moved: for honesty is a sufficient reward, and in our time the sole recompence to do well is to do well: but naughtiness will punish itself at last. As the diverb is, —

They that do well, shall have reward at last;
But they that ill, shall suffer for that's past.

Yea, but I am ashamed, disgraced, dishonoured, degraded, exploded: my notorious crimes and villainies are come to light ('tis bad to be found out), my filthy lust, abominable oppression, and avarice, lies open, my good name's lost, my fortune's gone, I have been stigmatized, whipt at post, arraigned, and condemned, I am a common obloquy, I have lost my ears; odious, execrable, abhorred of God and men. Be content, 'tis but a nine days' wonder, and as one sorrow drives out another, one passion another, one cloud another, one rumour is expelled by another; every day almost come new news unto our ears, as how the Sun was eclipsed, meteors seen i'th' air, monsters born, prodigies, how the Turks were overthrown in Persia, an Earthquake in Helvetia, Calabria, Japan, or China, an inundation in Holland, a great plague in Constantinople, a fire at Prague, a dearth in Germany, such a man is made a Lord, a Bishop, another hanged, deposed, pressed to death, for some murder, treason, rape, theft, oppression, all which we do hear at first with a kind of admiration, detestation, consternation, but by and by they are buried in silence: thy father's dead, thy brother robb'd, wife runs mad, neighbour hath kill'd himself; 'tis heavy, ghastly, fearful news at first, in every man's mouth, table talk; but after a while who speaks or thinks of it? It will be so with thee and thine offence, it will be forgotten in an instant, be it theft, rape, sodomy, murder, incest, treason, &c., thou art not the first offender, nor shalt thou be the last, 'tis no wonder; every hour such malefactors are called in question, nothing so common,

In every nation, under every sky. (JUVENAL)

Comfort thyself, thou art not the sole man. If he that were guiltless himself should fling the first stone at thee, and he alone should accuse thee that were faultless, how many executioners, how many accusers, wouldst thou have! If every man's sins were written in his forehead, and secret thoughts known, how many thousands would parallel, if not exceed, thine offence! It may be the Judge that gave sentence, the Jury that condemned thee, the spectators that gazed on thee, deserved much more, and were far more guilty than thou thyself. But it is thine infelicity to be taken, to be made a publick example of justice, to be a terror to the rest; yet should every man have his desert, thou wouldest peradventure be a Saint in comparison; doves are brought to judgement, poor souls are punished, the great ones do twenty thousand times worse, and are not so much as spoken of.

> *The net's not laid for kites or birds of prey,*
> *But for the harmless still our gins we lay.*   (TERENCE)

Be not dismayed then, to err is human, we are all sinners, daily and hourly subject to temptations, the best of us is an hypocrite, a grievous offender in God's sight; Noah, Lot, David, Peter, &c., how many mortal sins do we commit! Shall I say, be penitent, ask forgiveness, and make amends, by the sequel of thy life, for that foul offence thou hast committed? recover thy credit by some noble exploit, as Themistocles did, for he was a most debauched and vicious youth, but made the world amends by brave exploits; at last become a new man, and seek to be reformed. He that runs away in a battle, as Demosthenes said, may fight again; and he that hath a fall, may stand as upright as ever he did before. None need despair of a better day: a wicked liver may be reclaimed, and prove an honest man; he that is odious in present, hissed out, an exile, may be received again with all men's favours, and singular applause; so Tully was in Rome, Alcibiades in Athens. Let thy disgrace then be what it will, that which is past cannot be recalled; trouble not thyself, vex and grieve thyself no more, be it obloquy, disgrace, &c. No better way than to neglect, contemn, or seem not to regard it, to make no reckoning of it; much speaking means small strength; if thou be guiltless, it concerns thee not. Regard not the harmless shafts of an idle tongue. Doth the Moon care for the barking of a dog? They detract, scoff and rail, saith one, and bark at me on every side, but I, like that Albanian dog sometime given to Alexander for a present, I lie still and sleep, vindicate myself by contempt alone. Free from fear as Achilles in his armour, as a tortoise in his shell, I wrap myself in my virtue, or an urchin [or hedgehog] round, I care not for their blows, a lizard in camomile [a plant which the more it was trodden on grew the more], I decline their fury, and am safe.

> *Virtue and integrity are their own fence,*
> *Care not for envy or what comes from thence.*

Let them rail then, scoff, and slander, a wise man, Seneca thinks, is not moved, because he knows there is no remedy for it: Kings and Princes, wise, grave, prudent, holy, good men, divine, all are so served alike. Thou only, two-faced Janus, hast no derisive finger pointed behind thy back! Antevorta and Postvorta,* Jupiter's guardians, may not help in this case, they cannot protect; Moses had a Dathan, a Corah, David a Shimei, God himself is blasphemed: thou art not yet happy, if the crowd hath not yet mocked thee. It is an ordinary thing so to be misused; the chiefest men, and most understanding, are so vilified; let him take his course. And, as that lusty courser in Æsop, that contemned the poor ass, came by and by after with his bowels burst, a pack on his back, and was derided of the same ass: they shall be contemned and laughed to scorn of those whom they have formerly derided. Let them contemn, defame, or undervalue, insult, oppress, scoff, slander, abuse, wrong, curse and swear, feign and lie, do thou comfort thyself with a good conscience, rejoice at heart when they have all done, a good conscience is a continual feast, innocency will vindicate itself. And which the Poet gave out of Hercules, *he enjoys the anger of the gods,* enjoy thyself, though all the world be set against thee, contemn and say with him, *My posy is, not to be moved,* that my Palladium, my breast-plate, my buckler, with which I ward all injuries, offences, lies, slanders; I lean upon that stake of modesty, so receive and break asunder all that foolish force of livor and spleen. And whosoever he is that shall observe these short instructions, without all question he shall much ease and benefit himself.

In fine, if Princes would do justice, Judges be upright, Clergymen truly devout, and so live as they teach, if great men would not be so insolent, if soldiers would quietly defend us, the poor would be patient, rich men would be liberal and humble, Citizens honest, Magistrates meek, Superiors would give good example, subjects peaceable, young men would stand in awe: if Parents would be kind to their children, and they again obedient to their Parents, brethren agree amongst themselves, enemies be reconciled, servants trusty to their Masters, Virgins chaste, Wives modest, Husbands would be loving, and less jealous: if we could imitate Christ and his Apostles, live after God's laws, these mischiefs would not so frequently happen amongst us; but being most part so irreconcileable as we are, perverse, proud, insolent, factious, and malicious, prone to contention, anger and revenge, of such fiery spirits, so captious, impious, irreligious, so opposite to virtue, void of grace, how should it otherwise be? Many men are very testy by nature, apt to mistake, apt to quarrel, apt to provoke, and misinterpret to the worst every thing that is said or done, and thereupon heap unto their selves

* Antevorta was the goddess who presided over childbirth, Postvorta the goddess who reminded men of things past.

a great deal of trouble, and disquietness to others, smatterers in other men's matters, tale-bearers, whisperers, liars, they cannot speak in season, or hold their tongues when they should, they will speak more than comes to their share in all companies, and by those bad courses accumulate much evil to their own souls, (who begins by arguing, will end in quarrelling), their life is a perpetual brawl, they snarl, like so many dogs, with their wives, children, servants, neighbours, and all the rest of their friends, they can agree with nobody. But to such as are judicious, meek, submiss, and quiet, these matters are easily remedied: they will forbear upon all such occasions, neglect, contemn, or take no notice of them, dissemble, or wisely turn it off. If it be a natural impediment, as a red nose, squint eyes, crooked legs, or any such imperfection, infirmity, disgrace, reproach, the best way is to speak of it first thyself, and so thou shalt surely take away all occasions from others to jest at, or contemn, that they may perceive thee to be careless of it. Vatinius was wont to scoff at his own deformed feet, to prevent his enemies' obloquies and sarcasms in that kind; or else by prevention, as Cotys, King of Thrace, that brake a company of fine glasses presented to him, with his own hands, lest he should be overmuch moved when they were broken by chance. And sometimes again, so that it be discreetly and moderately done, it shall not be amiss to make resistance, to take down such a saucy companion; no better means to vindicate himself to purchase final peace: for he that suffers himself to be ridden, or through pusillanimity or sottishness will let every man baffle him, shall be a common laughing stock for all to flout at. As a cur that goes through a Village, if he clap his tail between his legs, and run away, every cur will insult over him, but if he bristle up himself, and stand to it, give but a counter-snarl, there's not a dog dares meddle with him. Much is in a man's courage and discreet carriage of himself.

Many other grievances there are, which happen to mortals in this life, from friends, wives, children, servants, masters, companions, neighbours, our own defaults, ignorance, errors, intemperance, indiscretion, infirmities, &c., and many good remedies to mitigate and oppose them, many divine precepts to counterpoise our hearts, special antidotes both in Scripture and human Authors, which whoso will observe shall purchase much ease and quietness unto himself. I will point at a few. Those Prophetical, Apostolical admonitions, are well known to all; what Solomon, Siracides, our Saviour Christ himself, hath said tending to this purpose, as, Fear God: obey the Prince: be sober and watch: pray continually: be angry, but sin not: remember thy last: fashion not yourselves to this world, &c., apply yourselves to the times: strive not with a mighty man: recompence good for evil: let nothing be done through contention or vain-glory, but with meekness of mind, every man esteeming of others better than himself: love one another; or that Epitome of the Law and the Prophets, which our Saviour inculcates, *love God above all, thy neighbour as thyself.* And *whatsoever you would that men should do unto you, so do unto them,* which Alexander Severus writ in letters of gold, and used as a motto; Hierom commends to Celantia as an excellent way, amongst so many enticements and worldly provocations, to rectify her life. Out of human Authors take these few cautions: Know thyself. Be contented with thy lot. Trust not wealth, beauty, nor parasites; they will bring thee to destruction. Have peace with all men, war with vice. Be not idle. Look before you leap. Beware of, Had I wist. Honour thy parents, speak well of friends. Be temperate in four things, talking, spending, looking and drinking. Watch thine eye. Moderate thine expences. Hear much, speak little. Bear and for-bear. If thou seest ought amiss in another, mend it in thyself. Keep thine own counsel, reveal not thy secrets, be silent in thine intentions. Give not ear to tale-tellers, babblers, be not scurrilous in conversa-tion. Jest without bitterness: give no man cause of offence: set thine house in order: take heed of suretyship. Trust and distrust: as a fox on the ice, take heed whom you trust. Live not beyond thy means. Give cheerfully. Pay thy dues willingly. Be not a slave to thy money. Omit not occasion, embrace opportunity, lose no time. Be humble to thy superiors, respective to thine equals, affable to all, but not familiar: flatter no man. Lie not, dissemble not. Keep thy word and promise, be constant in a good resolution. Speak truth. Be not opinionative, main-tain no factions. Lay no wagers, make no comparisons. Find no faults, meddle not with other men's matters. Admire not thyself. Be not proud or popular. Insult not. Stand in awe of fortune. Fear not that which cannot be avoided. Grieve not for that which cannot be recalled. Under-value not thyself. Accuse no man, commend no man, rashly. Go not to law without great cause. Strive not with a greater man. Cast not off an old friend. Take heed of a reconciled enemy. If thou come as a guest, stay not too long. Be not unthankful. Be meek, merciful, and patient. Do good to all. Be not fond of fair words. Be not a neuter in a faction. Moderate thy passions. Think no place without a witness. Admonish thy friend in secret, commend him in publick. Keep good company. Love others, to be beloved thyself. Love what you would be hating. Be slow to become a friend. Provide for a tempest. Stir not up hornets.

Do not prostitute thy soul for gain. Make not a fool of thyself to make others merry. Marry not an old crone or a fool for money. Be not over solicitous or curious. Seek that which may be found. Seem not greater than thou art. Take thy pleasure soberly. Thresh not the basil-weed [which by its smell breeds scorpions in men's brains]. Live merrily as thou canst. Take heed by other men's examples. Go as thou wouldst be met, sit as thou wouldst be found, yield to the time, follow the stream. Wilt thou live free from fears and cares? Live innocently, keep thyself upright, thou needest no other keeper, &c. Look for more in Isocrates, Seneca, Plutarch, Epictetus, &c., and for defect, consult with cheese-trenchers and painted clothes.*

MEMBER 8

Against Melancholy itself

EVERY man, saith Seneca, thinks his own burthen the heaviest, and a melancholy man above all others complains most; weariness of life, abhorring all company and light, fear, sorrow, suspicion, anguish of mind, bashfulness, and those other dread symptoms of body and mind, must needs aggravate this misery; yet, conferred to other maladies, they are not so heinous as they be taken. For first, this disease is either in habit, or disposition, curable, or incurable. If new and in disposition, 'tis commonly pleasant, and it may be helped. If inveterate, or an habit, yet they have lucid intervals, sometimes well, and sometimes ill; or if more continuate, as the Veientes were to the Romans, 'tis a more durable enemy than dangerous: and, amongst many inconveniences, some comforts are annexed to it. First, it is not catching, and, as Erasmus comforted himself, when he was grievously sick of the stone, though it was most troublesome, and an intolerable pain to him, yet it was no whit offensive to others, not loathsome to the spectators, ghastly, fulsome, terrible, as plagues, apoplexies, leprosies, wounds, sores, tetters, pox, pestilent agues are, which either admit of no company, terrify or offend those that are present. In this malady, that which is, is wholly to themselves, and those symptoms not so dreadful, if they be compared to the opposite extremes. They are most part bashful, suspicious, solitary, &c.,

* Cheese-trenchers, wooden platters to cut cheese on, had mottoes sometimes round the edge. Painted cloths, or painted clothes, were a cheap substitute for tapestry as a hanging for rooms; they were of canvas, adorned with heraldic devices, mottoes, texts, verses & proverbs.

therefore no such ambitious, impudent intruders, as some are, no sharkers, no cony-catchers, no prowlers, no smell-feasts, praters, panders, parasites, bawds, drunkards, whoremasters: necessity and defect compels them to be honest; as Micio told Demea in the comedy, if we be honest, 'twas poverty made us so: if we melancholy men be not as bad as he that is worst, 'tis our Dame Melancholy kept us so: 'twas not the will but the way that was wanting.

Besides, they are freed in this from many other infirmities, solitariness makes them more apt to contemplate, suspicion wary, which is a necessary humour in these times; for, truly, he that takes most heed is often circumvented and overtaken. Fear and sorrow keep them temperate and sober, and free them from many dissolute acts, which jollity and boldness thrust men upon: they are therefore no cut-throats, roaring boys, thieves, or assassinates. As they are soon dejected, so they are as soon by soft words and good persuasions reared. Wearisomeness of life makes them they are not so besotted on the transitory vain pleasures of the world. If they dote in one thing, they are wise and well understanding in most other. If it be inveterate, they are, most part doting, or quite mad, insensible to any wrongs, ridiculous to others, but most happy and secure to themselves. Dotage is a state which many much magnify and commend: so is simplicity and folly, as he said, may this madness, O gods, be with me for ever! Some think fools and dizzards live the merriest lives, as Ajax in Sophocles, 'tis the pleasantest life to know nothing: ignorance is a down-right remedy of evils. These curious Arts, and laborious Sciences, Galen's, Tully's, Aristotle's, Justinian's, do but trouble the world, some think; we might live better with that illiterate Virginian simplicity and gross ignorance; entire idiots do best; they are not macerated with cares, tormented with fears, and anxiety, as other wise men are: for, as he said, if folly were a pain, you should hear them howl, roar, and cry out in every house, as you go by in the street, but they are most free, jocund and merry, and in some Countries, as amongst the Turks, honoured for Saints, and abundantly maintained out of the common stock. They are no dissemblers, liars, hypocrites, for fools and mad men tell commonly truth. In a word, as they are distressed, so are they pitied, which some hold better than to be envied, better to be sad than merry, better to be foolish and quiet than to be wise, and still vexed; better to be miserable than happy; of two extremes it is the best.

SECTION 4 MEMBER 1

SUBSECTION 1 — *Of Physick which cureth with Medicines*

AFTER a long and tedious discourse of these six non-natural things, and their several rectifications, all which are comprehended in Diet, I am come now at last to Pharmaceutics, or that kind of Physick which cureth by Medicines, which Apothecaries most part make, mingle, or sell in their shops. Many cavil at this kind of Physick, and hold it unnecessary, unprofitable to this or any other disease, because those Countries which use it least live longest, and are best in health, as Hector Boethius relates of the Isles of Orcades, the people are still sound of body and mind without any use of Physick, they live commonly 120 years; and Ortelius, in his Itinerary of the Inhabitants of the Forest of Arden, they are very painful, long-lived, sound, &c. Martianus Capella, speaking of the Indians of his time, saith, they were (much like our western Indians now) bigger than ordinary men, bred coarsely, very long-lived, insomuch that he that died at an hundred years of age went before his time, &c. Damianus A-Goes, Saxo Grammaticus, Aubanus Bohemus, say the like of them that live in Norway, Lapland, Finmark, Biarmia, Corelia, all over Scandia, and those Northern Countries, they are most healthful and very long-lived, in which places there is no use at all of Physick, the name of it is not once heard. Dithmarus Bleskenius, in his accurate description of Iceland, 1607, makes mention amongst other matters of the inhabitants, and their manner of living, which is dried fish instead of bread, butter, cheese, and salt-meats, most part they drink water and whey, and yet without Physick or Physician they live many of them 250 years. I find the same relation by Lerius, and some other Writers, of Indians in America. Paulus Jovius, in his description of Britain, and Levinus Lemnius, observe as much of this our Island, that there was of old no use of Physick amongst us, and but little at this day, except it be for a few nice idle Citizens, surfeiting Courtiers, and stall-fed Gentlemen lubbers. The country people use kitchen Physick, and common experience tells us that they live freest from all manner of infirmities that make least use of Apothecaries' Physick. Many are overthrown by preposterous use of it, and thereby get their bane, that might otherwise have escaped; some think Physicians kill as many as they save, and who can tell how many murders they make in a year, that may freely kill folks, and have a reward for it? and, according to the Dutch proverb, a new Physician must have a

new Church-yard; and who daily observes it not? Many that did ill under Physicians' hands have happily escaped when they have been given
over by them, left to God and Nature and themselves. 'Twas Pliny's dilemma of old, Every disease is either curable or incurable, a man recov-
ers of it or is killed by it; both ways Physick is to be rejected. If it be
deadly, it cannot be cured; if it may be helped, it requires no Physician;
Nature will expel it of itself. Plato made it a great sign of an intemperate and corrupt Commonwealth, where Lawyers and Physicians did
abound; and the Romans distasted them so much, that they were often
banished out of their City, as Pliny and Celsus relate, for 600 years not
admitted. It is no Art at all, as some hold, no not worthy the name of a
liberal science (nor Law neither) as Pet. And. Canonherius, a Patrician
of Rome, and a great Doctor himself, one of their own tribe, proves by
16 Arguments, because it is mercenary as now used, base, and as Fiddlers play for a reward. Lawyers and doctors on the publick live, 'tis a
corrupt Trade, no Science, Art, no Profession; the beginning, practice
and progress of it, all is naught, full of imposture, incertainty and doth
generally more harm than good. The Devil himself was the first inventor of it: Medicine is my invention, said Apollo: and what was Apollo,
but the Devil? The Greeks first made an Art of it, and they were all deluded by Apollo's Sons, Priests, Oracles. If we may believe Varro, Pliny,
Columella, most of their best medicines were derived from his Oracles.
Æsculapius his son had his Temples erected to his Deity, and did many
famous cures, but, as Lactantius holds, he was a Magician, a mere
Impostor, and as his successors, Phaon, Podalirius, Melampius, Menecrates (another God) by charms, spells, and ministry of bad spirits, performed most of their cures. The first that ever wrote in Physick to any
purpose was Hippocrates, and his Disciple and Commentator Galen,
whom Scaliger calls a mere ravelling of Hippocrates, but, as Cardan
censures them, both immethodical and obscure, as all those old ones
are, their precepts confused, their medicines obsolete, and now most
part rejected. Those cures which they did, Paracelsus holds, were rather
done out of their Patients' confidence, and good opinion they had of
them, than out of any skill of theirs, which was very small, he saith,
they themselves idiots and infants, as are all their Academical followers.
The Arabians received it from the Greeks, and so the Latins, adding
new precepts and medicines of their own, but so imperfect still, that
through ignorance of Professors, Impostors, Mountebanks, Empiricks,
disagreeing of Sectaries, (which are as many almost as there be diseases), envy, covetousness, and the like, they do much harm amongst

us. They are so different in their consultations, prescriptions, mistaking many times the parties' constitution, disease, and causes of it, they give quite contrary Physick. One saith this, another that, out of singularity or opposition, as he said of Adrian, a multitude of Physicians hath killed the Emperor; more danger there is from the Physician than from the disease. Besides, there is much imposture and malice amongst them. All Arts (saith Cardan) admit of cozening, Physick amongst the rest doth appropriate it to herself; and tells a story of one Curtius, a Physisian in Venice, because he was a stranger, and practised among them, the rest of the Physicians did still cross him in all his precepts. If he prescribed hot medicines, they would prescribe cold, binders for purgatives, they changed everything about. If the party miscarried, they blamed Curtius, Curtius killed him, that disagreed from them: if he recovered, then they cured him themselves. Much emulation, imposture, malice, there is amongst them: if they be honest, and mean well, yet a knave Apothecary that administers the Physick, and makes the medicine, may do infinite harm, by his old obsolete doses, adulterine drugs, bad mixtures, substitutions, &c. See Fuchsius, Cordus' Dispensatory, and Brassivola. But it is their ignorance that doth more harm than rashness, their Art is wholly conjectural, if it be an Art, uncertain, imperfect, and got by killing of men, they are a kind of butchers, leeches, men-slayers; Chirurgeons, and Apothecaries especially, that are indeed the Physicians' hangmen, torturers, and common executioners; though, to say truth, Physicians themselves come not far behind; for according to that witty Epigram of Maximilianus Urentius, what's the difference? How (he asks) does the Surgeon differ from the Physician? One kills by hand, the other by drugs; and both differ from the hangman only in that they do slowly what he does quickly. But I return to their skill. Many diseases they cannot cure at all, as Apoplexy, Epilepsy, Stone, Stranguary, Gout.

Medicine cannot cure the knotty gout.   (OVID)

Quartan Agues, a common Ague sometimes stumbles them all; they cannot so much as ease, they know not how to judge of it. If by pulses, that doctrine, some hold, is wholly superstitious, and I dare boldly say with Andrew Dudeth, that variety of pulses, described by Galen, is neither observed, nor understood of any. And for urine, that is the Physicians' strumpet, the most deceitful thing of all, as Forestus and some other Physicians have proved at large: I say nothing of critick days, errors in indications, &c. The most rational of them, and skilful, are so often deceived, that as Tholosanus infers, I had rather believe and commit myself to a mere Empirick than to a mere Doctor, and I cannot sufficiently commend that custom of the Babylonians, that have no professed Physicians, but bring all their patients to the market to be cured: which Herodotus relates of the Egyptians, Strabo, Sardus, and Aubanus Bohemus of many other Nations. And those that prescribed Physick amongst them, did not so arrogantly take upon them to cure all diseases as our professors do, but some one, some another, as their skill and experience did serve. One cured the eyes, a second the teeth, a third the head, another the lower parts, &c., not for gain, but in charity, to do good; they made neither art, profession, nor trade of it, which in other places was accustomed: and therefore Cambyses, in Xenophon, told Cyrus, that to his thinking Physicians were like Tailors and Cobblers, the one mended our sick bodies, as the other did our clothes. But I will urge these cavelling and contumelious arguments no farther, lest some Physician should mistake me, and deny me Physick when I am sick: for my part, I am well persuaded of Physick: I can distinguish the abuse from the use in this and many other Arts and Sciences; wine and drunkenness are two distinct things. I acknowledge it a most noble and divine science, insomuch that Apollo, Æsculapius, and the first founders of it, were worthily counted Gods by succeeding ages, for the excellency of their invention. And whereas Apollo at Delos, Venus at Cyprus, Diana at Ephesus, and those other Gods, were confined and adored alone in some peculiar places, Æsculapius had his Temple and Altars everywhere, in Corinth, Lacedæmon, Athens, Thebes, Epidaurus, &c., (Pausanias records), for the latitude of his art, Deity, worth and necessity. With all virtuous and wise men, therefore, I honour the name, and calling, as I am enjoined to *honour the Physician for necessity's sake. The knowledge of the Physician lifted up his head, and in the sight of great men he shall be admired. The Lord hath created medicines of the earth, and he that is wise will not abhor them.* But of this noble subject how many panegyricks are worthily written! For my part, as Sallust said of Carthage, 'tis better to be silent than to say little. I have said, yet one thing I will add, that this kind of Physick is very moderately and advisedly to be used, upon good occasion, when the former of diet will not take place. And 'tis no other which I say than that which Arnoldus prescribes in his 8th Aphorism: A discreet and godly Physician doth first endeavour to expel a disease by medicinal diet, then by pure medicine; and in his ninth, he that may be cured by diet must not meddle with Physick. So in the 11th Aphorism: A modest and wise Physician will never hasten to use medicines, but upon urgent necessity, and that sparingly too; because (as he adds in his 13th Aphorism) : Whosoever takes much Physick in his youth shall soon bewail it in his old age; purgative Physick especially, which doth much debilitate nature. For which causes some Physicians refrain from the use of Purgatives, or else sparingly use them. Henricus Ayrerus, in a consultation for a melancholy person, would have him take as few purges as he could, because there be no such medicines which do not steal away some of our strength, and rob the parts of our body, weaken Nature, and cause that Cacochymia, which Celsus and others observe, or ill digestion, and bad juice through all the parts of it. Galen himself confesseth that purgative Physick is contrary to Nature, takes away some of our best spirits, and consumes the very substance of our bodies. But this without question is to be understood of such purges as are unseasonably or immoderately taken; they have their excellent use in this as well as most other infirmities. Of Alteratives and Cordials no man doubts, be they simples or compounds. I will, amongst that infinite variety of medicines which I find in every Pharmacopœia, every Physician, Herbalist, &c., single out some of the chiefest.

SUBSECTION 2 — *Simples proper to Melancholy, against Exotick Simples*

MEDICINES properly applied to Melancholy are either *Simple* or *Compound*. *Simples* are *Alterative* or *Purgative*. *Alterative* are such as correct, strengthen Nature, alter, any way hinder or resist the disease; and they be herbs, stones, minerals, &c., all proper to this humour. For as there be divers distinct infirmities, continually vexing us,

> *Diseases steal both day and night on men,*
> *For Jupiter hath taken voice from them,*   (HESIOD)

so there be several remedies, as he saith, for each disease a medicine, for every humour; and, as some hold, every clime, every country, and more than that, every private place, hath his proper remedies growing in it, peculiar almost to the domineering and most frequent maladies of it. As one discourseth, wormwood grows sparingly in Italy, because most part there they be misaffected with hot diseases; but henbane, poppy, and such cold herbs: with us in Germany and Poland great store of it in every waste. Baracellus and Baptista Porta give many instances and examples of it, and bring many other proofs. For that cause, belike, that learned Fuchsius of Nuremberg, when he came into a village, considered always what herbs did grow most frequently about it, and those he distilled in a silver limbeck, making use of others amongst them as occasion served. I know that many are of opinion our Northern simples are weak, unperfect, not so well concocted, of such force, as those in the Southern parts, not so fit to be used in Physick, and will therefore fetch their drugs afar off: Senna, Cassia out of Egypt, Rhubarb from Barbary, Aloes from Zocotora, Turbith [or Turpeth, a cathartick root], Agarick, Mirabolanes [or Indian Plums], Hermodactils [or Wild Saffron] from the East Indies, Tobacco from the West, and some as far as China, Hellebore from the Anticyræ, or that of Austria which bears the purple flower, which Mathiolus so much approves, and so of the rest. In the Kingdom of Valencia in Spain, Maginus commends two mountains, Mariola and Renagolosa, famous for simples; Leander Albertus, Baldus, a mountain near the lake Benacus, in the territory of Verona, to which all the herbalists in the Country continually flock: Ortelius one in Apulia, Munster mons Major in Histria: others Montpelier in France. Prosper Alpinus prefers Egyptian simples, Garcias ab Horto [prefers] Indian before the rest, another those of Italy, Crete, &c. Many times they are overcurious in this kind, whom Fuchsius taxeth, that they think they do nothing except they rake all over India, Arabia, Æthiopia, for remedies, and fetch their Physick from the three quarters of the World, and from beyond the Garamantes. Many an old wife or country woman doth often more good with a few known and common garden herbs than our bombast Physicians with all their prodigious, sumptuous, farfetched, rare, conjectural medicines. Without all question, if we have not these rare Exotick simples, we hold that at home which is in virtue equivalent unto them; ours will serve as well as theirs, if they be taken in proportionable quantity, fitted and qualified aright, if not much better, and more proper to our constitutions. But so 'tis for the most part, as Pliny writes to Gallus, we are careless of that which is near us, and follow that which is afar off, to know which we will travel and sail beyond the Seas, wholly neglecting that which is under our eyes. Opium in Turkey doth scarce offend, with us in a small quantity it stupifies; cicuta (or hemlock) is a strong poison in Greece, but with us it hath no such violent effects. I conclude with J. Voschius, who, as he much inveighs against those exotick medicines, so he promiseth by our European a full cure, and absolute, of all diseases; from beginning to end, our own simples agree best with us. It was a thing that Fernelius much laboured in his French practice, to reduce all his cure to our proper and domestick Physick: so did Janus Cornarius, and Martin Rulandus, in Germany, T. B.* with us, as appeareth by a treatise of his divulged in

* Timothy Bright.

our tongue 1615, to prove the sufficiency of English medicines to the cure of all manner of diseases. If our simples be not altogether of such force, or so apposite, it may be, if like industry were used, those far fetched drugs would prosper as well with us as in those Countries whence now we have them, as well as Cherries, Artichokes, Tobacco, and many such. There have been divers worthy Physicians, which have tried excellent conclusions in this kind, and many diligent, painful, Apothecaries, as Gesner, Besler, Gerard, &c., but amongst the rest, those famous publick Gardens of Padua in Italy, Nuremberg in Germany, Leyden in Holland, Montpelier in France, (and ours in Oxford now being constructed at the cost and charges of the Right Honourable the Lord Danvers, Earl of Danby), are much to be commended, wherein all exotick plants almost are to be seen, and liberal allowance yearly made for their better maintenance, that young students may be the sooner informed in the knowledge of them: which, as Fuchsius holds, is most necessary for that exquisite manner of curing, and as great a shame for a Physician not to observe them as for a workman not to know his axe, saw, square, or any other tool which he must of necessity use.

SUBSECTION 3 — *Alteratives, Herbs, other Vegetals, &c.*

AMONGST those 800 simples, which Galeottus reckons up, and many exquisite Herbalists have written of, these few following alone I find appropriated to this humour: of which some be Alteratives; which by a secret force, saith Renodeus, and special quality, expel future diseases, perfectly cure those which are, and many such incurable effects. This is as well observed in other plants, stones, minerals, and creatures, as in herbs, in other maladies, as in this. How many things are related of a man's skull! What several virtues of corns in a horse's leg, of a wolf's liver, &c., of divers excrements of beasts, all good against several diseases! What extraordinary virtues are ascribed unto plants! Priest pintle and rocket [or ragwort and colewort] enliven the member; the chaste-tree [or Abraham's balm] and waterlily quench the sperm; some herbs provoke lust; some again, as chaste-lamb, waterlily, quite extinguish seed; poppy causeth sleep, cabbage resisteth drunkenness, &c. and that which is more to be admired, that such and such plants should have a peculiar virtue to such particular parts, as to the head, Aniseeds, Foalfoot, Betony, Calamint, Eye-bright, Lavender, Bays, Roses, Rue, Sage, Marjoram, Peony, &c.; for the lungs, Calamint, Liquorice, Enula Campana, Hyssop, Horehound, Water Germander, &c.; for the heart, Borage, Bugloss, Saffron, Balm, Basil, Rosemary, Violet, Roses. &c.;

for the stomack, Wormwood, Mints, Betony, Balm, Centaury, Sorel, Purslain; for the liver, Darthspine, Germander, Agrimony, Fennel, Endive, Succory, Liverwort, Barberries; for the spleen, Maidenhair, Finger-fern, Dodder of Thyme, Hop, the rind of Ash, Betony; for the kidnies, Grumel, Parsley, Saxifrage, Plantain, Mallow; for the womb, Mugwort, Pennyroyal, Fetherfew, Savine, &c.; for the joints, Camomile, S. John's wort, Organ, Rue, Cowslips, Centaury the less, &c., and so to peculiar diseases. To this of Melancholy you shall find a Catalogue of Herbs proper, and that in every part. See more in Wecker, Renodeus, Heurnius, &c. I will briefly speak of them, as first of Alteratives, which Galen, in his third book of diseased parts, prefers before diminutives, and Trallianus brags that he hath done more cures on melancholy men by moistening than by purging of them.

In this Catalogue, Borage and Bugloss may challenge the chiefest place, whether in substance, juice, roots, seeds, flowers, leaves, decoctions, distilled waters, extracts, oils, &c., for such kind of herbs be diversely varied. Bugloss is hot and moist, and therefore worthily reckoned up amongst those herbs which expel melancholy, and exhilarate the heart (Galen saith, & Dioscorides). Pliny much magnifies this plant. It may be diversely used; as in Broth, in Wine, in Conserves, Syrops, &c. It is an excellent cordial, and against this malady most frequently prescribed: an herb indeed of such sovereignty that, as Diodorus, Pliny, Plutarch, &c., suppose, it was that famous Nepenthes of Homer, which Polydamna, Thonis's wife, (then King of Thebes in Ægypt), sent Helen for a token, of such rare virtue, that, if taken steept in wine, if wife and children, father and mother, brother and sister, and all thy dearest friends, should die before thy face, thou couldst not grieve or shed a tear for them. Helen's commended bowl to exhilarate the heart had no other ingredient, as most of our criticks conjecture, than this of Borage.

Honeyleaf Balm hath an admirable virtue to alter Melancholy, be it steeped in our ordinary drink, extracted, or otherwise taken. Cardan much admires this herb. It heats and dries, saith Heurnius, in the second degree, with a wonderful virtue comforts the heart, and purgeth all melancholy vapours from the spirits (Matthiolus). Besides they ascribe other virtues to it, as to help concoction, to cleanse the brain, expel all careful thoughts and anxious imaginations. The same words in effect are in Avicenna, Pliny, Simon Sethi, Fuchsius, Leobel, Dèlacampius, and every Herbalist. Nothing better for him that is melancholy than to steep this and Borage in his ordinary drink.

Matthiolus, in his fifth book of Medicinal Epistles, reckons up Scorzonera, not against poison only, falling sickness, and such as are vertiginous, but to this malady; the root of it taken by itself expels sorrow, causeth mirth and lightness of heart.

Antonius Musa, that renowned Physician to Cæsar Augustus, in his book which he writ of the virtues of Betony, wonderfully commends that herb, it preserves both body and mind from fears, cares, griefs, cures falling-sickness, this and many other diseases; to whom Galen subscribes.

Marigold is much approved against Melancholy, and often used therefore in our ordinary broth, as good against this and many other diseases.

Hop is a sovereign remedy; Fuchsius much extols it; it purgeth all choler, and purifies the blood. Matthiolus wonders the Physicians of his time made no more use of it, because it rarefies and cleanseth: we use it to this purpose in our ordinary beer, which before was thick and fulsome.

Wormwood, Centaury [a species of aster whose medicinal properties were said to have been discovered by the Centaur Chiron], Pennyroyal, are likewise magnified and much prescribed (as I shall after shew) especially in Hypochondriack Melancholy, daily to be used, sod [or seethed] in whey: and, as Ruffus Ephesius, Aretæus, relate, by breaking wind, and helping concoction, many melancholy men have been cured with frequent use of them alone.

And because the spleen and blood are often misaffected in Melancholy, I may not omit Endive, Succory, Dandelion, Fumitory, &c., which cleanse the blood; Scolopendria [Ferns], Cuscuta [or Dodders], Ceterach [or Miltwaste], Mugwort, Liverwort, Ash, Tamarisk, Genist [or Spanish Broom], Maidenhair, &c., which much help and ease the spleen.

To these I may add Roses, Violets, Capers, Fetherfew [or Feverfew], Scordium [or Water Germander], Stœchas [or French Lavender], Rosemary, Ros Solis [or Sun-Dew], Saffron, Ocyme [or Basil], sweet Apples, Wine, Tobacco, Sanders [or Sandalwood], &c., that Peruvian Chamico [or Wild Cane], of monstrous powers, Linshcosteus Datura; and to such as are cold the decoction of Guiacum, China [Roots], Sarsaparilla, Sassafras, the flowers of the Benedictus Thistle, which I find much used by Montanus in his consultations, Julius Alexandrinus, Lælius Eugubinus, and others. Bernardus Penottus prefers his Sun-Dew, or Dutch-Sindaw, before all the rest in this disease, and will admit of no herb upon the earth to be comparable to it. It excels Homer's Moly, cures this, falling-sickness, and almost all other infirmities. The same Penottus speaks of an excellent Balm out of Apponensis, which, taken to the quantity of three drops in a cup of wine, will cause a sudden alteration, drive away dumps, and cheer up the heart. Guianerius, in his Antidotary, hath many such. Jacobus de Dondis, the Aggregator, repeats Ambergrease, Nutmegs, and Allspice amongst the rest. But that cannot be general. Amber and Spice will make a hot brain mad, good for cold and moist. Garcias ab Horto hath many Indian Plants, whose virtues he much magnifies in this disease. Lemnius admires Rue, and commends it to have excellent virtue, to expel vain imaginations, Devils, and to ease afflicted souls. Other things are much magnified by writers, as an old Cock, a Ram's head, a Wolf's heart borne or eaten, which Mercurialis approves; Prosper Alpinus the water of Nilus, Gomesius all Sea water, and at seasonable times to be sea-sick: Goat's milk, Whey, &c.

SUBSECTION 4 — *Precious Stones, Metals, Minerals, Alteratives*

PRECIOUS Stones are diversely censured; many explode the use of them or any Minerals in Physick, of whom Thomas Erastus is the chief, in his Tract against Paracelsus, and in an Epistle of his to Peter Monavius: " That stones can work any wonders let them believe that list; no man shall persuade me, for my part I have found by experience there is no virtue in them." But Matthiolus, in his Comment upon Dioscorides, is as profuse on the other side in their commendation; so is Cardan, Renodeus, Alardus, Rueus, Encelius, Marbodeus, &c. Matthiolus specifies in Coral, and Oswaldus Crollius prefers the salt of Coral. Encelius will have them to be as so many several medicines against melancholy, sorrow, fear, dulness, and the like. Renodeus admires them, besides they adorn Kings' Crowns, grace the fingers, enrich our household-stuff, defend us from enchantments, preserve health, cure diseases, they drive away grief, cares, and exhilarate the mind. The particulars be these.

Granatus, a precious stone so called, because it is like the kernels of a Pomegranate, an unperfect kind of Ruby, it comes from Calicut; if hung about the neck, or taken in drink, it much resisteth sorrow, and recreates the heart. The same properties I find ascribed to the Jacinth and Topaz, they allay anger, grief, diminish madness, much delight and exhilarate the mind. If it be either carried about, or taken in a potion, it will increase wisdom, saith Cardan, expel fear; he brags that he hath cured many mad men with it, which, when they laid by the stone, were as mad again as ever they were at first. Petrus Bayerus and Fran.

Rueus, say as much of the Chrysolite, a friend of wisdom, an enemy to folly (Pliny, Solinus, Albertus, Cardan). Encelius highly magnifies the virtue of the Beryl, it much avails to a good understanding, represseth vain conceits, evil thoughts, causeth mirth, &c. In the belly of a swallow there is a stone found called Chelidonius [or Swallow-stone], which, if it be lapped in a fair cloth, and tied to the right arm, will cure lunaticks, mad men, make them amiable and merry.

There is a kind of Onyx, called a Chalcedony, which hath the same qualities, avails much against phantastick illusions which proceed from melancholy, preserves the vigour and good estate of the whole body.

The Eban stone, which Goldsmiths use to sleeken their gold with, borne about, or given to drink, hath the same properties, or not much unlike.

Lævinus Lemnius, amongst other Jewels makes mention of two more notable, Carbuncle and Coral, which drive away childish fears, Devils, overcome sorrow, and hung about the neck, repress troublesome dreams, which properties almost Cardan gives to that green coloured Emmetris, if it be carried about, or worn in a Ring; Rueus to the Diamond.

Nicholas Cabeus, a Jesuit of Ferrara, in the first book of his Magnetical Philosophy, speaking of the virtues of a loadstone, recites many several opinions; some say that, if it be taken in parcels inward, it will, like viper's wine, restore one to his youth, and yet, if carried about them, others will have it to cause melancholy; let experience determine.

Mercurialis admires the Emerald for his virtues in pacifying all affections of the mind; others the Sapphire, which is the fairest of all precious stones, of sky-colour, and a great enemy to black choler, frees the mind, mends manners, &c. Jacobus de Dondis, in his Catalogue of Simples, hath Ambergrease, the bone in a Stag's heart, a Monocerot's [or Unicorn's] horn, Bezoar's stone, (of which elsewhere), it is found in the belly of a little beast in the East Indies, brought into Europe by Hollanders and our Countrymen Merchants. Renodeus saith he saw two of these beasts alive in the Castle of the Lord of Vitry at Coubert.

Lapis Lazuli and Armenus, because they purge, shall be mentioned in their place.

Of the rest in brief thus much I will add out of Cardan, Renodeus, Rondoletius, &c., that almost all Jewels and precious stones have excellent virtues to pacify the affections of the mind, for which cause rich men so much covet to have them: and those smaller Unions [or Pearls] which are found in shells amongst the Persians and Indians, by the consent of all writers, are very cordial, and most part avail to the exhilaration of the heart.

Most men say as much of Gold, and some other Minerals, as these have done of precious stones. Erastus still maintains the opposite part. In his disputation against Paracelsus, he confesseth of Gold that it makes the heart merry, but in no other sense but as it is in a miser's chest: I am well content with myself at home, looking at my money in my strong-box, as he said in the Poet; it so revives the spirits, and is an excellent receipt against Melancholy.

> For gold in phisik is a cordial,
> Therefore he lovede gold in special.*

Potable [or drinkable] gold he discommends and inveighs against it, by reason of the corrosive waters which are used in it, which arguments our Dr. Guin urgeth against Dr. Antonius. Erastus concludes their Philosophical stones and potable gold, &c., to be no better than poison, a mere imposture, a nothing; digg'd out of that broody hill, belike, this goodly golden stone is, where the ridiculous mouse was brought to birth. Paracelsus and his Chemistical followers, as so many Prometheuses, will fetch fire from Heaven, will cure all manner of diseases with minerals, accounting them the only Physick on the other side. Paracelsus calls Galen, Hippocrates, and all their adherents, infants, idiots, Sophisters, &c. Away (he says) with those who jeer at Vulcanian metamorphoses, ignorant sprouts, backward and stubborn nurslings, &c., not worthy the name of Physicians, for want of these remedies; and brags that by them he can make a man live 160 years, or to the world's end; with their Alexipharmacums [or Antidotes], Panaceas, Mummias [Powdered Mummy?], Weapon Salve, and such Magnetical cures, Lamps of Life and Death, Balsams, Baths of Diana, Magico-Physical Electrum [or Amber], Martian Amulets, &c. What will not he and his followers effect? He brags moreover that he was the First of Physicians, and did more famous cures than all the Physicians in Europe besides; a drop of his preparations should go further than a dram or ounce of theirs, those loathsome and fulsome filthy potions, heteroclitical pills (so he calls them), horse medicines, at the sight of which the Cyclops Polyphemus would shudder. And, though some condemn their skill, and Magnetical cures, as tending to Magical superstition, witchery, charms, &c., yet they admire, stiffly vindicate nevertheless, and infinitely prefer them. But these are both in extremes, the middle sort approve of Min-

* Chaucer.

erals, though not in so high a degree. Lemnius commends Gold inwardly and outwardly used, as in Rings, excellent good in medicines, and such mixtures as are made for melancholy men, saith Wecker, to whom Renodeus subscribes, and many others. Matthiolus approves of Potable Gold, Mercury, with many such Chemical Confections, and goes so far in approbation of them, that he holds no man can be an excellent Physician that hath not some skill in Chemistical Distillations, and that chronick diseases can hardly be cured without mineral medicines. Look for Antimony among purgers.

SUBSECTION 5 — *Compound Alteratives; censure of Compounds, and mixt Physick*

PLINY bitterly taxeth all compound medicines: Men's knavery, imposture, and captious wits, have invented these shops, in which every man's life is set to sale: and by and by came in those compositions and inexplicable mixtures, far fetcht out of India and Arabia; a medicine for a botch must be had as far as the Red Sea, &c. And 'tis not without cause which he saith, for out of question they are much to blame in their compositions, whilst they make infinite variety of mixtures, as Fuchsius notes: They think they get themselves great credit, excel others, and to be more learned than the rest, because they make many variations; but he accounts them fools; and whilst they brag of their skill, and think to get themselves a name, they become ridiculous, bewray their ignorance and error. A few simples, well prepared and understood, are better than such an heap of nonsense, confused compounds, which are in Apothecaries' shops ordinarily sold; in which many vain, superfluous, corrupt, exolete things out of date, are to be had (saith Cornarius) a company of barbarous names given to Syrops, Julips, an unnecessary company of mixt medicines; a rude & undigested mass. Many times (as Agrippa taxeth) there is by this means more danger from the medicine than from the disease, when they put together they know not what, or leave it to an illiterate Apothecary to be made, they cause death and horror for health. Those old Physicians had no such mixtures; a simple potion of Hellebore in Hippocrates' time was the ordinary purge; and at this day, saith Mat. Riccius, in that flourishing Commonwealth of China, their Physicians give precepts quite opposite to ours, not unhappy in their Physick: they use altogether roots, herbs, and simples, in their medicines, and all their Physick in a manner is comprehended in an Herbal: no science, no school, no art, no degree; but, like a trade, every man in private is instructed of his Master. Cardan cracks that he can cure all diseases with water alone, as Hippocrates of old did most infirmities with one medicine. Let the best of our rational Physicians demonstrate and give a sufficient reason for those intricate mixtures, why just so many simples in Mithridate or Treacle,* why such and such quantity; may they not be reduced to half or a quarter? 'Tis vain to do with much, (as the saying is) what can be done with a little; 300 simples in a Julip, Potion, or a little Pill, to what end or purpose? I know not what Alkindus, Capivaccius, Montagna, and Simon Eitover, the best of them all and most rational have said in this kind; but neither he, they, nor any one of them, gives his reader, to my judgement, that satisfaction which he ought; why such, so many simples? Roger Bacon hath taxed many errors in his tract Concerning Measurements, explained some things, but not cleared. Mercurialis, in his book on the Composition of Medicine, gives instance in Hamech, and Philonium Romanum, which Hamech, an Arabian, and Philonius, a Roman, long since composed, but dully as the rest. If they be so exact, as by him it seems they were, and those mixtures so perfect, why doth Fernelius alter the one, and why is the other obsolete? Cardan taxeth Galen for presuming out of his ambition to correct Theriacum Andromachi [an Antidote for Poison], and we as justly may carp at all the rest. Galen's medicines are now exploded and rejected; what Nicholas Meripsa, Mesue, Celsus, Scribanius, Actuarius, &c., writ of old, are most part contemned. Mellichius, Cordus, Wecker, Quercetan, Renodeus, the Venetian, Florentine states, have their several receipts and magistrals [or Sovereign Recipes], they of Nuremberg have theirs, and Augustana Pharmacopœia, peculiar medicines to the meridian of the City: London hers, every City, Town, almost every private man, hath his own mixtures, compositions, receipts, magistrals, precepts, as if he scorned antiquity and all others, in respect of himself. But each man must correct and alter, to shew his skill, every opinionative fellow must maintain his own paradox, be it what it will; the Kings rage, the Greeks suffer: they dote, and in the mean time the poor patients pay for their new experiments, the Commonalty rue it.

* Mithridate or Treacle: the famous King Mithridates of Pontus, afraid of being poisoned, took small doses of poison every day to inure himself to their effects, and invented an antidote containing opium. This was elaborated into a prescription containing 55 ingredients by Damocrates, Nero's physician, and called Mithridatum Damocratis. It was again elaborated by Andromachus, another of Nero's physicians, the flesh of the poisonous snake Tyrus being added, and the number of ingredients increased; it was now called Theriaca Andromachi. The name Treacle, or Mithridate, was commonly applied to it; and because of its syrupy nature the word treacle has come down to us with its familiar meaning.

Thus others object, thus I may conceive out of the weakness of my apprehension; but, to say truth, there is no such fault, no such ambition, no novelty, or ostentation, as some suppose: but as one answers, this of compound medicines is a most noble and profitable invention, found out, and brought into Physick with great judgement, wisdom, counsel, and discretion. Mixt diseases must have mixt remedies, and such simples are commonly mixt, as have reference to the part affected, some to qualify, the rest to comfort, some one part, some another. Cardan and Brassavola both hold that no simple medicine is without hurt or offence; and, although Hippocrates, Erasistratus, Diocles, of old, in the infancy of this Art, were content with ordinary simples, yet now, saith Aëtius, necessity compelleth to seek for new remedies, and to make compounds of simples, as well to correct their harms if cold, dry, hot, thick, thin, insipid, noisome to smell, to make them savoury to the palate, pleasant to taste and take, and to preserve them for continuance by admixtion of sugar, honey, to make them last months and years for several uses. In such cases compound medicines may be approved, and Arnoldus in his 18th Aphorism doth allow of it. If simples cannot, necessity compels us to use compounds; so for receipts and magistrals, one day teacheth another, and they are as so many words or phrases, which come in and go out of fashion again, ebb and flow with the season, and, as wits vary, so they may be infinitely varied. Every man as he likes; so many men, so many minds; and yet all tending to good purpose, though not the same way. As arts and sciences, so Physick is still perfected amongst the rest. Time nourisheth knowledge, and experience teacheth us every day many things which our predecessors knew not of. Nature is not effete, as he saith, or so lavish, to bestow all her gifts upon an age, but hath reserved some for posterity, to shew her power, that she is still the same, and not old or consumed. Birds and beasts can cure themselves by nature, but men must use much labour and industry to find it out. But I digress.

Compound medicines are inwardly taken, or outwardly applied. Inwardly taken be either liquid or solid: liquid are fluid or consisting. Fluid, as Wines and Syrups. The wines ordinarily used to this disease are Wormwood-wine, Tamarisk, and Buglossatum, wine made of Borage and Bugloss; the composition of which is specified in Arnoldus Villanovanus, in his book On Wines, of Borage, Balm, Bugloss, Cinnamon, &c., and highly commended for its virtues. It drives away Leprosy, Scabs, clears the blood, recreates the spirits, exhilarates the mind, purgeth the brain of those anxious black melancholy fumes, and cleanseth the whole body of that black humour by urine. To which I add, saith Villanovanus, that " it will bring mad men, and such raging Bedlams as are tied in chains, to the use of their reason again; my conscience bears me witness, that I do not lie, I saw a grave matron helped by this means, she was so cholerick, and so furious sometimes, that she was almost mad, and beside herself, she said and did she knew not what, scolded, beat her maids, and was now ready to be bound, till she drank of this Borage wine, and by this excellent remedy was cured, which a poor foreigner, a silly beggar, taught her by chance, that came to crave an alms from door to door." — The juice of Borage, if it be clarified, and drunk in wine, will do as much, the roots sliced and steeped, &c., saith Ant. Mizaldus, who cites this story word for word out of Villanovanus, and so doth Magninus, a Physician of Milan, in his regimen of health. Such another excellent compound water I find in Rubeus, which he highly magnifies, out of Savanarola, for such as are solitary, dull, heavy or sad without a cause, or be troubled with trembling of heart. Other excellent compound waters for melancholy he cites in the same place, if their melancholy be not inflamed, or their temperature over hot. Euonymus hath a precious Aquavitae [or water of Life] to this purpose for such as are cold. But he and most commend Potable Gold, and every writer prescribes clarified whey, with Borage, Bugloss, Endive, Succory, &c., of Goat's milk especially, some indefinitely at all times, some thirty days together in the Spring, every morning fasting, a good draught. Syrups are very good, and often used to digest this humour in the heart, spleen, liver, &c., as Syrup of Borage, (there is a famous Syrup of Borage highly commended by Laurentius to this purpose in his Tract of Melancholy), of the Fruit of King Sabor, now obsolete, of Thyme and Epithyme, Hops, Scolopendria, Fumitory, Maidenhair, Bizantine, &c. These are most used for preparatives to other Physick, mixt with distilled waters of like nature, or in Julips otherwise.

Consisting are conserves or confections: conserves of Borage, Bugloss, Balm, Fumitory, Succory, Maidenhair, Violets, Roses, Wormwood, &c.; confections, Treacle, Mithridate, Eclegms, or Linctures, &c.; Solid, as Aromatical confections; hot, of Amber, Hot Pearls [concoctions of medicinal seeds], Flowers, Sweet Musk, the Electuary of Gems, the Gladdening Galen & Rhasis Electuary, Galingale, Cummin, Anise, Pepper, Ginger, Capers, Cinnamon; cold as Cold Pearls [certain medicinal seeds], Petals, Abbas Roses, Poppies, &c., as every Pharmacopœia will shew you, with tablets or losings [lozenges] that are made out of them; with Condites [or Preserves] and the like.*

Outwardly used as occasion serves, as Amulets, Oils hot and cold, as of Camomile, Stæchados, Violets, Roses, Almonds, Poppy, Nymphæa, Mandrake, &c., to be used after bathing, or to procure sleep.

Ointments composed of the said species, Oils and Wax, &c., as Poplar-Alabaster, some hot, some cold, to moisten, procure sleep, and correct other accidents.

Liniments are made of the same matter to the like purpose: emplasters of herbs, flowers, roots, &c., with oils and other liquors mixt and boiled together.

Cataplasms, salves, or poultices, made of green herbs, pounded, or sod in water till they be soft, which are applied to the Hypochondries [the Belly], and other parts, when the body is empty.

Cerotes [or plasters] are applied to several parts, and Frontals, to take away pain, grief, heat, procure sleep. Fomentations or sponges, wet in some decoctions, &c., epithemata, or those moist medicines, laid on linen, to bathe and cool several parts misaffected.

Sacculi, or little bags, of herbs, flowers, seeds, roots, and the like, applied to the head, heart, stomack, &c., odoraments, balls, perfumes, posies to smell to, all which have their several uses in melancholy, as shall be shewed, when I treat of the cure of the distinct species by themselves.

MEMBER 2

SUBSECTION 1 — *Purging Simples upward*

MELANAGOGA, or melancholy purging medicines, are either Simple or Compound, and that gently, or violently, purging upwards or downwards. These following purge upward. Asarum, or Asarabacca [Wildspikenard], which, as Mesue saith, is hot in the second degree, and dry in the third; it is commonly taken in wine, whey, or, as with us, the juice of two or three leaves, or more sometimes, pounded in posset-drink, qualified with a little Liquorice, or Aniseed, to avoid the fulsomeness of the taste, or as Fernelius' Mixture. Brassivola, On Cathartics, reckons it

---

* But since these were elaborate compounds, it is perhaps better to repeat, for the list of hot confections, their actual names: Diambra, Diamargaritum calidum, Dianthus, Diamoschum dulce, Electuarium de gemmis, lætificans Galen et Rhasis, Diagalinga, Diacimynum, Dianisum, Diatrion piperion, Diazinziber, Diacapers, Diacinnamonum; and for the cold: Diamargaritum frigidum, Diacorolli, Diarrhodon Abbatis, Diacodion.

up among those simples that only purge melancholy, and Ruellius confirms as much out of his experience, that it purgeth black choler, like Hellebore itself. Galen and Matthiolus ascribe other virtues to it, and will have it purge other humours as well as this.

Laurel, by Heurnius, is put amongst the strong purgers of melancholy; it is hot and dry in the fourth degree. Dioscorides adds other effects to it. Pliny sets down 15 berries in drink for a sufficient potion: it is commonly corrected with his opposites, cold and moist, as juice of Endive, Purslane, and is taken in a potion to seven grains and a half. But this, and Asarabacca, every Gentlewoman in the Country knows how to give, they are two common vomits.

Scilla, or Sea-Onion, is hot and dry in the third degree. Brassivola, out of Mesue, others, and his own experience, will have this simple to purge melancholy alone. It is an ordinary vomit, wine with squills, mixt with Rubel in a little white wine.

White Hellebore, which some call sneezing-powder, a strong purger upward, which many reject, as being too violent: Mesue and Averroes will not admit of it, by reason of danger of suffocation, great pain and trouble it puts the poor patient to, saith Dodonæus. Yet Galen and Dioscorides allow of it. It was indeed terrible in former times, as Pliny notes, but now familiar, insomuch that many took it in those days, that were students, to quicken their wits, which Persius objects to Accius the Poet, that he was drunk on Hellebore. It helps melancholy, the falling-sickness, madness, gout, &c., but not to be taken of old men, youths, such as are weaklings, nice, or effeminate, troubled with headache, high-coloured, or fear strangling, saith Dioscorides. Oribasius, an old Physician, hath written very copiously, and approves of it, in such affections, which can otherwise hardly be cured. Heurnius will not have it used but with great caution, by reason of its strength, and then when Antimony will do no good, which caused Hermophilus to compare it to a stout captain (as Codronchus observes) that will see all his soldiers go before him, and come, like the bragging soldier, last himself. When other helps fail in inveterate melancholy, in a desperate case, this vomit is to be taken. And yet for all this, if it be well prepared, it may be securely given at first. Matthiolus brags that he hath often, to the good of many, made use of it, and Heurnius, that he hath happily used it, prepared after his own prescript, and with good success. Christophorus à Vega is of the same opinion, that it may be lawfully given; and our Country Gentlewomen find it by their common practice that there is no such great danger in it. Dr. Turner, speaking of this plant in his Herbal, telleth us that in his time it was an ordinary receipt among good wives to give Hellebore in powder to two penny weight, and he is not much against it. But they do commonly exceed, for who so bold as blind Bayard? and prescribe it by pennyworths, and such irrational ways, as I have heard myself market folk ask for it in an Apothecary's shop: but with what success God knows; they smart often for their rash boldness and folly, break a vein, make their eyes ready to start out of their heads, or kill themselves. So that the fault is not in the Physick, but in the rude and undiscreet handling of it. He that will know therefore when to use, how to prepare it aright, and in what dose, let him read Heurnius, Brassivola, Godefridus Stegius, the Emperor Rodolphus' Physician, Matthiolus, and that excellent Commentary of Baptista Codronchus, which is worth them all, On White Hellebore, where he shall find great diversity of examples and receipts.

Antimony or Stibium, which our Chemists so much magnify, is either taken in substance, or infusion, &c., and frequently prescribed in this disease. It helps all infirmities, saith Matthiolus, which proceed from black choler, falling-sickness, and hypochondriacal passions; and for further proof of his assertion he gives several instances of such as have been freed with it: one of Andrew Gallus, a Physician of Trent, that, after many other essays, imputes the recovery of his health, next after God, to this remedy alone; another of George Handshius, that, in like sort, when other medicines failed, was by this restored to his former health, and which, of his knowledge, others have likewise tried, and by the help of this admirable medicine been recovered; a third of a Parish Priest at Prague in Bohemia, that was so far gone with melancholy, that he doted, and spake he knew not what, but after he had taken 12 grains of Stibium, (as I myself saw, and can witness [he saith] for I was called to see this miraculous accident), he was purged of a deal of black choler, like little gobbets of flesh, and all his excrements were as black blood (a Medicine fitter for a Horse than a Man): yet it did him so much good, that the next day he was perfectly cured. This very story of the Bohemian Priest Sckenkius relates word for word, with great approbation of it. Hercules de Saxoniâ calls it a profitable medicine, if it be taken after meat to 6 or 8 grains, of such as are apt to vomit. Rodericus à Fonseca, the Spaniard, and late Professor of Padua in Italy, extols it to this disease; so doth Lodovicus Mercatus, with many others. Jacobus Gervinus, a French Physician, on the other side, explodes all this, and saith he took three grains only, upon Matthiolus' and some others' commendation, but it almost killed him; whereupon he concludes, antimony is rather poison than a medicine. Th. Erastus concurs with him in his opinion, and so doth Ælian Montaltus. But what do I talk? 'tis the subject of whole books, I might cite a century of Authors pro and con. I will conclude with Zuinger, antimony is like Scanderbeg's sword, which is either good or bad, strong or weak, as the party is that prescribes or useth it; a worthy medicine, if it be rightly applied to a strong man, otherwise poison. For the preparing of it look in the Treasury of Euonymus, Quercetan, Oswaldus Crollius, Basilius Valentinus, &c.

Tobacco, divine, rare, superexcellent Tobacco, which goes far beyond all their panaceas, potable gold, and philosopher's stones, a sovereign remedy to all diseases. A good vomit, I confess, a virtuous herb, if it be well qualified, opportunely taken, and medicinally used, but, as it is commonly abused by most men, which take it as Tinkers do Ale, 'tis a plague, a mischief, a violent purger of goods, land, health, hellish, devilish, and damned Tobacco, the ruin and overthrow of body and soul.

SUBSECTION 2 — *Simples Purging Melancholy downward*

POLYPODY [Ferns], and Epithyme are, without all exceptions, gentle purgers of melancholy. Dioscorides will have them void flegm; but Brassivola, out of his experience, averreth that they purge this humour; they are used in decoction, infusion, &c., simple, mixt, &c.

Mirabolanes, all five kinds, are happily prescribed against melancholy and quartan agues, Brassivola speaks out of a thousand experiences; he gave them in pills, decoction, &c. Look for peculiar receipts in him.

Stœchas, Fumitory, Dodder, herb Mercury, roots of Capers, Genista or broom, Pennyroyal, and half-boiled Cabbage, I find in this Catalogue of purgers of black choler, Origan, Fetherfew, Ammoniack Salt, Saltpetre. But these are very gentle, Alypus, Dragon root, Centaury, Ditany, Colutea, which Fuchsius and others take for Senna, but most distinguish. Senna is in the middle of violent and gentle purgers downward, hot in the second degree, dry in the first. Brassivola calls it a wonderful herb against melancholy, it scours the blood, illightens the spirits, shakes off sorrow; a most profitable medicine, as Dodonæus terms it, invented by the Arabians, and not heard of before. It is taken divers ways, in powder, infusion, but most commonly in the infusion, with Ginger, or some cordial flowers added to correct it. Actuarius commends it sod in broth, with an old Cock, or in whey, which is the common conveyor of all such things as purge black choler; or steeped in wine, which Heurnius accounts sufficient, without any further correction.

Aloes by most is said to purge choler, but Aurelianus, Arculanus,

Julius Alexandrinus, Crato, prescribe it to this disease, as good for the stomack, and to open the Hæmrods, out of Mesue, Rhasis, Serapio, Avicenna. Menardus opposeth it; Aloes doth not open the veins, or move the Hæmrods, which Leonhartus Fuchsius likewise affirms; but Brassivola and Dodonæus defend Mesue out of their experience; let Valesius end the controversy.

Armenian Stone and Lapis Lazuli are much magnified by Alexander, Avicenna, Aëtius, and Actuarius, if they be well washed, that the water be no more coloured, fifty times, some say. That good Alexander (saith Guianerius) puts such confidence in this one medicine, that he thought all melancholy passions might be cured by it; and I, for my part, have oftentimes happily used it, and was never deceived in the operation of it [saith he].

The like may be said of Lapis Lazuli, though it be somewhat weaker than the other. Garcias ab Horto relates that the Physicians of the Moors familiarly prescribe it to all melancholy passions, and Matthiolus brags of that happy success which he still had in the administration of it. Nicholas Meripsa puts it amongst the best remedies; and if this will not serve (saith Rhasis) then there remains nothing but Armenian Stone and Hellebore itself. Valescus and Jason Pratensis much commend Hali's Powder,* which is made of it. James Damascen., Hercules de Saxoniâ, &c., speak well of it. Crato will not approve this; it and both Hellebores, he saith, are no better than poison. Victor Trincavellius found it, in his experience, to be very noisome, to trouble the stomack, and hurt their bodies that take it overmuch.

Black Hellebore, that most renowned plant, and famous purger of melancholy, which all antiquity so much used and admired, was first found out by Melampus, a Shepherd, (as Pliny records), who, seeing it to purge his Goats when they raved, practised it upon Elige and Calene, King Prœtus' daughters, that ruled in Arcadia, near the fountain Clitorius, and restored them to their former health. In Hippocrates' time it was in only request, insomuch that he writ a book of it, a fragment of which remains yet. Theophrastus, Galen, Pliny, Cælius Aurelianus, as ancient as Galen, Aretæus, Oribasius, a famous Greek, Aëtius, P. Ægineta, Galen's Ape, Actuarius, Trallianus, Cornelius Celsus, only remaining of the old Latins, extol and admire this excellent plant, and it was generally so much esteemed of the ancients for this disease amongst the rest, that they sent all such as were crazed, or that doted, to the Anticyrians, or to Phocis in Achaia, to be purged, where this plant was in abundance

* Pulvus Hali.

to be had. In Strabo's time it was an ordinary voyage; Sail to Anticyra, a common proverb among the Greeks and Latins to bid a dizzard oi a mad man go take Hellebore; as in Lucian, Menippus to Tantalus: " thou art out of thy little wit, O Tantalus, and must needs drink Hellebore, and that without mixture "; Aristophanes in Vespis, " Drink Hellebore," &c., and Harpax, in the Comedian, told Simo and Ballio, two doting fellows, that they had need to be purged with this plant. When that proud Menecrates had writ an arrogant letter to Philip of Macedon, he sent back no other answer but this, I advise you to take yourself off to Anticyra, noting thereby that he was crazed, and had much need of a good purge. Lilius Geraldus saith that Hercules, after all his mad pranks upon his wife and children, was perfectly cured by a purge of Hellebore, which an Anticyrian administered unto him. They that were sound commonly took it to quicken their wits (as Ennius of old, who never sallied forth to write of arms, but when well whittled himself, and as our Poets drink Sack to improve their inventions). I find it so registered by A. Gellius. Carneades, the Academick, when he was to write against Zeno the Stoick, purged himself with Hellebore first, which Petronius puts upon Chrysippus. In such esteem it continued for many ages, till at length Mesue and some other Arabians began to reject and reprehend it, upon whose authority for many following lustres it was much debased and quite out of request, held to be poison, and no medicine; and is still oppugned to this day by Crato and some Junior Physicians. Their reasons are because Aristotle said Henbane and Hellebore were poison; and Alexander Aphrodisiæus, in the Preface of his Problems, gave out that (speaking of Hellebore) quails fed on that which was poison to men. Galen confirms as much: Constantine the Emperor, in his Geoponicks, attributes no other virtue to it than to kill mice and rats, flies and mouldwarps, and so Mizaldus. Nicander of old, Gervinus, Sckenkius, and some other Neotericks that have written of poisons, speak of Hellebore in a chief place. Nicholas Leonicus hath a story of Solon, that, besieging I know not what City, steeped Hellebore in a spring of water, which by pipes was conveyed into the middle of the Town, and so either poisoned, or else made them so feeble and weak by purging, that they were not able to bear arms. Notwithstanding all these cavils and objections, most of our late writers do much approve of it. Gariopontus, Codronchus, & others, so that it be opportunely given. Jacobus de Dondis and all our Herbalists subscribe. Fernelius confesseth it to be a terrible purge, and hard to take, yet well given to strong men, and such as have able bodies. P. Forestus and Capivaccius forbid it to be taken in substance, but allow it in decoction or infusion, both which ways P. Monavius approves above all others; Jacchinus commends a receipt of his own preparing; Penottus another of his chemically prepared, Euonymus another. Hildesheim hath many examples how it should be used, with diversity of receipts. Heurnius calls it an innocent medicine howsoever, if it be well prepared. The root of it is only in use, which may be kept many years, and by some given in substance, as by Fallopius, and Brassavola amongst the rest, who brags that he was the first that restored it again to his use, and tells a story how he cured one Melatasta a mad man, that was thought to be possessed, in the Duke of Ferrara's Court, with one purge of black Hellebore in substance: the receipt is there to be seen; his excrements were like ink, he perfectly healed at once; Vidus Vidius, a Dutch Physician, will not admit of it in substance, to whom most subscribe, but, as before in the decoction, infusion, or which is all in all, in the extract, which he prefers before the rest, and calls a sweet medicine, an easy, that may be securely given to women, children, and weaklings. Baracellus terms it a medicine of great worth and note. Quercetan (and many others) tells wonders of the extract. Paracelsus above all the rest is the greatest admirer of this plant, and especially the extract; he calls it another Treacle, a terrestrial Balm, all in all, the sole and last refuge to cure this malady, the Gout, Epilepsy, Leprosy, &c. If this will not help, no Physick in the world can but mineral, it is the upshot of all. Matthiolus laughs at those that except against it, and though some abhor it out of the authority of Mesue, and dare not adventure to prescribe it, yet I (saith he) have happily used it six hundred times without offence, and communicated it to divers worthy Physicians, who have given me great thanks for it. Look for receipts, dose, preparation, and other cautions concerning this simple in him, Brassivola, Baracellus, Codronchus, and the rest.

SUBSECTION 3 — *Compound Purgers*

COMPOUND medicines which purge melancholy are either taken in the superior or inferior parts: superior at mouth or nostrils. At the mouth swallowed or not swallowed: if swallowed, liquid or solid: liquid, as compound wine of Hellebore, Scilla, or Sea-Onion, Senna, Wine with Squills, Helleboratum [a mixture containing chiefly Hellebore], which Quercetan so much applauds for melancholy and madness, either inwardly taken, or outwardly applied to the head, with little pieces of linen dipped warm in it. Oxymel Scillicum [a mixture of vinegar, honey,

&c., with squills], Syrupus Helleboratus major and minor in Quercetan, and Syrupus Genistae [Syrup of Broom] for Hypochondriacal Melancholy in the same Author, compound Syrup of Succory [or Chicory], of Fumitory, Polypody, &c., [and] Heurnius his purging Cock-broth. Some except against these Syrups, as appears by Udalrinus Leonorus his Epistle to Matthiolus, as most pernicious, and that out of Hippocrates, no raw things to be used in Physick; but this in the following Epistle is exploded, and soundly confuted by Matthiolus; many julips, potions, receipts, are composed of these, as you shall find in Hildesheim, Huernius, George Sckenkius, &c.

Solid purgers are confections, electuaries, pills by themselves, or compound with others, as of Lapis Lazuli, Red Armenian Earth, Indian Pills, of Fumitory, &c., confection of Hamech, which though most approve, Solenander bitterly inveighs against, so doth Rondoletius, Fernelius and others; confections of Senna, Polypody, Cassia, the Diacatholicon [purging all humours], Wecker's Electuary of Epithyme, Ptolemy's Hierologodium, of which divers receipts are daily made.

Aëtius commends Ruffus' Medicine [Rufus' Pills, of aloes and myrrh]. Trincavellius approves of Hiera; I find no better medicine, he saith. Heurnius adds pills of Epithyme, Indian pills. Mesue describes in the Florentine Antidotary, pills one would not wish to be without. Cochia with Hellebore, Arabian Pills, Fœtida [or Assafœtida], of five kinds of Myrobalans [or Indian Plums], &c. More proper to melancholy, not excluding, in the mean time, Turbith, Manna, Rhubarb, Agarick, Elescophe, &c. which are not so proper to this humour. For, as Montaltus holds, and Montanus, choler is to be purged, because it feeds the other: and some are of an opinion, as Erasistratus and Asclepiades maintained of old, against whom Galen disputes, that no Physick doth purge one humour alone, but all alike, or what is next. Most therefore in their receipts and magistrals which are coined here, make a mixture of several simples and compounds to purge all humours in general as well as this. Some rather use potions than pills to purge this humour because that, as Heurnius and Crato observe, this juice is not so easily drawn by dry remedies; and, as Montanus adviseth, all drying medicines are to be repelled, as Aloe, Hiera, and all pills whatsoever, because the disease is dry of itself.

I might here insert many receipts of prescribed potions, boles, &c. the doses of these, but that they are common in every good Physician, and that I am loth to incur the censure of Forestus, against those that divulge and publish medicines in their mother tongue, and lest I should give occasion thereby to some ignorant Reader to practise on himself, without the consent of a good Physician.

Such as are not swallowed, but only kept in the mouth, are Gargarisms [or Gargles], used commonly after a purge, when the body is soluble and loose. Or Apophlegmatisms, Masticatories, to be held and chewed in the mouth, which are gentle, as Hyssop, Origan, Pennyroyal, Thyme, Mustard; strong, as Pellitory, Pepper, Ginger, &c.

Such as are taken into the nostrils, Errhina [or Nose Medicines] are liquid, or dry, juice of Pimpernel, Onions, &c., Castor, Pepper, white Hellebore, &c. To these you may add odoraments, perfumes, and suffumigations, &c.

Taken into the inferior parts are Clysters strong or weak, Suppositories of Castilian soap, honey boiled to a consistence; or stronger of Scammony, Hellebore, &c.

These are all used, and prescribed to this malady upon several occasions, as shall be shewed in his place.

MEMBER 3

Chirurgical Remedies

IN letting of blood, three main circumstances are to be considered, *who, how much, when?* That is, that it be done to such a one as may endure it, or to whom it may belong, that he be of a competent age, not too young, nor too old, overweak, fat, or lean, sore laboured, but to such as have need, and are full of bad blood, noxious humours, and may be eased by it.

The quantity depends upon the party's habit of body, as he is strong or weak, full or empty, may spare more or less.

In the morning is the fittest time: some doubt whether it be best fasting, or full, whether the Moon's motion or aspect of Planets be to be observed, some affirm, some deny, some grant in acute, but not in chronick diseases, whether before or after Physic. 'Tis Heurnius' Aphorism, you must begin with blood-letting and not Physick; some except this peculiar malady. But what do I? Horatius Augenius, a Physician of Padua, hath lately writ 17 books of this subject, Jobertus, &c.

Particular kinds of blood-letting in use are three, first is that opening a Vein in the arm with a sharp knife, or in the head, knees, or any other part, as shall be thought fit.

Cupping-glasses, with or without scarification, saith Fernelius, they work presently, and are applied to several parts, to divert humours, aches, wind, &c.

Horse-leeches are much used in melancholy, applied especially to the Hæmrods. Horatius Augenius, Platerus, Altomarus, Piso, and many others, prefer them before any evacuations in this kind.

Cauteries or searing with hot irons, combustions, borings, lancings, which, because they are terrible, Dropax and Sinapismus are invented, by plasters to raise blisters, and eating medicines of pitch, mustard-seed, and the like.

Issues still to be kept open, made as the former, and applied in and to several parts, have their use here on divers occasions, as shall be shewed.

SECTION 5 MEMBER 1

SUBSECTION 1 — *Particular Cure of the three several kinds of Head-Melancholy*

THE general cures thus briefly examined and discussed, it remains now to apply these medicines to the three particular species or kinds, that, according to the several parts affected, each man may tell in some sort how to help or ease himself. I will treat of head-melancholy first, in which, as in all other good cures, we must begin with Diet, as a matter of most moment, able oftentimes of itself to work this effect. I have read, saith Laurentius, that in old diseases which have gotten the upper hand or an habit, the manner of living is to more purpose than whatsoever can be drawn out of the most precious boxes of the Apothecaries. This diet, as I have said, is not only in choice of meat and drink, but of all those other non-natural things. Let air be clear and moist most part: diet moistening, of good juice, easy of digestion, and not windy: drink clear, and well brewed, not too strong, nor too small. Make a melancholy man fat, as Rhasis saith, and thou hast finished the cure. Exercise not too remiss, nor too violent. Sleep a little more than ordinary. Excrements daily to be voided by art or nature; and, which Fernelius enjoins his Patient, above the rest, to avoid all passions and perturbations of the mind. Let him not be alone or idle (in any kind of melancholy); but still accompanied with such friends and familiars he most affects, neatly dressed, washed and combed, according to his ability at least, in clean sweet linen, spruce, handsome, decent, and good apparel; for nothing sooner dejects a man than want, squalor, nastiness, foul or old cloaths out of fashion. Concerning the medicinal part, he that will satisfy himself at large (in this precedent of diet) and see all at once the whole cure and manner of it in every distinct species, let him consult with Gordonius, Valescus, with Prosper Calenus, Laurentius, Ælian Montaltus, Donatus ab Altomari, Hercules de Saxoniâ, Savanarola, Sckenkius, Heurnius, Victorius Faventinus, Hildesheim, Felix Plater, Stockerus, Bruel, Petrus Bayerus, Forestus, Fuchsius, Cappivaccius, Rondoletius, Jason Pratensis, Sallustius Salvianus, Jacchinus, Lodovicus Mercatus, Alexander Messaria, Piso, Hollerius, &c., that have culled out of those old Greeks, Arabians, and Latins, whatsoever is observeable or fit to be used. Or let him read those counsels and consultations of Hugo Senensis, Renerus Solinander, Crato, Montanus, Lælius â Fonte Eugubinus, Fernelius, Julius Cæsar Claudinus, Mercurialis, Frambesarius, Sennertus, &c., wherein he shall find particular receipts, the whole method, preparatives, purgers, correctors, averters, cordials, in great variety and abundance: out of which, because every man cannot attend to read or peruse them, I will collect, for the benefit of the Reader, some few more notable medicines.

Subsection 2 — *Blood-letting*

Phlebotomy is promiscuously used before and after Physick, commonly before, and upon occasion is often reiterated, if there be any need at least of it. For Galen, and many others, make a doubt of bleeding at all in this kind of head-melancholy. If the malady, saith Piso, likewise Altomarus, Fuchsius, shall proceed primarily from the misaffected brain, the Patient in such case shall not need at all to bleed, except the blood otherwise abound, the veins be full, inflamed blood, and the party ready to run mad. In immaterial melancholy, which especially comes from a cold distemperature of spirits, Hercules de Saxoniâ will not admit of Phlebotomy; Laurentius approves it out of the authority of the Arabians; but as Mesue, Rhasis, Alexander appoint, especially in the head, to open the veins of the fore-head, nose, and ears, is good. They commonly set cupping-glasses on the party's shoulders, having first scarified the place; they apply horse-leeches on the head, and in all melancholy diseases, whether essential or accidental, they cause the Hæmrods to be opened, having the eleventh Aphorism of the 6th book of Hippocrates for their ground and warrant, which saith that in melancholy and mad men the varicous tumour or hœmorrhoides appearing doth heal the same. Valescus prescribes blood-letting in all three kinds, whom Sallustius Salvianus follows. If the blood abound, which is discerned by the fulness of the veins, his precedent diet, the party's laughter, age, &c., begin with the median or middle vein of the arm: if the blood be ruddy and clear, stop it; but if black in the spring time, or a good season, or thick, let it run, according to the party's strength: and some eight or twelve days after, open the head vein, and the veins in the forehead, or provoke it out of the nostrils, or cupping-glasses, &c. Trallianus allows of this, if there have been any suppression or stopping of blood at nose, or hemrods, or women's months, then to open a vein in the head or about the ankles. Yet he doth hardly approve of this course, if melancholy be sited in the head alone, or in any other dotage, except it primarily proceed from blood, or that the malady be increased by it; for blood-letting refrigerates and dries up, except the body be very full of blood, and a kind of ruddiness in the face. Therefore I conclude with Aretæus, before you let blood, deliberate of it, and well consider all circumstances belonging to it.

SUBSECTION 3 — *Preparatives and Purgers*

AFTER blood-letting we must proceed to other medicines; first prepare, and then purge, cleanse the Augean stables, make the body clean, before we hope to do any good. Gualter Bruel would have a practitioner begin first with a clyster of his, which he prescribes before blood-letting: the common sort, as Mercurialis, Montaltus, &c., proceed from lenitives to preparatives, and so to purgers. Lenitives are well known, the Lenitive Electuary, the Diaphænicum, the Diacatholicon, &c. Preparatives are usually Syrups of Borage, Bugloss, Apples, Fumitory, Thyme and Epithyme, with double as much of the same decoction or distilled water, or of the waters of Bugloss, Balm, Hops, Endive, Scolopendry, Fumitory, &c., or these sod in whey, which must be reiterated and used for many days together. Purges come last, which must not be used at all, if the malady may be otherwise helped, because they weaken nature, and dry so much; and in giving of them we must begin with the gentlest first. Some forbid all hot medicines, as Alexander, and Salvianus, &c.; hot medicines increase the disease by drying too much. Purge downward rather than upward, use potions rather than pills, and, when you begin Physick, persevere and continue in a course; for, as one observes, to stir up the humour (as one purge commonly doth) and not to prosecute doth more harm than good. They must continue in a course of Physick, yet not so that they tire and oppress nature, they must now and then remit, and let nature have some rest. The most gentle purges to begin with, are Senna, Cassia, Epithyme, Myrobalans, the Catholicon: if these prevail not, we may proceed to stronger, as the confection of Hamech, Indian Pills, Fumitories, of Assaieret, of Armenian Stone, and Lazuli, Senna Medicine. Or, if pills be too dry, some prescribe both Hellebores in the last place, amongst the rest Aretæus, because this disease will resist a gentle medicine. Laurentius and Hercules de Saxoniâ would have Antimony tried last, if the party be strong, and it warily given. Trincavellius prefers Hierologodium, to whom Francis Alexander subscribes, a very good medicine they account it. But Crato, in a counsel of his for the Duke of Bavaria's Chancellor, wholly rejects it.

I find a vast Chaos of medicines, a confusion of receipts and magistrals [or Sovereign Recipes], amongst writers, appropriated to this disease; some of the chiefest I will rehearse. To be sea-sick, first, is very good at seasonable times. The Helleborism of Matthiolus, with which he vaunts and boasts he did so many several cures: I never gave it (saith he) but, after once or twice, by the help of God they were happily cured. The manner of making it he sets down at large in his third book of Epistles to George Hankshius, a Physician. Gualter Bruel and Heurnius make mention of it with great approbation; so doth Sckenkius in his memorable cures, and experimental medicines. That famous Helleborism of Montanus which he so often repeats in his consultations and counsels, and cracks to be a most sovereign remedy for all melancholy persons, which he hath often given without offence, and found by long experience and observation to be such.

Quercetan prefers a Syrup of Hellebore in his Chemical Pharmacopœia, and Hellebore's Extract, of his invention likewise (a most safe medicine, and not unfit to be given children) before all remedies whatsoever.

Paracelsus, in his book of black Hellebore, admits this medicine, but as it is prepared by him. It is most certain (saith he) that the virtue of this herb is great, and admirable in effect, and little differing from Balm itself, and he that knows well how to make use hath more art than all their books contain, or all the doctors in Germany can show.

Ælianus Montaltus in his exquisite work on Diseases of the Head, sets a special receipt of his own, which in his practice he fortunately used; because it is but short I will set it down.

Take syrup of apples, 2 ounces; borage water, 4 ounces; black hellebore, steeped all night in a binding,* 6 or 8 grains; to be compounded by hand.

Other receipts of the same to this purpose you shall find in him. Valescus admires Hali's Powder, and Jason Pratensis after him: the confection of which our new London Pharmacopœia hath lately revived. Put case (saith he) all other medicines fail, by the help of God this alone shall do it, and 'tis a crowned medicine which must be kept in secret.

Take epithyme, one-half ounce; lapis lazuli and agarick, each 2 ounces; scammony, one drachm; cloves, 20; pulverize all, and of the powder make separate portions of 4 scruples each.†

To these I may add Arnold's Borage wine before mentioned, which Mizaldus calls a wonderful wine, and Stockerus vouchsafes to repeat word for word amongst other receipts. Rubeus his compound water out of Savanarola; Pinetus his balm; Cardan's Jacinth Powder, with which, in his book On Wonderful Cures, he boasts that he had cured many melancholy persons in eight days, which Sckenkius puts amongst his observeable medicines; Altomarus his syrup, with which he calls God so solemnly to witness, he hath in his kind done many excellent cures, and which Sckenkius mentioneth, Daniel Sennertus so much commends; Rulandus' admirable water for melancholy, which he names Golden Spirit of Life, Panacea, what not, and his absolute medicine of 50 Eggs, to be taken three in a morning, with a powder of his. Faventinus doubles this number of Eggs, and will have a hundred and one to be taken by three and three in like sort, which Sallustius Salvianus approves, with some of the same powder, till ail be spent, a most excellent remedy for all melancholy and madmen.

Take epithyme, thyme, each, 2 drachms; white sugar, 1 ounce; saffron, 3 grains; cinnamon, 1 drachm; mix, and make powder.‡

---

* The recipe says " *Ellebori nigri per noctem infusi in ligatura.*" This appears to mean that the herbs were tied together in a cloth bag & infused (dipped in hot water). Perhaps it should be emphasised that the chief ingredient of this recipe is a drastic hydragogic cathartic, producing in overdoses gastric and intestinal inflammation, violent vomiting, vertigo, cramp, convulsions, and sometimes death. It is nowadays employed in veterinary surgery — as Burton elsewhere quotes Paracelsus, a medicine " fitter for a horse than a man."

† Scammony is now used to cure worms in children; in large doses it is a violent gastro-intestinal irritant.

‡ Epithyme is the flower of thyme. The chief ingredient in this recipe is saffron, made from the autumnal crocus, about four thousand flowers being required to make an ounce; it was once highly valued as a medicine, so much so that pharmacists were

All these yet are nothing to those Chemical preparatives of Cheledony Water, quintessence of Hellebore, salts, extracts, distillations, oils, Potable Gold, &c. Dr. Anthony, in his book On Potable Gold, 1600, is all in all for it: And though all the schools of Galenists, with a wicked and unthankful pride and scorn, detest it in their practice, yet in more grievous diseases, when their vegetals will do no good, they are compelled to seek the help of minerals, though they use them rashly, unprofitably, slackly, and [saith he] to no purpose. Rhenanus, a Dutch Chemist, takes upon him to apologize for Anthony, and sets light by all that speak against him. But what do I meddle with this great Controversy, which is the subject of many volumes? Let Paracelsus, Quercetan, Crollius, and the brethren of the Rosy Cross defend themselves as they may. Crato, Erastus, and the Galenists oppugn Paracelsus. He brags on the other side he did more famous cures by this means than all the Galenists in Europe, and calls himself a Monarch, Galen, Hippocrates, infants, illiterate, &c. As Thessalus of old railed against those ancient Asclepiadean writers, he condemns others, insults, triumphs, overcomes all antiquity (saith Galen, as if he spake to him) declares himself a conqueror, and crowns his own doings. One drop of their Chemical preparatives shall do more good than all their fulsome potions. Erastus and the rest of the Galenists vilify them, on the other side, as Hereticks in Physick; Paracelsus did that in Physick which Luther in Divinity. A drunken rogue he was, a base fellow, a Magician, he had the Devil for his master, Devils his familiar companions, and what he did was done by the help of the Devil. Thus they contend and rail, and every Mart write books pro and con, and the matter is not settled yet; let them agree as they will, I proceed.

SUBSECTION 4 — *Averters*

AVERTERS and Purgers must go together, as tending all to the same purpose, to divert this rebellious humour, and turn it another way. In this range Clysters and Suppositories challenge a chief place, to draw this humour from the brain and heart to the more ignoble parts. Some would have them still used a few days between, and those to be made with the boiled seeds of Anise, Fennel, and bastard Saffron, Hops, Thyme, Epithyme, Mallows, Fumitory, Bugloss, Polypody, Senna,

---

burned, and others buried alive, in Nuremberg, in the fifteenth century, for adulterating it. But its value (it was supposed to be stimulant, antispasmodic, or narcotic) was traditional and largely fictitious, as modern experiments have shown that it possesses little activity. It was also used as a golden dye-stuff.

Diasene, Hamech, Cassia, Diacatholicon, Hierologodium, Oil of Violets, sweet Almonds, &c. For without question a Clyster, opportunely used, cannot choose in this, as most other maladies, but to do very much good; sometimes Clysters nourish, as they may be prepared, as I was informed not long since by a learned Lecture of our Natural Philosophy Reader, which he handled by way of discourse, out of some other noted Physicians. Such things as provoke urine most commend, but not sweat. Trincavellius in head melancholy forbids it. P. Bayerus and others approve frictions of the outward parts, and to bathe them with warm water. Instead of ordinary frictions, Cardan prescribes rubbing with Nettles till they blister the skin, which likewise Basardus Visontinus so much magnifies.

Sneezing, masticatories, and nasals, are generally received. Montaltus, Hildesheim, give several receipts of all three. Hercules de Saxoniâ relates of an Empirick in Venice, that he had a strong water to purge by the mouth and nostrils, which he still used in head-melancholy, and would sell for no gold.

To open months and Hemroids is very good Physick, if they have been formerly stopped. Faventinus would have them opened with horse-leeches, so would Hercules de Saxoniâ. Julius Alexandrinus thinks Aloes fitter: most approve horse-leeches in this case, to be applied to the fore-head, nostrils, and other places.

Montaltus, out of Alexander and others, prescribes cupping-glasses, and issues in the left thigh. Aretæus, Paulus Regolinus, Sylvius, will have them without scarification, applied to the shoulders and back, thighs and feet. Montaltus bids open an issue in the arms, or hinder part of the head. Piso enjoins ligatures, frictions, suppositories, and cupping-glasses, still without scarification, and the rest.

Cauteries and hot irons are to be used in the suture of the crown, and the seared or ulcerated place suffered to run a good while. 'Tis not amiss to bore the skull with an instrument, to let out the fuliginous vapours. Sallustus Salvianus, because this humour hardly yields to other Physick, would have the leg cauterized, or the left leg below the knee, and the head bored in two or three places, for that it much avails to the exhalation of the vapours. I saw (saith he) a melancholy man at Rome, that by no remedies could be healed, but when by chance he was wounded in the head, and the skull broken, he was excellently cured. Another, to the admiration of the beholders, breaking his head with a fall from on high, was instantly recovered of his dotage. Gordonius, would have these cauteries tried last, when no other Physick will serve:

The head to be shaved and bored to let out fumes, which without doubt will do much good; " I saw a melancholy man wounded in the head with a sword, his brain-pan broken; so long as the wound was open, he was well, but when his wound was healed, his dotage returned again." But Alexander Messaria, a Professor in Padua, will allow no cauteries at all; 'tis too stiff an humour, and too thick, as he holds, to be so evaporated.

Guianerius cured a Nobleman in Savoy, by boring alone, leaving the hole open a month together, by means of which, after two years' melancholy and madness, he was delivered. All approve of this remedy in the suture of the Crown; but Arculanus would have the cautery to be made with gold. In many other parts these cauteries are prescribed for melancholy men, as in the thighs, (Mercurialis), arms, legs; Montanus, Rodericus à Fonseca, &c. but most in the head, if other Physick will do no good.

SUBSECTION 5 — *Alteratives and Cordials, corroborating, resolving the Reliques, and mending the Temperament*

BECAUSE this Humour is so malign of itself, and so hard to be removed, the reliques are to be cleansed, by Alteratives, Cordials, and such means; the temper is to be altered and amended, with such things as fortify and strengthen the heart and brain, which are commonly both affected in this malady, and do mutually misaffect one another: which are still to be given every other day, or some few days inserted after a purge or like Physick, as occasion serves, and are of such force that many times they help alone, and as Arnoldus holds in his Aphorisms, are to be preferred before all other medicines, in what kind soever.

Amongst this number of Cordials and Alteratives I do not find a more present remedy than a cup of wine or strong drink, if it be soberly and opportunely used. It makes a man bold, hardy, courageous, whetteth the wit, if moderately taken, (and, as Plutarch saith,) it makes those, which are otherwise dull, to exhale and evaporate like frankincense, or quicken (Xenophon adds) as oil doth fire. A famous cordial Matthiolus calls it, an excellent nutriment to refresh the body, it makes a good colour, a flourishing age, helps concoction, fortifies the stomack, takes away obstructions, provokes urine, drives out excrements, procures sleep, clears the blood, expels wind and cold poisons, attenuates, concocts, dissipates, all thick vapours, and fuliginous humours. And that which is all in all to my purpose, it takes away fear and sorrow.

Bacchus drives away fierce cares.   (HORACE)

It glads the heart of man; the sweet school of mirth. Helen's bowl, the sole Nectar of the Gods, or that true Nepenthes in Homer, which puts away care and grief, as Oribasius and some others will, was naught else but a cup of good wine. *It makes the mind of the King and of the fatherless both one, of the bond and free-man, poor and rich; it turneth all his thoughts to joy and mirth, makes him remember no sorrow or debt, but enricheth his heart, and makes him speak by talents.* It gives life itself, spirits, wit, &c. For which cause the Antients called Bacchus, Liber Pater, Releaser, and sacrificed to Bacchus and Pallas still upon an Altar. *Wine measurably drunk, and in time, brings gladness and cheerfulness of mind, it cheereth God and men:* Bacchus, giver of joy, &c.; it makes an old wife dance, and such as are in misery to forget evil, and be merry.

> *Wine makes a troubled soul to rest,*
> *Though feet with fetters be opprest.* (TIBULLUS)

Demetrius in Plutarch, when he fell into Seleucus' hands, and was prisoner in Syria, spent his time with dice and drink, that he might so ease his discontented mind, and avoid those continual cogitations of his present condition wherewith he was tormented. Therefore Solomon *bids wine be given to him that is ready to perish, and to him that hath grief of heart; let him drink that he forget his poverty, and remember his misery no more.* It easeth a burdened soul, nothing speedier, nothing better: which the Prophet Zachary perceived, when he said, *that in the time of Messias they of Ephraim should be glad, and their heart should rejoice as through wine.* All which makes me very well approve of that pretty description of a feast in Bartholomæus Anglicus, when grace was said, their hands washed, and the Guests sufficiently exhilarated, with good discourse, sweet musick, dainty fare, as a Corollary to conclude the feast, and continue their mirth, a grace cup came in to cheer their hearts, and they drank healths to one another again and again. Which (as J. Fredericus Matenesius) was an old custom in all ages in every Commonwealth, so as they be not enforced to drink by coercion, but as in that Royal Feast of Assuerus which lasted 180 days, *without compulsion they drank by order in golden vessels,* when and what they would themselves. This of drink is a most easy and parable remedy, a common, a cheap, still ready against fear, sorrow, and such troublesome thoughts, that molest the mind; as brimstone with fire, the spirits on a sudden are enlightened by it. No better Physick (saith Rhasis) for a melancholy man: and he that can keep company, and carouse, needs no other medicines, 'tis enough. His Country-man, Avicenna, proceeds further yet, and will have him that is troubled in mind, or melancholy, not to drink only, but now and then to be drunk: excellent good Physick it is for this and many other diseases. Magninus will have them to be so once a month at least, and gives his reasons for it, because it scours the body by vomit, urine, sweat, of all manner of superfluities, and keeps it clean. Of the same mind is Seneca the Philosopher in his book On Tranquillity, it is good sometimes to be drunk, it helps sorrow, depresseth cares, and so concludes his Tract with a cup of wine: Take, dearest Serenus, what conduces to tranquillity of mind. But these are Epicureal tenents, tending to looseness of life, Luxury and Atheism, maintained alone by some Heathens, dissolute Arabians, profane Christians, and are exploded by Rabbi Moses, Gulielmus Placentius, Valescus de Taranta, and most accurately ventilated by Jo. Sylvaticus, a late writer and Physician of Milan, where you shall find this tenent copiously confuted.

Howsoever you say, if this be true that wine and strong drink have such virtue to expel fear and sorrow, and to exhilarate the mind, ever hereafter let's drink and be merry.

> Come, lusty Lydia, fill's a cup of sack,
> And, sirrah drawer, bigger pots we lack,
> And Scio wines that have so good a smack.   (HORACE)

I say with him in A. Gellius, let us maintain the vigour of our souls with a moderate cup of wine, (cups made to give gladness, &c.), and drink to refresh our mind; if there be any cold sorrow in it, or torpid bashfulness, let's wash it all away. — Now drown your cares in wine, so saith Horace, so saith Anacreon,

> Drink, then, while we may,
> For Death is on his way.

Let's drive down care with a cup of wine: and so say I too (though I drink none myself), for all this may be done, so that it be modestly, soberly, opportunely used; so that they be not drunk with wine, wherein is excess, which our Apostle forewarns; for, as Chrysostom well comments on that place, 'tis for mirth, wine, but not for madness: and will you know where, when, and how, that is to be understood? Would you know where wine is good? hear the Scriptures, Give Wine to them that are in sorrow, or, as Paul bid Timothy drink wine for his stomack's sake, for concoction, health, or some such honest occasion. Otherwise, as Pliny telleth us, if singular moderation be not had, nothing so pernicious, 'tis mere Vinegar, a flattering demon, poison itself. But hear a more fearful doom: Woe be to him that makes his neighbour drunk, *shameful spewing shall be upon his glory.* Let not good fellows triumph therefore, (saith Matthiolus), that I have so much commended wine; if it be immoderately taken, instead of making glad, it confounds both body and soul, it makes a giddy head, a sorrowful heart. And 'twas well said of the Poet of old, Wine causeth mirth and grief; nothing so good for some, so bad for others, especially as one observes, that are hot or inflamed. And so of spices, they alone, as I have shewed, cause head-melancholy themselves, they must not use wine as an ordinary drink, or in their diet. But to determine with Laurentius, wine is bad for mad men, and such as are troubled with heat in their inner parts or brains; but to melancholy, which is cold (as most is), Wine soberly used may be very good.

I may say the same of the decoction of China roots, Sassafras, Sarsaparilla, Guaiacum. China, saith Manardus, makes a good colour in the face, takes away melancholy, and all infirmities proceeding from cold; even so Sarsaparilla provokes sweat mightily, Guaiacum dries, Claudinus. Montanus, Cappivaccius, make frequent and good use of Guaiacum, and China, so that the liver be not incensed, good for such as are cold, as most melancholy men are, but by no means to be mentioned in hot.

The Turks have a drink called Coffee (for they use no wine), so named of a berry as black as soot, and as bitter, (like that black drink which was in use amongst the Lacedæmonians, and perhaps the same), which they sip still off, and sup as warm as they can suffer; they spend much time in those Coffee-houses, which are somewhat like our Ale-houses or Taverns, and there they sit chatting and drinking to drive away the time, and to be merry together, because they find by experience that kind of drink so used helpeth digestion, and procureth alacrity. Some of them take Opium to this purpose.

Borage, Balm, Saffron, Gold, I have spoken of; Montaltus commends Scorzonera roots condite [or preserved]. Garcias ab Horto makes mention of an herb called Datura, which, if it be eaten, for 24 hours following takes away all sense of grief, makes them incline to laughter and mirth: and another called bang, like in effect to Opium, which puts them for a time into a kind of Extasis, and makes them gently to laugh. One of the Roman Emperors had a seed, which he did ordinarily eat to exhilarate himself. Christophorus Ayrerus prefers Bezoar's stone, and the confection of Alkermes, before other cordials, and Amber in some cases. Alkermes comforts the inner parts; and Bezoar stone hath an especial virtue against all melancholy affections, it refresheth the heart, and corroborates the whole body. Amber provokes urine, helps the body, breaks wind, &c. After a purge, three or four grains of Bezoar stone, and three grains of Ambergrease drunk, or taken in Borage, or Bugloss water, in which gold hot hath been quenched, will do much good, and the purge shall diminish less (the heart so refreshed) of the strength and substance of the body.

> *Take Alkermes confection, half an ounce; Bezoar stone,*
> *1 scruple; powdered finest white Amber, 2 scruples, with*
> *syrup of citron rind; make an electuary.**

To Bezoar's stone most subscribe, Manardus, and many others; it takes away sadness, and makes merry him that useth it (saith Garcias ab Horto): " I have seen some that have been much diseased with faintness, swooning, and melancholy, that, taking the weight of three grains of this stone in the water of Oxtongue, have been cured." Garcias ab Horto brags how many desperate cures he hath done upon melancholy men by this alone, when all Physicians had forsaken them. But Alchermes many except against; in some cases it may help, if it be good and of the best, such as that of Montpelier in France, which Jodocus Sincerus so much magnifies, and would have no traveller omit to see it made. But it is not so general a medicine as the other. Fernelius suspects Alchermes, by reason of its heat; nothing (saith he) sooner exasperates this disease than the use of hot working meats and medicines, and would have them for that cause warily taken. I conclude therefore of this and all other medicines, as Thucydides of the plague at Athens, no remedy could be prescribed for it, there is no Catholick medicine to be had: that which helps one is pernicious to another.

Medicine of Cold Pearls [certain medicinal seeds], of Amber, of Borage, the Gladdening Electuary of Galen & Rhasis, of Gems, of Sweet and Bitter Musk, the Conciliator Electuary, Syrup of Cydonian Apples, conserves of Roses, Violets, Fumitory, Enula campana, Satyrion, Lemons, Orange-pills condite, &c., have their good use.

> *Take musk and sweet marjoram, each, 2 drachms;*
> *bugloss, borage, sweet violets, each 1 ounce; to mix*
> *with syrup of apples.*

Every Physician is full of such receipts; one only I will add for the rareness of it, which I find recorded by many learned Authors, as an

---

* Alkermes, a compound cordial made of cider, rose-water, sugar, fragrantly flavored, and colored red by kermes, a dyestuff made from a Mediterranean insect. Bezoar stone, certain calculi or concretions found in the stomachs of animals, once esteemed as an antidote for poison.

approved medicine against dotage, head-melancholy, and such diseases of the brain. Take a Ram's head that never meddled with an Ewe, cut off at a blow, and, the horns only taken away, boil it well skin and wool together, after it is well sod, take out the brains, and put these spices to it, Cinnamon, Ginger, Nutmeg, Mace, Cloves, in equal parts of half an ounce, mingle the powder of these spices with it, and heat them in a platter upon a chafing-dish of coals together, stirring them well, that they do not burn; take heed it be not overmuch dried, or dryer than a Calves brains ready to be eaten. Keep it so prepared, and for three days give it the patient fasting, so that he fast two hours after it. It may be eaten with bread in an egg, or broth, or any way, so it be taken. For fourteen days let him use this diet, drink no wine, &c. Gesner, Caricterius, mention this medicine, though with some variation; he that list may try it, and many such.

Odoraments to smell to, of Rose-water, Violet flowers, Balm, Rose-cakes, Vinegar, &c. do much recreate the brains and spirits, according to Solomon, *they rejoice the heart,* and, as some say, nourish: 'tis a question commonly controverted in our schools, whether odors nourish; let Ficinus decide it, many arguments he brings to prove it: as of Democritus, that lived by the smell of bread alone, applied to his nostrils, for some few days, when for old age he could eat no meat. Ferrerius speaks of an excellent confection of his making, of wine, saffron, &c., which he prescribed to dull, weak, feeble, and dying men, to smell to, and by it to have done very much good, as if he had given them drink. Our noble and learned Lord Verulam, in his book Concerning Life and Death, commends therefore all such cold smells as any way serve to refrigerate the spirits. Montanus prescribes a form which he would have his melancholy Patient never to have out of his hands. If you will have them spagirically [or chemically] prepared, look in Oswaldus Crollius.

Irrigation of the head shaven, of the flowers of water-lillies, lettuce, violets, camomile, wild mallows, wether's head, &c., must be used many mornings together. Montanus would have the head so washed once a week. Lælius à Fonte Eugubinus, for an Italian Count troubled with head-melancholy, repeats many medicines which he tried, but two alone which did the cure; use of whey made of goat's milk, with the extract of Hellebore, and irrigations of the head with water-lillies, lettuce, violets, camomile, &c., upon the suture of the crown. Piso commends a ram's lungs applied hot to the fore part of the head, or a young lamb divided in the back, exenterated, [disembowelled], &c. All acknowledge the chief cure to consist in moistening throughout. Some, saith Laurentius, use powders, and caps to the brain, but, forasmuch as such aromatical things are hot and dry, they must be sparingly administered.

Unto the heart we may do well to apply bags, epithemes, ointments, of which Laurentius gives examples. Bruel prescribes an epitheme for the heart, of bugloss, borage, water-lily, violet waters, sweet wine, balm leaves, nutmegs, cloves, &c.

For the Belly, make a Fomentation of oil, in which the seeds of cummin, rue, carrots, dill, have been boiled.

Baths are of wonderful great force in this malady, much admired by Galen, Aëtius, Rhasis, &c., of sweet water, in which is boiled the leaves of mallows, roses, violets, water-lilies, wether's head, flowers of Bugloss, Camomile, Melilot, &c. Guianerius would have them used twice a day, and when they come forth of the Baths, their back bones to be anointed with oil of Almonds, Violets, Nymphæa, fresh Capon-grease, &c.

Amulets and things to be borne about I find prescribed, taxed by some, approved by Renodeus, Platerus, (amulets, he saith, are not to be neglected), and others; look for them in Mizaldus, Porta, Albertus, &c. Bassardus Visontinus commends Hypericon, or S. John's Wort, gathered on a Friday in the hour of Jupiter, when it comes to his effectual operation (that is about the full Moon in July): so gathered, and borne or hung about the neck, it mightily helps this affection, and drives away all phantastical spirits. Philes, a Greek Author that flourished in the time of Michael Palæologus, writes that a Sheep or Kid's skin, whom a Wolf worried, ought not at all to be worn about a man, because it causeth palpitation of the heart, not for any fear, but a secret virtue which Amulets have. A ring made of the hoof of an ass's right fore-foot carried about, &c. I say with Renodeus, they are not altogether to be rejected. Peony doth cure Epilepsy, precious stones most diseases, a Wolf's dung borne with one helps the Cholick, a Spider an Ague, &c. Being in the Country in the vacation time not many years since at Lindley in Leicestershire, my Father's house, I first observed this Amulet of a Spider in a nut-shell lapped in silk, &c., so applied for an Ague by my Mother *; whom, although I knew to have excellent Skill in Chirurgery, sore eyes, aches, &c., and such experimental medicines, as all the country where she dwelt can witness, to have done many famous and good cures upon divers poor folks, that were otherwise destitute of help, yet, among all other experiments, this methought was most absurd and ridiculous, I could see no warrant for it. Why a Spider

* Mistress Dorothy Burton, she died 1629. — Burton's note.

for a fever? For what Antipathy? till at length, rambling amongst authors (as often I do) I found this very medicine in Dioscorides, approved by Matthiolus, repeated by Aldrovandus, in his chapter on Spiders, in his book on Insects, I began to have a better opinion of it, and to give more credit to Amulets, when I saw it in some parties answer to experience. Such medicines are to be exploded that consist of words, characters, spells, and charms, which can do no good at all, but out of a strong conceit, as Pomponatius proves; or the Devil's policy, who is the first founder and teacher of them.

SUBSECTION 6 — *Correctors of Accidents to procure Sleep. Against fearful Dreams, Redness, &c.*

WHEN you have used all good means and helps of alteratives, averters, diminutives, yet there will be still certain accidents to be corrected and amended, as waking, fearful dreams, flushing in the face to some, ruddiness, &c.

Waking, by reason of their continual cares, fears, sorrows, dry brains, is a symptom that much crucifies melancholy men, and must therefore be speedily helped, and sleep by all means procured, which sometimes is a sufficient remedy of itself without any other Physick. Sckenkius, in his observations, hath an example of a woman that was so cured. The means to procure it are inward or outward. Inwardly taken, are simples, or compounds; simples, as Poppy, Nymphæa, Violets, Roses, Lettuce, Mandrake, Henbane, Nightshade, or Solanum, Saffron, Hemp-seed, Nutmegs, Willows with their seeds, juice, decoctions, distilled waters, &c. Compounds are syrups, or Opiates, syrup of Poppy, Violets, Verbasco, which are commonly taken with distilled waters.

> *Take diacodium, 1 ounce; diascordium, one-half drachm; lettuce water, 3 and a half ounces; make a mingled potion; to be taken at bed-time.**

Nicholas' Rest, Philonium Romanum,† Triphera Magna [a gentle caustick], Pills of Cynoglossa [or Borage], Diascordium, Laudanum of Paracelsus, Opium, are in use, &c. Country folks commonly make a posset of hemp-seed, which Fuchsius in his Herbal so much discommends, yet I have seen the good effect, and it may be used where better medicines are not to be had.

---

* Diacodium, a syrup made of poppies; diascordium, a medicine invented by Fracastorius as a remedy for plague, containing water-germander (or perhaps garlic)

† Philonium Romanum, a medicine invented by Philon, of Tarsus, an ancient physician; it was composed of opium, saffron, pyrethrum, euphorbium, pepper, henbane, spikenard, honey, and other ingredients.

Laudanum of Paracelsus is prescribed in two or three grains, with a dram of Dioscordium, which Oswaldus Crollius commends. Opium itself is most part used outwardly, to smell to in a ball, though commonly so taken by the Turks to the same quantity for a cordial, and at Goa in the Indies; the dose 40 or 50 grains.

Rulandus calls Nicholas' Rest the last refuge, but of this and the rest look for peculiar receipts in Victorius Faventinus, Heurnius, Hildesheim, &c. Outwardly used, as oil of Nutmegs by extraction or expression, with Rose-water to anoint the temples, oils of Poppy, Nenuphar, Mandrake, Purslain, Violets, all to the same purpose.

Montanus much commends odoraments of Opium, Vinegar, and Rosewater. Laurentius prescribes Pomanders and nodules; see the receipts in him; Codronchus, wormwood to smell to.

Poplar-alabaster Ointments are used to anoint the temples, nostrils, or, if they be too weak, they mix Saffron and Opium. Take a grain or two of Opium, and dissolve it with three or four drops of Rose-water in a spoon, and after mingle with it as much Poplar Ointment as a nut, use it as before: or else take half a dram of Opium, Poplar Ointment, oil of Nenuphar, Rose-water, Rose-vinegar, of each half an ounce, with as much virgin wax as a nut; anoint your temples with some of it, at bed-time.

Sacks of Wormwood, Mandrake, Henbane, Roses, made like pillows and laid under the Patient's head, are mentioned by Cardan and Mizaldus, to anoint the soles of the feet with the fat of a dormouse, the teeth with ear-wax of a dog,* swine's gall, hare's ears: charms, &c.

Frontlets are well known to every good wife, Rose-water and Vinegar, with a little woman's milk, and Nutmegs grated upon a Rose-cake applied to both temples.

For an Emplaister, take of Castorium a dram and half, of Opium half a scruple, mixt both together with a little water of life, make two small plaisters thereof, and apply them to the temples.

Rulandus prescribes Epithemes, and lotions of the head, with the decoction of flowers of Nymphæa, Violet-leaves, Mandrake roots, Henbane, white Poppy. Hercules de Saxoniâ, rainwater, or droppings, &c. Lotions of the feet do much avail of the said herbs: by these means, saith Laurentius, I think you may procure sleep to the most melancholy men in the world. Some use horse-leeches behind the ears, and apply Opium to the place.

Bayerus sets down some remedies against fearful dreams, and such as walk and talk in their sleep. Baptista Porta, to procure pleasant

* Scarcely possible to believe, says Burton's Latin footnote.

dreams and quiet rest, would have you take Hippoglossa, or the herb Horse-tongue, Balm, to use them or their distilled waters after supper, &c. Such men must not eat Beans, Pease, Garlick, Onions, Cabbage, Venison, Hare, use black wines, or any meat hard of digestion at supper, or lie on their backs, &c.

Boorish shyness, bashfulness, flushing in the face, high colour, ruddiness, are common grievances, which much torture many melancholy men, when they meet a man, or come in company of their betters, strangers, after a meal, or if they drink a cup of wine or strong drink, they are as red and fleckt, and sweat, as if they had been at a Mayor's Feast; particularly if fear overcomes them, it [that is to say, bashfulness] exceeds, they think every man observes, takes notice of it: and fear alone will effect it, suspicion without any other cause. Sckenkius speaks of a waiting Gentlewoman in the Duke of Savoy's Court, that was so much offended with it, that she kneeled down to him, and offered Biarus, a Physician, all that she had to be cured of it. And 'tis most true that Antony Lodovicus saith in his book On Shame, bashfulness either hurts or helps; such men I am sure it hurts. If it proceed from suspicion or fear, Felix Plater prescribes no other remedy but to reject and contemn it: he is shielded by the crowd, as a worthy Physician in our town said to a friend of mine in like case, complaining without a cause, suppose one looked red, what matter is it? make light of it, who observes it?

If it trouble at or after meals, (as Jobertus observes) after a little exercise or stirring, for many are then hot and red in the face, or if they do nothing at all, especially women; he would have them let blood in both arms, first one, then another, two or three days between, if blood abound, to use frictions of the other parts, feet especially, and washing of them, because of that consent which is betwixt the head and the feet. And withal to refrigerate the face, by washing it often with Rose, Violet, Nenuphar, Lettuce, Lovage waters, and the like: but the best of all is that Virgin Milk, or strained liquor of Litharge [Protoxide of Lead]. It is diversely prepared; by Jobertus thus: Take litharge, 1 ounce; white lead, 3 drachms; camphire, 2 scruples; to be dissolved in water of nightshade, lettuce, nenuphar, each, 3 ounces, white wine vinegar 2 ounces; let it settle for several hours, then put through a philter; keep in a glass vessel, and moisten the face twice or thrice a day. Quercetan commends the water of frogs' spawn for ruddiness in the face. Crato would fain have them use all Summer the condite flowers of Succory, Strawberry-water, Roses, (cupping-glasses are good for the time), and to defecate impure blood with the infusion of Senna, Savory,

Balm-water. Hollerius knew one cured alone with the use of Succory boiled, and drunk for five months, every morning in the Summer.

It is good overnight to anoint the face with Hare's blood, and in the morning to wash it with strawberry and cowslip-water, the juice of distill'd Lemons, juice of cowcumbers, or to use the seeds of Melons, or kernels of Peaches beaten small, or the roots of arum, and mixt with wheat bran to bake it in an oven, and to crumble it in strawberry-water, or to put fresh cheese curds to a red face.

> *Take kernels of Persian melon-seeds, to*
> *each ounce a half-scruple; strawberry-*
> *water, 2 pounds; mix; apply by hand.*

If it trouble them at meal times that flushing, as oft it doth, with sweating or the like, they must avoid all violent passions and actions, as laughing, &c., strong drink, and drink very little, one draught saith Crato, and that about the midst of their meal; avoid at all times in-durate salt, and especially spice and windy meat.

Crato prescribes the condite fruit of wild rose to a Nobleman his Patient, to be taken before dinner or supper, to the quantity of a chestnut. It is made of sugar, as that of Quinces. The decoction of the roots of sow-thistle before meat by the same Author is much approved. To eat of a baked Apple some advise, or of a preserved Quince, Cum-minseed prepared with meat instead of salt, to keep down fumes: not to study, or to be intentive after meals.

To apply cupping-glasses to the shoulders is very good. For the other kind of ruddiness which is settled in the face with pimples, &c., because it pertains not to my subject, I will not meddle with it. I refer you to Crato's Counsels, Arnoldus, Ruland, Peter Forestus on redness, to Pla-terus, Mercurialis, Ulmus, Randoletius, Heurnius, Menadous, and others, that have written largely of it.

Those other grievances and symptoms of head-ache, palpitation of heart, vertigo, deliquium, &c., which trouble many melancholy men, because they are copiously handled apart in every Physician, I do voluntarily omit.

MEMBER 2

Cure of Melancholy over all the Body

WHERE the melancholy blood possesseth the whole body with the Brain, it is best to begin with blood-letting. The Greeks prescribe the Median, or middle vein, to be opened, and so much blood to be taken away as the Patient may well spare, and the cut that is made must be wide enough. The Arabians hold it fittest to be taken from that arm on which side there is more pain and heaviness in the head: if black blood issue forth, bleed on, if it be clear and good, let it be instantly suppressed, because the malice of melancholy is much corrected by the goodness of the blood. If the party's strength will not admit much evacuation in this kind at once, it must be assayed again and again: if it may not be conveniently taken from the arm, it must be taken from the knees and ancles, especially to such men or women whose hemrods or months have been stopped. If the malady continue, it is not amiss to evacuate in a part, in the forehead, & to virgins in the ancles, which are melancholy for love-matters; so to widows that are much grieved and troubled with sorrow and cares: for bad blood flows in the heart, and so crucifies the mind. The hemrods are to be opened with an instrument, or horse-leeches, &c. See more in Montaltus. Sckenkius hath an example of one that was cured by an accidental wound in his thigh, much bleeding freed him from melancholy. Diet, Diminutives, Alteratives, Cordials, Correctors, as before, intermixt as occasion serves; all their study must be to make a melancholy man fat, and then the cure is ended. Diuretica, or medicines to procure urine, are prescribed by some in this kind, hot and cold: hot where the heat of the liver doth not forbid; cold where the heat of the liver is very great. Amongst hot are Parsley roots, Lovage, Fennel, &c. cold, Melon-seeds, &c., with whey of Goat's-milk, which is the common conveyer.

To purge and purify the blood use Sowthistle, Succory, Senna, Endive, Carduus Benedictus, Dandelion, Hop, Maidenhair, Fumitory, Bugloss, Borage, &c., with their juice, decoctions, distilled waters, syrups, &c.

Oswaldus Crollius much admires salt of Corals in this case, and Aëtius, Hieram Archigenis [Archigenes' Medicine], which is an excellent medicine to purify the blood for all melancholy affections, falling sickness, none to be compared to it.

MEMBER 3

SUBSECTION 1 — *Cure of Hypochondriacal Melancholy*

IN this cure, as in the rest, is especially required the rectification of those six non-natural things above all, as good diet, which Montanus enjoins a French Nobleman, to have an especial care of it, without which all other remedies are in vain. Blood-letting is not to be used, except the Patient's body be very full of blood, and that it be derived from the liver and spleen to the stomack and his vessels, then to draw it back, to cut the inner vein of either arm, some say the salvatella, [a vein between the ring finger and the little finger], and, if the malady be continuate, to open a vein in the forehead.

Preparatives and Alteratives may be used as before, saving that there must be respect had as well to the Liver, Spleen, Stomack, Hypochondries, as to the heart and brain. To comfort the Stomack and inner parts against wind and obstructions, by Aretæus, Galen, Aëtius, Aurelianus, &c., and many latter writers, are still prescribed the decoctions of Wormwood, Centaury, Pennyroyal, Betony sod in whey, and daily drunk: many have been cured by this medicine alone.

Prosper Alpinus and some others as much magnify the water of Nilus against this malady, an especial good remedy for windy melancholy. For which reason belike Ptolemæus Philadelphus, when he married his daughter Berenice to the King of Assyria (as Celsus records) to his great charge caused the water of Nilus to be carried with her, and gave command that during her life she should use no other drink. I find those that commend use of Apples in splenetick and this kind of melancholy, (Lambswool some call it), which, howsoever approved, must certainly be corrected of cold rawness and wind.

Codronchus magnifies the oil and salt of Wormwood above all other remedies, which works better and speedier than any simple whatsoever, and much to be preferred before all those fulsome decoctions, and infusions, which much offend by reason of their quantity; this alone, in a small measure taken, expels wind, and that most forcibly, moves urine, cleanseth the stomack of all gross humours, crudities, helps appetite, &c. Arnoldus hath a Wormwood wine which he would have used, which every Pharmacopœia speaks of.

Diminutives and purgers may be taken as before, of hiera, manna, cassia, which Montanus in this kind prefers before all other simples, and these must be often used, still abstaining from those which are more violent, lest they do exasperate the stomack, &c., and the mischief by that means be increased; though in some Physicians I find very strong purgers, Hellebore itself, prescribed in this affection. If it long continue, vomits may be taken after meat, or otherwise gently procured with warm water, oxymel, &c., now and then. Fuchsius prescribes Hellebore; but still take heed in this malady, which I have often warned, of hot medicines, because, (as Salvianus adds), drought follows heat, which increaseth the disease : and yet Baptista Sylvaticus forbids cold medicines, because they increase obstructions, and other bad symptoms. But this varies as the parties do, and 'tis not easy to determine which to use. The stomack most part in this infirmity is cold, the liver hot ; scarce therefore (which Montanus insinuates) can you help the one, and not hurt the other : much discretion must be used ; take no Physick at all, he concludes, without great need. Lælius Eugubinus, for an hypochondriacal German Prince, used many medicines, but it was after signified to him in letters, that the decoction of China and Sassafras, and salt of Sassafras, wrought him an incredible good. In his 108th consultation, he used as happily the same remedies ; this to a third might have been poison, by overheating his liver and blood.

For the other parts look for remedies in Savanarola, Gordonius, Massaria, Mercatus, Johnson, &c. One for the spleen, amongst many other, I will not omit, cited by Hildesheim, prescribed by Matthiolus Flaccius, and out of the authority of Benevenius. Antony Benevenius in an hypochondriacal passion cured an exceeding great swelling of the spleen with Capers alone, a meat befitting that infirmity, and frequent use of the water of a Smith's Forge ; by this Physick he helped a sick man whom all other Physicians had forsaken, that for seven years had been Splenetick. And of such force is this water, that those creatures that drink of it have commonly little or no spleen. See more excellent medicines for the Spleen in him and Lodovicus Mercatus, who is a great magnifier of this medicine. This steel-drink is much likewise commended to this disease by Daniel Sennertus, and admired by J. Cæsar Claudinus, he calls steel the proper Alexipharmacum of this malady, and much magnifies it ; look for receipts in them. Averters must be used to the liver and spleen, and to scour the Meseraick Veins ; and they are either to open, or provoke urine. You can open no place better than the Hemrods, which if by horse-leeches they be made to flow, there may be again such an excellent remedy, as Plater holds. Sallustus Salvianus will admit no other phlebotomy but this ; and by his experience in an hospital which he kept he found all mad and melancholy men worse for other blood-letting. Laurentius calls this of horse-leeches a sure remedy to empty the spleen and Meseraick Membrane. Only Montanus is against it ; to other men (saith he) this opening of the hæmrods seems to be a profitable remedy ; for my part I do not approve of it, because it draws away the thinnest blood, and leaves the thickest behind.

Aëtius, Vidus Vidius, Mercurialis, Fuchsius, recommend Diureticks, or such things as provoke urine, as Aniseeds, Dill, Fennel, Germander, ground Pine, sod [seethed] in water, drunk in powder; and yet P. Bayerus is against them, and so is Hollerius; all melancholy men (saith he) must avoid such things as provoke urine, because by them the subtle or thinnest is evacuated, the thicker matter remains.

Clysters are in good request. Trincavellius esteems of them in the first place, and Hercules de Saxoniâ is a greater approver of them. I have found (saith he) by experience that many hypochondriacal melancholy men have been cured by the sole use of Clysters, receipts are to be had in him.

Besides those fomentations, irrigations, inunctions, odoraments, prescribed for the head, there must be the like used for the Liver, Spleen, Stomack, Hypochondries, &c. In crudity (saith Piso) 'tis good to bind the stomack hard, to hinder wind, and to help concoction.

Of inward medicines I need not speak; use the same Cordials as before. In this kind of melancholy some prescribe Treacle in Winter, especially before or after purges, or in the Spring, as Avicenna; Trincavellius, Mithridate; Montaltus, Peony seeds, Unicorn's horn, bone of the heart of a stag, &c.

Amongst Topicks, or outward medicines, none are more precious than Baths, but of them I have spoken. Fomentations to the Hypochondries are very good of wine and water, in which are sod [seethed] Southern-wood, Melilot, Epithyme, Mugwort, Senna, Polypody, as also Plaisters, Liniments, Ointments for the Spleen, Liver, and Hypochondries, of which look for examples in Laurentius, Jobertus, Montanus, Montaltus, Hercules de Saxoniâ, Faventinus. And so of Epithemes, digestive powders, bags, oils. Octavius Horatianus prescribes chalastick [or laxative] Cataplasms, or dry purging medicines: Piso, Dropaces of pitch, and oil of Rue, applied at certain times to the stomack, to the metaphrene, or part of the back which is over against the heart; Aëtius, sinapisms; Montaltus would have the thighs to be cauterised, Mercurialis prescribes beneath the knees; Lælius Eugubinus will have the cautery made in the right thigh, and so Montanus. The same Montanus approves of issues in the arms or hinder part of the head. Bernardus Paternus, would have issues made in both the thighs: Lodovicus Mercatus prescribes them near the Spleen, or near the region of the belly, or in either of the thighs. Ligatures, Frictions, and Cupping-glasses above or about the belly, without scarification, which Felix Platerus so much approves, may be used as before.

SUBSECTION 2 — *Correctors to expel Wind. Against Costiveness, &c.*

In this kind of Melancholy one of the most offensive symptoms is wind, which, as in the other species, so in this, hath great need to be corrected and expelled.

The medicines to expel it are either inwardly taken or outwardly. Inwardly to expel wind, are simples or compounds: simples are herbs, roots, &c. as Galanga, Gentian, Angelica, Enula, Calamus Aromaticus, Valerian, Zeodoti, Iris, condite Ginger, Aristolochy, Cicliminus, China [Roots], Dittander, Pennyroyal, Rue, Calamint, Bay-berries and Bay-leaves, Betony, Rosemary, Hyssop, Sabine, Centaury, Mint, Camomile, French Lavender, Chaste-lamb, Broom-flowers, Origan, Orange-pills, &c., Spices, as Saffron, Cinnamon, Bezoar Stone, Myrrh, Mace, Nut-megs, Pepper, Cloves, Ginger, seeds of Anise, Fennel, Amni, Cary, Nettle, Rue, &c., Juniper berries, grana Paradisi; Compounds, of Anise, Galingale, Cinnamon, Calaminth, the Electuary of Laurel, the Blessed Laxative, the Powder Against Flatulence, the Florentian Antidote, the Charming Powder, Aromatick Rose Wine,* Treacle, Mithridate, &c. This one caution of Gualter Bruel is to be observed in the administering of these hot medicines and dry, that, whilst they covet to expel wind, they do not inflame the blood and increase the disease. Sometimes (as he saith) medicines must more decline to heat, sometimes more to cold, as the circumstances require, and as the parties are inclined to heat or cold.

Outwardly taken to expel winds, are oils, as of Camomile, Rue, Bays, &c. fomentations of the Hypochondries, with the decoctions of Dill, Pennyroyal, Rue, Bay-leaves, Cummin, &c., bags of Camomile-flowers, Aniseed, Cummin, Bays, Rue, Wormwood, Ointments of the Oil of Spikenard, Wormwood, Rue, &c. Aretæus prescribes Cataplasms of Camomile-flowers, Fennel, Aniseeds, Cummin, Rosemary, Worm-wood-leaves, &c.

Cupping-glasses applied to the Hypochondries, without scarification, do wonderfully resolve wind. Fernelius much approves of them at the lower end of the belly; Lodovicus Mercatus calls them a powerful remedy, and testifieth moreover out of his own knowledge how many he hath seen suddenly eased by them. Julius Cæsar Claudinus admires

---

* The Compounds, by their own names, run: Dianisum, Diagalanga, Diaciminum, Diacalaminth, Electuarium de Baccis Lauri, Benedicta Laxativa, Pulvis ad Flatus, Antid. Florent, Pulvis Carminativus, Aromaticum Rosatum, &c. The " Florentian Anti-dote " may be simply a reference to the Florentine Antidotary.

these Cupping-glasses, which he calls (out of Galen) a kind of enchant-ment, they cause such present help.

Empiricks have a myriad of medicines, as to swallow a bullet of lead, &c., which I voluntarily omit. Amatus Lusitanus for an Hypochondriacal person that was extremely tormented with wind, prescribes a strange remedy. Put a pair of bellows' end into a Clyster pipe, and applying it into the fundament, open the bowels, so draw forth the wind; nature abhors a vacuum. He vaunts he was the first invented this remedy, and by means of it speedily eased a melancholy man. Of the cure of this flatuous melancholy read more in Fienus.

Against Head-ache, Vertigo, Vapours which ascend forth of the stomack to molest the head, read Hercules de Saxoniâ and others.

If Costiveness offend in this, or in any other of the three species, it is to be corrected with suppositories, clysters, or lenitives, powder of Senna, condite [or preserved] Prunes, &c.

Make lenitive electuaries of
juice of roses, each 1 ounce.

Take as much as a Nutmeg at a time, half an hour before dinner or supper, or Mastic pills, 1 oz. in 6 pills, a pill or two at a time. See more in Montanus, Hildesheim. P. Cnemander and Montanus commend Cyprian Turpentine, which they would have familiarly taken, to the quantity of a small Nut, two or three hours before dinner and supper, twice or thrice a week, if need be; for, besides that it keeps the belly soluble, it clears the stomack, opens obstructions, cleanseth the liver, provokes urine.

These in brief are the ordinary medicines which belong to the cure of melancholy, which, if they be used aright, no doubt may do much good. Saith Bessardus, a good choice of particular receipts must needs ease, if not quite cure, not one, but all or most, as occasion serves.

Where one thing by itself may fail,
The many serve to cure our ail. (OVID)

THE THIRD PARTITION

ANALYSIS OF THE THIRD PARTITION

Love and love melancholy, Memb. 1. Sect. 1.

Preface or Introduction. *Subsect.* 1.

Love's definition, pedigree, object, fair, amiable, gracious, and pleasant, from which comes beauty, grace, which all desire and love, parts affected.

Division or kinds, *Subs.* 2.

Natural, in things without life, as love and hatred of elements; and with life, as vegetable, vine and elm, sympathy, antipathy, &c.

Sensible, as of beasts, for pleasure, preservation of kind, mutual agreement, custom, bringing up together, &c.

Rational, Simple, which hath three objects, as *M.* 1.

Profitable, *Subs.* 1. — Health, wealth, honour, we love our benefactors: nothing so amiable as profit, or that which hath a show of commodity.

Pleasant, *Subs.* 2. — Things without life, made by art, pictures, sports, games, sensible objects, as hawks, hounds, horses; or men themselves, for similitude of manners, natural affection, as to friends, children, kinsmen, &c., for glory such as commend us.

Of women, as — Before marriage, as *Heroical Mel. Sect.* 2, *vide* ♈

Or after marriage, as *Jealousy, Sect.* 3, *vide* 8

Honest, *Subs.* 3. — Fucate in show, by some error or hypocrisy; some seem and are not; or truly for virtue, honesty, good parts, learning, eloquence, &c.

Mixed of all three, which extends to *M.* 3. — Common good, our neighbour, country, friends, which is charity; the defect of which is cause of much discontent and melancholy.

or — In excess, *vide* II.

God, *Sect.* 4. — In defect, *vide* ♏.

♈ **Heroical or Love-Melancholy, in which consider,**

Memb. 1.
His pedigree, power, extent to vegetables and sensible creatures, as well as men, to spirits, devils, &c.
His name, definition, object, part affected, tyranny.

Causes, *Memb.* 2.

Stars, temperature, full diet, place, country, clime, condition, idleness, *S.* 1.

Natural allurements, and causes of love, as beauty, its praise, how it allureth.

Comeliness, grace, resulting from the whole or some parts, as face, eyes, hair, hands, &c. *Subs.* 2.

Artificial allurements, and provocations of lust and love, gestures, apparel, dowry, money, &c.

Quest. Whether beauty owe more to Art or Nature? *Subs.* 3.

Opportunity of time and place, conference, discourse, music, singing, dancing, amorous tales, lascivious objects, familiarity, gifts, promises, &c. *Subs.* 4.

Bawds and Philters. *Subs.* 5.

Symptoms or signs, *Memb.* 3.

Of body — Dryness, paleness, leanness, waking, sighing, &c.

Quest. An detur pulsus amatorius?

or

Of mind. — Bad, as — Fear, sorrow, suspicion, anxiety, &c. A hell, torment, fire, blindness, &c. Dotage, slavery, neglect of business.

or

Good, as — Spruceness, neatness, courage, aptness to learn music, singing, dancing, poetry, &c.

Prognostics; despair, madness, phrensy, death, *Memb.* 4.

Cures, *Memb.* 5.

By labour, diet, physic, abstinence, *Subs.* 1.

To withstand the beginnings, avoid occasions, fair and foul means, change of place, contrary passion, witty inventions, discommend the former, bring in another, *Subs.* 2.

By good counsel, persuasion, from future miseries, inconveniences, &c., *Subs.* 3.

By philters, magical, and poetical cures, *Subs.* 4.

To let them have their desire disputed *pro* and *con.* Impediments removed, reasons for it, *Subs.* 5.

8 Jealousy, *Sect.* 3.

His name, definition, extent, power, tyranny, *Memb.* 1.

Division, Equivocations, kinds, *Subs.* 1.
- Improper
  - To many beasts, as swans, cocks, bulls.
  - To kings and princes, of their subjects, successors.
  - To friends, parents, tutors over their children, or otherwise.
- or
- Proper
  - Before marriage, corrivals, &c.
  - After, as in this place or present subject.

Causes, *Sect.* 2.
- In the parties themselves,
  - Idleness, impotency in one party, melancholy, long absence.
  - They have been naught themselves. Hard usage, unkindness, wantonness, inequality of years, persons, fortunes, &c.
- or
- from others.
  - Outward enticements and provocations of others.

Symptoms, *Memb.* 2.
Fear, sorrow, suspicion, anguish of mind, strange actions, gestures, looks, speeches, locking up, outrages, severe laws, prodigious trials, &c.

Prognostics, *Memb.* 3.
Despair, madness, to make away themselves, and others.

Cures, *Memb.* 4.
- By avoiding occasions, always busy, never to be idle.
- By good counsel, advice of friends, to contemn or dissemble it. *Subs.* 1.
- By prevention before marriage. Plato's communion.
- To marry such as are equal in years, birth, fortunes, beauty, of like conditions, &c.
- Of a good family, good education. To use them well.

Religious melancholy, *Sect.* 4.

A proof that there is such a species of melancholy, name, object God, what his beauty is, how it allureth, part and parties affected, superstitious, idolaters, prophets, heretics, &c., *Subs.* 1.

II. In excess of such as do that which is not required. *Memb.* 1.

Causes, *Subs.* 2.
- From others,
  - The devil's allurements, false miracles, priests for their gain. Politicians, to keep men in obedience, bad instructors, blind guides.
- or
- from themselves.
  - Simplicity, fear, ignorance, solitariness, melancholy, curiosity, pride, vain-glory, decayed image of God.

Symptoms, *Subs.* 3.
- General
  - Zeal without knowledge, obstinacy, superstition, strange devotion, stupidity, confidence, stiff defence of their tenets, mutual love & hate of other sects, belief of incredibilities, impossibilities.
  - Of heretics, pride, contumacy, contempt of others, wilfulness, vain-glory, singularity, prodigious paradoxes.
- or
- Particular.
  - In superstitious blind zeal, obedience, strange works, fasting, sacrifices, oblations, prayers, vows, pseudo-martyrdom, mad and ridiculous customs, ceremonies, observations.
  - In pseudo-prophets, visions, revelations, dreams, prophecies, new doctrines, &c., of Jews, Gentiles, Mahometans, &c.

Prognostics, *Subs.* 4.
New doctrines, paradoxes, blasphemies, madness, stupidity, despair, damnation.

Cures, *Subs.* 5.
By physic, if need be, conference, good counsel, persuasion, compulsion, correction, punishment. *Quæritur an cogi debent? Affir.*

In defect, as *Memb.* 2.

Secure, void of grace and fears.
Epicures, atheists, magicians, hypocrites, such as have cauterised consciences, or else are in a reprobate sense, worldly-secure, some philosophers, impenitent sinners, *Subs.* 1.

or

Distrustful, or too timorous, as desperate. In despair consider,

Causes, *Subs.* 2.
- The devil and his allurements, rigid preachers, that wound their consciences, melancholy, contemplation, solitariness.
- How melancholy and despair differ. Distrust, weakness of faith. Guilty conscience for offence committed, misunderstanding Scr.

Symptoms, *Subs.* 3.
Fear, sorrow, anguish of mind, extreme tortures and horror of conscience, fearful dreams, conceits, visions, &c.

Prognostics.
Blasphemy, violent death, *Subs.* 4.

Cures, *S.* 5.
Physic, as occasion serves, conference, not to be idle or alone. Good counsel, good company, all comforts and contents, &c.

THE THIRD PARTITION

LOVE–MELANCHOLY

THE FIRST SECTION, MEMBER, SUBSECTION

The Preface

HERE will not be wanting, I presume, one or other that will much discommend some part of this Treatise of Love-Melancholy, and object (which Erasmus in his Preface to Sir Thomas More suspects of his) that it is too light for a Divine, too Comical a subject, to speak of Love-Symptoms, too phantastical, and fit alone for a wanton Poet, a feeling young love-sick gallant, an effeminate Courtier, or some such idle person. And 'tis true they say: for by the naughtiness of men it is so come to pass, as Caussinus observes, that the very name of Love is odious to chaster ears. And therefore some again out of an affected gravity, will dislike all for the name's sake before they read a word; dissembling with him in Petronius, and seem to be angry that their ears are violated with such obscene speeches, that so they may be admired for grave Philosophers, and staid carriage. They cannot abide to hear talk of Love-toys, or amorous discourses; in mien and gesture, what strikes the eye, in their outward actions averse; and yet in their cogitations they are all out as bad, if not worse than others.

> *To read my book, the virgin shy*
> *May blush, while Brutus standeth by;*
> *But when he's gone, read through what's writ,*
> *And never stain a cheek for it.* (MARTIAL)

But let these cavillers and counterfeit Catos know that, as the Lord John answered the Queen in that Italian Guazzo, an old, a grave, discreet man is fittest to discourse of Love matters, because he hath likely more experience, observed more, hath a more staid judgement, can better discern, resolve, discuss, advise, give better cautions and more solid precepts, better inform his auditors in such a subject, and by reason of his riper years sooner divert. Besides, there is nothing here to be excepted at; Love is a species of melancholy, and a necessary part of this my Treatise, which I may not omit; so Jacob Mycillus pleadeth for himself in his translation of Lucian's Dialogues, and so do I; I must and will perform my task. And that short excuse of Mercerus for his edition of Aristænetus shall be mine: If I have spent my time ill to write, let them not be so idle as to read. — But I am persuaded that it is not so ill spent. I ought not to excuse or repent myself of this subject, on which many grave and worthy men have written whole volumes; Plato, Plutarch, Plotinus, Maximus Tyrius, Alcinous, Avicenna, Leon Hebræus, in three large Dialogues, Xenophon in his Symposium, Theophrastus (if we may believe Athenaeus), Picus Mirandula, Marius Aequicola, both in Italian, Kornmannus, in his Outline of Love, Petrus Godefridus hath handled in three books, P. Hædus, and which almost every Physician, as Arnoldus Villanovanus, Valleriola in his Medical Observations, Aelian Montaltus and Laurentius in their Treatises of Melancholy, Jason Pratensis, Valescus de Taranta, Gordonius, Hercules de Saxoniâ, Savanarola, Langius, &c., have treated of apart, and in their works. I excuse myself therefore with Peter Godefridus, Valleriola, Ficinus, and in Langius' words: Cadmus Milesius writ fourteen books of Love, and why should I be ashamed to write an Epistle in favour of young men, of this subject? A company of stern Readers dislike the second of the Æneids, & tax Virgil's gravity for inserting such amorous passages in an heroical subject; but Servius, his commentator, justly vindicates the Poet's worth, wisdom, and discretion in doing as he did. Castalio would not have young men read the Canticles, because to his thinking it was too light and amorous a tract, a Ballad of Ballads, as our old English translation hath it. He might as well forbid the reading of Genesis, because of the loves of Jacob and Rachel, the stories of Shechem and Dinah, Judah and Tamar: reject the book of Numbers, for the fornications of the people of Israel with the Moabites: that of Judges, for Samson and Delilah's embracings: that of the Kings, for David and Bathsheba's adulteries, the incest of Ammon and Tamar, Solomon's Concubines, &c., the stories of Esther, Judith, Susanna, and many such. Dicaearchus, and some other, carp at Plato's majesty, that he would vouchsafe to indite such Love toys; amongst the rest, for that dalliance with Agathon:

> *When Agathon I kissed,*
> *My very soul, I wist,*
> *Was on my lips; yet sick,*
> *It must return so quick.**

* This Plato, of course, was the Comic Poet, not Plato the Philosopher as is implied.

For my part, saith Maximus Tyrias, a great Platonist himself, I do
not only admire but stand amazed to read that Plato and Socrates both
should expel Homer from their City, because he writ of such light and
wanton subjects, because he brought in Juno cohabiting with Jove on
Ida, covered with an immortal cloud, Vulcan's net, Mars' and Venus'
fopperies before all the Gods, because Apollo fled when he was persecuted by Achilles, the Gods were wounded and ran whining away,
as Mars that roared louder than Stentor, and covered nine acres of
ground with his fall; Vulcan was a Summer's day falling down from
Heaven, and in Lemnos Isle brake his leg, with such ridiculous passages; when as both Socrates and Plato by his testimony writ lighter
themselves: (as he follows it) what can be more absurd than for grave
Philosophers to treat of such fooleries, to admire Autolycus, Alcibiades,
for their beauties as they did, to run after, to gaze, to dote on fair
Phædrus, delicate Agathon, young Lysis, fine Charmides? Doth this
become grave Philosophers? Thus peradventure Callias, Thrasyma-
chus, Polus, Aristophanes, or some of his adversaries and emulators
might object; but neither they nor Anytus and Meletus, his bitter enemies, that condemned him for teaching Critias to tyrannize, his impiety for swearing by dogs and plane trees, for his juggling sophistry,
&c., never so much as upbraided him with impure Love, writing or
speaking of that subject; and therefore without question, as he concludes, both Socrates and Plato in this are justly to be excused. But
suppose they had been a little over-seen, should divine Plato be de-
famed? No, rather, as he said of Cato's drunkenness, if Cato were
drunk, it should be no vice at all to be drunk. They reprove Plato then,
but without cause, (as Ficinus pleads), for all Love is honest and good,
and they are worthy to be loved that speak well of Love. Being to
speak of this admirable affection of Love, (saith Valleriolla), there lies
open a vast and philosophical field to my discourse, by which many
lovers become mad: let me leave my more serious meditations, wander
in these Philosophical fields, and look into those pleasant Groves of
the Muses, where with unspeakable variety of flowers we may make Garlands to ourselves, not to adorn us only, but with their pleasant smell
and juice to nourish our souls, and fill our minds desirous of knowledge, &c. After an harsh and unpleasing discourse of Melancholy, which
hath hitherto molested your patience, and tired the author, give him
leave with Godefridus the lawyer and Laurentius to recreate himself in
this kind after his laborious studies, since so many grave Divines and
worthy men have without offence to manners, to help themselves and

others, voluntarily written of it. Heliodorus, a Bishop, penned a Love
story of Theagenes and Chariclea, and when some Catos of his time
reprehended him for it, chose rather, saith Nicephorus, to leave his
Bishoprick than his book. Æneas Sylvius, an ancient Divine, and past
40 years of age (as he confesseth himself), afterwards Pope Pius
Secundus, indited that wanton history of Euryalus and Lucretia. And
how many Superintendents of learning could I reckon up, that have
written of light Phantastical subjects! Beroaldus, Erasmus, Alphera-
tius, twenty-four times printed in Spanish, &c. Give me leave then to
refresh my Muse a little, and my weary Readers, to expatiate in this
delightsome field, as Fonseca terms it, to season a surly discourse with
a more pleasant aspersion of Love matters. As the Poet invites us, 'tis
good to sweeten our life with some pleasing toys to relish it; and, as
Pliny tells us, most of our students love such pleasant subjects. Though
Macrobius teach us otherwise, that those old sages banished all such
light tracts from their studies to nurses' cradles, to please only the
ear, yet out of Apuleius I will oppose as honorable Patrons, Solon,
Plato, Xenophon, Adrian, &c., that as highly approve of these Treatises.
On the other side methinks they are not to be disliked, they are not so
unfit. I will not peremptorily say as Aretine did, I will tell you such
pretty stories, that foul befall him that is not pleased with them;
neither will I say, may these things be agreeable to hear and pleasant
to remember, with that confidence, as Beroaldus doth his enarrations
on Propertius. I will not expect or hope for that approbation which
Lipsius gives to his Epictetus: the more I read, the more shall I covet
to read. I will not press you with my pamphlets, or beg attention, but
if you like them you may. Pliny holds it expedient, and most fit, to
season our works with some pleasant discourse; Synesius approves it,
a pause for play is permitted, the Poet admires it:

> *Profit and pleasure, then, to mix with art,*
> *T' inform the judgement, not offend the heart,*
> *Shall gain all votes.*   (HORACE)

And there be those, without question, that are more willing to read
such toys than I am to write. Let me not live, saith Aretine's Antonia,
if I had not rather hear thy discourse than see a play! No doubt but
there be more of her mind, ever have been, ever will be, as Hierome
bears me witness. A far greater part had rather read Apuleius than
Plato: Tully himself confesseth he could not understand Plato's
Timaeus, and therefore cared less for it; but every school-boy hath
that famous testament of Grunnius Corocotta Porcellus at his finger's

ends. The Comical Poet made this his only care and sole study, to please
the people, tickle the ear, and to delight:

> *I care not, so I am able*
>
> *To please the audience with my fable.*   (TERENCE)

But mine earnest intent is as much to profit as to please; and these
my writings, I hope, shall take like gilded pills, which are so composed
as well to tempt the appetite and deceive the palate, as to help and
medicinally work upon the whole body; my lines shall not only recreate
but rectify the mind. I think I have said enough; if not, let him that is
otherwise minded remember that of Apuleius Maudaurensis, he was in
his life a Philosopher, (as Ausonius apologizeth for him), in his Epigrams a Lover, in his precepts most severe, in his Epistle to Caerellia a
wanton. Annianus, Sulpicius, Evenus, Menander, and many old Poets
besides, did write Fescennines [or wanton verses], Atellanes [or droll
comedies], and lascivious songs, jocose things; yet they had virtuous
ways, they were chaste, severe, and upright livers.

> *Be the poet free from smutch,*
>
> *But his verses far from such;*
>
> *For the Muse is at her best*
>
> *When she's laughing and undressed.*   (CATULLUS)

I am of Catullus' opinion, and make the same apology in mine own
behalf. This that I write depends much on the opinion and authority
of others; nor perchance am I mad myself, I only follow in the steps of
those that are. Yet I may be a little off; we have all been mad at one
time or another; you yourself, I think, are touched, and this man, and
that man, so I must be, too.

> *I am a man; and naught in man can be*
>
> *That I can reckon wholly strange to me.*   (TERENCE)

And, which Martial urgeth for himself, accused of the like fault, I as
justly plead:

> *Wanton though my pages seem*
>
> *Do not my own life so deem.*

Howsoever my lines err, my life is honest:

> *Jocund my Muse is, but my life is chaste.*   (OVID)

But I presume I need no such apologies. I need not, as Socrates in Plato,
cover his face when he spake of Love, or blush and hide mine eyes, as
Pallas did in her hood, when she was consulted by Jupiter about Mercury's marriage; it is no such lascivious, obscene, or wanton discourse;
I have not offended your chaster ears with any thing that is here written, as many French and Italian Authors in their modern language of

late have done, nay some of our Latin Pontifical writers, Zanchius, Asorius, Abulensis, Burchardus, &c., whom Rivet accuseth to be more lascivious than Virgil in his Priapian verses, Petronius in his Catalectics, Aristophanes in his Lysistrata, Martial, or any other Pagan profane writer, who have so badly sinned (Barthius notes), in this kind of writing, that chaste minds abhor for their obscenities many most ingenious works. 'Tis not scurrile, this, but chaste, honest, most part serious, and even of religion itself. Incensed (as Ficinus said) with the love of finding love, we have sought it, and found it. More yet, I have augmented and added something to this light Treatise (if light) which was not in the former Editions; I am not ashamed to confess it, with a good Author, that overborne by the importunity of friends, who asked me to enlarge and better my book, I have addressed my otherwise reluctant mind to the work; and now for the sixth time have I taken pen in hand and devoted myself to writings foreign enough to my studies and profession, stealing a few hours from serious occupations and giving them if you please to refreshment and play:

> *I trim my sails, and trace once more*
> *The same course that was mine before,* (HORACE)

though I was hardly ignorant that new detractors would not be wanting to blame my additions.

And thus much I have thought good to say by way of preface, lest any man (which Godefridus feared in his book) should blame in me lightness, wantonness, rashness, in speaking of Love's causes, enticements, remedies, lawful and unlawful loves, and lust itself. I speak it only to tax and deter others from it, not to teach, but to show the vanities and fopperies of this heroical or Herculean Love, and to apply remedies unto it. I will treat of this with like liberty as of the rest.

> *I will tell all, that you in turn*
> *May tell all those who wish to learn;*
> *And when this writing is antique,*
> *Still in its pages may men seek.* (CATULLUS)

Condemn me not, good Reader, then, or censure me too hardly, if some part of this Treatise to thy thinking as yet be too light, but consider better of it. To the pure all things are pure; a naked man to a modest woman is no otherwise than a picture, as Augusta Livia truly said; and evil mind, evil thoughts, 'tis as 'tis taken. If in thy censure it be too light, I advise thee, as Lipsius did his reader for some places of Plautus, avoid them then, as if they were the rocks of the Sirens; if they like thee not, let them pass; or oppose that which is good to that which is bad, and reject not therefore all. For to invert that verse of Martial, and with Hierom Wolfius to apply it to my present purpose, some is good, some bad, some is indifferent. I say farther with him yet, I have inserted foolish trifles that I might not be too oppressive, and jests from the market-place, the theatres, the streets, nay even the cook-shops, some things more homely, light or comical, the offering of Gratius,* &c., which I would request every man to interpret to the best, and, as Julius Cæsar Scaliger besought Cardan, *though you should prefer a somewhat more polite amusement, by the immortal Gods, Hieronymus Cardan, take me not badly amiss;* I beseech thee, good reader, not to mistake me, or misconstrue what is here written; by the Muses and Charities, and by the grace of all the Poets, gentle reader, do not take me ill. 'Tis a Comical subject; in sober sadness I crave pardon of what is amiss, and desire thee to suspend thy judgement, wink at small faults, or to be silent at least; but if thou likest, speak well of it, and wish me good success.

> *O Arethusa, one last time*
> *Give inspiration to my rhyme!* (VIRGIL)

I am resolved howsoever, willy nilly, to go fearlessly into the arena, in the Olympics, with those Elean wrestlers in Philostratus, boldly to shew myself in this common Stage, and in this Tragi-Comedy of Love to act several parts, some Satirically, some Comically, some in a mixt tone, as the subject I have in hand gives occasion, and present Scene shall require or offer itself.

SUBSECTION 2 — *Love's Beginning, Object, Definition, Division*

LOVE's limits are ample and great, and a spacious walk it hath, beset with thorns, and for that cause, which Scaliger reprehends in Cardan, not lightly to be passed over. Lest I incur the same censure, I will examine all the kinds of Love, his nature, beginning, difference, objects, how it is honest or dishonest, a virtue or vice, a natural passion or a disease, his power and effects, how far it extends: of which, although something hath been said in the first Partition, in those Sections of Perturbations (for Love and hatred are the first and most common passions, from which all the rest arise, and are attendant, as Piccolomineus holds, or, as Caussinus, the Primum Mobile of all other affections, which carry them all about them), I will now more copiously dilate, through all his parts and several branches, that so it may better appear what Love is, and how it varies with the objects, how in defect, or

---

* Gratius, a Latin poet who wrote of dogs and hunting.

(which is most ordinary and common) immoderate, and in excess, causeth melancholy.

Love, universally taken, is defined to be a Desire, as a word of more ample signification: and though Leon Hebræus, the most copious writer of this subject, in his third Dialogue make no difference, yet in his first he distinguisheth them again, and defines Love by desire. Love is a voluntary affection, and desire to enjoy that which is good. Desire wisheth, Love enjoys: the end of the one is the beginning of the other: that which we love is present; that which we desire is absent. It is worth the labour, saith Plotinus, to consider well of Love, whether it be a God or a Devil, or passion of the mind, or partly God, partly Devil, partly passion. He concludes Love to participate of all three, to arise from desire of that which is beautiful and fair, and defines it to be an action of the mind desiring that which is good. Plato calls it the great Devil, for its vehemency, and sovereignty over all other passions, and defines it an appetite, by which we desire some good to be present. Ficinus in his comment adds the word fair to this definition, Love is a desire of enjoying that which is good and fair. Austin dilates this common definition, and will have love to be a delectation of the heart for something which we seek to win, or joy to have, coveting by desire, resting in joy. Scaliger taxeth these former definitions, and will not have love to be defined by Desire or Appetite: for when we enjoy the things we desire, there remains no more appetite: as he defines it, Love is an affection by which we are either united to the thing we love, or perpetuate our union; which agrees in part with Leon Hebræus.

Now this Love varies as its object varies, which is always good, amiable, fair, gracious, and pleasant. All things desire that which is good, as we are taught in the Ethicks, or at least that which to them seems to be good; as Austin well infers, thou wilt wish no harm I suppose, no ill in all thine actions, thoughts or desires, wish ill to none; thou wilt not have bad corn, bad soil, a naughty tree, but all good; a good servant, a good horse, a good son, a good friend, a good neighbour, a good wife. From this goodness comes Beauty; from Beauty, Grace, and Comeliness, which result as so many rays from their good parts, make us to love, and so to covet it: for were it not pleasing and gracious in our eyes, we should not seek. No man loves, saith Aristotle, but he that was first delighted with comeliness and beauty. As this fair object varies, so doth our Love; for, as Proclus holds, every fair thing is amiable, and what we love is fair and gracious in our eyes, or at least we do so apprehend and still esteem of it. Amiableness is the object of

Love, the scope and end is to obtain it, for whose sake we love, and which our mind covets to enjoy. And it seems to us especially fair and good; for good, fair, and unity, cannot be separated. Beauty shines, Plato saith, and by reason of its splendour and shining causeth admiration; and the fairer the object is, the more eagerly it is sought. For, as the same Plato defines it, Beauty is a lively shining or glittering brightness, resulting from effused good, by ideas, seeds, reasons, shadows, stirring up our minds, that by this good they may be united and made one.

Others will have beauty to be the perfection of the whole composition, caused out of the congruous symmetry, measure, order and manner of parts; and that comeliness which proceeds from this beauty is called grace, and from thence all fair things are gracious. For grace and beauty are so wonderfully annexed, so sweetly and gently win our souls, and strongly allure, that they confound our judgement and cannot be distinguished. Beauty and Grace are like those beams and shinings that come from the glorious and divine Sun, which are diverse, as they proceed from the diverse objects, to please and affect our several senses. As the species of beauty are taken at our eyes, ears, or conceived in our inner soul, as Plato disputes at large in his Dialogue on Beauty, Phædrus, Hippias, and, after many sophistical errors confuted, concludes that beauty is a grace in all things, delighting the eyes, ears and soul itself; so that, as Valesius infers hence, whatsoever pleaseth our ears, eyes, and soul, must needs be beautiful, fair, and delightsome to us. And nothing can more please our ears than musick, or pacify our minds. Fair houses, pictures, orchards, gardens, fields, a fair hawk, a fair horse is most acceptable unto us; whatsoever pleaseth our eyes and ears, we call beautiful and fair; pleasure belongeth to the rest of the senses, but grace and beauty to these two alone. As the objects vary and are diverse, so they diversely affect our eyes, ears, and soul itself; which gives occasion to some to make so many several kinds of Love as there be objects: one beauty ariseth from God, of which and divine Love S. Dionysius, with many Fathers and Neotericks, have written just volumes, On the Love of God, as they term it, many parænetical discourses; another from his creatures; there is a beauty of the body, a · beauty of the soul, a beauty from virtue, a beauty of martyrs, Austin calls it, which we see with the eyes of our mind; which beauty, as Tully saith, if we could discern with these corporeal eyes, would cause admirable affections, and ravish our souls. This other beauty, which ariseth from those extreme parts, and graces which proceed from ges-

tures, speeches, several motions, and proportions of creatures, men and
women (especially from women, which made those old Poets put the
three Graces still in Venus' company, as attending on her, and holding
up her train) are infinite almost, and vary their names with their objects, as love of money, covetousness, love of beauty, lust, immoderate
desire of any pleasure, concupiscence, friendship, love, good will, &c.,
and is either virtue or vice, honest, dishonest, in excess, defect, as shall
be shewed in his place; heroical love, religious love, &c. which may
be reduced to a twofold division, according to the principal parts which
are affected, the brain and liver: love and friendship, which Scaliger,
Valesius and Melancthon, warrant out of Plato, from that speech of
Pausanias, belike, that makes two Venuses and two loves: One Venus is
ancient, without a mother, and descended from heaven, whom we call
celestial; the younger begotten of Jupiter and Dione, whom commonly
we call Venus.

Ficinus in his comment upon this place, following Plato, calls these
two loves two Devils, or good and bad Angels according to us, which
are still hovering about our souls: The one rears to heaven, the other
depresseth us to hell; the one good, which stirs us up to the contemplation of that divine beauty, for whose sake we perform Justice, and
all godly offices, study Philosophy, &c., the other base, and, though
bad, yet to be respected; for indeed both are good in their own natures;
procreation of children is as necessary as that finding out of truth, but
therefore called bad because it is abused, and withdraws our soul from
the speculation of that other to viler objects; so far Ficinus. S. Austin
hath delivered as much in effect. Every creature is good, and may be
loved well or ill: and two Cities make two Loves, Jerusalem and Babylon, the Love of God the one, the Love of the world the other; of these
two cities we all are Citizens, as by examination of ourselves we may
soon find, and of which: the one Love is the root of all mischief, the
other of all good. So he will have those four cardinal virtues to be
nought else but Love rightly composed; he calls virtue the order of
Love, whom Thomas following, confirms as much, and amplifies in
many words. Lucian to the same purpose hath a division of his own,
one love was born in the sea, which is as various and raging in young
men's breasts as the sea itself, and causeth burning lust: the other is
that golden chain which was let down from heaven, and with a divine
Fury ravisheth our souls, made to the image of God, and stirs us up
to comprehend the innate and incorruptible beauty, to which we were
once created. Beroaldus hath expressed all this in an Epigram of his.

If divine Plato's tenents they be true,
　Two Veneres, two loves there be;
The one from heaven, unbegotten still,
　Which knits our souls in unity.
The other famous over all the world,
　Binding the hearts of gods and men;
Dishonest, wanton, and seducing, she
　Rules whom she will, both where and when.

This twofold division of Love, Origen likewise follows in his Comment on the Canticles, one from God, the other from the Devil, as he holds, (understanding it in the worser sense) which many others repeat and imitate. Both which (to omit all subdivisions) in excess or defect, as they are abused, or degenerate, cause melancholy in a particular kind, as shall be shewed in his place. Austin, in another Tract, makes a threefold division of this Love, which we may use well or ill: God, our neighbour, and the world: God above us, our neighbour next us, the world beneath us. In the course of our desires God hath three things, the world one, our neighbour two. Our desire to God is either from God, with God, or to God, and ordinarily so runs. From God, when it receives from him, whence, and for which it should love him: with God, when it contradicts his will in nothing: to God, when it seeks to him, and rests itself in him. Our Love to our neighbour may proceed from him, and run with him, not to him; from him, as when we rejoice of his good safety, and well doing; with him when we desire to have him a fellow and companion of our journey in the way of the Lord; not in him, because there is no aid, hope, or confidence, in man. From the world our Love comes, when we begin to admire the Creator in his works, and glorify God in his creatures; with the world it should run, if, according to the mutability of all temporalities, it should be dejected in adversity, or over elevated in prosperity; to the world, if it would settle itself in its vain delights and studies. — Many such partitions of Love I could repeat, and Subdivisions, but lest (which Scaliger objects to Cardan) I confound filthy burning lust with pure and divine Love, I will follow that accurate Division of Leon Hebræus, in the Dialogue, betwixt Sophia and Philo, where he speaks of Natural, Sensible, and Rational Love, and handleth each apart. Natural Love or Hatred is that Sympathy or Antipathy which is to be seen in animate and inanimate creatures, in the four Elements, Metals, Stones, heavy things go downward, as a Stone to his Centre, Fire upward, and rivers to the Sea. The Sun, Moon, and Stars go still round, performing gladly their natural tasks, for love of perfection. This Love is manifest, I say, in inanimate creatures. How comes a load-stone to draw iron to it? jet, chaff? the ground to covet showers, but for Love? No creature, S. Hierom concludes, is to be found, that doth not love something, no stock, no stone, that hath not some feeling of love. 'Tis more eminent in Plants, Herbs, and is especially observed in vegetals; as betwixt the Vine and Elm a great Sympathy, betwixt the Vine and the Cabbage, betwixt the Vine and Olive,

The Virgin Goddess flees from Bacchus, (ALCIATI)

betwixt the Vine and Bays a great antipathy, the Vine loves not the Bay nor his smell, and will kill him, if he grow near him; the Burr and the Lintle cannot endure one another, the Olive and the Myrtle embrace each other, in roots and branches, if they grow near. Read more of this in Piccolomineus, Crescentius, Baptista Porta, Fracastorius. Of the Love and Hatred of Planets consult with every Astrologer: Leon Hebræus gives many fabulous reasons, and moralizeth them withal. Sensible Love is that of brute beasts, of which the same Leon Hebræus, assigns these causes. First for the pleasure they take in the Act of Generation, male and female love one another. Secondly for the preservation of the species, and desire of young brood. Thirdly for the mutual agreement, as being of the same kind: the Pig is regarded by the Pig as the most beautiful thing in the world, the Dog by the Dog, the Cow by the Cow, the Ass by the Ass, as Epicharmus held, and according to that Adage of Diogenianus,

Jackdaw percheth beside Jackdaw,

they much delight in one another's company,

The grasshopper loves the grasshopper aye,
Likewise the ant the ant, they say, (THEOCRITUS)

and birds of a feather will flock together. Fourthly for custom, use, and familiarity, as if a dog be trained up with a Lion and a Bear, contrary to their natures, they will love each other. Hawks, dogs, horses, love their masters and keepers: many stories I could relate in this kind, but see Gillius, those two Epistles of Lipsius, of dogs and horses, A. Gellius, &c. Fifthly, for bringing up, as if a bitch bring up a kid, a hen ducklings, an hedge-sparrow a cuckoo, &c.

The third kind is Cognitive Love, as Leo calls it, Rational Love, Intellectual Love, and is proper to men, on which I must insist. This appears in God, Angels, Men. God is love itself, the fountain of Love, the Disciple of love, as Plato styles him; the servant of peace, the God of love and peace; have peace with all men, and God is with you.

By this Love (saith Gerson) we purchase Heaven, and buy the Kingdom of God. This Love is either in the Trinity itself, for the Holy Ghost is the Love of the Father and the Son, &c., or towards us his creatures, as in making the world. Love made the world, Love built Cities, is the soul of the world, invented Arts, Sciences, and all good things, incites us to virtue and humanity, combines and quickens; keeps peace on earth, quietness by sea, mirth in the winds and elements, expels all fear, anger, and rusticity: is a round circle still from good to good; for Love is the beginner and end of all our actions, the efficient and instrumental cause, as our Poets in their Symbols, Impresses, Emblems of rings, squares, &c., shadow unto us.

> *If first and last of any thing you wit,*
> *Cease; love's the sole and only cause of it.*

Love, saith Leo, made the world, and afterwards, in redeeming of it, " God so loved the world, that he gave his only begotten son for it." " Behold what love the Father hath shewed on us, that we should be called the sons of God." Or by his sweet providence, in protecting of it; either all in general, or his Saints elect and Church in particular, whom he keeps as the apple of his eye, whom he loves freely, as Hosea speaks, and dearly respects. Dearer to the gods than to himself is man. Not that we are fair, nor for any merit or grace of ours, for we are most vile and base; but out of his incomparable love and goodness, out of his divine Nature. And this is that Homer's golden chain, which reacheth down from Heaven to Earth, by which every creature is annexed, and depends on his Creator. He made all, saith Moses, " and it was good," and he loves it as good.

The love of Angels and living souls, is mutual amongst themselves, towards us militant in the Church, and all such as love God; as the Sun beams irradiate the Earth from those celestial Thrones, they by their well-wishes reflect on us; eager are they in good will to men, constant in guidance, there is joy in Heaven for every sinner that repenteth; they pray for us, are solicitous for our good, pure spirits. Where charity reigns, sweet desire, joy and love of God are there also. Love proper to mortal men is the third Member of this subdivision, and the subject of my following discourse.

MEMBER 2

SUBSECTION 1 — *Love of Men, which varies as his objects, profitable,*
pleasant, honest

VALESIUS defines this love which is in men, to be an affection of both
powers, Appetite, and Reason. The rational resides in the Brain, the
other in the Liver (as before hath been said out of Plato and others)
the heart is diversely affected of both, and carried a thousand ways by
consent. The sensitive faculty most part over-rules reason, the Soul is
carried hood-winkt, and the understanding captive like a beast. The
heart is variously inclined, sometimes they are merry, sometimes sad,
and from Love arise Hope and Fear, Jealousy, Fury, Desperation. Now
this Love of men is diverse, and varies, as the object varies, by which
they are enticed, as virtue, wisdom, eloquence, profit, wealth, money,
fame, honour, or comeliness of person, &c. Leon Hebræus, in his first
Dialogue, reduceth them all to these three, Profitable, Pleasant, Honest,
(out of Aristotle, belike), of which he discourseth at large ; and whatsoever is beautiful and fair, is referred to them, or any way to be desired. To profitable, is ascribed health, wealth, honour, &c., which is
rather Ambition, Desire, Covetousness, than Love. Friends, Children,
Love of women, all delightful and pleasant objects, are referred to the
second. The love of honest things consists in virtue and wisdom, and is
preferred before that which is profitable and pleasant: Intellectual
about that which is honest. St. Austin calls profitable, worldly ; pleasant,
carnal ; honest, spiritual. Of and from all three result Charity, Friendship and true Love, which respects God and our neighbour. Of each of
these I will briefly dilate, and shew in what sort they cause melancholy.

   Amongst all these fair enticing objects, which procure Love, and
bewitch the Soul of man, there is none so moving, so forcible, as profit ;
and that which carrieth with it a shew of commodity. Health indeed is
a precious thing, to recover and preserve which we will undergo any
misery, drink bitter potions, freely give our goods : restore a man to his
health, his purse lies open to thee, bountiful he is, thankful and beholding to thee ; but give him wealth and honour, give him gold, or
what shall be for his advantage and preferment, and thou shalt command his affections, oblige him eternally to thee, heart, hand, life and
all, is at thy service, thou art his dear and loving friend, good and
gracious Lord and Master, his Mæcenas ; he is thy slave, thy vassal,

most devote, affectioned, and bound in all duty: tell him good tidings in this kind, there spoke an Angel, a blessed hour that brings in gain, he is thy creature, and thou his creator, he hugs and admires thee; he is thine for ever. No Loadstone so attractive as that of profit, none so fair an object as this of gold: nothing wins a man sooner than a good turn; bounty and liberality command body and soul.

Good turns doth pacify both God and men,
And Jupiter himself is won by them. (OVID)

Gold of all other is a most delicious object, a sweet light, a goodly lustre it hath; and, saith Austin, we had rather see it than the Sun. Sweet and pleasant in getting, in keeping; it seasons all our labours, intolerable pains we take for it, base employments, endure bitter flouts and taunts, long journeys, heavy burdens, all are made light and easy by this hope of gain;

At home I think I have what's best,
Counting the money in my chest. (HORACE)

The sight of gold refresheth our spirits, and ravisheth our hearts, as that Babylonian garment and golden wedge did Achan in the camp, the very sight and hearing sets on fire his soul with desire of it. It will make a man run to the Antipodes, or tarry at home and turn parasite, lie, flatter, prostitute himself, swear and bear false witness; he will venture his body, kill a king, murder his father, and damn his soul to come at it. As he well observed, the mass of gold is fairer than all your Grecian pictures, that Apelles, Phidias, or any doting painter could ever make: we are enamoured with it.

The promptest prayer, to all the temples known,
Is, Let increase of riches be my own: (JUVENAL)

All our labours, studies, endeavours, vows, prayers and wishes, are to get, how to compass it. This is the great Goddess we adore and worship, this is the sole object of our desire. If we have it, as we think, we are made for ever, thrice happy, Princes, Lords, &c. If we lose it, we are dull, heavy, dejected, discontent, miserable, desperate, and mad. Our estate and well being ebbs and flows with our commodity; and, as we are endowed or enriched, so are we beloved and esteemed: it lasts no longer than our wealth; when that is gone, and the object removed, farewell friendship: as long as bounty, good cheer, and rewards were to be hoped, friends enough; they were tied to thee by the teeth, and would follow thee as Crows do a Carcass: but when thy goods are gone and spent, the lamp of their Love is out, and thou shalt be contemned, scorned, hated, injured. Lucian's Timon, when he lived in prosperity, was the sole spectacle of Greece, only admired; who but Timon? Everybody loved, honoured, applauded him, each man offered him his service, and sought to be kin to him; but when his gold was spent, his fair possessions gone, farewell Timon: none so ugly, none so deformed, so odious an object as Timon, no man so ridiculous on a sudden, they gave him a penny to buy a rope; no man would know him.

'Tis the general humour of the world, commodity steers our affections throughout, we love those that are fortunate and rich, that thrive, or by whom we may receive mutual kindness, hope for like courtesies, get any good, gain, or profit; hate those, and abhor, on the other side, which are poor and miserable, or by whom we may sustain loss or inconvenience. And even those that were now familiar and dear unto us, our loving and long friends, neighbours, kinsmen, allies, with whom we have conversed and lived as so many Geryons for some years past, striving still to give one another all good content and entertainment, with mutual invitations, feastings, disports, offices, for whom we would ride, run, spend ourselves, and of whom we have so freely and honourably spoken, to whom we have given all those turgent titles, and magnificent elogiums, most excellent and most noble, worthy, wise, grave, learned, valiant, &c., and magnified beyond measure: if any controversy arise betwixt us, some trespass, injury, abuse, some part of our goods be detained, a piece of Land come to be litigious, if they cross us in our suit, or touch the string of our commodity, we detest and depress them upon a sudden: neither affinity, consanguinity, or old acquaintance, can contain us, but the vainglorious avoid the wretched. A golden apple sets all together by the ears, as if a marrow-bone, or honeycomb, were flung amongst Bears: Father and Son, Brother and Sister, kinsmen are at odds: and look what malice, deadly hatred can invent, that shall be done, dreadful, ill-omened, pestilential, savage, beastly, mutual injuries, desire of revenge, and how to hurt them, him and his, are all our studies. If our pleasures be interrupt, we can tolerate it: our bodies hurt, we can put it up and be reconciled: but touch our commodities, we are most impatient: fair becomes foul, the Graces are turned to Harpies, friendly salutations to bitter imprecations, mutual feastings to plotting villainies, minings, and counterminings; good words to Satires and invectives, we revile against him, nought but his imperfections are in our eyes, he is a base knave, a Devil, a Monster, a Caterpillar, a Viper, an Hog-rubber, &c. What began as a lovely woman turns out to have a fish's tail. The Scene is altered on a sudden, Love is turned to hate, mirth to melancholy: so furiously are we most part bent, our affections fixed, upon this object of commodity, and upon money, the desire of which in excess is covetousness. Ambition tyrannizeth over our souls, as I have shewed, and in defect crucifies as much, as if a man by negligence, ill husbandry, improvidence, prodigality, waste and consume his goods and fortunes, beggary follows, and melancholy, he becomes an abject, odious and worse than an Infidel, in not providing for his family.

SUBSECTION 2 — *Pleasant Objects of Love*

PLEASANT Objects are infinite, whether they be such as have life, or be without life. Inanimate are Countries, Provinces, Towers, Towns, Cities, as he said, we see a fair Island by description when we see it not. The Sun never saw a fairer City, 'tis as charming as Tempe in Thessaly, Orchards, Gardens, pleasant walks, Groves, Fountains, &c. The heaven itself is said to be fair or foul: fair buildings, fair pictures, all artificial, elaborate and curious works, clothes, give an admirable lustre: we admire, and gaze upon them, as children do on a Peacock: a fair Dog, a fair Horse and Hawk, &c. The Thessalian loves a colt, the Egyptian a bullock, the Lacedaemonian a young dog, &c., such things we love, are most gracious in our sight, acceptable unto us, and whatsoever else may cause this passion, if it be superfluous or immoderately loved, as Guianerius observes. These things in themselves are pleasing and good, singular ornaments, necessary, comely, and fit to be had; but when we fix an immoderate eye, and dote on them over much, this pleasure may turn to pain, bring much sorrow, and discontent unto us, work our final overthrow, and cause melancholy in the end. Many are carried away with those bewitching sports of gaming, hawking, hunting, and such vain pleasures, as I have said: some with immoderate desire of fame, to be crowned in the Olympicks, knighted in the field, &c., and by these means ruinate themselves. The lascivious dotes on his fair mistress, the glutton on his dishes, which are infinitely varied to please the palate, the epicure on his several pleasures, the superstitious on his idol, and fats himself with future joys, as Turks feed themselves with an imaginary persuasion of a sensual Paradise: so several pleasant objects diversely affect divers men. But the fairest objects and enticings proceed from men themselves, which most frequently captivate, allure, and make them dote beyond all measure upon one another, and that for many respects. First, as some suppose, by that secret force of stars: (What star brings me to thee?) They do singularly dote on such a man, hate such again, and can give no reason for it. I do not love thee, Sir, &c. Alexander admired Hephæstion, Adrian Antinous, Nero Sporus, &c. The physicians refer this to their temperament, Astrologers to trine and sextile Aspects, or opposite of their several Ascendants, Lords of their genitures, love and hatred of Planets; Cicogna, to concord and discord of Spirits; but most to outward Graces. A merry companion is welcome and acceptable to all men, and therefore, saith Gomesius, Princes and great men entertain Jesters and players commonly in their Courts. But, 'tis similitude of manners which ties most men in an inseparable link, as if they be addicted to the same studies or disports, they delight in one another's companies, birds of a feather will gather together: if they be of diverse inclinations, or opposite in manners, they can seldom agree. Secondly, affability, custom, and familiarity, may convert nature many times, though they be different in manners, as if they be Country-men, fellow students, colleagues, or have been fellow-soldiers, brethren in affliction (for calamity joineth unlike men together), affinity, or some such accidental occasion, though they cannot agree amongst themselves, they will stick together like burrs, and hold against a third: so after some discontinuance, or death, enmity ceaseth; or in a foreign place.

> *Envy feeds on the living, after death 'twill tire;*
> *Hatred rests in the grave, with grief and ire.*   (OVID)

A third cause of Love and hate may be mutual offices, the receiving of benefits, commend him, use him kindly, take his part in a quarrel, relieve him in his misery, thou winnest him for ever; do the opposite, and be sure of a perpetual enemy. Praise and dispraise of each other do as much, though unknown, as Scioppius by Scaliger and Casaubonus: Mule scratcheth Mule, who but Scaliger with him? what Encomiums, Epithets, Elogiums! Master of Wisdom, perpetual dictator, ornament of literature, wonder of Europe, noble Scaliger, incredible excellence of genius, &c., in every respect more comparable to Gods than men, we venerate his writings on bended knees as like unto those [Roman] shields fallen from Heaven, &c., but when they began to vary, none so absurd as Scaliger, so vile and base, as his books, Concerning the Bordone Family,* & other Satirical invectives, may witness. Ovid in Ibis, Archil-

---

* Joseph Lustus Scaliger had asserted himself to be a scion of the ancient house of La Scala, princes and rulers of Verona; his son, Joseph Justus Scaliger, took him at his word and wrote a life of his father in which these claims were put forth. Scioppius wrote a sarcastic book, The Suppositious Scaliger, undertaking to show that he was really the son of a schoolmaster named Bordone. J. J. Scaliger replied with a Confutation of the Bordone Fable. But he was unable to prove his father's claims, and the calling in question of his lineage and his father's veracity is said to have hastened his death.

ochus himself, was not so bitter. Another great tie or cause of Love is consanguinity; parents are dear to their children, children to their parents, brothers and sisters, cousins of all sorts, as an hen and chickens, all of a knot: every crow thinks her own bird fairest. Many memorable examples are in this kind, and 'tis monstrous, if they do not: a mother cannot forget her child; Solomon so found out the true owner: love of parents may not be concealed, 'tis natural, descends, and they that are inhuman in this kind, are unworthy of that air they breathe, and of the four elements; yet many unnatural examples we have in this rank, of hard-hearted parents, disobedient children, of disagreeing brothers, nothing so common. The love of kinsmen is grown cold, many kinsmen, (as the saying is) few friends; if thine estate be good, and thou able to requite their kindness, there will be mutual correspondence, otherwise thou art a burden, most odious to them above all others. The last object that ties man and man, is comeliness of person, and beauty alone, as men love women with a wanton eye: which, above all, is termed Heroical, or Love-melancholy. Other Loves (saith Piccolomineus) are so called with some contraction, as the Love of wine, gold, &c., but this of women is predominant in an higher strain, whose part affected is the liver, and this Love deserves a longer explication, and shall be dilated apart in the next Section.

SUBSECTION 3 — *Honest objects of Love*

BEAUTY is the common object of all Love, as jet draws a straw, so doth beauty love: virtue and honesty are great motives, and give as fair a lustre as the rest, especially if they be sincere and right, not fucate, but proceeding from true form, and an incorrupt judgement; those two Venus twins, Eros and Anteros, are then most firm and fast. For many times otherwise men are deceived by their flattering Gnathos, dissembling Chamæleons, out-sides, hypocrites, that make a shew of great love, learning, pretend honesty, virtue, zeal, modesty, with affected looks and counterfeit gestures: feigned protestations often steal away the hearts and favours of men, and deceive them, the appearance and shadow of virtue, when as in truth and indeed there is no worth or honesty at all in them, no truth, but mere hypocrisy, subtilty, knavery, and the like. As true friends they are, as he that Cælius Secundus met by the highway side; and hard it is in this temporising age to distinguish such companions, or to find them out. Such Gnathos as these for the most part belong to great men, and by this glozing flattery, affability, and such like philters, so dive and insinuate into their favours, that they are taken for men of excellent worth, wisdom, learning, demi-Gods, and so screw themselves into dignities, honours, offices: but these men cause harsh confusion often, and as many stirs as Rehoboam's Counsellors in a common-wealth, overthrow themselves and others. Tandlerus, and some authors, make a doubt whether Love and Hatred may be compelled by philters or characters; Cardan, and Marbodius, by precious stones and amulets; Astrologers by election of times, &c., as I shall elsewhere discuss. The true object of this honest Love is virtue, wisdom, honesty, real worth, inward beauty, and this Love cannot deceive or be compelled: may you be loved that are worthy of love; Love itself is the most potent philter, virtue and wisdom, favour creating favour, the sole and only grace, not counterfeit, but open, honest, simple, naked, descending from heaven, as our Apostle hath it, an infused habit from God, which hath given several gifts, as wit, learning, tongues, for which they shall be amiable and gracious, as to Saul stature and a goodly presence. Joseph found favour in Pharaoh's court for his person; and Daniel with the Princes of the Eunuchs. Christ was gracious with God and men. There is still some peculiar grace, as of good discourse, eloquence, wit, honesty, which is the first mover and a most forcible loadstone to draw the favours and good wills of men's eyes, ears, and affections, unto them. When Jesus spake, *they were all astonished at his answers, and wondered at his gracious words which proceeded from his mouth.* An Orator steals away the hearts of men, and as another Orpheus, he pulls them to him by speech alone: a sweet voice causeth admiration; and he that can utter himself in good words, in our ordinary phrase, is called a proper man, a divine spirit. For which cause belike, our old Poets, the senate and populace of poets, made Mercury the Gentleman-usher to the Graces, Captain of eloquence, and those Charites to be Jupiter and Eurymone's daughters, descended from above. Though they be otherwise deformed, crooked, ugly to behold, those good parts of the mind denominate them fair. Plato commends the beauty of Socrates; yet who was more grim of countenance, stern and ghastly to look upon? So are and have been many great Philosophers, as Gregory Nazianzen observes, deformed most part in that which is to be seen with the eyes, but most elegant in that which is not to be seen. Often under a threadbare coat lies an excellent understanding. Æsop, Democritus, Aristotle, Politianus, Melancthon, Gesner, &c., withered old men, old Satyrs very harsh and impolite to the eye; but who were so terse, polite, eloquent, generally learned, temperate and modest? No man then living was so fair as Alcibiades, so lovely to the eye, as Boethius observes, but he had a most deformed soul.

Honesty, virtue, fair conditions, are great enticers to such as are well given, and much avail to get the favour and good will of men. Abdolonymus in Curtius, a poor man, (but, which mine Author notes, the cause of this poverty was his honesty), for his modesty and continency from a private person (for they found him digging in his garden) was saluted King, and preferred before all the Magnificoes of his time, a purple embroidered garment was put upon him, and they bade him wash himself, and, as he was worthy, take upon him the style and spirit of a King, continue his continency and the rest of his good parts. Titus Pomponius Atticus, that noble Citizen of Rome, was so fair conditioned, of so sweet a carriage, that he was generally beloved of all good men, of Cæsar, Pompey, Antony, Tully, of divers sects, &c., many estates (Cornelius Nepos writes) following him only for his worth. To hear of rich works, &c., it is worthy of your attention, Livy cries, you that scorn all but riches, and give no esteem to virtue, except they be wealthy withal. Q. Cincinnatus had but four acres, and by the consent of the Senate was chosen Dictator of Rome. Of such account were Cato, Fabricius, Aristides, Antonius, Probus, for their eminent worth: so Cæsar, Trajan, Alexander admired for valour, Hephæstio loved Alexander, but Parmenio the King: Titus, the delight of mankind, and which Aurelius Victor hath of Vespasian, the dilling [or darling] of his time, as Edgar Etheling was in England, for his excellent virtues: their memory is yet fresh, sweet, and we love them many ages after, though they be dead: he leaves behind a sweet memory of himself, saith Lipsius of his friend, living and dead they are all one. I have ever loved as thou knowest (so Tully wrote to Dolabella) Marcus Brutus for his great wit, singular honesty, constancy, sweet conditions; and believe it, there is nothing so amiable and fair as virtue. — I do mightily love Calvisinus (so Pliny writes to Sossius), a most industrious, eloquent, upright man, which is all in all with me: the affection came from his good parts. And, as S. Austin comments on the 84th Psalm, there is a peculiar beauty of justice, an inward beauty, which we see with the eyes of our hearts, love, and are enamoured with, as in Martyrs, though their bodies be torn in pieces with wild beasts, yet this beauty shines, and we love their virtues. The Stoicks are of opinion that a wise man is only fair; and Cato contends the same, that the lineaments of the mind are far fairer than those of the body, incomparably beyond them: wisdom and valour, according to Xenophon, especially deserve the name of beauty, & denominate one fair; and (as Austin holds) fairer is the truth of the Christians than the Helen of the Greeks. " Wine is strong, the king is strong, women are strong, but truth overcometh all things." " Blessed is the man that findeth wisdom, and getteth understanding: for the merchandise thereof is better than silver, and the gain thereof better than gold; it is more precious than pearls, and all the things thou canst desire are not to be compared to her." A wise, true, just, upright, and good man, I say it again, is only fair. It is reported of Magdalen, Queen of France, and wife to Lewis 11th, a Scottish woman by birth, that, walking forth in an evening with her Ladies, she spied M. Alanus, one of the King's Chaplains, a silly, old, hard-favoured man, fast asleep in a bower, and kissed him sweetly; when the young Ladies laughed at her for it, she replied, that it was not his person that she did embrace and reverence, but, with a Platonick love, the divine beauty of his soul. Thus in all ages virtue hath been adored, admired, a singular lustre hath proceeded from it: and the more virtuous he is, the more gracious, the more admired.

No man so much followed upon earth, as Christ himself; & as the Psalmist saith, *he was fairer than the sons of men.* Chrysostom, Bernard, Austin, Cassiodore, Hierome, interpret it of the beauty of his person; there was a divine Majesty in his looks, it shined like Lightning, and drew all men to it: but Basil, Cyril, Esay, Theodoret, Arnobius, &c., of the beauty of his divinity, justice, grace, eloquence, &c. Thomas of both; and so doth Baradius, and Peter Morales, adding as much of Joseph and the Virgin Mary, she excelled all others in beauty, according to that prediction of the Cumæan Sybil. Be they present or absent, near us, or afar off, this beauty shines, and will attract men many miles to come and visit it. Plato and Pythagoras left their Country to see those wise Egyptian Priests: Apollonius travelled into Æthiopia, Persia, to consult with the Magi, Brachymanes, Gymnosophists. The Queen of Sheba came to visit Solomon; and many, saith Hierom, went out of Spain and remote places a thousand miles, to behold that eloquent Livy; not to see the most beautiful of cities, nor the city-world of Octavian, but to see and hear this man. No beauty leaves such an impression, strikes so deep, or links the souls of men closer than virtue. No painter, no Graver, no Carver, can express virtue's lustre, or those admirable rays that come from it, those enchanting rays that enamour posterity, those everlasting rays that continue to the world's end. Many, saith Favorinus, that loved and admired Alcibiades in his youth, knew not, cared not, for Alcibiades a man; now seeking him they ask, where is Alcibiades: but the beauty of Socrates is still the same; virtue's lustre never fades, is ever fresh and green to all succeeding ages, and a most attractive loadstone, to draw and combine such as are present. For that reason, belike, Homer feigns the three Graces to be linked and tied hand in hand, because the hearts of men are so firmly united with such graces. O sweet bands (Seneca exclaims) which so happily combine, that those which are bound by them love their binders, desiring withal much more harder to be bound; and, as so many Geryons, to be united into one. For the nature of true friendship is to combine, to be like affected, of one mind;

> *To will and nill alike, and be*
> *Of the same mind eternally,*   (SILIUS ITALICUS)

as the Poet saith, still to continue one and the same. And where this Love takes place, there is a peace and quietness, a true correspondence, perfect amity, a Diapason of vows and wishes, the same opinions, as betwixt David and Jonathan, Damon and Pythias, Pylades and Orestes, Nisus and Euryalus, Theseus and Pirithous, they will live and die together, and prosecute one another with good turns (for those bound in love put away evil), not only living, but when their friends are dead, with Tombs and Monuments, Dirges, Epitaphs, Elegies, Inscriptions, Pyramids, Obelisks, Statues, Images, Pictures, Histories, Poems, Annals, Feasts, Anniversaries, many ages after (as Plato's Scholars did), they will make offerings to their spirits still, omit no good office that may tend to the preservation of their names, honours, and eternal memory. He did express his son in colours, in wax, in brass, in ivory, in marble, gold and silver, (as Pliny reports of a Citizen in Rome) and, in a great Auditory not long since, recited a just volume of his life. In another place, speaking of an Epigram which Martial had composed in praise of him: He gave me as much as he might, and would have done more if he could; though what can a man give more than honour, glory, and eternity? But that which he wrote, peradventure, will not continue; yet he wrote it to continue. — 'Tis all the recompence a poor scholar can make his well deserving Patron, Mæcenas, friend, to mention him in his works, to dedicate a book to his name, to write his life, &c., as all our Poets, Orators, Historiographers, have ever done, and the greatest revenge such men take of their adversaries, to persecute them with Satires, Invectives, &c., and 'tis both ways of great moment, as Plato gives us to understand. Paulus Jovius in the Fourth book of the Life and Deeds of Pope Leo Decimus, his noble Patron, concludes in these words: Because I cannot honour him as other rich men do, with like endeavour, affection, and piety, I have undertaken to write his life; since my fortunes will not give me leave to make a more sumptuous monument, I will perform those rites to his sacred ashes which a small, perhaps, but a liberal wit can afford. But I rove. Where this true love is wanting, there can be no firm peace, friendship from teeth outward, counterfeit, or from some by-respects, so long dissembled, till they have satisfied their own ends, which upon every small occasion breaks out into enmity, open war, defiance, heart-burnings, whispering, calumnies, contentions, and all manner of bitter melancholy discontents. And those men which have no other object of their Love than greatness, wealth, authority, &c., are rather feared than beloved; they neither love nor are loved; and howsoever borne with for a time, yet for their tyranny and oppression, griping, covetousness, currish hardness, folly, intemperance, imprudence, and such like vices, they are generally odious, abhorred of all, both God and men. Wife and children, friends, neighbours, all the world forsakes them, would fain be rid of them, and are compelled many times to lay violent hands on them, or else God's judgements overtake them: instead of graces come Furies. So when fair Abigail, a woman of singular wisdom, was acceptable to David, Nabal was churlish and evil-conditioned; and therefore Mordecai was received, when Haman was executed, Haman the favourite, " that had his seat above the other Princes, to whom all the King's servants that stood in the gates bowed their knees and reverenced." Though they flourish many times, such Hypocrites, such temporizing Foxes, and blear the world's eyes by flattery, bribery, dissembling their natures, or other men's weakness, that cannot so soon apprehend their tricks, yet in the end they will be discerned, and precipitated in a moment: " surely, saith David, thou hast set them in slippery places "; as so many Sejanuses, they will come down to the Gemonian steps; and, as Eusebius in Ammianus, that was in such authority, exalted to Imperial command, be cast down headlong on a sudden. Or put case they escape, and rest unmasked to their lives' end, yet, after their death, their memory stinks as a snuff of a candle put out, and those that durst not so much as mutter against them in their lives, will prosecute their name with Satires, Libels, and bitter imprecations, they shall have a bad name in all succeeding ages, and be odious to the world's end.

MEMBER 3

Charity composed of all three kinds, Pleasant, Profitable, Honest

BESIDES this Love that comes from Profit, pleasant, honest, (for one good turn asks another in equity) that which proceeds from the law of nature, or from discipline and Philosophy, there is yet another Love compounded of all these three, which is Charity, and includes piety, dilection, benevolence, friendship, even all those virtuous habits; for Love is the circle equant of all other affections, (of which Aristotle dilates at large in his Ethicks,) and is commanded by God, which no man can well perform, but he that is a Christian, and a true regenerate man. This is to love God above all, and our neighbour as ourself; for this Love is a communicating light, apt to illuminate itself as well as others. All other objects are fair, and very beautiful, I confess; kindred, alliance, friendship, the Love that we owe to our country, nature, wealth, pleasure, honour, and such moral respects, &c. of which read copious Aristotle in his Morals; a man is beloved of a man, in that he is a man; but all these are far more eminent and great, when they shall proceed from a sanctified spirit, that hath a true touch of Religion, and a reference to God. Nature binds all creatures to love their young ones: an Hen to preserve her brood will run upon a Lion, an Hind will fight with a Bull, a Sow with a Bear, a silly Sheep with a Fox. So the same nature urgeth a man to love his Parents,

　　　　　――― *all the Gods would hate me, father,*
　　Did I not cherish thee more than my very eyes!　(TERENCE)
and this Love cannot be dissolved, as Tully holds, without detestable offence: but much more God's commandment, which enjoins a filial Love, and an obedience in this kind. The Love of brethren is great, and like an arch of stones, where, if one be displaced, all comes down; no Love so forcible & strong, honest, to the combination of which nature, fortune, virtue, happily concur; yet this Love comes short of it.

　　Sweet and proper 'tis to die for one's country;　(HORACE)
it cannot be expressed, what a deal of Charity that one name of Country contains.

　　　Love of one's country serves instead of wages.
The Decii, Horatii, Curii, Scævola, Regulus, Codrus, did sacrifice themselves, for their Country's peace and good.

　　　One day the Fabii stoutly warred,
　　　One day the Fabii were destroyed.　(OVID)
Fifty thousand Englishmen lost their lives willingly near Battle Abbey in defence of their Country. P. Æmilius speaks of six Senators of Calais, that came with halters in their hands to the King of England, to die for the rest. This love makes so many writers take such pains, so many Historiographers, Physicians, &c., or at least as they pretend, for common safety, and their country's benefit. Friendship is an holy name, and

a sacred communion of friends. As the Sun is in the Firmament, so is friendship in the world, a most divine and heavenly band. As nuptial Love makes, this perfects mankind, and is to be preferred (if you will stand to the judgment of Cornelius Nepos) before affinity or consanguinity; the cords of Love bind faster than any other wreath whatsoever. Take this away, and take all pleasure, joy, comfort, happiness, and true content, out of the world; 'tis the greatest tie, the surest Indenture, strongest band, and, as our modern Maro decides it, is much to be preferred before the rest.

> *Hard is the doubt, and difficult to deem,*
> *When all three kinds of Love together meet;*
> *And do dispart the heart with power extreme,*
> *Whether shall weigh the balance down; to wit,*
> *The dear affection unto kindred sweet,*
> *Or raging fire of Love to women kind,*
> *Or zeal of friends, combin'd by virtues meet;*
> *But of them all, the band of virtuous mind,*
> *Methinks the gentle heart should most assured bind.*
>
> *For natural affection soon doth cease,*
> *And quenchèd is with Cupid's greater flame;*
> *But faithful friendship doth them both suppress,*
> *And them with mastering discipline doth tame,*
> *Through thoughts aspiring to eternal fame.*
> *For as the soul doth rule the earthly mass,*
> *And all the service of the body frame,*
> *So Love of soul doth Love of body pass,*
> *No less than perfect gold surmounts the meanest brass.*
>
> (SPENSER)

A faithful friend is better than gold, a medicine or misery, an only possession; yet this Love of friends, nuptial, heroical, profitable, pleasant, honest, all three Loves put together, are little worth, if they proceed not from a true Christian illuminated soul, if it be not done for God's sake. *Though I had the gift of Prophecy, spake with the tongues of men and Angels, though I feed the poor with all my goods, give my body to be burned, and have not this love, it profiteth me nothing,* 'tis a glittering sin without charity. This is an all-apprehending love, a deifying love, a refined, pure, divine love, the quintessence of all love, the true Philosopher's stone; as Austin infers, he is no true friend that loves not God's truth. And therefore this is true Love indeed, the cause of all good to mortal men, that reconciles all creatures, and glues them together in perpetual amity and firm league, and can no more abide bitterness, hate, malice, than fair and foul weather, light, and darkness, sterility and plenty, may be together. As the Sun in the Firmament, (I say) so is Love in the world; and for this cause 'tis Love without an addition, Love pre-eminent, Love of God and Love of men. The Love of God begets the Love of man; and by this Love of our neighbour the Love of God is nourished and increased. By this happy union of Love all well governed families and Cities are combined, the heavens annexed, and divine souls complicated, the world itself composed, and all that is in it conjoined in God, and reduced to one. This Love causeth true and absolute virtues, the life, spirit and root of every virtuous action, it finisheth prosperity, easeth adversity, corrects all natural incumbrances, inconveniences, sustained by Faith and Hope, which with this our Love make an indissoluble twist, a Gordian knot, an Æquilateral Triangle, *and yet the greatest of them is Love,* which inflames our souls with a divine heat, and being so inflamed, purgeth, and so purged, elevates to God, makes an atonement, and reconciles us unto him. That other Love infects the soul of man, this cleanseth; that depresses, this rears: that causeth cares and troubles, this quietness of mind; this informs, that deforms, our life; that leads to repentance, this to heaven. For if once we be truly link'd and touched with this charity, we shall love God above all, *our neighbour as ourself,* as we are enjoined; perform those duties and exercises, even all the operations of a good Christian.

This Love suffereth long, it is bountiful, envieth not, boasteth not itself, it is not puffed up, it deceiveth not, it seeketh not his own things, it is not provoked to anger, it thinketh not evil, it rejoiceth not in iniquity, but in truth. It suffereth all things, believeth all things, hopeth all things, ———— it covereth all trespasses, ———— a multitude of sins, ———— as our Saviour told the woman in the Gospel, that washed his feet, *many sins were forgiven her, for she loved much,* ———— *it will defend the fatherless and the widow,* ———— *will seek no revenge, or be mindful of wrong,* ———— *will bring home his brother's ox if he go astray,* as 'tis commanded, ———— *will resist evil, give to him that asketh, and not turn from him that borroweth, bless them that curse him, love his enemy,* ———— *bear his brother's burden.* He that so loves will be hospitable, and distribute to the necessities of the Saints; he will, if it be possible, have peace with all men, *feed his enemy, if he be hungry, if he be athirst, give him drink,* he will perform those seven works of mercy, *he will make himself equal to them of the lower sort, rejoice with them that rejoice, weep with them that weep,* he will speak truth to his neighbour, be courteous and tender-hearted, *forgiving others for Christ's sake, as God forgave him,* ——— *he will be like-minded,* ——— *of one judgement ; be humble, meek, long-suffering,* ——— *forbear, forget and forgive,* and what he doth, shall be heartily done to God, and not to men; *be pitiful and courteous,* ——— *seek peace and follow it.* He will love his brother *not in word and tongue, but in deed and truth,* ——— *and he that loves God, Christ will love him that is begotten of him,* &c.

Thus should we willingly do, if we had a true touch of this charity, of this divine Love, if we would perform this which we are enjoined, forget and forgive, and compose ourselves to those Christian Laws of Love. Angelical souls, how blessed, how happy should we be, so loving, how might we triumph over the devil, and have another heaven upon earth!

But this we cannot do; and which is the cause of all our woes, miseries, discontent, melancholy, want of this charity. We do press one another by turns, insult, contemn, vex, torture, molest, and hold one another's noses to the grind-stone hard, provoke, rail, scoff, calumniate, challenge, hate, abuse (hard-hearted, implacable, malicious, peevish, inexorable as we are) to satisfy our lust or private spleen, for toys, trifles, and impertinent occasions, spend ourselves, goods, friends, fortunes, to be revenged on our adversary, to ruin him and his. 'Tis all our study, practice, and business, how to plot mischief, mine, countermine, defend and offend, ward ourselves, injure others, hurt all; as if we were born to do mischief; and that with such eagerness and bitterness, with such rancour, malice, rage and fury, we prosecute our intended designs, that neither affinity or consanguinity, love or fear of God or men can contain us: no satisfaction, no composition will be accepted, no offices will serve, no submission; though he shall upon his knees, as Sarpedon did to Glaucus in Homer, acknowledging his error, yield himself with tears in his eyes, beg his pardon, we will not relent, forgive, or forget, till we have confounded him and his, made dice of his bones, as they say, see him rot in prison, banish his friends, followers, and the whole hated stock, rooted him out and all his posterity. Monsters of men as we are, Dogs, Wolves, Tigers, Fiends, incarnate Devils, we do not only contend, oppress, and tyrannize ourselves, but, as so many fire-brands, we set on, and animate others: our whole life is a perpetual combat, a conflict, a set battle, a snarling fit: the goddess of discord is settled in our tents, all are contaminated, opposing wit to wit, wealth to wealth, strength to strength, fortunes to fortunes, friends to friends, as at a sea-fight, we turn our broad sides, or two millstones with continual attrition, we fire ourselves, or break one another's backs, and both are ruined and consumed in the end. Miserable wretches, to fat and enrich ourselves, we care not how we get it, by what manner of means, how many thousands we undo, whom we oppress, by whose ruin and downfall we arise, whom we injure, fatherless children, widows, common societies, to satisfy our own private lust. Though we have myriads, abundance of wealth and treasure, (pitiless, merciless, remorseless, and uncharitable in the highest degree) and our poor brother in need, sickness, in great extremity, and now ready to be starved for want of food, we had rather, as the Fox told the Ape, his tail should sweep the ground still, than cover his buttocks; rather spend it idly, consume it with dogs, hawks, hounds, unnecessary buildings, in riotous apparel, ingurgitate, or let it be lost, than he should have part of it; rather take from him that little which he hath than relieve him.

Like the dog in the manger, we neither use it ourselves, let others make use of, or enjoy it; part with nothing while we live: for want of disposing our household, and setting things in order, set all the world together by the ears after our death. Poor Lazarus lies howling at his gates for a few crumbs, he only seeks chippings, offals; let him roar and howl, famish, and eat his own flesh, he respects him not. A poor decayed kinsman of his sets upon him by the way in all his jollity, and runs begging bareheaded by him, conjuring by those former bonds of friendship, alliance, consanguinity, &c., uncle, cousin, brother, father,

> *By these tears and by that hand of thine,*
> *If any wise I have deserved well of thee,*
> *If aught of mine hath ever been sweet to thee,*
> *Pity me!*   (VIRGIL)

Shew some pity for Christ's sake, pity a sick man, an old man, &c., he cares not, ride on: pretend [that is, assert] sickness, inevitable loss of limbs, goods, plead suretyship, or shipwrack, fires, common calamities, shew thy wants and imperfections,

> ———— *by holy Osiris swearing,*
> *Believe me, I deceive thee not, O help me!*   (HORACE)

Swear, protest, take God and all his Angels to witness,

> *Seek out some stranger!*   (HORACE)

thou art a counterfeit crank [or one who feigns phrenzy to get money], a cheater, he is not touched with it,

> *Everywhere is the poor man neglected,*   (OVID)

ride on, he takes no notice of it. Put up a supplication to him in the name of a thousand Orphans, an Hospital, a Spittle, a Prison as he goes by, they cry out to him for aid, ride on, you speak to a deaf man, he cares not, let them eat stones, devour themselves with vermin, rot in their own dung, he cares not. Shew him a decayed haven, a bridge, a school, a fortification, &c., or some publick work, ride on; good your Worship, your Honour, for God's sake, your country's sake, ride on. But shew him a roll wherein his name shall be registered in golden letters, and commended to all posterity, his arms set up, with his devices to be seen, and then peradventure he will stay and contribute; or if thou canst thunder upon him, as Papists do, with satisfactory and meritorious works, or persuade him by this means he shall save his soul out of Hell, and free it from Purgatory (if he be of any religion) then in all likelihood he will listen and stay; or that he have no children, no near kinsman, heir, he cares for at least, or cannot well tell otherwise how or where to bestow his possessions (for carry them with him he cannot) it may be then he will buiid some School or Hospital in his life, or be induced to give liberally to pious uses after his death. For, I dare boldly say, vain glory, that opinion of merit, and this enforced necessity, when they know not otherwise how to leave, or what better to do with them, is the main cause of most of our good works. I will not urge this to derogate from any man's charitable devotion, or bounty in this kind, to censure any good work; no doubt there be many sanctified, heroical, and worthy-minded men, that in true zeal, and for virtue's sake (divine spirits) that out of commiseration and pity extend their liberality, and, as much as in them lies, do good to all men, clothe the naked, feed the hungry, comfort the sick and needy, relieve all, forget and forgive injuries, as true charity requires; yet most part there is a deal of hypocrisy in this kind, much default and defect. Cosmo de Medici, that rich citizen of Florence, ingenuously confessed to a near friend of his, that would know of him why he built so many publick and magnificent palaces, and bestowed so liberally on Scholars, not that he loved learning more than others, but to eternize his own name, to be immortal by the benefit of Scholars; for when his friends were dead, walls decayed, and all Inscriptions gone, books would remain to the world's end. The lanthorn in Athens was built by Xenocles, the Theatre by Pericles, the famous port Piræus by Themicles, Pallas Palladium by Phidias, the Parthenon by Callicrates; but these brave monuments are decayed all, and ruined long since, their builders' names alone flourish by mediation of writers. And as he said of that Marian oak, now cut down and dead, no plant can grow so long as that which is set and manured by those everliving wits. Allon bacuth, that weeping oak, under which Deborah, Rebecca's nurse, died, and was buried, may not survive the memory of such everlasting monuments. Vain glory and emulation (as to most men) was the cause efficient, and to be a trumpeter of his own fame, Cosmo's sole intent so to do good, that all the world might take notice of it. Such for the most part is the charity of our times, such our Benefactors, Mæcenases and Patrons. Shew me, amongst so many myriads, a truly devout, a right, honest, upright, meek, humble, a patient, innocuous, innocent, a merciful, a loving, a charitable man! Lives there an honest man amongst us? Shew me a Caleb or a Joshua!

　　　　　Sing for me, Muse, the man, &c.　　(HORACE)

shew a virtuous woman, a constant wife, a good neighbour, a trusty servant, an obedient child, a true friend, &c. Crows in Africa are not so scant. He that shall examine this iron age wherein we live, where love is cold, Astræa gone from earth, Justice fled with her assistants, virtue expelled,

　　　　　——————*sister of Justice, unsullied Faith,*
　　　　　And naked Truth,　　(HORACE)

all goodness gone, where vice abounds, the Devil is loose, & see one man vilify & insult over his brother, as if he were an innocent, or a block, oppress, tyrannize, prey upon, torture him, vex, gall, torment and crucify him, starve him, where is charity? He that shall see men swear and forswear, lie and bear false witness, to advantage themselves, prejudice others, hazard goods, lives, fortunes, credit, all, to be revenged on their enemies, men so unspeakable in their lusts, unnatural in malice, such bloody designments, Italian blaspheming, Spanish renouncing, &c., may well ask where is charity? He that shall observe so many law-suits, such endless contentions, such plotting, undermining, so much money spent with such eagerness and fury, every man for himself, his own ends, the Devil for all: so many distressed souls, such lamentable complaints, so many factions, conspiracies, seditions, oppressions, abuses, injuries, such grudging, repining, discontent, so much emulation, envy, so many brawls, quarrels, monomachies, &c., may well inquire what is become of charity? when we see and read of such cruel wars, tumults, uproars, bloody battles, so many men slain, so many cities ruinated, &c., (for what else is the subject of all our stories almost, but Bills, Bows, and Guns?) so many murders and massacres, &c., where is Charity? Or see men wholly devote to God, Churchmen, professed Divines, holy men, to make the trumpet of the gospel the trumpet of war, a company of Hell-born Jesuits, and fiery-spirited Friars, hold the torch to all seditions: as so many firebrands set all the world by the ears (I say nothing of their contentious and railing books, whole ages spent in writing one against another, and that with such virulency and bitterness, satires like Bion's and poisonous wit), and by their bloody inquisitions, that in thirty years Bale saith, consumed 39 Princes, 148 Earls, 235 Barons, 14,755 Commons, worse than those ten persecutions, may justly doubt where is Charity? For Heaven's sake, what sort of Christians are these? Are these Christians? I beseech you, tell me. He that shall observe and see these things, may say to them as Cato to Cæsar, sure I think thou art of opinion there is neither Heaven, nor Hell. Let them pretend religion, zeal, make what shews they will, give alms, [be] peace-makers, frequent sermons, if we may guess at the tree by the fruit, they are no better than Hypocrites, Epicures, Atheists, with the " fool in their hearts they say there is no God." 'Tis no marvel, then, if being so uncharitable, hardhearted as we are, we have so frequent and so many discontents, such melancholy fits, so many bitter pangs, mutual discords, all in a combustion, often complaints, so common grievances, general mischiefs, so many tragedies on earth, devastating mankind, so many pestilences, wars, uproars, losses, deluges, fires, inundations, God's vengeance, and all the plagues of Egypt, come not upon us, since we are so currish one towards another, so respectless of God and our neighbours, and by our crying sins pull these miseries upon our own heads. Nay more, 'tis justly to be feared, which Josephus once said of his Countrymen Jews, if the Romans had not come when they did to sack their City, surely it had been swallowed up with some earthquake, deluge, or fired from Heaven as Sodom and Gomorrah: their desperate malice, wickedness, and peevishness, was such. 'Tis to be suspected, if we continue these wretched ways, we may look for the like heavy visitations to come upon us. If we had any sense or feeling of these things, surely we should not go on as we do in such irregular courses, practise all manner of impieties; our whole carriage would not be so averse from God. If a man would but consider, when he is in the midst and full career of such prodigious and uncharitable actions, how displeasing they are in God's sight, how noxious to himself, as Solomon told Joab, *the Lord shall bring this blood upon their heads,* ———— *sudden desolation and destruction shall come like a whirlwind upon them: affliction, anguish, the reward of his hand shall be given him, &c.,* ———— *they shall fall into the pit they have digged for others,* and when they are scraping, tyrannizing, getting, wallowing in their wealth, *this night, O fool, I will take away thy soul,* what a severe account they must make; and how gracious on the other side a charitable man is in God's eyes. *Blessed are the merciful, for they shall obtain mercy. He that lendeth to the poor,* gives to God; and how *it shall be restored to them again,* ———— how by their patience and long suffering they shall *heap coals on their enemies' heads,* ———— and *he that followeth after righteousness and mercy shall find righteousness and glory;* surely they would check their desires, curb in their unnatural, inordinate affections, agree amongst themselves, abstain from doing evil, amend their lives, and learn to do well. *Behold how comely and good a thing it is for brethren to live together in union: it is like the precious ointment, &c.* How odious to contend one with the other! Why do we contend and vex one another? behold death is over our heads, and we must shortly give an account of all our uncharitable words and actions: think upon it, and be wise!

SECTION 2 MEMBER 1

SUBSECTION I — *Heroical love causing Melancholy. His Pedigree,
Power, and Extent*

IN the precedent Section mention was made, amongst other pleasant objects, of the comeliness and beauty which proceeds from women, that causeth Heroical, or Love-melancholy, is more eminent above the rest, and properly called Love. The part affected in men is the liver, and therefore called Heroical, because commonly Gallants, Noblemen, and the most generous spirits are possessed with it. His power and extent is very large, and in that twofold division of Love, Love and Friendship, those two Venuses, which Plato and some other make mention of, it is most eminent, and par excellence called Venus, as I have said, or Love itself. Which, although it be denominated from men, and most evident in them, yet it extends and shews itself in vegetal and sensible creatures, those incorporeal substances (as shall be specified) and hath a large dominion of sovereignty over them. His pedigree is very ancient, derived from the beginning of the world, as Phædrus contends, and his parentage of such antiquity, that no Poet could ever find it out. Hesiod makes Earth and Chaos to be Love's parents, before the Gods were born.

Love was created first, before the gods.

Some think it is the self same fire Prometheus fetched from heaven. Plutarch will have Love to be the son of Iris and Favonius, but Socrates in that pleasant Dialogue of Plato, when it came to his turn to speak of Love, (of which subject Agathon, the Rhetorician, the eloquent Agathon, that Chanter Agathon, had newly given occasion), in a poetical strain.

telleth this tale. When Venus was born, all the Gods were invited to a banquet, and, amongst the rest, Porus the God of bounty and wealth; Penia or poverty came a begging to the door; Porus, well whittled with Nectar, (for there was no wine in those days), walking in Jupiter's garden, in a Bower met with Penia, and in his drink got her with child, of whom was born Love; and, because he was begotten on Venus' birth day, Venus still attends upon him. The moral of this is in Ficinus. Another tale is there, borrowed out of Aristophanes. In the beginning of the world, men had four arms, and four feet, but for their pride, because they compared themselves with the Gods, were parted into halves, and now peradventure by love they hope to be united again and made one. Otherwise thus; Vulcan met two lovers, and bid them ask what they would, and they should have it; but they made answer, O Vulcan the Gods' great Smith, we beseech thee to work us anew in thy furnace, and of two make us one; which he presently did, and ever since true lovers are either all one, or else desire to be united. Many such tales you shall find in Leon Hebræus, and their moral to them. The reason why Love was still painted young, (as Phornutus and others will) is because young men are most apt to love; soft, fair, and fat, because such folks are soonest taken: naked, because all true affection is simple and open: he smiles, because merry and given to delights: hath a quiver, to shew, his power none can escape: is blind, because he sees not where he strikes, whom he hits, &c. His power and sovereignty is expressed by the poets, in that he is held to be a God, and a great commanding God, above Jupiter himself; the great Daimon, as Plato calls him, the strongest and merriest of all the Gods, according to Alcinous and Athenæus. As Euripides, Love is the God of Gods and govenor of men; for we must do all homage to him, keep an holy day for his Deity, adore in his Temples, worship his image (a God divine, and no mere Shrine), sacrifice to his altar, that conquers all, and rules all. I had rather contend with Bulls, Lions, Bears, and Giants, than with Love; he is so powerful, enforceth all to pay tribute to him, domineers over all, and can make mad and sober whom he list; insomuch that Cæcilius, in Tully's Tusculans, holds him to be no better than a fool, or an idiot, that doth not acknowledge Love to be a great God, that can make sick and cure whom he list. Homer and Stesichorus were both made blind, if you will believe Leon Hebræus, for speaking against his god-head. And though Aristophanes degrade him, and say that he was scornfully rejected from the counsel of the Gods, had his wings clipped besides, that he might come no more amongst them, and to his farther disgrace banished heaven for ever, and confined to dwell on earth, yet he is of that power, majesty, omnipotency, and dominion, that no creature can withstand him.

Cupid rules with the power of the Gods,
And not great Jove himself can give him odds. (SOPHOCLES)

He is more than Quarter-Master with the Gods, he divides the empire of the Sea with Thetis, of the Shades with Æacus, of Heaven with Jupiter, and hath not so much possession as dominion. Jupiter himself was turned into a Satyr, a Shepherd, a Bull, a Swan, a golden shower, and what not, for love; that as Lucian's Juno right well objected to him, Thou art Cupid's whirligig: how did he insult over all the other Gods, Mars, Neptune, Pan, Mercury, Bacchus, and the rest! Lucian brings in Jupiter complaining of Cupid that he could not be quiet for him; and the Moon lamenting that she was so impotently besotted on Endymion, even Venus herself confessing as much, how rudely and in what sort her own son Cupid had used her, being his mother, now drawing her to mount Ida for the love of that Trojan Anchises, now to Libanus for that Assyrian youth's sake. And although she threatened to break his bow and arrows, to clip his wings, and whipped him besides on the bare buttocks with her pantophle, [or slipper] yet all would not serve, he was too head-strong and unruly. That monster-conquering Hercules was tamed by him:

Whom neither beasts nor enemies could tame,
Nor Juno's might subdue, Love quell'd the same. (OVID)

Your bravest soldiers and most generous spirits are enervated with it, when they surrender to feminine blandishments and defile themselves with embraces. Apollo, that took upon him to cure all diseases, could not help himself of this; and therefore Socrates calls Love a tyrant, and brings him triumphing in a Chariot, whom Petrarch imitates in his triumph of Love, and Fracastorius in an elegant Poem expresseth at large, Cupid riding, Mars and Apollo following his Chariot, Psyche weeping, &c.

In vegetal creatures what sovereignty Love hath by many pregnant proofs and familiar examples may be proved, especially of palm trees, which are both he and she, and express not a sympathy but a love-passion, as by many observations have been confirmed. Boughs live for love, and every flourishing tree in turn feels the passion: palms nod mutual vows, poplar sighs to poplar, plane to plane, and alder murmurs to alder. Constantine gives an instance out of Florentius his Georgicks, of a Palm-tree that loved most fervently, and would not be comforted until such time her Love applied himself unto her; you might see the two trees bend, and of their own accords stretch out their boughs to embrace and kiss each other: they will give manifest signs of mutual love. Ammianus Marcellinus reports that they marry one another, and fall in love if they grow in sight; and when the wind brings the smell to them, they are marvellously affected. Philostratus observes as much, and Galen, they will be sick for love, ready to die and pine away, which the husbandmen perceiving, saith Constantine, stroke many Palms that grow together, and so stroking again the Palm that is enamoured, they carry kisses from the one to the other: or tying the leaves and branches of the one to the stem of the other, will make them both flourish and prosper a great deal better: which are enamoured, they can perceive, by the bending of boughs, and inclination of their bodies. If any man think this which I say to be a tale, let him read that story of two palm trees in Italy, the male growing at Brundusium, the female at Otranto (related by Jovianus Pontanus in an excellent Poem, sometime Tutor to Alphonso Junior, King of Naples, his Secretary of State, and a great Philosopher), which were barren, and so continued a long time, till they came to see one another growing up higher, though many Stadiums asunder. Pierius in his Hieroglyphicks, and Melchior Guilandinus, in his Tract on Papyrus, cites this story of Pontanus for a truth. See more in Salmuth, Mizaldus, Sand's voyages, &c.

If such fury be in vegetals, what shall we think of sensible creatures? how much more violent and apparent shall it be in them!

> *All kind of creatures in the earth,*
> *And fishes of the sea,*
> *And painted birds do rage alike*
> *This love bears equal sway.* (VIRGIL)
> *This God rules earth and the deep seas alike.* (PROPERTIUS)

Common experience and our sense will inform us, how violently brute beasts are carried away with this passion, horses above the rest, the lust of mares is noted. Cupid, in Lucian, bids Venus his mother be of good cheer, for he was now familiar with Lions, and oftentimes did get on their backs, hold them by the mane, and ride them about like horses, and they would fawn upon him with their tails. Bulls, Bears, and Boars, are so furious in this kind, they kill one another: but especially Cocks, Lions, and Harts, which are so fierce that you may hear them fight half a mile off, saith Turberville, and many times kill each other, or compel them to abandon the rut, that they may remain masters in their places; and when one hath driven his corrival away, he raiseth his nose up into the air, and looks aloft, as though he gave thanks to nature, which affords him such great delight. How Birds are affected in this kind, appears out of Aristotle, he will have them to sing for joy or in hope of their venery which is to come.

First the birds of the air, O Goddess, of thee
And thy coming aware, are smit to the heart by thy power.

(LUCRETIUS)

Fishes pine away for love and wax lean, if Gomesius's authority may be taken, and are rampant too, some of them. Peter Gellius tells wonders of a Triton in Epirus: there was a well not far from the shore, where the country wenches fetched water; they, the Tritons, to ravish them, would set upon them and carry them to the Sea, and there drown them, if they would not yield; so Love tyrannizeth in dumb creatures. Yet this is natural for one beast to dote upon another of the same kind; but what strange fury is that, when a Beast shall dote upon a man! Saxo Grammaticus hath a story of a Bear that loved a woman, kept her in his den a long time, and begot a son of her, out of whose loins proceeded many Northern Kings: this is the original belike of that common tale of Valentine and Orson. Ælian, Pliny, Peter Gellius are full of such relations. A Peacock in Leucadia loved a maid, and when she died the Peacock pined. A Dolphin loved a boy called Hernias, and when he died, the fish came on land, and so perished. The like, adds Gellius, out of Apion, a Dolphin at Puteoli loved a child, would come often to him, let him get on his back, and carry him about, and when by sickness the child was taken away, the Dolphin died. Every book is full (saith Busbequius, the Emperor's Orator, with the Grand Seignior not long since), and yields such instances, to believe which I was always afraid, lest I should be thought to give credit to fables, until I saw a Lynx, which I had from Assyria, so affected towards one of my men, that it cannot be denied but that he was in love with him. When my man was present, the beast would use many notable enticements, and pleasant motions, and when he was going, hold him back, and look after him when he was gone, very sad in his absence, but most jocund when he returned: and when my man went from me, the beast expressed his love with continual sickness, and after he had pined away some few days, died. — Such another story he hath of a Crane of Majorca, that loved a Spaniard, that would walk any way with him, and in his absence seek about for him, make a noise that he might hear her, and knock at his door, and when he took his last farewell, famished herself. Such pretty pranks can love play with Birds, Fishes, Beasts: Venus keeps the keys of the air, earth, and sea, and alone retains the rulership of all. And

if all be certain that is credibly reported, with the Spirits of the Air, and
Devils of Hell themselves, who are as much enamoured and dote (if I
may use that word) as any other creatures whatsoever. For if those
stories be true that are written of Incubi and Succubi, of Nymphs,
lascivious Fauns, Satyrs, and those Heathen gods which were Devils,
those lascivious Telchines [or Elves], of whom the Platonists tell so
many fables; or those familiar meetings in our days, and company of
Witches and Devils, there is some probability for it. I know that Biarmannus, Wierus, and some others stoutly deny it, that the Devil hath
any carnal copulation with women, that the Devil takes no pleasure in
such facts, they be mere phantasies, all such relations of Incubi, Succubi,
lies and tales: but Austin doth acknowledge it; Erastus, on Lamias,
Jacobus Sprenger and his colleagues, &c., Zanchius, Dandinus, Bodine,
and Paracelsus, a great champion of this Tenent amongst the rest, which
give sundry peculiar instances, by many testimonies, proofs, and confessions, evince it. Hector Boethius, in his Scottish History, hath three
or four such examples, which Cardan confirms out of him, of such as
have had familiar company many years with them, and that in the habit
of men and women.

Philostratus, in his Fourth Book of his Life of Apollonius, hath a
memorable instance in this kind, which I may not omit, of one Menippus
Lycius, a young man 25 years of age, that going betwixt Cenchreæ and
Corinth, met such a phantasm in the habit of a fair gentlewoman, which,
taking him by the hand, carried him home to her house in the suburbs
of Corinth, and told him she was a Phœnician by birth, and if he would
tarry with her, he should hear her sing and play, and drink such wine as
never any drank, and no man should molest him; but she being fair and
lovely would live and die with him, that was fair and lovely to behold.
The young man, a Philosopher, otherwise staid and discreet, able to
moderate his passions, though not this of love, tarried with her a while to
his great content, and at last married her, to whose wedding, among
other guests, came Apollonius, who by some probable conjectures found
her out to be a Serpent, a Lamia, and that all her furniture was like
Tantalus' gold described by Homer, no substance, but mere illusions.
When she saw herself descried, she wept, and desired Apollonius to be
silent, but he would not be moved, and thereupon she, plate, house, and
all that was in it, vanished in an instant: many thousands took notice
of this fact, for it was done in the midst of Greece.

Sabine, in his Comment on the 10th. of Ovid's Metamorphoses, at the
tale of Orpheus, telleth us of a Gentleman of Bavaria, that for many

months together bewailed the loss of his dear wife; at length the Devil
in her habit came and comforted him, and told him, because he was so
importunate for her, that she would come and live with him again, on
that condition he would be new married, never swear and blaspheme as
he used formerly to do; for if he did, she should be gone: he vowed it,
married, and lived with her, she brought him children, and governed his
house, but was still pale and sad, and so continued, till one day falling
out with him, he fell a swearing; she vanished thereupon, and was never
after seen. This I have heard, saith Sabine, from persons of good credit,
which told me that the Duke of Bavaria did tell it for a certainty to the
Duke of Saxony.

One more I will relate out of Florilegus, about the year 1058, an
honest Historian of our nation, because he telleth it so confidently, as a
thing in those days talked of all over Europe. A young Gentleman of
Rome, the same day that he was married, after dinner with the Bride
and his friends went a walking into the fields, and towards evening to
the Tennis Court to recreate himself; whilst he played, he put his ring
upon the finger of a statue of Venus, which was thereby, made in brass;
after he had sufficiently played, and now made an end of his sport, he
came to fetch his ring, but Venus had bowed her finger in, and he could
not get it off. Whereupon loath to make his company tarry at present,
there he left it, intending to fetch it the next day, or at some more convenient time, went thence to supper, and so to bed. In the night, when he
should come to perform those nuptial rites, Venus steps between him
and his wife, (unseen or felt of her) and told him that she was his wife,
that he had betrothed himself unto her by that ring, which he put upon
her finger: she troubled him for some following nights. He, not knowing how to help himself, made his moan to one Palumbus, a learned
Magician in those days, who gave him a letter, and bid him at such a
time of the night, in such a crossway, at the Town's end, where old
Saturn would pass by, with his associates in procession, as commonly
he did, deliver that script with his own hands to Saturn himself; the
young man, of a bold spirit, accordingly did it; and when the old fiend
had read it, he called Venus to him, who rode before him, and commanded her to deliver his ring, which forthwith she did, and so the
gentleman was freed.

Many such stories I find in several Authors to confirm this which I
have said: as that more notable among the rest, of Philinium and
Machates in Phlegon's Tract On Marvellous Things, and, though many
be against it, yet I for my part will subscribe to Lactantius, God sent

Angels to the tuition of men; but whilst they lived amongst us, that mischievous all-commander of the Earth, and hot in lust, enticed them by little and little to this vice, and defiled them with the company of women. And Anaxagoras: Many of those spiritual bodies overcome by the love of Maids, and lust, failed, of whom those were born we call Giants. Justin Martyr, Clemens Alexandrinus, Sulpicius Severus, Eusebius, &c., to this sense make a twofold fall of Angels, one from the beginning of the world, another a little before the deluge, as Moses teacheth us, openly professing that these Genii can beget, and have carnal copulation with women. At Japan in the East Indies, at this present (if we may believe the relation of travellers) there is an Idol called Teuchedy, to whom one of the fairest virgins in the country is monthly brought, and left in a private room, in the Fotoqui, or Church, where she sits alone to be deflowered. At certain times the Teuchedy (which is thought to be the Devil) appears to her, and knoweth her carnally. Every month a fair Virgin is taken in, but what becomes of the old, no man can tell. In that goodly temple of Jupiter Belus in Babylon, there was a fair Chapel, saith Herodotus, an eye-witness of it, in which was a brave bed, a table of gold, &c., into which no creature came but one only woman, which their God made choice of, as the Chaldæan Priests told him, and that their God lay with her himself, as at Thebes in Egypt was the like done of old. So that you see this is no news, the Devils themselves, or their juggling Priests, have played such pranks in all ages. Many Divines stiffly contradict this; but I will conclude with Lipsius, that since examples, testimonies, and confessions of those unhappy women are so manifest on the other side, and many, even in this our Town of Louvain, that it is likely to be so; one thing I will add, that I suppose that in no age past, I know not by what destiny of this unhappy time, there have never appeared or showed themselves so many lecherous Devils, Satyrs, and Genii, as in this of ours, as appears by the daily narrations, and judicial sentences upon record. - - Read more of this question in Plutarch, Austin, Wierus, Giraldus Cambrensis, the Hammer of Witches [by Jacob Sprenger, the Cologne Inquisitor], Jacobus Reussus, Godelman, Erastus, Valesius, John Nider, Delrio, Lipsius, Bodine, Pererius, King James, &c.

SUBSECTION 2 — *How Love tyrannizeth over men. Love, or Heroical Melancholy, his definition, part affected*

YOU have heard how this tyrant Love rageth with brute beasts and spirits; now let us consider what passions it causeth amongst men.

Naughty Love, to what dost thou not compel our mortal hearts? How it tickles the hearts of mortal men, I am almost afraid to relate, amazed, and ashamed, it hath wrought such stupend and prodigious effects, such foul offences. Love indeed (I may not deny) first united provinces, built Cities, and by a perpetual generation makes and preserves mankind, propagates the Church; but if it rage, it is no more Love, but burning Lust, a Disease, Phrensy, Madness, Hell. 'Tis death, 'tis an immedicable calamity, 'tis a raging madness; 'tis no virtuous habit this, but a vehement perturbation of the mind, a monster of nature, wit, and art; as Alexis in Athenæus sets it out, manfully rash, womanishly timid, furiously headlong, bitter sweet, a caressing blow, &c. It subverts kingdoms, overthrows cities, towns, families; mars, corrupts, and makes a massacre of men; thunder and lightning, wars, fires, plagues, have not done that mischief to mankind, as this burning lust, this brutish passion. Let Sodom and Gomorrah, Troy, (which Dares Phrygius, and Dictys Cretensis will make good) and I know not how many cities bear record. Helen was not the first petticoat that caused a war, &c., all succeeding ages will subscribe: Joan of Naples in Italy, Frédégunde and Brunhalt in France, all histories are full of these Basilisks. Besides those daily monomachies, murders, effusion of blood, rapes, riot, and immoderate expense, to satisfy their lust, beggary, shame, loss, torture, punishment, disgrace, loathsome diseases that proceed from thence, worse than calentures and pestilent fevers, those often Gouts, Pox, Arthritis, palsies, cramps, Sciatica, convulsions, aches, combustions, &c., which torment the body, that feral melancholy which crucifies the Soul in this life, and everlasting torments in the world to come.

Notwithstanding they know these and many such miseries, threats, tortures, will surely come upon them; rewards, exhortations, to the contrary; yet either out of their own weakness, a depraved nature, or love's tyranny, which so furiously rageth, they suffer themselves to be led " like an ox to the slaughter "; (easy the descent to Avernus), they go down headlong to their own perdition, they will commit folly with beasts, men " leaving the natural use of women," as Paul saith, " burned in lust one towards another, and man with man wrought filthiness."

Semiramis with a horse, Pasiphae with a bull, Aristo Ephesius with a she-ass, Fulvius with a mare, others with dogs, goats, &c., from such combinations in ancient days were sprung monsters, Centaurs, Silvanuses, and prodigious sights to affright mankind. And not with brutes only, but men among themselves, which sin is vulgarly called Sodomy; this vice was customary in old times with the Orientals, the Greeks without question, the Italians, Africans, Asiaticks: Hercules * had Hylas,

* Lilius Giraldus, his life. — Burton's note.

Polycletus, Dion, Pirithous, Abderus and the Phrygian, and 'tis given out by some that Eurystheus even was his minion. Socrates used to frequent the Gymnasium because of the beauty of the youngsters, feeding his hungry eyes on that spectacle, wherefore Philebus and Phædo were corrivals, as Charmides and other Dialogues of Plato sufficiently show; and in truth it was this very Socrates who said of Alcibiades: gladly would I keep silent, and indeed I am averse, he offers too much incentive to wantonness. Theodoretus censures this. Plato himself delighted in Agathon, Xenophon in Clinias, Virgil in Alexis, Anacreon in Bathyllus. But of the portentous lusts of Nero, Claudius and others of infamous memory, assailed by Petronius, Suetonius, and others, exceeding all belief, how much more might be looked for here; but 'tis an ancient ill. Among the Asiaticks, Turks, Italians, the vice is customary to this day; sodomy is [in a manner of speaking] the Diana of the Romans; they make a practice of this everywhere among the Turks — sowing seed among the rocks, as the poet saith, ploughing the sands; nor are there lacking complaints of it even in the married state, where an opposite part is used from that which is lawful; nothing a more familiar sin among the Italians, who following Lucianus and Tatius, defend themselves in many writings. Johannes de la Casa, Bishop Beventius, calls it a holy act, the smug rascal, and goes so far as to say that Venus should not otherwise be used. Nothing more common among monks and priestlings, an inordinate passion even to death and madness. Angelus Politianus, because of the love of boys, laid violent hands on himself. And terrible to say, in our own country, within memory, how much that detestable sin hath raged. For, indeed, in the year 1538, the most prudent King Henry the Eighth, through the venerable Doctors of Laws, Thomas Lee and Richard Layton, inspected the cloisters of cowls and companies of priests and votaries, and found among them so great a number of wenchers, gelded youths, debauchees, catamites, boy-things, pederasts, Sodomites, (as it saith in Bale), Ganymedes, &c., that in every one of them you may be certain of a new Gomorrah. But see, if you please, the catalogue of these things in Bale: girls (he saith) are not able to sleep in their beds because of necromantick Friars. If 'tis thus among monks, votaries, and such-like saintly rascals, what may we not suspect in towns, in palaces? what among nobles, what in cellars, how much nastiness, how much filth! I am silent meanwhile as to the other uncleannesses of self-defiling monks, scarce to be named. Rodericus a Castro tells that they take turns scourging each other with whips, by way of incitation to Venus, that they have Spintrias [or those that seek out and invent new and monstrous actions of lust], Succubas, Ambubaias [or Dancing-Girls], and those wanton-loined womanlings, Tribadas, that fret each other by turns, and fulfill Venus, even among Eunuchs, with their so artful secrets. Nay, then, what wonder that a woman in Constantinople, being mad in love with another woman, dared an incredible thing, went through the ceremonial of marriage disguised as a man, and in short was married: but consult the author, Busbequius, yourself. I pass over those Egyptian Salinarios [or Dissectors] who couch with beautiful cadavers; and their insane lust, who are in love with idols and images: too well known is the fable of Pygmalion, in Ovid; or Mundus and Paulina, in Hegesippus, in that chapter of his Jewish Wars on Pontius, the legate of Cæsar (look in Pliny), the same that crucified Christ; of the picture of Atalanta and Helena, so inflaming to desire that one wanted to ravish them away, but that they were painted on a wall; another loved the statue of Good Fortune madly (saith Ælianus), another Bona Dea. And no part free from lewdness, no orifice not defiled and given over to shameful lust: Heliogabalus, saith Lampridius in his life of him, welcomed lust at every gateway of his body. Hostius made a looking-glass and so arranged it as to see his virility falsely magnified to his delight, acting both the man and woman at once, a nastiness and abomination even to speak of. 'Tis plain truth, what Plutarch's Gryllus objects to in Ulysses; moreover, he saith, we have not to this day, in the matter of men with men or women with women, so many sorts of vile actions as among your memorable and famous heroes, as Hercules following beardless comrades, mad for his friends, &c.; you are not able to confine your desires within their natural boundaries, but rather, like overflooding rivers, bring about violence, filthiness, turmoil, and confusion of nature in regard to love; for not only men go with goats, swine, and horses, but women are inflamed with mad passion for beasts, whence Minotaurs, Centaurs, Silvanuses, Sphynxes, &c. — Neither do I argue the contrary, nor bring things to the light which it is not proper for all to know, but for the learned only, for whose sake, like Rodericus, I would wish to have written; neither for light wits nor for depraved minds have I made note of these nasty sins, and I am unwilling to inquire any longer into such evils.

I come at last to that Heroical Love, which is proper to men and women, is a frequent cause of melancholy, and deserves much rather to be called burning lust, than by such an honourable title. There is an honest love, I confess, which is natural, a secret snare to captivate the hearts of men, as Christopher Fonseca proves, a strong allurement, of a most attractive, occult, adamantine property, and powerful virtue, and no man living can avoid it. He is not a man, but a block, a very stone, and either a God or a Nebuchadnezzar, he hath a gourd for his head, a pepon [or pumpkin] for his heart, that hath not felt the power of it, and a rare creature to be found, one in an age,

Whom no maiden's beauty ever inflamed, (JUVENAL)

for once at least we have been mad, dote we either young or old, as he [Chaucer] said, and none are excepted but Minerva and the Muses: so Cupid in Lucian complains to his Mother Venus, that, amongst all the rest, his arrows could not pierce them. But this nuptial love is a common passion, and honest, for men to love in the way of marriage; as matter seeks form, so woman man. You know marriage is honourable, a blessed calling, appointed by God himself in Paradise, it breeds true peace, tranquillity, content and happiness, than which no holier union exists or ever did, as Daphnæus in Plutarch could well prove (and which gives immortality to human kind), when they live without jarring, scolding, lovingly, as they should do.

Thrice happy they, and more than that,
   Whom bond of love so firmly ties,
That without brawls till death them part,
   'Tis undissolved and never dies. (HORACE)

As Seneca lived with his Paulina, Abraham and Sarah, Orpheus and Eurydice, Arria and Pœtus, Artemisia and Mausolus, Rubenius Celer, that would needs have it engraven on his tomb, he had led his life with Ennea, his dear wife, forty three years eight months, and never fell out. There is no pleasure in this world comparable to it, 'tis the height of mortal good,

Delight of Gods and men, kind Venus. (LUCRETIUS)

As one holds, there's something in a woman beyond all human delight; a magnetick virtue, a charming quality, an occult and powerful motive. The husband rules her as head, but she again commands his heart, he is her servant, she his only joy and content: no happiness is like unto it, no love so great as this of man and wife, no such comfort, as a sweet wife,

---

* The line is usually translated, "Who burned with lust for a girl he had never seen," but the context calls for the meaning given above, and it has been so translated by previous editors of Burton.

Mighty is love, but most in naked wedlock, (PROPERTIUS)
when they love at last as fresh as they did at first,
Growing old in love and years together, (SIMONIDES)
as Homer brings Paris kissing Helena, after they had been married ten
years, protesting withal that he loved her as dear as he did the first
hour that he was betrothed. And in their old age when they make much
of one another, saying as he did to his wife in the Poet,

Dear wife, let's live in love and die together,
As hitherto we have in all good will:
Let no day change or alter our affections,
But let's be young to one another still. (AUSONIUS)

Such should conjugal love be, still the same, and as they are one flesh,
so should they be of one mind, as in an Aristocratical government, one
consent, Geryon-like, join in one, have one heart in two bodies, will and
nill the same. A good wife, according to Plutarch, should be as a looking-glass, to represent her husband's face and passion. If he be pleasant,
she should be merry; if he laugh, she should smile; if he look sad, she
should participate of his sorrow, and bear a part with him, and so they
should continue in mutual love one towards another:

No age shall part my love from thee, sweet wife,
Though I live Nestor or Tithonus' life. (PROPERTIUS)

And she again to him, as the Bride saluted the Bridegroom of old in
Rome, Be thou still Caius, I'll be Caia.

'Tis an happy state this indeed, when the fountain is blessed (saith
Solomon) " and he rejoiceth with the wife of his youth, and she is to
him as the loving Hind, and pleasant Roe, and he delights in her continually."

But this love of ours is immoderate, inordinate, and not to be comprehended in any bounds. It will not contain itself within the union
of marriage, or apply to one object, but is a wandering, extravagant, a
domineering, a boundless, an irrefragable, a destructive passion: sometimes this burning lust rageth after marriage, and then it is properly
called Jealousy; sometimes before, and then it is called Heroical Melancholy; it extends sometimes to corrivals, &c., begets rapes, incests,
murders: Marcus Antonius embraced his sister Faustina, Caracalla his
stepmother Julia, Nero his mother, Caligula his sisters, Cinyras his
daughter Myrrha, &c. But it is confined within no terms of blood, years,
sex, or whatsoever else. Some furiously rage before they come to discretion or age. Quartilla in Petronius never remembered she was a maid:
and the wife of Bath in Chaucer cracks,

Since I was twelve years old, believe,
*Husbands at Kirk-door had I five.**

Aretine's Lucretia sold her Maiden-head a thousand times before she was twenty-four years old, nor were those lacking who could make it whole again. Rahab that harlot began to be a professed quean at ten years of age, and was but fifteen when she hid the spies, as Hugh Broughton proves, to whom Serrarius the Jesuit subscribes. Generally women begin to sprout hair, as they call it, or yearn for a male, as Julius Pollux cites, out of Aristophanes, at fourteen years old, then they do offer themselves, and some plainly rage. Leo Afer saith, that in Africa a man shall scarce find a Maid at fourteen years of age, they are so forward, and many amongst us after they come into the teens, do not live without husbands, but linger [or sicken]. What pranks in this kind the middle age have played, is not to be recorded.

Though I spoke with an hundred tongues, with an hundred mouths,
                                                                    (VIRGIL)

no tongue can sufficiently declare, every story is full of men and women's insatiable lust, Neros, Heliogabaluses, Bonoses, &c. Cœlius burned for Aufilenus, Quinctius for Aufilena, &c. They neigh after other men's wives (as Jeremiah complaineth) like fed horses, or range like Town Bulls, ravishers of virginity and widowhood, as many of our great ones do. Solomon's wisdom was extinguished in this fire of lust, Samson's strength enervated, piety in Lot's daughters quite forgot, gravity of Priesthood in Eli's sons, reverend old age in the Elders that would violate Susanna, filial duty in Absalom to his stepmothers, brotherly love in Amnon towards his sister. Human, divine laws, precepts, exhortations, fear of God and men, fair, foul means, fame, fortunes, shame, disgrace, honour, cannot oppose, stave off, or withstand the fury of it, love overcomes all, &c. No cord, nor cable, can so forcibly draw, or hold so fast, as Love can do with a twin'd thread. The scorching beams under the Æquinoctial, or extremity of cold within the circle Arctick, where the very Seas are frozen, cold or torrid zone cannot avoid, or expel this heat, fury and rage of mortal men.

Why vainly seek to flee? Love will pursue you
Even as far as Scythian Tanais.   (PROPERTIUS)

Of women's unnatural, unsatiable lust, what Country, what Village

---

* Quoted from memory. The lines in Chaucer are:
    For, lordinges, sith I twelf yeer was of age,
    Thonked be god that is eterne on lyve,
    Housbondes at chirche-dore I have had fyve.

doth not complain? Mother and daughter sometimes dote on the same man, father and son, master and servant on one woman.

> *What have desire and lust unbridled left*
> *Chaste and inviolate upon the earth?*   (EURIPIDES)

What breach of vows and oaths, fury, dotage, madness, might I reckon up! Yet this is more tolerable in youth, and such as are still in their hot blood; but for an old fool to dote, to see an old lecher, what more odious, what can be more absurd? and yet what so common? Who so furious?

> *Those who love in age,*
> *All the more madly rage.*   (PLAUTUS)

Some dote then more than ever they did in their youth. How many decrepit, hoary, harsh, writhen, bursten-bellied, crooked, toothless, bald, blear-eyed, impotent, rotten, old men shall you see flickering still in every place! One gets him a young wife, another a courtisan, and when he can scarce lift his leg over a sill, and hath one foot already in Charon's boat, when he hath the trembling in his joints, the gout in his feet, a perpetual rheum in his head, a continuate cough, his sight fails him, thick of hearing, his breath stinks, all his moisture is dried up and gone, may not spit from him, a very child again, that cannot dress himself, or cut his own meat, yet he will be dreaming of, and honing after wenches, what can be more unseemly? Worse it is in women than in men, when she is in her declining years, an old widow, a mother so long since (in Pliny's opinion) she doth very unseemly seek to marry, yet whilst she is so old a crone, a beldam, she can neither see, nor hear, go nor stand, a mere carcass, a witch, and scarce feel; she catterwauls, and must have a stallion, a champion, she must and will marry again, and betroth herself to some young man, that hates to look on her but for her goods, abhors the sight of her, to the prejudice of her good name, her own undoing, grief of friends, and ruin of her children.

But to enlarge or illustrate this power and effects of love is to set a candle in the Sun. It rageth with all sorts and conditions of men, yet is most evident among such as are young and lusty, in the flower of their years, nobly descended, high fed, such as live idly, and at ease; and for that cause (which our Divines call burning lust) this mad and beastly passion, as I have said, is named by our Physicians Heroical Love, and a more honourable title put upon it, Noble Love, as Savanarola styles it, because Noble men and women make a common practice of it, and are so ordinarily affected with it. Avicenna calleth this passion Ilishi. and defines it to be a disease or melancholy vexation, or anguish of mind, in which a man continually meditates of the beauty, gesture, manners of his Mistress, and troubles himself about it: desiring (as Savanarola adds) with all intentions and eagerness of mind to compass or enjoy her, as commonly Hunters trouble themselves about their sports, the covetous about their gold and goods, so is he tormented still about his Mistress. Arnoldus Villanovanus, in his book of Heroical Love, defines it a continual cogitation of that which he desires, with a confidence or hope of compassing it: which definition his Commentator cavils at. For continual cogitation is not the kind, but a symptom, of Love; we continually think of that which we hate and abhor as well as that which we love; and many things we covet and desire without all hope of attaining. Carolus à Lorme, in his Questions, makes a doubt, whether this heroical love be a disease: Julius Pollux determines it. They that are in love are likewise sick; to be lustful, lecherous, wanton, to be raging in desire, is certainly to be sick. Arnoldus will have it improperly so called, and a malady rather of the body than mind. Tully in his Tusculans defines it a furious disease of the mind, Plato madness itself, Ficinus, his Commentator, a species of madness, " for many have run mad for women," but Rhasis a melancholy passion, and most Physicians make it a species or kind of melancholy (as will appear by the Symptoms) and treat of it apart: whom I mean to imitate, and to discuss it in all his kinds, to examine his several causes, to shew his symptoms, indications, prognosticks, effects, that so it may be with more facility cured.

The part affected in the mean time, as Arnoldus supposeth, is the former part of the head for want of moisture, which his Commentator rejects. Langius will have this passion sited in the liver, and to keep residence in the heart, to proceed first from the eyes, so carried by our spirits, and kindled with imagination in the liver and heart; the liver will compel one to love, as the saying is, He will strike through the liver, as Cupid in Anacreon. For some such cause belike Homer feigns Tityus' liver (who was enamoured on Latona) to be still gnawed by two Vultures day and night in Hell, for that young men's bowels thus enamoured, are so continually tormented by love. Gordonius will have the testicles an immediate subject or cause, the liver an antecedent. Fracastorius agrees in this with Gordonius, from thence originally come the images of desire, erection, &c.; it calls for an exceeding titillation of the part, adds Guastivinus, so that until the seed is put forth there is no end of frisking voluptuousness and continual remembrance of venery. But properly it is a passion of the brain, as all other melancholy, by reason of corrupt imagination, and so doth Jason Pratensis, (who writes copiously of this Erotical love), place and reckon it amongst the affections of the brain. Melancthon confutes those that make the liver a part affected, and Guianerius, though many put all the affections in the heart, refers it to the brain. Ficinus will have the blood to be the part affected. Jo. Frietagius supposeth all four affected, heart, liver, brain, blood; but the major part concur upon the brain, 'tis an injury, a lesion of the fancy, and both imagination and reason are misaffected; because of his corrupt judgement, and continual meditation of that which he desires, he may truly be said to be melancholy. If it be violent, or his disease inveterate, as I have determined in the precedent partitions, both imagination and reason are mis-affected, first one, then the other.

MEMBER 2

SUBSECTION 1 — *Causes of Heroical Love, Temperature, full Diet, Idleness, Place, Climate, &c.*

OF all causes the remotest are stars. Ficinus saith they are most prone to this burning lust, that have Venus in Leo in their Horoscope, when the Moon and Venus be mutually aspected, or such as be of Venus' complexion. Plutarch interprets Astrologically that tale of Mars and Venus, in whose genitures Mars and Venus are in conjunction, they are commonly lascivious, and if women, queans; as the good wife of Bath confessed in Chaucer;

> J folwed ay myn inclinacioun
> By vertu of my constellacioun.

But of all those Astrological Aphorisms which I have ever read, that of Cardan is most memorable, for which, howsoever he be bitterly censured by Marinus Marcennus, a malapert Friar, and some others (which he himself suspected), yet methinks it is free, downright, plain and ingenuous. In his eighth Geniture or example, he hath these words of himself: When Venus and Mercury are in conjunction, Mercury in the ascendant, I am so urged with thoughts of love that I cannot rest. And a little after, he saith: The thought of the pleasures of love torments me perpetually, and inasmuch as it is not permissable to find satisfaction in deed, or at least shameful, I am continually sunk in the feigned pleasures of fancy. And again he saith: Because of the mingled dominion of the Moon and Mercury, I am deeply inclined toward wantonness, given over to foul and obscene lust. ———— So far Cardan of himself, confessing what use he made of the time allotted to study, and for this he is traduced by Marcennus whenas in effect he saith no more than what Gregory Nazianzen of old to Chilo his scholar, Visionary women offered themselves to me, by their surpassing grace and marvellous beauty making trial of my chastity; and though I escaped the sin of fornication, yet in my secret heart I ravished their virgin flowers. ———— But to the point. They are more apt to masculine venery, at whose birth Venus is in a masculine sign, and Saturn in other parts of the heaven or in opposition. Ptolemy, saith his commentator Cardan, knew of these things, proved them true, and wrote of them in his Aphorisms. Thomas Campanella, in his remonstrances against amatory madness in his book of Astrology, hath collected many previous aphorisms, which who will may consult. The Chiromanticks are full of conjectures concerning the girdle of Venus, the mount of Venus, as to which teachings you may look in Taisnerus, Johan. de Indagine, Goclenius, and others, if it please you. Physicians divine wholly from the temperature and complexion; phlegmatick persons are seldom taken, according to Ficinus, naturally melancholy less than they, but once taken they are never freed; though many are of opinion flatuous or hypochondriacal melancholy are most subject of all others to this infirmity. Valescus assigns their strong imagination for a cause, Bodine abundance of wind, Gordonius of seed, and spirits, or atomi in the seed, which cause their violent and furious passions. Sanguine thence are soon caught, young folks most apt to love, and by their good wills, saith Lucian, would have a bout with every one they see: the colt's evil is common to all complexions. Theomnestus, a young and lusty gallant, acknowledgeth (in the said Author) all this to be verified in him: I am so amorously given, you may sooner number the Sea sands, and Snow falling from the skies, than my several loves. Cupid hath shot all his arrows at me, I am deluded with various desires, one love succeeds another, and that so soon, that before one is ended, I begin with a second; she that is last is still fairest, and she that is present pleaseth me most: as an Hydra's head my loves increase, no Iolaus can help me. Mine eyes are so moist a refuge and sanctuary of love, that they draw all beauties to them, and are never satisfied. I am in a doubt what fury of Venus this should be. Alas, how have I offended her so to vex me, what Hippolytus am I! What Telchin is my Genius? Or is it a natural imperfection, an hereditary passion? — Another in Anacreon confesseth that he had twenty sweet-hearts in Athens at once, fifteen at Corinth, as many at Thebes, at Lesbos, and at Rhodes, twice as many in Ionia, thrice in Caria, twenty thousand in all: or in a word, as the leaves of the forest, &c.

> *Canst count the leaves in May,*
> *Or sands i' th' ocean sea?*
> *Then count my loves I pray.*

His eyes are like a balance, apt to propend each way, and to be weighed down with every wench's looks; his heart a weathercock, his affection tinder, or naptha itself, which every fair object, sweet smile, or mistress' favour sets on fire. Guianerius refers all this to the hot temperature of the testicles; Ferandus, a Frenchman, in his Erotique Melancholy, (which book came first to my hands after the Third Edition) to certain atomi in the seed, such as are very spermatick and full of seed. I find the same in Aristotle, if they cannot be rid of the seed, they cannot stop burning, for which cause these young men that be strong set, of able bodies, are so subject to it. Hercules de Saxoniâ hath the same words in effect. But most part, I say, such are aptest to love that are young and lusty, live at ease, stall-fed, free from cares, like cattle in a rank pasture, idle and solitary persons, they must needs be goatish, as Guastavinius recites out of Censorinus.

> *The mind is apt to lust, and hot or cold,*
> *As corn luxuriates in a better mould.* (OVID)

The place itself makes much wherein we live, the clime, air, and discipline if they concur. In our Mysia, saith Galen, near to Pergamus, thou shalt scarce find an adulterer, but many at Rome, by reason of the delights of the seat. It was that plenty of all things which made Corinth so infamous of old, and the opportunity of the place to entertain those foreign comers; every day strangers came in at each gate from all quarters. In that one Temple of Venus a thousand whores did prostitute themselves, as Strabo writes, besides Lais and the rest of better note. All nations resorted thither as to a school of Venus. Your hot and Southern countries are prone to lust, and far more incontinent than those that live in the North, as Bodine discourseth at large. The Asiaticks are amorous; so are Turks, Greeks, Spaniards, Italians, even all that latitude: and in those Tracts such as are more fruitful, plentiful, and delicious, as Valentia in Spain, Capua in Italy, a luxurious abode, Tully terms it, and (which Hannibal's soldiers can witness) Canopus in Egypt, Sybaris, Phæacia, Baiæ, Cyprus, Lampsacus. In Naples the fruits of the soil and pleasant air enervate their bodies, and alter constitutions: insomuch, that Florus calls it a contest of Bacchus and Venus, but Foliet admires it. In Italy and Spain they have their stews in every great City, as in Rome, Venice, Florence, wherein some say dwell ninety thousand inhabitants of which ten thousand are Courtisans; and yet for all this, every Gentleman almost hath a peculiar Mistress; fornications, adulteries are nowhere so common: the city is one great bawdy house; how should a man live honest among so many provocations? now if vigour of youth, greatness, liberty I mean, and that impunity of sin which Grandees take unto themselves in this kind shall meet, what a gap must it needs open to all manner of vice, with what fury will it rage! For, as Maximus Tyrius the Platonist observes, lewdness follows wherever there is a weak disposition, and precipitate license, and unbridled rashness, &c.; what will not lust effect in such persons? For commonly Princes and great men make no scruple at all of such matters, but with that whore in Spartian, they think they may do what they list, profess it publickly, and rather brag with Proculus (that writ to a friend of his in Rome, what famous exploits he had done in that kind) than any way be abashed at it. Nicholas Sanders relates of Henry the 8th (I know not how truly) he saw very few pretty maids that he did not desire, and desired fewer whom he did not enjoy: nothing so familiar amongst them, 'tis most of their business. Sardanapalus, Messalina, and Joan of Naples, are not comparable to meaner men and women; Solomon of old had a thousand Concubines, Ahasuerus his Eunuchs and keepers, Nero his Tigillinus, Pandars, and Bawds, the Turks, Muscovites, Mogors, Xeriffs of Barbary, and Persian Sophies, are no whit inferior to them in our times. The most beautiful girls are all brought (saith Jovius) before the Emperor; and those he leaves, the Nobles have; they press and muster up wenches as we do soldiers, and have their choice of the rarest beauties their countries can afford, and yet all this cannot keep them from adultery, incest, sodomy, buggery, and such prodigious lusts. We may conclude that, if they be young, fortunate, rich, high-fed, and idle withal, it is almost impossible they should live honest, not rage, and precipitate themselves into those inconveniences of burning lust.

Such idleness hath kings and thriving towns
Ere now laid in the dust.   (CATULLUS)

* Idleness overthrows all, in the empty heart love reigns, love tyrannizeth in an idle person. Thou dost overflow with longing, Antipho. If thou hast nothing to do, thou shalt be haled in pieces with envy, lust, some passion or other. Those with nothing to do find something evil to do. 'Tis Aristotle's Simile, as match or touchwood takes fire, so doth an idle person love. Why was Ægisthus a whoremaster? You need not ask

a reason of it. Ismenadora stole Bacho, a woman forced a man as Aurora did Cephalus: no marvel, saith Plutarch, great riches make women behave like men: she was rich, fortunate and jolly, and doth but as men do in that case, as Jupiter did by Europa, Neptune by Amyone. The Poets therefore did well to feign all Shepherds Lovers, to give themselves to songs and dalliances, because they lived such idle lives. For love, as Theophrastus defines it, is an affection of an idle mind, or as Seneca describes it, youth begets it, riot maintains it, idleness nourisheth it, &c., which makes Gordonius the Physician call this disease the proper passion of Nobility. Now if a weak judgement and a strong apprehension do concur, how, saith Hercules de Saxoniâ, shall they resist? Savanarola appropriates it almost to Monks, Friars, and religious persons, because they live solitary, fare daintily, and do nothing: and well he may, for how should they otherwise choose?

Diet alone is able to cause it: a rare thing to see a young man or a woman that lives idly, and fares well, of what condition soever, not to be in love. Alcibiades was still dallying with wanton young women, immoderate in his expenses, effeminate in his apparel, ever in love, but why? he was over-delicate in his diet, too frequent and excessive in banquets. Lust and security domineer together, as S. Hierome averreth. All which the wife of Bath in Chaucer freely justifies, —

ffor al so siker as colo engendrith hapl.
A likerous mouth most han a likerous tapl.

Especially if they shall further it by choice Diet, as many times those Sybarites and Phæacians do, feed liberally, and by their good will eat nothing else but lascivious meats. Noble Wine first of all, Pulse, Beans, Roots of all sorts well preserved, and liberally sprinkled with Pepper, Garden Chard, Lettuces, Rocket, Rape, Scallions, Onions, Pistachio Nuts, Sweet Almonds, Electuaries, Syrups, Broths, Snails, Oysters, Fishes, richly prepared young Fowls, the Fries or testicular parts of animals, Condiments of divers kinds, assorted Sweets, Pigeon-pies, &c. And whatsoever Physicians may prescribe to those suffering from impotency in matters of love, they have as it were an Aphrodisiack in delicacies and sumptuous repasts: in Honey mixtures, exquisite and exotick Fruits, Allspices, Cakes, Meat-broths, smoothly powerful Wine, all that the Kitchen, the Pharmacopœia and the Shops are able to offer. And having stuffed themselves with all this victual, like those who made ready for Chrysis herself [a harlot in Terence], having medicined themselves with scallions and snails, so as to be capable of addressing themselves to Venus, and exerting themselves in the lists, who would not then exceedingly rage with lust, who would not run wholly mad? Inflammation of the belly is quickly worked off in venery, Hierome saith. After benching, then comes wenching. Who can then contain himself? Immoderate drinking foments lust, saith Augustine; a smooth devil, Bernardus; the milk of venery, Aristophanes. Not Ætna, nor Vesuvius, is so fiery as young bellies full of wine, adds Hierome. That the vines might prosper, Lampsacus was of old dedicated to Priapus; and Venus listened to Bacchus as well as to Orpheus. If the wine is unmixed, and is taken by itself before food (whither is Bacchus carrying me, full of his influence?) shall we not expect fury and madness? Gomesius puts salt among those things which are wont to provoke tempests of lust, and maintains that women are made wanton through being corroded by salt: 'twas from the Ocean, they say, that Venus rose.

> Why so many harlots stray
> In Venetia every day?
> 'Tis Venus risen from the sea.   (KORNMANNUS)

And from this Ocean goddess, in a word, peradventure, from salt comes salacity. So many Bacchic disorders disgraced the loves of old time that the statues of Bacchus were discrowned. Cubebs steeped in wine are used by the East Indians to incite to venery, and the Surax root by the Africans. China roots have the same effect, and others of the sort are mentioned. Baptista Porta brought some from India, of which he and Theophrastus made mention. (These are not only eaten, but applied to the parts, that they may have as much pleasure, and as many times, as possible; some succeeding twelve, others sixty times.) A multitude of like things are in Rhasis, Matthiolus, Mizaldus, and other medicos, always with the same warning, not to meddle with these things ignorantly, but beware of the dangerous reefs of such virility, lest you be destroyed.

SUBSECTION 2 — *Other Causes of Love-Melancholy, Sight, Beauty from the Face, Eyes, other parts, and how it pierceth*

MANY such causes may be reckoned up, but they cannot avail, except opportunity be offered of time, place, and those other beautiful objects, or artificial enticements, as kissing, conference, discourse, gestures concur, with such like lascivious provocations. Kornmannus, in his book, The Outline of Love, makes five degrees of lust, out of Lucian belike, which he handles in five Chapters: Sight, Speech, Company, Kissing, Handling. Sight, of all other, is the first step of this unruly love, though sometimes it be prevented by relation or hearing, or rather incensed. For there be those so apt, credulous and facile to love, that if they hear of a proper man, or woman, they are in love before they see them, and that merely by relation, as Achilles Tatius observes. Such is their intemperance and lust, that they are as much maimed by report as if they saw them. Callisthenes, a rich young Gentleman of Byzantium in Thrace, hearing of Leucippe, Sostratus' fair daughter, was far in love with her, and out of fame and common rumour so much incensed that he would needs have her to be his wife. And sometimes by reading they are so affected, as he in Lucian confesseth of himself: I never read that place of Panthea in Xenophon, but I am as much affected as if I were present with her. Such persons commonly feign a kind of beauty to themselves; and so did those three Gentlewomen, in Balthasar Castilio, fall in love with a young man, whom they never knew, but only heard him commended: or by reading of a letter; for there is a grace cometh from hearing, as a moral Philosopher informeth us, as well as from sight; and the species [or lineaments] of love are received into the phantasy by relation alone; both senses affect. Sometimes we love those that are absent, saith Philostratus, and gives instance in his friend Athenodorus, that loved a Maid at Corinth whom he never saw; we see with the eyes of our understanding.

But the most familiar and usual cause of Love is that which comes by sight, which conveys those admirable rays of beauty and pleasing graces to the heart. Plotinus derives love from sight, Eros as if 'twere δρασις [seeing]. The eyes are the harbingers of love, and the first step of love is sight, as Lilius Giraldus proves at large, they as two sluices let in the influences of that divine, powerful, soul-ravishing, and captivating beauty, which, as one saith, is sharper than any dart or needle, wounds deeper into the heart, and opens a gap through our eyes to that lovely wound, which pierceth the soul itself. " Through it love is kindled like a fire." This amazing, confounding, admirable, amiable Beauty, than which in all Nature's treasure (saith Isocrates) there is nothing so majestical and sacred, nothing so divine, lovely, precious, 'tis nature's Crown, gold and glory; good if not best, and often triumphing over the best, whose power hence may be discerned; we contemn and abhor generally such things as are foul and ugly to behold, account them filthy, but love and covet that which is fair. 'Tis beauty in all things, which pleaseth and allureth us, a fair hawk, a fine garment, a goodly building, a fair house, &c. That Persian Xerxes, when he destroyed all those Temples of the Gods in Greece, caused that of Diana to be spared alone for that excellent beauty and magnificence of it. Inanimate beauty can so command. 'Tis that which Painters, Artificers, Orators, all aim at, as Erixymachus, the Physician in Plato, contends: It was beauty first that ministered occasion to art, to find out the knowledge of carving, painting, building, to find out models, perspectives, rich furnitures, and so many rare inventions. Whiteness in the Lily, red in the Rose, purple in the Violet, a lustre in all things without life, the clear light of the Moon, the bright beams of the Sun, splendour of Gold, purple, sparkling Diamond, the excellent feature of the Horse, the Majesty of the Lion, the colour of Birds, Peacocks' tails, the silver scales of Fish, we behold with singular delight and admiration. And which is rich in plants, delightful in flowers, wonderful in beasts, but most glorious in men, doth make us affect and earnestly desire it, as when we hear any sweet harmony, an eloquent tongue, see any excellent quality, curious work of man, elaborate art, or ought that is exquisite, there ariseth instantly in us a longing for the same. We love such men, but most part for comeliness of person; we call them Gods and Goddesses, divine, serene, happy, &c. And of all mortal men they alone (Calcagninus holds) are free from calumny; we backbite, wrong, hate, renowned, rich, and happy men, we repine at their felicity, they are undeserving, we think, fortune is a stepmother to us, a parent to them. We envy (saith Isocrates) wise, just, honest men, except with mutual offices and kindnesses, some good turn or other, they extort this love from us; only fair persons we love at first sight, desire their acquaintance, and adore them as so many Gods: we had rather serve them than command others, and account ourselves the more beholding to them, the more service they enjoin us; though they be otherwise vicious, unhonest, we love them, favour them, and are ready to do them any good office for their beauty's sake, though they have no other good quality beside. As that eloquent Phavorinus breaks out in Stobæus: Speak, fair youth, speak Autolycus, thy words are sweeter than Nectar; speak O Telemachus, thou art more powerful than Ulysses; speak Alcibiades, though drunk, we will willingly hear thee as thou art. — Faults in such are no faults. For when the said Alcibiades had stolen Anytus his gold and silver plate, he was so far from prosecuting so foul a fact (though every man else condemned his impudence and insolency) that he wished it had been more, and much better (he loved him dearly) for his sweet sake. No worth is eminent in such lovely persons, all imperfections hid; for hearing, sight, touch, &c., our mind and all our senses are captivated. Many men have been preferred for their person alone, chosen Kings, as amongst the Indians, Persians, Æthiopians of old; the properest man of person the country could afford was elected their Sovereign Lord; virtue seems even lovelier in a lovely body; and so have many other nations thought and done, as Curtius observes; for there is a majestical presence in such men; and so far was beauty adored amongst them, that no man was thought fit to reign that was not in all parts complete and supereminent. Archidamus, King of Lacedæmon, had like to have been deposed, because he married a little wife; they would not have their royal issue degenerate. Who would ever have thought that Adrian the Fourth, an English Monk's Bastard (as Papirius Massovius writes in his life) a poor forsaken child, should ever come to be Pope of Rome? But why was it? As he follows it out of Nubrigensis, for he " ploughs with his heifer," he was wise, learned, eloquent, of a pleasant, a promising countenance, a goodly proper man; he had, in a word, a winning look of his own, and that carried it, for that he was especially advanced. So Saul was a goodly person and a fair. Maximinus elected Emperor, &c. Branchus the son of Apollo, whom he begot of Jance, Succron's daughter, (saith Lactantius), when he kept King Admetus' Herds in Thessaly, now grown a man, was an earnest suitor to his mother to know his father; the Nymph denied him, because Apollo had conjured her to the contrary; yet, overcome by his importunity, at last she sent him to his father; when he came into Apollo's presence, kissing reverently the god's cheeks, he carried himself so well, and was so fair a young man, that Apollo was infinitely taken with the beauty of his person, he could scarce look off him, and said he was worthy of such parents, gave him a crown of gold, the spirit of Divination, and in conclusion made him a Demi-god. A Goddess beauty is, whom the very Gods adore; she is love's mistress, love's harbinger, love's loadstone, a witch, a charm, &c. Beauty is a dower of itself, a sufficient patrimony, an ample commendation, an accurate epistle, as Lucian, Apuleius, Tiraquellus, and some others conclude. Beauty deserves a Kingdom, saith Abulensis, immortality, and more have got this honour and eternity for their beauty than for all other virtues besides: and such as are fair are worthy to be honoured of God and men. That Idalian Ganymedes was therefore fetched by Jupiter into Heaven, Hephæstion dear to Alexander, Antinous to Adrian. Plato calls beauty, for that cause, a privilege of Nature, nature's master-piece, a dumb comment; Theophrastus, a silent fraud; still rhetorick, Carneades, that persuades without speech, a kingdom without a guard, because beautiful persons command as so many Captains; Socrates, a

tyranny, which tyrannizeth over tyrants themselves; which made Diogenes belike call proper women Queens, because men were so obedient
to their commands. They will adore, cringe, compliment, and bow to a
common wench (if she be fair) as if she were a Noble woman, a Countess, a Queen, or a Goddess. Those intemperate young men of Greece
erected at Delphi a golden Image, with infinite cost, to the eternal
memory of Phryne the Courtisan, as Ælian relates, for she was a most
beautiful woman, in so much, saith Athenæus, that Apelles and Praxiteles drew Venus' picture from her. Thus young men will adore and honour beauty; nay, Kings themselves, I say, will do it, and voluntarily
submit their sovereignty to a lovely woman. " Wine is strong, Kings are
strong, but a woman strongest," as Zorobabel proved at large to King
Darius, his Princes and Noblemen: " Kings sit still and command Sea
and Land, &c., all pay tribute to the King; but women make Kings pay
tribute, and have dominion over them. When they have got gold and
silver, they submit all to a beautiful woman, give themselves wholly
to her, gape and gaze on her, and all men desire her more than gold or
silver, or any precious thing: they will leave Father and Mother, and
venture their lives for her, labour and travail to get, and bring all their
gains to women, steal, fight, and spoil, for their Mistress' sakes. And no
King so strong, but a fair woman is stronger than he is. All things (as
he proceeds) fear to touch the King; yet I saw him, and Apame his
concubine, the Daughter of the famous Bartacus, sitting on the right
hand of the King, and she took the Crown off his head, and put it on her
own, and struck him with her left hand; yet the King gaped and gazed
on her, and when she laughed, he laughed, and when she was angry, he
flattered to be reconciled to her." So beauty commands even Kings
themselves; nay whole Armies and Kingdoms are captivated together
with their Kings. Beauty conquers arms, loveliness takes war itself
captive; we are conquered by looks, who are not conquered in battle.
And 'tis a great matter, saith Xenophon, and of which all fair persons
may worthily brag, that a strong man must labour for his living, if he
will have ought, a valiant man must fight and endanger himself for it,
a wise man speak, shew himself, and toil; but a fair and beautiful person doth all with ease, he compasseth his desire without any painstaking; God and men, Heaven and Earth, conspire to honour him;
every one pities him above other, if he be in need, and all the world is
willing to do him good. Chariclea fell into the hands of Pirates, but
when all the rest were put to the edge of the sword, she alone was preserved for her person. When Constantinople was sacked by the Turk,

Irene escaped, and was so far from being made a captive, that she even captivated the Grand Seignior himself. So did Rosamond insult over King Henry the Second:

> ——————— *I was so fair an object,*
> *Whom fortune made my king, my love made subject;*
> *He found by proof the privilege of beauty,*
> *That it had power to countermand all duty.*   (DANIEL)

It captivates the very Gods themselves, even the severest of them,

> *The God of Gods, for beauty's sake of old,*
> *Became a swan, a bull, a shower of gold.*   (STROZA FILIUS)

And those evil spirits are taken with it, as I have already proved. The Barbarians stand in awe of a fair woman, and at a beautiful aspect a fierce spirit is pacified. For when as Troy was taken, and the wars ended (as Clemens Alexandrinus quotes out of Euripides) angry Menelaus, with rage and fury armed, came with his sword drawn to have killed Helena with his own hands, as being the sole cause of all those wars and miseries: but when he saw her fair face, as one amazed at her divine beauty, he let his weapon fall, and embraced her besides, he had no power to strike so sweet a creature. The edge of a sharp sword (as the saying is) is dulled with a beautiful aspect, and severity itself is overcome. Hyperides the Orator, when Phryne his Client was accused at Athens for her lewdness, used no other defence in her cause, but tearing her upper garment, disclosed her naked breast to the Judges, with which comeliness of her body, and amiable gesture, they were so moved and astonished, that they did acquit her forthwith, and let her go. O noble piece of Justice! mine Author exclaims, and who is he that would not rather lose his seat and robes, forfeit his office, than give sentence against the majesty of beauty? Such prerogatives have fair persons, and they alone are free from danger. Parthenopæus was so lovely and fair, that when he fought in the Theban wars, if his face had been by chance bare, no enemy would offer to strike at, or hurt him. Such immunities hath beauty; beasts themselves are moved with it. Sinalda was a woman of such excellent feature, and a Queen, that when she was to be trodden on by wild horses for a punishment, the wild beasts stood in admiration of her person (Saxo Grammaticus) and would not hurt her. Wherefore did that royal Virgin in Apuleius, when she fled from the thieves' den, in a desert, make such an Apostrophe to her Ass on whom she rode: (for what knew she to the contrary but that he was an Ass?) If you will bring me back to my parents, and my beautiful lover, what thanks shall I not owe you, what honour, what provender shall I not supply you? She would comb him, dress him, feed him, and trick him every day herself, and he should work no more, toil no more, but rest and play, &c. And besides, she would have a dainty picture drawn, in perpetual remembrance, a Virgin riding upon an Ass's back with this motto, A captured fleeing royal Virgin riding on an Ass. Why said she all this? why did she make such promises to a dumb beast? but that she perceived the poor Ass to be taken with her beauty; for he did often kiss her feet as she rid, offer to give consent as much as in him was to her delicate speeches, and besides he had some feeling, as she conceived, of her misery. And why did Theagenes' horse in Heliodorus curvet, prance, and go so proudly, but that sure, as mine Author supposeth, he was in love with his Master? A fly lighted on Malthius' cheek as he lay asleep, but why? Not to hurt him, as a parasite of his standing by well perceived, but certainly to kiss him, as ravished with his divine looks. Inanimate creatures, I suppose, have a touch of this. When a drop of Psyche's Candle fell on Cupid's shoulder, I think, sure, it was to kiss it. When Venus ran to meet her rose-cheeked Adonis, as an elegant Poet of ours sets her out,

> ———— *the bushes in the way*
> *Some catch her by the neck, some kiss her face,*
> *Some twine about her legs to make her stay,*
> *And all did covet her for to embrace.* (SHAKESPEARE)

As Heliodorus holds, the air itself is in love: for when Hero played upon her Lute,

> *The wanton air in twenty sweet forms danc't*
> *After her fingers.* (CHAPMAN)

And those lascivious winds staid Daphne when she fled from Apollo:

> *The winds sought to undress her, and each gust*
> *Played with her garments as in wanton lust.* (OVID)

The wind Boreas loved Hyacinthus, and Orithyia, Erectheus' daughter of Athens; he took her away by force, as she was playing with other wenches at Ilissus, and begat Zetes and Calais his two sons of her. That seas and waters are enamoured with this our beauty is all out as likely as that of the air and winds; for when Leander swimmed in the Hellespont, Neptune with his Trident did beat down the waves, but they

> *Still mounted up, intending to have kiss'd him,*
> *And fell in drops like tears because they missed him.* (MARLOWE)

The River Alpheus was in love with Arethusa, as she tells the tale herself,

And having with her hand wrung dry her fair green hanging hair,
The River Alphey's ancient loves she thus began to tell:
I was (quoth she) a Nymph of them that in Achaia dwell, &c.   (OVID)
When our Thames and Isis meet,
The air resounds with kisses, pale their arms
With twining grow, their necks with mutual clasps. (LELAND)
Inachus and Peneus, and how many loving rivers can I reckon up, whom
beauty hath enthrall'd! I say nothing all this while of Idols them-
selves that have committed Idolatry in this kind, of looking glasses
that have been rapt in love (if you will believe Poets) when their
Ladies and Mistresses looked on to dress them.

Though I no sense at all of feeling have,
Yet your sweet looks do animate and save;
And when your speaking eyes do this way turn,
Methinks my wounded members live and burn. (ANGERIANUS)
I could tell you such another story of a spindle that was fired by a fair
Lady's looks, or fingers, some say, I know not well whether, but fired it
was, by report, and of a cold bath that suddenly smoked, and was very
hot, when naked Cælia came into it,

We marvel why it raises such a steam, &c.
But of all the tales in this kind, that is the most memorable of Death
himself, when he should have stroken a sweet young Virgin with his
dart, he fell in love with the object. Many more such could I relate,
which are to be believed with a poetical faith. So dumb and dead
creatures dote, but men are mad, stupefied many times at the first sight
of beauty, amazed, as that fisherman in Aristænetus, that espied a
Maid bathing herself by the Sea side, —

From head to foot my limbs seem'd paralys'd,
My spirits, as in a dream, were all bound up. (STOBÆUS)
And as Lucian, in his Images, confesseth of himself, that he was at his
Mistress' presence void of all sense, immoveable, as if he had seen a
Gorgon's head: which was no such cruel monster (as Cælius interprets
it) but the very quintessence of beauty, some fair creature, as without
doubt the Poet understood in the first fiction of it, at which the spectators were amazed. Poor wretches are compelled at the very sight of
her ravishing looks to run mad, or make away themselves.

They wait the sentence of her scornful eyes;
And whom she favours lives, the other dies. (MARLOWE)
Heliodorus brings in Thyamis almost besides himself, when he saw
Chariclea first, and not daring to look upon her a second time, for he

thought it unpossible for any man living to see her, and contain him-self. The very fame of beauty will fetch them to it many miles off (such an attractive power this loadstone hath) and they will seem but short, they will undertake any toil or trouble, long journeys, Penia or Atalanta shall not overgo them, through Seas, Deserts, Mountains, and dangerous places, as they did to gaze on Psyche: many mortal men came far and near to see that glorious object of her age, as Paris for Helena, Corœbus to Troy, —

Who in those days had come to windy Troy,
Haply through violent passion for Cassandra.   (VIRGIL)

King John of France, once prisoner in England, came to visit his old friends again, crossing the Seas; but the truth is, his coming was to see the Countess of Salisbury, the Non-pareil of those times, and his dear Mistress. That infernal God Plutus came from Hell itself, to steal Proserpine; Achilles left all his friends for Polyxena's sake, his enemy's daughter; and all the Grecian Gods forsook their heavenly mansions for that fair Lady, Philo Dioneus daughter's sake, the Para-gon of Greece in those days; so graceful was she that all the gods were rivals for her favour.

The gods are conquered by a girl's loveliness.   (JOHANNES SECUNDUS)

They will not only come to see, but as a Falconer makes an hungry Hawk hover about, follow, give attendance and service, spend goods, lives, and all their fortunes to attain;

Were beauty under twenty locks kept fast,
Yet love breaks through, and picks them all at last.

When fair Hero came abroad, the eyes, hearts, and affections of her spectators were still attendant on her.

So far above the rest fair Hero shined,
And stole away the enchanted gazer's mind.   (MARLOWE)

When Peter Aretine's Lucretia came first to Rome, and that the fame of her beauty was spread abroad, they came in (as they say) thick and threefold to see her, and hovered about her gates, as they did of old to Lais of Corinth and Phryne of Thebes, —

At whose doors lay all Greece.   (PROPERTIUS)

Every man sought to get her Love, some with gallant and costly ap-parel, some with an affected pace, some with musick, others with rich gifts, pleasant discourse, multitude of followers; others with letters, vows, and promises, to commend themselves, and to be gracious in her eyes. Happy was he that could see her, thrice happy that enjoyed her company. Charmides in Plato was a proper young man, in comeliness of person, and all good qualities, far exceeding others; whensoever fair Charmides came abroad, they seemed all to be in love with him (as Critias describes their carriage) and were troubled at the very sight of him; many came near him, many followed him wheresoever he went; as those lovers of beauty did Acontius, if at any time he walked abroad: the Athenian Lasses stared on Alcibiades; Sappho and the Miletian women on Phaon the fair. Such lovely sights do not only please, entice, but ravish & amaze. Cleonymus, a delicate & tender youth, present at a feast which Androcles his uncle made in the Piræus at Athens, when he sacrificed to Mercury, so stupified the guests, Dineas, Aristippus, Agasthenes, and the rest (as Charidemus in Lucian relates it) that they could not eat their meat, they sate all supper time gazing, glancing at him, stealing looks, and admiring of his beauty. Many will condemn these men that are so enamoured for fools; but some again commend them for it; many reject Paris' judgement, and yet Lucian approves of it; admiring Paris for his choice; he would have done as much himself, and by good desert in his mind; beauty is to be preferred before wealth or wisdom. Athenæus holds it not such indignity for the Trojans and Greeks to contend ten years, to spend so much labour, lose so many men's lives for Helen's sake, for so fair a Lady's sake;

> Such a mistress, of so surpassing beauty,
> Scarcely mortal.   (HOMER)

That one woman was worth a kingdom, a hundred thousand other women, a world itself. Well might Stesichorus be blind for carping at so fair a creature; and a just punishment it was. The same testimony gives Homer of the old men of Troy, that were spectators of that single combat betwixt Paris and Menelaus at the Scæan [or Western] gate; when Helena stood in presence, they said all, the war was worthily prolonged and undertaken for her sake. The very gods themselves (as Homer and Isocrates record) fought more for Helena than they did against the Giants. When Venus lost her son Cupid, she made proclamation by Mercury, that he that could bring tidings of him should have seven kisses; a noble reward some say; and much better than so many golden talents; seven such kisses to many men were more precious than seven Cities, or so many Provinces. One such a kiss alone would recover a man if he were a dying. Great Alexander married Roxane, a poor man's child, only for her person. 'Twas well done of Alexander, and heroically done, I admire him for it. Orlando was mad for Angelica, and who doth not condole his mishap? Thisbe died for Pyramus, Dido for Æneas; who doth not weep, as (before his conversion) Austin did in commiseration of her estate? she died for him, methinks (as he said) I could die for her!

But this is not the matter in hand, what prerogative this Beauty hath, of what power and sovereignty it is, and how far such persons that so much admire, and dote upon it, are to be justified; no man doubts of these matters; the question is how and by what means Beauty produceth this effect? By sight: the Eye betrays the soul, and is both Active and Passive in this business; it wounds and is wounded, is an especial cause and instrument, both in the subject, and in the object. As tears, it begins in the eyes, descends to the breast, it conveys these beauteous rays, as I have said, unto the heart. I saw, I was undone. Mars sees her, and would have her at first sight. Shechem saw Dinah, the daughter of Leah, and defiled her; Jacob [loved] Rachel, for she was beautiful and fair: David spied Bathsheba afar off; the Elders Susanna, as that Orthomenian Strato saw fair Aristoclea, the daughter of Theophanes, bathing herself at that Hercyne well in Lebadea; and were captivated in an instant. Their eyes saw, their breasts were ravaged with flames. Amnon fell sick for Tamar's sake. The beauty of Esther was such that she found favour, not only in the sight of Ahasuerus, " but of all those that looked upon her." Gerson, Origen, and some others, contended that Christ himself was the fairest of the sons of men, and Joseph next unto him, and they will have it literally taken; his very person was such, that he found grace and favour of all those that looked upon him. Joseph was so fair, that as the ordinary Gloss hath it, they ran to the top of the walls and to the windows to gaze on him, as we do commonly to see some great personage go by: and so Matthew Paris describes Matilda the Empress going through Cologne. P. Morales the Jesuit saith as much of the Virgin Mary. Antony no sooner saw Cleopatra, but, saith Appian, he was enamoured on her. Theseus at the first sight of Helen was so besotted, that he esteemed himself the happiest man in the world if he might enjoy her, and to that purpose kneeled down, and made his pathetical prayers unto the gods. Charicles, by chance espying that curious picture of smiling Venus naked in her Temple, stood a great while gazing, as one amazed; at length he brake into that mad passionate speech: O fortunate God Mars, that wast bound in chains, and made ridiculous for her sake! He could not contain himself, but kissed her picture, I know not how oft, and heartily desired to be so disgraced as Mars was. And what did he that his Betters had not done before him?

The other gods desire the like disgrace.   (OVID)

When Venus came first to Heaven, her comeliness was such, that (as mine Author saith) all the gods came flocking about, and saluted her, each of them went to Jupiter, and desired he might have her to be his wife. When fair Autolycus came in presence, as a candle in the dark his beauty shined, all men's eyes (as Xenophon describes the manner of it) were instantly fixed on him, and moved at the sight, insomuch that they could not conceal themselves, but in gesture or looks it was discerned and expressed. Those other senses, hearing, touching, may much penetrate and affect, but none so much, none so forcible as sight. Achilles was moved in the midst of a battle by fair Briseis, Ajax by Tecmessa; Judith captivated that great Captain Holofernes; Delilah, Samson; Rosamund, Henry the Second, Roxalana, Solyman the Magnificent, &c. A fair woman overcomes fire and sword.

Nought under heaven so strongly doth allure
The sense of man and all his mind possess,
As beauty's loveliest bait, that doth procure
Great warriors oft their rigour to suppress,
And mighty hands forget their manliness,
Drawne with the power of an heart-robbing eye,
And wrapt in fetters of a golden tress,
That can with melting pleasaunce mollify
Their harden'd hearts enur'd to blood and cruelty.   (SPENSER)

Clitiphon ingenuously confesseth that he no sooner came in Leucippe's presence, but that he did tremble at heart and looked with desirous eyes; he was wounded at the first sight, his heart panted, and he could not possibly turn his eyes from her. So doth Calasiris in Heliodorus, Isis' Priest, a reverend old man, complain, who, by chance at Memphis seeing that Thracian Rhodophis, might not hold his eyes off her: I will not conceal it, she overcame me with her presence, and quite assaulted my continency, which I had kept unto mine old age; I resisted a long time my bodily eyes with the eyes of my understanding; at last I was conquered, and as in a tempest carried headlong. ———— Xenopeithes, a Philosopher, railed at women down-right for many years together, scorned, hated, scoffed at them; coming at last into Daphnis a fair maid's company (as he condoles his mishap to his friend Demaretus) though free before, was far in love, and quite overcome upon a sudden. I confess I am taken, she, only she, has touched my feelings, and shaken my mind. I could hold out no longer. Such another mishap, but worse, had Stratocles, the Physician, that blear-eyed old man, full of snivel (so Prodromus describes him); he was a severe woman-hater all

his life, a bitter persecutor of the whole sex, he called them asps and
vipers, he forswore them all still, and mocked them wheresoever he
came, in such vile terms, that, if thou hadst heard him, thou wouldest
have loathed thine own Mother and Sisters for his words' sake. Yet this
old doting fool was taken at last with that celestial and divine look of
Myrilla, the daughter of Anticles the gardener, that smirking wench,
that he shaved off his bushy beard, painted his face, curl'd his hair, wore
a Laurel Crown to cover his bald pate, and for her love besides was
ready to run mad. For the very day that he married, he was so furious,
(a terrible, a monstrous long day), he could not stay till it was night,
but, the meat scarce out of his mouth, without any leave taking, he
would needs go presently to bed. What young man therefore, if old men
be so intemperate, can secure himself? Who can say, I will not be
taken with a beautiful object, I can, I will contain? No, saith Lucian
of his Mistress, she is so fair, that if thou dost but see her, she will
stupify thee, kill thee straight, and, Medusa like, turn thee to a stone,
thou canst not pull thine eyes from her, but as an adamant doth iron;
she will carry thee bound headlong whither she will herself, infect thee
like a Basilisk. It holds both in men and women. Dido was amazed at
Æneas' presence; and, as he feelingly verified out of his experience,

> *I lov'd her not as others, soberly,*
> *But as a madman rageth, so did I.*   (PLAUTUS)

So Musæus of Leander, he never takes his eyes from her; and Chaucer
of Palamon:

> He caste his eyen upon Emelia,
> And therewithal he blent and cryed ah!
> As though he stongen were unto the herte.

If you desire to know more particularly what this Beauty is, how it
doth influence, how it doth fascinate (for as all hold love is a fascination) thus in brief. This comeliness or beauty ariseth from the due
proportion of the whole, or from each several part. For an exact delinea-
tion of which, I refer you to Poets, Historiographers, and those amorous
Writers, to Lucian's Images and Charidemus, Xenophon's description
of Panthea, Petronius' Catalects, Heliodorus' Chariclea, Tatius' Leucippe, Longus Sophista's Daphnis and Chloe, Theodorus Prodromus
his Rhodanthe, Aristænetus' and Philostratus' Epistles, Balthasar Castilio, Laurentius, Æneas Sylvius his Lucretia, and every Poet almost,
which have most accurately described a perfect beauty, an absolute
feature, and that through every member, both in men and women. Each
part must concur to the perfection of it; for as Seneca saith, she is no

fair woman, whose arm, thigh, &c., are commended, except the face and all the other parts be correspondent. And the face especially gives a lustre to the rest: the Face is it that commonly denominates fair or foul; the Face is Beauty's Tower; and though the other parts be deformed, yet a good face carries it, (the face and not the wife is loved), that alone is most part respected, principally valued, and of itself able to captivate.

Glycera's face, too fair to see!   (HORACE)

Glycera's too fair a face was it that set him on fire, too fine to be beheld. When Chærea saw the singing wench's sweet looks, he was so taken, that he cried out, O fair face, I'll never love any but her, look on any other hereafter but her, I am weary of these ordinary beauties, away with them. The more he sees her, the worse he is; the sight burns, as in a burning-glass the Sun beams are recollected to a centre, the rays of Love are projected from her eyes. It was Æneas' countenance ravished Queen Dido, he had an Angelical face.

O sacred looks, befitting Majesty,

Which never mortal wight could safely see.   (PETRONIUS)

Although for the greater part this beauty be most eminent in the face, yet many times those other members yield a most pleasing grace, and are alone sufficient to enamour. An high brow like unto the bright heavens, white and smooth like the polished Alabaster; a pair of cheeks of Vermilion colour, in which Love lodgeth; Love that basks all night on a girl's soft cheeks; a coral lip, temple of delights, in which

A thousand kisses shalt thou find,

Yet still a thousand lurk behind,

the most pleasant seat of the graces, a sweet-smelling flower, from which Bees may gather honey, a dell of thyme and roses, &c.

Come, bees, to my lady's lips,

There roses breathe, &c.   (JOHANNES SECUNDUS)

A white and round neck, that Milky Way, dimple in the chin, black eyebrows, Cupid's bows, sweet breath, white and even teeth, which some call the sale-piece, a fine soft round pap, gives an excellent grace,

What splendour of swelling breasts, as of Parian marble!   (LOCHÆUS)

and makes a pleasant valley, a milky vale, between two chalky hills, sisterly little breasts, snowy companions, that merely to see them arouse desire,

Beautiful breasts made perfect for caresses,   (OVID)

again

Those calm unyielding breasts inflame the sight.

A flaxen hair; golden hair was ever in great account, for which Virgil commends Dido,

Not yet had Proserpine clipped her golden hair,   (VIRGIL)

and

All her yellow hair bound up in gold.   (VIRGIL)

Apollonius will have Jason's golden hair to be the main cause of Medea's dotage on him. Castor and Pollux were both yellow-hair'd; Paris, Menelaus, and most amorous young men have been such in all ages, smooth and sweet, as Baptista Porta infers, lovely to behold. Homer so commends Helena, makes Patroclus and Achilles both yellow-hair'd; lovely-hair'd Venus, and Cupid himself, was yellow-hair'd, with crisp hair glittering like gold, like that neat picture of Narcissus in Callistratus; for so Psyche spied him asleep; Briseis, Polyxena, were all yellow-hair'd,

———— *and Hero the fair,*

Whom young Apollo courted for her hair.   (MARLOWE)

Leland commends Guithera, King Arthur's wife, for a fair flaxen hair; so Paulus Æmilius sets out Clodoveus, that lovely King of France. Synesius holds every effeminate fellow or adulterer is fair hair'd: & Apuleius adds that Venus herself, Goddess of Love, cannot delight, though she come accompanied with the Graces, and all Cupid's train to attend upon her, girt with her own girdle, and smell of Cinnamon and Balm, yet if she be bald or bad hair'd, she cannot please her Vulcan. Which belike makes our Venetian Ladies at this day to counterfeit yellow hair so much, great women to calamistrate [with a curling-iron] and curl it up, with that glitter to take all captive, to adorn their head with spangles, pearls, and made flowers, and all Courtiers to affect a pleasing grace in this kind. In a word, the hairs are Cupid's nets, to catch all comers, a brushy wood, in which Cupid builds his nest, and under whose shadow all Loves a thousand several ways sport themselves.

A little soft hand, pretty little mouth, small, fine, long fingers, 'tis that which Apollo did admire in Daphne; a straight and slender body, a small foot, and well proportioned leg, hath an excellent lustre, bearing the body like the foundation of a temple. Clearchus vowed to his friend Amynander, in Aristænetus, that the most attractive part in his Mistress, to make him love and like her first, was her pretty leg and foot; a soft and white skin, &c., have their peculiar graces, a cloud is not softer, by Pollux, than the surface of her lovely breasts. Though in men these parts are not so much respected; a grim Saracen sometimes, a Pyracmon with naked limbs, a martial hirsute face pleaseth best; a black man is a pearl in a fair woman's eye, and is as acceptable as lame Vulcan was to Venus; for he being a sweaty fuliginous blacksmith, was dearly beloved of her, when fair Apollo, nimble Mercury, were rejected, and the rest of the sweet-fac'd gods forsaken. Many women (as Petronius observes) are hot after dirty ones, (as many men are more moved with kitchen-wenches, and a poor market-maid, than all these illustrious Court and City Dames) will sooner dote upon a slave, a servant, a Dirt-dauber, a Blacksmith, a Cook, a Player, if they see his naked legs or brawny arms, like that Huntsman Meleager in Philostratus, though he be all in rags, obscene and dirty, besmeared like a ruddle-man, [or digger of red clay], a gipsy, or a chimney-sweeper, than upon a Noble Gallant, Nireus, Hephæstion, Alcibiades, or those embroidered Courtiers full of silk and gold. Justine's wife, a Citizen of Rome, fell in love with Pylades, a Player, and was ready to run mad for him, had not Galen himself helped her by chance. Faustina the Empress doted on a Fencer.

Not one of a thousand falls in love, but there is some peculiar part or other which pleaseth most, and inflames him above the rest. A company of young Philosophers on a time fell at variance, which part of a woman was most desirable, and pleased best? some said the forehead, some the teeth, some the eyes, cheeks, lip, neck, chin, &c., the controversy was referred to Lais of Corinth to decide; but she, smiling, said they were a company of fools; for suppose they had her where they wished, what would they first seek? Yet, this notwithstanding, I do easily grant, nor, I think, would any of you contradict me, all parts are attractive, but especially the eyes, — sparkling and bright as stars, — which are Love's Fowlers; the shoeing-horns, the hooks of Love (as Arandus will) the guides, touchstone, judges, that in a moment cure mad men, and make sound folks mad, the watchmen of the body; what do they not? How vex they not? All this is true, and (which Athæneus and Tatius hold) they are the chief seats of Love, and as James Lernutius hath facetely expressed in an elegant Ode of his, —

> *I saw Love sitting in my mistress' eyes*
> *Sparkling, believe it, all posterity,*
> *And his attendants playing round about,*
> *With bow and arrows ready for to fly.*

Scaliger calls the eyes, Cupid's arrows; the tongue, the lightning of Love; the paps, the tents: Balthasar Castilio, the causes, the chariots, the lamps of Love,

Eyes emulating stars in light,
Enticing gods at the first sight ;

Love's Orators, Petronius.

O sweet and pretty speaking eyes,
Where Venus, love, and pleasure lies.

Love's Torches, Touch-box, Naptha, and Matches, Tibullus.

Tart Love, when he will set the gods on fire.
Lightens the eyes as torches to desire.

Leander, at the first sight of Hero's eyes, was incensed, saith Musæus.

Love's torches 'gan to burn first in her eyes,
And set his heart on fire which never dies :
For the fair beauty of a virgin pure
Is sharper than a dart, and doth inure
A deeper wound, which pierceth to the heart,
By the eyes, and causeth such a cruel smart.

A modern Poet brings in Amnon complaining of Tamar, —

It was thy beauty, 'twas thy pleasing smile,
Thy grace and comeliness did me beguile ;
Thy rose-like cheeks, and unto purple fair,
Thy lovely eyes and golden knotted hair.   (JACOB CORNELIUS)

Philostratus Lemnius cries out on his Mistress' Basilisk eyes, those two burning-glasses, they had so inflamed his soul, that no water could quench it. What a tyranny (saith he) what a penetration of bodies is this ! thou drawest with violence, and swallowest me up, as Charybdis doth Sailors, with thy rocky eyes ; he that falls into this gulf of Love, can never get out. — Let this be the Corollary then, the strongest beams of beauty are still darted from the eyes.

For who such eyes with his can see,
And not forthwith enamoured be?   (LOECHÆUS)

And as men catch dotterels [or plovers], by putting out a leg or an arm, with those mutual glances of the eyes they first inveigle one another.

'Twas Cynthia's eyes that first ensnared poor me.   (PROPERTIUS)

Of all eyes, (by the way), black are most amiable, enticing, and fairer, which the Poet observes in commending of his Mistress.

Wonderful black eyes and jet-black hair,

which Hesiod admires in his Alcmena,

From her black eyes, and from her golden face,
As if from Venus, came a lovely grace.

and Triton in his Milane —

My black-eyed beauty.

Homer useth that Epithet of Ox-eyed, in describing Juno, because a round black eye is the best, the Sun of Beauty, and farthest from black the worse: which Polydore Virgil taxeth in our Nation; we have grey eyes for the most part. Baptista Porta puts grey colour upon children, they be childish eyes, dull and heavy. Many commend on the other side Spanish Ladies, and those Greek Dames at this day, for the blackness of their eyes, as Porta doth his Neapolitan young wives. Suetonius describes Julius Cæsar to have been of a black quick sparkling eye: and although Averroes, in his Colliget, will have such persons timorous, yet without question they are most amorous.

Now, last of all, I will shew you by what means beauty doth fascinate, bewitch, as some hold, and work upon the soul of a man by the eye. For certainly I am of the Poet's mind, Love doth bewitch, and strangely change us.

> *Love mocks our senses, curbs our liberties,*
> *And doth bewitch us with his art and rings,*
> *I think some devil gets into our entrails,*
> *And kindles coals, and heaves our souls from th' hinges.*

Heliodorus proves at large that Love is witchcraft, it gets in at our eyes, pores, nostrils, ingenders the same qualities, and affections in us, as were in the party whence it came. The manner of the fascination, as Ficinus declares it, is thus: Mortal men are then especially bewitched, when as by often gazing one on the other, they direct sight to sight, join eye to eye, and so drink and suck in Love between them; for the beginning of this disease is the Eye; and therefore he that hath a clear Eye, though he be otherwise deformed, by often looking upon him, will make one mad, and tie him fast to him by the eye. — Leonard. Varius telleth us, that by this interview, the purer spirits are infected, the one Eye pierceth through the other with his rays, which he sends forth, and many men have those excellent piercing eyes, that, which Suetonius relates of Augustus, their brightness is such, they compel their spectators to look off, and can no more endure them than the Sun beams. Barradius reports as much of our Saviour Christ, and Peter Morales of the Virgin Mary, whom Nicephorus describes likewise to have been yellow-hair'd, of a wheat colour, but of a most amiable and piercing eye. The rays, as some think, sent from the eyes, carry certain spiritual vapours with them, and so infect the other party, and that in a moment. I know, they that hold that sight goes inward, will make a doubt of this; but Ficinus proves it from blear-eyes, that by sight alone, make others blear-eyed: and it is more than manifest, that the vapour of the corrupt blood doth get in together with the rays, and so by the contagion the spectators' eyes are infected. Other arguments there are of a Basilisk, that kills afar off by sight, as that Ephesian did of whom Philostratus speaks, of so pernicious an eye, he poisoned all he looked steadily on : and that other argument, of menstruous women, out of Aristotle's Problems : full of disease, Capivaccius adds, and Septalius the Commentator, that contaminate a looking-glass with beholding it. So the beams that come from the Agent's heart, by the eyes infect the spirits about the patients, inwardly wound, and thence the spirits infect the blood. To this effect she complained in Apuleius, Thou art the cause of my grief, thy eyes piercing through mine eyes to mine inner parts, have set my bowels on fire, and therefore pity me that am now ready to die for thy sake. Ficinus illustrates this with a familiar example of that Marrhusian Phædrus and Theban Lycias : Lycias he stares on Phædrus' face, and Phædrus fastens the balls of his eyes upon Lycias, and with those sparkling rays sends out his spirits. The beams of Phædrus' eyes are easily mingled with the beams of Lycias', and spirits are joined to spirits. This vapour begot in Phædrus' heart, enters into Lycias' bowels : and that which is a greater wonder, Phædrus' blood is in Lycias' heart, and thence come those ordinary love speeches, my sweetheart Phædrus, and mine own self, my dear bowels ! And Phædrus again to Lycias, O my light, my joy, my soul, my life ! Phædrus follows Lycias, because his heart would have his spirits ; and Lycias follows Phædrus, because he loves the seat of his spirits ; both follow, but Lycias the earnester of the two : the river hath more need of the fountain than the fountain of the river ; as iron is drawn to that which is touched with a loadstone, but draws not it again : so Lycias draws Phædrus. But how comes it to pass then, that the blind man loves, that never saw ? We read, in the Lives of the Fathers, a story of a child that was brought up in the wilderness, from his infancy, by an old Hermit : now come to man's estate, he saw by chance two comely women wandering in the woods : he asked the old man what creatures they were, he told him Fairies ; after awhile talking casually, the Hermit demanded of him, which was the pleasantest sight that ever he saw in his life ? he readily replied, the two Fairies he spied in the wilderness. So that, without doubt, there is some secret loadstone in a beautiful woman, a magnetick power, a natural inbred affection, which moves our concupiscence, as he sings,

> *Methinks I have a mistress yet to come,*
> *And still I seek, I love, I know not whom.*

'Tis true indeed of natural and chaste love, but not of this Heroical passion, or rather brutish burning lust of which we treat; we speak of wandering, wanton, adulterous eyes, which, as he saith, lie still in wait, as so many soldiers, and when they spy an innocent spectator fixed on them, shoot him through, and presently bewitch him: especially when they shall gaze and gloat, as wanton lovers do one upon another, and with a pleasant eye-conflict participate each other's souls. Hence you may perceive how easily, and how quickly, we may be taken in love, since at the twinkling of an eye Phædrus' spirits may so perniciously infect Lycias' blood. Neither is it any wonder, if we but consider how many other diseases closely and as suddenly, are caught by infection, Plague, Itch, Scabs, Flux, &c. The spirits taken in, will not let him rest that hath received them, but egg him on.

And the mind seeks the body whence came the love-wound.

(LUCRETIUS)

And we may manifestly perceive a strange eduction of spirits, by such as bleed at nose after they be dead, at the presence of their murderer; but read more of this in Lemnius, Valleriola, Valesius against Ficinus, Cardan, Libanius, &c.

SUBSECTION 3 — *Artificial Allurements of Love, Causes and Provocations to Lust, Gestures, Clothes, Dower, &c.*

NATURAL Beauty is a strong loadstone of itself, as you have heard, a great temptation, and pierceth to the very heart; a girl's modest beauty wounds my sight; but much more when those artificial enticements and provocations of Gestures, Clothes, Jewels, Pigments, Exornations, shall be annexed unto it; those other circumstances, opportunity of time and place, shall concur, which of themselves alone were all sufficient, each one in particular, to produce this effect. It is a question much controverted by some wise men, whether natural or artificial objects be more powerful? but not decided: for my part, I am of opinion, that, though Beauty itself be a great motive, and give an excellent lustre in beggary, as a Jewel on a dunghill will shine, and cast his rays, it cannot be suppressed, which Heliodorus feigns of Chariclea, though she were in beggar's weeds: yet, as it is used, artificial is of more force, and much to be preferred.

So toothless Ægle seems a pretty one,
Set out with new-bought teeth of Indy bone:
So foul Lycoris blacker than berry
Herself admires, now finer than cherry.   (MARTIAL)

John Lerius the Burgundian is altogether on my side. For whereas (saith he) at our coming to Brasil, we found both men and women naked as they were born, without any covering, so much as of their privities, and could not be persuaded, by our Frenchmen that lived a year with them, to wear any; many will think [saith he] that our so long commerce with naked women must needs be a great provocation to lust; but he concludes otherwise, that their nakedness did much less entice them to lasciviousness, than our women's clothes. And I dare boldly affirm (saith he) that those glittering attires, counterfeit colours, headgears, curled hairs, plaited coats, cloaks, gowns, costly stomachers, guarded and loose garments, and all those other accoutrements, where-with our country-women counterfeit a beauty, and so curiously set out themselves, cause more inconvenience in this kind, than that barbarian homeliness, although they be no whit inferior unto them in beauty. I could evince the truth of this by many other arguments, but I appeal (saith he) to my companions at that present, which were all of the same mind. — His country-man Montaigne, in his Essays, is of the same opinion, and so are many others; out of whose assertions thus much in brief we may conclude: that beauty is more beholding to Art than Nature, and stronger provocations proceed from outward ornaments, than such as nature hath provided. It is true, that those fair sparkling eyes, white neck, coral lips, turgent paps, rose-coloured cheeks, &c., of themselves are potent enticers; but when a comely, artificial, well-composed look, pleasing gesture, an affected carriage shall be added, it must needs be far more forcible than it was, when those curious needle-works, variety of colours, purest dyes, jewels, spangles, pendants, lawn, lace, tiffanies, fair and fine linen, embroideries, calamistrations [or hair-curlings], ointments, &c., shall be added, they will make the veriest dowdy otherwise a Goddess, when nature shall be furthered by Art. For it is not the eye of itself that enticeth to lust, but an " adulter-ous eye," as Peter terms it, a wanton, a rolling, lascivious eye: a wander-ing eye, which Isaiah taxeth. Christ himself and the Virgin Mary had most beautiful eyes, as amiable eyes as any persons, saith Barzadius, that ever lived, but withal so modest, so chaste, that whosoever looked on them, was freed from that passion of burning lust; if we may believe Gerson and Bonaventure, there was no such Antidote against it, as the Virgin Mary's face. 'Tis not the eye, but carriage of it, as they use it, that causeth such effects. When Pallas, Juno, Venus, were to win Paris' favour for the golden Apple, as it is elegantly described in that pleasant interlude of Apuleius, Juno came with majesty upon the stage, Minerva with gravity, but Venus came in smiling with her gracious graces, and exquisite musick, as if she had danced, and which was the main matter of all, she danced with her rolling eyes: they were the Brokers and Harbingers of her suit. So she makes her brags in a modern Poet,

> *Soon could I make my brow to tyrannise,*
> *And force the world do homage to mine eyes.*   (DANIEL)

The eye is a secret Orator, the first bawd, the gateway of love, and with private looks, winking, glances and smiles, as so many dialogues, they make up the match many times, and understand one another's meanings, before they come to speak a word. Euryalus and Lucretia were so mutually enamoured by the eye, and prepared to give each other entertainment, before ever they had conference: he asked her good will with his eye; she did favour him, and gave consent with a pleasant look. That Thracian Rhodopis was so excellent at this dumb Rhetorick, that if she had but looked upon any one almost (saith Calasiris) she would have bewitched him, and he could not possibly escape it. For, as Salvianus observes, the eyes are the windows of our souls, by which as so many channels, all dishonest concupiscence gets into our hearts. They reveal our thoughts, and as they say, the face is the index of the mind, but the eye of the countenance, —

> *Why look upon me with such wanton eyes?*   (BUCHANAN)

I may say the same of smiling, gait, nakedness of parts, plausible gestures, &c. To laugh is the proper passion of a man, an ordinary thing to smile, but those counterfeit, composed, affected, artificial, and reciprocal, those counter-smiles are the dumb shews and prognosticks of greater matters, which they most part use, to inveigle and deceive; though many fond lovers again are so frequently mistaken, and led into a fool's paradise. For if they see but a fair Maid laugh, or shew a pleasant countenance, use some gracious words or gestures, they apply it all to themselves, as done in their favour, sure she loves them, she is willing, coming, &c.

> *When a fool sees a fair maid for to smile,*
> *He thinks she loves him, 'tis but to beguile.*

They make an Art of it, as the Poet telleth us,

> *Who can believe? to laugh maids make an art,*
> *And seek a pleasant grace to that same part.*   (OVID)

And 'tis as great an enticement as any of the rest. She makes thine heart leap with a pleasing gentle smile of hers. I love Lalage as much for smiling, as for discoursing; 'Twas delightful, as he said in Petronius of his Mistress, being well pleased, she gave so sweet a smile. It won

Ismenias, as he confesseth, Ismene smiled so lovingly the second time
I saw her, that I could not choose but admire her: and Galla's sweet
smile quite overcame Faustus the Shepherd. All other gestures of the
body will enforce as much. Daphnis in Lucian was a poor tattered
wench, when I knew her first, said Crobyle, but now she is a stately
piece indeed, hath her Maids to attend her, brave attires, money in her
purse, &c., and will you know how this came to pass? by setting out
herself after the best fashion, by her pleasant carriage, affability, sweet
smiling upon all, &c. Many women dote upon a man for his compliment
only, and good behaviour, they are won in an instant; too credulous to
believe that every light, wanton suitor, who sees or makes love to them,
is instantly enamoured, he certainly dotes on, admires them, will surely
marry, when as he means nothing less, 'tis his ordinary carriage in all
such companies. So both delude each other, by such outward shews,
and amongst the rest, an upright, a comely grace, courtesies, gentle
salutations, cringes, a mincing gate, a decent and an affected pace, are
most powerful enticers, and which the Prophet Esay, a Courtier himself,
and a great observer, objected to the daughters of Sion, " they minced
as they went, and made a tinkling with their feet." To say the truth,
what can they not effect by such means?

> *Whilst nature decks them in their best attires*
> *Of youth and beauty which the world admires.*

She sets you all afire with her voice, her hand, her walk, her breast, her
face, her eyes. When Art shall be annexed to Beauty, when wiles and
guiles shall concur: for to speak as it is, Love is a kind of legerdemain,
mere juggling, a fascination. When they shew their fair hand, fine foot
and leg withal, saith Balthazar Castilio, they set us a longing, and so
when they pull up their petticoats, and outward garments, as usually
they do to shew their fine stockings, and those of purest silken dye,
gold fringes, laces, embroiderings, (it shall go hard but when they go
to Church, or to any other place, all shall be seen) 'tis but a springe to
catch woodcocks; and as Chrysostom telleth them down-right, though
they say nothing with their mouths, they speak in their gate, they speak
with their eyes, they speak in the carriage of their bodies. And what
shall we say otherwise of that baring of their necks, shoulders, naked
breasts, arms and wrists, to what end are they but only to tempt men to
lust?

> *Pray, why display those milk-white breasts and paps*
> *Without the modesty-piece? 'Tis but to say,*
> *" Ask me, and I surrender; " 'tis but to*
> *Invite your lovers to the field of Love.* (JOVIANUS PONTANUS)

There needs no more, as Fredericus Matenesius well observes, but a Crier to go before them so dressed, to bid us look out, a trumpet to sound, or for defect, a sow-gelder to blow, —

> *Look out, look out and see*
> *What object this may be*
> *That doth perstringe mine eye;*
> *A gallant lady goes*
> *In rich and gaudy clothes,*
> *But whither away God knows,** *

or to what end and purpose? But to leave all these phantastical raptures, I'll prosecute mine intended Theme. Nakedness, as I have said, is an odious thing of itself, an antidote to love, yet it may be so used, in part, and at set times, that there can be no such enticement as it is:

> *Chaste Diana, and naked Venus, neither is quite to my mind,*
> *The one has nothing wanton about her, the other too much, I find.*
>
> (AUSONIUS)

David so espied Bathsheba, the Elders Susanna; Apelles was enamoured with Campaspe, when he was to paint her naked. Tiberius supped with Sestius Gallus, an old lecher, waited on by naked girls; some say as much of Nero, and Pontus Heuter of Carolus Pugnax. Amongst the Babylonians, it was the custom of some lascivious queans to dance frisking in that fashion, saith Curtius, and Sardus writes of others to that effect. The Tuscans, at some set banquets, had naked women to attend upon them, which Leonicus confirms of such other bawdy nations. Nero would have filthy pictures still hanging in his chamber, which is too commonly used in our times; and Heliogabalus had others perform Venus in his presence that he might be aroused to the same. So things may be abused. A servant maid in Aristænetus spied her Master and Mistress through the key-hole merrily disposed; upon the sight she fell in love with her Master. Antoninus Caracalla observed his mother-in-law with her breasts amorously laid open, he was so much moved, that he said, Oh that I might! which she by chance over-hearing, replied as impudently, Thou mayest do what thou wilt. And upon that temptation he married her: this object was not in cause, not the thing itself, but that unseemly, undecent carriage of it.

When you have all done, the greatest provocations of lust are from our apparel; God makes, they say, man shapes, and there is no motive like unto it;

> *Which doth even beauty beautify,*
> *And most bewitch a wretched eye.* (SIDNEY)

---

* If you can tell how, you may sing this to the tune a sow-gelder blows. — B's note.

A filthy knave, a deformed quean, a crooked carkass, a maukin, a witch, a rotten post, an hedge-stake, may be so set out, and tricked up, that it shall make as fair a shew, as much enamour as the rest: many a silly fellow is so taken. One calls it the first snare of lust; Bossus, a fatal reed; the greatest bawd, saith Matenesius, and with tears of blood to be deplored. Not that comeliness of clothes is therefore to be condemned, and those usual ornaments: there is a decency and decorum in this, as well as in other things, fit to be used, becoming several persons, and befitting their estates; he is only phantastical, that is not in fashion, and like an old Image in Arras hangings, when a manner of Attire is generally received: but when they are so new-fangled, so unstaid, so prodigious in their Attires, beyond their means and fortunes, unbefitting their age, place, quality, condition, what should we otherwise think of them? Why do they adorn themselves with so many colours of herbs, fictitious flowers, curious needleworks, quaint devices, sweet-smelling odours, with those inestimable riches of precious stones, pearls, rubies, diamonds, emeralds, &c.? Why do they crown themselves with gold and silver, use coronets, and tires of several fashions, deck themselves with pendants, bracelets, ear-rings, chains, girdles, rings, pins, spangles, embroideries, shadows, rabatoes [or turned-down collars], versicolour ribbands? Why do they make such glorious shews with their scarfs, feathers, fans, masks, furs, laces, tiffanies, ruffs, falls, cauls [or hair-nets], cuffs, damasks, velvets, tinsels, cloth of gold, silver, tissue? with colours of heavens, stars, planets? the strength of metals, stones, odours, flowers, birds, beasts, fishes, and whatsoever Africa, Asia, America, sea, land, art, and industry of man can afford? Why do they use and covet such novelty of inventions, such new-fangled tires, and spend such inestimable sums on them? To what end are those crisped, false hairs, painted faces, as the Satirist observes, such a composed gate, not a step awry? Why are they like so many Sybarites, or Nero's Poppæa, Ahasuerus' Concubines, so costly, so long a dressing as Cæsar was marshalling his army, or an hawk in pruning? They take a year to trim and comb themselves; a gardener takes not so much delight and pains in his garden, an horseman to dress his horse, scour his armour, a mariner about his ship, a merchant his shop and shop-book, as they do about their faces, and all those other parts: such setting up with corks, straightening with whalebones, why is it but, as a day-net catcheth Larks, to make young men stoop unto them? Philocharus, a gallant in Aristænetus, advised his friend Polyænus to take heed of such enticements, for it was the sweet sound and motion of his Mistress' spangles and bracelets, the smell of her ointments, that captivated him first. Saith Lucian, to what use are pins, pots, glasses, ointments, irons, combs, bodkins, setting-sticks? Why bestow they all their patrimonies and husbands' yearly revenues on such fooleries? why use they dragons, wasps, snakes, for chains, enamelled jewels on their necks, ears? They had more need some of them be tied in Bedlam with iron chains, have a whip for a fan, and haircloths next to their skins, and instead of wrought smocks, have their cheeks stigmatised with a hot iron; I say, some of our Jezebels instead of painting, if they were well served. But why is all this labour, all this cost, preparation, riding, running, far-fetched, and dear bought stuff? Because forsooth they would be fair and fine, and where nature is defective, supply it by art.

Who blushes not by nature, doth by art,   (OVID)
and to that purpose they anoint and paint their faces, to make Helen of Hecuba — a distorted dwarf an Europa. To this intent they crush in their feet and bodies, hurt and crucify themselves, some in lax clothes, an hundred yards I think in a gown, a sleeve; and sometimes again so close, as to show their naked shape. Now long tails and trains, and then short, up, down, high, low, thick, thin, &c., now little or no bands, then as big as cart wheels; now loose bodies, then great fardingales and close girt, &c. Why is all this, but with the whore in the Proverbs, to intoxicate some or other? A snare for the eyes, one therefore calls it, and the trap of lust, and sure token, as an Ivy-bush is to a Tavern.

> *O Glycere, in that you paint so much,*
> *Your hair is so bedeckt in order such,*
> *With rings on fingers, bracelets in your ear,*
> *Although no prophet, tell I can, I fear.*

To be admired, to be gazed on, to circumvent some novice, as many times they do, that instead of a Lady he loves a cap and a feather, instead of a maid that should have true color, a solid body, and plenty of juice, (as Chærea describes his mistress in the Poet), a painted face, a ruff-band, fair and fine linen, a coronet, a flower.

He thinks that nature which is due to art,   (STROZA, FILIUS)
a wrought waistcoat he dotes on, or a pied petticoat, a pure dye instead of a proper woman. For generally, as with rich furred Conies, their cases are far better than their bodies, and like the bark of a Cinnamon tree which is dearer than the whole bulk, their outward accoutrements are far more precious than their inward endowments. 'Tis too commonly so.

> *With gold and jewels all is covered,*
> *And with a strange tire we are won,*
> *(While she's the least part of herself),*
> *And with such baubles quite undone.*   (OVID)

Why do they keep in so long together, a whole winter sometimes, and will not be seen but by torch or candle-light, and come abroad with all the preparation may be, when they have no business, but only to shew themselves?

> *They come to see, and to be seen, forsooth.* (OVID)
> *For what is beauty if it be not seen,*
> *Or what is't to be seen, if not admir'd,*
> *And though admir'd, unless in love desir'd?* (DANIEL)

Why do they go with such counterfeit gait, which Philo Judæus reprehends them for, and use (I say it again) such gestures, apish, ridiculous, undecent Attires, Sybaritical tricks, use those sweet perfumes, powders, and ointments, in publick, flock to hear sermons so frequent, is it for devotion? or rather, as Basil tells them, to meet their sweethearts, and see fashion; for, as he saith, commonly they come so provided to that place, with such curious compliments, with such gestures and tires, as if they should go to a dancing-school, a stage-play, or bawdy-house, fitter than a Church,

> *When such a she-priest comes her mass to say,*
> *Twenty to one they all forget to pray.* (DRAYTON)

They make those holy Temples consecrated to godly Martyrs, and religious uses, the shops of impudence, dens of whores and thieves, and little better than brothel-houses. When we shall see these things daily done, their husbands bankrupts, if not cornutos, their wives light huswives, daughters dishonest; and hear of such dissolute acts, as daily we do, how should we think otherwise? what is their end, but to deceive and inveigle young men? As tow takes fire, such enticing objects produce their effect, how can it be altered? When Venus stood before Anchises (as Homer feigns in one of his Hymns) in her costly robes, he was instantly taken, —

> *When Venus stood before Anchises first,*
> *He was amazed to see her in her tires;*
> *For she had on a hood as red as fire,*
> *And glittering chains, and ivy-twisted spires,*
> *About her tender neck were costly brooches,*
> *And necklaces of gold-enamell'd ouches.*

So when Medea came in presence of Jason first, attended by her Nymphs and Ladies, as she is described by Apollonius [Rhodius]:

> *A lustre followed them like flaming fire,*
> *And from their golden borders came such beams,*
> *Which in his eyes provok'd a sweet desire.*

Such a relation we have in Plutarch, when the Queens came and offered themselves to Antony, with divers presents, and enticing ornaments, Asiatick allurements, with such wonderful joy and festivity, they did so inveigle the Romans, that no man could contain himself, all was turned to delight and pleasure. The women transformed themselves to Bacchus shapes, the men-children to Satyrs and Pans; but Antony himself was quite besotted with Cleopatra's sweet speeches, philters, beauty, pleasing tires: for when she sailed along the River Cydnus, with such incredible pomp, in a gilded ship, herself dressed like Venus, her maids like the Graces, her Pages like so many Cupids, Antony was amazed, and rapt beyond himself. Heliodorus brings in Damæneta, Step-mother to Cnemon, whom she saw in his scarfs, rings, robes and coronet, quite mad for the love of him. It was Judith's Pantofles that ravished the eyes of Holofernes. And Cardan is not ashamed to confess, that, seeing his wife the first time all in white, he did admire, and instantly love her. If these outward ornaments were not of such force, why doth Naomi give Ruth counsel how to please Boaz? And Judith seeking to captivate Holofernes, washed and anointed herself with sweet ointments, dressed her hair, and put on costly attires. The riot in this kind hath been excessive in times past; no man almost came abroad, but curled and anointed, one spent as much as two funerals at once, and with perfumed hairs, — our grey hairs, saith Horace, made odorous with roses and Syrian nard. What strange things doth Suetonius relate in this matter of Caligula's riot. And Pliny. Read more in Dioscorides, Ulmus, Arnoldus, Randoletius On Cosmetics and Adornments, for it is now an art, as it was of old, (so Seneca records), perfumery is a trade. Women are bad, and men worse, no difference at all betwixt their and our times. Good manners (as Seneca complains) are extinct with wantonness, in tricking up themselves men go beyond women, they wear harlot's colours, and do not walk, but jet and dance, he-women, she-men, more like Players, Butterflies, Baboons, Apes, Anticks, than men. So ridiculous moreover we are in our attires, and for cost so excessive, that, as Hierome said of old, the price of a villa goes into a fillet, ten sesterces into a garment; 'tis an ordinary thing to put a thousand oaks and an hundred oxen into a suit of apparel, to wear a whole Manor on his back. What with shoe-ties, hangers, points, caps and feathers, scarfs, bands, cuffs, &c., in a short space their whole patrimonies are consumed. Heliogabalus is taxed by Lampridius, and admired in his age, for wearing jewels in his shoes, a common thing in our times, not for Emperors and Princes, but almost for serving-men & tailors: all the flowers, stars, constellations, gold &

precious stones, do condescend to set out their shoes. To repress the luxury of those Roman Matrons, there was the Valerian Law, & the Oppian, & a Cato to contradict; but no Laws will serve to repress the pride and insolency of our days, the prodigious riot in this kind. Lucullus' wardrobe is put down by our ordinary Citizens; and a Cobbler's wife in Venice, a Courtesan in Florence, is no whit inferior to a Queen, if our Geographers say true: and why is all this? Why do they glory in their jewels (as he saith) or exult and triumph in the beauty of clothes? why is all this cost? to incite men the sooner to burning lust. They pretend decency and ornament; but let them take heed, lest, while they set out their bodies, they do not damn their souls; 'tis Bernard's counsel: shine in jewels, stink in conditions; have purple robes, and a torn conscience. Let them take heed of Esay's Prophecy, that their slippers and tires be not taken from them, [their] sweet balls, bracelets, ear-rings, veils, wimples, crisping-pins, glasses, fine linen, hoods, lawns, and sweet savours, they become not bald, burnt, and stink upon a sudden. And let Maids beware, as Cyprian adviseth, lest, while they wander too loosely abroad, they lose not their virginities: and, like Egyptian Temples, seem fair without, but prove rotten carkasses within. How much better were it for them to follow that good counsel of Tertullian! To have their eyes painted with chastity, the Word of God inserted into their ears, Christ's yoke tied to the hair, to subject themselves to their husbands. If they would do so, they should be comely enough, clothe themselves with the silk of sanctity, damask of devotion, purple of piety and chastity, and so painted, they shall have God himself to be a suitor. Let whores and queans prank up themselves, let them paint their faces with minium and ceruse, they are but fuels of lust, and signs of a corrupt soul: if ye be good, honest, virtuous, and religious Matrons, let sobriety, modesty, and chastity, be your honour, and God himself your love and desire. Then a woman smells best, when she hath no perfume at all; no Crown, Chain, or Jewel (Guevarra adds) is such an ornament to a Virgin, or virtuous woman, as chastity is: more credit in a wise man's eye and judgment they get by their plainness, and seem fairer than they that are set out with baubles, as a Butcher's meat is with pricks [or skewers], puffed up and adorned, like so many jays, with variety of colours. It is reported of Cornelia, that virtuous Roman Lady, great Scipio's daughter, Titus Sempronius' wife, and the Mother of the Gracchi, that being by chance in company with a companion, a strange gentlewoman (some light huswife belike, that was dressed like a May-Lady, and as most of our gentlewomen are, was more solicitous of her head-tire than of her health, that spent her time betwixt a comb and a glass, and had rather be fair than honest, as Cato said, and have the Commonwealth turned topsy turvy than her tires marred) and she did naught but brag of her fine Robes and Jewels, and provoked the Roman Matron to shew hers: Cornelia kept her in talk till her children came from school, and these, said she, are my Jewels, and so deluded and put off a proud, vain, phantastical huswife. How much better were it for our Matrons to do as she did, to go civilly and decently, to use gold as it is gold, and for that use it serves, and when they need it, than to consume it in riot, beggar their husbands, prostitute themselves, inveigle others, and peradventure damn their own souls! How much more would it be for their honour and credit! Thus doing, as Hierome said of Blæsilla, Furius did not so triumph over the Gauls, Papirius of the Samnites, Scipio of Numantia, as she did by her temperance; always clad soberly, &c. They should insult and domineer over lust, folly, vain-glory, all such inordinate, furious, and unruly passions.

But I am over tedious, I confess, and whilst I stand gaping after fine clothes, there is another great allurement (in the world's eye at least) which had like to have stolen out of sight, and that is money, 'tis from the dowry that love's arrows come, money makes the match; they look only to money, 'tis like sauce to their meat, a good dowry with a wife. Many men, if they do hear but of a great portion, a rich heir, are more mad, than if they had all the beauteous ornaments, and those good parts Art and Nature can afford, they care not for honesty, bringing up, birth, beauty, person, but for money.

> *Our dogs and horses still from the best breed*
> *We carefully seek, and well may they speed:*
> *But for our wives, so they prove wealthy,*
> *Fair or foul, we care not what they be.* (THEOGNIS)

If she be rich, then she is fair, fine, absolute and perfect, then they burn like fire, they love her dearly, like pig and pie, and are ready to hang themselves if they may not have her. Nothing so familiar in these days, as for a young man to marry an old wife, as they say, for a piece of gold; an ass laden with money; and though she be an old crone, and have never a tooth in her head, neither good conditions, nor good face, a natural fool, but only rich, she shall have twenty young Gallants to be suitors in an instant. As she said in Suetonius, 'tis not for her sake, but for her lands or money; and an excellent match it were (as he added) if she were away. So, on the other side, many a young lovely Maid will cast away herself upon an old, doting, decrepit dizzard, that is rheu-

matick and gouty, hath some twenty diseases, perhaps but one eye, one
leg, never a nose, no hair on his head, wit in his brains, nor honesty, if he
have land or money, she will have him before all other suitors.

If only rich, a very barbarian pleases.   (OVID)

If he be rich, he is the man, fine man, and a proper man, she'll go to
Jacaktres or Tidore with him; Galesimus of the golden mountain. Sir
Giles Goosecap, Sr Amorous La-Fool, shall have her. And as Philematium in Aristænetus told Eumusus, hang him that hath no money, 'tis
to no purpose to talk of marriage without means, trouble me not with
such motions; let others do as they will, I'll be sure to have one shall
maintain me fine and brave. Most are of her mind; the question of his
qualities shall come last; for his conditions [or behaviours], she shall
enquire after them another time, or when all is done, the match made,
and every body gone home. Lucian's Lycia was a proper young Maid,
and had many fine Gentlemen to her suitors; Ethecles, a Senator's son,
Melissus, a Merchant, &c., but she forsook them all for one Passius, a
base, hirsute, bald-pated knave; but why was it? His Father lately died,
and left him sole heir of his goods and lands. This is not amongst your
dust-worms alone, poor snakes that will prostitute their souls for money,
but with this bait you may catch our most potent, puissant, and illustrious Princes. That proud upstart domineering Bishop of Ely, in the
time of Richard the First, Viceroy in his absence, as Nubrigensis relates
it, to fortify himself, and maintain his greatness, married his poor kins-
women (which came forth of Normandy by droves) to the chiefest
Nobles of the land, and they were glad to accept of such matches, fair
or foul, for themselves, their Sons, Nephews, &c. Who would not have
done as much for money and preferment? as mine author adds. Vortigern, King of Britain, married Rowena the daughter of Hengist, the
Saxon Prince, his mortal enemy; but wherefore? she had Kent for her
dowry. Iagello the great Duke of Lithuania, 1386, was mightily enamoured on Hedenga, insomuch that he turned Christian from a Pagan,
and was baptized himself by the name of Uladislaus, and all his subjects
for her sake: but why was it? she was daughter and heir of Poland, and
his desire was to have both Kingdoms incorporated into one. Charles the
Great was an earnest suitor to Irene the Empress, but, saith Zonaras,
for the sake of rulership, to annex the Empire of the East to that of the
West. Yet what is the event of all such matches, that are so made for
money, goods, by deceit, or for burning lust, what follows? they are
almost mad at first, but 'tis a mere flash; as chaff and straw soon fired,
burn vehemently for a while, yet out in a moment: so are all such

matches made by those allurements of burning lust; where there is no respect of honesty, parentage, virtue, religion, education, and the like, they are extinguished in an instant, and instead of love, comes hate; for joy, repentance, and desperation itself. Franciscus Barbarus, in his first book On Uxoriousness, hath a story of one Philip of Padua, that fell in love with a common whore, and was now ready to run mad for her; his Father, having no more sons, let him enjoy her; but after a few days, the young man began to loathe, could not so much as endure the sight of her, and from one madness fell into another. Such event commonly have all these lovers; and he that so marries, or for such respects, let them look for no better success than Menelaus had with Helen, Vulcan with Venus, Theseus with Phædra, Minos with Pasiphæ, and Claudius with Messalina; shame, sorrow, misery, melancholy, discontent.

SUBSECTION 4 — *Importunity and opportunity of time, place, conference, discourse, singing, dancing, musick, amorous tales, objects,
kissing, familiarity, tokens, presents, bribes, promises, protestations, tears, &c.*

ALL these allurements hitherto are afar off, and at a distance; I will come nearer to those other degrees of Love, which are conference, kiss-ing, dalliance, discourse, singing, dancing, amorous tales, objects, pres-ents, &c., which as so many Sirens steal away the hearts of men and women. For, as Tatius observes, It is no sufficient trial of a Maid's affection by her eyes alone, but you must say something that shall be more available, and use such other forcible engines; therefore take her by her hand, wring her fingers hard, and sigh withal; if she accept this in good part, and seem not to be much averse, then call her Mistress, take her about the neck and kiss her, &c. — But this cannot be done except they first get opportunity of living or coming together, ingress, egress, and regress; letters and commendations may do much, outward gestures and actions: but when they come to live near one another, in the same street, village, or together in an house, Love is kindled on a sudden. Many a Serving-man by reason of this opportunity and impor-tunity inveigles his Master's daughter, many a Gallant loves a Dowdy, many a Gentleman runs upon his Wife's Maids, many Ladies dote upon their [serving] men as the Queen in Ariosto did upon the Dwarf, many matches are so made in haste, and they compelled as it were by necessity so to love, which, had they been free, come in company of others, seen that variety which many places afford, or compared them to a third, would never have looked one upon another. (Hungry dogs will eat dirty puddings.) Or had not that opportunity of discourse & familiarity been offered, they would have loathed and contemned those, whom for want of better choice, and other objects, they are fatally driven on, and by reason of their hot blood, idle life, full diet, &c., are forced to dote upon them that come next. And many times those which at the first sight cannot fancy or affect each other, but are harsh and ready to disagree, offended with each other's carriage, like Benedick and Beatrice in the Comedy, and in whom they find many faults, by this living together in a house, conference, kissing, colling, and such like allurements, begin at last to dote insensibly one upon another.

It was the greatest motive that Potiphar's wife had to dote upon Joseph, and Clitophon upon Leucippe, his Uncle's Daughter, because the plague being at Byzantium, it was his fortune for a time to sojourn with her, to sit next her at the Table, as he telleth the tale himself in Tatius, (which though it be but a fiction, is grounded upon good observation, and doth well express the passions of lovers), he had opportunity to take her by the hand, and after a while to kiss and handle her paps, &c.; which made him almost mad. Ismenius the Orator makes the like confession in Eustathius, when he came first to Sosthenes' house, and sate at table with Cratisthenes his friend, Ismene, Sosthenes' daughter, waiting on them with her breasts open, arms half bare, after the Greek fashion in those times, naked armed, as Daphne was when she fled from Phœbus (which moved him much), was ever ready to give attendance on him, to fill him drink, her eyes were never off him, those speaking eyes, courting eyes, enchanting eyes; but she was still smiling on him, and when they were risen, that she had gotten a little opportunity, she came and drank to him, and withal trod upon his toes, and would come and go, and when she could not speak for the company, she would wring his hand, and blush when she met him: and by this means first she overcame him, she would kiss the cup and drink to him, and smile, and drink where he drank on that side of the cup, by which mutual compressions, kissings, wringing of hands, treading of feet, &c., I sipt and sipt, and sipt so long, till at length I was drunk in love upon a sudden. Philochorus, in Aristænetus, met a fair maid by chance, a mere stranger to him, he looked back at her, she looked back at him again, and smiled withal.

Of that day death and disaster came. (VIRGIL)
It was the sole cause of his farther acquaintance and love, that undid him.

'Tis never safe to yield to blandishments. (PROPERTIUS)
This opportunity of time and place, with their circumstances, are so

forcible motives, that it is unpossible almost for two young folks, equal in years, to live together, and not be in love, especially in great houses, Princes' Courts, where they are idle in their eminence, fare well, live at ease, and cannot tell otherwise how to spend their time.

Put an Hippolytus there, he'd soon be a Priapus. (OVID)

Achilles was sent by his Mother Thetis to the Island of Scyros in the Ægean Sea (where Lycomedes then reigned) in his nonage to be brought up, to avoid that hard destiny of the Oracle (he should be slain at the siege of Troy): and for that cause was nurtured in the Gynecium [or women's side of the house], amongst the King's children in a woman's habit, but see the event; he comprest Deidamia, the King's fair daughter, and had a fine son, called Pyrrhus, by her. Peter Abelard the Philosopher, as he tells the tale himself, being set by Fulbert her Uncle to teach Heloise his lovely Niece, and to that purpose sojourned in his house, had committed his tender lamb to an hungry wolf, I use his own words, he soon got her good will, and he read her more of Love than any other Lecture; such pretty feats can opportunity plea; already under one roof, soon of one mind, &c. But when, as I say, youth, wine, and night, shall concur (night, conspirator with love and sleep), 'tis a wonder they be not all plunged over head and ears in love; for youth is benign to love, a favouring condition, a very combustible matter, naptha itself, the fuel of Love's fire, and most apt to kindle it. If there be seven servants in an ordinary house, you shall have three couples in some good liking at least, and amongst idle persons how should it be otherwise? Living at Rome, saith Aretine's Lucretia, in the flower of my fortunes, rich, fair, young, and so well brought up, my conversation, age, beauty, fortune, made all the world admire and love me. — Night alone, that one occasion is enough to set all on fire, and they are so cunning in great houses, that they make their best advantage of it. Many a Gentlewoman, that is guilty to herself of her imperfections, paintings, impostures, will not willingly be seen by day, but as Castilio noteth, in the night; she hates the day like a dor-mouse, and above all things loves torches and candle-light, and if she must come abroad in the day, she covets, as in a Mercer's shop, a very obfuscate and obscure light. And good reason she hath for it: blemishes are not seen at night, and many an amorous gull is fetched over by that means. Gomesius gives instance in a Florentine Gentleman, that was so deceived with a wife, she was so radiantly set out with rings and jewels, lawns, scarfs, laces, gold, spangles, and gaudy devices, that the young man took her to be a goddess (for he never saw her but by torch-light), but after the wedding solemnities, when as he

698]   ANATOMY OF MELANCHOLY   [Part. 3, Sect. 2

viewed her the next morning without her tires, and in a clear day, she was so deformed, lean, yellow, riveld [or wrinkled], &c., such a beastly creature in his eyes, that he could not endure to look upon her. Such matches are frequently made in Italy, where they have no other opportunity to woo, but when they go to Church, or, as in Turkey, see them at a distance, they must interchange few or no words, till such time they come to be married, and then as Sardus and Bohemus relate of those old Lacedæmonians, the Bride is brought into the chamber, with her hair girt about her, the Bridegroom comes in, and unties the knot, and must not see her at all by day-light, till such time as he is made a Father by her. In those hotter Countries these are ordinary practices at this day; but in our Northern parts, amongst Germans, Danes, French, and Britains, the continent of Scandia and the rest, we assume more liberty in such causes; we allow them, as Bohemus saith, to kiss coming and going, to talk merrily, sport, play, sing, and dance, so that it be modestly done, go to the Ale-house and Tavern together. And 'tis not amiss, though Chrysostom, Cyprian, Hierome, and some other of the Fathers speak bitterly against it : but that is the abuse which is commonly seen at some drunken matches, dissolute meetings, or great unruly feasts. A young pickitivanted [or peak'd-bearded], trim-bearded fellow, saith Hierome, will come with a company of compliments, and hold you up by the arm as you go, and wringing your fingers, will so be enticed or entice : one drinks to you, another embraceth, a third kisseth, and all this while the Fiddler plays or sings a lascivious song; a fourth singles you out to dance, one speaks by becks and signs, and that which he dares not say, signifies by passions; amongst so many and so great provocations of pleasure, lust conquers the most hard and crabbed minds, and scarce can a man live honest amongst feastings, and sports, or at such great-meetings. For as he goes on, she walks along, and with the ruffling of her clothes makes men look at her, her shoes creak, her paps tied up, her waist pulled in to make her look small, she is straight girded, her hairs hang loose about her ears, her upper garment sometimes falls, and sometimes tarries, to shew her naked shoulders, and as if she would not be seen, she covers that in all haste which voluntarily she shewed. — And not [only] at Feasts, Plays, Pageants, and such assemblies, but as Chrysostom objects, these tricks are put in practice at Service-time in Churches, and at the Communion itself. If such dumb shews, signs, and more obscure significations of Love can so move, what shall they do that have full liberty to sing, dance, kiss, coll, to use all manner of discourse and dalliance? What shall he do that is beleaguered on all sides?

After whom so many rosy maids inquire,
Whom dainty dames and loving wights desire,
In every place, still, and at all times sue,
Whom gods and gentle goddesses do woo. (JOVIANUS PONTANUS)
How shall he contain? The very tone of some of their voices, a pretty
pleasing speech, an affected tone they use, is able of itself to captivate a
young man; but when a good wit shall concur, art and eloquence, fascinating speech, pleasant discourse, sweet gestures, the Sirens themselves
cannot so enchant. P. Jovius commends his Italian Countrywomen, to
have an excellent faculty in this kind, above all other nations, and
amongst them the Florentine Ladies: some prefer Roman and Venetian
Courtesans, they have such pleasing tongues, and such elegancy of
speech, that they are able to overcome a Saint.

Songs too have charms: let girls learn how to sing;
A charming voice will serve instead of looks. (OVID)
Often a pleasing voice brings fame, saith Petronius in his fragment of
pure impurities, I mean his Satyricon; she sang so sweetly, that she
charmed the air, and thou wouldst have thought thou hadst heard a
consort of Sirens. O good God, when Lais speaks, how sweet it is! Philo-
caus exclaims in Aristænetus. To hear a fair young Gentlewoman play
upon the Virginals, Lute, Viol, and sing to it, which as Gellius observes,
are the chief delight of Lovers, must needs be a great enticement. Parthenis was so taken.

Greedily my mind drinks in that lovely voice.
O sister Harpedona (she laments) I am undone, how sweetly he sings!
I'll speak a bold word, he is the properest man that ever I saw in my
life! O how sweetly he sings! I die for his sake, O that he would love
me again! — If thou didst but hear her sing, saith Lucian, thou wouldst
forget father and mother, forsake all thy friends, and follow her. Helen
is highly commended by Theocritus the Poet for her sweet voice and
musick, none could play so well as she, and Daphnis in the same Idyll:

How sweet a face hath Daphnis, how lovely a voice!
Honey itself is not so pleasant in my choice.
A sweet voice and musick are powerful enticers. Those Samian singing
wenches, Aristonica, Oenanthe and Agathoclea, insulted over Kings
themselves, as Plutarch contends. Argus had an hundred eyes, all so
charmed by one silly pipe, that he lost his head. Clitiphon complains in
Tatius of Leucippe's sweet tunes, he heard her play by chance upon the
Lute, and sing a pretty song to it, in commendations of a Rose, out of
old Anacreon belike;

Rose, the fairest of all flowers,
Rose, delight of higher powers,
Rose, the joy of mortal men,
Rose, the pleasure of fine women,
Rose, the Grace's ornament,
Rose, Dione's sweet content.

To this effect the lovely Virgin with a melodious Air upon her golden wired Harp or Lute, I know not well whether, played and sang, and that transported him beyond himself, and that ravished his heart. It was Jason's discourse as much as his beauty, or any other of his good parts, which delighted Medea so much.

Eloquence equally with beauty moves the heart.   (APOLLONIUS)

It was Cleopatra's sweet voice, and pleasant speech, which inveigled Antony, above the rest of her enticements. As a bull's horns are bound with ropes, so are men's hearts with pleasant words. Her words burn as fire. Roxalana bewitched Solyman the Magnificent; and Shore's wife by this engine overcame Edward the Fourth;

In her sole self the stolen charms of all.   (CATULLUS)

The wife of Bath in Chaucer confesseth all this out of her experience.

Thou sepst, some folk despre us for richesse,
Som for our shap, and som for our fairness;
And some, for she can outher singe or daunce,
And som, for gentilesse and daliaunce.

Peter Aretine's Lucretia telleth as much and more of herself, I counterfeited honesty, as if I had been more than a Vestal virgin, I looked like a wife, I was so demure and chaste, I did add such gestures, tunes, speeches, signs and motions upon all occasions, that my spectators and auditors were stupified, enchanted, fastened all to their places, like so many stocks and stones. ———— Many silly Gentlewomen are fetched over in like sort, by a company of gulls and swaggering companions, that frequently bely Noblemen's favours, rhyming Corybantiasmics, Thrasonian Rhodomonts or Bombomachides, that have nothing in them but a few players' ends, and compliments, vain braggadocians, impudent intruders, that can discourse at table of Knights and Lords' combats, like Lucian's Leontichus, of other men's travels, brave adventures, and such common trivial news, ride, dance, sing old ballet tunes, and wear their clothes in fashion, with a good grace; a fine sweet gentleman, a proper man, who could not love him? She will have him, though all her friends say no, though she beg with him! Some again are incensed by reading amorous toys, Amadis de Gaul, Palmerin de Oliva, the Knight of the Sun, &c., or hearing such tales of lovers, descriptions of their persons, lascivious discourses, such as Astyanassa, Helena's waiting-woman, by the report of Suidas, writ of old, of the various positions in love-making, and after her, Philænis and Elephantis; or those light tracts of Aristides Milesius (mentioned by Plutarch) and found by the Persians in Crassus' Army amongst the spoils, Aretine's Dialogues, with ditties, Love-songs, &c., must needs set them on fire, with such like pictures as those of Aretine, or wanton objects in what kind soever; no stronger engine than to hear or read of Love-toys, fables, and discourses, (one saith) and many by this means are quite mad. At Abdera in Thrace, (Andromeda, one of Euripides' Tragedies, being played), the spectators were so much moved with the object, and those pathetical Love-speeches of Perseus, amongst the rest, O Cupid, Prince of Gods and Men, &c., that every man almost a good while after spake pure Iambicks, and raved still on Perseus' speech, O Cupid, Prince of Gods and Men! As Car-men, Boys, and Prentices, when a new song is published with us, go singing that new tune still in the streets; they continually acted that Tragical part of Perseus, and in every man's mouth was, O Cupid, in every street, O Cupid, in every house almost, O Cupid, Prince of Gods and Men, pronouncing still like stage-players, O Cupid; they were so possessed all with that rapture, and thought of that pathetical Love-speech, they could not for a long time after forget, or drive it out of their minds, but, O Cupid, Prince of Gods and Men, was ever in their mouths. This belike made Aristotle forbid young men to see Comedies, or to hear amorous tales.

O therefore let not youths to girls
Have easy access.   (MARTIAL)

Let not young folks meddle at all with such matters. And this made the Romans, as Vitruvius relates, put Venus' Temple in the Suburbs, that youths might not become accustomed to love-making, to avoid all occasions and objects. For what will not such an object do? Ismenius, as he walked in Sosthenes' garden, being now in love, when he saw so many lascivious pictures, Thetis' marriage, and I know not what, was almost beside himself. And to say truth, with a lascivious object who is not moved, to see others dally, kiss, dance? And much more when he shall come to be an Actor himself.

To kiss and to be kissed, which amongst other lascivious provocations, is as a burden in a song, and a most forcible battery, as infectious, Xenophon thinks, as the poison of a spider; a great allurement, a fire itself, the prologue of burning lust (as Apuleius adds), lust itself.

It hath the very quintessence of Venus's nectar.   (HORACE)

A strong assault, that conquers Captains, and those all-commanding forces,

> *You conquer with swords, but are conquered with a kiss.*
>
> (HEINSIUS)

Aretine's Lucretia, when she would in kindness overcome a suitor of hers, and have her desire of him, took him about the neck, and kissed him again and again, and to that, which she could not otherwise effect, she made him so speedily and willingly condescend. And 'tis a continual assault,

> *Beginning ever, ending never,*   (PETRONIUS)

always fresh, and ready to begin as at first, a kiss that hath no close, yet is ever new, and hath a fiery touch with it.

> *The least touch of her body,*
> *And you're all ablaze already.*   (PETRONIUS)

Especially when they shall be lasciviously given, as he feelingly said, when Fotis gave him a hard kiss, laced in her arms, with lips twisted cunningly.

> *So sharply sweet her kiss,*
> *'Tis less a kiss than a wound;*
> *And at my lips, my soul*
> *Lies in a breathless swound.*   (In AULUS GELLIUS)

The soul and all is moved; with the shock of many kisses, saith Petronius, the lips ache, and breaths are mixt breathlessly, and in the stress of mutual embraces the soul is at its last gasp:

> ———— *Hotly cleaving each to each,*
> *And by each other's eager lips transpierced,*
> *Your souls will stray: such lovers may ye be.*   (PETRONIUS)

They breathe out their souls and spirits together with their kisses, saith Balthasar Castilio, change hearts and spirits, and mingle affections, as they do kisses, and it is rather a connexion of the mind than of the body. And although these kisses be delightsome and pleasant, Ambrosial kisses, such as Ganymede gave Jupiter, sweeter than Nectar, Balsom, Honey, Love-dropping kisses; for

> *The Gilliflower, the Rose is not so sweet,*
> *As sugared kisses be when Lovers meet,*

yet they leave an irksome impression, like that of Aloes or Gall,

> *At first ambrose itself was not sweeter,*
> *At last black hellebore was not so bitter.*   (CATULLUS)

They are deceitful kisses,

> *Why dost within thine arms me lap,*
> *And with false kisses me entrap?*   (BUCHANAN)

They are destructive, and the more the worse:

A thousand kisses, that were my utter ruin. (OVID)

They are the bane of these miserable Lovers. There be honest kisses I deny not, the respectful kiss, friendly kisses, modest kisses, Vestal-Virgin kisses, officious and ceremonial kisses, &c. Kissing and embracing are proper gifts of nature to a man: but these are too lascivious kisses,

With arms about my neck enfolded tight, (OVID)

too continuate, and too violent; they cling like Ivy, close as an Oyster, bill as Doves, meretricious [or courtesan's] kisses, biting of lips, with other tricks, mouth-suckings (saith Lucian), such as the lips can scarce be withdrawn from, with bitings between, and with open mouth caressing the paps, &c., such kisses as she gave to Giton, in Petronius, innumerable kisses not unpleasing to the lad, assaulting the neck, &c. More than kisses, or too homely kisses: as those that he [Apuleius] spake of, having had from her the seven sweet kinds of love, with such other obscenities that vain Lovers use, which are abominable and pernicious. If, as Peter de Ledesmo holds, *every kiss a man gives his wife after marriage be a mortal sin,* or that of Hierome, *whoever is hotly in love with his own wife is an adulterer,* or that of Thomas Secundus, *handling and kissing is a mortal sin,* or that of Durandus, *married folks should abstain from caresses during the entire time when the nuptial deed is interdicted,* what shall become of all such immodest kisses, and obscene actions, the forerunners of brutish lust, if not lust itself? What shall become of them, that often abuse their own wives? But what have I to do with this?

That which I aim at, is to shew you the progress of this burning lust: to epitomize therefore all this which I have hitherto said, with a familiar example out of that elegant Musæus; observe but with me those amorous proceedings of Leander and Hero. They began first to look one on the other with a lascivious look,

With becks and nods he first began
*   To try the wench's mind,*
With becks and nods and smiles again
*   An answer he did find.*
And in the dark he took her by the hand,
And wrung it hard, and sighed grievously,
And kiss'd her too, and woo'd her as he might,
With Pity me, sweetheart, or else I die,
And with such words and gestures as there past,
He won his Mistress' favour at the last.

The same proceeding is elegantly described by Apollonius in his Argonauticks, betwixt Jason and Medea, by Eustathius in the eleven books of the loves of Ismenias and Ismene, Achilles Tatius betwixt his Clitophon and Leucippe, Chaucer's neat poem of Troilus and Cresseide; and in that notable tale in Petronius of a Soldier and a Gentlewoman of Ephesus, that was so famous all over Asia for her chastity, and that mourned for her husband: the Soldier wooed her with such Rhetorick as Lovers use to do, — why struggle against love, &c., at last, breaking down her resistance, he got her good will, not only to satisfy his lust, but to hang her dead husband's body on the cross (which he watched instead of the thieves) that was newly stolen away, whilst he wooed her in her Cabin. These are tales you will say, but they have most significant Morals, and do well express those ordinary proceedings of doting Lovers.

Many such allurements there are, Nods, Jests, Winks, Smiles, Wrestlings, Tokens, Favours, Symbols, Letters, Valentines, &c. For which cause belike Godefridus would not have women learn to write. Many such provocations are used when they come in presence, they will and will not.

> My Mistress with an apple woos me,
> And hastily to covert goes
> To hide herself, but would be seen
> With all her heart before, God knows. (VIRGIL)

Hero so tripped away from Leander as one displeased,

> Yet as she went full often lookt behind,
> And many poor excuses did she find
> To linger by the way, —— (MARLOWE)

but if he chance to overtake her, she is most averse, nice and coy, —

> She refuses, and struggles, but desires above all to be conquered.
> (BAPTISTA MANTUANUS)

> She seems not won, but won she is at length,
> In such wars women use but half their strength. (MARLOWE)

Sometimes they lie open and are most tractable and coming, apt, yielding, & willing to embrace, to take a green gown, with that Shepherdess in Theocritus, to let their Coats, &c., to play and dally, at such seasons, and to some, as they spy their advantage; and then coy, close again, so nice, so surly, so demure, you had much better tame a colt, catch or ride a wild horse, than get her favour, or win her love, not a look, not a smile, not a kiss for a kingdom. Aretine's Lucretia was an excellent Artisan in this kind, as she tells her own tale: Though I was by nature and art most beautiful and fair, yet by these tricks I seem'd to be far more amiable than I was. For that which men earnestly seek and cannot attain, draws on their affection with a most furious desire. I had a suitor lov'd me dearly (saith she) and the more he gave me, the more eagerly he wooed me, the more I seemed to neglect, to scorn him, and (which I commonly gave others), I would not let him see me, converse with me, no not have a kiss. To gull him the more, and fetch him over (for him only I aimed at) I personated mine own servant to bring in a present from a Spanish Count, whilst he was in my company, as if he had been the Count's servant, which he did excellently well perform : The Count de monte Turco, my Lord and Master, hath sent your Ladyship a small present, and part of his hunting, a piece of Venison, a Pheasant, a few Partridges, &c., (all which she bought with her own money) commends his love and service to you, desiring you to accept of it in good part, and he means very shortly to come and see you. Withal she shewed him rings, gloves, scarfs, coronets, which others had sent her, when there was no such matter, but only to circumvent him. By these means (as she concludes) I made the poor Gentleman so mad, that he was ready to spend himself, and venture his dearest blood for my sake. Philinna in Lucian practised all this long before, as it shall appear unto you by her discourse ; for when Diphilus her sweetheart came to see her (as his daily custom was) she frowned upon him, would not vouchsafe him her company, but kissed Lamprias, his corrival, at the same time before his face : but why was it ? To make him (as she telleth her mother that chid her for it) more jealous ; to whetten his love, to come with a greater appetite, and to know that her favour was not so easy to be had. Many other tricks she used besides this (as she there confesseth) for she would fall out with, and anger him of set purpose, pick quarrels upon no occasion, because she would be reconciled to him again. As the old saying is, the falling out of lovers is the renewing of love ; and according to that of Aristænetus, love is increased by injuries, as the Sunbeams are more gracious after a cloud. And surely this Aphorism is most true ; for as Ampelis informs Chrysis in the said Lucian, If a lover be not jealous, angry, waspish, apt to fall out, sigh and swear, he is no true lover. To kiss and coll, hang about her neck, protest, swear, and wish, are but ordinary symptoms, signs of the beginning and growth of love ; but if he be jealous, angry, apt to mistake, &c., breathe easily, sweet sister, he is thine own ; yet if you let him alone, humour him, please him, &c., and that he perceive once he hath you sure, without any corrival, his love will languish, and he will not care so much for you. Hitherto (saith she) can I speak out of experience; Demophantus, a rich fellow, was a suitor of mine; I seem'd to neglect him, and gave better entertainment to Callides the Painter before his face; at first he went his way all in a chafe, cursing and swearing, but at last he came submitting himself, vowing and protesting that he loved me most dearly, I should have all he had, and that he would kill himself for my sake. Therefore I advise thee (dear sister Chrysis) and all maids, not to use your suitors over kindly; 'twill make them proud and insolent; but now and then reject them, estrange thyself, and if you will list to me, shut him out of doors once or twice, let him dance attendance; follow my counsel, and by this means you shall make him mad, come off roundly, stand to any conditions, and do whatsoever you will have him. — These are the ordinary practices; yet, in the said Lucian, Melissa, methinks, had a trick beyond all this; for when her suitor came coldly on, to stir him up, she writ one of his corrival's names and her own in a paper, Melissa loves Hermotimus, Hermotimus Melissa, causing it to be stuck upon a post, for all gazers to behold, and lost it in the way where he used to walk; which when the silly novice perceived, he instantly apprehended it was so, came raving to me, &c.: and so, when I was in despair of his love, four months after I recovered him again. — Eugenia drew Timocles for her Valentine, and wore his name a long time after in her bosom; Camæna singled out Pamphilus to dance, at Myson's wedding (some say) for there she saw him first; Felicianus overtook Cælia by the high-way side, offered his service, thence came further acquaintance, and thence came love. But who can repeat half their devices; what Aretine experienced, what conceited Lucian, or wanton Aristænetus? They will deny and take, stiffly refuse, and yet earnestly seek the same, repel to make them come with more eagerness, fly from if you follow, but if averse, as a shadow they will follow you again; with a regaining retrait, a gentle reluctancy, a smiling threat, a pretty pleasant peevishness, they will put you off, and have a thousand such several enticements. For as he saith,

> 'Tis not enough though she be fair of hue,
> For her to use this vulgar compliment :
> But pretty toys and jests, and saws and smiles,
> Are far beyond what beauty can attempt.   (PETRONIUS)

For this cause, belike, Philostratus, in his Images, makes divers Loves, some young, some of one age, some of another, some winged, some of one sex, some of another, some with torches, some with golden apples, some with darts, gins, snares, and other engines in their hands, as

Propertius hath prettily painted them out, and which some interpret, divers enticements, or divers affections of Lovers, which if not alone, yet jointly may batter and overcome the strongest constitutions.

It is reported of Decius and Valerianus, those two notorious persecutors of the Church, that when they could enforce a young Christian by no means (as Hierome records) to sacrifice to their idols, by no torments or promises, they took another course to tempt them: they put him into a fair Garden, and set a young Courtesan to dally with him; she took him about the neck and kissed him, and that which is not to be named, fondled with the hands, &c., and all those enticements which might be used, that whom Torments could not, Love might batter and beleaguer. But such was his constancy, she could not overcome, and when this last engine would take no place, they left him to his own ways. At Berkeley in Gloucestershire, there was in times past a Nunnery (saith Gualterus Mapes, an old Historiographer, that lived 400 years since) of which there was a noble and a fair Lady Abbess: Godwin, that subtil Earl of Kent travelling that way (seeking not her but hers) leaves a Nephew of his, a proper young Gallant (as if he had been sick) with her, till he came back again, and gives the young man charge so long to counterfeit, till he had deflowered the Abbess, and as many besides of the Nuns as he could, and leaves him withal rings, jewels, girdles, and such toys to give them still, when they came to visit him. The young man, willing to undergo such a business, played his part so well, that in short space he got up most of their bellies, and when he had done, told his Lord how he had sped; his Lord makes instantly to the Court, tells the King how such a Nunnery was become a bawdy house, procures a visitation, gets them to be turned out, and begs the lands to his own use. This story I do therefore repeat, that you may see of what force these enticements are, if they be opportunely used, and how hard it is even for the most averse and sanctified souls to resist such allurements. John Major, in the life of John the Monk, that lived in the days of Theodosius, commends the Hermit to have been a man of singular continency, and of a most austere life; but one night by chance the Devil came to his Cell in the habit of a young market wench that had lost her way, and desired for God's sake some lodging with him. The old man let her in, and after some common conference of her mishap, she began to inveigle him with lascivious talk and jests, to play with his beard, to kiss him, and do worse, till at last she overcame him. As he went to address himself to that business, she vanished on a sudden, and the Devils in the air laughed him to scorn. Whether this be a true story, or a tale, I will not much contend, it serves to illustrate this which I have said.

Yet were it so, that these of which I have hitherto spoken, and such like enticing baits be not sufficient, there be many others, which will of themselves intend this passion of burning lust, amongst which, dancing is none of the least; and it is an engine of such force, I may not omit it. Petrarch calls it the spur of lust, a circle of which the Devil himself is the centre. Many women that use it have come dishonest home, most indifferent, none better. Another terms it, the companion of all filthy delights and enticements, and 'tis not easily told what inconveniences come by it, what scurrile talk, obscene actions, and many times such monstrous gestures, such lascivious motions, such wanton tunes, meretricious kisses, homely embracings, —

> Comes now some Gaditanian with his troop
> Of naughty singers, and the wanton pranks
> Of much applauded dancing girls that stoop
> And rouse desire with undulating flanks —
> (JUVENAL)

that it will make the spectators mad. When that Epitomizer of Trogus had to the full described and set out King Ptolemy's riot, as a chief engine and instrument of his overthrow, he adds fiddling and dancing; the King was not a spectator only, but a principal actor himself. A thing nevertheless frequently used, and part of a Gentlewoman's bringing up, to sing, dance, and play on the Lute, or some such instrument, before she can say her Pater Noster, or ten Commandments. 'Tis the next way their Parents think to get them husbands, they are compelled to learn, and by that means, from earliest years their thoughts run to wantonness. 'Tis a great allurement as it is often used, and many are undone by it. Thais, in Lucian, inveigled Lamprias in a dance. Herodias so far pleased Herod, that she made him swear to give her what she would ask, John Baptist's head in a platter. Robert, Duke of Normandy, riding by Falais, spied Arletta a fair maid, as she danced on a green, and was so much enamoured with the object, that he must needs lie with her that night, (of whom he begat William the Conqueror; by the same token she tore her smock down, saying, &c.). Owen Tudor won Queen Katherine's affection in a dance, falling by chance with his head in her lap. Who cannot parallel these stories out of his experience? Speucippus, a noble gallant in that Greek Aristænetus, seeing Panareta a fair young Gentlewoman dancing by accident, was so far in love with her, that for a long time after he could think of nothing but Panareta: he came raving home full of Panareta. Who would not admire her, who would not love her, that should but see her dance as I did? O admirable, O divine Panareta! I have seen old and new Rome, many fair Cities, many proper women, but never any like to Panareta, they are dross, dowdies all to Panareta! O how she danced, how she tript, how she turn'd, with what a grace! happy is that man that shall enjoy her! O most incomparable, only Panareta! — When Xenophon in the Symposium or Banquet, had discoursed of love, and used all the engines that might be devised, to move Socrates amongst the rest, to stir him the more, he shuts up all with a pleasant interlude or dance of Dionysus and Ariadne: First Ariadne dressed like a bride came in and took her place; by and by Dionysus entered, dancing to the Musick. The spectators did all admire the young man's carriage; and Ariadne herself was so much affected with the sight, that she could scarce sit. After a while Dionysus beholding Ariadne, and incensed with love, bowing to her knees, embraced her first, and kissed her with a grace; she embraced him again, and kissed him with like affection, &c., as the dance required: but they that stood by and saw this, did much applaud and commend them both for it. And when Dionysus rose up, he raised her up with him, and many pretty gestures, embraces, kisses, and love compliments passed between them; which when they saw fair Bacchus and beautiful Ariadne so sweetly and so unfeignedly kissing each other, so really embracing, they swore they loved indeed, and were so inflamed with the object, that they began to rouse up themselves, as if they would have flown. At the last when they saw them still so willing embracing, and now ready to go to the Bride-chamber, they were so ravished with it, that they that were unmarried swore they would forthwith marry, and those that were married, called instantly for their horses, and galloped home to their wives. What greater motive can there be than this burning lust? What so violent an oppugner? Not without good cause therefore so many general Councils condemn it, so many Fathers abhor it, so many grave men speak against it. Use not the company of a woman, saith Siracides, that is a singer or a dancer; neither hear, lest you be taken in her craftiness. Hædus holds, lust in Theatres is not seen, but learned. Gregory Nazianzen, that eloquent Divine (as he relates the story himself), when a noble friend of his solemnly invited him, with other Bishops, to his daughter Olympia's wedding, refused to come: for it is absurd to see an old gouty Bishop sit amongst dancers, he held it unfit to be a spectator, much less an actor. Tully writes, he is not a sober man that danceth; for some such reason (belike) Domi-

tian forbade the Roman Senators to dance, and for that fact removed
many of them from the Senate. But these, you will say, are lascivious
and Pagan dances, 'tis the abuse that causeth such inconvenience, and
I do not well therefore to condemn, speak against, or innocently to
accuse the best and pleasantest thing (so Lucian calls it) that belongs
to mortal men. You mis-interpret, I condemn it not; I hold it notwithstanding an honest disport, a lawful recreation, if it be opportune,
moderately and soberly used: I am of Plutarch's mind, that which respects pleasure alone, honest recreation, or bodily exercise, ought not
to be rejected and contemned; I subscribe to Lucian, 'tis an elegant
thing, which cheereth up the mind, exerciseth the body, delights the
spectators, which teacheth many comely gestures, equally affecting the
ears, eyes, and soul itself. Sallust discommends singing and dancing in
Sempronia, not that she did sing and dance, but that she did it in
excess, 'tis the abuse of it: and Gregory's refusal doth not simply condemn it, but in some folks. Many will not allow men and women to
dance together, because it is a provocation to lust: they may as well,
with Lycurgus and Mahomet, cut down all Vines, forbid the drinking
of wine, for that it makes some men drunk.

> *There's nothing good that cannot evil be.*
> *Fire is good, yet evil too, we see.* (OVID)

I say of this, as of all other honest recreations, they are like fire, good
and bad, and I see no such inconvenience, but that they may so dance,
if it be done at due times, and by fit persons: and conclude with
Wolfongus Hider, and most of our modern divines: If the dancing is
decorous, sober, modest, and in the plain view of good men and honest
matrons, and at fitting times, it may and should be approved. " There
is a time to mourn, a time to dance." Let them take their pleasures
then, and as Apuleius said of old, young men and maids flourishing in
their age, fair and lovely to behold, well attired, and of comely carriage,
dancing a Greek galliard, and as their dance required, kept their time,
now turning, now tracing, now apart, now altogether, now a courtesy,
then a caper, &c.; and it was a pleasant sight, to see those pretty knots,
and swimming figures. The Sun and Moon (some say) dance about the
earth, the three upper Planets about the Sun as their centre, now stationary, now direct, now retrograde, now in apogee then in perigee,
now swift, then slow, occidental, oriental, they turn round, jump and
trace, Venus and Mercury about the Sun with those thirty three Maculæ
or Bourbonian planets, dancers about the harping Sun, saith Fromundus. Four Medicean stars dance about Jupiter, two Austrian about

Saturn, &c., and all (belike) to the musick of the Spheres. Our greatest Councillors, and staid Senators, at some times dance, as David before the Ark, Miriam, Judith, (though the Devil hence perhaps hath brought in those bawdy Bacchanals), and well may they do it. The greatest Soldiers, as Quintilianus, Æmilius Probus, Cælius Rhodiginus, have proved at large, still use it in Greece, Rome, and the most worthy Senators, sing, and dance. Lucian, Macrobius, Libanius, Plutarch, Julius Pollux, Athenæus, have written just tracts in commendation of it. In this our age it is in much request in those Countries, as in all civil Commonwealths, as Alexander ab Alexandro hath proved at large, amongst the Barbarians themselves nothing so precious; all the World allows it.

> *Croesus, I despise your gold,*
> *All your Asia I'd have sold,*
> *Traded, given, or thrown away,*
> *For sweet-limb'd dancers young and gay.*
>
> (EROTOPÆDIA OF ANGERIANUS)

Plato, in his Common-wealth, will have dancing-schools to be maintained, that young folks might meet, be acquainted, see one another, and be seen; nay more, he would have them dance naked, and scoffs at them that laugh at it. But Eusebius, and Theodoret, worthily lash him for it; and well they might: for as one saith, the very sight of naked parts causeth enormous, exceeding concupiscences, and stirs up both men and women to burning lust. There is a mean in all things: this is my censure in brief; dancing is a pleasant recreation of body and mind, if sober and modest (such as our Christian dances are) if tempestively [or timely] used; a furious motive to burning lust, if, as by Pagans heretofore, unchastely abused. But I proceed.

If these allurements do not take place, for Simierus, that great master of dalliance, shall not behave himself better, the more effectually to move others, and satisfy their lust, they will swear and lie, promise, protest, forge, counterfeit, brag, bribe, flatter and dissemble of all sides. 'Twas Lucretia's counsel in Aretine, if you would profit from your admirers, promise, pretend, swear and forswear, lie and cheat, and they put it well in practice, as Apollo to Daphne, —

> *Delphos, Claros, and Tenedos serve me,*
> *And Jupiter is known my sire to be.* (OVID)

The poorest swains will do as much: I have a thousand sheep, good store of cattle, and they are all at her command; house, land, goods, are at her service, as he is himself. Dinomachus, a Senator's Son in

Lucian, in love with a wench inferior to him in birth and fortunes, the sooner to accomplish his desire, wept unto her, and swore he loved her with all his heart, and her alone, and that as soon as ever his Father died, (a very rich man, and almost decrepit), he would make her his wife. The Maid by chance made her Mother acquainted with the business, who being an old Fox, well experienced in such matters, told her daughter, now ready to yield to his desire, that he meant nothing less, for dost thou think he will ever care for thee, being a poor wench, that may have his choice of all the beauties in the City, one Noble by birth, with so many talents, as young, better qualified, and fairer than thyself? Daughter, believe him not: the Maid was abasht, and so the matter broke off. When Jupiter wooed Juno first (Lilius Giraldus relates it out of an old Comment on Theocritus) the better to effect his suit, he turned himself into a Cuckoo, and spying her one day walking alone, separated from the other Goddesses, caused a tempest suddenly to arise, for fear of which she fled to shelter: Jupiter to avoid the storm likewise flew into her lap, whom Juno for pity covered in her Apron. But he turned himself forthwith into his own shape, began to embrace and offer violence unto her, but she by no means would yield, till he vowed and swore to marry her, and then she gave consent. This fact was done at Thornax hill, which ever after was called Cuckoo hill, and in perpetual remembrance there was a Temple erected to Juno Teleia in the same place. So powerful are fair promises, vows, oaths, and protestations. It is an ordinary thing too in this case to belie their age, which widows usually do, that mean to marry again, and bachelors too sometimes, coming on to forty, to say they are younger than they are. Charmides, in the said Lucian, loved Philematium, an old Maid of five and forty years, she swore to him she was but two and thirty next December. But to dissemble in this kind is familiar of all sides, and often it takes.

> *'Tis no great thing so to deceive*
> *One who cannot but believe,* (OVID)

'tis soon done, no such great mastery,

> *Vast, in all truth, the renown, and ample the spoils,* (VIRGIL)

and nothing so frequent as to belie their estates, to prefer their suits, and to advance themselves. Many men, to fetch over a young woman, widows, or whom they love, will not stick to crack, forge, and feign, anything comes next, bid his boy fetch his cloak, rapier, gloves, jewels, &c., in such a chest, scarlet, golden, tissue breeches, &c., when there is no such matter; or make any scruple to give out, as he did in Petronius, that he was Master of a Ship, kept so many servants, and to personate their part the better, take upon them to be gentlemen of good houses, well descended and allied, hire apparel at brokers, some Scavenger or pricklouse Tailors to attend upon them for the time, swear they have great possessions, bribe, lie, cog, and foist, how dearly they love, how bravely they will maintain her, like any Lady, Countess, Duchess, or Queen; they shall have gowns, tires, jewels, coaches, and caroches, choice diet, —

> *The heads of Parrots, tongues of Nightingales,*
> *The brains of Peacocks, and of Ostriches,*
> *Their bath shall be the juice of Gilliflowers,*
> *Spirit of Roses and of Violets,*
> *The milk of Unicorns, &c.*

as old Volpone courted Cælia in the Comedy, when as they are no such men, not worth a groat, but mere sharkers, to make a fortune, to get their desire, or else pretend love to spend their idle hours, to be more welcome, and for better entertainment. The conclusion is, they mean nothing less.

> *Oaths, vows, promises, are much protested;*
> *But when their mind and lust is satisfied,*
> *Oaths, vows, promises, are quite neglected.* (CATULLUS)

Though he solemnly swear by the Genius of Cæsar, by Venus' shrine, Hymen's deity, by Jupiter, and all the other gods, give no credit to his words. For when Lovers swear, Venus laughs, Venus laughs at lovers' lies, Jupiter himself smiles, and pardons it withal; as grave Plato gives out, of all perjury, that alone for love matters is forgiven by the gods. If promises, lies, oaths, and protestations will not avail, they fall to bribes, tokens, gifts, and such like feats. 'Tis by gold that love is won; as Jupiter corrupted Danaë with a golden shower, and Liber Ariadne with a lovely Crown (which was afterwards translated into the Heavens, and there for ever shines); they will rain Chickens, Florins, Crowns, Angels, all manner of coins and stamps in her lap. And so must he certainly do that will speed, make many feasts, banquets, invitations, send her some present or other every foot [of the way]. He must give feasts and presents galore, (saith Hædus), he must be very bountiful and liberal, seek and sue, not to her only, but to all her followers, friends, familiars, fiddlers, panders, parasites, and household-servants; he must insinuate himself, and surely will, to all, of all sorts, messengers, porters, carriers; no man must be unrewarded, or unrespected. I had a suitor (saith Aretine's Lucretia) that when he came to my house, flung gold and silver about as if it had been chaff. Another suitor I had was a very cholerick fellow, but I so handled him that for all his fuming, I brought him upon his knees. If there had been an excellent bit in the market, any novelty, fish, fruit, or fowl, muskadel, or malmsey, or a cup of neat wine in all the city, it was presented presently to me, though never so dear, hard to come by, yet I had it: the poor fellow was so fond at last, that I think, if I would, I might have had one of his eyes out of his head. A third suitor was a merchant of Rome, and his manner of wooing was with exquisite musick, costly banquets, poems, &c. I held him off till at length he protested, promised, and swore if I gave him my virginity, I should have all he had, house, goods and lands, only for lying with me. Neither was there ever any Conjurer, I think, to charm his spirits, that used such attention, or mighty words, as he did exquisite phrases; or General of any army, so many stratagems to win a city, as he did tricks and devices to get the love of me. Thus men are active and passive, and women not far behind them in this kind. Bold are women, both in love and hate.

> For half so boldely can ther no man
> Swere and lyen as a womman can.

They will crack, counterfeit, and collogue, as well as the best, with handkerchiefs, and wrought nightcaps, purses, posies, and such toys: as he justly complained,

> *Why dost thou send me violets, my dear?*
> *To make me burn more violent, I fear,*
> *With violets too violent thou art,*
> *To violate and wound my gentle heart.*   (JOVIANUS PONTANUS)

When nothing else will serve, the last refuge is their tears. 'Twixt tears and sighs I write this (I take love to witness), saith Chelidonia to Philonius. Those burning torches are now turned to floods of tears. Aretine's Lucretia, when her sweetheart came to Town, wept in his bosom, that he might be persuaded those tears were shed for joy of his return. Quartilla, in Petronius, when nought would move, fell a weeping; and, as Balthazar Castilio paints them out, To these crocodile's tears, they will add sobs, fiery sighs, and sorrowful countenance, pale colour, leanness, and if you do but stir abroad, these fiends are ready to meet you at every turn, with such a sluttish, neglected habit, dejected look, as if they were now ready to die for your sake; and how saith he, shall a young novice thus beset, escape? But believe them not.

> *Trust not your hearts to girls, the sea's more certain*
> *Than woman's faith.*   (PETRONIUS)

Thou thinkest peradventure because of her vows, tears, smiles, and protestations, she is solely thine, thou hast her heart, hand, and affection, when as indeed there is no such matter, as the Spanish Bawd said, she will have one sweetheart in bed, another in the gate, a third sighing at home, a fourth, &c. Every young man she sees and likes, hath as much interest, and shall as soon enjoy her as thyself. On the other side, which I have said, men are as false, let them swear, protect, and lie;

What they tell you, they've told a thousand girls. (OVID)

They love some of them those eleven thousand Virgins at once, [of whom later], and make them believe each particular, he is besotted on her, or love one till they see another, and then her alone: like Milo's wife in Apuleius, who could not see a good looking youth without employing all her charms to corrupt him. 'Tis their common compliment in that case, they care not what they swear, say, or do. One while they slight them, care not for them, rail down right and scoff at them, and then again they will run mad, hang themselves, stab and kill, if they may not enjoy them. Henceforth therefore, let not Maids believe them. These tricks and counterfeit passions are more familiar with women; Today shall end my sorrow or my life, quoth Phædra to Hippolytus. Joessa, in Lucian, told Pythias, a young man, to move him the more, that if he would not have her, she was resolved to make away herself: There is a Nemesis, and it cannot choose but grieve and trouble thee, to hear that I have either strangled or drowned myself for thy sake. — Nothing so common to this sex, as oaths, vows, and protestations, and as I have already said, tears, which they have at command; for they can so weep, that one would think their very hearts were dissolved within them, and would come out in tears, their eyes are like rocks, which still drop water; saith Aristænetus, they wipe away their tears like sweat, weep with one eye, laugh with the other; or as children weep and cry, they can both together.

Care not for women's tears, I counsel thee,
They teach their eyes as much to weep as see. (OVID)

And as much pity is to be taken of a woman weeping, as of a goose going barefoot. When Venus lost her son Cupid, she sent a Cryer about to bid every one that met him take heed.

Take heed of Cupid's tears, if cautelous,
And of his smiles and kisses, I thee tell,
If that he offer't, for they be noxious,
And very poison in his lips doth dwell. (MOSCHUS)

A thousand years, as Castilio conceives, will scarce serve to reckon up those allurements and guiles, that men and women use to deceive one another with.

SUBSECTION 5 — *Bawds, Philters, Causes*

WHEN all other Engines fail, that they can proceed no further of themselves, their last refuge is to fly to Bawds, Panders, Magical Philters, and Receipts, rather than fail, to the Devil himself.

They will move Hell, if Heaven will not hear them.   (VIRGIL)

And by those indirect means many a man is overcome, and precipitated into this malady, if he take not good heed. For these Bawds first, they are every where so common, and so many, that as he said of old Croton, all here either inveigle, or be inveigled, we may say of most of our Cities, there be so many professed, cunning bawds in them. Besides, bawdry is become an art, or a liberal science, as Lucian calls it; and there be such tricks and subtilties, so many nurses, old women, Pandars, letter-carriers, beggars, Physicians, Friars, Confessors, employed about it, that no one pen could deal with it all,

Not even in three hundred verses
One your vileness rehearses.   (PLAUTUS)

Such occult notes, Stenography, Polygraphy, mind reading, or magnetical telling of their minds, which Cabeus the Jesuit, by the way, counts fabulous and false; cunning conveyances in this kind, that neither Juno's jealousy, nor Danae's custody, nor Argo's vigilancy can keep them safe. 'Tis the last and common refuge to use an assistant, such as that Catanean Phillippa was to Joan Queen of Naples; a Bawd's help, an old woman in the business, as Myrrha did when she doted on Cinyras, and could not compass her desire, the old Jade her Nurse was ready at a pinch, saying, Fear it not, if it be possible to be done, I will effect it. There's no woman that a woman can't come over, as Cælestina said, let him or her be never so honest, watched, and reserved, 'tis hard but one of these old women will get access: and scarce shall you find, as Austin observes, in a Nunnery a maid alone; if she cannot have egress, before her window you shall have an old woman, or some prating Gossip tell her some tales of this Clerk, and that Monk, describing or commending some young Gentleman or other unto her. — As I was walking in the street (saith a good fellow in Petronius) to see the town served one evening, I spied an old woman in a corner selling of Cabbages and Roots (as our Hucksters do Plums, Apples, and such like fruits); mother (quoth I), can you tell where I dwell? she being well pleased with my foolish urbanity, replied, And why sir should I not tell? with that she rose up and went before me; I took her for a wise woman, and by and by she led me into a by-lane, and

told me there I should dwell; I replied again I knew not the house; but
I perceived on a sudden by the naked queans, that I was now come into
a bawdy-house, and then too late I began to curse the treachery of this
old Jade. ———— Such tricks you shall have in many places, and
among the rest it is ordinary in Venice, and in the Island of Zante, for
a man to be Bawd to his own wife. No sooner shall you land or come
on shore, but as the Comical Poet hath it,

> *The courtesans within the place are wont*
> *To send their slaves and girls down to the harbour,*
> *Whenever any strange ship comes in port;*
> *They ask the vessel's name, and where it comes from,*
> *Then swoop upon the officers and crew.* (PLAUTUS)

These white Devils have their Panders, Bawds, and Factors, in every
place, to seek about and bring in customers, to tempt and way-lay
novices, and silly travellers. And when they have them once within
their clutches, as Ægidius Maserius in his comment upon Valerius
Flaccus describes them, with promises and pleasant discourse, with
gifts, tokens, and taking their opportunities, they lay nets which Lucretia cannot avoid, and baits that Hippolytus himself would swallow;
they make such strong assaults and batteries, that the Goddess of Virginity cannot withstand them: give gifts and bribes to move Penelope,
and with threats able to terrify Susanna. How many Proserpinas with
those catchpoles doth Pluto take! These are the sleepy rods with which
their souls touched descend to hell; this the glew or lime with which
the wings of the mind once taken cannot fly away; the Devil's ministers
to allure, entice, &c. Many young men and maids without all question
are inveigled by these Eumenides and their associates. But these are
trivial and well known. The most sly, dangerous, and cunning bawds,
are your knavish Physicians, Empiricks, Mass-Priests, Monks, Jesuits,
and Friars. Though it be against Hippocrates' oath, some of them will
give a dram, a promise to restore maidenheads, and do it without danger, make an abort if need be; keep down their paps, hinder conception,
procure lust, make them able with Satyrions, and now and then step
in themselves. No Monastery so close, house so private, or prison so
well kept, but these honest men are admitted to censure and ask questions, to feel their pulse beat at their bed side, and all under pretence of
giving Physick. Now as for Monks, Confessors, and Friars, as he said,

> *That Stygian Pluto dares not tempt or do,*
> *What an old hag or monk will undergo,* (ÆNEAS SYLVIUS)

either for himself, to satisfy his own lust, for another, if he be hired thereto, or both at once, having such excellent means. For under colour of visitation, auricular confession, comfort, and penance, they have free egress and regress, and corrupt God knows how many. They can use trades some of them, practise Physick, use exorcisms, &c.

> For ther as wont to walken was an Elf,
> There walketh now the Limitour himself,
> In every bush, and under every tree,
> Ther is non other Incubus but he.

In the Mountains betwixt Dauphiné and Savoy, the Friars persuaded the good wives to counterfeit themselves possessed, that their husbands might give them free access, and were so familiar in those days with some of them, that, as one observes, wenches could not sleep in their beds for Necromantick Friars: and the good Abbess in Boccaccio may in some sort witness, that rising betimes mistook and put on the Friar's breeches instead of her veil or hat. You have heard the story, I presume, of Paulina, a chaste matron in Hegesippus, whom one of Isis' Priests did prostitute to Mundus, a young Knight, and made her believe it was their God Anubis. Many such pranks are played by our Jesuits, sometimes in their own habits, sometimes in others, like soldiers, courtiers, citizens, scholars, gallants, and women themselves. Proteus-like in all forms, and disguises, they go abroad in the night, to inescate [or allure] and beguile young women, or to have their pleasure of other men's wives: and if we may believe some relations, they have wardrobes of several suits in their Colleges for that purpose. Howsoever in publick they pretend much zeal, seem to be very holy men, and bitterly preach against adultery, fornication, there are no verier Bawds or whoremasters in a Country. Whose soul they should gain to God, they sacrifice to the Devil. But I spare these men for the present.

The last battering engines are Philters, Amulets, Spells, Charms, Images, and such unlawful means; if they cannot prevail of themselves by the help of Bawds, Panders, and their adherents, they will fly for succour to the Devil himself. I know there be those that deny the Devil can do any such thing, (Crato, and many Divines), there is no other fascination than that which comes by the eyes, of which I have formerly spoken; and if you desire to be better informed, read Camerarius. It was given out of old, that a Thessalian wench had bewitched King Philip to dote upon her, and by Philters enforced his love; but when Olympias, the Queen, saw the Maid of an excellent beauty, well brought up, and qualified: these, quoth she, were the Philters which inveigled King Philip; those the true charms, as Henry to Rosamund, —

One accent from thy lips the blood more warms
Than all their philters, exorcisms, and charms. (DRAYTON)

With this alone Lucretia brags, in Aretine, she could do more than all Philosophers, Astrologers, Alchemists, Necromancers, Witches, and the rest of the crew. As for herbs and Philters, [saith she,] I could never skill of them, the sole Philter that ever I used was kissing and embracing, by which alone I made men rave like beasts stupified, and compelled them to worship me like an Idol. In our time 'tis a common thing, saith Erastus in his book On Lamias, for witches to take upon them the making of these Philters, to force men and women to love and hate whom they will, to cause tempests, diseases, &c., by Charms, Spells, Characters, Knots.

Love-potions from Thessaly he sells. (JUVENAL)

St. Hierome proves that they can do it, (as in Hilarion's life), he hath a story of a young man that with a Philter made a Maid mad for the love of him, which Maid was afterward cured by Hilarion. Such instances I find in John Nider. Plutarch records of Lucullus that he died of a Philter, and that Cleopatra used Philters to inveigle Antony, amongst other allurements. Eusebius reports as much of Lucretius the Poet. Panormitan hath a story of one Stephen, a Neapolitan Knight, that by a Philter was forced to run mad for love. But of all others, that which Petrarch relates of Charles the Great, is most memorable. He foolishly doted upon a woman of mean favour and condition, many years together, wholly delighting in her company, to the great grief and indignation of his friends and followers. When she was dead, he did embrace her corpse, as Apollo did the bay-tree for his Daphne, and caused her Coffin (richly embalmed and decked with Jewels) to be carried about with him, over which he still lamented. At last a venerable Bishop that followed his Court, prayed earnestly to God (commiserating his Lord and Master's case) to know the true cause of this mad passion, and whence it proceeded; it was revealed to him in fine, that the cause of the Emperor's mad love lay under the dead woman's tongue. The Bishop went hastily to the carkass, and took a small ring thence; upon the removal the Emperor abhorred the Corpse, and instead of it fell as furiously in love with the Bishop, he would not suffer him to be out of his presence: which when the Bishop perceived, he flung the ring into the midst of a great Lake, where the King then was. From that hour the Emperor, neglecting all his other houses, dwelt at Aix, built a fair house in the midst of the Marsh, to his infinite expense, and a Temple by it, where after he was buried, and in which City all his posterity ever since use to be crowned. Marcus the Heretick is accused by Irenæus to have inveigled a young Maid by this means; and some writers speak hardly of the Lady Katherine Cobham, that by the same Art she circumvented Humphrey Duke of Gloucester to be her husband. Sicinius Æmilianus summoned Apuleius to come before Claudius Maximus, Proconsul of Africa, that he, being a poor fellow, had bewitched by Philters Pudentilla, an ancient rich Matron, to love him, and being worth so many thousand sesterces, to be his wife. Agrippa attributes much in this kind to Philters, Amulets, Images: and Salmuth saith, 'tis an ordinary practice at Fez, in Africa, there are many tricksters there, who bring lovers to bed together, as skilful all out as that Hyperborean Magician, of whom Cleodemus in Lucian tells so many fine feats, perform'd in this kind. But Erastus, Wierus, and others, are against it; they grant indeed such things may be done, but (as Wierus discourseth) not by Charms, Incantations, Philters, but the Devil himself; he contends as much; so doth Freitagius, Andreas Cisalpinus, and so much Sigismundus Schereczius proves at large. Unchaste women by the help of these witches, the Devil's kitchen-maids, have their Loves brought to them in the night, and carried back again by a phantasm flying in the Air in the likeness of a Goat. I have heard (saith he) divers confess that they have been so carried on a Goat's back to their sweet-hearts, many miles in a night. — Others are of opinion that these feats, which most suppose to be done by Charms and Philters, are merely effected by natural causes, as by man's blood chemically prepared, which much avails, saith Ernestus Burgravius, in a Revelatory Lamp of Life and Death, to procure love and hate (so huntsmen make their dogs love them and farmers their pullen [poultry]), 'tis an excellent Philter, as he holds, but not fit to be made common: and so be apples of madness, Mandrake roots, Mandrake apples, precious stones, dead men's clothes, candles, apples of drunkenness, swine's bread [the herb of cyclamen], Hippomanes [which is the venomus humour that comes from a mare in heat], a certain hair in a Wolf's tail, &c., of which Rhasis, Dioscorides, Porta, Wecker, Rubeus, Mizaldus, Albertus, treat: a swallow's heart, dust of a dove's heart, vipers' tongues are much valued, asses' brains, horses' pintles, cauls, the rope with which a man hath been hanged, a stone from an eagle's nest, &c. See more in Sckenkius, which are as forcible, and of as much virtue, as that fountain Salmacis in Vitruvius, Ovid, Strabo, that made all such mad for love that drank of it, or that hot bath at Aix in Germany, wherein Cupid once dipt his arrows, which ever since hath a peculiar virtue to make them lovers all that wash in it. But hear the Poet's own description of it.

> *Whence this heat of waters tost*
> *Bubbling upward from earth's frost?*
> *Cupid once his arrows hot*
> *Dipt in waters of this spot,*
> *And delighted with the sound*
> *Of waters steaming from the ground,*
> *' Lo,' he said, ' boil on for ever,*
> *Keeping memory of my quiver ! '*
> *Since when 'tis a magick spring,*
> *And who dares bathe here feels love's sting.*

These above-named remedies have happily as much power as that bath of Aix, or Venus' enchanted girdle, in which, saith Natalis Comes, Love-toys and dalliance, pleasantness, sweetness, persuasions, subtilties, gentle speeches, and all witchcraft to enforce love, was contained. Read more of these in Agrippa's Occult Philosophy, the Hammer of Witches, Delrio, Wierus, Pomponatius on Incantations, Ficinus on the Theology of Plato, Calcagninus, &c.

MEMBER 3

Symptoms or signs of Love-Melancholy, in Body, Mind, good, bad, &c.

SYMPTOMS are either of Body or Mind; of body, Paleness, Leanness, dryness, &c. Let everyone that loves be pale, for lovers 'tis the proper hue, as the Poet [Ovid] describes lovers; love causeth leanness. Avicenna makes hollow eyes, dryness, symptoms of this disease, to go smiling to themselves, or acting as if they saw or heard some delectable object. Valleriola, Laurentius, Ælianus Montaltus, Langius, deliver as much, the body lean, pale,

Like one who hath trodden barefoot on a snake,　(JUVENAL)

hollow-ey'd, their eyes are hidden in their heads, they pine away, and look ill with waking, cares, sighs, eyes that rivall'd the sunny locks of Phœbus lose their lustre, with groans, griefs, sadness, dulness, want of appetite, &c. A reason of all this, Jason Pratensis gives, because of the distraction of the spirits, the Liver doth not perform his part, nor turns the aliment into blood as it ought; and for that cause the members are weak for want of sustenance, they are lean and pine, as the herbs of my garden do this month of May, for want of rain. The Green-sickness

therefore often happeneth to young women, a Cachexia, or an evil habit
to men, besides their ordinary sighs, complaints and lamentations,
which are too frequent. As drops from a Still, doth Cupid's fire provoke
tears from a true Lover's eyes.

> *The mighty Mars did oft for Venus shriek,*
> *Privily moistening his horid cheek*
> *With womanish tears, ——*   (SPENSER)

with many such like passions. When Chariclea was enamoured on
Theagenes, as Heliodorus sets her out, she was half distracted, and
spake she knew not what, sighed to herself, lay much awake, and was
lean upon a sudden: and when she was besotted on her son-in-law, she
had ugly paleness, hollow eyes, restless thoughts, short wind, &c.
Euryalus, in an Epistle sent to Lucretia his Mistress, complains amongst
other grievances, thou hast taken my stomack and my sleep from me.
So he [Chaucer] describes it aright:

> His slepe, his mete, his drinke is him byraft,
> That lene he wex, and drie as is a shaft,
> His eyen holwe, and grisly to behold,
> His hewe falwe, and pale as ashen cold,
> And solitary he was and ever alone,
> And waking all the night, making his mone.

Theocritus makes a fair maid of Delphi, in love with a young man of
Minda confess as much,

> *No sooner seen I had, than mad I was,*
> *My beauty fail'd, and I no more did care*
> *For any pomp, I knew not where I was,*
> *But sick I was, and evil I did fare;*
> *I lay upon my bed ten days and nights,*
> *A skeleton I was in all men's sights.*

All these passions are well expressed by that Heroical Poet in the
person of Dido:

> *Unhappy Dido could not sleep at all,*
> *But lies awake, and takes no rest:*
> *And up she gets again, whilst care and grief,*
> *And raging love torments her breast.*   (VIRGIL)

Accius Sannazarius in the same manner feigns his Lycoris tormenting
herself for want of sleep, sighing, sobbing, and lamenting; and Eustathius his Ismenias much troubled, and panting at heart at the sight of
his mistress, he could not sleep, his bed was thorns. All make leanness,
want of appetite, want of sleep ordinary Symptoms, and by that means
they are brought often so low, so much altered and changed, that as he

[Terence] jested in the Comedy, one can scarce know them to be the same men.

Let sleepless nights make thin the young men's bodies,
  Care, too, and the grief that comes from violent love. (OVID)

Many such Symptoms there are of the body to discern lovers by,

For who is there can hide his love? (OVID)

Can a man, said Solomon, carry fire in his bosom, and not burn? It will hardly be hid, though they do all they can to hide it, it must out; by more than a thousand Symptoms it may be descried.

The more concealed, the more it breaks to light. (OVID)

'Twas Antiphanes the Comedian's observation of old, Love and Drunkenness cannot be concealed, words, looks, gestures, all will betray them: but two of the most notable signs are observed by the Pulse and Countenance. When Antiochus the son of Seleucus was sick for Stratonice his Mother-in-law, and would not confess his grief, or the cause of his disease, Erasistratus the Physician found him by his Pulse and Countenance to be in love with her, because that when she came in presence, or was named, his pulse varied, and he blushed besides. In this very sort was the love of Charicles, the son of Polycles, discovered by Panacius the Physician, as you may read the story at large in Aristænetus. By the same signs Galen brags that he found out Justa, Boëthius the Consul's wife, to dote on Pylades the Player, because at his name still she both altered Pulse and Countenance, as Poliarchus did at the name of Argenis. Franciscus Valesius denies there is any such pulse of love, or that love may be so discerned; but Avicenna confirms this of Galen out of his experience, and Gordonius; their pulse, he saith, is inordinate and swift, if she go by whom he loves; Langius, Nevisanus, Valescus de Taranta, Guianerius. Valleriola sets down this for a Symptom, difference of Pulse, neglect of business, want of sleep, often sighs, blushings, when there is any speech of their Mistress, are manifest signs. But amongst the rest, Josephus Struthius, that Polonian, in the fifth Book of his Doctrine of Pulses, holds that this, and all other passions of the mind, may be discovered by the Pulse. And if you will know, saith he, whether the men suspected be such or such, touch their arteries, &c. And in his fourth Book, he speaks of this particular Pulse, Love makes an unequal pulse, &c.; he gives instance of a Gentlewoman, a Patient of his, whom by this means he found to be much enamoured, and with whom: he named many persons, but at the last when his name came whom he suspected, her pulse began to vary, and to beat swifter, and so by often feeling her pulse, he perceived what the matter was. Apollonius, poetically setting down the meeting of Jason and Medea, makes them both to blush at one another's sight, and at the first they were not able to speak. " I'm all trembling & chill at the very sight of her, Parmeno " (Terence). Phædria trembled at the sight of Thais, others sweat, blow short, tremble in their knees, are troubled with palpitation of heart upon the like occasion, saith Aristænetus, their heart is at their mouth, leaps, these burn and freeze, (for love is fire, ice, hot, cold, itch, fever, phrenzy, pleurisy, what not?) they look pale, red, and commonly blush at their first congress; and sometimes, through violent agitation of spirits, bleed at nose, or when she is talked of; which very sign Eustathius makes an argument of Ismene's affection, that, when she met her Sweetheart by chance, she changed her countenance to a Maiden-blush. 'Tis a common thing amongst Lovers, as Arnulphus, that merry, conceited Bishop, hath well expressed in a facete Epigram of his,

> *Their faces answer, and by blushing say,*
> *How both affected are, they do bewray.*

But the best conjectures are taken from such symptoms as appear when they are both present; all their speeches, amorous glances, actions, lascivious gestures, will bewray them, they cannot contain themselves, but that they will be still kissing. Stratocles the Physician upon his Wedding day, when he was at dinner, could not eat his meat for kissing the Bride, &c. First a word, and then a kiss, then some other Compliment, and then a kiss, then an idle question, then a kiss, and when he had pumped his wits dry, can say no more, kissing and colling are never out of season.

> *Never ceasing, still beginning,*   (PETRONIUS)

'tis never at an end, another kiss, and then another, another, and another, &c.

> *Come hither, O Thelayra!* (LŒCHEUS)

Come, kiss me, Corinna!

> *A hundred hundred kisses,*
> *A hundred thousand kisses,*
> *A thousand thousand kisses,*
> *Thousands of thousands altogether,*
> *As drops of water in the Sicilian Sea,*
> *As many as there are stars in the sky,*
> *Upon your rosy knees,*
> *Upon your swelling lips,*
> *Upon your speaking eyes,*
> *I fix with unceasing passion,*
> *O lovely Neæra!* (JOHANNES SECUNDUS)

As Catullus to Lesbia,

> —————— *first give a hundred,*
> *Then a thousand, then another*
> *Hundred, then unto the other*
> *Add a thousand, and so more, &c.**

Till you equal with the store all the grass, &c. So Venus did by her
Adonis, the Moon with Endymion, they are still dallying and culling, as
so many Doves, and that with alacrity and courage,

> *With indrawn breath, hungrily breast to breast,*
> *With mingling of spittle, and teeth against mouths hard pressed.*
> (LUCRETIUS)

With such hard kisses on the mouth that the lips can scarce be withdrawn, head thrown back, as Lamprias in Lucian kist Thais, Philippus
her in Aristænetus, in a phrenzy of love cleaving so hotly that 'twas hard
to free the lips, he bruised his whole mouth against her. Aretine's Lucretia, by a suitor of hers was so saluted, and 'tis their ordinary fashion,

> *With bitten lips, and clashing of mouth on mouth.*   (LUCRETIUS)

They cannot, I say, contain themselves, they will be still not only joining
hands, kissing, but embracing, treading on their toes, &c., diving into
their bosoms, and that as a welcome pleasance, as Philostratus confesseth to his Mistress; and Lamprias in Lucian, with the hand secretly in
the bosom, feeling their paps, and that scarce honestly sometimes; as
the old man in the Comedy well observed of his son, Did not I see thee
put thy hand into her bosom? Go to, with many such love tricks. Juno
in Lucian, complains to Jupiter of Ixion, he looked so attentively on
her, and sometimes would sigh and weep in her company: And when I
drank by chance, and gave Ganymede the cup, he would desire to drink
still in the very cup that I drank of, and in the same place where I
drank, and would kiss the cup, and then look steadily on me, and sometimes sigh, and then again smile. If it be so they cannot come near to
dally, have not that opportunity, familiarity, or acquaintance, to confer
and talk together; yet, if they be in presence, their eyes will bewray
them: as the common saying is, Where I look, I like; and where I like,
I love; but they will lose themselves in her looks.

> *Each, with bright glances at the other's face,*
> *Demanded silently tidings of our love.*   (OVID)

They cannot look off whom they love, they will deflower her with their
eyes, be still gazing, staring, stealing faces, smiling, glancing at her, as

---

* Translated or imitated by M[r]. B. Johnson, our arch poet, in his 119th epigram.
— Burton's note.

Apollo on Leucothöe, the Moon on her Endymion, when she stood still
in Caria, and at Latmos caused her Chariot to be stayed. They must all
stand and admire, or, if she go by, look after her as long as they can see
her; she is the charioteer of the soul, as Anacreon calls her, they cannot
go by her door or window, but, as an Adamant, she draws their eyes to
it, though she be not there present, they must needs glance that way, and
look back to it. Aristænetus of Euxitheus, Lucian in Images, of himself,
and Tatius of Clitophon say as much, he never could turn his eyes away
from Leucippe, and many Lovers confess, when they came in their Mistress' presence, they could not hold off their eyes, but looked wistly and
steadfastly on her, with an unwinking glance, with much eagerness and
greediness, as if they would look through, or should never have enough
sight of her, —

Rooted motionless in one set gaze. (VIRGIL)

So she will do by him, drink to him with her eyes, nay drink him up,
devour him, swallow him, as Martial's Mamurra is remembered to have
done:

She looked at the sweet lads, eating them up with her eyes. (MARTIAL)

There is a pleasant story to this purpose in Vertomannus. The Sultan of
Sana's wife in Arabia, because Vertomannus was fair and white, could
not look off him, from Sun-rising to Sun-setting she could not desist, she
made him one day come into her chamber, for two hours' space she still
gazed on him, averting not one glance of her eyes, observing him as
though he were Cupid himself. A young man in Lucian fell in love with
Venus' picture, he came every morning to her Temple, and there continued all day long from Sun-rising to Sun-set, unwilling to go home at
night, sitting over against the Goddess' Picture, he did continually look
upon her, and mutter to himself I know not what. If so be they cannot
see them whom they love, they will still be walking and waiting about
their Mistress' doors, taking all opportunity to see them; as in Longus
Sophista, Daphnis and Chloe, two Lovers, were still hovering at one
another's gates, he sought all occasions to be in her company, to hunt in
Summer, and catch Birds in the Frost about her Father's house in the
Winter, that she might see him, and he her. A King's Palace was not so
diligently attended, saith Aretine's Lucretia, as my house was when I
lay in Rome, the porch and street was ever full of some, walking or
riding, on set purpose to see me, their eye was still upon my window as
they passed by, they could not choose but look back to my house when
they were past, and sometimes hem, or cough, or take some impertinent
occasion to speak aloud, that I might look out and observe them. 'Tis

so in other places, 'tis common to every Lover, 'tis all his felicity to be
with her, to talk with her, he is never well but in her company, and will
walk seven or eight times in a day through the street where she dwells,
and make sleeveless [or idle] errands to see her, plotting still where,
when, and how to visit her,

Now let soft whispers in the dusk of evening
Be renewed at the appointed hour. (HORACE)

And when he is gone, he thinks every minute an hour, every hour as long
as a day, ten days a whole year, till he see her again —
If thou dost reckon the time, which we who love reckon so carefully.
(OVID)

And if thou be in love, thou wilt say so too, and at length, Farewell,
beautiful one, farewell, Sweetheart. Farewell, my dearest Argenis, once
more farewell, farewell. And though he is to meet her by compact, and
that very shortly, perchance to-morrow, yet loath to depart, he'll take
his leave again and again, and then come back again, look after, and
shake his hand, wave his hat afar off. Now gone, he thinks it long till
he see her again, and she him, the clocks are surely set back, the hour's
past.

I, thy hostess, I, thy Rhodopeian Phyllis,
Wonder why beyond the promis'd time thou'rt absent. (HORACE)

She looks out at window still to see whether he come, and by report
Phyllis went nine times to the Sea side that day, to see if her Demophoon
were approaching, and Troilus to the City gates, to look for his Creseid.
She is ill at ease, and sick till she see him again, peevish in the mean
time, discontent, heavy, sad, and why comes he not? where is he? why
breaks he promise? why tarries he so long? sure he is not well; sure he
hath some mischance, sure he forgets himself and me, with infinite such.
And then confident again, up she gets, out she looks, listens and enquires,
hearkens, kens [looks about] ; every man afar off is sure he, every stirring
in the street, now he is there, that's he; an evil day, she says, the longest
day that ever was; so she raves, restless and impatient; for love brooks
no delays : the time's quickly gone that's spent in her company, the miles
short, the way pleasant, all weather is good whilst he goes to her house,
heat or cold, though his teeth chatter in his head, he moves not, wet or
dry, 'tis all one; wet to the skin, he feels it not, cares not at least for it,
but will easily endure it, and much more, because it is done with alacrity, and for his Mistress' sweet sake ; let the burthen be never so heavy,
Love makes it light. Jacob served seven years for Rachel, and it was
quickly gone, because he loved her. None so merry, if he may happily

enjoy her company, he is in heaven for a time; and if he may not, dejected in an instant, solitary, silent, he departs weeping, lamenting, sighing, complaining.

But the Symptoms of the mind in Lovers are almost infinite, and so diverse, that no Art can comprehend them: though they be merry sometimes, and rapt beyond themselves for joy, yet most part, Love is a plague, a torture, an hell, a bitter-sweet passion at last. 'Tis a sweet bitterness, a delicious pain, a gay torment:

> *Sweeter than honey, it pleases me;*
> *More bitter than gall, it teases me.*

Like a Summer Fly, or Sphine's wings, or a Rainbow of all colours, fair, foul, and full of variation, though most part irksome and bad. For in a word, the Spanish Inquisition is not comparable to it; a torment and execution it is, as he calls it in the Poet, an unquenchable fire, and what not? From it, saith Austin, arise biting cares, perturbations, passions, sorrows, fears, suspicions, discontents, contentions, discords, wars, treacheries, enmities, flattery, cozening, riot, lust, impudence, cruelty, knavery, &c.

> *Pains and plaints, regrets and endless tears,*
> *Weariness and care, bitterness and fears,*   (MARULLUS)

these be the companions of lovers, and the ordinary symptoms, as the Poet repeats them.

> *In love these vices are: suspicions,*
> *Peace, war, and impudence, detractions,*
> *Dreams, cares, and errors, terrors and affrights,*
> *Immodest pranks, devices, sleights and flights,*
> *Heart-burnings, wants, neglects, desire of wrong,*
> *Loss continual, expense, and hurt among.*   (TERENCE)

Every Poet is full of such Catalogues of Love Symptoms; but fear and sorrow may justly challenge the chief place. Though Hercules de Saxoniâ will exclude fear from Love Melancholy, yet I am otherwise persuaded. 'Tis full of fear, anxiety, doubt, care, peevishness, suspicion, it turns a man into a woman, which made Hesiod, belike, put Fear and Paleness [as] Venus' daughters, because fear and love are still linked together. Moreover, they are apt to mistake, amplify, too credulous sometimes, too full of hope and confidence, and then again very jealous, unapt to believe or entertain any good news. The Comical Poet hath prettily painted out this passage amongst the rest, in a Dialogue betwixt Micio and Æschines, a gentle father and a love-sick son: M. *Be of good cheer, my son, thou shalt have her to wife. Æ. Ah father, do you mock me now?* M. *I mock thee, why?* Æ. *That which I so earnestly desire, I more suspect and fear.* M. *Get you home, and send for her to be your wife.* Æ. *What now, a wife, now father,* &c. — These doubts, anxieties, suspicions, are the least part of their torments; they break many times from passions to actions, speak fair, and flatter, now most obsequious and willing, by and by they are averse, wrangle, fight, swear, quarrel, laugh, weep: and he that doth not so by fits, Lucian holds, is not thoroughly touched with this Loadstone of Love. So their actions and passions are intermixt, but of all other passions, Sorrow hath the greatest share; Love to many is bitterness itself; Plato calls it a bitter potion, an agony, a plague.

> *O take away this plague, this mischief from me,*
> *Which as a numbness over all my body,*
> *Expels my joys, and makes my soul so heavy.*   (CATULLUS)

Phædria had a true touch of this, when he cried out,

> *O Thais, would thou hadst of these my pains a part,*
> *Or, as it doth me now, so it would make thee smart.*   (TERENCE)

So had that young man, when he roared again for discontent,

> *I am vext and toss'd, and rack'd on Love's wheel;*
> *Where not, I am; but where am, do not feel.*   (PLAUTUS)

The Moon, in Lucian, made her moan to Venus, that she was almost dead for love, and after a long tale, she broke off abruptly and wept, O Venus, thou knowest my poor heart. Charmides, in Lucian, was so impatient, that he sobb'd and sighed, and tore his hair, and said he would hang himself: I am undone, O sister Tryphæna, I cannot endure these love pangs, what shall I do? — O ye Gods, free me from these cares and miseries! out of the anguish of his Soul, Theocles prays. Shall I say, most part of a Lover's life is full of agony, anxiety, fear, and grief, complaints, sighs, suspicions, and cares, (heigh-ho, my heart is wo), full of silence and irksome solitariness?

> *Frequenting shady bowers in discontent,*
> *To the air his fruitless clamours he will vent,*

except at such times that he hath lucid intervals, pleasant gales, or sudden alterations; as, if his Mistress smile upon him, give him a good look, a kiss, or that some comfortable message be brought him, his service is accepted, &c.

He is then too confident, and rapt beyond himself, as if he had heard the Nightingale in the Spring before the Cuckoo, or as Callisto was at Melibœa's presence, Who ever saw so glorious a sight, what man ever enjoyed such delight? More content cannot be given of the Gods, wished, had, or hoped, of any mortal man. There is no happiness in the world comparable to his; no content, no joy to this, no life to Love, he is in Paradise.

Who lives so happy as myself? what bliss
In this our life may be compared to this? (CATULLUS)

He will not change fortune in that case with a Prince. Whilst he is pleasing to her, the Persian Kings are not so jovial as he is. O happy day; so Chærea exclaims when he came from Pamphila, his Sweetheart, well pleased; he could find in his heart to be killed instantly, lest, if he live longer, some sorrow or sickness should contaminate his joys. A little after, he was so merrily set upon the same occasion, that he could not contain himself. Is't possible (O my Countrymen) for any living to be so happy as myself! No, sure, it cannot be, for the Gods have shewed all their power, all their goodness in me. Yet by and by, when this young Gallant was crossed in his Wench, he laments, and cries, and roars downright. I am undone. The Virgin's gone, and I am gone; she's gone, she's gone, and what shall I do? where shall I seek her, where shall I find her, whom shall I ask? what way, what course shall I take? what will become of me? He was weary of his life, sick, mad and desperate. 'Tis not Chærea's case this alone, but his, and his, and every Lover's in the like state. If he hear ill news, have bad success in his suit, she frown upon him, or that his Mistress in his presence respect another more, (as Hædus observes), prefer another suitor, speak more familiarly to him, or use more kindly than himself, if by nod, smile, message, she discloseth herself to another, he is instantly tormented, none so dejected as he is, utterly undone, a cast-away, a dead man, the scorn of fortune, a monster of fortune, worse than naught, the loss of a Kingdom had been less. Aretine's Lucretia made very good proof of this, as she relates it herself: For when I made some of my suitors believe I would betake myself to a Nunnery, they took on, as if they had lost Father and Mother, because they were for ever after to want my company. All other labour was light; but this might not be endured, for I cannot be without thy company, mournful Amyntas, painful Amyntas, careful Amyntas; better a Metropolitan City were sackt, a Royal Army overcome, an Invincible Armada sunk, and twenty thousand Kings should perish, than her little finger ache, so zealous are they, and so tender of her good. They would all turn Friars for my sake, as she follows it, in hope by that means to meet, or see me again, as my Confessors, at stool-ball, or at barley-break. And so afterwards, when an importunate suitor came, If I had bid my Maid say that I was not at leisure, not within, busy, could not speak with him, he was instantly astonished, and stood like a pillar of marble; another went swearing, chafing, cursing, foaming.

That voice was like the wrath of God,

the voice of a Mandrake had been sweeter musick; but he to whom I gave entertainment, was in the Elysian fields, ravished for joy, quite beyond himself. 'Tis the general humour of all Lovers, she is their stern, Pole-star, and guide,

The delight and desire of the soul.   (LOCHÆUS)

As a Tulipant to the Sun (which our Herbalists call Narcissus) when it shines, is a glorious Flower exposing itself; but when the Sun sets, or a tempest comes, it hides itself, pines away, and hath no pleasure left (which Carolus Gonzaga, Duke of Mantua, in a cause not unlike, sometimes used for an Impress) do all enamoratoes to their Mistress, she is their Sun, their prime mover or informing breath; this, one hath elegantly expressed by a windmill, still moved by the wind, which otherwise hath no motion of itself. He is wholly animated from her breath, his soul lives in her body, she keeps the keys of his life; his fortune ebbs and flows with her favour, a gracious or bad aspect turns him up or down,

The light of my mind, Lucia, at thy light is lit.

Howsoever his present state be pleasing or displeasing, 'tis continuate so long as he loves, he can do nothing, think of nothing but her; desire hath no rest, she is his Cynosure [or North Star], his Hesper and Vesper, his morning and evening Star, his Goddess, his Mistress, his life, his soul, his every thing, dreaming, waking, she is always in his mouth: his heart, eyes, ears, and all his thoughts are full of her. His Laura, his Victorina, his Columbina, Flavia, Flaminia, Cælia, Delia, or Isabella, (call her how you will), she is the sole object of his senses, the substance of his soul, he magnifies her above measure, he is full of her, can breathe nothing but her. I adore Melibœa, saith Love-sick Callisto, I believe in Melibœa, I honour, admire, and love, my Melibœa: his soul was sowced, imparadised, imprisoned in his Lady. When Thais took her leave of Phædria, Sweetheart (she said) will you command me any further service? He readily replied, and gave this in charge, —

Dost ask (my dear) what service I will have?
To love me day and night is all I crave,
To dream on me, to expect, to think on me,
Depend and hope, still covet me to see,
Delight thyself in me, be wholly mine,
For know, my love, that I am wholly thine.

But all this needed not, you will say, if she affect once, she will be his, settle her love on him, on him alone.

Seeing and hearing him, though they be parted, (VIRGIL)

she can, she must think and dream of nought else but him, continually of him, as did Orpheus on his Eurydice.

On thee, sweet wife, was all my song,
Morn, Evening, and all along. (VIRGIL)

And Dido upon her Æneas:

And ever and anon she thinks upon the man
That was so fine, so fair, so blythe, so debonair. (VIRGIL)

Clitophon, in the first book of Achilles Tatius, complaineth how that his Mistress Leucippe tormented him much more in the night than in the day: For all day long he had some object or other to distract his senses, but in the night all ran upon her: all night long he lay awake and could think of nothing else but her, he could not get her out of his mind; towards morning, sleep took a little pity on him, he slumbered a while, but all his dreams were of her.

In the dark night I speak, embrace, and find
That fading joys deceive my careful mind. (BUCHANAN)

The same complaint Euryalus makes to his Lucretia, day and night I think of thee, I wish for thee, I talk of thee, call on thee, look for thee, hope for thee, delight myself in thee, day and night I love thee. Morning, Evening, all is alike with me, I have restless thoughts,

Thee with waking eyes and anxious mind I follow all night.
(PETRONIUS)

Still I think on thee. The soul is not where it lives, but where it loves. I live and breathe in thee, I wish for thee. O happy day that shall restore thee to my sight! In the mean time he raves on her; her sweet face, eyes, actions, gestures, hands, feet, speech, length, breadth, height, depth, and the rest of her dimensions, are so surveyed, measured, and taken, by that Astrolabe of Phantasy, and that so violently sometimes, with such earnestness and eagerness, such continuance, so strong an imagination, that at length he thinks he sees her indeed; he talks with her, he embraceth her, Ixion-like, a cloud for Juno, as he said, I see and meditate of nought but Leucippe. Be she present or absent, all is one;

Though her fair presence is wanting,
The love which it kindled stays, (OVID)

that impression of her beauty is still fixed in his mind; as he that is bitten with a mad dog, thinks all he sees dogs, dogs in his meat, dogs in his dish, dogs in his drink: his Mistress is in his eyes, ears, heart, in all

his senses. Valleriola had a Merchant his Patient in the same predicament: and Ulricus Molitor, out of Austin, hath a story of one, that
through vehemency of his love passion, still thought he saw his Mistress
present with him, she talked with him, still embracing him.

Now if this passion of Love can produce such effects, if it be pleasantly intended, what bitter torments shall it breed, when it is with fear
& continual sorrow, suspicion, care, agony, as commonly it is, still accompanied, what an intolerable pain must it be!

> *Mount Gargarus hath not so many stems,*
> *As Lover's breast hath grievous wounds,*
> *And linked cares, which love compounds.*

When the King of Babylon would have punished a Courtier of his, for
loving of a young Lady of the Royal blood, and far above his fortunes,
Apollonius in presence by all means persuaded to let him alone; for to
love, and not enjoy, was a most unspeakable torment, no tyrant could
invent the like punishment; as a gnat at a candle, in a short space he
would consume himself. For Love is a perpetual flux, an anguish of the
soul, a warfare, every lover a soldier, a grievous wound is love still, & a
Lover's heart is Cupid's quiver, a consuming fire, an inextinguishable
fire. As Ætna rageth, so doth Love, and more than Ætna, or any material
fire. Vulcan's flames are but smoke to this. For fire, saith Xenophon,
burns them alone that stand near it, or touch it; but this fire of Love
burneth and scorcheth afar off, and is more hot and vehement than any
material fire; 'tis a fire in a fire, the quintessence of fire. For when Nero
burnt Rome, as Callisto urgeth, he fired houses, consumed men's bodies
and goods; but this fire devours the soul itself, and one soul is worth
100,000 bodies. No water can quench this wild fire.

> *A fire he took into his breast,*
> > *Which water could not quench,*
> *Nor Herb, nor Art, nor Magic spells*
> > *Could quell, nor any drench,* (MANTUAN)

except it be tears and sighs, for so they may chance find a little ease.

> *So thy white neck, Neæra, me, poor soul,*
> *Doth scorch, thy cheeks, thy wanton eyes that roll:*
> *Were it not for my dropping tears that hinder,*
> *I should be quite burnt up forthwith to cinder.* (MARULLUS)

This fire strikes like lightning, which made those old Grecians paint
Cupid in many of their Temples with Jupiter's thunder-bolts in his
hands; for it wounds, and cannot be perceived how, whence it came,
where it pierced,

I burn, and my breast hath a secret wound, (OVID)
and can hardly be discerned at first.

> *A gentle wound, an easy fire it was,*
> *And fly at first, and secretly did pass.* (VIRGIL)

But by and by it began to rage and burn amain;

> *This fiery vapour rageth in the veins,*
> *And scorcheth entrails as when fire burns*
> *An house, it nimbly runs along the beams,*
> *And at the last the whole it overturns.* (SENECA)

Abraham Hoffemannus relates out of Plato, how that Empedocles the Philosopher was present at the cutting up of one that died for love, his heart was combust, his liver smoky, his lungs dried up, insomuch that he verily believed his soul was either sod or roasted, through the vehemency of Love's fire. Which belike made a modern writer of amorous Emblems express Love's fury by a pot hanging over the fire, and Cupid blowing the coals. As the heat consumes the water, so doth Love dry up his radical moisture. Another compares Love to a melting torch, which stood too near the fire.

> *The nearer he unto his mistress is,*
> *The nearer he unto his ruin is.* (GROTIUS)

So that to say truth, as Castilio describes it, the beginning, middle, end of Love is nought else but sorrow, vexation, agony, torment, irksomeness, wearisomeness, so that to be squalid, ugly, miserable, solitary, discontent, dejected, to wish for death, to complain, rave, and to be peevish, are the certain signs, and ordinary actions of a Love-sick person. This continual pain and torture makes them forget themselves, if they be far gone with it, in doubt, despair of obtaining, or eagerly bent, to neglect all ordinary business.

> *The works unfinished hang, the threatening walls,*
> *And turrets mounting upward to the skies.* (VIRGIL)

Love-sick Dido left her works undone, so did Phædra,

> *The web of Pallas languishes, the work*
> *Even in Phædra's hands is left undone.*

Faustus, in Mantuan, took no pleasure in any thing he did,

> *No rest, no labor, pleased my love-sick breast,*
> *My faculties were asleep, my mind was dull,*
> *I lost my zest for poesy and song.*

And 'tis the humour of them all, to be careless of their persons, and their estates, as the shepherd in Theocritus, their beards flag, and they have no more care of pranking themselves, or of any business, they care not, as they say, which end goes forward.

> *Forgetting flocks of sheep and country farms,*
> *The silly shepherd always mourns and burns.*

Love-sick Chærea when he came from Pamphila's house, and had not so good welcome as he did expect, was all amort, Parmeno meets him, *Why art thou so sad, man? whence com'st, how dost?* but he sadly replies, *I have so forgotten myself, I neither know where I am, nor whence I come, nor whither I will, what I do.* P. *How so?* Ch. *I am in love.*

> *Living, I die, and know not what I do.* (TERENCE)

He that erst had his thoughts free (as Philostratus Lemnius, in an Epistle of his, describes this fiery passion) and spent his time like an hard student, in those delightsome philosophical precepts, he that with the Sun and Moon wandered all over the world, with Stars themselves ranged about, and left no secret or small mystery in Nature unsearched, since he was enamoured, can do nothing now but think and meditate of Love-matters, day and night composeth himself how to please his Mistress; all his study, endeavour, is to approve himself to his Mistress, to win his Mistress' favour, to compass his desire, to be counted her servant. When Peter Abelard, that great scholar of his age,

> *To whom alone was known whate'er is knowable,* *

was now in love with Heloise, he had no mind to visit or frequent Schools and Scholars any more. Very tedious it was, (as he confesseth) to go to the disputations, or linger there, all his mind was on his new Mistress.

Now to this end and purpose, if there be any hope of obtaining his suit, to prosecute his cause, he will spend himself, goods, fortunes for her, and though he lose and alienate all his friends, be threatened, be cast off, and disinherited; for as the Poet saith, who can set bounds to love? though he be utterly undone by it, disgraced, go a begging, yet for her sweet sake, to enjoy her, he will willingly beg, hazard all he hath, goods, lands, shame, scandal, fame, and life itself.

> *I'll never rest or cease my suit,*
> *'Till she or death do make me mute.* (PLAUTUS)

Parthenis in Aristænetus was fully resolved to do as much. I may have better matches, I confess, but farewell shame, farewell honour, farewell honesty, farewell friends and fortune, &c. O Harpedona, keep my counsel, I will leave all for his sweet sake, I will have him, say no more, against all the world I am resolved, I will have him. Gobryas the Cap-

* His epitaph.

tain, when he had espied Rhodanthe, the fair captive Maid, fell upon his knees before Mystylus the General, with tears, vows, and all the Rhetorick he could, by the scars he had formerly received, the good service he had done, or whatsoever else was dear unto him besought his Governor he might have the captive Virgin to be his wife, as a reward of his worth and service; and moreover, he would forgive him the money which was owing, and all reckonings besides due unto him, I ask no more, no part of booty, no portion, but Rhodanthe to be my wife. And when as he could not compass her by fair means, he fell to treachery, force and villainy, and set his life at stake at last, to accomplish his desire. 'Tis a common humour this, a general passion of all Lovers, to be so affected, and which Æmilia told Aretinus a Courtier in Castilio's discourse, Surely, Aretinus, and if thou wert not so indeed, thou didst not love; ingenuously confess, for if thou hadst been thoroughly enamoured, thou wouldst have desired nothing more than to please thy Mistress. For that is the law of love, to will and nill the same.

Undoubtedly this may be pronounced of them all, they are very slaves, drudges for the time, mad-men, fools, dizzards, melancholy, beside themselves, and as blind as Beetles. Their dotage is most eminent; as Seneca holds, Jupiter himself cannot love and be wise both together; the very best of them, if once they be overtaken with this passion, the most staid, discreet, grave, generous and wise, otherwise able to govern themselves, in this commit many absurdities, many indecorums, unbefitting their gravity and persons.

> *Whoever loves is a slave, his beloved's captive,*
> *Wearing the yoke tamely upon his neck.*   (MANTUAN)

Samson, David, Solomon, Hercules, Socrates, &c., are justly taxed of indiscretion in this point; the middle sort are betwixt hawk and buzzard; and although they do perceive and acknowledge their own dotage, weakness, fury, yet they cannot withstand it: as well may witness those expostulations, and confessions of Dido in Virgil:

> *She began to speak, but silent became in mid-utterance.*

Phædra in Seneca:

> *Reason is overcome and sway'd by passion,*
> *The potent god of love reigns in her soul.*

Myrrha in Ovid:

> *She sees and knows her fault, and doth resist,*
> *Against her filthy lust she doth contend.*
> *And whither go I, what am I about?*
> *And God forbid! yet doth it in the end.*

Again:

> *With raging lust she burns, and now recalls*
> *Her vow, and then despairs, and when 'tis past,*
> *Her former thoughts she'll prosecute in haste,*
> *And what to do she knows not at the last.*

She will and will not, abhors, and yet, as Medea did, doth it:

> *Reason pulls one way, burning lust another,*
> *She sees and knows what's good, but she doth neither.*   (OVID)
> *Beguiling love, and passion, what a gate*
> *You've led me!*   (BUCHANAN)

The major part of Lovers are carried headlong like so many brute beasts, reason counsels one way, thy friends, fortunes, shame, disgrace, danger and an ocean of cares that will certainly follow; yet this furious lust precipitates, counterpoiseth, weighs down on the other; though it be their utter undoing, perpetual infamy, loss, yet they will do it, and become at last void of sense; degenerate into dogs, hogs, asses, brutes; as Jupiter into a Bull, Apuleius an Ass, Lycaon a Wolf, Tereus a Lapwing, Callisto a Bear,* Elpenor and Gryllus into Swine by Circe. For what else may we think those ingenious Poets to have shadowed in their witty fictions and Poems, but that a man once given over to his lust (as Fulgentius interprets that of Apuleius, Alciati of Tereus) is no better than a beast.

> *I was a King, my Crown a witness is,*
> *But by my filthiness am come to this.*   (ALCIATI)

Their blindness is all out as great, as manifest as their weakness and dotage, or rather an inseparable companion, an ordinary sign of it. Love is blind, as the saying is, Cupid's blind, and so are all his followers.

> *Who loves a frog, thinks the frog as fair as Diana.*

Every Lover admires his Mistress, though she be very deformed of her self, ill-favoured, wrinkled, pimpled, pale, red, yellow, tanned, tallow-faced, have a swollen Juggler's platter-face, or a thin, lean, chitty-face, have clouds in her face, be crooked, dry, bald, goggle-ey'd, blear-ey'd, or with staring eyes, she looks like a squis'd [or squeez'd] cat, hold her head still awry, heavy, dull, hollow-eyed, black or yellow about the eyes, or squint-eyed, sparrow-mouthed, Persean hook-nosed, have a sharp Fox nose, a red nose, China flat great nose, snub-nose with wide nostrils, a nose like a promontory, gubber-tushed, rotten teeth, black, uneven, brown teeth, beetle-browed, a Witch's beard, her breath stink all over the room, her nose drop winter and summer, with a Bavarian poke [or

---

* An immodest woman is like a bear. — Burton's note.

pouch] under her chin, a sharp chin, lave eared [or big-eared], with a long crane's neck, which stands awry too, with hanging breasts, her dugs like two double jugs, or else no dugs, in the other extreme, bloody-faln [or chilblain'd] fingers, she have filthy long unpared nails, scabbed hands or wrists, a tanned skin, a rotten carkass, crooked back, she stoops, is lame, splay-footed, as slender in the middle as a Cow in the waist, gouty legs, her ankles hang over her shoes, her feet stink, she breeds lice, a mere changeling, a very monster, an auf [or oaf, or elf], imperfect, her whole complexion savours, an harsh voice, incondite gesture, vile gait, a vast virago, or an ugly Tit, a slug, a fat fustilugs, a truss, a long lean raw-bone, a skeleton, a sneaker, (suppose, as the poet saith, her unseen beauties somewhat better), and to thy judgement looks like a merd in a lanthorn, whom thou couldest not fancy for a world, but hatest, loathest, and wouldest have spit in her face, or blow thy nose in her bosom, the very antidote of love to another man, a dowdy, a slut, a scold, a nasty, rank, rammy, filthy, beastly quean, dishonest peradventure, obscene, base, beggarly, rude, foolish, untaught, peevish, Irus' daughter, Thersites' sister, Grobian's scholar, if he love her once, he admires her for all this, he takes no notice of any such errors, or imperfections of body or mind.

> *These very things enchant him then,*
> *As upon Agna's nose the wen*
> *Charms poor Balbinus,* (HORACE)

he had rather have her than any woman in the world. If he were a King, she alone should be his Queen, his Empress. O that he had but the wealth and treasure of both the Indies to endow her with, a carrack [or great ship] of Diamonds, a chain of Pearl, a cascanet of Jewels (a pair of calf-skin gloves of four pence a pair were fitter) or some such toy, to send her for a token, she should have it with all his heart; he would spend myriads of crowns for her sake. Venus herself, Panthea, Cleopatra, Tarquin's Tanaquil, Herod's Mariamne, or Mary of Burgundy, if she were alive, would not match her,

> *Her beauty beats Helen's, who did inspire*
> *The Trojan War,*

(let Paris himself be Judge), renowned Helena comes short, that Rhodopeian Phyllis, Larissæan Coronis, Babylonian Thisbe, Polyxena, Laura, Lesbia, &c., your counterfeit Ladies were never so fair as she is.

> *Whate'er is pretty, pleasant, facete, well,*
> *Whate'er Pandora had, she doth excel.* (LOECHAEUS)

Diana was not to be compared to her, nor Juno, nor Minerva, nor any Goddess. Thetis' feet were as bright as silver, the ancles of Hebe clearer than Crystal, the arms of Aurora as ruddy as the Rose, Juno's breasts as white as Snow, Minerva wise, Venus fair; but what of this? Dainty, come thou to me! She is all in all,

Fairest of fair, that fairness doth excel. (SPENSER)

Euemerus, in Aristænetus, so far admireth his Mistress' good parts, that he makes proclamation of them, and challengeth all comers in her behalf. Who ever saw the beauties of the East, or of the West, let them come from all quarters, all, and tell truth, if ever they saw such an excellent feature, as this is! A good fellow in Petronius cries out, no tongue can tell his Lady's fine feature, or express it,

No tongue can her perfections tell,
In whose each part all tongues may dwell. (SIDNEY)

Most of your Lovers are of his humour and opinion. She is second to none, a rare creature, a Phœnix, the sole commandress of his thoughts, Queen of his desires, his only delight: as Triton now feelingly sings, that Love-sick Sea-God.

Fair Leucothoe, black Melæne please me well,
But Galatea doth by odds the rest excel.

(CALCAGNINUS)

All the gracious Eulogies, Metaphors, Hyperbolical comparisons of the best things in the world, the most glorious names; whatsoever, I say, is pleasant, amiable, sweet, grateful, and delicious, are too little for her.

His Phœbe is so fair, she is so bright,
She dims the Sun's lustre, and the Moon's light.

Stars, Suns, Moons, Metals, sweet-smelling Flowers, Odours, Perfumes, Colours, Gold, Silver, Ivory, Pearls, Precious Stones, Snow, painted Birds, Doves, Honey, Sugar, Spice, cannot express her, so soft, so tender, so radiant, sweet, so fair is she: softer than a coney's fur, &c.

Fine Lydia, my Mistress, white and fair,
The milk, the Lily do not thee come near;
The Rose so white, the Rose so red to see,
And Indian Ivory comes short of thee. (PETRONIUS)

Such a description our English Homer makes of a fair Lady:

That Emelie, that fairer was to sene,
Than is the lilie upon his stalke grene:
And fressher than the May with floures newe,
For with the rose-colour strofe hire hewe;
I no't which was the finer of hem two.

In this very phrase Polyphemus courts Galatea:

> *Whiter Galatea than the white withy-wind,*
> *Fresher than a field, higher than a tree,*
> *Brighter than glass, more wanton than a kid,*
> *Softer than swan's down, or ought that may be.*   (OVID)

So she admires him again in that conceited Dialogue of Lucian, which Joannes Secundus, an Elegant Dutch modern Poet, hath translated into verse. When Doris, and those other Sea-Nymphs, upbraided her with her ugly mis-shapen Lover Polyphemus; she replies, they speak out of envy and malice:

> *Plainly 'tis envy prompts, since he*
> *Doth not love you as he doth me.*

Say what they could, he was a proper man. And as Heloise writ to her Sweetheart Peter Abelard, she had rather be his vassal, his Quean, than the world's Empress or Queen, she would not change her love for Jupiter himself.

To thy thinking she is a most loathsome creature, and as when a country-fellow discommended once that exquisite picture of Helena, made by Zeuxis, for he saw no such beauty in it; Nicomachus, a love-sick spectator replied, Take mine eyes, and thou wilt think she is a Goddess; dote on her forthwith, count all her vices, virtues; her imperfections, infirmities, absolute and perfect. If she be flat-nosed, she is lovely; if hook-nosed, kingly; if dwarfish and little, pretty; if tall, proper and man-like, our brave British Boadicea; if crooked, wise; if monstrous, comely; her defects are no defects at all, she hath no deformities. Though she be nasty, fulsome, as Sostratus's bitch, or Parmeno's sow: thou hadst as lieve have a snake in thy bosom, a toad in thy dish, and callest her witch, devil, hag, with all the filthy names thou canst invent; he admires her, on the other side, she is his Idol, Lady, Mistress, Venerilla [or Little Venus], Queen, the quintessence of beauty, an Angel, a Star, a Goddess.

> *Thou art my Vesta, thou my Goddess art,*
> *Thy hallowed Temple only is my heart.*   (DRAYTON)

The fragrancy of a thousand Courtesans is in her face: 'tis not Venus' picture that, nor the Spanish Infanta's as you suppose (good Sir) no Princess, or King's daughter; no, no, but his divine Mistress forsooth, his dainty Dulcinea, his dear Antiphila, to whose service he is wholly consecrate, whom he alone adores.

> *To whom conferr'd a Peacock's undecent,*
> *A squirrel's harsh, a Phœnix too frequent.*   (MARTIAL)

All the Graces, veneries, elegances, pleasures, attend her. He prefers her before a Myriad of Court-Ladies.

> *He that commends Phyllis or Neæra*
> *Or Amaryllis, or Galatea,*
> *Tityrus or Melibœa, by your leave,*
> *Let him be mute, his Love the praises have.* (ARIOSTO)

Nay, before all the Gods and Goddesses themselves. So Quintus Catulus admired his squint-eyed friend Roscius.

> *By your leave, gentle Gods, this I'll say true,*
> *There's none of you that have so fair a hue.* (CICERO)

All the bombast Epithets, pathetical adjuncts, incomparably fair, curiously neat, divine, sweet, dainty, delicious, &c., pretty diminutives, Little Heart, Little Kiss, &c., pleasant names may be invented, bird, mouse, lamb, puss, pigeon, pigsney, kid, honey, love, dove, chicken, &c., he puts on her.

> *My honey, my heart, my sweetness,*
> *My rabbit, my little kiss,* (MARULLUS)

my life, my light, my jewel, my glory, my sweet Margaret, my sole delight and darling! And as Rhodomant courted Isabella:

> *By all kind words and gestures that he might,*
> *He calls her his dear heart, his sole beloved,*
> *His joyful comfort, and his sweet delight,*
> *His Mistress, and his Goddess, and such names,*
> *As loving Knights apply to lovely Dames.* (ARIOSTO)

Every cloath she wears, every fashion, pleaseth him above measure; her hand,

> *O such fingers on that hand of hers!*

pretty foot, pretty coronets, [or head-dresses], her sweet carriage, sweet voice, tone, O that pretty tone, her divine and lovely looks, her every thing, lovely, sweet, amiable and pretty, pretty, pretty! Her very name (let it be what it will) is the most pretty pleasing name; I believe now there is some secret power and virtue in names, every action, sight, habit, gesture, he admires, whether she play, sing, or dance, in what tires soever she goeth, how excellent it was, how well it became her, never the like seen or heard.

> *She wears a thousand dresses*
> *In a thousand charming ways.* (TIBULLUS)

Let her wear what she will, do what she will, say what she will, 'tis all becoming. He applauds and admires every thing she wears, saith, or doth.

What e'er she doth, or whither e'er she go,
A sweet and pleasing grace attends forsooth;
Or loose, or bind her hair, or comb it up,
She's to be honoured in what she doth.   (TIBULLUS)

Let her be dressed or undressed, all is one, she is excellent still, beautiful, fair, and lovely to behold. Women do as much by men, nay more,
far fonder, weaker, and that by many parasangs. Come to me, my
dear Lysias (saith Musarium in Aristænetus) come quickly Sweetheart,
all other men are Satyrs, mere clowns, block-heads to thee, nobody to
thee: thy looks, words, gestures, actions, &c., are incomparably beyond
all others. Venus was never so much besotted on her Adonis, Phædra so
delighted in Hippolytus, Ariadne in Theseus, Thisbe in her Pyramus,
as she is enamoured on her Mopsus.

Be thou the Marigold, and I will be the Sun,
Be thou the Friar, and I will be the Nun.

I could repeat centuries of such. Now tell me what greater dotage, or
blindness can there be than this in both sexes? and yet their slavery is
more eminent, a greater sign of their folly than the rest.

They are commonly slaves, captives, voluntary servants, a lover is
the slave of his beloved, as Castilio terms him, his Mistress' servant,
her drudge, prisoner, bond-man, what not? He composeth himself
wholly to her affections, to please her; and, as Æmilia said, makes himself her lackey; all his cares, actions, all his thoughts, are subordinate
to her will and commandment; her most devote, obsequious, affection-
ate, servant and vassal. For Love (as Cyrus in Xenophon well observed)
is a mere tyranny, worse than any disease, and they that are troubled
with it, desire to be free, and cannot, but are harder bound than if they
were in iron chains. What greater captivity or slavery can there be (as
Tully expostulates) than to be in love? Is he a free man over whom a
woman domineers, to whom she prescribes Laws, commands, forbids
what she will herself? that dares deny nothing she demands; she asks,
he gives; she calls, he comes; she threatens, he fears; I account this
man a very drudge. And as he follows it, Is this no small servitude for
an enamorite to be every hour combing his head, stiffening his beard,
perfuming his hair, washing his face with sweet waters, painting, curl-
ing, and not to come abroad but sprucely crowned, decked and appar-
elled?

Yet these are but toys in respect, to go to the Barber, Baths, Theatres, &c., he must attend upon her wherever she goes, run along the
streets by her doors and windows to see her, take all opportunities,

sleeveless errands, disguise, counterfeit shapes, and as many forms as Jupiter himself ever took; and come every day to her house (as he will surely do if he be truly enamoured) and offer her service, and follow her up and down from room to room, as Lucretia's suitors did, he cannot contain himself, but he will do it, he must and will be where she is, sit next her, still talking with her. If I did but let my glove fall by chance (as the said Aretine's Lucretia brags) I had one of my suitors, nay two or three at once ready to stoop and take it up, and kiss it, and with a low congee deliver it unto me: if I would walk, another was ready to sustain me by the arm; a third to provide fruits, Pears, Plums, Cherries, or whatsoever I would eat or drink. — All this and much more he doth in her presence, and when he comes home, as Troilus to his Creseid, 'tis all his meditation to recount with himself his actions, words, gestures, what entertainment he had, how kindly she used him in such a place, how she smiled, how she graced him, and that infinitely pleased him; then he breaks out, O sweet Areusa, O my dearest Antiphila, O most divine looks, O lovely graces, and thereupon instantly he makes an Epigram, or a Sonnet to five or seven tunes, in her commendation, or else he ruminates how she rejected his service, denied him a kiss, disgraced him, &c., and that as effectually torments him. And these are his exercises betwixt comb and glass, Madrigals, Elegies, &c., these his cogitations till he see her again. But all this is easy and gentle, and the least part of his labour and bondage, no hunter will take such pains for his Game, Fowler for his sport, or Soldier to sack a City, as he will for his Mistress' favour.

> *I will be your companion, nought shall fright me,*
> *Nor rugged rocks, nor tusk of savage boar,*

as Phædra to Hippolytus. No danger shall affright; for if that be true the Poets feign, Love is the son of Mars and Venus; as he hath delights, pleasures, elegancies from his Mother, so hath he hardness, valour, and boldness, from his father. And 'tis true that Bernard hath: nothing so boisterous, nothing so tender as Love. If once therefore enamoured, he will go, run, ride many a mile to meet her, day and night, in a very dark night, endure scorching heat, cold, wait in frost and snow, rain, tempests, till his teeth chatter in his head, those Northern winds and showers cannot cool or quench his flames of love. By unseasonable night he is not deterred, he will, take my word, he will sustain hunger, thirst, penetrate all, overthrow all, love will find out a way, through thick and thin he will go to her; he will swim through an Ocean, ride post over the Alps, Apennines, or Pyrenean hills, fire, flood, whirlpools, though it rain daggers with their points downwards, light or dark, all is one:

Dew-drenched through the darkness Faunus came to the grotto,

for her sweet sake he will undertake Hercules' twelve Labours, endure hazard, &c., he feels it not. What shall I say (saith Hædus) of their great dangers they undergo, single combats they undertake, how they will venture their lives, creep in at windows, gutters, climb over walls to come to their sweethearts, (anointing the doors and hinges with oil, because they should not creak, tread soft, swim, wade, watch, &c.), and if they be surprised, leap out at windows, cast themselves headlong down, bruising or breaking their legs or arms, and sometimes losing life itself, as Callisto did for his lovely Meliboea? Hear some of their own confessions, protestations, complaints, proffers, expostulations, wishes, brutish attempts, labours in this kind. Hercules served Omphale, put on an apron, took a distaff and spun; Thraso the soldier was so submissive to Thais, that he was resolved to do whatsoever she enjoined. I give myself to Thais, I am at her service. Philostratus, in an Epistle to his Mistress: I am ready to die, Sweetheart, if it be thy will; allay his thirst whom thy star has scorched and undone; the fountains and rivers deny no man drink that comes; the fountain doth not say, thou shalt not drink, nor the apple, thou shalt not eat, nor the fair meadow, walk not in me, but thou alone wilt not let me come near thee, or see thee, contemned and despised I die for grief. Polyænos, when his Mistress Circe did but frown upon him in Petronius, drew his sword, and bade her kill, stab, or whip him to death, he would strip himself naked, and not resist. Another will take a journey to Japan, uncaring for the troubles of a long voyage. A third (if she say it) will not speak a word for a twelve-month's space, her command shall be most inviolably kept. A fourth will take Hercules' club from him, and, with that Centurion in the Spanish Cælestina, will kill ten men for his Mistress Areusa, for a word of her mouth, he will cut bucklers in two like pippins, and flap down men like flies, saying to her, Choose how you will have him killed. Galeatus of Mantua did a little more, for when he was almost mad for love of a fair Maid in the City, she to try him, belike, what he would do for her sake, bade him, in jest, leap into the River Po, if he loved her; he forthwith did leap headlong off the bridge, and was drowned. Another at Ficinum in like passion, when his Mistress by chance (thinking no harm I dare sware) bade him go hang, the next night at her doors hanged himself. Money (saith Xenophon) is a very acceptable and welcome guest, yet I had rather give it my dear Cleinias, than take it of others, I had rather serve him, than command others, I had rather be his drudge, than take my ease, undergo any danger for his sake, than live in security. For I had rather see Cleinias than all the world besides, and had rather want the sight of all other things, than him alone; I am angry with the night and sleep that I may not see him, and thank the light and Sun because they shew me my Cleinias; I will run into the fire for his sake, and if you did but see him, I know that you likewise would run with me. So Philostratus to his Mistress: Command me what you will, I will do it; bid me go to Sea, I am gone in an instant; take so many stripes, I am ready; run through the fire, and lay down my life and soul at thy feet, 'tis done. So did Æolus to Juno,

> *O Queen, it is thy pains to enjoin me still,*
> *And I am bound to execute thy will.* (VIRGIL)

And Phædra to Hippolytus,

> *O call me sister, call me servant, choose,*
> *Or rather servant, I am thine to use.*
> *It shall not grieve me to the snowy hills,*
> *Or frozen Pindus' tops forthwith to climb,*
> *Or run through fire, or through an Army,*
> *Say but the word, for I am always thine.* (SENECA)

Callicratides, in Lucian, breaks out in this passionate speech: O God of heaven, grant me this life for ever to sit over against my Mistress, and to hear her sweet voice, to go in and out with her, to have every other business common with her; I would labour when she labours, sail when she sails; he that hates her should hate me; and if a tyrant kill her, he should kill me; if she should die, I would not live, and one grave should hold us both.

> *When she dies, my love shall likewise be at rest in the tomb.*
> (BUCHANAN)

Abrocomas in Aristænetus makes the like petition for his Delphis.

> *Gladly I'd live with thee, or gladly die.* (HORACE)

'Tis the same strain which Theagenes used to his Chariclea: So that I may but enjoy thy love, let me die presently; Leander to his Hero, when he besought the Sea waves to let him go quietly to his Love, and kill him coming back.

> *Spare me while I go, o'erwhelm me returning.* (MARTIAL)

'Tis the common humour of them all, to contemn death, to wish for death, to confront death in this case, caring neither for wild beasts, nor fire, nor precipices, nor straits, nor of weapons, nor of heavy seas: 'tis their desire (saith Tyrius) to die.

He fears not death, nay, he desires to run
Upon the very swords. (SENECA)

Though a thousand dragons or devils kept the gates, Cerberus himself,
Sciron and Procrustes lay in wait, and the way as dangerous, as inac-
cessible as hell, through fiery flames and over burning coulters, he will
adventure for all this. And as Peter Abelard lost his testicles for his
Heloise, he will (I say) not venture an incision, but life itself. For how
many gallants offered to lose their lives for a night's lodging with
Cleopatra in those days! And in the hour and moment of death, 'tis
their sole comfort to remember their dear Mistress, as Zerbino slain
in France, and Brandimart in Barbary; as Arcite did his Emily:

> ————when he felte death,
> Dusked been his eyen two, faded his breath,
> But on his lady yet caste he his eye,
> His laste word was, mercy Emely.
> His spirit changed, and out wente there,
> Whither I cannot tell, ne where.

When Captain Gobrias by an unlucky accident had received his death's
wound, miserable man that I am (instead of other devotions) he cries
out, Shall I die before I see Rhodanthe my Sweetheart? Saith mine
Author, so Love triumphs, contemns, insults over death itself. Thirteen
proper young men lost their lives for that fair Hippodamia's sake, the
daughter of Œnomaus, King of Elis: when that hard condition was proposed of death or victory, they made no account of it, but courageously
for love died, till Pelops at last won her by a sleight. As many gallants
desperately adventured their dearest blood for Atalanta the daughter of
Schœneus, in hope of marriage, all vanquished and overcome, till Hip-
pomenes by a few golden apples happily obtained his suit. Perseus of
old fought with a Sea-monster for Andromeda's sake; and our S. George
freed the King's daughter of Sabea, (the Golden Legend is mine Author), that was exposed to a Dragon, by a terrible Combat. Our Knights
Errant, and the Sir Lancelots of these days, I hope will adventure as
much for Ladies' favours, as the Squire of Dames, Knight of the Sun,
Sir Bevis of Southampton, or that renowned Peer

> *Orlando, who long time had lovéd dear*
> *Angelica the fair, and for her sake*
> *About the world, in nations far and near,*
> *Did high attempts perform and undertake.* (ARIOSTO)

He is a very dastard, a coward, a block and a beast, that will not do as
much, but they will sure, they will; for 'tis an ordinary thing for these

inamoratos of our times, to say and do more, to stab their arms, carouse in blood, or as that Thessalian Thero, that bit off his own thumb, to make his Corrival do as much. 'Tis frequent with them to challenge the field for their Lady and Mistress' sake, to run a tilt,

> *That either bears (so furiously they meet)*
> *The other down under the horses' feet,*   (SPENSER)

and then up and to it again,

> *And with their axes both so sorely pour,*
> *That neither plate nor mail sustained the stour,*
> *But riveld wreak like rotten wood asunder,*
> *And fire did flash like lightning after thunder,*

and in her quarrel, to fight so long, till their head-piece, bucklers, be all broken, and swords hackt like so many saws; for they must not see her abused in any sort, 'tis blasphemy to speak against her, a dishonour without all good respect to name her. 'Tis common with these creatures, to drink healths upon their bare knees, though it were a mile to the bottom (no matter of what mixture) off it comes. If she bid them, they will go barefoot to Jerusalem, to the great Cham's Court, to the East Indies, to fetch her a bird to wear in her hat: and with Drake and Cavendish sail round about the world for her sweet sake, with adverse winds, serve twice seven years, as Jacob did for Rachel; do as much as Gismunda the daughter of Tancredus, Prince of Salerna, did for Guiscardus her true love, eat his heart when he died; or as Artemisia drank her husband's bones beaten to powder, and so bury him in herself, and endure more torments than Theseus or Paris. With such sacrifices as these (as Aristænetus holds) Venus is well pleased. Generally they undertake any pain, any labour, any toil, for their Mistress' sake, love and admire a servant, not to her alone, but to all her friends and followers, they hug and embrace them for her sake; her dog, picture, and every thing she wears, they adore it as a relique. If any man come from her, they feast him, reward him, will not be out of his company, do him all offices, still remembering, still talking of her:

> *For though the object of thy love be absent*
> *Her image stays, her sweet name rings in thine ears.*   (LUCRETIUS)

The very Carrier that comes from him to her is a most welcome guest, and if he bring a letter, she will read it twenty times over; and as Lucretia did by Euryalus, kiss the letter a thousand times together, and then read it: and Chelidonia by Philonius, after many sweet kisses, put the letter in her bosom,

And kiss again, and often look thereon,
And stay the Messenger that would be gone, (ARISTÆNETUS)
and ask many pretty questions, over and over again, as how he looked,
what he did, and what he said? In a word,

He strives to please his Mistress and her maid,
Her servants, and her dog, and's well apaid. (PLAUTUS)
If he get any remnant of hers, a busk-point, a feather of her fan, a
shoe-tie, a lace, a ring, a bracelet of hair,

Some token snatched from her arm,
Or hardly resisting finger, (HORACE)
he wears it for a favour on his arm, in his hat, finger, or next his heart.
Her picture he adores twice a day, and for two hours together will not
look off it; as Laodomia did by Protesilaus, when he went to war, sit
at home with his picture before her; a garter or a bracelet of hers is
more precious than any Saint's Relique, he lays it up in his casket (O
blessed Relique) and every day will kiss it: if in her presence, his eye is
never off her, and drink he will where she drank, if it be possible, in
that very place, &c. If absent, he will walk in the walk, sit under that
tree where she did use to sit, in that bower, in that very seat,

And sadly prints his kisses on the doors, (LUCRETIUS)
many years after sometimes, though she be far distant, and dwell many
miles off, he loves yet to walk that way still, to have his chamber
window look that way: to walk by that River's side which (though far
away) runs by the house where she dwells, he loves the wind blows
to that coast.

O happy Western winds that blow that way,
For you shall see my love's fair face to-day. (BUCHANAN)
He will send a message to her by the wind,

Ye Alpine breezes, mountain winds,
Bear her these tidings. (FRACASTORIUS)
He desires to confer with some of her acquaintance, for his heart is
still with her, to talk of her, admiring and commending her, lamenting,
moaning, wishing himself any thing for her sake, to have opportunity
to see her, O that he might but enjoy her presence! So did Philostratus
to his Mistress: O happy ground on which she treads, and happy were
I if she would tread upon me! I think her countenance would make the
Rivers stand, and when she comes abroad, birds will sing and come
about her.

The fields will laugh, the pleasant valleys burn,
And all the grass will into flowers turn.
All the air will breathe ambrosia.

When she is in the meadow, she is fairer than any flower, for that lasts but for a day; the river is pleasing, but it vanisheth on a sudden, but thy flower doth not fade, thy stream is greater than the Sea. If I look upon the Heaven, methinks, I see the Sun fallen down to shine below, and thee to shine in his place, whom I desire. If I look upon the night, methinks I see two more glorious Stars, Hesperus and thyself. A little after he thus courts his Mistress: If thou goest forth of the City, the protecting Gods that keep the town, will run after to gaze upon thee: if thou sail upon the Seas, as so many small boats, they will follow thee: what River would not run into the Sea? Another, he sighs and sobs, swears he hath an heart bruised to powder, dissolved and melted within him, or quite gone from him, to his Mistress' bosom belike; he is an Oven, a Salamander in the fire, so scorched with love's heat; he wisheth himself a saddle for her to sit on, a posy for her to smell to, and it would not grieve him to be hanged, if he might be strangled in her garters; he would willingly die to-morrow, so that she might kill him with her own hands. Ovid would be a Flea, a Gnat, a Ring, Catullus a Sparrow,

> *O that I might thus play with thee*
> *And set my mind from sorrow free.*

Anacreon, a glass, a gown, a chain, any thing:

> *But I a looking-glass would be,*
> *Still to be lookt upon by thee,*
> *Or I, my Love, would be thy gown,*
> *By thee to be worn up and down;*
> *Or a pure well full to the brims,*
> *That I might wash thy purer limbs:*
> *Or, I'd be precious balm to 'noint,*
> *With choicest care each choicest joint;*
> *Or, if I might, I would be fain*
> *About thy neck thy happy chain,*
> *Or would it were my blessed hap*
> *To be the lawn o'er thy fair pap.*
> *Or would I were thy shoe, to be*
> *Daily trod upon by thee.* (Englished by Mr. B. Holliday)

O thrice happy man that shall enjoy her: as they that saw Hero in Musæus, and Salmacis to Hermaphroditus,

> *Happy thy mother, happy thy nurse,*
> *But happiest she, the bride that shares thy bed.*   (OVID)

The same passion made her break out in the Comedy, happy are his bed-fellows; and as she said of Cyrus, blessed is that woman that shall be his wife, nay thrice happy she that shall enjoy him but a night. Such a night's lodging is worth Jupiter's Sceptre. O what a blissful night would it be, how soft, how sweet a bed! She will adventure all her estate for such a night, for a Nectarean, a balsam kiss alone.

> *Happy is he who sees thee,*
> *Happier he who hears thee,*
> *A demigod he who kisses thee,*
> *A god he who possesses thee.* (GREEK ANTHOLOGY)

The Sultan of Sana's wife in Arabia, when she had seen Vertomannus, that comely Traveller, lamented to herself in this manner, O God, thou hast made this man whiter than the Sun; but me, mine husband, and all my children black; I would to God he were mine husband, or that I had such a son; she fell a weeping, and so impatient for love at last, that (as Potiphar's wife did by Joseph) she would have had him gone in with her, she sent away Gazella, Tegeia, Galzerana, her waiting maids, loaded him with fair promises and gifts, and wooed him with all the Rhetorick she could,

> *Grant this last favour to your hapless lover.* (VIRGIL)

But when he gave not consent, she would have gone with him, and left all, to be his page, his servant, or his lackey, so that she might enjoy him; threatening moreover to kill herself, &c. Men will do as much and more for women, spend goods, lands, lives, fortunes; Kings will leave their Crowns, as King John for Matilda the Nun at Dunmow.

> *But kings in this yet privileg'd may be,*
> *I'll be a monk, so I may live with thee.* (DRAYTON)

The very Gods will endure any shame, be a spectacle as Mars and Venus were to all the rest; so did Lucian's Mercury wish, and peradventure so dost thou. They will adventure their lives with alacrity,

> *I would not fear to die for her,* (HORACE)

nay more, I will die twice, nay twenty times for her. If she die, there's no remedy, they must die with her, they cannot help it. A Lover, in Calcagninus, wrote this on his darling's Tomb:

> *Quincia my dear is dead, but not alone,*
> *For I am dead, and with her I am gone:*
> *Sweet smiles, mirth, graces, all with her do rest,*
> *And my soul, too, for 'tis not in my breast.*

How many doting Lovers upon the like occasion might say the same! But these are toys in respect, they will hazard their very souls for their Mistress' sake.

One said, to heaven would I not
      Desire at all to go,
If that at mine own house I had
      Such a fine wife as Hero.   (MUSAEUS)

Venus forsook Heaven for Adonis' sake. Old January, in Chaucer,
thought when he had his fair May, he should never go to heaven, he
should live so merrily here on earth; had I such a Mistress, he protests,

I would not envy their prosperity,
The Gods should envy my felicity.   (BUCHANAN)

Another as earnestly desires to behold his Sweetheart, he will adventure and leave all this, and more than this, to see her alone.

If all my mischiefs were recompensed,
And God would give me what I requested,
I would my Mistress' presence only seek,
Which doth my heart in prison captive keep.   (PETRARCH)

But who can reckon up the dotage, madness, servitude and blindness,
the foolish phantasms and vanities of Lovers, their torments, wishes,
idle attempts?

Yet for all this, amongst so many irksome, absurd, troublesome
symptoms, inconveniences, phantastical fits and passions, which are
usually incident to such persons, there be some good and graceful qualities in Lovers, which this affection causeth. As it makes wise men fools,
so many times it makes fools become wise; it makes base fellows become generous, cowards courageous, as Cardan notes out of Plutarch;
covetous, liberal and magnificent; clowns, civil; cruel, gentle; wicked
profane persons, to become religious; slovens, neat; churls, merciful;
and dumb dogs, eloquent: your lazy drones, quick and nimble; love
tames savage breasts; that fierce, cruel and rude Cyclops Polyphemus
sighed, and shed many a salt tear, for Galatea's sake. No passion causeth greater alterations, or more vehement of joy or discontent. Plutarch
saith that the soul of a man in love is full of perfumes and sweet odours,
and all manner of pleasing tones and tunes, insomuch that it is hard
to say (as he adds) whether love do mortal men more harm than good.
It adds spirits, and makes them otherwise soft and silly, generous and
courageous. Ariadne's love made Theseus so adventurous, and Medea's
beauty Jason so victorious; love drives out fear. Plato is of opinion that
the love of Venus made Mars so valorous. A young man will be much
abashed to commit any foul offence that shall come to the hearing or
sight of his Mistress. As he that desired of his enemy, now dying, to lay
him with his face upward, lest his Sweetheart should say he was a

Coward. And if it were possible to have an Army consist of Lovers, such as love, or are beloved, they would be extraordinary valiant and wise in their Government, modesty would detain them from doing amiss, emulation incite them to do that which is good and honest, and a few of them would overcome a great company of others. There is no man so pusillanimous, so very a dastard, whom Love would not incense, make of a divine temper, and an heroical spirit. As he said in like case, though the heavens should fall, nothing can terrify, nothing can dismay them; but as Sir Blandamour and Paridell, those two brave Fairy Knights, fought for the love of fair Florimell in presence ——

> And drawing both their swords with rage anew,
> Like two mad mastives each other slew,
> And shields did share, and mailes did rash, and helms did hew:
> So furiously each other did assail,
> As if their souls at once they would have rent
> Out of their breasts, that streams of blood did trail
> Adown, as if their springs of life were spent,
> That all the ground with purple blood was sprent,
> And all their armour stained with bloody gore;
> Yet scarcely once to breathe would they relent.
> So mortal was their malice and so sore,
> That both resolved (than yield) to die before.

Every base Swain in love will dare to do as much for his dear Mistress' sake. He will fight, and fetch that famous buckler of Argos, to do her service, adventure at all, undertake any enterprize. And as Serranus the Spaniard, then Governor of Sluys, made answer to Marquess Spinola, if the enemy brought 50,000 Devils against him, he would keep it. The nine Worthies, Oliver and Roland, and forty dozen of Peers are all in him, he is all metal, armour of proof, more than a man, and in this case improved beyond himself. For, as Agathon contends, a true Lover is wise, just, temperate and valiant. I doubt not therefore, but if a man had such an Army of Lovers (as Castilio supposeth) he might soon conquer all the world, except by chance he met with such another Army of Inamoratos to oppose it. For so perhaps they might fight as that fatal Dog, and fatal Hare in the Heavens, course one another round, and never make an end. Castilio thinks Ferdinand King of Spain would never have conquered Granada had not Queen Isabel and her Ladies been present at the siege; it cannot be expressed what courage the Spanish Knights took, when the Ladies were present, a few Spaniards overcame a multitude of Moors. They will undergo any danger whatsoever, as Sir Walter Manny in Edward the Third's time, stuck full of Ladies' favours, fought like a Dragon. For, as Plato holds, only Lovers will die for their friends, and in their Mistress' quarrel. And for that cause he would have women follow the Camp, to be spectators and encouragers of noble actions: upon such an occasion, the Squire of Dames himself, Sir Lancelot, or Sir Tristram, Cæsar, or Alexander, shall not be more resolute, or go beyond them.

Not courage only doth Love add, but, as I said, subtilty, wit, and many pretty devises,

For love inspires to stratagems and frauds. (MANTUAN)

Jupiter, in love with Leda, and not knowing how to compass his desire, turn'd himself into a Swan, and got Venus to pursue him in the likeness of an Eagle; which she doing, for shelter he fled to Leda's lap, Leda embraced him, and so fell fast asleep, but he took her asleep, by which means Jupiter had his will. Infinite such tricks can Love devise, such fine feats in abundance, with wisdom and wariness:

Who can deceive a lover?

All manner of civility, decency, compliment, and good behaviour, polite graces, and merry conceits. Boccaccio hath a pleasant tale to this purpose, which he borrowed from the Greeks, and which Beroaldus hath turned into Latin, Bebelius in verse, of Cimon and Iphigenia. This Cimon was a fool, a proper man of person, and the Governor of Cyprus' son, but a very ass; insomuch that his father, being ashamed of him, sent him to a Farm-house he had in the Country to be brought up; where by chance, as his manner was, walking alone, he espied a gallant young Gentlewoman named Iphigenia, a Burgomaster's daughter of Cyprus, with her maid, by a brook side in a little thicket, fast asleep in her smock, where she had newly bathed herself. When Cimon saw her, he stood leaning on his staff, gaping on her immoveable, and in a maze. At last he fell so far in love with the glorious object, that he began to rouse himself up, to bethink what he was, would needs follow her to the City, and for her sake began to be civil, to learn to sing and dance, to play on Instruments, and got all those Gentlemen-like qualities and compliments in a short space, which his friends were most glad of. In brief, he became, from an Idiot and a Clown, to be one of the most complete Gentlemen in Cyprus, did many valorous exploits, and all for the love of Mistress Iphigenia. In a word, I may say thus much of them all, let them be never so clownish, rude and horrid, Grobians [or slovens] and sluts, if once they be in love, they will be most neat and spruce; for love is foremost in the nicenesses of elegance, they will follow the fashion, begin to trick up, and to have a good opinion of themselves; for Venus is mother of the graces; a ship is not so long a-rigging, as a young Gentlewoman a-trimming up herself against her Sweetheart comes. A Painter's shop, a flowery Meadow, no so gracious aspect in Nature's storehouse as a young maid, a Novista or Venetian Bride, that looks for a husband, or a young man that is her suitor; composed looks, composed gait, clothes, gestures, actions, all composed; all the graces, elegancies in the world are in her face. Their best robes, ribbons, chains, Jewels, Lawns, Linnens, Laces, Spangles, must come on, before all things they must study to be elegant, they are beyond all measure coy, nice, and too curious on a sudden: 'tis all their study, all their business, how to wear their clothes neat, to be polite and terse, and to set out themselves. No sooner doth a young man see his Sweetheart coming, but he smugs up himself, pulls up his cloak now fallen about his shoulders, ties his garters, points, sets his band, cuffs, slicks his hair, twires his beard, &c. When Mercury was to come before his Mistress,

> *He put his cloak in order, that the lace,*
> *And hem, and gold-work all might have his grace.*   (OVID)

Salmacis would not be seen of Hermophroditus, till she had spruced up herself first.

> *Nor did she come, although 'twas her desire,*
> *Till she composed herself, and trimm'd her tire,*
> *And set her looks to make him to admire.*   (OVID)

Venus had so ordered the matter, that when her son Æneas was to appear before Queen Dido, he was like a God, for she was the tire-woman herself, to set him out with all natural and artificial impostures. As Mother Mamæa did her son Severus, new chosen Emperor, when he was to be seen of the people first. When the hirsute Cyclopical Polyphemus courted Galatea:

> *And then he did begin to prank himself,*
> *To plait and comb his head, and beard to shave,*
> *And look his face i' th' water as a glass,*
> *And to compose himself for to be brave.*   (OVID)

He was upon a sudden now spruce and keen, as a new-ground hatchet. He now began to have a good opinion of his own feature, and good parts, now to be a gallant.

> *Come now, my Galatea, scorn me not,*
> *Nor my poor presents; for but yesterday*
> *I saw myself i' th' water, and methought*
> *Full fair I was, then scorn me not I say.*   (OVID)

'Tis the common humour of all Suitors to trick up themselves, to be prodigal in apparel, faultless as a lotus, neat, comb'd and curl'd, with powdered hairs, with a long Love-lock, a flower in his ear, perfumed gloves, rings, scarfs, feathers, points, &c., as if he were a Prince's Ganymede, with every day new suits, as the fashion varies; going as if he trod upon eggs, and as Heinsius writ to Primerius, If once he be besotted on a Wench, he must lie awake a-nights, renounce his book, sigh and lament, now and then weep for his hard hap, and mark above all things what Hats, Bands, Doublets, Breeches, are in fashion, how to cut his beard, and wear his lock, to turn up his Mushatos, and curl his head, prune his pickitivant [or peaked beard], or if he wear it abroad, that the East side be correspondent to the West; he may be scoffed at otherwise, as Julian that Apostate Emperor was for wearing a long hirsute goatish beard, fit to make ropes with, as in his Misopogon, or that Apologetical Oration he made at Antioch to excuse himself, he doth ironically confess, it hindered his kissing; but he did not much esteem it [kissing], as it seems by the sequel, I do not exert myself, said he, in the giving and taking of kisses; yet (to follow mine Author) it may much concern a young lover, he must be more respectful in this behalf, he must be in league with an excellent Tailor, Barber, —

A barber boy, yet such an artist
As Nero's Thalamus was, (MARTIAL)

— have neat shoe-ties, points, garters, speak in Print, walk in Print, eat and drink in Print, and that which is all in all, he must be mad in Print.

Amongst other good qualities an amorous fellow is endowed with, he must learn to sing and dance, play upon some instrument or other, as without all doubt he will, if he be truly touched with this Loadstone of Love. For as Erasmus hath it, Love will make them Musicians, and to compose Ditties, Madrigals, Elegies, Love Sonnets, and sing them to several pretty tunes, to get all good qualities may be had. Jupiter perceived Mercury to be in love with Philologia, because he learned languages, polite speech, (for Suadela [the Goddess of Persuasion], herself was Venus' daughter, as some write), Arts and Sciences, all to ingratiate himself and please his Mistress. 'Tis their chiefest study to sing, dance; and without question, so many Gentlemen and Gentlewomen would not be so well qualified in this kind, if love did not incite them. Who, saith Castilio, would learn to play, or give his mind to Musick, learn to dance, or make so many rhymes, Love-songs, as most do, but for women's sake, because they hope by that means to purchase their good wills, and win their favour? We see this daily verified in our young women and wives, they that being maids took so much pains to sing, play, and dance, with such cost and charge to their Parents, to get those graceful qualities, now being married, will scarce touch an instrument, they care not for it. Constantine makes Cupid himself to be a great dancer, by the same token as he was capering amongst the Gods, he flung down a bowl of Nectar, which distilling upon the white Rose, ever since made it red; and Callistratus, by the help of Dædalus, about Cupid's Statue made a many of young Wenches still a dancing, to signify belike that Cupid was much affected with it, as without all doubt he was. For at his and Psyche's wedding, the Gods being present to grace the Feast, Ganymede filled Nectar in abundance (as Apuleius describes it), Vulcan was the Cook, the Hours made all fine with Roses and Flowers, Apollo played on the harp, the Muses sang to it, but his Mother Venus danced to his and their sweet content. Witty Lucian, in that Pathetical Love passage, or pleasant description of Jupiter's stealing of Europa, and swimming from Phœnicia to Crete, makes the Sea calm, the winds hush, Neptune and Amphitrite riding in their Chariot to break the waves before them, the Tritons dancing round about, with every one a Torch, the Sea-Nymphs half naked, keeping time on Dolphins' backs, and singing Hymenæus, Cupid nimbly tripping on the top of the waters, and Venus herself coming after in a shell, strewing Roses and Flowers on their heads. Praxiteles in all his pictures of Love, feigns Cupid ever smiling, and looking upon dancers; and in Saint Mark's Garden in Rome, (whose work I know not), one of the most delicious pieces is a many of Satyrs dancing about a wench asleep. So that dancing still is, as it were, a necessary appendix to love matters. Young Lasses are never better pleased, than when as upon an Holiday after Even-song, they may meet their Sweethearts, and dance about a May-pole, or in a Town-Green under a shady Elm. Nothing so familiar in France, as for Citizens' wives and maids to dance a round in the streets, and often too, for want of better instruments, to make good Musick of their own voices, and dance after it. Yea, many times this Love will make old men and women, that have more toes than teeth, dance, —— " John come kiss me now," mask and mum; for Comus and Hymen love masks, and all such merriments above measure, will allow men to put on women's apparel in some cases, and promiscuously to dance, young and old, rich and poor, generous and base, of all sorts. Paulus Jovius taxeth Augustine Niphus the Philosopher, for that being an old man, and a publick Professor, a father of many children, he was so mad for the love of a young maid (that which many of his friends were ashamed to see), an old gouty fellow, yet would dance after

Fiddlers. Many laughed him to scorn for it, but this omnipotent love would have it so.

Love hasty with his purple staff did make
Me follow, and the dance to undertake. (ANACREON)

And 'tis no news this, no indecorum: for why? a good reason may be given of it. Cupid and Death met both in an Inn, and being merrily disposed, they did exchange some arrows from either quiver; ever since young men die, and oftentimes old men dote.

Therefore youth dies, therefore the near-dead love. (BELLIUS)

And who can then withstand it? If once we be in love, young or old, though our teeth shake in our heads, like Virginal Jacks, or stand parallel asunder like the arches of a bridge, there's no remedy, we must dance trenchmore * for a need, over tables, chairs, and stools, &c. And princum prancum is a fine dance. Plutarch doth in some sort excuse it, and telleth us moreover in what sense, Love teacheth music, how Love makes them that had no skill before, learn to sing and dance; he concludes, 'tis only that power and prerogative Love hath over us. Love (as he holds) will make a silent man speak, a modest man most officious; dull, quick; slow, nimble; and that which is most to be admired, an hard, base, untractable churl, as fire doth iron in a Smith's forge, free, facile, gentle, and easy to be entreated. Nay, 'twill make him prodigal in the other extreme, and give an hundred sesterces for a night's lodging, as they did of old to Lais of Corinth, or two hundred drachmas for a single night, as Mundus to Paulina,† spend all his fortunes (as too many do in like case) to obtain his suit. For which cause many compare Love to wine, which makes men jovial and merry, frolick and sad, whine, sing, dance, and what not.

But above all the other Symptoms of Lovers, this is not lightly to be over-passed, that likely of what condition soever, if once they be in love, they turn to their ability, Rhymers, Ballet-makers, and Poets. For, as Plutarch saith, they will be Witnesses and Trumpeters of their Paramours' good parts, bedecking them with verses and commendatory songs, as we do statues with gold, that they may be remembered and admired of all. Ancient men will dote in this kind sometimes as well as the rest; the heat of love will thaw their frozen affections, dissolve the ice of age, and so far enable them, though they be sixty years of age above the girdle, to be scarce thirty beneath. Jovianus Pontanus makes an old fool rhyme, and turn Poetaster to please his Mistress.

* Trenchmore, a boisterous country dance.
† See page 718.

Sweet Marian, do not mine age disdain,
For thou canst make an old man young again.

They will be still singing amorous songs and ditties (if young especially) and cannot abstain, though it be when they go to, or should be
at Church. We have a pretty story to this purpose in Westmonasteri-·
ensis, an old Writer of ours (if you will believe it). In the year 1012, at
Colewiz, in Saxony, on Christmas Eve, a company of young men and
maids, whilst the Priest was at Mass in the Church, were singing catches
and love-songs in the Church-yard; he sent to them to make less noise,
but they sung on still; and if you will, you shall have the very song
itself:

A fellow rid by the greenwood side,
And fair Meswinde was his bride,
Why stand we so, and do not go?

This they sung, he chaft, till at length, impatient as he was, he prayed
to S. Magnus, Patron of the Church, they might all there sing and dance
till that time twelvemonth, and so they did, without meat and drink,
wearisomeness or giving over, till at year's end they ceased singing, and
were absolved by Herebertus, Archbishop of Cologne. They will in all
places be doing thus, young folks especially, reading love stories, talking of this or that young man, such a fair maid, singing, telling or hearing lascivious tales, scurrile tunes, such objects are their sole delight,
their continual meditation; and as Guastavinius adds, of an abundance
of seed comes much thought of love, continual memories, &c., an earnest
longing comes hence, itching body, itching mind, amorous conceits,
tickling thoughts, sweet and pleasant hopes: hence it is, they can think,
discourse willingly, or speak almost of no other subject. 'Tis their only
desire, if it may be done by Art, to see their husband's picture in a
glass, they'll give any thing to know when they shall be married, how
many husbands they shall have, by Cromnysmantia, a kind of Divination with Onions laid on the Altar on Christmas Eve, or by fasting on
S. Agnes' Eve or Night, to know who shall be their first husband; or
by Alphitomantia, by beans in a Cake, &c., to burn the same. This Love
is the cause of all good conceits, neatness, exornations, plays, elegancies,
delights, pleasant expressions, sweet motions, and gestures, joys, comforts, exultancies, and all the sweetness of our life, what would life be
worth, or what pleasure without Venus? Let me live no longer than I
may love, saith a mad merry fellow in Mimnermus. This Love is that
salt that seasoneth our harsh and dull labours, and gives a pleasant
relish to our other unsavoury proceedings; when love goes, the shadows

gather, old age with its stiff joints, disease, &c. All our feasts almost, masques, mummings, banquets merry meetings, weddings, pleasing songs, fine tunes, Poems, Love-stories, Plays, Comedies, Atellanes [or Farces], Jigs, Fescennines, [or Facetious Verses], Elegies, Odes, &c., proceed hence. Danaus the son of Belus, at his daughter's wedding at Argos, instituted the first plays (some say) that ever were heard of, Symbols, Emblems, Impresses, Devices, if we shall believe Jovius, Contiles, Paradine, Camillus de Camillis, may be ascribed to it: most of our Arts and Sciences; painting amongst the rest, was first invented, saith Patritius, for love's sake. For when the daughter of Deburiades the Sicyonian, was to take leave of her Sweetheart, now going to wars, to comfort herself in his absence, she took his picture with coal upon a wall, as the candle gave the shadow, which her Father admiring perfected afterwards, and it was the first picture by report that ever was made. And long after, Sicyon for painting, carving, statuary, musick, and Philosophy, was preferred before all the Cities in Greece. Apollo was the first inventor of Physic, Divination, Oracles; Minerva found out weaving, Vulcan curious Ironwork, Mercury letters, but who prompted all this into their heads? Love. Never had they found out such things, had they not loved; they loved such things, or some party, for whose sake they were undertaken at first. 'Tis true, Vulcan made a most admirable Brooch or neck-lace, which long after Axion and Temenus, Phegeus' sons, for the singular worth of it, consecrated to Apollo at Delphi, but Pharyllus the Tyrant stole it away, and presented it to Aristo's wife, on whom he miserably doted (Parthenius tells the story out of Phylarchus); but why did Vulcan make this excellent ouch? to give Hermione, Cadmus' wife, whom he dearly loved. All our Tilts and Tournaments, Orders of the Garter, Golden Fleece, &c., owe their beginnings to love, and many of our histories. By this means, saith Jovius, they would express their loving minds to their Mistress, and to the beholders. 'Tis the sole object almost of Poetry, all our invention tends to it, all our songs, and therefore Hesiod makes the Muses and Graces still follow Cupid, and, as Plutarch holds, Menander and the rest of the Poets were Love's Priests, whatever those old Anacreons, all our Greek and Latin Epigrammatists, Love-writers, Antony Diogenes the most ancient, whose Epitome we find in Photius' Bibliotheca, Longus Sophista, Eustathius, Achilles Tatius, Aristænetus, Heliodorus, Plato, Plutarch, Lucian, Parthenius, Theodorus Prodromus, Ovid, Catullus, Tibullus, &c., our new Ariostos, Boiardos, Authors of Arcadia, Urania, Fairy Queen, &c., Marullus, Lotichius, Angerianus, Stroza,

Secundus, Capellanus, &c., with the rest of those facete modern Poets, have written in this kind, are but as so many Symptoms of Love. Their whole books are a Synopsis, or Breviary of Love, the Portuous [or Portesse, or Breviary] of Love, Legends of Lovers' lives and deaths, and of their memorable adventures, nay more, as Nevisanus the Lawyer holds, there never was any excellent Poet, that invented good fables, or made laudable verses, which was not in love himself; had he not taken a quill from Cupid's wings, he could never have written so amorously as he did.

> *Wanton Propertius and witty Gallus,*
> *Subtile Tibullus, and learned Catullus,*
> *It was Cynthia, Lesbia, Lycoris,*
> *That made you poets all; and if Alexis,*
> *Or Corinna chance my paramour to be,*
> *Virgil and Ovid shall not despise me.* (MARTIAL)
> *Not Thracian Orpheus shall vanquish me in song,*
> *Nor Linus.* (VIRGIL)

Petrarch's Laura made him so famous, Astrophel's Stella, and Jovianus Pontanus' Mistress was the cause of his Roses, Violets, Lilies, profligacies, flatteries, jests, elegance, Spikenard, Spring, Garland, Frankincense, Mars, Pallas, Venus, Grace, Saffron, Laurel, Perfume, Costum [the herb Zedoary], Tears, Myrrh, the Muses, and the rest of his Poems. Why are Italians at this day generally so good Poets and Painters? Because every man of any fashion amongst them hath his Mistress. The very rusticks and hog-rubbers, Menalcas and Corydon, stinking of horse-dirt, those fulsome knaves, if once they taste of this Love-liquor, are inspired in an instant. Instead of those accurate Emblems, curious Impresses, gaudy Masques, Tilts, Tournaments, &c., they have their Wakes, Whitsun-ales, Shepherds'-feasts, meetings on holy-days, country-dances, roundelays, writing their names on trees, true-lovers'-knots, pretty gifts.

> *With tokens, hearts divided, and half rings,*
> *Shepherds are in their Loves as coy as Kings.*

Choosing Lords, Ladies, Kings, Queens, and Valentines, &c., they go by couples,

> *Corydon's Phillis, Nysa and Mopsus,*
> *With dainty Dousibel and Sir Tophus.*

Instead of Odes, Epigrams, and Elegies, &c., they have their Ballads, Country-tunes, *O the Broom, the bonny bonny Broom,* Ditties and Songs, *Bess a Bell she doth excel,* — they must write likewise and indite all in rhyme.

Thou honeysuckle of the hawthorn hedge,
Vouchsafe in Cupid's cup my heart to pledge;
My heart's dear blood, sweet Cis, is thy carouse,
Worth all the ale in Gammer Gubbin's house.
I say no more, affairs call me away,
My father's horse for provender doth stay.
Be thou the Lady Cressetlight to me,
Sir Trolly Lolly will I prove to thee.
Written in haste, farewell, my Cowslip sweet,
Pray let's a Sunday at the alehouse meet.   (ROWLANDS)

Your most grim Stoicks and severe Philosophers will melt away with this passion, and if Athenæus bely them not, Aristippus, Apollodorus, Antiphanes, &c., have made love-songs and Commentaries of their Mistress' praises, Orators wrote Epistles, Princes given Titles, Honours, what not? Xerxes gave to Themistocles Lampsacus to find him wine, Magnesia for bread, and Myus for the rest of his diet. The Persian Kings allotted whole Cities to like use, one whole City served to dress her hair, another her neck, a third her hood. Ahasuerus would have given Esther half his Empire, and Herod bid Herodias ask what she would, she should have it. Caligula gave an 100,000 sesterces to his Courtisan at first word to buy her pins, and yet, when he was solicited by the Senate to bestow something to repair the decayed walls of Rome for the Commonwealth's good, he would give but 6,000 sesterces at most. Dionysius, that Sicilian tyrant, rejected all his privy Councillors, and was so besotted on Myrrha, his favourite and Mistress, that he would bestow no office, or in the most weightiest business of the Kingdom do ought, without her especial advice, prefer, depose, send, entertain no man, though worthy and well-deserving, but by her consent; and he again whom she commended, howsoever unfit, unworthy, was as highly approved. Kings and Emperors, instead of Poems, build Cities; Adrian built Antinoe in Egypt, besides Constellations, Temples, Altars, Statues, Images, &c., in the honour of his Antinous. Alexander bestowed infinite sums, to set out his Hephæstion to all eternity. Socrates professeth himself Love's servant, ignorant in all arts and sciences, a Doctor alone in love-matters, saith Maximus Tyrius, his sectator [or follower], a teacher of these matters, &c., and this he spake openly, at home and abroad, at publick feasts, in the Academy, in the Piraeus, the Lyceum, under the plane trees, &c., the very blood-hound of beauty, as he is styled by others. But I conclude there is no end of Love's Symptoms, 'tis a bottomless pit. Love is subject to no dimensions; not to be surveyed by any art or engine: and besides, I am of Hædus' mind, no man can discourse of love-matters, or judge of them aright, that hath not made trial in his own person, or, as Æneas Sylvius adds, hath not a little doted, been mad or love-sick himself. I confess I am but a novice, a Contemplator only,

I'm not in love, nor know what love may be.

I have a tincture; for why should I lie, dissemble or excuse it, yet I'm a man, &c. not altogether inexpert in this subject, I am not a teacher of love, and what I say is merely reading, the follies of others, by mine own observation, and others' relation.

MEMBER 4

Prognosticks of Love-Melancholy

WHAT Fires, Torments, Cares, Jealousies, Suspicions, Fears, Griefs, Anxieties, accompany such as are in love, I have sufficiently said: the next question is, what will be the event of such miseries, what they fore-tell. Some are of opinion that this love cannot be cured, there flowers no balm to sain them, it accompanies them to the last.

The same love slays alike the sheep and the shepherd,   (VIRGIL)

and is so continuate, that by no persuasion almost it may be relieved. Bid me not love, said Euryalus, bid the Mountains come down into the plains, bid the Rivers run back to their fountains; I can as soon leave to love, as the Sun leave his course.

First seas shall want their fish, the mountains shade,
Woods singing birds, the wind's murmur shall fade,
Than my fair Amaryllis' love allay'd.   (BUCHANAN)

Bid me not love, bid a deaf man hear, a blind man see, a dumb speak, lame run, counsel can do no good, a sick man cannot relish, no Physick can ease me.

Those arts help not their master which help all,

as Apollo confessed, and Jupiter himself could not be cured.

Physick can soon cure every disease,

Excepting love, that can it not appease.   (PROPERTIUS)

But whether love may be cured or no, and by what means, shall be explained in his place; in the mean time, if it take his course, and be not otherwise eased or amended, it breaks out often into outrageous and prodigious events. As Tatius observes, Love and Bacchus are so violent Gods, so furiously rage in our minds, that they make us forget all honesty, shame, and common civility. For such men ordinarily as are throughly possessed with this humour, become senseless and mad, for it is insane love as the Poet calls it, beside themselves, and as I have proved, no better than beasts, irrational, stupid, headstrong, void of fear of God or men, they frequently forswear themselves, spend, steal, commit incests, rapes, adulteries, murders, depopulate Towns, Cities, Countries, to satisfy their lust.

> *A Devil 'tis, and 'mischief such doth work,*
> *As never yet did Pagan, Jew, or Turk.* (R. T.)

The wars of Troy may be a sufficient witness; and as Appian saith of Antony and Cleopatra, their Love brought themselves and all Egypt into extreme and miserable calamities, the end of her is as bitter as worm-wood, and as sharp as a two-edged sword. *Her feet go down to death, her steps lead on to hell. She is more bitter than death, and the sinner shall be taken by her.* He that runs head-long from the top of a rock, is not in so bad a case, as he that falls into the gulf of love. For hence, saith Platina, comes Repentance, Dotage, they lose themselves, their wits, and make shipwrack of their fortunes altogether: madness, to make away themselves and others, violent death. Saith Gordonius, the prognostication is, they will either run mad or die. For if this passion continue, saith Ælian Montaltus, it makes the blood hot, thick, and black; and if the inflammation get into the brain, with continual meditation and waking, it so dries it up, that madness follows, or else they make away themselves.

O Corydon, Corydon, what madness hath seized upon you? (VIRGIL) Now, as Arnoldus adds, it will speedily work these effects, if it be not presently helped; they will pine away, run mad, and die upon a sudden; saith Valescus, quickly mad, if good order be not taken.

> *Oh heavy yoke of love, which whoso bears,*
> *Is quite undone, and that at unawares.* (CALCAGNINUS)

So she confessed of herself in the Poet,

> *I shall be mad before it be perceived,*
> *A hair-breadth off scarce am I, now distracted.* (LUCIAN)

As mad as Orlando for his Angelica, or Hercules for his Hylas,

> *He went he car'd not whither, mad he was,*
> *The cruel God so tortur'd him, alas!* (THEOCRITUS)

At the sight of Hero I cannot tell how many ran mad,

> *And whilst he doth conceal his grief,*
> *Madness comes on him like a thief.* (MUSÆUS)

Go to Bedlam for examples. It is so well known in every village, how many have either died for love, or voluntarily made away themselves, that I need not much labour to prove it; Death is the common Catastrophe to such persons.

> *Would I were dead! for nought, God knows,*
> *But death can rid me of these woes.*   (ANACREON)

As soon as Euryalus departed from Siena, Lucretia, his Paramour, never looked up, no jests could exhilarate her sad mind, no joys comfort her wounded and distressed soul, but a little after she fell sick and died. But this is a gentle end, a natural death, such persons commonly make away themselves:

> *Gladly the impatient spirit*
> *Is effused upon the vacant air.*   (PRODROMUS)

So did Dido:

> *" O let me die," she said; " 'tis pleasant thus*
> *To journey to the shadows."*

Pyramus and Thisbe, Medea, Coresus and Callirhoe, Theagenes the Philosopher, and many Myriads besides, and so will ever do,

> *For this one dead I also have a hand that's brave,*
> *I too have love: twill gird me for the grave.*   (OVID)
> *Who ever heard a story of more woe,*
> *Than that of Juliet and her Romeo?*   (SHAKESPEARE)

Read Parthenius on Romances, and Plutarch's Love-stories, all tending almost to this purpose. Valleriola hath a lamentable narration of a Merchant his patient, that raving through impatience of love, had he not been watched, would every while have offered violence to himself. Amatus Lusitanus hath such another story, and Felix Plater a third of a young Gentleman that studied Physick, and for the love of a Doctor's daughter, having no hope to compass his desire, poisoned himself. In the year 1615, a Barber in Frankfort, because his wench was betrothed to another, cut his own throat. At Neuburg the same year a young man, because he could not get her parents' consent, killed his sweetheart, and afterwards himself, desiring this of the Magistrate, as he gave up the Ghost, that they might be buried in one grave, which Gismunda besought of Tancredus her Father, that she might be in like sort buried with Guiscardus her Lover, that so their bodies might lie together in the grave, as their souls wander about in the Elysian fields,

> *Whom relentless love consumed with wasting pain,*   (VIRGIL)

in a myrtle grove they dwell.

> *Even in death, the pang doth never leave them*   (VIRGIL)

You have not yet heard the worst, they do not offer violence to themselves in this rage of lust, but unto others, their nearest and dearest friends. Catiline killed his only Son, for the love of Aurelia Orestilla, because she would not marry him while his son yet lived. Laodice, the sister of Mithridates, poisoned her husband, to give content to a base fellow whom she loved. Alexander to please Thais, a Concubine of his, set Persepolis on fire. Nereus' wife, a widow and Lady of Athens, for the love of a Venetian Gentleman, betrayed the City; and he for her sake murthered his wife, the daughter of a Noble man in Venice. Constantine Despota made away Catherine his wife, turned his son Michael and his other children out of doors, for the love of a base Scrivener's daughter in Thessalonica, with whose beauty he was enamoured. Leucophrye betrayed the City where she dwelt, for her sweetheart's sake, that was in the enemy's Camp. Pithidice, the Governor's daughter of Methinia, for the love of Achilles, betrayed the whole Island to him, her Father's enemy. Diognetus did as much, in the city where he dwelt, for the love of Polycrite, Medea for the love of Jason; she taught him how to tame the fire-breathing, brass-feeted Bulls, and kill the mighty Dragon that kept the golden fleece; and tore her little brother Absyrtus in pieces, that her Father Aëetes might have something to detain him, while she ran away with her beloved Jason, &c. Such Acts and Scenes hath this Tragicomedy of love.

MEMBER 5

SUBSECTION 1 — *Cure of Love-Melancholy, by Labour, Diet, Physick, Fasting, &c.*

ALTHOUGH it be controverted by some, whether Love-Melancholy may be cured, because it is so irresistible and violent a passion; for, as you know,

It is an easy passage down to hell,
But to come back, once there, you cannot well. (VIRGIL)

Yet without question, if it be taken in time, it may be helped, and by many good remedies amended. Avicenna sets down seven compendious ways how this malady may be eased, altered and expelled. Savanarola, 9 principal observations, Jason Pratensis prescribes eight rules besides Physick, how this passion may be tamed, Laurentius 2 main precepts, Arnoldus, Valleriola, Montaltus, Hildesheim, Langius, and others inform us otherwise, and yet all tending to the same purpose. The sum of which I will briefly epitomize (for I light my Candle from their Torches) and enlarge again upon occasion, as shall seem best to me, and that after mine own method. The first rule to be observed in this stub-born and unbridled passion, is exercise and diet. It is an old and well known sentence, without Ceres and Bacchus, Venus grows cold. As an idle sedentary life, liberal feeding, are great causes of it, so the opposite, labour, slender and sparing diet, with continual business, are the best and most ordinary means to prevent it.

> *Take idleness away, and put to flight*
> *Are Cupid's arts, his torches give no light.*   (OVID)

Minerva, Diana, Vesta, and the nine Muses were not enamoured at all, because they never were idle.

> *In vain are all your flatteries,*
> *In vain are all your knaveries,*
> *Delights, deceits, procacities,*
> *Sighs, kisses, and conspiracies,*
> *And whate'er is done by Art,*
> *To bewitch a Lover's heart.*   (BUCHANAN)

'Tis in vain to set upon those that are busy. 'Tis Savanarola's third rule, to be occupied with many and large affairs, and Avicenna's precept, —

> *Love yields to business; be at work, you're safe.*   (OVID)

To be busy still, and as Guianerius enjoins, about matters of great moment, if it may be. Magninus adds, never to be idle, but at the hours of sleep.

> *For if thou dost not ply thy book,*
> *By candle-light to study bent,*
> *Employ'd about some honest thing,*
> *Envy or Love shall thee torment.*   (HORACE)

No better Physick than to be always occupied, seriously intent.

> *Why dost thou ask, poor folks are often free*
> *And dainty places still molested be?*   (SENECA)

Because poor people fare coarsely, work hard, go wool-ward and bare.

> *Poverty hath not means to feed love fat.*   (OVID)

Guianerius therefore prescribes his patient to go with hair-cloth next his skin, to go bare-footed, and bare-legged in cold weather, to whip himself now and then, as Monks do, but above all, to fast. Not with sweet wine, mutton and pottage, as many of those Tenterbellies [or Gluttons] do, howsoever they put on Lenten faces, and whatsoever they pretend, but from all manner of meat. Fasting is an all-sufficient remedy of itself, for, as Jason Pratensis holds, the bodies of such persons that feed liberally, and live at ease, are full of bad spirits and Devils, devilish thoughts; no better Physick for such parties, than to fast. Hildesheim, to this of hunger, adds often baths, much exercise and sweat, but hunger and fasting he prescribes before the rest. And 'tis indeed our Saviour's Oracle, " This kind of devil is not cast out but by fasting and prayer," which makes the Fathers so immoderate in commendation of fasting. As Hunger, saith Ambrose, is a friend of Virginity, so is it an enemy to lasciviousness, but fulness overthrows chastity, and fostereth all manner of provocations. If thine horse be too lusty, Hierome adviseth thee to take away some of his provender; by this means those Pauls, Hilaries, Antonies, and famous Anchorites, subdued the lust of the flesh; by this means Hilarion made his ass, as he called his own body, leave kicking, (so Hierome relates of him in his life) when the Devil tempted him to any such foul offence. By this means those Indian Brachmanes kept themselves continent, they lay upon the ground covered with skins, as the Redshanks [or Highlanders] do on Hadder [or Heather], and dieted themselves sparingly on one dish, which Guianerius would have all young men put in practice; and if that will not serve, Gordonius would have them soundly whipped, or, to cool their courage, kept in prison, and there be fed with bread and water, till they acknowledge their error, and become of another mind. If imprisonment and hunger will not take them down, according to the direction of that Theban Crates, time must wear it out; if time will not, the last refuge is an halter. But this, you will say, is comically spoken. Howsoever, Fasting by all means must be still used; and as they must refrain from such meats formerly mentioned, which cause venery, or provoke lust, so they must use an opposite diet. Wine must be altogether avoided of the younger sort. So Plato prescribes, and would have the Magistrates themselves abstain from it, for example's sake, highly commending the Carthaginians for their temperance in this kind. And 'twas a good edict, a commendable thing, so that it were not done for some sinister respect, as those old Egyptians abstained from Wine, because some fabulous Poets had given out, Wine sprang first from the blood of the Giants, or out of superstition, as our modern Turks, but for temperance, it being a poison to the mind and an encourager of faults, a plague itself if immoderately taken. Women of old for that cause, in hot Countries, were forbid the use of it; and as severely punished for drinking of wine, as for adultery, and young folks, as Leonicus hath recorded, out of Athenæus and others; and is still practised in Italy and some other Countries of Europe, and Asia, as Claudius Minos hath well illustrated in his Comment on the 23rd Emblem of Alciati. So choice is to be made of other diet.

Eringoes are not good for to be taken,
And all lascivious meats must be forsaken.   (OVID)

Those opposite meats which ought to be used are Cowcumbers, Melons, Purselan, Water-Lilies, Rue, Woodbine, Ammi, Lettice, which Lemnius so much commends, and Mizaldus, to this purpose; Vitex before the rest, which, saith Magninus, hath a wonderful virtue in it. Those Athenian women, in their solemn feasts called Thesmophoria, were to abstain nine days from the company of men, during which time, saith Ælian, they laid a certain herb named Hanea [agnos, agnus castus, or chaste-lamb], in their beds, which assuaged those ardent flames of love, and freed them from the torments of that violent passion. See more in Porta, Matthiolus, Crescentius, &c., and what every Herbalist almost and Physician hath written, in their chapters on Satyriasis and Priapism, Rhasis amongst the rest. In some cases again, if they be much dejected and brought low in body, and now ready to despair through anguish, grief, and too sensible a feeling of their misery, a cup of wine and full diet is not amiss, and, as Valescus adviseth, together with other worthy means, the frequent use of Venus, which Langius approves out of Rhasis (he urgeth to frequent indulgence), and Guianerius seconds it as a very profitable remedy.

When of Venus thou art fain,
And a serving-maid stands by,
Wouldst thou rather keep thy pain
Than take what's nearest? No, not I!   (HORACE)

Jason Pratensis subscribes to this counsel of the Poet, such voiding may be relied on to heal at once or at least mitigate the sickness. As it did the raging lust of Ahasuerus, who in the impatient assuaging of his passions deflowered new virgins each night. And to be drunk too by fits; but this is mad Physick, if it be at all to be permitted. If not, yet some pleasure is to be allowed, as that which Vives speaks of: A lover that hath as it were lost himself through impotency, impatience, must be called home as a traveller by musick, feasting, good wine, if need be, to drunkenness itself, which many so much commend for the easing of the mind, all kinds of sports and merriments, to see fair pictures, hangings, buildings, pleasant fields, Orchards, Gardens, Groves, Ponds, Pools, Rivers, fishing, fowling, hawking, hunting, to hear merry tales, and pleasant discourse, reading, to use exercise till he sweat, that new spirits may succeed, or by some vehement affection or contrary passion, to be diverted, till he be fully weaned from anger, suspicion, cares, fears, &c., and habituated into another course. Mayest thou (as Sempronius adviseth Callisto his love-sick Master) still have a pleasant companion to sing and tell merry tales, songs, and facete histories, sweet discourse, &c. And as the melody of musick, merriment, singing, dancing, doth augment the passion of some Lovers, as Avicenna notes, so it expelleth it in others, and doth very much good. These things must be warily applied, as the parties' Symptoms vary, and they shall stand variously affected.

If there be any need of Physick, that the humours be altered, or any new matter aggregated, they must be cured as melancholy men. Carolus à Lorme, amongst other questions discussed for his degree at Montpelier in France, hath this, Whether amantes (lovers) and amentes (mad men) be cured by the same remedies? he affirms it; for love extended is mere madness. Such Physick then as is prescribed, is either inward or outward, as hath been formerly handled in the precedent partition in the cure of Melancholy. Consult with Valleriola, Lodovicus Mercatus, Daniel Sennertus, Jacobus Ferrandus, the Frenchman, in his Tract on Erotick Love, Forestus, Jason Pratensis and others for peculiar receipts. Amatus Lusitanus cured a young Jew that was almost mad for love, with the syrup of Hellebore, and such other evacuations and purges, which are usually prescribed to black choler; Avicenna confirms as much, if need require, and blood-letting above the rest, which makes amantes no more amentes, lovers come to themselves, and keep in their right mind. 'Tis the same which the Salernitan school, Jason Pratensis, Hildesheim, &c., prescribe, blood-letting to be used as a principal remedy. Those old Scythians had a trick to cure all appetite of burning lust, by letting themselves blood under the ears, and to make both men and women barren, as Sabellicus in his Enneads relates of them. Which Salmuth, out of Hippocrates and Benzo, say still is in use amongst the Indians, a reason of which Langius gives.

Here they make medicines to allay lust, such as putting Camphor on the parts, and carrying it in the breeches (one saith) keeps the pintle flaccid. A noble virgin being sick with this affliction, a Physician prescribed for her, among other things, that she wear on her back for twenty days a thin sheet of lead pierced with many holes; and for the drying up of seed he ordered that she be very sparing of victual, and chew frequently a preparation of coriander, lettuce-seed and vinegar, and so freed her of the malady. Further, they hinder or prevent coitus by a willow-leaf rubbed and drunk, and if frequently used, they cease from it wholly. Topaz is likewise recommended, worn in a ring; the right stone of a wolf, brayed; and oil or water of roses will cause weari ness of venery, writes Alexander Benedictus; buttermilk, Canabis seed, and Camphor are also commended. Carrying a Verbena herb extinguisheth lust, and pulverized frog, beheaded and dried up. To extinguish coitus, anoint the genitals and belly and chest with water in which opium Thebaicum has been dissolved; Camphor is in the highest degree inimical to lust, and dried coriander diminishes coitus and hinders erection; mustard drink does the same. Give verbena in a potion, and the pintle will not lift for six days; dried mint with vinegar in the uterus, the genitals smeared with juice of Henbane or Hemlock, quiets the appetite for coitus, &c. Take seeds of lettuce, purslain, coriander, each, 1 drachm; dried mint, one-half drachm; white sugar, 4 ounces; let all be pulverized very fine, then mixt with water of Nenuphar, and made into lozenges; take one in the morning on arising. Many similar receipts are to be found in Hildesheim, Mizaldus, Porta, and the others.

SUBSECTION 2 — *Withstand the beginnings, avoid occasions, change his place: fair and foul means, contrary passions, with witty inventions: to bring in another, and discommend the former*

OTHER good rules and precepts are enjoined by our Physicians, which, if not alone, yet certainly conjoined may do much; the first of which is, to withstand the beginnings; he that will but resist at first, may easily be a conqueror at the last. Balthasar Castilio urgeth this prescript above the rest, when he shall chance (saith he) to light upon a woman that hath good behaviour joined with her excellent person, and shall perceive his eyes with a kind of greediness to pull unto them this image of beauty, and carry it to the heart: shall observe himself to be somewhat incensed with this influence, which moveth within: when he shall discern those subtile spirits sparkling in her eyes to administer more fuel to the fire, he must wisely withstand the beginnings, rouse up reason, stupefied almost, fortify his heart by all means, and shut up all those passages, by which it may have entrance. — 'Tis a precept which all concur upon.

> *Thy quick disease, whilst it is fresh to-day,*
> *By all means crush, thy feet at first step stay.* (OVID)

Which cannot speedier be done, than if he confess his grief and passion to some judicious friend (the more he conceals, the greater is his pain) that by his good advice may happily ease him on a sudden; and withal to avoid occasions, or any circumstance that may aggravate his disease, to remove the object by all means; for who can stand by a fire and not burn?

Shoot back, ye volts, and cast her out of doors,
That has drunk up the blood of me her lover. (PLAUTUS)

'Tis good therefore to keep quite out of her company, which Hierome so much labours to Paula, to Nepotian; Chrysostom so much inculcates, Cyprian, and many other Fathers of the Church, Siracides in his ninth chapter, Jason Pratensis, Savanarola, Arnoldus, Valleriola, &c., and every Physician that treats of this subject. Not only to avoid, as Gregory Tholosanus exhorts, kissing, dalliance, all speeches, tokens, love-letters, and the like, or as Castilio, to converse with them, hear them speak, or sing (thou hadst better hear, saith Cyprian, a serpent hiss), those amiable smiles, admirable graces, and sweet gestures, which their presence affords,

Let them not bend their heads to bite their wonted little kisses,
Nor press with gentle touches the nipples of their misses, (LIPSIUS)

but all talk, name, mention, or cogitation of them, and of any other women, persons, circumstance, amorous book or tale, that may administer any occasion of remembrance. Prosper adviseth young men not to read the Canticles, and some parts of Genesis at other times; but for such as are enamoured, they forbid, as before, the name mentioned, &c., especially all sight, they must not so much as come near, or look upon them.

'Tis best to shun the sight and food of love,
Turn the mind wholly from the thought thereof. (LUCRETIUS)

Gaze not on a Maid, saith Siracides, turn away thine eyes from a beautiful woman; " avert thine eyes," saith David, or if thou dost see them, as Ficinus adviseth, let not thine eye be intent on lust, do not intend [or attend to] her more than the rest: for, as Propertius holds, 'tis by this food that love grows fat, Love as a snow-ball inlargeth itself by sight: but as Hierome to Nepotian, either see all alike, or let all alone; make a league with thine eyes, as Job did, and that is the safest course, let all alone, see none of them. Nothing sooner revives, or waxeth sore again, as Petrarch holds, than Love doth by sight. As Pomp renews ambition; the sight of gold, covetousness, a beauteous object sets on fire this burning lust. The sight of drink makes one dry, and the sight of meat increaseth appetite. 'Tis dangerous therefore to see. A young Gentleman in merriment, would needs put on his Mistress' clothes, and walk abroad alone, which some of her suitors espying, stole him away for her that he represented. So much can sight enforce. Especially if he have been formerly enamoured, the sight of his Mistress strikes him into a new fit, and makes him rave many days after.

> *A sickly man a little thing offends,*
> *As brimstone doth a fire decayed renew,*
> *And make it burn afresh, doth Love's dead flames,*
> *If that the former object it review.*   (OVID)

Or, as the Poet compares it to embers in ashes, which the wind blows, a scald head (as the saying is) is soon broken, dry wood quickly kindles, and when they have been formerly wounded with sight, how can they by seeing but be inflamed? Ismenias acknowledgeth as much of himself, when he had been long absent, and almost forgotten his Mistress, at the first sight of her, as straw in a fire, I burned afresh, and more than ever I did before. Chariclea was as much moved at the sight of her dear Theagenes, after he had been a great stranger. Myrtila in Aristænetus swore she would never love Pamphilus again, and did moderate her passion, so long as he was absent; but the next time he came in presence, she could not contain, she broke her vow, and did profusely embrace him. Hermotinus a young man (in the said Author) is all out as unstaid, he had forgot his Mistress quite, and by his friends was well weaned from her love, but seeing her by chance, he remembered his old flame, he raved amain, she did appear as a blazing-star, or an Angel, to his sight. And it is the common passion of all lovers to be overcome in this sort. For that cause, belike, Alexander discerning this inconvenience and danger that comes by seeing, when he heard Darius' wife so much commended for her beauty, would scarce admit her to come in his sight, foreknowing belike that of Plutarch, how full of danger it is to see a proper woman; and though he was intemperate in other things, yet in this he carried himself bravely. And so when as Araspes, in Xenophon, had so much magnified that divine face of Panthea to Cyrus, by how much she was fairer than ordinary, by so much he was the more unwilling to see her. Scipio, a young man of 23 years of age, and the most beautiful of the Romans, equal in person to that of Grecian Cleinias, or Homer's Nireus, at the siege of a City in Spain, when as a noble and a most fair young Gentlewoman was brought unto him, and he had heard she was betrothed to a Lord, rewarded her, and sent her back to her sweetheart. S. Austin, as Gregory reports of him, would not live in the house with his own sister. Xenocrates lay with Lais of Corinth all night, and would not touch her. Socrates, though all the City of Athens supposed him to dote upon fair Alcibiades, yet when he had an opportunity to lie in the chamber with him all to himself, and was wooed by him besides, as the said Alcibiades publickly confessed, he scornfully rejected him. Petrarch, that had so magnified his Laura in several Poems, when by the Pope's means she was offered unto him, would not accept of her. It is a good happiness to be free from this passion of Love, and great discretion it argues in such a man that he can so contain himself; but when thou art once in love, to moderate thyself (as Heliodorus saith) is a singular point of wisdom.

> *To avoid such nets is no such mastery,*
> *But ta'en, to escape is all the victory.* (LUCRETIUS)

But forasmuch as few men are free, so discreet Lovers, or that can contain themselves, and moderate their passions, to curb their senses, as not to see them, not to look lasciviously, not to confer with them, such is the fury of this head-strong passion of raging lust, and their weakness, as Haedus terms it, such a furious desire nature hath inscribed, such unspeakable delight,

> *The fury of holy Venus*
> *Brings madness among men,*

which neither reason, counsel, poverty, pain, misery, drudgery, the throes of travail, &c., can deter them from; we must use some speedy means to correct and prevent that, and all other inconveniences, which come by conference and the like. The best, readiest, surest way, and which all approve, is, change of scene, to send them several ways, that they may neither hear of, see, nor have opportunity to send to one another again, or live together he alone with her alone, as so many Gilbertines.* Be long away from home, 'tis Savanarola's fourth rule, and Gordonius' precept, send him to travel. 'Tis that which most run upon, as so many hounds with full cry, Poets, Divines, Philosophers, Physicians, all; change country, saith Valesius; as a sick man, he must be cured by change of air, Tully. The best remedy is to get thee gone, Jason Pratensis; change air and soil, Laurentius.

> *Flee the cherished shore.* (VIRGIL)
> *'Tis best to keep away from neighboring haunts.* (OVID)
> *Go then and tread the long and distant ways,*
> *Safety is but in flight.*

Travelling is an Antidote of Love. For this purpose, saith Propertius, my parents sent me to Athens; time and absence wear away pain and grief, as fire goes out for want of fuel.

> *As far as eye can see, so far the soul can love.* (PROPERTIUS)

But so as they tarry out long enough: a whole year [Socrates in] Xenophon prescribes Critobulus: some will hardly be weaned under. All this

---

* Gilbertines, a double order comprising both monks and nuns, founded by St. Gilbert of Sempringham in England in the 12th century.

Heinsius merrily inculcates in an Epistle to his friend Primerius : first fast, then tarry, thirdly change thy place, fourthly think of an halter. If change of place, continuance of time, absence, will not wear it out, with those precedent remedies, it will hardly be removed : but these commonly are of force. Felix Plater had a baker to his patient, almost mad for the love of his maid, and desperate ; by removing her from him, he was in a short space cured. Isæus, a Philosopher of Assyria, was a most dissolute liver in his youth, openly lustful, in love with all he met ; but after he betook himself by his friend's advice to his study, and left women's company, he was so changed, that he cared no more for Plays, nor Feasts, nor Masks, nor Songs, nor Verses, fine clothes, nor no such love-toys ; he became a new man upon a sudden, (saith mine Author) as if he had lost his former eyes. Peter Godefridus, in the last Chapter of his third Book, hath a story out of S. Ambrose, of a young man, that meeting his old love, after long absence, on whom he had extremely doted, would scarce take notice of her ; she wondered at it, that he should so lightly esteem her, called him again, spoke persuasively, and told him who she was, I am So-and-so, she said : but he replied, he was not the same man : tore himself away, as Æneas fled from Dido, not vouchsafing her any farther parley, loathing his folly, and ashamed of that which formerly he had done.

I am not as foolish as I was, Neæra, (BUCHANAN)

O Neæra, put your tricks, and practise hereafter upon some body else, you shall befool me no longer. Petrarch hath such another tale of a young Gallant, that loved a wench with one eye, and for that cause by his parents was sent to travel into far Countries ; after some years he returned, and meeting the maid for whose sake he was sent abroad, asked her how, and by what chance she lost her eye ? No, said she, I have lost none, but you have found yours : signifying thereby, that all Lovers were blind ; as Fabius saith, Lovers cannot judge of beauty, nor scarce of anything else, as they will easily confess, after they return unto themselves, by some discontinuance or better advice, wonder at their own folly, madness, stupidity, blindness, be much abashed, and laugh at Love, and call't an idle thing, condemn themselves, that ever they should be so besotted or misled ; and be heartily glad they have so happily escaped.

If so be (which is seldom) that change of place will not effect this alteration, then other remedies are to be annexed, fair and foul means, as to persuade, promise, threaten, terrify, or to divert by some contrary passion, rumour, tales, news, or some witty invention, to alter his affection; by some greater sorrow to drive out the less, saith Gordonius, as that his house is on fire, his best friends dead, his money stolen, that he is made some great Governor, or hath some honour, office, some inheritance is befallen him, he shall be a Knight, a Baron: or by some false accusation, as they do to such as have the hiccup, to make them forget it. Saint Hierome, in his epistle to Rusticus the Monk, hath an instance of a young man of Greece, that lived in a Monastery in Egypt, that by no labour, no continence, no persuasion, could be diverted, but at last by this trick he was delivered. The Abbot sets one of his Convent to quarrel with him, and with some scandalous reproach or other to defame him before company, and then to come and complain first, the witnesses were likewise suborned for the Plaintiff. The young man wept, and when all were against him, the Abbot cunningly took his part, lest he should be overcome with immoderate grief: but what need many words? By this invention he was cured, and alienated from his pristine love-thoughts. — Injuries, slanders, contempts, disgraces,

————— *the affront of slighted beauty,*   (VIRGIL)

are very forcible means to withdraw men's affections; as Lucian saith, Lovers reviled or neglected, contemned or misused, turn love to hate. Comest thou back? Not for all thine entreaties, I'll never love thee more. What's she to me? So Zephyrus hated Hyacinthus because he scorned him and preferred his corrival Apollo; he will not come again though he be invited. Tell him but how he was scoffed at behind his back ('tis the counsel of Avicenna), that his Love is false, and entertains another, rejects him, cares not for him, or that she is a fool, a nasty quean, a slut, a vixen, a scold, a Devil; or which Italians commonly do, that he or she hath some loathsome filthy disease, gout, stone, strangury, falling-sickness, and they are hereditary, not to be avoided, he is subject to a Consumption, hath the Pox, that he hath three or four incurable tetters, issues: that she is bald, her breath stinks, she is mad by inheritance, and so are all the kindred, an hare-brain, with many other secret infirmities, which I will not so much as name, belonging to women. That he is an Hermaphrodite, an Eunuch, imperfect, impotent, a spendthrift, a gamester, a fool, a gull, a beggar, a whoremaster, far in debt, and not able to maintain her, a common drunkard, his mother was a witch, his father hang'd, that he hath a Wolf [or running sore] in his bosom, a sore leg, he is a Leper, hath some incurable disease, that he will surely beat her, he cannot hold his water, that he cries out or walks in the night, will stab his bed-fellow, tell all his secrets in his sleep, and that no body dare lie with him, his house is haunted with spirits, with such fearful and trag-

ical things, able to avert and terrify any man or woman living. Gordonius adviseth in this manner; and having brought secretly a menstruous rag, if these things will not persuade, draw it forth of a sudden,
flourish it before the face, crying out, Such is thy beloved; and if this
will not cure him, he is not a man, but a devil incarnate. Avicenna saith
the same: Let some old woman tell of filthy things concerning women.
So Arculanus, Rhasis, &c.

Withal, as they do discommend the old, for the better affecting a more
speedy alteration, they must commend another Paramour, set him or her
to be wooed, or woo some other that shall be fairer, of better note, better
fortune, birth, parentage, much to be preferred,

> *Thou'lt find another Alexis, if he disdain thee.*   (VIRGIL)

by this means, which Jason Pratensis wisheth, to turn the stream of
affection another way,

> *A new love thrusteth out the old,*   (OVID)

or, as Valesius adviseth, by subdividing to diminish it, as a great River
cut into many channels, runs low at last.

> *Take, I advise, two mistresses at once.*   (OVID)

If you suspect to be taken, be sure, saith the Poet, to have two Mistresses at once, or go from one to another. As he that goes from a good fire
in cold weather, is loath to depart from it, though in the next room there
be a better, which will refresh him as much; there's as much difference
of shes as fires; or bring him to some publick shews, plays, meetings,
where he may see variety, and he shall likely loathe his first choice:
carry him but to the next Town, yea, peradventure to the next house,
and as Paris lost Ænone's love by seeing Helena, and Cressida forsook
Troilus by conversing with Diomede, he will dislike his former Mistress,
and leave her quite behind him, as Theseus left Ariadne fast asleep in
the Island of Dia, to seek her fortune, that was erst his loving Mistress.
As he said [in Petronius] Doris is but a dowdy to this. As he that looks
himself in a glass, forgets his Physiognomy forthwith, this flattering
glass of love will be diminished by remove; after a little absence, it will
be remitted, the next fair object will likely alter it. A young man in
Lucian was pitifully in love, he came to the Theatre by chance, and by
seeing other fair objects there, was fully recovered, and went merrily
home, as if he had taken a dram of oblivion. A Mouse (saith an Apolo-
ger) was brought up in a chest, there fed with fragments of bread and
cheese, thought there could be no better meat, till coming forth at last,
and feeding liberally of other variety of viands, loathed his former life:
moralize this fable by thyself. Plato, in his seventh book of his Republic,
hath a pretty fiction of a City under ground, to which by little holes

some small store of light came; the inhabitants thought there could not be a better place, and at their first coming abroad they might not endure the light; but, after they were accustomed a little to it, they deplored their fellows' misery that lived under ground. A silly Lover is in like state, none so fair as his Mistress at first, he cares for none but her; yet after a while, when he hath compared her with others, he abhors her name, sight, and memory. 'Tis generally true; for as he observes, one fire drives out another, and such is women's weakness, that they love commonly him that is present. And so do many men (as he confesseth), he loved Amy till he saw Flora, and when he saw Cynthia, forgat them both: but fair Phyllis was incomparably beyond them all, Chloris surpassed her, and yet when he espied Amaryllis, she was his sole Mistress; O divine Amaryllis! &c. how lovely, how tall, how comely, she was (saith Polemius) till he saw another, and then she was the sole subject of his thoughts. In conclusion, her he loves best he saw last. Triton the Sea-God first loved Leucothoë, till he came in presence of Milæne, she was the Commandress of his heart, till he saw Galatea; but (as she complains) he loved another eftsoons, another, and another. 'Tis a thing which by Hierom's report, hath been usually practised. Heathen Philosophers drive out one love with another, as they do a peg, or pin with a pin. Which those seven Persian Princes did to Ahasuerus, that they might requite the desire of Queen Vashti with the love of others. Pausanias, in Eliacis, saith that therefore one Cupid was painted to contend with another, and to take the Garland from him, because one love drives out another.

One passion diminisheth another's power,   (OVID)

and Tully, disputing with C. Cotta, makes mention of three several Cupids, all differing in office. Felix Plater in the first book of his observations, boasts how he cured a widower in Basil, a Patient of his, by this stratagem alone, that doted upon a poor servant his maid, when friends, children, no persuasion could serve to alienate his mind: they motioned him to another honest man's daughter in the Town, whom he loved, and lived with, long after, abhorring the very name and sight of the first. After the death of Lucretia, Euryalus would admit of no comfort, till the Emperor Sigismund married him to a noble Lady of his Court, and so in short space he was freed.

SUBSECTION 3 — *By counsel and persuasion, foulness of the fact, men's, women's faults, miseries of marriage, events of lust, &c.*

As there be divers causes of this burning lust, or heroical love, so there be many good remedies to ease and help; amongst which, good counsel

and persuasion, which I should have handled in the first place, are of
great moment, and not to be omitted. Many are of opinion, that in this
blind head-strong passion counsel can do no good.

> *Which thing hath neither judgment, or an end,*
> *How should advice or counsel it amend?*   (TERENCE)
> *For what term shall be set to love?*   (VIRGIL)

But without question, good counsel and advice must needs be of great
force, especially if it shall proceed from a wise, fatherly, reverend, discreet person, a man of authority, whom the parties do respect, stand in
awe of, or from a judicious friend, of itself alone, it is able to divert and
suffice. Gordonius, the Physician, attributes so much to it, that he would
have it by all means used in the first place : I counsel him that would
not be poisoned to turn from her, pointing to mortal perils, the judgment of hell, the joys of Paradise. He would have some discreet men to
dissuade them, after the fury of passion is a little spent, or by absence
allayed ; for it is as intempestive at first to give counsel, as to comfort
parents when their children are in that instant departed ; to no purpose
to prescribe Narcoticks, Cordials, Nectarines, Potions, Homer's Nepenthes, or Helena's Bowl, &c. She will not cease to beat her breast, she
will lament and howl for a season : let passion have his course a while,
and then he may proceed, by fore-shewing the miserable events and
dangers which will surely happen, the pains of Hell, joys of Paradise,
and the like, which by their preposterous courses they shall forfeit or
incur ; and 'tis a fit method, a very good means. For what Seneca said of
Vice, I say of Love, 'tis learned of itself, but hardly left without a Tutor.
'Tis not amiss therefore to have some such overseer, to expostulate and
shew them such absurdities, inconveniences, imperfections, discontents,
as usually follow ; which their blindness, fury, madness, cannot apply
unto themselves, or will not apprehend through weakness : and good for
them to disclose themselves, to give ear to friendly admonitions. Tell
me, Sweetheart (saith Tryphæna, to love-sick Charmides in Lucian)
what is it that troubles thee : peradventure I can ease thy mind, and
further thee in thy suit ; and so without question she might, and so
mayest thou, if the Patient be capable of good counsel, and will hear at
least what may be said.

If he love at all, she is either an honest woman or a whore. If dishonest, let him read, or inculcate to him, that fifth of Solomon's Proverbs, Ecclesiastes 26, Ambrose in his book of Abel and Cain, Philo Judæus, Platina's Dialogue on Loves, Espencæus, and those three books of
Peter Hædus On the Disdain of Love, Æneas Sylvius' tart Epistle, which

he wrote to his friend Nicholas of Wartburg, which he calls a medicine for illicit love, &c. For what's an whore, as he saith, but a poller [or fleecer] of youth, ruin of men, a destruction, a devourer of patrimonies, a downfall of honour, fodder for the Devil, the gate of death, and supplement of hell? Such love is a snare to the soul, &c., a bitter honey, sweet poison, delicate destruction, a voluntary mischief, a defiling filth, a dung-pit. And as Peter Aretine's Lucretia, a notable quean, confesseth: gluttony, anger, envy, pride, sacrilege, theft, slaughter, were all born that day that a whore began her profession; for, as she follows it, her pride is greater than a rich churl's, she is more envious than the pox, as malicious, as melancholy, as covetous as Hell. If from the beginning of the world any were bad, worse, worst, bad in the superlative degree, 'tis a whore; how many have I undone, caused to be wounded, slain! O Antonia, thou seest what I am without, but within, God knows, a puddle of iniquity, a sink of sin, a pocky quean. — Let him now that so dotes meditate on this; let him see the event and success of others, Samson, Hercules, Holofernes, &c. Those infinite mischiefs attend it: if she be another man's wife he loves, 'tis abominable in the sight of God and men: adultery is expressly forbidden in God's Commandment, a mortal sin, able to endanger his soul: if he be such a one that fears God, or have any Religion, he will eschew it, and abhor the loathsomeness of his own fact. If he love an honest maid, 'tis to abuse, or marry her: if to abuse, 'tis fornication, a foul fact (though some make light of it) and almost equal to adultery itself. If to marry, let him seriously consider what he takes in hand, look before he leap, as the proverb is, or settle his affections, and examine first the party, and condition of his estate and hers, whether it be a fit match, for fortunes, years, parentage, and such other circumstances, whether it be of Venus herself; whether it be likely to proceed; if not, let him wisely stave himself off at the first, curb in his inordinate passion, and moderate his desire, by thinking of some other subject, divert his cogitations. Or if it be not for his good, as Æneas, forewarned by Mercury in a dream, left Dido's love, and in all haste got him to Sea,

> *Calling his comrades three,*
> *He bids them quietly*
> *Prepare the ships for sea,*

and although she did oppose with vows, tears, prayers, and imprecation,

> *He is not moved by sigh or tear,*
> *Her pleading voice he will not hear.*

Let thy Mercury, reason, rule thee against all allurements, seeming de-

lights, pleasing inward or outward provocations. Thou mayst do this if
thou wilt, a father dotes not on his own daughter, a brother on a sister:
and why? because it is unnatural, unlawful, unfit. If he be sickly, soft,
deformed, let him think of his deformities, vices, infirmities; if in debt,
let him ruminate how to pay his debts: if he be in any danger, let him
seek to avoid it; if he have any law-suit, or other business, he may do
well to let his love matters alone, and follow it, labour in his vocation,
whatever it is. But if he cannot so ease himself, yet let him wisely pre-
meditate of both their estates; if they be unequal in years, she young
and he old, what an unfit match must it needs be, an uneven yoke, how
absurd and undecent a thing it is! as Lycinus in Lucian told Timolaus,
for an old bald crook-nosed knave, to marry a young wench; how odious
a thing it is to see an old Lecher! What should a bald fellow do with a
comb, a dumb doter with a pipe, a blind man with a looking-glass, and
thou with such a wife? How absurd is it for a young man to marry an
old wife for a piece of good[s]! But put case she be equal in years, birth,
fortunes, and other qualities correspondent, he doth desire to be coupled
in marriage, which is an honourable estate, but for what respects? Her
beauty belike, and comeliness of person, that is commonly the main
object, she is a most absolute form in his eye at least, she hath the
Paphian's beauty, the elegancies of the Graces, but do other men affirm
as much? or is it an error in his judgement? our eyes and other senses
will commonly deceive us; it may be, to thee thyself upon a more serious
examination, or after a little absence, she is not so fair as she seems.
Some things seem and are not so; compare her to another standing by,
'tis a touchstone to try, confer hand to hand, body to body, face to face,
eye to eye, nose to nose, neck to neck, &c., examine every part by itself,
then altogether, in all postures, several sites, and tell me how thou likest
her. It may be not she that is so fair, but her coats, or put another in her
clothes, and she will seem all out as fair; as the Poet then prescribes,
separate her from her clothes: suppose thou saw her in a base beggar's
weed, or else dressed in some old hirsute attires out of fashion, foul
linen, coarse raiment, besmeared with soot, colly [or smut], perfumed
with Opoponax, Sagapenum, Assafœtida, or some such filthy gums, dirty,
about some undecent action or other; or in such a case as Brassivola
the Physician found Malatasta, his patient, after a potion of Hellebore,
which he had prescribed: with hands on the ground and hinder parts
elevated to heaven (as that Socratic in Aristophanes, who while writing
geometrick figures on the earth, seemed to be grubbing for truffles)
blackening the white wall with bile, and what is worse, the whole room

and himself defiled, &c., all to bewrayed, or worse; if thou saw'st her (I say), wouldst thou affect her as thou dost? Suppose thou beheldest her in a frosty morning, in cold weather, in some passion or perturbation of mind, weeping, chafing, &c. rivel'd and ill-favoured to behold. She many times that in a composed look seems so amiable and delicious, of so handsome a figure, if she do but laugh or smile, makes an ugly sparrow-mouthed face, and shews a pair of uneven, loathsome, rotten, foul teeth: she hath a black skin, gouty legs, a deformed crooked carkass under a fine coat. It may be for all her costly tires she is bald, and though she seem so fair by dark, by candle-light, or afar off at such a distance, as Callicratides observed in Lucian, if thou shouldst see her near, or in a morning, she would appear more ugly than a beast; if you but carefully consider what comes forth of mouth and nostrils and other bodily conduits, you ne'er saw viler stuff. Follow my counsel, see her undrest, see her, if it be possible, out of her attires, stripped of her borrowed feathers; it may be she is like Æsop's Jay, or Pliny's Cantharides,* she will be loathsome, ridiculous, thou wilt not endure her sight: or suppose thou saw'st her sick, pale, in a Consumption, on her death-bed, skin and bones, or now dead, the embrace of whom was most pleasant, as Bernard saith, will be horrible to see.

> *She that smelled so sweet of yore,*
> *Smelleth now, but sweet no more.†*

As a posy, she smells sweet, is most fresh and fair one day, but dried up, withered, and stinks another. Beautiful Nireus, by that Homer so much admired, once dead, is more deformed than Thersites, and Solomon deceased, as ugly as Marcolphus: thy lovely Mistress, that was erst dearer to thee than thine eyes, once sick or departed, is worse than any dirt or dunghill. Her embraces were not so acceptable, as now her looks be terrible: thou hadst better behold a Gorgon's head than Helena's carkass.

Some are of opinion, that to see a woman naked, is able of itself to alter his affection; and it is worthy of consideration, saith Montaigne the Frenchman in his Essays, that the skilfullest masters of amorous dalliance, appoint for a remedy of venereous passions, a full survey of the body; which the Poet insinuates,

> *The love stood still, that ran in full career,*
> *When once it saw those parts should not appear.* (OVID)

It is reported of Seleucus King of Syria, that seeing his wife Stratonice's

---

* A fly that hath golden wings but a poisoned body. — Burton's note.
† From the Epigram on Rosamund the Fair, mistress to Henry II. of England.

bald pate, as she was undressing her by chance, he could never affect her after. Raymond Lully, the Physician, spying an ulcer or canker in his Mistress' breast, whom he so dearly loved, from that day following abhorr'd the looks of her. Philip, the French King, as Nubrigensis relates it, married the King of Denmark's daughter, and after he had used her as a wife one night, because her breath stunk, they say, or for some other secret fault, sent her back again to her father. Peter Matthaeus in the life of Lewis the Eleventh, finds fault with our English Chronicles, for writing how Margaret the King of Scots' daughter, and wife to Lewis the XI. French King, was for bad breath rejected by her husband. Many such matches are made for by-respects, or some seemly comeliness, which, after honey-moon's past, turn to bitterness: for burning lust is but a flash, a Gunpowder passion; and hatred oft follows in the highest degree, dislike and contempt.

> When the skin's no longer tight,
> And the teeth no longer white,   (JUVENAL)

when they wax old, and ill-favoured, they may commonly no longer abide them.

> Thou'rt offensive to me now,   (JUVENAL)

be gone, they grow stale, fulsome, loathsome, odious, thou art a beastly, filthy quean, hast the face of one straining at stool, thou art Saturn's hind-end, withered and dry,

> Now that wrinkles spoil thine airs,
> And the grey is in thy hairs.   (OVID)

(I say) be gone, the door's open, off with you.

Yea, but you will infer, your Mistress is complete, of a most absolute form in all men's opinions, no exceptions can be taken at her, nothing may be added to her person, nothing detracted, she is the mirror of women for her beauty, comeliness, and pleasant grace, unimitable, of unmixt pleasures, unmixt charms, she is the Ointment-Box of Love, the Casket of Graces, a mere magazine of natural perfections, she hath all the Loves and Graces, a thousand aspects and forms, in each part absolute and complete,

> Gladsome cheeks, rosy mouth, languishing eyes,   (LOCHÆUS)

to be admired for her person, a most incomparable, unmatchable piece, a golden child, made in the image of the goddesses, a Phoenix, a blossoming little Venus, a Nymph, a Fairy, like Venus herself when she was a maid, second to none, a mere quintessence, a breathing flower, sweet marjoram, a feminine prodigy, put case she be, how long will she continue?

Each day weareth away the flower's beauty. (SENECA)

Each day detracts from her person, and this beauty is a fragile good, a mere flash, a Venice glass, quickly broken,

> *Beauty is a dubious boon*
> *To mortals, and departeth soon,* (SENECA)

it will not last. As that fair flower Adonis, which we call an Anemone, flourisheth but one month, this gracious, all-commanding beauty fades in an instant. It is a jewel soon lost, the Painter's Goddess, a false truth, a mere picture. " Favour is deceitful, and beauty is vanity," Proverbs.

> *A little gem, bubble, is beauty pale,*
> *A rose, dew, snow, smoke, wind, air, naught at all.* (BAUHUSIUS)

If she be fair, as the saying is, she is commonly a fool; if proud, scornful (arrogance follows beauty), or dishonest; rare is the union of beauty and modesty; can she be fair and honest too? Aristo, the son of Agasi-cles, married a Spartan Lass, the fairest Lady in all Greece next to Helen, but, for her conditions [or character] the most abominable and beastly creature of the world. So that I would wish thee to respect, with Seneca, not her person, but qualities. Will you say that's a good blade, which hath a gilded scabbard, embroidered with gold and jewels? No, but that which hath a good edge and point, well-tempered metal, able to resist. This beauty is of the body alone, and what is that, but as Gregory Nazianzen telleth us, a mock of time and sickness? or as Boethius, as mutable as a flower, and 'tis not nature so makes us, but most part the infirmity of the beholder. For ask another, he sees no such matter: I pray thee tell me how thou likest my Sweetheart, as she asked her sister in Aristænetus; whom I so much admire, methinks he is the sweetest Gentleman, the properest man that ever I saw: but I am in love, I con-fess, and cannot therefore well judge. But be she fair indeed, golden-haired, as Anacreon his Bathyllus, (to examine particulars), she have

> *Sparkling eyes and milky neck.* (BRUGENSIS)

a pure sanguine complexion, little mouth, coral lips, white teeth, soft and plump neck, body, hands, feet, all fair and lovely to behold, com-posed of all graces, elegancies, an absolute piece,

> *Let my Melita's eyes like Juno's be,*
> *Her hand Minerva's, Venus's her breasts,*
> *And her leg Amphitrite's, &c.* (BRUGENSIS)

Let her head be from Prague, paps out of Austria, belly from France, back from Brabant, hands out of England, feet from Rhine, buttocks from Switzerland, let her have the Spanish gait, the Venetian tire Italian compliment and endowments;

Let her eyes shine as bright as stars, her neck
Bloom as the rose, her hair outshine pure gold,
Her honey lips display the ruddy blush,
Let her in all her glory outdo Venus
And all the goddesses, &c.   (PETRONIUS)

Let her be such a one throughout, as Lucian deciphers in his Images;
as Euphranor of old painted Venus, Aristænetus describes Lais, another
Helen, Chariclea, Leucippe, Lucretia, Pandora; let her have a box of
beauty to repair herself still, such a one as Venus gave Phaon, when he
carried her over the Ford; let her use all helps Art and Nature can
yield; be like her, and her, and whom thou wilt, or all these in one; a
little sickness, a fever, small pox, wound, scar, loss of an eye, or limb, a
violent passion, a distemperature of heat or cold, mars all in an instant,
disfigures all; child-bearing, old age, that Tyrant Time, will turn Venus
to Erinnys; raging Time, care, rivels her upon a sudden; after she hath
been married a small while, and the black ox hath trodden on her toe,
she will be so much altered, and wax out of favour, thou wilt not know
her. One grows too fat, another too lean, &c., modest Matilda, pretty
pleasing Peg, sweet singing Susan, mincing merry Moll, dainty dancing
Doll, neat Nancy, jolly Joan, nimble Nell, kissing Kate, bouncing Bess
with black eyes, fair Phyllis with fine white hands, fiddling Frances, tall
Tib, slender Sib, &c., will quickly lose their grace, grow fulsome, stale,
sad, heavy, dull, sour, and all at last out of fashion. Where now the
speaking look, the pleasing pleasantries, the blandishing smiles? &c.
Those fair sparkling eyes will look dull, her soft coral lips, will be pale,
dry, cold, rough, and blue, her skin rugged, that soft and tender surface
will be hard and harsh, her whole complexion change in a moment, and
as Matilda writ to King John,

I am not now as when thou saw'st me last,
That favour soon is vanishèd and past:
That rosy blush lapt in a lilly vale,
Now is with morphew overgrown and pale.   (DRAYTON)

'Tis so in the rest, their beauty fades as a tree in winter, which Deianira
hath elegantly expressed in the Poet:

And as a tree that in the green wood grows,
With fruit and leaves, and in the Summer blows,
In Winter like a stock deformèd shows:
Our beauty takes his race and journey goes,
And doth decrease, and lose, and come to nought,
Admir'd of old, to this by child-birth brought:

And mother hath bereft me of my grace,
And crooked old age coming on apace. (SENECA)

To conclude with Chrysostom, When thou seest a fair and beautiful person, (a brave Bonaroba, or well-dress'd woman, a beautiful Donna who'd make your mouth water, a merry girl and one not hard to love) * a comely woman, having bright eyes, a merry countenance, a shining lustre in her look, a pleasant grace, wringing thy soul, and increasing thy concupiscence; bethink with thyself that it is but earth thou lovest, a mere excrement, which so vexeth thee, which thou so admirest, and thy raging soul will be at rest. Take her skin from her face, and thou shalt see [saith Chrysostom] all loathsomeness under it, that beauty is a superficial skin and bones, nerves, sinews: suppose her sick, now rivel'd, hoary-headed, hollow-cheeked, old: within she is full of filthy fleam, stinking, putrid, excremental stuff: snot and snivel in her nostrils, spittle in her mouth, water in her eyes, what filth in her brains, &c. ———— Or take her at her best, and look narrowly upon her in the light, stand nearer her, nearer yet, thou shalt perceive almost as much, and love less; as Cardan well writes, they love less who see sharply, though Scaliger deride him for it: if he see her near, or look exactly at such a posture, whosoever he is, according to the true rules of symmetry and proportion, those I mean of Albert Durer, Lomatius, and Taisnier, examine him of her. If he be a good judge of fine faces, he shall find many faults in Physiognomy, and ill colour, ill form, one side of the face likely bigger than the other, or crooked nose, bad eyes, prominent veins, concavities about the eyes, wrinkles, pimples, red streaks, freckons [or freckles], hairs, warts, neves [or moles], inequalities, roughness, scabredity, paleness, yellowness, and as many colours as are in a Turkey-cock's neck, many indecorums in their other parts; what you wish is to lop something off, one leers, another frowns, a third gapes, squints, &c. And 'tis true that he [Cardan] saith, seldom shall you find an absolute face without fault, as I have often observed; not in the face alone is this defect or disproportion to be found, but in all the other parts, of body and mind; she is fair indeed, but foolish; pretty, comely, and decent, of a majestical presence, but peradventure imperious, unhonest, self-will'd: she is rich, but deformed; hath a sweet face, but bad carriage, no bringing up, a rude and wanton flirt; a neat body she hath, but it is a nasty quean otherwise, a very slut, of a bad kind. As flowers in a garden have colour some, but no smell, others have

---

* The words in parentheses are Burton's interjection into the celebrated passage on woman's beauty by the great Christian divine.

a fragrant smell, but are unseemly to the eye; one is unsavoury to the taste as rue, as bitter as wormwood, and yet a most medicinal cordial flower, most acceptable to the stomack; so are men and women, one is well qualified, but of ill proportion, poor and base: a good eye she hath, but a bad hand and foot, a fine leg, bad teeth, a vast body, &c. Examine all parts of body and mind, I advise thee to enquire of all. See her angry, merry, laugh, weep, hot, cold, sick, sullen, dressed, undressed, in all attires, sites, gestures, passions, eat her meals, &c., and in some of these you will surely dislike. Yea, not her only let them observe, but her parents, how they carry themselves: for what deformities, defects, incumbrances of body or mind be in them, at such an age, they will likely be subject to, be molested in like manner, they will take after their father or mother. And with all let him take notice of her companions, in publick gatherings (as Quiverra prescribes) and whom she converseth with. Show me your company, I'll tell you who you are. According to Thucydides, she is commonly the best, that is least talked of abroad. For if she be a noted reveller, a gadder, a singer, a pranker or dancer, then take heed of her. For what saith Theocritus?

> *Dance less, ye merry girls, the rakish goat*
> *Will lead you else another dance ere long!*

Young men will do it, when they come to it. Fauns and Satyrs will certainly play wreeks [pay them out] when they come in such wanton Bacchis' or Elenora's presence. Now when they shall perceive any such obliquity, indecency, disproportion, deformity, bad conditions, &c., let them still ruminate on that, and as Hædus adviseth out of Ovid, note their faults, vices, errors, and think of their imperfections; 'tis the next way to divert and mitigate Love's furious head-strong passions, as a Peacock's feet, and filthy comb, they say, make him forget his fine feathers, and pride of his tail; she is lovely, fair, well-favoured, well qualified, courteous and kind: But if she be not so to me, what care I how kind she be? I say with Philostratus, beautiful to others, she is a tyrant to me, and so let her go. Besides these outward neves, or open faults, errors, there be many inward infirmities, secret, some private (which I will omit), and some more common to the sex, sullen fits, evil qualities, filthy diseases, in this case fit to be considered; the filthiness of women, in the first place the menstrual dirtinesses, which Savanarola exposes, Platina censures at length, Lodovicus Boncialus, Pet. Hædus, Albertus, and many other Physicians touch on. A Lover, in Calcagninus' Apologies, wished with all his heart he were his Mistress' Ring, to hear, embrace, see, and do, I know not what: O thou fool, quoth the Ring, if thou wer'st in my room, thou shouldst hear, observe and see things abominable and shameful, that which would make thee loathe and hate her, yea, peradventure, all women for her sake.

I will say nothing of the vices of their minds, their pride, envy, inconstancy, weakness, malice, self-will, lightness, insatiable lust, jealousy. " No malice like to a woman's, no bitterness like to hers," and as the same Author urgeth, " Who shall find a virtuous woman? " He makes a question of it. They know neither good nor bad, be it better or worse (as the Comical Poet hath it) beneficial or hurtful, they will do what they list.

> *Snares of the human race, torment of life,*
> *Spoils of the night, bitterest cares of the day,*
> *Torture of husbands, and the ruin of youths.*   (LOCHÆUS)

And to that purpose were they first made, as Jupiter insinuates in the Poet * ;

> *The fire that bold Prometheus stole from me,*
> *With plagues call'd Women shall revengèd be,*
> *On whose alluring and enticing face*
> *Poor mortals doting, shall their death embrace.*   (HESIOD)

In fine, as Diogenes concludes in Nevisanus, they have all their faults.

> Everiche of hem hath some vice,
> If one be full of villany,
> Another hath a likerous eye,
> If one be full of wantonness,
> Another is a chideress.

When Leander was drowned, the inhabitants of Sestos consecrated Hero's Lantern to Anteros, and he that had good success in his love, should light the candle: but never any man was found to light it; which I can refer to nought, but the inconstancy and lightness of women.

> *For in a thousand, good there is not one ;*
> *All be so proud, unthankful, and unkind,*
> *With flinty hearts, careless of others' moan,*
> *In their own lusts carried most headlong blind,*
> *But more herein to speak I am forbidden :*
> *Sometime for speaking truth one may be chidden.*   (ARIOSTO)

I am not willing, you see, to prosecute the cause against them, and therefore take heed you mistake me not, I say nothing against any good woman, I honour the sex, with all good men, and as I ought to do, rather than displease them, I will voluntarily take the oath which Mercurius Britannicus took : Never have I, in word or act, borne malice

---

* See our English Tatius book 1 — Burton's note. [See Index.]

against that most noble sex, &c. Let Simonides, Mantuan, Platina, Peter Aretine, and such women-haters bear the blame, if ought be said amiss; I have not writ a tenth of that which might be urged out of them and others; a single book would not hold all the satire and invective that has been written against women. And that which I have said (to speak truth) no more concerns them than men, though women be more frequently named in this Tract; (to apologize once for all) I am neither partial against them, or therefore bitter: what is said of the one, change but the name, may most part be understood of the other. My words are like Pauso's picture in Lucian, of whom, when a good fellow had bespoke an horse to be painted with his heels upward, tumbling on his back, he made him passant [or walking, with three hoofs on the ground and the left fore-foot lifted], now when the fellow came for his piece, he was very angry, and said, it was quite opposite to his mind; but Pauso instantly turned the Picture upside down, shewed him the horse at that site which he requested, and so gave him satisfaction. If any man take exception at my words, let him alter the name, read him for her, and 'tis all one in effect.

But to my purpose. If women in general be so bad (and men worse than they) what a hazard is it to marry! where shall a man find a good wife, or a woman a good husband? A woman a man may eschew, but not a wife: wedding is undoing (as some say), marrying marring, wooing woeing: a wife is a fever hectick, as Scaliger calls her, and not to be cured but by death, as out of Menander; Athenæus adds,

> *Thou wadest into a sea itself of woes;*
> *In Libyck and Ægean each man knows*
> *Of thirty not three ships are cast away,*
> *But on this rock not one escapes, I say.*

The worldly cares, miseries, discontents, that accompany marriage, I pray you learn of them that have experience, for I have none; by books the mind is warned. For my part, I'll not dissemble with him,

> *Go away, girls, you're a deceitful lot,*
> *No married life for me,*

many married men exclaim at the miseries of it, and rail at wives down right; I never tried, but as I hear some of them say, an Irish Sea is not so turbulent and raging as a litigious wife.

> *Scylla and Charybdis are less dangerous,*
> *There is no beast that is so noxious.*   (SENECA)

Which made the Devil, belike, as most interpreters hold, when he had taken away Job's goods, health, children, friends, to persecute him the more, leave his wicked wife, as Pineda proves out of Tertullian, Cyprian, Austin, Chrysostom, Prosper, Gaudentius, &c., to vex and gall him worse than all the fiends in hell, as knowing the conditions of a bad woman. Jupiter hath given man no more pestilential evil, saith Simonides. *Better dwell with a Dragon or a Lion, than keep house with a wicked wife. Better dwell in a wilderness. No wickedness like to her. She makes a sorry heart, an heavy countenance, a wounded mind, weak hands, and feeble knees.* A woman and death are two the bitterest things in the world.

> *Saying, You must wed today,*
> *Go hang yourself, he seem'd to say.*   (TERENCE)

And yet for all this we bachelors desire to be married; with that Vestal Virgin, we long for it.

> *Happy nuptials! let me die,*
> *Unless those wedded sweets I try.*   (SENECA)

'Tis the sweetest thing in the world, I would I had a wife, saith he,

> *For fain would I leave a single life,*
> *If I could get me a good wife.*

Heigh-ho for a husband, cries she, a bad husband, nay the worst that ever was, is better than none: O blissful marriage, O most welcome marriage, and happy are they that are so coupled: we do earnestly seek it, and are never well till we have effected it. But with what fate? like those birds in the Emblem, that fed about a cage, so long as they could fly away at their pleasure, liked well of it; but when they were taken, and might not get loose, though they had the same meat, pined away for sullenness, and would not eat. So we commend marriage, so long as we are wooers, may kiss and coll at our pleasure, nothing is so sweet, we are in heaven as we think: but when we are once tied, and have lost our liberty, marriage is an hell, give me my yellow hose again: a mouse in a trap lives as merrily, we are in a purgatory some of us, if not hell itself. As the proverb is, 'tis fine talking of war, and marriage sweet in contemplation, till it be tried: and then as wars are most dangerous, irksome, every minute at death's door, so is, &c. When those wild Irish Peers, saith Stanihurst, were feasted by King Henry the Second (at what time he kept his Christmas at Dublin) and had tasted of his Prince-like cheer, generous wines, dainty fare, had seen his massy plate of silver, gold, enamell'd, beset with jewels, golden candle-sticks, goodly rich hangings, brave furniture, heard his trumpets sound, Fifes, Drums, and his exquisite musick in all kinds: when they had observed his majestical presence as he sat in purple robes, crowned, with his sceptre,

&c., in his royal seat, the poor men were so amazed, enamoured, and taken with the object, that they were weary and ashamed of their own sordidity and manner of life. They would all be English forthwith; who but English! but when they had now submitted themselves, and lost their former liberty, they began to rebel some of them, others repent of what they had done, when it was too late. 'Tis so with us Bachelors, when we see and behold those sweet faces, those gaudy shews that women make, observe their pleasant gestures and graces, give ear to their Siren tunes, see them dance, &c., we think their conditions are as fine as their faces, we are taken with dumb signs, we rush to embrace them, we rave, we burn, and would fain be married. But when we feel the miseries, cares, woes, that accompany it, we make our moan many of us, cry out at length, and cannot be released. If this be true now, as some out of experience will inform us, farewell wiving for my part, and as the Comical Poet merrily saith,

> *Foul fall him that brought the second match to pass,*
> *The first I wish no harm, poor man, alas!*
> *He knew not what he did, nor what it was.**

What shall I say to him that marries again and again, who puts his neck into the halter a second time? I pity him not, for the first time he must do as he may, bear it out sometimes by the head and shoulders, and let his next neighbour ride, or else run away, or as that Syracusan in a tempest, when all ponderous things were to be exonerated out of the ship, because she was his heaviest burthen, fling his wife in the Sea. But this I confess is Comically spoken, and so I pray you take it. In sober sadness, marriage is a bondage, a thraldom, a yoke, an hindrance to all good enterprises, (" he hath married a wife and cannot come ") a stop to all preferments, a rock on which many are saved, many impinge, and are cast away: not that the thing is evil in itself, or troublesome, but full of all contentment and happiness, one of the three things which please God, " when a man and his wife agree together," an honourable and happy estate, who knows it not? If they be sober, wise, honest, as the Poet infers,

> *If fitly match'd be man and wife.*
> *No pleasure's wanting to their life.* (EURIPIDES)

But to undiscreet sensual persons, that as brutes are wholly led by sense, it is a fearful plague, many times an Hell itself, and can give little or no content, being that they are often so irregular and prodigious in their lusts, so diverse in their affections. As Aelius Verus said, a wife is a name of honour, not of pleasure: she is fit to bear the office,

---

* Translated [from Eubulus] by my brother, Ralph Burton. — Burton's note.

govern a family, to bring up children, sit at board's end and carve; as some carnal men think and say, they had rather go to the stews, or have now and then a snatch as they can come by it, borrow of their neighbours, than have wives of their own; except they may, as some Princes and great men do, keep as many Courtisans as they will themselves, fly out recklessly, meddling with others' wives; [they had rather] that polygamy of Turks, Lex Julia, which Cæsar once enforced in Rome (though Levinus Torrentius and others suspect it) that every great man might marry, and keep as many wives as he would, or Irish divorcement were in use: but as it is, 'tis hard, and gives not that satisfaction to these carnal men, beastly men as too many are. What still the same, to be tied * to one, be she never so fair, never so virtuous, is a thing they may not endure, to love one long. Say thy pleasure, and counterfeit as thou wilt, as Parmeno told Thais, one man will never please thee; nor one woman many men. But as Pan replied to his Father Mercury, when he asked whether he was married, No Father, no, I am a Lover still, and cannot be contented with one woman. Pitys, Echo, the Mænades, and I know not how many besides, were his Mistresses, he might not abide marriage. Variety delights; 'tis loathsome and tedious, what, one still? which the Satirist said of Iberina, is verified in most,

> *'Tis not one man will serve her by her will,*
> *As soon she'll have one eye as one man still.* (JUVENAL)

As capable of any impression as primal matter itself, that still desires new forms; like the Sea, their affections ebb and flow. Husband is a cloak for some to hide their villainy; once married she may fly out at her pleasure, the name of Husband is a sanctuary to make all good. It comes to this (saith Seneca) that they take a husband only to get a lover. They are right and straight, as true Trojans as mine host's daughter, that Spanish wench in Ariosto, as good wives as Messalina. Many men are as constant in their choice, and as good husbands as Nero himself, they must have their pleasure of all they see, and are in a word far more fickle than any woman.

> ffor either they be full of jealousye,
> Our masterfull, or loven noveltye.

Good men have often ill wives, as bad as Xanthippe was to Socrates, Elenora to St. Lewis † Isabella to our Edward the Second: and good wives are as often matched to ill husbands, as Mariamne to Herod, Serena to Diocletian, Theodora to Theophilus, and Thyra to Gurmunde.

---

* For better for worse, for richer for poorer, in sickness and in health, &c., 'tis a hard saying to a sensual man. — Burton's note.

† Should be Lewis the Seventh.

But I will say nothing of dissolute and bad husbands, of Bachelors and their vices; their good qualities are a fitter subject for a just volume, too well known already in every village, town and city, they need no blazon; and lest I should mar any matches, or dis-hearten loving Maids, for this present I will let them pass.

Being that men and women are so irreligious, depraved by nature, so wandering in their affections, so brutish, so subject to disagreement, so unobservant of marriage rites, what shall I say? If thou beest such a one, or thou light on such a wife, what concord can there be, what hope of agreement? 'tis not yoked with each other but provoked with each other, as the Reed and Fern in the Emblem, averse and opposite in nature: 'tis twenty to one thou wilt not marry to thy contentment: but as in a lottery forty blanks were drawn commonly for one prize, out of a multitude you shall hardly choose a good one: a small ease hence then, little comfort.

> *If he or she be such a one,*
> *Thou hadst much better be alone.*   (SIMONIDES)

If she be barren, she is not ——————— &c. If she have children, and thy state be not good, though thou be wary and circumspect, thy charge will undo thee, she will sink your whole establishment by her fecundity, thou wilt not be able to bring them up, and what greater misery can there be, than to beget children, to whom thou canst leave no other inheritance but hunger and thirst? when thou art oppressed by hunger, shrill voices cry for bread, piercing the father's heart: what so grievous as to turn them up to the wide world, to shift for themselves? No plague like to want: and when thou hast good means, and art very careful of their education, they will not be ruled. Think but of that old proverb, great men's sons seldom do well. Would that I had either remained single or not had children! Augustus exclaims in Suetonius. Jacob had his Reuben, Simeon, and Levi: David an Amnon, an Absalom, an Adonijah; wise men's sons are commonly fools, insomuch that Spartian concludes, they had been much better to have been childless. 'Tis too common in the middle sort; thy son's a drunkard, a gamester, a spendthrift; thy daughter a fool, a whore; thy servants lazy drones and thieves; thy neighbours devils, they will make thee weary of thy life. If thy wife be froward, when she may not have her will, thou hadst better be buried alive; she will be so impatient, raving still, and roaring like Juno in the Tragedy, there's nothing but tempests, all is in an uproar. If she be soft and foolish, thou wert better have a block, she will shame thee, and reveal thy secrets; if wise and learned, well qualified, there is as much danger on the other side, saith Nevisanus, she will be too insolent and peevish,

> *Some simple rustick at Venusium bred,*
> *O let me, rather than Cornelia, wed,*
> *If to great virtues, greater pride she join,*
> *And count her ancestors as current coin.* (JUVENAL)

Take heed; if she be a slut, thou wilt loathe her; if proud, she'll beggar thee, she'll spend thy patrimony in baubles, all Arabia will not serve to perfume her hair, saith Lucian: if fair and wanton, she'll make thee a Cornuto; if deformed, she will paint. If her face be filthy by nature, she will mend it by art, which who can endure? If she do not paint, she will look so filthy, thou canst not love her, and that peradventure will make thee unhonest. Cromerus relates of Casimirus, that he was unchaste, because his wife Aleida the daughter of Henry, Landgrave of Hesse, was so deformed. If she be poor, she brings beggary with her (saith Nevisanus), misery and discontent. If you marry a maid, it is uncertain how she proves, perhaps she will not suit you. If young, she is likely wanton and untaught; if lusty, too lascivious; and if she be not satisfied, you know where and when, nothing but quarrels, all is in an uproar, and there is little quietness to be had: if an old maid, 'tis an hazard she dies in child-bed; if a rich widow, thou dost halter thyself, she will make all away before hand, to her other children, &c. Who can endure a virago for a wife? she will hit thee still in the teeth with her first husband: if a young widow, she is often unsatiable and immodest. If she be rich, well descended, bring a great dowry, or be nobly allied, thy wife's friends will eat thee out of house and home, she will be so proud, so high-minded, so imperious. For

> *Sure, of all ills with which mankind are curst,*
> *A wife who brings you money is the worst.* (JUVENAL)

There's nothing so intolerable, thou shalt be as the Tassell of a Gosshawk, she will ride upon thee, domineer as she list, wear the breeches in her oligarchical government, and beggar thee besides. Rich wives force us into slavery, (as Seneca hits them), who accepts a dowry, loses rulership. They will have sovereignty, they will have attendance, they will do what they list. In taking a dowry thou losest thy liberty, hazardest thine estate.

> *These and others be the ills*
> *Of large dowries — frightful bills,* (PLAUTUS)

with many such inconveniences. Say the best, she is a commanding servant; thou hadst better have taken a good housewife maid in her smock. Since then there is such hazard, if thou be wise, keep thyself as thou art, 'tis good to match, much better to be free. To be a father is very pleasant, to be a free man is still more so. Art thou young? then match not yet; if old, match not at all. And therefore, with that Philosopher, [Thales], still make answer to thy friends that importune thee to marry, 'tis yet unseasonable, and ever will be.

Consider withal how free, how happy, how secure, how heavenly, in respect, a single man is; as he said in the Comedy, And that which all my neighbours admire and applaud me for, account so great an happiness, I never had a wife; consider how contentedly, quietly, neatly, plentifully, sweetly and how merrily he lives! He hath no man to care for but himself, none to please, no charge, none to control him, is tied to no residence, no cure to serve, may go and come, when, whither, live where he will, his own master, and do what he list himself. Consider the excellency of Virgins, marriage replenisheth earth, but virginity Paradise; Elias, Eliseus, John Baptist, were Bachelors: Virginity is a precious Jewel, a fair garland, a never-fading flower; for why was Daphne turned to a green bay-tree, but to shew that virginity is immortal?

> As the sequestered flower that grows within
> Some fenced-in garden, to the herd unknown,
> Ne'er turned up by the plough, fanned by the air,
> By the sun strengthened, by the shower reared,
> So is the virgin in her maiden state,
> Dear to her friends, but if her flower be ta'en,
> She is undone and meets no more regard.　(catullus)

Virginity is a fine picture, as Bonaventure calls it, a blessed thing in itself, and if you will believe a Papist, meritorious. And although there be some inconveniences, irksomeness, solitariness, &c., incident to such persons, want of those comforts, tending in sickness, &c., embracing, dalliance, kissing, colling, &c., those furious motives and wanton pleasures a new married wife most part enjoys; yet they are but toys in respect, easily to be endured, if conferred to those frequent incumbrances of marriage; solitariness may be otherwise avoided with mirth, musick, good company, business, employment; in a word, he shall have less of joy and less of sorrow; for their good nights he shall have good days. And methinks sometime or other, amongst so many rich Bachelors, a benefactor should be found to build a monastical College for old, decayed, deformed, or discontented maids to live together in, that have lost their first loves, or otherwise miscarried, or else are willing howsoever to lead a single life. The rest, I say, are toys in respect, and sufficiently recompensed by those innumerable contents and incomparable privileges of Virginity. Think of these things, confer both lives, and consider last of all these commodious prerogatives a Bachelor hath, how well he is esteemed, how heartily welcome to all his friends, as Tertullian observes, with what counterfeit courtesies they will adore him, follow him, present him with gifts; it cannot be believed (saith Ammianus) with what humble service he shall be worshipped, how loved and respected: if he want children (and have means) he shall be often invited, attended on by Princes, and have advocates to plead his cause for nothing, as Plutarch adds. Wilt thou then be reverenced, and had in estimation?

———— *If you'd have the Prince's friendship,*
Let there be no little son to sport in your hall,
Nor daughter dearer still. 'Tis a barren wife
That curries favour with your Noble friends.   (JUVENAL)

Live a single man, marry not, and thou shalt soon perceive how those Succession-hunters, (for so they were called of old) will seek after thee, bribe and flatter thee for thy favour, to be thine heir or executor: Arruntius and Haterius, those famous parasites in this kind, as Tacitus and Seneca have recorded, shall not go beyond them. Periplectomenes, that good personate old man, well understood this in Plautus; for when Pleusides exhorted him to marry, that he might have children of his own, he readily replied in this sort,

Whilst I have kin, what need I brats to have?
Now I live well, and as I will, most brave.
And when I die, my goods I'll give away
To them that do invite me every day,
That visit me, and send me pretty toys,
And strive who shall do me most courtesies.

This respect thou shalt have in like manner, living as he did, a single man.

But if thou marry once, bethink thyself what a slavery it is, what an heavy burthen thou shalt undertake, how hard a task thou art tied to (for as Hierome hath it, who hath a wife is a bondman, bound to serve her), and how continuate, what squalor attends it, what irksomeness, what charges; for wife and children are a perpetual bill of charges; besides a Myriad of cares, miseries, and troubles; for as that Comical Plautus merrily and truly said, he that wants trouble must get to be Master of a Ship, or marry a Wife; and as another seconds him, wife and children have undone me; so many, and such infinite, incumbrances accompany this kind of life. Furthermore, a wife is a shrew, &c., or as he said, in the Comedy, I have married a wife, what misery it has brought me! sons were born, other cares followed.

All gifts and invitations cease, no friend will esteem thee, and thou shalt be compelled to lament thy misery, and make thy moan with Bartholomæus Scheræus, that famous Poet Laureate, and Professor of Hebrew in Witenberg: I had finished this work long since, but that (I use his own words) amongst many miseries which almost broke my back, a shrew to my wife, tormented my mind above measure, and beyond the rest. So shalt thou be compelled to complain, and to cry out at last, with Phoroneus the Lawyer, How happy had I been, if I had wanted a wife! If this which I have said will not suffice, see more in Lemnius, Espencæus, Kornmannus, Platina, Barbarus, Arnisæus, and him that is worth them all, Nevisanus, the Lawyer, almost in every page.

SUBSECTION 4 — *Philters, Magical, and Poetical cures*

WHERE persuasions and other remedies will not take place, many fly to unlawful means, Philters, Amulets, Magick Spells, Ligatures, Characters, Charms, which as a wound with a spear of Achilles, is so made and caused, must so be cured. If forced by Spells and Philters, saith Paracelsus, it must be eased by Characters, and by Incantations. See Fernelius. Sckenkius hath some examples of such as have been so magically caused and magically cured, and by witch-craft: so saith Baptista Codronchus. 'Tis not permitted to be done, I confess; yet often attempted: see more in Wierus on the Devil's Tricks, of Remedies through Philters, Delrio on Magick. Cardan reckons up many magnetical medicines, as to piss through a ring, &c. Mizaldus, Baptista Porta, Jason Pratensis, Lobelius, Matthiolus, &c., prescribe many absurd remedies: The root of a Mandrake drunk, parings from as Ass's hoof, the excrement of his beloved placed under his pillow without her knowledge, when he smells the foul odor, love is dissolved. Eating the egg of a night-owl causeth abstemiousness, according to Iarcha the Indian gymnosophist, as related by Philostratus; drinking the blood of the beloved taketh away all feeling of love; Faustina the wife of Marcus Aurelius, being seized by love for a gladiator, was completely set free by the axiom of the Chaldæans, as told by Julius Capitolinus. Some of our Astrologers will effect as much by Characteristical Images, Seals of

Hermes, or Solomon, of Chael,* &c., the seal of a woman with dishev-
elled hair, &c. Our old Poets and Phantastical writers have many fabulous remedies for such as are love-sick, as that of Protesilaus' tomb in
Philostratus, in his dialogue betwixt Phœnix and Vinitor. Vinitor upon
occasion discoursing of the rare virtues of that shrine, telleth him, that
Protesilaus' Altar and Tomb cures almost all manner of diseases, consumptions, dropsies, quartan agues, sore eyes, and amongst the rest,
such as are love-sick shall there be helped. But the most famous is
Leucata Petra, that renowned Rock in Greece, of which Strabo writes,
not far from Saint Maura, saith Sands, from which rock if any Lover
flung himself down headlong, he was instantly cured.† Venus, after the
death of Adonis, when she could take no rest for love,

> *When hearts burn with raging flame,* (CATULLUS)

came to the Temple of Apollo to know what she should do to be eased
of her pain: Apollo sent her to Leucata Petra, where she precipitated
herself, and was forthwith freed, and when she would needs know of
him a reason of it, he told her again, that he had often observed Jupiter,
when he was enamoured on Juno, thither go to ease and wash himself,
and after him divers others. Cephalus for the love of Pelater, Desoneius'
daughter, leapt down here, that Lesbian Sappho for Phaon, on whom
she miserably doted;

> *Stricken by the gadfly of love, rushed headlong from the summit,*
>
> (MENANDER)

hoping thus to ease herself, and to be free of her love-pangs.

> *Hither Deucalion came, when Pyrrha's love*
> *Tormented him, and leapt down to the Sea,*
> *And had no harm at all, but by and by*
> *His Love was gone and chasèd quite away.* (OVID)

This medicine Joseph Scaliger speaks of, Salmuth, and other writers.
Pliny reports, that amongst the Cyziceni, there is a Well consecrated
to Cupid, of which, if any Lover taste, his passion is mitigated: and
Anthony Verdurius saith, that amongst the Antients there was Amor
Lethes; he took burning torches, and extinguished them in the river;
his statue was to be seen in the Temple of Venus Eleusina, of which
Ovid makes mention, and saith, that all Lovers of old went thither on

---

* Chael, an ancient Hebrew physician, who is said to have made as many as thirty-
two sigils for the cure of disease. See Marcus Antonius Zimara's *Antrum Magico-Medi-
cum*, vol. 1, p. 178 (Frankfort, 1625–6).

† The moral is, vehement fear expels love. — Burton's note.

pilgrimage, that would be rid of their love-pangs. Pausanias, in Phocicis, writes of a Temple dedicated to Venus in the vault, at Naupactus in Achaia (now Lepanto) in which your widows that would have second husbands made their supplications to the Goddess: all manner of suits concerning Lovers were commenced, and their grievances helped. The same Author, in Achaicis, tells as much of the river Selemnus in Greece; if any Lover washed himself in it, by a secret virtue of that water (by reason of the extreme coldness belike) he was healed of Love's torments, the cause and remedy of love being the same; which if it be so, that water, as he holds, is better than any gold. Where none of all these remedies will take place, I know no other, but that all Lovers must make an head, and rebel, as they did in Ausonius, and crucify Cupid, till he grant their request, or satisfy their desires.

SUBSECTION 5 — *The last and best Cure of Love-Melancholy is, to let them have their desire*

THE last refuge and surest remedy, to be put in practice in the utmost place, when no other means will take effect, is, to let them go together, and enjoy one another; so saith Guianerius. Æsculapius himself, to this malady, cannot invent a better remedy, (saith Jason Pratensis) than that a Lover have his desire.

> *And let them both be joinèd in a bed,*
> *And let Æneas fair Lavinia wed.*

'Tis the special cure, to let them bleed in the hymenean vein, for love is a pleurisy, and if it be possible, so let it be,

> *And the wished-for joy is taken.*

Arculanus holds it the speediest and the best cure, 'tis Savanarola's last precept, a principal infallible remedy, the last, sole, and safest refuge.

> *Julia alone can quench my desire,*
> *With neither ice nor snow, but with like fire.* (PETRONIUS)

When you have all done, saith Avicenna, there is no speedier or safer course, than to join the parties together according to their desires and wishes, the custom and form of law; and so we have seen him quickly restored to his former health, that was languished away to skin and bones; after his desire was satisfied, his discontent ceased, and we thought it strange; our opinion is therefore, that in such cases Nature is to be obeyed. Aretæus, an old Author, hath an instance of a young man, when no other means could prevail, was so speedily relieved. What remains then but to join them in marriage?

Give and take their ticklish kisses,
Urging on to newer blisses,
Tasting one another's charms,
Sporting in each other's arms.   (JOVIANUS PONTANUS)

They may then kiss and coll, lie and lock babies in one another's eyes, as their sires before them did, they may then satiate themselves with love's pleasures, which they have so long wished and expected;

In one slumber now held fast,
All their fevers sweetly past,
Quiet in one bed at last.

Yea, but 'tis hard, 'tis difficult, this cannot conveniently be done, by reason of many and several impediments. Sometimes both parties themselves are not agreed: Parents, Tutors, Masters, Guardians, will not give consent; Laws, Customs, Statutes hinder; poverty, superstition, fear and suspicion: many men dote on one woman, all at once and once for all: she dotes as much on him, or them, and in modesty must not, cannot woo, as unwilling to confess, as willing to love: she dares not make it known, shew her affection, or speak her mind. And hard is the choice (as it is in Euphues) when one is compelled either by silence to die with grief, or by speaking to live with shame. In this case almost was the fair Lady Elizabeth, Edward the Fourth his daughter, when she was enamoured on Henry the Seventh, that noble young Prince, and new saluted King, when she brake forth into that passionate speech, O that I were worthy of that comely Prince! but my father being dead, I want friends to motion such a matter. What shall I say? I am all alone, and dare not open my mind to any. What if I acquaint my mother with it? bashfulness forbids. What if some of the Lords? audacity wants. O that I might but confer with him, perhaps in discourse I might let slip such a word that might discover mine intention! How many modest maids may this concern, I am a poor servant, what shall I do? I am a fatherless child, and want means, I am blithe and buxom, young and lusty, but I have never a suitor; as she said [in the play], a company of silly fellows, [they] look belike that I should woo them and speak first: fain they would and cannot woo; how can I begin? Being merely passive they may not make suit, with many such lets and inconveniences, which I know not; what shall we do in such a case? sing Fortune my Foe? ——

Some are so curious in this behalf, as those old Romans, our modern Venetians, Dutch and French, that if two parties dearly love, the one noble, the other ignoble, they may not by their Laws match, though

equal otherwise in years, fortunes, education, and all good affection. In
Germany, except they can prove their gentility by three descents, they
scorn to match with them. A noble man must marry a noble woman : a
Baron, a Baron's daughter; a Knight, a Knight's; a Gentleman, a
Gentleman's; as slaters sort their slates, do they degrees and families.
If she be never so rich, fair, well-qualified otherwise, they will make
him forsake her. The Spaniards abhor all widows; the Turks repute
them old women, if past five and twenty. But these are too severe Laws,
and strict Customs, we must make some concession to love, we are all
the sons of Adam, 'tis opposite to Nature, it ought not to be so. Again,
he loves her most impotently, she loves not him, and so on the other
hand. Pan loved Echo, Echo Satyrus, Satyrus Lyda.

> *For each did hate a lover, yet each with love did burn,*
> *And as each hurt the other, so each was hurt in turn.* (MOSCHUS)

They love and loath of all sorts, he loves her, she hates him; and is
loathed of him on whom she dotes. Cupid hath two darts, one to force
love, all of Gold, and that sharp, another blunt, of Lead, and that to
hinder; this dispels, that creates love. This we see too often verified in
our common experience. Coresus dearly loved that Virgin Callirrhoe,
but the more he loved her, the more she hated him. Œnone loved Paris,
but he rejected her; they are stiff of all sides, as if beauty were therefore created to undo, or be undone. I give her all attendance, all observance, I pray and intreat, fair Mistress pity me, I spend myself, my
time, friends and fortunes to win her favour (as he complains in the
Eclogue), I lament, sigh, weep, and make my moan to her, but she is
hard as flint, as fair and hard as a Diamond, she will not respect or hear
me; she has no compassion on my tears, flees from my prayers, is inflexible to my demands. What shall I do?

> *I wooed her as a young man should do,*
> *But Sir, she said, I love not you.*
> *Rock, marble, heart of oak with iron barr'd,*
> *Frost, flint or adamants are not so hard.* (ANGERIANUS)

I give, I bribe, I send presents, but they are refused. [As Virgil hath it :]
Corydon, thou art but a yokel! thy beloved cares nothing for gifts.
I protest, I swear, I weep; she neglects me for all this, she derides me,
contemns me, she hates me : Phillida flouts me : stiff, churlish, rocky
still.

And 'tis most true, many Gentlewomen are so nice, they scorn all
suitors, crucify their poor Paramours, and think nobody good enough
for them, as dainty to please as Daphne herself,

Many did woo her, but she scorn'd them still,
And said she would not marry by her will.   (OVID)

One while they will not marry, as they say at least (when as they intend nothing less), another while not yet, when 'tis their only desire, they rave upon it. She will marry at last, but not him: he is a proper man indeed, and well qualified, but he wants means: another of her suitors hath good means, but he wants wit; one is too old, another too young, too deformed, she likes not his carriage: a third too loosely given, he is rich, but base born: she will be a Gentlewoman, a Lady, as her Sister is, as her Mother is: she is all out as fair, as well brought up, hath as good a portion, and she looks for as good a match, as Matilda or Dorinda: if not, she is resolved as yet to tarry; so apt are young maids to boggle at every object, so soon won or lost with every toy, so quickly diverted, so hard to be pleased. In the mean time, one suitor pines away, languisheth in love, another sighs and grieves, she cares not: and which Stroza objected to Ariadne,

Is no more mov'd with those sad sighs and tears,
Of her sweetheart, than raging sea with prayers:
Thou scorn'st the fairest youth in all our city,
And mak'st him almost mad for love to die.

They take a pride to prank up themselves, to make young men enamoured, to captivate the men but despise them when captive; to dote on them, and to run mad for their sakes,

Whilst niggardly their favours they discover,
They love to be belov'd, yet scorn the Lover.   (VIRGIL)

All suit and service is too little for them, presents too base: they delight in tormenting and fleecing their lovers. As Atalanta, they must be over-run, or not won. Many young men are as obstinate, and as curious in their choice, as tyrannically proud, insulting, deceitful, false-hearted, as irrefragable and peevish on the other side, Narcissus-like,

Young men and maids did to him sue,
But in his youth, so proud, so coy was he,
Young men and maids bade him adieu.   (OVID)

Echo wept and wooed him by all means above the rest, love me for pity, or pity me for love, but he was obstinate, he would rather die than give consent. Psyche ran whining after Cupid,

Fair Cupid, thy fair Psyche to thee sues,
A lovely lass a fine young gallant wooes,   (FRACASTORIUS)

but he rejected her nevertheless. Thus many Lovers do hold out so long,

doting on themselves, stand in their own light, till in the end they come
to be scorned and rejected, as Stroza's Gargiliana was,

> *Both young and old do hate thee scornèd now,*
> *That once was all their joy and comfort too,*

as Narcissus was himself,

> ———*Who, despising many,*
> *Died ere he could enjoy the love of any.*

They begin to be contemned themselves of others, as he was of his
shadow, and take up with a poor curate, or an old serving-man at last,
that might have had their choice of right good matches in their youth,
like that generous Mare in Plutarch, which would admit of none but
great Horses, but when her tail was cut off, and mane shorn close, and
she now saw herself so deformed in the water, when she came to drink,
she was contented at last to be covered by an Ass. Yet this is a common
humour, will not be left, and cannot be helped.

> *I love a maid, she loves me not: full fain*
> *She would have me, but I not her again;*
> *So Love to crucify men's souls is bent:*
> *But seldom doth it please or give content.* (AUSONIUS)

Their love danceth in a ring, and Cupid hunts them round about, he
dotes, is doted on again, their affection cannot be reconciled. Oftentimes
they may and will not, 'tis their own foolish proceeding that mars all,
they are too distrustful of themselves, too soon dejected: say she be
rich, thou poor; she young, thou old; she lovely and fair, thou most
ill-favoured and deformed; she noble, thou base; she spruce and fine,
but thou an ugly Clown: never despair, there's hope enough yet:
Mopsus takes Nysa! is there aught we lovers may not hope? — put
thyself forward once more, as unlikely matches have been and are
daily made, see what will be the event. Many leave roses and gather
thistles, loathe honey and love verjuice: our likings are as various as
our palates. But commonly they omit opportunities, taking a kiss, all
else they miss, &c., they neglect the usual means and times.

> *He that will not when he may,*
> *When he will he shall have nay.*

They look to be wooed, sought after, and sued to. Most part they will
and cannot, either for the above-named reasons, or for that there is a
multitude of suitors equally enamoured, doting all alike; and where
one alone must speed, what shall become of the rest? Hero was beloved
of many, but one did enjoy her; Penelope had a company of suitors,
yet all missed of their aim. In such cases he or they must wisely and

warily unwind themselves, unsettle his affections by those rules above prescribed, shake off this senseless passion, divert his cogitations, or else bravely bear it out, as Turnus did, Lavinia is thine to wed, when he could not get her, with a kind of heroical scorn he bid Æneas take her, or with a milder farewell, let her go, Take Phyllis for thyself, take her to you, God give you joy, Sir. The Fox in the Emblem would eat no grapes, but why? because he could not get them! care not thou for that which may not be had.

Many such inconveniences, lets and hindrances there are, which cross their projects, and crucify poor Lovers, which sometimes may, sometimes again cannot, be so easily removed. But put case they be reconciled all, agreed hitherto, suppose this love or good liking be betwixt two alone, both parties well pleased, there is mutual love and great affection: yet their Parents, Guardians, Tutors, cannot agree, thence all is dashed, the match is unequal: one rich, another poor: an hardhearted, unnatural, a covetous Father will not marry his son, except he have so much money, all are mad for money, as Chrysostom notes, nor join his daughter in marriage, to save her dowry, or for that he cannot spare her for the service she doth him, and is resolved to part with nothing whilst he lives, not a penny, though he may peradventure well give it, he will not till he dies, and then as a pot of money broke, it is divided amongst them that gaped after it so earnestly. Or else he wants means to set her out, he hath no money, and though it be to the manifest prejudice of her body and soul's health, he cares not, he will take no notice of it, she must and shall tarry. Many slack and careless Parents measure their children's affections by their own, they are now cold and decrepit themselves, past all such youthful conceits, and they will therefore starve their children's Genius, have them with old heads on young shoulders, they must not marry, as he said in the Comedy: they will stifle nature, their young bloods must not participate of youthful pleasures, but be as they are themselves, old on a sudden. And 'tis a general fault amongst most Parents in bestowing of their children, the Father wholly respects wealth, when through his own folly, riot, indiscretion, he hath embezzled his estate, to recover himself, he confines and prostitutes his eldest son's love and affection to some fool, or ancient, or deformed piece for money; he shall marry the daughter of rich parents, a red-hair'd, blear-eyed, big-mouth'd, crooknosed wench — and though his son utterly dislike, with Clitipho in the Comedy [of Terence], I cannot, father: if she be rich (he replies), he must and shall have her, she is fair enough, young enough;

if he look or hope to inherit his lands, he shall marry, not when or whom he loves, but whom his Father commands, when and where he likes, his affection must dance attendance upon him. His daughter is in the same predicament forsooth, as an empty boat she must carry what, where, when, and whom, her Father will. So that in these businesses, the Father is still for the best advantage. Now the mother respects good kindred, most part the son a proper woman. All which Livy exemplifies; a Gentleman and a Yeoman woo'd a wench in Rome (contrary to that statute that the gentry and commonalty must not match together), the matter was controverted: the Gentleman was preferred by the Mother's voice, she wanted a richer marriage: the overseers stood for him that was most worth, &c. But parents ought not to be so strict in this behalf, Beauty is a dowry of itself all-sufficient; Rachel was so married by Jacob, and Bonaventure denies that he so much as venially sins, that marries a maid for comeliness of person. The Jews, if they saw amongst the captives a beautiful woman, some small circumstances observed, might take her to wife. They should not be too severe in that kind, especially if there be no such urgent occasion, or grievous impediment. 'Tis good for a commonwealth. Plato holds, that in their contracts young men should never avoid the affinity of poor folks, or seek after rich. Poverty and base parentage may be sufficiently recompensed by many other good qualities, modesty, virtue, religion, and choice bringing up. I am poor, I confess, but am I therefore contemptible, and an abject? Love itself is naked, the Graces, the Stars, and Hercules was clad in a Lion's skin. Give something to virtue, love, wisdom, favour, beauty, person; be not all for money. Besides, you must consider, that Love cannot be compelled, they must affect as they may: Fate rules even what the toga hides; as the saying is, marriage and hanging goes by destiny, matches are made in Heaven.

> *It lies not in our power to love or hate,*
> *For will in us is overrul'd by fate.*   (MARLOWE)

A servant maid in Aristænetus loved her Mistress' Minion, which when her Dame perceived, in a jealous humour she dragg'd her about the house by the hair of the head, and vexed her sore. The wench cried out, O Mistress, fortune hath made my body your servant, but not my soul! Affections are free, not to be commanded. Moreover it may be to restrain their ambition, pride, and covetousness, to correct those hereditary diseases of a family, God in his just judgement assigns & permits such matches to be made. For I am of Plato and Bodine's mind, that Families have their bounds and periods as well as Kingdoms, beyond which for extent or continuance they shall not exceed, six or seven hundred years, as they there illustrate by a multitude of examples, and which Peucer and Melancthon approve, but in a perpetual tenor (as we see by many pedigrees of Knights, Gentlemen, Yeomen) continue as they began, for many descents with little alteration. Howsoever, let them I say, give something to youth, to love; they must not think they can fancy whom they appoint. This is a free passion, as Pliny said in a Panegyrick of his, and may not be forced. Love craves liking, as the saying is, it requires mutual affections, a correspondency: it cannot be given nor taken away; it may not be learned, Ovid himself cannot teach us how to love, Solomon describe, Apelles paint, or Helena express it. They must not therefore compel or intrude; for who (as Fabius urgeth) can love with an estranged mind? but consider withal the miseries of enforced marriages; take pity upon youth: and such above the rest as have daughters to bestow, should be very careful and provident to marry them in due time. Siracides calls it a weighty matter to perform, so to marry a daughter to a man of understanding in due time. As Lemnius admonisheth, virgins must be provided for in season, to prevent many diseases, of which Rodericus a Castro, and Lod. Mercatus, have both largely discoursed. And therefore as well to avoid these feral maladies, 'tis good to get them husbands betimes, as to prevent other gross inconveniences, and for a thing that I know besides; when the time and age for marriage hath come, as Chrysostom adviseth, let them not defer it; they perchance will marry themselves else, or do worse. If Nevisanus the Lawyer do not impose, they may do it by right: for as he proves out of Curtius, and some other Civilians, a Maid past 25 years of age, against her parents' consent, may marry such a one as is unworthy of, and inferior to her, and her Father by law must be compelled to give her a competent dowry. Mistake me not in the mean time, or think that I do apologize here for any headstrong unruly wanton flirts. I do approve that of S. Ambrose which he hath written touching Rebecca's spousals: A woman should give unto her parents the choice of her husband, lest she be reputed to be malapert and wanton, if she take upon her to make her own choice, for she should rather seem to be desired by a man, than to desire a man herself. To those hard parents alone I retort that of Curtius (in the behalf of modester Maids) that are too remiss and careless of their due time and riper years. For if they tarry longer, to say truth, they are past date, and nobody will respect them. A woman with us in Italy (saith Aretine's Lucretia) 24 years of age, is old already, past the best, of no account.

An old fellow, as Lysistrata confesseth in Aristophanes, though grey-haired, can have as wife a young maid, and 'tis no news for an old fellow to marry a young wench: but as he follows it, a woman's term is brief, and if 'tis not used in time, no one wants her for a wife; who cares for an old Maid? she may sit and wait. A virgin, as the Poet holds, a desirous and sportive girl, is like a flower, a Rose withered on a sudden.

> *She that was erst a Maid as fresh as May,*
> *Is now an old Crone, time so steals away.*   (AUSONIUS)

Let them take time then while they may, make advantage of youth, and as he prescribes,

> *Fair Maids, go gather Roses in the prime,*
> *And think that as a flower so goes on time.*   (AUSONIUS)

Let's all love, whiles we are in the flower of years, fit for Love-matters, and while time serves: for

> *Suns that set may rise again,*
> *But if once we lose this light,*
> *'Tis with us perpetual night.** (CATULLUS)

Time past cannot be recall'd. But we need no such exhortation, we are all commonly too forward: yet if there be any escape, and all be not as it should, as Diogenes struck the Father when the son swore, because he taught him no better; if a maid or young man miscarry, I think their Parents oftentimes, Guardians, Overseers, Governours, (saith Chrysostom) are in as much fault, and as severely to be punished, as their children, in providing for them no sooner.

Now for such as have free liberty to bestow themselves, I could wish that good counsel of the Comical old man were put in practice,

> *That rich men would marry poor maidens some,*
> *And that without dowry, and so bring them home,*
> *So would much concord be in our city,*
> *Less envy should we have, much more pity.*   (PLAUTUS)

If they would care less for wealth, we should have much more content and quietness in a Common-wealth. Beauty, good bringing up, methinks, is a sufficient portion of itself; their beauty is girls' dowry, and he doth well that will accept of such a wife. Eubulides in Aristænetus married a poor man's child, of a merry countenance, and heavenly visage, in pity of her estate, and that quickly. Acontius, coming to Delos to sacrifice to Diana, fell in love with Cydippe, a noble lass, and wanting means to get her love, flung a golden apple into her lap, with this inscription upon it,

* Translated by Mr. B. Jonson. — Burton's note.

I swear by all the Rites of Diana,
I'll come and be thy husband if I may.

She considered of it, and upon some small enquiry of his person and estate was married unto him.

Blessed is the wooing,
That is not long a doing,

as the saying is; when the parties are sufficiently known to each other, what needs such scrupulosity, so many circumstances? dost thou know her conditions, her bringing up, like her person? let her means be what they will, take her without any more ado. Dido and Æneas were accidently driven by a storm both into one cave, they made a match upon it; Masinissa was married to that fair captive Sophonisba, King Syphax' wife, the same day that he saw her first, to prevent Scipio and Lælius, lest they should determine otherwise of her. If thou lovest the party, do as much: good education and beauty is a competent dowry, stand not upon money. Mens' hearts once were made of gold (saith Theocritus) and troth met troth, in days of old; in the golden world men did so (in the reign of Ogyges belike, before staggering Ninus began to domineer) if all be true that is reported: and some few nowadays will do as much, here and there one; 'tis well done methinks, and all happiness befall them for so doing. Leontius, a Philosopher of Athens, had a fair daughter called Athenais, (saith mine author) of a comely carriage, he gave her no portion but her bringing up, out of some secret foreknowledge of her fortune, bestowing that little which he had amongst his other children. But she, thus qualified, was preferred by some friends to Constantinople to serve Pulcheria, the Emperor's sister, of whom she was baptized and called Eudocia. Theodosius the Emperor in short space took notice of her excellent beauty and good parts, and a little after, upon his sister's sole commendation, made her his wife: 'twas nobly done of Theodosius. Rhodope was the fairest Lady in her days in all Egypt; she went to wash her, and by chance (her maids meanwhile looking but carelessly to her clothes) an Eagle stole away one of her shoes, and laid it in Psammetichus the King of Egypt's lap at Memphis: he wondered at the excellency of the shoe, and pretty foot, but more at the deed of the eagle, at the manner of the bringing of it: and caused forthwith proclamation to be made, that she that owned that shoe, should come presently to his Court; the Virgin came and was forthwith married to the King. I say this was heroically done, and like a Prince: I commend him for it, and all such as have means, that will either do (as he did) themselves, or so for love, &c. marry their children. If he be rich, let him take such a one as wants, if she be virtuously given; for as Siracides adviseth, Forego not a wife and good woman; for her grace is above gold. If she have fortunes of her own, let her take * a man. Danaus of Lacedæmon had a many daughters to bestow, and means enough for them all, he never stood enquiring after great matches, as others used to do, but sent for a company of brave young gallants home to his house, and bid his daughters choose every one one, whom she liked best, and take him for her husband, without any more ado. This act of his was much approved in those times. But in this Iron age of ours we respect riches alone (for a maid must buy her husband now, with a great dowry, if she will have him), covetousness and filthy lucre mars all good matches, or some such by-respects. Crales, a Servian Prince (as Nicephorus Gregoras relates it), was an earnest suitor to Eudocia the Emperor's sister; though her brother much desired it, yet she could not abide him, for he had three former wives, all basely abused; but the Emperor still, because he was a great Prince, and a troublesome neighbour, much desired his affinity, and to that end betrothed his own daughter Simonida to him, a little girl five years of age (he being forty-five) and five years elder than the Emperor himself: such disproportionable and unlikely matches can wealth and a fair fortune make. And yet not that alone, it is not only money, but sometimes vain-glory, pride, ambition, do as much harm as wretched covetousness itself in another extreme. If a Yeoman have one sole daughter, he must over-match her, above her birth and calling, to a Gentleman forsooth, because of her great portion, too good for one of her own rank, as he supposeth. A Gentleman's daughter and heir must be married to a Knight baronet's eldest son at least; and a Knight's only daughter to a Baron himself, or an Earl, and so upwards, her great dowry deserves it. And thus striving for more honour to their wealth, they undo their children, many discontents follow, and oftentimes they ruinate their Families. Paulus Jovius gives instance in Galeatius the second, that Heroical Duke of Milan, who sought foreign matrimonial alliances, honourable indeed and of royal state, but hurtful and almost fatal to him and his successors; he married his eldest son John Galeatius to Isabella, the King of France his sister, but she was so great a burden to her father-in-law, he spent two hundred thousand gold pieces on her appointments, her entertainment at Milan was so costly, that it almost undid him. His daughter Violanta was married to Lionel, Duke of Clarence, the youngest son to Edward the Third, King of England, but he was welcomed with such incredible magnificence, that a King's purse

* " Make," in text.

was scarce able to bear it; for besides many rich presents of horses, arms, plate, money, jewels, &c., he made one dinner for him and his company, in which were thirty-two messes, and as much provision left as would serve ten thousand men: but a little after Lionel died, devoting himself to his bride and untimely entertainments, and to the Duke's great loss, the solemnity was ended. So can titles, honours, ambition, make many brave, but unfortunate matches, of all sides, for by-respects, though both crazed in body and mind, most unwilling, averse, and often unfit; so love is banished, and we feel the smart of it in the end. But I am too lavish peradventure in this subject.

Another let or hindrance is strict and severe Discipline, Laws and rigorous customs that forbid men to marry at set times, and in some places: as Prentices, Servants, Collegiates, States of lives in Copy-holds, or in some base inferior Offices, *thou mayst crave*, in such cases, *thou canst not have*, as he * said. They see but as prisoners through a grate, they covet and catch but as Tantalus the waters that recede from his lips. Their love is lost, and vain it is in such an estate to attempt. 'Tis a grievous thing to love and not enjoy. They may indeed, I deny not, marry if they will, and have free choice some of them; but in the mean time their case is desperate, they hold a Wolf by the ears, they must either burn or starve. 'Tis a sophistical dilemma, hard to resolve. If they marry, they forfeit their estates, they are undone and starve themselves through beggary and want: if they do not marry, in this heroical passion they furiously rage, are tormented, and torn to pieces by their predominate affections.

Every man hath not the gift of continence, let him pray for it then, as Beza adviseth in his Tract on Divorce, because God hath so called him to a single life, in taking away the means of marriage: Paul would have gone from Mysia to Bithynia, but the Spirit suffered him not, and thou wouldst peradventure be a married man with all thy will, but that protecting Angel holds it not fit. The devil too sometimes may divert by his ill suggestions, and mar many good matches, as the same Paul was willing to see the Romans, but hindered of Satan, he could not.

There be those that think they are necessitated by Fate, their Stars have so decreed, and therefore they grumble at their hard fortune, they are well inclined to marry, but one rub or other is ever in the way: I know what Astrologers say in this behalf, what Ptolemy, Skoner, what Leovitius, in his first Example of Geniture, which Sextus ab Heminga takes to be the Horoscope of Hieronymus Wulfius, what Pezelius, Origanaus, and Leovitius his illustrator, Garceus, what Junc-

* Apuleius.

tine, Protanus, Campanella, what the rest (to omit those Arabian conjectures as to marriage, as to lasciviousness, the threefold Venus, &c.,
and those resolutions upon a question, whether he will obtain a mistress,
&c.) determine in this behalf, for example, whether he was born to have
a wife, whether he will win a spouse easily or hardly, how many marriages, when, what kind of wives, as to their mutual love, both in men's
and women's genitures, by the examination of the seventh house, the
Almutens [or prevailing planets in the horoscope], Lords and Planets
there, a Moon dominant and Sun ascendant, &c., by particular Aphorisms, whether the Lord of the Seventh, in the Seventh or the Second,
awards a better wife, a slave or one not noble in the Twelfth, if Venus
in the Twelfth ———— with many such, too tedious to relate. Yet let
no man be troubled, or find himself grieved with such Predictions, as
Hier. Wolfius well saith in his Astrological Dialogue, these are not decrees, they be but conjectures, the Stars incline, but not enforce. The
heavenly bodies have power over our bodies, these being but of vile
clay; but they bind not the rational mind, for that is under the dominion of God only. Wisdom, diligence, discretion, may mitigate, if not
quite alter, such decrees; everyone is the architect of his own fortune,
those who are cautious and prudent compass their desires. Let no man
then be terrified or molested with such Astrological Aphorisms, or be
much moved, either to vain hope or fear, from such predictions, but let
every man follow his own free will in this case, and do as he sees cause.
Better it is indeed to marry than burn for their soul's health, but for
their present fortunes by some other means to pacify themselves, and
divert the stream of this fiery torrent, to continue as they are, rest satisfied, lamenting the flower of virginity thus ungathered, deploring their
misery with that Eunuch in Libanius, since there is no help or remedy,
and with Jephthah's daughter to bewail their virginities.

Of like nature is superstition, those rash vows of Monks and Friars,
and such as live in religious Orders, but far more tyrannical and much
worse. Nature, youth, and his furious passion forcibly inclines, and
rageth on the one side: but their Order and Vow checks them on the
other.

Thy beauty doth such vows forbid. (OVID)

What Merits and Indulgences they heap unto themselves by it, what
commodities, I know not; but I am sure, from such rash vows, and
inhuman manner of life proceed many inconveniences, many diseases,
many vices, mastupration, satyriasis, priapism, melancholy, madness,

fornication, adultery, buggary, sodomy, theft, murder, and all manner of mischiefs: read but Bale's Catalogue of Sodomites at the Visitation of Abbies here in England, Henry Stephan his Apology for Herodotus, that which Ulricus writes in one of his Epistles, that Pope Gregory, when he saw 6,000 skulls and bones of infants taken out of a fish-pond near a Nunnery, thereupon retracted that decree of Priests' marriages, which was the cause of such a slaughter, was much grieved at it, and purged himself by repentance. Read many such, and then ask what is to be done, is this vow to be broke or not? No, saith Bellarmine, better burn or fly out than to break thy vow. And Coster saith it is absolutely a greater sin for a Priest to marry, than to keep a concubine at home. Gregory de Valence maintains the same, as those Essenes and Montanists of old. Insomuch that many Votaries, out of a false persuasion of merit and holiness in this kind, will sooner die than marry, though it be to the saving of their lives. In the year 1419, Pius 2, [being] Pope, James Rossa, Nephew to the King of Portugal, and then elect Archbishop of Lisbon, being very sick at Florence, when his Physicians told him that his disease was such he must either lie with a wench, marry, or die, cheerfully chose to die. Now they commended him for it: but S. Paul teacheth otherwise, Better marry than burn, and as S. Hierome gravely delivers it, There's a difference betwixt God's ordinances, and men's laws: and therefore Cyprian boldly denounceth, it is abominable, impious, adulterous, and sacrilegious, what men make and ordain after their own furies to cross God's laws. Georgius Wicelius, one of their own arch Divines, exclaims against it, and all such rash monastical vows, and would have such persons seriously to consider what they do, whom they admit, lest they repent it at last. For either, as he follows it, you must allow them Concubines, or suffer them to marry, for scarce shall you find three Priests of three thousand, in their prime that are not troubled with burning lust. Wherefore I conclude, it is an unnatural and impious thing to bar men of this Christian liberty, too severe and inhuman an edict.

> The silly wrenne, the titmouse also,
> The little redbrest have free election,
> To flyen y-fere and together gone,
> Whereas hem list, aboute environ,
> As they of kinde have inclination,
> And as Nature, empresse and guide,
> Of everything list to provide.
> But man alone, alas the hard stond,
> Full cruelly by kindes ordinance

Constrained is, and by statutes bound,
And debarred from all suche pleasance;
What meaneth this, what is this pretence
Of lawes, I wis, against all right of kinde,
Without a cause, so narrow men to binde? *

Many Lay-men repine still at Priests' marriages above the rest, and not at Clergymen only, but all of the meaner sort and condition, they would have none marry but such as are rich and able to maintain wives, because their parish belike shall be pestered with orphans, and the world full of beggars: but these are hard-hearted, unnatural, monsters of men, shallow politicians, they do not consider that a great part of the world is not yet inhabited as it ought, how many Colonies into America, Terra Australis Incognita, Africa, may be sent! Let them consult with Sir William Alexander's Book of Colonies, Orpheus Junior's Golden Fleece, Captain Whitburne, Mr. Hagthorpe, &c., and they shall surely be otherwise informed. Those politick Romans were of another mind, they thought their City and Country could never be too populous. Adrian the Emperor said he had rather have men than money. Augustus Cæsar made an oration in Rome to bachelors to persuade them to marry; some countries compelled them to marry of old, as Jews, Turks, Indians, Chinese, amongst the rest in these days, who much wonder at our discipline to suffer so many idle persons to live in Monasteries, and often marvel how they can live honest. In the Isle of Maragnan the Governor and petty King there did wonder at the Frenchmen, and admire how so many Friars, and the rest of their company could live without wives, they thought it a thing unpossible, and would not believe it. If these men should but survey our multitudes of religious houses, observe our numbers of Monasteries all over Europe, 18 Nunneries in Padua, in Venice 31 Cloisters of Monks, 28 of Nuns, &c., from the claw guessing what size the beast must be, 'tis to this proportion in all other Provinces and Cities, what would they think, do they live honest? Let them dissemble as they will, I am of Tertullian's mind, that few can contain but by compulsion. O chastity (saith he) thou art a rare Goddess in the world, not so easily got, seldom continuate: thou may'st now and then be compelled either for defect of nature, or if discipline persuade, decrees enforce; — or for some such by-respects, sullenness, discontent, they have lost their first loves, may not have whom they will themselves, want of means, rash vows, &c. But can he willingly contain? I think not. Therefore, either out of commiseration of human imbecility, in policy, or to prevent a far worse inconvenience, for they

* Lydgate.

hold it some of them as necessary as meat and drink, and because vigour of youth, the state and temper of most men's bodies, do so furiously desire it, they have heretofore in some Nations liberally admitted polygamy and stews, an hundred thousand Courtisans in grand Cairo in Egypt, as Radzivilius observes, are tolerated, besides boys: how many at Fessa, Rome, Naples, Florence, Venice, &c.? and still in many other Provinces and Cities of Europe they do as much, because they think young men, Church-men, and servants amongst the rest, can hardly live honest. The consideration of this belike made Vibius, the Spaniard, when his friend Crassus that rich Roman gallant lay hid in the Cave, to gratify him the more, send two lusty lasses to accompany him all the while he was there imprisoned; and Surenas the Parthian General, when he warred against the Romans, to carry about with him 200 Concubines, as the Swiss Soldiers do now commonly their wives. But because this course is not generally approved, but rather contradicted as unlawful, and abhorred, in most Countries they do much encourage them to marriage, give great rewards for such as have many children, and mulct those that will not marry; the Law of three children, and in A. Gellius, Ælian, Valerius, we read that three children freed the father from painful offices, and five from all contribution. " A woman shall be saved by bearing children." Epictetus would have all marry, and as Plato will, he that marrieth not before 35 years of his age must be compelled or punished, and the money consecrated to Juno's Temple, or applied to publick uses. They account him in some Countries unfortunate that dies without a wife, a most unhappy man, as Boethius infers, and if at all happy, yet unhappy in his supposed happiness. They commonly deplore his estate, and much lament him for it; O my sweet son! &c. See Lucian, Sands, &c.

Yet notwithstanding many with us are of the opposite part, they are married themselves, and for others, let them burn, fire, and flame, they care not, so they be not troubled with them. Some are too curious, and some too covetous, they may marry when they will, both for ability and means, but so nice, that except, as Theophilus, the Emperor, was presented, by his Mother Euphrosyne, with all the rarest beauties of the Empire in the Great Chamber of his Palace at once, and bid to give a golden apple to her he liked best. If they might so take and choose whom they list out of all the fair Maids their Nation affords, they could happily condescend to marry: otherwise, &c., why should a man marry, saith another Epicurean rout, what's matrimony but a matter of money? why should free nature be entrenched on, confined or obliged,

to this or that man or woman, with these manacles of body and goods?
&c. There are those too, that dearly love, admire and follow women, all
their lives long, like Penelope's suitors, never well but in their companies, wistly gazing on their beauties, observing close, hanging after
them, dallying still with them, and yet dare not, will not, marry. Many
poor people, and of the meaner sort, are too distrustful of God's providence, they will not, dare not for such worldly respects, fear of want,
woes, miseries, or that they shall light, as Lemnius saith, on a scold, a
slut, or a bad wife. And therefore turning away from Venus they spend
a joyless youth, they are resolved to live single, as Epaminondas
did, —

There's nothing better than a single life, (HORACE)
— and ready with Hippolytus to abjure all women, detest, abhor, flee,
execrate them all. But alas, poor Hippolytus, thou knowest not what
thou sayest, 'tis otherwise, Hippolytus. Some make a doubt whether a
Scholar should marry; if she be fair, she will bring him back from his
grammar to his horn-book, or else with kissing and dalliance she will
hinder his study; if foul, with scolding, he cannot well intend to both,
as Philippus Beroaldus, that great Bononian [or Bolognian] Doctor,
once writ, 'tis sure to hinder the study of letters; but he recanted at
last, and in a solemn sort with true conceived words he did ask the world
and all women forgiveness. But you shall have the story as he relates
himself, in his Commentaries on the sixth of Apuleius: For a long time
I lived a single life, I could not abide marriage, but as a rambler, (to
use his own words) I took a snatch where I could get it, nay more, I
railed at marriage downright, and in a publick auditory when I did
interpret that sixth Satire of Juvenal, out of Plutarch and Seneca, I
did heap up all the dicteries [or sayings] I could against women; but
now recant with Stesichorus, I sing a Palinode, I approve of marriage,
I am glad I am a married man, I am heartily glad I have a wife, so
sweet a wife, so noble a wife, so young, so chaste a wife, so loving a
wife, and I do wish and desire all other men to marry, and especially
Scholars; that as of old Marcia did by Hortensius, Terentia by Tullius,
Calphurnia to Plinius, Pudentilla to Apuleius, hold the candle whilst
their husbands did meditate and write, so theirs may do to them, and
as my dear Camilla doth to me. Let other men be averse, rail then and
scoff at women, and say what they can to the contrary, a single man is
an happy man, &c., but this is a toy,

Reject not in your prime sweet love and mirth; (HORACE)
these men are too distrustful and much to blame, to use such speeches,

Forbear to blame on womankind
The guilt that in one girl you find. (HORACE)

They must not condemn all for some. As there be many bad, there be some good wives; as some be vicious, some be virtuous: read what Solomon hath said in their praises, and Siracides. " Blessed is the man that hath a virtuous wife, for the number of his days shall be double. A virtuous woman rejoiceth her husband, and she shall fulfil the years of his life in peace. A good wife is a good portion, an help, a pillar of rest."

Who takes a wife, hath brother and sister too. (APHRANIUS)

He that hath no wife wandereth to and fro mourning. Women are the sole, only joy, and comfort of a man's life, born for the use and pleasure of men, and the founding of a family.

Joy of the human race, solace in life,
By night caressing, and by day the object
Of pleasant care, the strong desire of men,
The hope of lads. (LOECHAEUS)

A wife is a young man's Mistress, a middle age's companion, an old man's Nurse : sharer of joys and sorrows, a prop, an help, &c.

Man's best possession is a loving wife,
She tempers anger and diverts all strife. (EURIPIDES)

There is no joy, no comfort, no sweetness, no pleasure in the world like to that of a good wife. With what harmony, saith our Latin Homer, a loving wife and constant husband lead their lives ; she is still the same in sickness and in health, his eye, his hand, his bosom-friend, his partner at all times, his other self, not to be separated by any calamity, but ready to share all sorrow, discontent, and as the Indian women do, live and die with him, nay more, to die presently for him. Admetus, King of Thessaly, when he lay upon his death-bed, was told by Apollo's Oracle, that if he could get any body to die for him, he should live longer yet, but when all refused, his parents, although decrepit, friends and followers, forsook him, Alcestis his wife, though young, most willingly undertook it ; what more can be desired or expected? And although on the other side there be an infinite number of bad husbands (I should rail downright against some of them) able to discourage any women ; yet there be some good ones again, and those most observant of Marriage Rites. An honest Country-fellow (as Fulgosus relates it) in the kingdom of Naples, at plough by the Sea side, saw his wife carried away by Mauritanian Pirates, he ran after in all haste, up to the chin first, and when he could wade no longer, swam, calling to the Governo.

of the ship to deliver his wife, or if he must not have her restored, to let him follow as a prisoner, for he was resolved to be a Galley-slave, his drudge, willing to endure any misery, so that he might but enjoy his dear wife. The Moors, seeing the man's constancy, and relating the whole matter to their Governor at Tunis, set them both free, and gave them an honest pension to maintain themselves during their lives. I could tell many stories to this effect; but put case it often prove otherwise, because marriage is troublesome, wholly therefore to avoid it is no argument; he that will avoid trouble must avoid the world (Eusebius). Some trouble there is in marriage, I deny not. And if matrimony be a burden, saith Erasmus, yet there be many things to sweeten it, a pleasant wife, pretty children, *the chief delight of the sons of men*. And howsoever, though it were all troubles, it must willingly be undergone for publick good's sake.

> *Hear me, O my countrymen, saith Susarion,*
> *Women are nought, yet no life without one.* (STOBÆUS)

Say they are evils, yet they are necessary evils, and for our own ends we must make use of them to have issue, to give pleasure and restore the race, and to propagate the Church. For to what end is a man born? why lives he, but to increase the world? and how shall he do that well, if he do not marry? Saith Nevisanus, matrimony makes us immortal, and according to Tacitus, 'tis the sole and chief prop of an Empire.

He lives contemptibly through whom none else has life,   (PALINGENIUS)
which Pelopidas objected to Epaminondas, he was an unworthy member of a Common-wealth, that left not a child after him to defend it; and as Trismegistus to his son Tatius, have no commerce with a single man: holding belike that a bachelor could not live honestly as he should; and with Georgius Wicelius, a great Divine and holy man, who of late by twenty-six arguments commends marriage as a thing most necessary for all kind of persons, most laudable and fit to be embraced: and is persuaded withal, that no man can live and die religiously, and as he ought, without a wife, he is false, an enemy to the Common-wealth, injurious to himself, destructive to the world, an apostate to nature, a rebel against Heaven and Earth. Let our wilful, obstinate, and stale Bachelors ruminate of this. If we could live without wives, as Marcellus Numidicus said in A. Gellius, we would all want them, but because we cannot, let all marry, and consult rather to the publick good, than their own private pleasure or estate. It were an happy thing, as wise Euripides hath it, if we could buy children with gold and silver, and be so provided, without women's company, but that may not be.

Earth, air, sea, land, eftsoon would come to nought,
The world itself should be to ruin brought. (SENECA)

Necessity therefore compels us to marry.

But what do I trouble myself, to find arguments to persuade to, or commend marriage? behold a brief abstract of all that which I have said, and much more, succinctly, pithily, pathetically, perspicuously, and elegantly delivered in twelve motives to mitigate the miseries of marriage, by Jacobus de Voragine.

1. Hast thou means? thou hast one to keep and increase it.
2. Hast none? thou hast one to help to get it.
3. Art in prosperity? thine happiness is doubled.
4. Art in adversity? she'll comfort, assist, bear a part of thy burden to make it more tolerable.
5. Art at home? she'll drive away melancholy.
6. Art abroad? she looks after thee going from home, wishes for thee in thine absence, and joyfully welcomes thy return.
7. There's nothing delightsome without society, no society so sweet as matrimony.
8. The band of conjugal love is adamantine.
9. The sweet company of kinsmen increaseth, the number of parents is doubled, of brothers, sisters, nephews.
10. Thou art made a father by a fair and happy issue.
11. Moses curseth the barrenness of matrimony, how much more a single life?
12. If nature escape not punishment, surely thy will shall not avoid it.

All this is true, say you, and who knows it not? but how easy a matter is it to answer these motives, and to make an Antiparody quite opposite unto it? To exercise myself I will essay.

1. Hast thou means? thou hast one to spend it.
2. Hast none? thy beggary is increased.
3. Art in prosperity? thy happiness is ended.
4. Art in adversity? like Job's wife, she'll aggravate thy misery, vex thy soul, make thy burden intolerable.
5. Art at home? she'll scold thee out of doors.
6. Art abroad? If thou be wise, keep thee so, she'll perhaps graft horns in thine absence, scowl on thee coming home.
7. Nothing gives more content than solitariness, no solitariness like this of a single life.
8. The band of marriage is adamantine, no hope of losing it, thou art undone.

9. Thy number increaseth, thou shalt be devoured by thy wife's friends.

10. Thou art made a cornuto by an unchaste wife, and shalt bring up other folks' children instead of thine own.

11. Paul commends marriage, yet he prefers a single life.

12. Is marriage honourable? What an immortal crown belongs to virginity!

So Siracides himself speaks as much as may be for and against women, so doth almost every Philosopher plead for and against, every Poet thus argues the case (though what cares the common man what they say?), so can I conceive peradventure, and so canst thou: when all is said, yet since some be good, some bad, let's put it to the venture. I conclude therefore with Seneca, Why dost thou lie alone, let thy youth and best days to pass away? Marry whilst thou mayest, whilst thou art yet able, yet lusty,

Find her to whom you may say, "Thou art my only pleasure," (OVID) make thy choice, and that freely, forthwith, make no delay, but take thy fortune as it falls. 'Tis true,

> *Unhappy he who lights on a bad wife,*
> *Happy he who obtains a good one.* (EURIPIDES)

'Tis an hazard both ways I confess, to live single, or to marry; it may be bad, it may be good; as it is a cross and calamity on the one side, so 'tis a sweet delight, an incomparable happiness, a blessed estate, a most unspeakable benefit, a sole content on the other; 'tis all in the proof. Be not then so wayward, so covetous, so distrustful, so curious and nice, but let's all marry, lie in mutual warm embrace. Take me to thee, and thee to me, to morrow is St. Valentine's day, let's keep it Holiday for Cupid's sake, for that great God Love's sake, for Hymen's sake, and celebrate Venus' Vigil with our Ancestors for company together, singing as they did,

To-morrow let him love who ne'er loved yet,
Nor let him who e'er loved before forget,
'Tis tuneful spring, the world's new-born in spring
It is love's season, birds then pairing sing,
'Tis then the woods renew their annual green. (PERVIGILIUM VENERIS)

Let him that is averse from marriage read more in Barbarus, Lemnius, P. Godefridus, Nevisanus, Alex. ab Alexandro, Tunstall, Erasmus' tracts In Praise of Matrimony, &c., and I doubt not but in the end he will rest satisfied, recant with Beroaldus, do penance for his former folly, singing some penitential ditties, desire to be reconciled to the

Deity of this great God Love, go a pilgrimage to his Shrine, offer to his Image, sacrifice upon his altar, and be as willing at last to embrace marriage as the rest. There will not be found, I hope, no, not in that severe family of Stoicks, who shall refuse to submit his grave beard, and supercilious looks to the clipping of a wife, or disagree from his fellows in this point. For what more willingly (as Varro holds) can a proper man see than a fair wife, a sweet wife, a loving wife? Can the world afford a better sight, sweeter content, a fairer object, a more gracious aspect?

Since then this of marriage is the last and best refuge and cure of Heroical love, all doubts are cleared, and impediments removed; I say again, what remains, but that according to both their desires, they be happily joined, since it cannot otherwise be helped. God send us all good wives, every man his wish in this kind, and me mine!

> And God that all this wyde world hath wrought,
> Send him his love that hath it dere y-bought.

If all parties be pleased, ask their Banns, 'tis a match. Rhodanthe and Dosicles shall go together, Clitiphon and Leucippe, Theagenes and Chariclea, Poliarchus hath his Argenis,* Lysander Calista, (to make up the mask) and Iphis enjoys his Ianthe.

> And Troilus in lust and in quiete
> Is with Creseide, his owne herte swete.

And although they have hardly past the pikes, through many difficulties and delays brought the match about, yet let them take this of Aristæ-netus (that so marry) for their comfort: after many troubles and cares, the marriages of Lovers are more sweet and pleasant. As we commonly conclude a Comedy with a wedding, and shaking of hands, let's shut up our discourse, and end all with an Epithalamium.

Happiness to bride and groom! God give them joy together! Hymen, lead the wedding home, Hymen Hymenaeus, come! 'Tis well done, and not without the aid of the gods, 'tis an happy conjunction, a fortunate match, an even couple, they both excel in gifts of body and mind, are both equal in years, youth, vigour, alacrity, she is fair and lovely as Lais or Helena, he as another Cleinias or Alcibiades, —

> *Then modestly go sport and toy,*
> *And let's have every year a boy.* (CATULLUS)

Go give a sweet smell as Incense, and bring forth flowers as the Lily: that we may say hereafter, Faith, Pamphilus has got a son. In the mean time I say,

* John Barclay's poem of that name.

O gentle youths, go sport yourselves betimes,
Let not the Doves outpass your murmurings,
  Or Ivy-clasping arms, or oyster kissings.   (GALLIENUS)

And in the morn betime, as those Lacedæmonian Lasses saluted Helena
and Menelaus, singing at their windows, and wishing good success, do
we at yours:

Good morrow, Master Bridegroom, and Mistress Bride,
Many fair lovely Bairns to you betide!
Let Venus to you mutual love procure,
Let Saturn give you riches to endure.
Long may you sleep in one another's arms,
Inspiring sweet desire, and free from harms.   (THEOCRITUS)

Even all your lives long,

  The love of Turtles hap to you,
  And Ravens' years still to renew.   (ERASMUS)

Let the Muses sing, (as he said) the Graces dance, not at their weddings
only, but all their days long; so couple their hearts, that no irksomeness
or anger ever befall them. Let him never call her other name than my
joy, my light, or she call him otherwise than sweet-heart. To this happiness of theirs, let not old age any whit detract, but as their years, so
let their mutual love and comfort increase. And when they depart this
life,

  Because they have so sweetly liv'd together,
  Let not one die a day before the other,
  He bury her, she him, with even fate,
  One hour their souls let jointly separate.   (OVID)
  O happy both! if that my lines have power,
  No time shall ever make your memory fade.   (VIRGIL)

And this is enough said of love, subject, as Kornmannus said, to correction by those who know better. Who would more of the remedies of
love, let them read Jason Pratensis, Arnoldus, Montaltus, Savanarola,
Langius, Valescus, Crimisonus, Alexander Benedictus, Laurentius,
Valleriola, the poet Ovid, and our Chaucer, with whom I conclude.

  For myne wordes here and every part,
  I speak hem alle under correcioun,
  Of you that feeling have in love's art,
  And put it all in your discrecion,
  To increse or maken diminucion,
  Of my language, that I you beseech:
  But now to purpose of my rather speech.

SECTION — MEMBER

SUBSECTION 1 — *Jealousy, its Equivocations, Name, Definition, Extent, several kinds ; of Princes, Parents, Friends. In Beasts, Men : before marriage, as Corrivals ; or after, as in this place*

VALESCUS DE TARANTA, Ælian Montaltus, Felix Platerus, Guianerius, put Jealousy for a cause of Melancholy, others for a Symptom; because melancholy persons, amongst these passions and perturbations of the mind, are most obnoxious to it. But methinks for the latitude it hath, and that prerogative above other ordinary Symptoms, it ought to be treated of as a Species apart, being of so great and eminent note, so furious a passion, and almost of as great extent as Love itself, as Benedetto Varchi holds, No Love without a mixture of Jealousy; who's not jealous, loves not. For these causes I will dilate, and treat of it by itself, as a bastard-branch, or kind of Love-Melancholy, which, as Heroical Love goeth commonly before marriage, doth usually follow, torture, and crucify in like sort, deserves therefore to be rectified alike, requires as much care and industry, in setting out the several causes of it, prognosticks and cures. Which I have more willingly done, that he that is or hath been jealous, may see his error as in a glass; he that is not, may learn to detest, avoid it himself, and dispossess others that are any wise affected with it.

Jealousy is described and defined to be a certain suspicion which the Lover hath of the party he chiefly loveth, lest he or she should be enamoured of another: or any eager desire to enjoy some beauty alone, to have it proper to himself only: a fear or doubt, lest any foreigner should participate or share with him in his love. Or (as Scaliger adds) a fear of losing her favour, whom he so earnestly affects. Cardan calls it, a zeal for love, and a kind of envy lest any man should beguile us. Ludovicus Vives defines it in the very same words, or little differing in sense.

There be many other Jealousies, but improperly so called all; as that of Parents, Tutors, Guardians, over their children, friends whom they love, or such as are left to their wardship or protection.

Storax, young master's not returned from supper,
Nor any of the slaves that went to meet him; (TERENCE)
as the old man in the Comedy cried out in passion, and from a solicitous fear and care he had of his adopted son; not of beauty, but lest they should miscarry, do amiss, or any way discredit, disgrace (as Vives

notes) or endanger themselves and us. Ægeus was so solicitous for his
son Theseus, (when he went to fight with the Minotaur) of his success,
lest he should be foiled; fear always will believe the worst. We are still
apt to suspect the worst in such doubtful cases, as many wives in their
husbands' absence, fond mothers in their children's, lest if absent they
should be misled or sick, and are continually expecting news from
them, how they do fare, and what is become of them, they cannot endure to have them long out of their sight. Oh my sweet son! O my dear
child! &c. Paul was jealous over the Church of Corinth, as he confesseth, " with a godly jealousy, to present them a pure Virgin to Christ ";
and he was afraid still lest, as the Serpent beguiled Eve through his
subtilty, so their minds should be corrupted from the simplicity that
is in Christ. God himself in some sense is said to be jealous, " I am a
jealous God, and will visit "; so, " Shall thy jealousy burn like fire for
ever? " But these are improperly called Jealousies, and by a Metaphor,
to shew the care and solicitude they have of them. Although some
Jealousies express all the Symptoms of this which we treat of, fear,
sorrow, anguish, anxiety, suspicion, hatred, &c., the object only varied.
That of some fathers is very eminent to their sons and heirs; for though
they love them dearly being children, yet now coming towards man's
estate they may not well abide them, the son and heir is commonly sick
of the father, and the father again may not well brook his eldest son,
they are full of quarrels and enmities. But that of Princes is most notorious, as when they fear corrivals, (if I may so call them), successors,
emulators, subjects, or such as they have offended. Impatience ever goes
with power; they are still suspicious, lest their authority should be
diminished, as one observes; and as Commines hath it, it cannot be
expressed what slender causes they have of their grief and suspicion, a
secret disease that commonly lurks and breeds in Princes' families.
Sometimes it is for their honour only, as that of Adrian the Emperor,
that killed all his emulators. Saul envied David; Domitian Agricola,
because he did excel him, obscure his honour as he thought, eclipse his
fame. Juno turned Prœtus' daughters into Kine, for that they contended
with her for beauty; Cyparissæ, King Etocles' children, were envied of
the Goddesses for their excellent good parts, and dancing amongst the
rest, saith Constantine,* & for that cause flung down head-long from
heaven, and buried in a pit, but the earth took pity of them, and brought
out cypress trees to preserve their memories. Niobe, Arachne, and
Marsyas can testify as much. But it is most grievous when it is for a
kingdom itself, or matters of commodity, it produceth lamentable

* In his Husbandry.

effects, especially amongst Tyrants, and such as are more feared than beloved of their subjects, that get and keep their sovereignty by force, and fear, as Phalaris, Dionysius, Periander held theirs. For though fear, cowardice, and jealousy, in Plutarch's opinion, be the common causes of tyranny, as in Nero, Caligula, Tiberius, yet most take them to be symptoms. For what slave, what hang-man (as Bodine well expresseth this passion) can so cruelly torture a condemned person, as this fear and suspicion? Fear of death, infamy, torments, are those furies and vultures that vex and disquiet tyrants, and torture them day and night, with perpetual terrors and affrights, envy, suspicion, fear, desire of revenge, and a thousand such disagreeing perturbations, turn and affright the soul out of the hinges of health, and more grievously wound and pierce, than those cruel masters can exasperate and vex their prentices or servants, with clubs, whips, chains, and tortures. Many terrible examples we have in this kind, amongst the Turks especially, many jealous outrages; Selimus killed Cornutus his youngest brother, five of his Nephews, Mustapha Bassa, and divers others. Bajazet, the second Turk, jealous of the valour and greatness of Achmet Bassa, caused him to be slain. Solyman the Magnificent murdered his own Son Mustapha; and 'tis an ordinary thing amongst them to make away their brothers, or any competitors, at the first coming to the Crown: 'tis all the solemnity they use at their fathers' funerals. What mad pranks in his jealous fury did Herod of old commit in Jewry, when he massacred all the children of a year old! Valens the Emperor in Constantinople, when as he left no man alive of quality in his kingdom that had his name begun with Theo; Theodoti, Theognosti, Theodosii, Theoduli, &c., they went all to their long home, because a wizard told him that name should succeed in his Empire! And what furious designs hath John Basilius,* that Muscovian tyrant, practised of late! It is a wonder to read that strange suspicion, which Suetonius reports of Claudius Cæsar and of Domitian, they were afraid of every man they saw; and which Herodian [reports] of Antoninus and Geta, those two jealous brothers, the one could not endure so much as the other's servants, but made away him, his chiefest followers, and all that belonged to him, or were his well-wishers. Maximinus, perceiving himself to be odious to most men, because he was come to that height of honour out of base beginnings, and suspecting his mean parentage would be objected to him, caused all the Senators that were nobly descended to be slain in a jealous humour, turned all the servants of Alexander his predecessor out of doors, and slew many of them, because they lamented their master's death, suspecting them to be traitors

* Ivan the Terrible.

for the love they bare to him. When Alexander in his fury had made Clitus his dear friend to be put to death, and saw now (saith Curtius) an alienation in his subjects' hearts, none durst talk with him, he began to be jealous of himself, lest they should attempt as much on him, and said, they lived like so many wild beasts in a wilderness, one afraid of another. Our modern stories afford us many notable examples. Henry the Third of France, jealous of Henry of Lorraine, Duke of Guise, Anno 1588, caused him to be murdered in his own chamber. Lewis the Eleventh was so suspicious, he durst not trust his children, every man about him he suspected for a traitor: many strange tricks Commines telleth of him. How jealous was our Henry the Fourth of King Richard the Second, so long as he lived, after he was deposed! and of his own son Henry, in his later days! which the Prince well perceiving, came to visit his father in his sickness, in a watchet velvet gown, full of oilet [or eyelet] holes, and with needles sticking in them, (as an emblem of jealousy) and so pacified his suspicious father, after some speeches and protestations, which he had used to that purpose. Perpetual imprisonment, as that of Robert Duke of Normandy, in the days of Henry the First, forbidding of marriage to some persons, with such like edicts and prohibitions, are ordinary in all states. In a word (as he [R. Tofte in his Blason of Jealousy] said) three things cause Jealousy, a mighty state, a rich treasure, a fair wife; or where there is a crackt title, much tyranny, and many exactions. In our state, as being freed from all these fears and miseries, we may be most secure and happy under the reign of our fortunate Prince.

> *His fortune hath indebted him to none,*
> *But to all his people universally;*
> *And not to them but for their love alone,*
> *Which they account as placèd worthily.*
> *He is so set, he hath no cause to be*
> *Jealous, or dreadful of disloyalty;*
> *The pedestal whereon his greatness stands,*
> *Is held of all our hearts, and all our hands.* (DANIEL)

But I rove, I confess. These equivocations, Jealousies, and many such, which crucify the souls of men, are not here properly meant, or in this distinction of ours included, but that alone which is for beauty, tending to love, and wherein they can brook no corrival, or endure any participation: and this Jealousy belongs as well to brute beasts, as men. Some creatures, saith Vives, Swans, Doves, Cocks, Bulls, &c., are jealous as well as men, and as much moved, for fear of communion.

In Venus' cause what mighty battles make
Your raving bulls, and stirs for their herd's sake:
And harts and bucks, that are so timorous,
Will fight and roar, if once they be but jealous. (SENECA)

In Bulls, Horses, Goats, this is most apparently discerned; Bulls especially, he will not admit another Bull to feed in the same pasture, saith Oppian: which Stephanus Bathorius, late king of Poland, used as an Impress, with that motto, A kingdom admits not of two kings. R. T., in his Blazon of Jealousy, telleth a story of a Swan about Windsor; that finding a strange Cock with his mate, did swim I know not how many miles after to kill him, and when he had done so, came back and killed his hen; a certain truth, he saith, done upon Thames, as many Watermen, and neighbour Gentlemen can tell. They keep their faith; for my part, I do believe it may be true; for Swans have ever been branded with that Epithet of Jealousy.

𝔗𝔥𝔢 jealous swanne against his death that singeth,
And eke the owle that of death bode bringeth.

Some say as much of Elephants, that they are more jealous than any other creatures whatsoever; and those old Egyptians, as Pierius informeth us, express in their Hieroglyphicks the passion of Jealousy by a Camel; because that fearing the worst still about matters of Venery, he loves solitudes, that he may enjoy his pleasure alone, and he will quarrel and fight with whosoever comes next, man or beast, in his jealous fits. I have read as much of Crocodiles; and if Peter Martyr's authority be authentick, you shall have a strange tale to that purpose confidently related. Another story of the jealousy of dogs, see in Hieronymus Fabricius.

But this furious passion is most eminent in men, and is as well amongst Bachelors, as married men. If it appear amongst Bachelors, we commonly call them rivals or corrivals, a metaphor derived from a River; for as a River, saith Acron and Donatus, divides a common ground betwixt two men, and both participate of it; so is a woman indifferent betwixt two suitors, both likely to enjoy her; and thence comes this emulation, which breaks out many times into tempestuous storms, and produceth lamentable effects, murder itself, with much cruelty, many single combats. They cannot endure the least injury done unto them before their Mistress, and in her defence will bite off one another's noses; they are most impatient of any flout, disgrace, least emulation or participation in that kind. Memmius bites the arm of Largus. Memmius the Roman (as Tully tells the story), being corrival with Largus at Terracina, bit him by the arm, which fact of his was so famous, that it afterwards grew to a proverb in those parts. Phædria could not abide his corrival Thraso; for when Parmeno demanded, whether he would command him any more service: No more (saith he) but to speak in his behalf, and to drive away his corrival if he could. Constantine, in the eleventh book of his husbandry, chapter 11, hath a pleasant tale of the Pine-tree: she was once a fair Maid, whom Phineus and Boreas, two corrivals, dearly sought; but jealous Boreas broke her neck, &c. And in his 18th chapter he telleth another tale of Mars, that in his jealousy slew Adonis. Petronius calleth this passion a furious emulation; and their symptoms are well expressed by Sir Geoffrey Chaucer in his first Canterbury tale. It will make the nearest and dearest friends fall out; they will endure all other things to be common, goods, lands, monies, participate of each other's pleasures, and take in good part any disgraces, injuries in another kind; but as Propertius well describes it in an Elegy of his, in this they will suffer nothing, have no corrivals.

> *Stab me with sword, or poison strong*
> *Give me to work my bane:*
> *So thou court not my lass, so thou*
> *From Mistress mine refrain.*
> *Command myself, my body, purse,*
> *As thine own goods take all,*
> *And as my ever dearest friend,*
> *I ever use thee shall.*
> *O spare my Love, to have alone*
> *Her to myself I crave,*
> *Nay, Jove himself I'll not endure*
> *My Rival for to have.* (In R. T.)

This Jealousy which I am to treat of, is that which belongs to married men, in respect of their own wives; to whose estate, as no sweetness, pleasure, happiness, can be compared in the world, if they live quietly and lovingly together; so if they disagree or be jealous, those bitter pills of sorrow and grief, disastrous mischiefs, mischances, tortures, gripings, discontents, are not to be separated from them. A most violent passion it is where it taketh place, an unspeakable torment, a hellish torture, an infernal plague, as Ariosto calls it, a fury, a continual fever, full of suspicion, fear and sorrow, a martyrdom, a mirth-marring monster. " The sorrow and grief of heart of one woman jealous of another, is heavier than death," as Peninnah did Hannah, " vex her and upbraid her sore." 'Tis a main vexation, a most intolerable burden, a corrosive to all content, a frenzy, a madness itself, as Benedetto Varchi proves out of that select Sonnet of Giovanni de la Casa, that reverend Lord, as he styles him.

SUBSECTION 2 — *Causes of Jealousy. Who are most apt. Idleness, Melancholy, Impotency, long Absence, Beauty, Wantonness, naught themselves. Allurements from time, place, persons, bad usage, Causes*

ASTROLOGERS make the stars a cause or sign of this bitter passion, and out of every man's Horoscope will give a probable conjecture whether he will be jealous or no, and at what time, by direction of the significators to their several promissors: their Aphorisms are to be read in Albubator, Pontanus, Scheiner, Junctine, &c. Bodine ascribes a great cause to the country or clime, and discourseth largely there of this subject, saying, that Southern men are more hot, lascivious, and jealous, than such as live in the North; they can hardly contain themselves in those hotter climes, but are most subject to prodigious lusts. Leo Afer telleth incredible things almost of the lust and jealousy of his Countrymen of Africa, and especially such as live about Carthage, and so doth every Geographer of them in Asia, Turkey, Spaniards, Italians. Germany hath not so many drunkards, England Tobacconists, France Dancers, Holland Mariners, as Italy alone hath jealous husbands. And in Italy some account them of Piacenza more jealous than the rest. In Germany, France, Britain, Scandia, Poland, Muscovy, they are not so troubled with this feral malady, although Damianus à Goes, which I do much wonder at, in his Topography of Lapland, and Herbastein of Russia, against the stream of all other Geographers, would fasten it upon those Northern inhabitants. Altomarus, Poggius, and Munster in his description of Baden, reports that men and women of all sorts go commonly into the Baths together, without all suspicion, the name of Jealousy (saith Munster) is not so much as once heard of among them. In Friesland the women kiss him they drink to, and are kissed again of those they pledge. The virgins in Holland go hand in hand with young men from home, glide on the Ice, such is their harmless liberty, and lodge together abroad without suspicion, which rash Sansovinus, an Italian, makes it a great sign of unchastity. In France, upon small acquaintance, it is usual to court other men's wives, to come to their houses, and accompany them arm in arm in the streets, without imputation. In the most Northern Countries young men and maids familiarly dance together, men and their wives, which, Siena only excepted, Italians may not abide. The Greeks on the other side have their private baths for men and women, where they must not come near, not so much as see one another: and as Bodine observes, the Italians could never endure this, or a Spaniard, the very conceit of it would make him mad: and for that cause they lock up their women, and will not suffer them to be near men, so much as in the Church, but with a partition between. He telleth moreover, how that, when he was Embassador in England, he heard Mendoza the Spanish Legate finding fault with it as a filthy custom for men and women to sit promiscuously in Churches together: but Dr. Dale, the Master of the Requests, told him again, that it was indeed a filthy custom in Spain, where they could not contain themselves from lascivious thoughts in their holy places, but not with us. Baronius in his Annals, out of Eusebius, taxeth Licinius the Emperor for a decree of his made to this effect, that men might not enter the church at the same time with women; for being prodigiously naught [that is, naughty] himself, he so esteemed others. But we are far from any such strange conceits, and will permit our wives and daughters to go to the Tavern with a friend, as Aubanus saith, innocently enough, and suspect nothing, to kiss coming and going, as Erasmus writes in one of his Epistles, which they cannot endure. England is a paradise for women, and hell for horses: Italy a paradise for horses, hell for women, as the diverb goes. Some make a question whether this headstrong passion rage more in women than men, as Montaigne. But sure it is more outrageous in women, as all other melancholy is, by reason of the weakness of their sex. Scaliger concludes against women: Besides their inconstancy, treachery, suspicion, dissimulation, superstition, pride (for all women are by nature proud), desire of sovereignty, if they be great women (he gives instance in Juno) bitterness and jealousy are the most remarkable affections.

> *Tiger, boar, bear, viper, lioness,*
> *A woman's fury cannot express.* (OVID)

Some say red-headed women, pale-coloured, black-eyed, and of a shrill voice, are most subject to jealousy.

> *High colour in a woman choler shows,*
> *Naught are they, peevish, proud, malicious;*
> *But worst of all, red, shrill, and jealous.* (R. T.)

Comparisons are odious, I neither parallel them with others, nor debase them any more: men and women are both bad, and too subject to this pernicious infirmity. It is most part a symptom and cause of Melancholy, as Plater and Valescus teach us: melancholy men are apt to be jealous, and jealous apt to be melancholy.

> *Pale jealousy, child of insatiate love,*
> *Of heart-sick thoughts with melancholy bred,*
> *A hell-tormenting fear no faith can move,*
> *By discontent with deadly poison fed;*
> *With heedless youth and error vainly led:*
> *A 'mortal plague, a virtue-drowning flood,*
> *A hellish fire not quenchèd but with blood.* (DRAYTON)

If idleness concur with melancholy, such persons are most apt to be jealous; 'tis Nevisanus' note, An idle woman is presumed to be lascivious, and often jealous. A woman left alone to think, thinks ill; and 'tis not unlikely, for they have no other business to trouble their heads with.

More particular causes be these which follow. Impotency first, when a man is not able of himself to perform those dues which he ought unto his wife: for though he be an honest liver, hurt no man, yet Trebatius the Lawyer may make a question, whether he give every one their own; and therefore when he takes notice of his wants, and perceives her to be more craving, clamorous, unsatiable and prone to lust, than is fit, he begins presently to suspect, that wherein he is defective, she will satisfy herself, she will be pleased by some other means. Cornelius Gallus hath elegantly expressed this humour in an Epigram to his Lycoris:

> *She now seeks other youths and other loves,*
> *Calls me a worn-out, good-for-naught old man.*

For this cause is most evident in old men, that are cold and dry by nature, and married to those full of juice, to young wanton wives, with old doting Janivere in Chaucer, they begin to mistrust all is not well.

> ——————— She was yong, and he was olde,
> And therefore he feared to be a cuckolde.

And how should it otherwise be? Old age is a disease of itself, loathsome, full of suspicion and fear; when it is at best, unable, unfit for such matters. As welcome to a young woman as snow in harvest, saith Nevisanus; marry a lusty Maid, and she will surely graft horns on thy head. All women are slippery, often unfaithful to their husbands (as Æneas Sylvius seconds him) but to old men most treacherous: they had rather lie with a corse, than such a one. Youths hate, women despise him. On the other side, many men, saith Hieronymus, are suspicious of their wives, if they be lightly given, but old folks above the rest. Insomuch that she did not complain without a cause, in Apuleius, of an old bald bedridden knave she had to her goodman: Poor woman as I am, what shall I do? I have an old grim sire to my husband, as bald as a coot, as little and as unable as a child, a bedful of bones, he keeps all the doors barred and lockt upon me, woe is me, what shall I do? He was jealous, and she made him a cuckold for keeping her up: suspicion without a cause, hard usage, is able of itself to make a woman fly out, that was otherwise honest, bad usage aggravates the matter. As Nevisanus holds, when a woman thinks her husband watcheth her, she will sooner offend; they sin openly, all shame is gone, rough handling makes them worse: as the good wife of Bath in Chaucer brags,

In his owene grece I made him frye,
For angre and for verray jealousye.

Of two extremes, this of hard usage is the worst. 'Tis a great fault (for some men are uxorious) to be too fond of their wives, to dote on them as Senior Deliro on his Fallace, to be too effeminate, or as some do, to be sick for their wives, breed children for them, and like the Tiberini lie in for them, as some birds hatch eggs by turns, they do all women's offices: Cælius Rhodiginus makes mention of a fellow out of Seneca, that was so besotted on his wife, he could not endure a moment out of her company, he wore her scarf when he went abroad next his heart, and would never drink but in that cup she began first. We have many such fondlings that are their wives' pack-horses and slaves, (as the Comical Poet hath it, there's no greater misery to a man than to let his wife domineer), to carry her muff, dog, and fan, let her wear the breeches, lay out, spend and do what she will, go and come, whither, when she will, they give consent.

Here take my muff, and do you hear, good man;
Now give me Pearl, and carry you my fan, &c.   (CHALONER)

Many brave and worthy men have trespassed in this kind, and many noble Senators and soldiers (as Pliny notes) have lost their honour in being uxorious, so sottishly over-ruled by their wives; and therefore Cato in Plutarch made a bitter jest on his fellow Citizens, the Romans, we govern all the world abroad, and our wives at home rule us. These offend in one extreme; but too hard and too severe, are far more offensive on the other. As just a cause may be long absence of either party, when they must of necessity be much from home, as Lawyers, Physicians, Mariners, by their professions; or otherwise make frivolous impertinent journeys, tarry long abroad to no purpose, lie out, and are gadding still, upon small occasions, it must needs yield matter of suspicion, when they use their wives unkindly in the mean time, and never tarry at home, it cannot choose but engender some such conceit.

If thou be absent long, thy wife then thinks,
Th' art drunk, at ease, or with some pretty minx,
'Tis well with thee, or else beloved of some,
Whilst she, poor soul, doth fare full ill at home.   (TERENCE)

Hippocrates the Physician had a smack of this disease; for when he was to go from home as far as Abdera, and some other remote cities of Greece, he writ to his friend Dionysius (if at least those Epistles be his) to oversee his wife in his absence, (as Apollo set a Raven to watch his Coronis) although she lived in his house with her father and mother, whom he knew would have a care of her; yet that would not satisfy his jealousy, he would have his special friend Dionysius to dwell in his house with her all the time of his peregrination, and to observe her behaviour, how she carried herself in her husband's absence, and that she did not lust after other men: for a woman had need to have an overseer to keep her honest; they are bad by nature, and lightly given all, and if they be not curbed in time, as an unproined tree, they will be full of wild branches, and degenerate of a sudden. Especially in their husband's absence. Though one Lucretia were trusty, and one Penelope, yet Clytæmnestra made Agamemnon cuckold; and no question there be too many of her conditions. If their husbands tarry too long abroad upon unnecessary business, well they may suspect: or if they run one way, their wives at home will fly out another, tit for tat. Or if present, and give them not that content which they ought, (at first unwelcome, soon hateful, the nights in which nothing is accomplished but sleeping), they cannot endure to lie alone, or to fast long. Peter Godefridus, in his second book of Love, and sixth chapter, hath a story out of S. Anthony's life, of a Gentleman, who, by that good man's advice, would not meddle with his wife in the Passion Week, but for his pains she set a pair of horns on his head. Such another he hath out of Abstemius, one persuaded a new married man to forbear the three first nights, and he should all his life time after be fortunate in cattle, but his impatient wife would not tarry so long: well he might speed in cattle, but not in children. Such a tale hath Heinsius of an impotent and slack scholar, a mere student, and a friend of his, that, seeing by chance a fine damsel sing and dance, would needs marry her; the match was soon made, for he was young and rich, of good family, smooth of body, skilled in many arts, like that Apollo in Apuleius. The first night, having liberally taken his liquor (as in that country they do) my fine scholar was so fusled that he no sooner was laid in bed, but he fell fast asleep, never waked till morning, and then much abashed, when the fair morn with

purple hue 'gan shine, he made an excuse, I know not what, out of Hippocrates of Cos, &c., and for that time it went current; but when as
afterward he did not play the man as he should do, she fell in league
with a good fellow, and whilst he sat up late at his study about those
Criticisms, mending some hard places in Festus or Pollus, came cold to
bed, and would tell her still what he had done, she did not much regard
what he said, &c. She would have another matter mended much rather,
which he did not perceive was corrupt: thus he continued at his study
late, she at her sport elsewhere, enjoying festive nights, hating all
scholars for his sake, till at length he began to suspect, and turned a
little yellow, as well he might; for it was his own fault; and if men be
jealous in such cases (as oft it falls out) the mends is in their own hands,
they must thank themselves. Who will pity them, saith Neander, or
be much offended with such wives, if they deceive and cornute those
that cozened them first? A Lawyer's wife in Aristænetus, because her
husband was negligent in his business, slack in his bed-labours, threatened to cornute him: and did not stick to tell Philinna, one of her
gossips, as much, and that aloud for him to hear: If he follow other
men's matters, and leave his own, I'll have an Orator shall plead my
cause, I care not if he know it.

A fourth eminent cause of jealousy may be this, when he that is deformed, and, as Pindar says of Vulcan, without natural graces, hirsute,
ragged, yet virtuously given, will marry some fair nice piece, or light
housewife, begins to misdoubt (as well he may) she doth not affect him.
Beauty and honesty have ever been at odds. Abraham was jealous of his
wife, because she was fair: so was Vulcan of his Venus, when he made
her creaking shoes, saith Philostratus, that he might hear by them
when she stirred, which Mars was not well pleased with. Good cause had
Vulcan to do as he did, for she was no honester than she should be. Your
fine faces have commonly this fault, and it is hard to find; saith Francis
Philelphus in an Epistle to Saxola his friend, a rich man honest, a proper
woman not proud or unchaste. Can she be fair and honest too?

Oft has the serpent lain 'neath colored grass,
Beauteous seeming, oft has an evil will
Found purchasers without the husband's knowledge.   (HORACE)

He that marries a wife that is snowt fair [or fair-looking] alone, let him
look, saith Barbarus, for no better success than Vulcan had with Venus,
or Claudius with Messalina. And 'tis impossible almost in such cases the
wife should contain, or the good man not be jealous: for when he is
so defective, weak, ill proportioned, unpleasing in those parts which

women most affect, and she most absolutely fair and able on the other side, if she be not very virtuously given, how can she love him? and although she be not fair, yet if he admire her, and think her so, in his conceit she is absolute, he holds it impossible for any man living not to dote as he doth, to look on her, and not lust, not to covet, and if he be in company with her, not to lay siege to her honesty: or else out of a deep apprehension of his infirmities, deformities, and other men's good parts, out of his own little worth and desert, he distrusts himself (for what is jealousy but distrust?) he suspects she cannot affect him, or be not so kind and loving as she should, she certainly loves some other man better than himself.

Nevisanus will have barrenness to be a main cause of Jealousy. If her husband cannot play the man, some other shall, they will leave no remedies unassayed, and thereupon the good man grows jealous; I could give an instance, but be it as it is.

I find this reason given by some men, because they have been formerly naught themselves, they think they may be so served by others, they turned up trump before the cards were shuffled, they shall have therefore like for like.

> *Wretch as I was, I taught her bad to be,*
> *And now mine own sly tricks are put on me.*   (TIBULLUS)

As the saying is, ill dispositions cause ill suspicions.

> *There is none jealous, I durst pawn my life,*
> *But he that hath defil'd another's wife,*
> *And for that he himself hath gone astray,*
> *He straightway thinks his wife will tread that way.*   (WITHER)

To these two above named causes, or incendiaries of this rage, I may very well annex those circumstances of time, place, persons, by which it ebbs and flows, the fuel of this fury, as Vives truly observes; and such like accidents or occasions, proceeding from the parties themselves, or others, which much aggravate and intend this suspicious humour. For many men are so lasciviously given, either out of a depraved nature, or too much liberty, which they do assume unto themselves, by reason of their greatness, in that they are Noblemen (for license to sin and company in the sinning are great motives) though their own wives be never so fair, noble, virtuous, honest, wise, able, and well given, they must have change.

> *Who being match'd to wives most virtuous,*
> *Noble and fair, fly out lascivious.*   (MARULLUS)

What's granted is not wanted, that which is ordinary is unpleasant. Nero (saith Tacitus) abhorred Octavia his own wife, a noble virtuous Lady, and loved Acte, a base quean in respect. Cerinthus rejected Sulpicia, a nobleman's daughter, and courted a poor servant maid. 'Tis more pleasure to reap in strange fields, for that stolen waters be more pleasant: or, as Vitellius the Emperor was wont to say, the most delightful loves are those that are most dangerous, like stolen Venison, still the sweetest is that love, which is most difficultly attained: they like better to hunt by stealth in another man's walk, than to have the fairest course that may be at game of their own.

As Sun and Moon in Heaven change their course,
So they change loves, though often to the worse. (PROPERTIUS)

Or that some fair object so forcibly moves them, they cannot contain themselves, be it heard or seen, they will be at it. Nessus the Centaur, was by agreement to carry Hercules and his wife over the River Evenus; no sooner had he set Deianira on the other side, but he would have offered violence unto her, leaving Hercules to swim over as he could: and though her husband was a spectator, yet would he not desist till Hercules with a poisoned arrow shot him to death. Neptune saw by chance that Thessalian Tyro, Enipeus' wife, he forthwith in the fury of his lust counterfeited her husband's habit, and made him cuckold. Tarquin heard Collatine commend his wife, and was so far enraged, that in midst of the night to her he went. Theseus stole Ariadne, ravished that Trœzenian Anaxo, Antiope, and, now being old, Helena, a girl not yet ready for an husband. Great men are most part thus affected all, as an horse they neigh, saith Jeremiah, after their neighbour's wives, and if they be in company with other women, though in their own wives' presence, they must be courting and dallying with them. Juno in Lucian, complains of Jupiter, that he was still kissing Ganymede before her face, which did not a little offend her: and besides, he was a counterfeit Amphitryo, a bull, a swan, a golden shower, and played many such bad pranks, too long, too shameful, to relate.

Or that they care little for their own Ladies, and fear no Laws, they dare freely keep whores at their wives' noses. 'Tis too frequent with noblemen to be dishonest; as he [Seneca] said long since, piety, chastity, and such like virtues are for private men; not to be much looked after in great Courts: and which Suetonius said of the good Princes of his time, they might be all engraven in one Ring, we may truly hold of chaste potentates of our age. For great personages will familiarly run out in this kind, and yield occasion of offence. Montaigne in his Essays gives instances in Cæsar, Mahomet the Turk, that sacked Constantinople, and Ladislaus King of Naples, that besieged Florence: great men, and great soldiers, are commonly great ———— &c., 'tis approved, they are good doers. Mars and Venus are equally balanced in their actions.

A dove within a head-piece made her nest,
'Twixt Mars and Venus see an interest. (PETRONIUS)

Especially if they be bald, for bald men have ever been suspicious (read more in Aristotle), as Galba, Otho, Domitian, and remarkable Cæsar amongst the rest. Citizens, look to your wives, we are bringing a bald adulterer *; besides, this bald Cæsar, saith Curio in Suetonius, was husband to all women; he made love to Eunoe, Queen of Mauritania, to Cleopatra, to Postumia, wife to Servius Sulpicius, to Lollia, wife to Gabinius, to Tertulla of Crassus, and to Mucia, Pompey's wife, and I know not how many besides: and well he might, for if all be true that I have read, he had a license to lie with whom he list. Among the other honors decreed to Cæsar (as Suetonius and Dion relate) was the right to couple with any woman he pleased. Every private History will yield such variety of instances: otherwise good, wise, discreet men, virtuous and valiant, but too faulty in this. Priam had fifty sons, but seventeen alone lawfully begotten. Philippus Bonus left fourteen bastards. Laurence Medices a good Prince and a wise, but, saith Machiavel, prodigiously lascivious. None so valiant as Castruccius Castrucanus, but as the said author hath it, none so incontinent as he was. And 'tis not only predominant in Grandees, this fault: but if you will take a great man's testimony, 'tis familiar with every base soldier in France, (and elsewhere I think). This vice (saith mine Author) is so common with us in France, that he is of no account, a mere coward, not worthy the name of a soldier, that is not a notorious whoremaster. In Italy he is not a gentleman, that besides his wife hath not a Courtesan and a mistress. 'Tis no marvel then, if poor women in such cases be jealous, when they shall see themselves manifestly neglected, contemned, loathed, unkindly used: their disloyal husbands to entertain others in their rooms, and many times to court Ladies to their faces: other men's wives to wear their jewels: how shall a poor woman in such a case moderate her passion?

How felt you then, Dido, beholding this? (VIRGIL)

How, on the other side, shall a poor man contain himself from this feral malady, when he shall see so manifest signs of his wife's inconstancy? when as, like Milo's wife, she dotes upon every young man she sees, or as Martial's Sota, deserts her husband and follows Clitus. Though her husband be proper and tall, fair and lovely to behold, able

* The song sung by Cæsar's soldiers on the occasion of his Gallic triumph.

to give contentment to any one woman, yet she will taste of the forbidden fruit: Juvenal's Iberina to an hair, she is as well pleased with
one eye as one man. If a young gallant come by chance into her presence, a Fastidius Brisk, that can wear his clothes well in fashion, with a
lock, gingling spur, a feather, that can cringe, and withal compliment,
court a Gentlewoman, she raves upon him. O what a lovely proper man
he was, another Hector, an Alexander, a goodly man, a demi-god, how
sweetly he carried himself, with how comely a grace, such were his eyes,
his hands, his air, how neatly he did wear his clothes!

What gallant mien, how stout of spirit and arms!   (VIRGIL)

how bravely did he discourse, ride, sing, and dance, &c. and then she
begins to loathe her husband, repugnant to his kiss, to hate him and his
filthy beard, his goatish complexion, as Doris said of Polyphemus, he is
a rammy fulsome fellow, a goblin-faced fellow, he smells, he stinks, he
belches onions and garlic, how like a dizzard, a fool, an ass he looks, how
like a clown he behaves himself! she will not come near him by her
good will, but wholly rejects him, as Venus did her fuliginous Vulcan at
last,

No god will have him at his board, no goddess in her bed.   (VIRGIL)

So did Lucretia, a Lady of Siena, after she had but seen Euryalus,
thought but of him when she returned home, she would not hold her
eyes off him in his presence,

So noble was his air and grace of mien,   (VIRGIL)

and in his absence could think of none but him, she loathed her husband
forthwith, might not abide him.

All against the laws of matrimony,
She did abhor her husband's phis'nomy,

and sought all opportunity to see her sweetheart again. Now when the
good man shall observe his wife so lightly given, to be so free, and
familiar with every gallant, her immodesty and wantonness, (as Camerarius notes) it must needs yield matter of suspicion to him, when she
still pranks up herself beyond her means and fortunes, makes impertinent journeys, unnecessary visitations, stays out so long, with such and
such companions, so frequently goes to plays, masks, feasts, and all
publick meetings, shall use such immodest gestures, free speeches, and
withal shew some distaste of her own husband; how can he choose,
though he were another Socrates, but be suspicious, and instantly jealous?

She'll force him to transgress Socratic bounds.   (CHALONER)

More especially when he shall take notice of their more secret and sly tricks, which to cornute their husbands they commonly use, (while you're at the games, she's making game of you), they pretend love, honour, chastity, and seem to respect them before all men living, saints in shew, so cunningly can they dissemble, they will not so much as look upon another man in his presence, so chaste, so religious, and so devout, they cannot endure the name or sight of a quean, an harlot, out upon her! and in their outward carriage are most loving and officious, will kiss their husband, and hang about his neck, (dear husband, sweet husband) and with a composed countenance, salute him, especially when he comes home, or if he go from home, weep, sigh, lament, and take upon them to be sick and swoon, (like Jocundo's wife in Ariosto, when her husband was to depart) and yet arrant, &c. they care not for him,

> *Aye me, the thought (quoth she) makes me so 'fraid,*
> *That scarce the breath abideth in my breast ;*
> *Peace, my sweet love and wife, Jocundo said,*
> *And weeps as fast, and comforts her his best, &c.*
> *All this might not assuage the woman's pain,*
> *Needs must I die before you come again,*
> *Nor how to keep my life I can devise,*
> *The doleful days and nights I shall sustain,*
> *From meat my mouth, from sleep will keep mine eyes, &c.*
> *That very night that went before the morrow,*
> *That he had pointed surely to depart,*
> *Jocundo's wife was sick, and swoon'd for sorrow,*
> *Amid his arms, so heavy was her heart.*

And yet for all these counterfeit tears and protestations, Jocundo coming back in all haste for a jewel he had forgot,

> *His chaste and yoke-fellow he found*
> *Yok'd with a knave, all honesty neglected,*
> *The adulterer sleeping very sound,*
> *Yet by his face was easily detected :*
> *A beggar's brat bred by him from his cradle,*
> *And now was riding on his master's saddle.*

Thus can they cunningly counterfeit, as Platina describes their customs, kiss their husbands whom they had rather see hanging on a Gallows, and swear they love him dearer than their own lives, whose soul they would not ransom for their little dogs. Many of them seem to be precise and holy forsooth, and will go to such a Church, to hear such a good man by all means, an excellent man, when 'tis for no other intent (as he follows it) than to see and to be seen, to observe what fashions are in use, to meet some Pandar, Bawd, Monk, Friar, or to entice some good fellow. For they persuade themselves, as Nevisanus shews, that it is neither sin nor shame to lie with a Lord or a parish Priest, if he be a proper man, and though she kneel often, and pray devoutly, 'tis (saith Platina) not for her husband's welfare, or children's good, or any friend, but for her sweetheart's return, her Pandar's health. If her husband would have her go, she feigns herself sick, her head aches, and she can not stir: but if her Paramour ask as much, she is for him in all seasons, at all hours of the night. In the kingdom of Malabar, and about Goa in the East-Indies, the women are so subtile, that with a certain drink they give them to drive away cares as they say, they will make them sleep for twenty-four hours, or so intoxicate them that they can remember nought of that they saw done, or heard, and by washing of their feet, restore them again, and so make their husbands cuckolds to their faces. Some are ill disposed at all times, to all persons they like, others more wary to some few, at such and such seasons, as Augusta Livia, she takes no passenger unless the ship is full [that is, only dallied with lovers when already pregnant by her husband]. But as he said,

> No pen could write, no tongue attain to tell,
> By force of eloquence, or help of art,
> Of women's treacheries the hundredth part. (ARIOSTO)

Both, to say truth, are often faulty; men and women give just occasions in this humour of discontent, aggravate and yield matter of suspicion: but most part of the chief causes proceed from other adventitious accidents and circumstances, though the parties be free, and both well given themselves. The undiscreet carriage of some lascivious gallant (and on the other hand of some light woman) by his often frequenting of an house, bold unseemly gestures, may make a breach, and by his over familiarity, if he be inclined to yellowness, colour him quite out. If he be poor, basely born, saith Benedetto Varchi, and otherwise unhandsome, he suspects him the less, but if a proper man, such as was Alcibiades in Greece, and Castruccius Castrucanus in Italy, well descended, commendable for his good parts, he taketh on the more, and watcheth his doings. Theodosius the Emperor gave his wife Eudocia a golden apple, when he was a suitor to her, which she long after bestowed upon a young gallant in the Court, of her especial acquaintance. The Emperor, espying this apple in his hand, suspected forthwith, more than was, his wife's dishonesty, banished him the Court, and from that day following forbare to accompany her any more. A rich merchant had a fair wife; according to his custom he went to travel; in his absence a good fellow tempted his wife: she denied him, yet he, dying a little after, gave her a legacy for the love he bore her. At his return her jealous husband, because she had got more by land than he had done at Sea, turned her away upon suspicion.

Now when those other circumstances of time and place, opportunity and importunity, shall concur, what will they not effect?

Fair opportunity can win the coyest she that is,
So wisely he takes time, as he'll be sure he will not miss:
Then he that loves her gamesome vein, and tempers toys with art,
Brings love that swimmeth in her eyes, to dive into her heart.

As at Plays, Masks, great feasts and banquets, one singles out his wife to dance, another courts her in his presence, a third tempts her, a fourth insinuates with a pleasing compliment, a sweet smile, ingratiates himself with an amphibological [or equivocal] speech; as that merry companion in the Satirist did to his Glycerium, sitting by her, and paddling palms and pinching fingers;

Take what you will from my garden-close,
If you'll give me what in your garden grows;

with many such, &c., and then, as he [Chaucer] saith,

𝕾𝖍𝖊 𝖒𝖆𝖞 𝖓𝖔 𝖜𝖍𝖞𝖑𝖊 𝖎𝖓 𝖈𝖍𝖆𝖘𝖙𝖎𝖙𝖊𝖊 𝖆𝖇𝖞𝖉𝖊,
𝕿𝖍𝖆𝖙 𝖎𝖘 𝖆𝖘𝖘𝖆𝖎𝖑𝖑𝖊𝖉 𝖚𝖕𝖔𝖓 𝖊𝖇𝖊𝖗𝖞 𝖘𝖞𝖉𝖊.

For after a great feast,

In wine a woman knows not her own husband.   (PROPERTIUS)

Noah (saith Hierome) shewed his nakedness in his drunkenness, which for six hundred years he had covered in soberness. Lot lay with his daughters in his drink, as Cinyras with Myrrha,

For what does love in drink scruple to do?   (JUVENAL)

The most continent may be overcome, or if otherwise they keep bad company, they are modest of themselves, and dare not offend, confirmed by others, grow impudent, and confident, and get an ill habit.

One violates her bed for gain, another
Seduces other wives to have companions
In guilt.   (EURIPIDES)

Or if they dwell in suspected places, as in an infamous Inn, near some Stews, near Monks, Friars, Nevisanus adds, where be many tempters and solicitors, idle persons, that frequent their companies, it may give just cause of suspicion. Martial of old inveighed against them that counterfeited a disease to go to the Bath, for so, many times,

Penelope comes back an unchaste Helen.

Æneas Sylvius puts in a caveat against Princes' Courts, because there be so many brave Suitors to tempt, &c. If you leave her in such a place, you shall likely find her in company you like not, either they come to her, or she is gone to them. Kornmannus makes a doubting jest in his lascivious Country, How much discount on the chastity of a virgin to whom Scholars have frequent approach? And Baldus, the Lawyer, scoffs on, when a Scholar talks with a maid, or another man's wife in private, it is presumed he saith not a Pater Noster. Or if I shall see a Monk or a Friar climb up by a ladder at midnight into a Virgin's or Widow's chamber-window, I shall hardly think he then goes to administer the Sacraments, or to take her Confession. These are the ordinary causes of jealousy, which are intended or remitted, as the circumstances vary.

MEMBER 2

Symptoms of Jealousy, fear, sorrow, suspicion, strange actions, gestures, outrages, locking up, oaths, trials, laws, &c.

OF all passions, as I have already proved, Love is most violent, and of those bitter potions which this Love Melancholy affords, this bastard Jealousy is the greatest, as appears by those prodigious Symptoms which it hath, and that it produceth. For besides Fear and Sorrow, which is common to all Melancholy, anxiety of mind, suspicion, aggravation, restless thoughts, paleness, meagreness, neglect of business, and the like, these men are farther yet misaffected, and in an higher strain. 'Tis a more vehement passion, a more furious perturbation, a bitter pain, a fire, a pernicious curiosity, a gall corrupting the honey of our life, madness, vertigo, plague, hell, they are more than ordinarily disquieted, they lose the blessing of peace of mind, as Chrysostom observes; and though they be rich, keep sumptuous tables, be nobly allied, yet they are most miserable, they are more than ordinarily discontent, more sad, more than ordinarily suspicious. Jealousy, saith Vives, begets unquietness in the mind night and day: he hunts after every word he hears, every whisper, and amplifies it to himself (as all melancholy men do in other matters) with a most unjust calumny of others, he misinterprets every thing is said or done, most apt to mistake or misconster, he pries into every corner, follows close, observes to an hair. 'Tis proper to Jealousy so to do,

> *Pale hag, infernal fury, pleasure's smart,*
> *Envy's observer, prying in every part.* (DANIEL)

Besides those strange gestures of staring, frowning, grinning, rolling of eyes, menacing, ghastly looks, broken pace, interrupt, precipitate, half-turns. He will sometimes sigh, weep, sob for anger,

Such thunder-storms in sooth pour down their showers,

swear and belie, slander any man, curse, threaten, brawl, scold, fight; and sometimes again flatter, and speak fair, ask forgiveness, kiss and coll, condemn his rashness and folly, vow, protest and swear he will never do so again; and then eftsoons, impatient as he is, rave, roar, and lay about him like a mad man, thump her sides, drag her about perchance, drive her out of doors, send her home, he will be divorced forthwith, she is a whore, &c., by and by with all submiss compliment intreat her fair, and bring her in again, he loves her dearly, she is his sweet, most kind, and loving wife, he will not change, not leave her for a Kingdom; so he continues off and on, as the toy takes him, the object moves him, but most part brawling, fretting, unquiet he is, accusing and suspecting not strangers only, but Brothers and Sisters, Father and Mother, nearest and dearest friends. He thinks with those Italians,

Who doth it not in the family
Is one who doth it never or seldomly.

And through fear conceives unto himself things almost incredible and impossible to be effected. As an Heron when she fishes, still prying on all sides, or as a Cat doth a Mouse, his eye is never off hers; he gloats on him, on her, accurately observing on whom she looks, who looks at her, what she saith, doth, at dinner, at supper, sitting, walking, at home, abroad, he is the same, still inquiring, mandering [or crying for her], gazing, listening, affrighted with every small object; why did she smile, why did she pity him, commend him? why did she drink twice to such a man? why did she offer to kiss, to dance? &c., a whore, a whore, an arrant whore! All this he confesseth in the Poet,

Each thing affrights me, I do fear,
Ah pardon me my fear,
I doubt a man is hid within
The clothes that thou dost wear.   (PROPERTIUS)

Is't not a man in woman's apparel? is not somebody in that great chest, or behind the door, or hangings, or in some of those barrels? May not a man steal in at the window with a ladder of ropes, or come down the chimney, have a false key, or get in when he is asleep? If a Mouse do but stir, or the wind blow, a casement clatter, that's the villain, there he is; by his good will no man shall see her, salute her, speak with her, she shall not go forth of his sight, so much as to do her needs. Argus did not so keep his Cow, that watchful Dragon the Golden fleece, or Cerberus the coming in of Hell, as he keeps his wife. If a dear friend or near kinsman come as guest to his house, to visit him, he will never let him be out of his own sight and company, lest peradventure, &c. If the necessity of his business be such that he must go from home, he doth either lock her up, or commit her with a deal of injunctions and protestations to some trusty friends, him and her he sets and bribes to oversee: one servant is set in his absence to watch another, and all to observe his wife, and yet all this will not serve, though his business be very urgent, he will, when he is half way, come back again in all post haste, rise from supper, or at midnight, and be gone, and sometimes leave his business undone, and as a stranger court his own wife in some disguised habit. Though there be no danger at all, no cause of suspicion, she live in such a place, where Messalina herself could not be dishonest if she would, yet he suspects her as much as if she were in a bawdy house, some Prince's Court, or in a common Inn, where all comers might have free access. He calls her on a sudden all to naught, she is a strumpet, a light-housewife, a bitch, an arrant whore. No persuasion, no protestation, can divert this passion, nothing can ease him, secure or give him satisfaction. It is most strange to report, what outrageous acts by men and women have been committed in this kind; by women especially, that will run after their husbands into all places and companies, as Jovianus Pontanus' wife did by him, follow him whithersoever he went, it matters not, or upon what business, raving, like Juno in the Tragedy, miscalling, cursing, swearing, and mistrusting every one she sees. Gomesius, in his third Book of the life and deeds of Francis Ximenes, sometime Archbishop of Toledo, hath a strange story of that incredible jealousy of Joan Queen of Spain, wife to King Philip, mother of Ferdinand and Charles the Fifth, Emperors; when her husband Philip, either for that he was tired with his wife's jealousy, or had some great business, went into the Low Countries, she was so impatient and melancholy upon his departure, that she would scarce eat her meat, or converse with any man; and though she were with child, the season of the year very bad, the wind against her, in all haste she would to sea after him. Neither Isabella her Queen Mother, the Archbishop, or any other friend, could persuade her to the contrary, but she would after him. When she was now come into the Low Countries, and kindly entertained by her husband, she could not contain herself, but in a rage ran upon a yellow-hair'd wench, with whom she suspected her husband to be naught, cut off her hair, did beat her black and blue, and so dragged her about. It is an ordinary thing for women in such cases to scrat the faces, slit the noses, of such as they suspect; as Henry the Second's importune [or cruel] Juno did by Rosamond at Woodstock: for she complains in a modern Poet, she scarce spake,

> But flies with eager fury to my face,
> Offering me most unwomanly disgrace.
> Look how a tigress, &c.
> So fell she on me in outrageous wise,
> As could disdain and jealousy devise.   (DANIEL)

Or if it be so they dare not, or cannot execute any such tyrannical injustice, they will miscall, rail and revile, bear them deadly hate and malice, as Tacitus observes, the hatred of a jealous woman is inseparable against such as she suspects.

> Winds, weapons, flames make not such hurly-burly,
> As raving women turn all topsy-turvy.   (SENECA)

So did Agrippina by Lollia and Calpurnia in the days of Claudius. But women are sufficiently curbed in such cases, the rage of men is more eminent, and frequently put in practice. See but with what rigour those jealous husbands tyrannize over their poor wives. In Greece, Spain, Italy, Turkey, Africa, Asia, and generally over all those hot Countries, your women are your land, to be ploughed at your will; Mahomet in his Alcoran gives this power to men; your wives are as your land, till them, use them, intreat them fair or foul, as you will yourselves.

> I' faith, women live under hard conditions,   (PLAUTUS)

they lock them still in their houses, which are as so many prisons to them, will suffer nobody to come at them, or their wives to be seen abroad. They must not so much as look out. And if they be great persons, they have Eunuchs to keep them, as the Grand Seignior among the Turks, the Sophies of Persia, those Tartarian Mogors, and Kings of China. Saith Riccius, they geld innumerable infants to this purpose; the King of China maintains 10,000 Eunuchs in his family to keep his wives. The Xeriffes of Barbary keep their Courtesans in such strict manner, that if any man come but in sight of them, he dies for it; and if they chance to see a man, and do not instantly cry out, though from their windows, they must be put to death. The Turks have I know not how many black deformed Eunuchs (for the white serve for other ministeries) to this purpose sent commonly from Egypt, deprived in their childhood of all their privities, and brought up in the Seraglio at Constantinople, to keep their wives; which are so penned up they may not confer with any living man, or converse with younger women, have a Cucumber or Carrot sent in to them for their diet, but sliced, for fear,

———— &c., and so live, and are left alone to their unchaste thoughts all the days of their lives. The vulgar sort of women, if at any time they come abroad, which is very seldom, to visit one another, or to go to their Baths, are so covered, that no man can see them, as the Matrons were in old Rome, carried in a litter or chair, so Dion and Seneca record; they all walk veil'd, which Alexander ab Alexandro relates of the Parthians, which, with Andreas Tiraquellus his Commentator, I rather think should be understood of Persians. I have not yet said all, they do not only lock them up, but lock up their private parts: hear what Bembus relates, in book 6 of his Venetian History, of those inhabitants that dwell about Quiloa in Africa. The Lusitanians, he saith, border upon certain tribes who sew up the parts of female infants at birth, leaving a way for the urine, and when they grow up, give them in marriage thus sewn up, so that it is the husband's first business to cut apart the fettered nether lips of the maiden. In some parts of Greece at this day, like those old Jews, they will not believe their wives are honest, without seeing the sheet stained from the first night; our countryman Sands, in his Peregrination, saith, it is severely observed in Zacynthus, or Zante; and Leo Afer in his time at Fez, in Africa, they will not credit virginity without seeing the bloody napkin, otherwise she is sent back shamed to her parents. Those sheets are publickly shewed by their Parents, and kept as a sign of incorrupt Virginity. The Jews of old examined their maids as to the condition of the membrane called Hymen, which Laurentius in his Anatomy, and others, copiously confute; 'tis no sufficient trial, they contend. And yet others again defend it, Gaspar Bartholinus, Pinæus of Paris, Albertus Magnus, &c., and think they speak too much in favour of women. Ludovicus Boncialus asserts that that natural constriction of the labia, in which they would have virginity to consist, can be brought about by astringent medicines; and if they have been deflowered, wise women (he says) thus befool us. Alsarius Crucius Genuensis says the same. So Avicenna, &c. An old bawdy nurse in Aristænetus (like that Spanish Cœlestina, who made women of five thousand virgins, and by her art restored as many women to virginity), when a fair maid of her acquaintance wept & made her moan to her, how she had been deflowered, and now ready to be married, was afraid it would be perceived, comfortably replied, Fear not, daughter, I'll teach thee a trick to help it. But this is aside from our path. To what end are all those Astrological questions, whether a virgin, whether chaste, whether a woman? and such strange absurd trials in Albertus Magnus, &c., by stones, perfumes, to make them piss, and confess J know not what in their sleep; some jealous brain was the first founder of them.

And to what passion may we ascribe those severe laws against jealousy, adulterers, as amongst the Hebrews, amongst the Egyptians (read Bohemus of the Carthaginians, of Turks), amongst the Athenians of old, Italians at this day, wherein they are to be severely punished, cut in pieces, burned, buried alive, with several expurgations [or trials of virtue], &c., are they not as so many symptoms of incredible jealousy? we may say the same of those Vestal Virgins that fetched water in a sieve, as Tatia did in Rome, in the year 800 from the founding of the city, before the Senators; and Æmilia, innocent virgin, that ran over hot irons, as Emma, Edward the Confessor's mother, did, the King himself being a spectator, with the like. We read in Nicephorus that Cunegunda, the wife of Henricus Bavarus, Emperor, suspected of adultery, trod upon red hot coulters, and had no harm: such another story we find in Regino; in Aventinus and Sigonius, of Charles the Third, and his wife Richarda, in the year 887, that was so purged with hot irons. Pausanias saith that he was once an eye-witness of such a miracle at Diana's Temple, a maid without any harm at all walked upon burning coals. Pius the Second, in his description of Europe, relates as much, that it was commonly practised at Diana's Temple, for women to go barefoot over hot coals, to try their honesties. Plinius, Solinus, and many writers, make mention of Feronia's Temple, and Dionysius Halicarnasseus of Memnon's statue, which were used to this purpose; Tatius of Pan his Cave (much like old S. Wilfrid's needle in Yorkshire), wherein they did use to try maids, whether they were honest * : when Leucippe went in, a sweet sound was heard. Austin relates many such examples, all which Lavater contends to be done by the illusion of Devils; though Thomas ascribes it to good Angels. Some, saith Austin, compel their wives to swear they be honest, as if perjury were a lesser sin than adultery; some consult Oracles, as Pheron that blind King of Egypt. Others reward, as those old Romans use to do; if a woman were contented with one man, she had a crown of Chastity bestowed on her. When all this will not serve, saith Alexander Gaguinus, the Muscovites, if they suspect their wives, will beat them till they confess; and if that will not avail, like those wild Irish, be divorced at their pleasures, or

---

* " Within the Church, St. Wilfrid's Needle was in our grandfather's remembrance very famous. A narrow hole this was in the Crypts, or close vaulted room under the ground, whereby women's honesty was tried. For such as were chaste did easily pass through, but as many as had played false were miraculously, I know not how, held fast, and could not creep through." — Camden's Britannia.

else knock them on the heads, as the old Gauls have done in former ages. Of this Tyranny of Jealousy, read more in Parthenius, Camerarius, Cælia's Epistles, Tho. Chaloner, Ariosto, Felix Platerus, &c.

MEMBER 3

Prognosticks of Jealousy, Despair, Madness, to make away themselves and others

THOSE which are jealous, most part, if they be not otherwise relieved, proceed from suspicion to hatred, from hatred to frenzy, madness, injury, murder, and despair.

> *A plague by whose most damnable effect,*
> *Divers in deep despair to die have sought,*
> *By which a man to madness near is brought,*
> *As well with causeless as with just suspect.*   (ARIOSTO)

In their madness many times, saith Vives, they make away themselves, and others. Which induceth Cyprian to call it a fruitful mischief, the seminary of offences, and fountain of murders. Tragical examples are too common in this kind, both new and old, in all ages, as of Cephalus and Procris, Pheron of Egypt, Tereus, Atreus, and Thyestes. Alexander Pheræus was murdered of his wife, on suspicion of keeping a mistress, Tully saith. Antoninus Verus was so made away by Lucilla; Demetrius, the son of Antigonus, and Nicanor, by their wives; Hercules poisoned by Deianira, Cæcinna murdered by Vespasian, Justina a Roman Lady by her husband. Amestris, Xerxes' wife, because she found her husband's cloak in Masistes his house, cut off Masistes his wife's paps, and gave them to the dogs, flayed her besides, and cut off her ears, lips, tongue, and slit the nose of Artaynta her daughter. Our late writers are full of such outrages.

Paulus Æmilius, in his History of France, hath a Tragical story of Chilpericus the First his death, made away by Frédégonde his Queen. In a jealous humour he came from hunting, and stole behind his wife, as she was dressing and combing her head in the Sun, gave her a familiar touch with his wand, which she mistaking for her lover, said, Ah, Landre, a good Knight should strike before, and not behind: but when she saw herself betrayed by his presence, she instantly took order to make him away. Hierome Osorius, in the eleventh book of the deeds of Emanuel, King of Portugal, to this effect hath a Tragical Narration of

one Ferdinandus Calderia, that wounded Gotherinus, a noble Countryman of his, at Goa in the East Indies, and cut off one of his legs, for
that he looked, as he thought, too familiarly upon his wife, which was
afterwards a cause of many quarrels, and much bloodshed. Guianerius
speaks of a silly jealous fellow, that seeing his child new born, included
in a kell, thought sure a Franciscan, that used to come to his house, was
the father of it, it was so like the Friar's Cowl, and thereupon threatened the Friar to kill him: Fulgosus, of a woman in Narbonne, that cut
off her husband's privities in the night, because she thought he played
false with her. The story of Jonuses Bassa, and fair Manto his wife, is
well known to such as have read the Turkish History, and that of Joan
of Spain, of which I treated in my former Section. Her jealousy, saith
Gomesius, was cause of both their deaths: King Philip died for grief a
little after, as Martian his Physician gave it out, and she for her part,
after a melancholy discontented life, misspent in lurking holes and
corners, made an end of her miseries. Felix Plater, in the first book of
his Observations, hath many such instances, of a Physician of his acquaintance, that was first mad through jealousy, and afterwards desperate; of a Merchant that killed his wife in the same humour, and after
precipitated himself [from a window]; of a Doctor of Law, that cut
off his man's nose: of a Painter's wife in Basil, in the year 1600, that
was mother of nine children, and had been 27 years married, yet afterwards jealous, and so impatient, that she became desperate, and would
neither eat nor drink in her own house, for fear her husband should
poison her. 'Tis a common sign this; for when once the humours are
stirred, and the imagination misaffected, it will vary itself in divers
forms; and many such absurd symptoms will accompany even madness
itself. Sckenkius hath an example of a jealous woman, that by this
means had many fits of the mother: and in his first book, of some that
through jealousy ran mad: of a Baker that gelded himself to try his
wife's honesty, &c. Such examples are too common.

MEMBER 4

SUBSECTION 1 — *Cure of Jealousy: by avoiding occasions, not to be
idle: of good counsel: to contemn it, not to watch or lock them up:
to dissemble it, &c.*

As of all other Melancholy, some doubt whether this malady may be
cured or no, they think 'tis like the Gout, or Switzers, whom we com-

monly call Walloons, those hired Soldiers, if once they take possession
of a Castle they can never be got out.

> *This is that cruel wound, against whose smart*
> *No liquor's force prevails, or any plaster,*
> *No skill of stars, no depth of magick art,*
> *Devisèd by that great clerk Zoroaster;*
> *A wound that so infects the soul and heart,*
> *As all our sense and reason it doth master:*
> *A wound whose pang and torment is so durable,*
> *As it may rightly callèd be incurable.*   (ARIOSTO)

Yet what I have formerly said of other Melancholy, I will say again,
it may be cured, or mitigated at least, by some contrary passion, good
counsel and persuasion, if it be withstood in the beginning, maturely
resisted, and as those Ancients hold, the nails of it be pared before
they grow too long. No better means to resist or repel it, than by avoiding idleness, to be still seriously busied about some matters of importance, to drive out those vain fears, foolish fantasies, and irksome suspicions out of his head, and then to be persuaded by his judicious
friends, to give ear to their good counsel and advice, and wisely to consider, how much he discredits himself, his friends, dishonours his children,
disgraceth his family, publisheth his shame, and as a Trumpeter of his
own misery, divulgeth, macerates, grieves himself and others; what an
argument of weakness it is, how absurd a thing in its own nature, how
ridiculous, how brutish a passion, how sottish, how odious; for as
Hierome well hath it, others hate him, and at last he hates himself for
it; how hare-brain a disease, mad and furious! If he will but hear them
speak, no doubt he may be cured. Joan, Queen of Spain, of whom I
have formerly spoken, under pretence of changing air, was sent to
Complutum, or Alcala de Henares, where Ximenes the Archbishop of
Toledo then lived, that by his good counsel (as for the present she was)
she might be eased. For a disease of the soul, if concealed, tortures and
overturns it, and by no physick can sooner be removed than by a discreet man's comfortable speeches. I will not here insert any consolatory
sentences to this purpose, or forestall any man's invention, but leave it
every one to dilate and amplify as he shall think fit in his own judgement: let him advise with Siracides. *Be not jealous over the wife of
thy bosom;* read that comfortable and pithy speech to this purpose of
Ximenes in the Author himself, as it is recorded by Gomesius; consult
with Chaloner, or Cælia in her Epistles, &c. Only this I will add, that
if it be considered aright, which causeth this jealous passion, be it just

or unjust, whether with or without cause, true or false, it ought not so heinously to be taken; 'tis no such real or capital matter, that it should make so deep a wound. 'Tis a blow that hurts not, an insensible smart, grounded many times upon false suspicion alone, and so fostered by a sinister conceit. If she be not dishonest, he troubles and macerates himself without a cause; or put case, which is the worst, he be a cuckold, it cannot be helped, the more he stirs in it, the more he aggravates his own misery. How much better were it in such a case to dissemble, or contemn it! why should that be feared, which cannot be redressed? Saith Vives, many women when they see there is no remedy, have been pacified; and shall men be more jealous than women? 'Tis some comfort in such a case to have companions,

'Tis a relief to have companions in misery.

Who can say he is free? who can assure himself he is not one already, or secure himself as to the future? If it were his case alone, it were hard; but being as it is almost a common calamity, 'tis not so grievously to be taken. If a man have a lock, which every man's key will open, as well as his own, why should he think to keep it private to himself? In some Countries they make nothing of it, saith Leo Afer, in many parts of Africa (if she be past fourteen) there's not a Nobleman that marries a maid, or that hath a chaste wife; 'tis so common; as the Moon gives horns once a month to the world, do they to their husbands at least. And 'tis most part true which that Caledonian Lady, Argentocoxus a British Prince his wife, told Julia Augusta, when she took her up for dishonesty, We Britons are naught at least with some few choice men of the better sort, but you Romans lie with every base knave, you are a company of common whores. Severus the Emperor in his time made laws for the restraint of this vice; and as Dion Nicæus relates in his life, three thousand cuckold-makers, or as Philo calls them, false coiners, and clippers of nature's money, were summoned into the Court at once. And yet, the Miller sees not all the water that goes by his mill: no doubt, but as in our days, these were of the Commonalty, all the great ones were not so much as called in question for it. Martial's Epigram, I suppose, might have been generally applied in those licentious times, thy goods, lands, money, wits, are thine own, but, neighbour Candidus, your wife is common. Husband and Cuckold in that age, it seems, were reciprocal terms; the Emperors themselves did wear Actæon's badge; how many Cæsars might I reckon up together, and what a catalogue of cornuted Kings and Princes in every story! Agamemnon, Menelaus, Philip of Greece, Ptolemæus of Egypt, Lucullus, Cæsar, Pompeius,

Cato, Augustus, Antonius, Antoninus, &c., that wore fair plumes of Bull's feathers in their crests. The bravest Soldiers and most Heroical spirits could not avoid it. They have been active and passive in this business, they have either given or taken horns. King Arthur, whom we call one of the Nine Worthies, for all his great valour, was unworthily served by Mordred one of his Round-Table Knights: and Guithera, or Helena Alba, his fair wife, as Leland interprets it, was an arrant honest woman. Saith mine Author, I could willingly wink at a fair Lady's faults, but that I am bound by the laws of History to tell the truth: against his will, God knows, did he write it, and so do I repeat it. I speak not of our times all this while, we have good, honest, virtuous men and women, whom fame, zeal, fear of God, Religion and superstition contains; and yet for all that, we have too many Knights of this order, so dubbed by their wives, many good women abused by dissolute husbands. In some places, and such persons, you may as soon enjoin them to carry water in a sieve, as to keep themselves honest. What shall a man do now in such a case? What remedy is to be had? How shall he be eased? By suing a divorce? that is hard to be effected: if not rightfully, then carefully, they carry the matter so cunningly, that though it be as common as Simony, as clear and as manifest as the nose in a man's face, yet it cannot be evidently proved, or they likely taken in the fact: they will have a knave Gallus to watch, or with that Roman Sulpicia, all made fast and sure,

> *Lest he should see her now, not as before*
> *With fine Cadurcian linen covered o'er,*
> *But lying naked with her paramour.*

She will hardly be surprised by her husband, be he never so wary. Much better then to put it up, the more he strives in it, the more he shall divulge his own shame; make a virtue of necessity, and conceal it. Yea, but the world takes notice of it, 'tis in every man's mouth: let them talk their pleasure, of whom speak they not in this sense? From the highest to the lowest, they are thus censured all: there is no remedy then but patience. It may be 'tis his own fault, and he hath no reason to complain, 'tis tit for tat, she is bad, he is worse. Bethink thyself, hast thou not done as much for some of thy neighbours? why dost thou require that of thy wife, which thou wilt not perform thyself? Thou rangest like a Town Bull, why art thou so incensed if she tread awry?

> *Be it that some woman break chaste wedlock's laws,*
> *And leaves her husband and becomes unchaste:*
> *Yet commonly it is not without cause,*
> *She sees her man in sin her goods to waste,*

She feels that he his love from her withdraws,
And hath on some perhaps less worthy placed,
Who strike with sword, the scabbard them may strike,
And sure love craveth love, like asketh like. (ARIOSTO)

She will ever study, saith Nevisanus, to pay back equally, she will quit it if she can. And therefore, as well adviseth Siracides, teach her not an evil lesson against thyself, which as Jansenius, Lyranus, on this text, and Carthusianus interpret, is no otherwise to be understood, then that she do thee not a mischief. I do not excuse her in accusing thee; but if both be naught, mend thyself first; for as the old saying is, A good husband makes a good wife.

Yea, but thou repliest, 'Tis not the like reason betwixt man and woman, through her fault my children are bastards, I may not endure it, let her scowl, brawl, and spend, I care not, so she be honest, I could easily bear it; but this I cannot, I may not, I will not; my faith, my fame, mine eye must not be touched, as the diverb is. I say the same of my wife, touch all, use all, take all but this. I acknowledge that of Seneca to be true, there is no sweet content in the possession of any good thing, without a companion, this only excepted, I say, This. And why this? Even this which thou so much abhorrest, it may be for thy progeny's good, better be any man's son than thine, to be begot of base Irus, poor Seius, or mean Mævius, the Town Swineherd's, a Shepherd's son: and well is he that, like Hercules, he hath any two fathers; for thou thyself hast peradventure more diseases than an horse, more infirmities of body and mind, a canker'd soul, crabbed conditions; make the worst of it, as it is incurable, so it is insensible. But art thou sure it is so? The fellow attends to your business? doth he so indeed? It may be thou art over suspicious, and without a cause, as some are: if it be born at eight months, or like him, and him they fondly suspect, he got it; if she speak or laugh familiarly with such or such men, then presently she is naught with them, such is thy weakness: whereas charity, or a well-disposed mind, would interpret all unto the best. S. Francis, by chance, seeing a Friar familiarly kissing another man's wife, was so far from misconceiving it, that he presently kneeled down, and thanked God there was so much charity left: but they, on the other side, will ascribe nothing to natural causes, indulge nothing to familiarity, mutual society, friendship; but out of a sinister suspicion, presently lock them close, watch them, thinking by those means to prevent all such inconveniences, that's the way to help it; whereas by such tricks they do aggravate the mischief.

'Tis but in vain to watch that which will away.

None can be kept resisting for her part;
Though body be kept close, within her heart
Advoutry lurks, t' exclude it there's no art.   (OVID)

Argus with an hundred eyes cannot keep her, these love alone many a
time evaded, as in Ariosto.

If all our hairs were eyes, yet sure, they said,
We husbands of our wives should be betrayed.

Hierome holds, to what end is all your custody? A dishonest woman
cannot be kept, an honest woman ought not to be kept, necessity is a
keeper not to be trusted. That which many covet, can hardly be preserved, as Salisburiensis thinks. I am of Æneas Sylvius' mind, Those
jealous Italians do very ill to lock up their wives; for women are of
such a disposition, they will most covet that which is denied most, and
offend least when they have free liberty to trespass. It is in vain to
lock her up if she be dishonest; and as our great Mr. Aristotle calls it,
too tyrannical a task, most unfit: for when she perceives her husband
observes her and suspects, she sins more freely, saith Nevisanus. She
is exasperated, seeks by all means to vindicate herself, and will therefore offend, because she is unjustly suspected. The best course then is
to let them have their own wills, give them free liberty, without any
keeping.

In vain our friends from this do us dehort,
For beauty will be where is most resort.   (DANIEL)

If she be honest, as Lucretia to Collatinus, Laodamia to Protesilaus,
Penelope to her Ulysses, she will so continue her honour, good name,
credit,

Ulysses shall my only husband be.   (OVID)

And as Phocion's wife in Plutarch, called her husband her wealth,
treasure, world, joy, delight, orb and sphere, she will hers. The vow she
made unto her good man, love, virtue, religion, zeal, are better keepers
than all those locks, Eunuchs, prisons; she will not be moved.

First I desire the earth to swallow me,
Before I violate mine honesty,
Or thunder from above drive me to hell,
With those pale ghosts, and ugly nights to dwell.
                                        (VIRGIL)

She is resolv'd with Dido to be chaste; though her husband be false,
she will be true: and as Octavia writ to her Antony:

These walls that here do keep me out of sight,
Shall keep me all unspotted unto thee,

And testify that I will do thee right,
I'll never stain thine house, though thou shame me.   (DANIEL)

Turn her loose to all those Tarquins and Satyrs, she will not be tempted. In the time of Valence the Emperor, saith St. Austin, one Archidamus, a Consul of Antioch, offered an hundred pound of gold to a fair young wife, and besides to set her husband free, who was then a dark prisoner, to be his concubine for a single night; but the chaste matron would not accept of it. When one commended Theano's fine arm to his fellows, she took him up short, Sir, 'tis not common; she is wholly reserved to her hus- band. Bilia had an old man to her spouse, and his breath stunk, so that no body could abide it abroad, coming home one day, he reprehended his wife, because she did not tell him of it: she vowed unto him she had told him, but that she thought every man's breath had been as strong as his. Tigranes and Armenia his Lady were invited to supper by King Cyrus: when they came home, Tigranes asked his wife, how she liked Cyrus, and what she did especially commend in him? she swore she did not observe him; when he replied again, what then she did observe, whom she looked on? She made answer, her husband that said he would die for her sake. Such are the properties and conditions of good women: and if she be well given, she will so carry herself; if otherwise she be naught, use all the means thou canst, she will be naught. Not the wish, but the lover, is lacking; she hath so many lies, excuses, as an hare hath muses, [or loopholes], tricks, Pandars, Bawds, shifts to deceive, 'tis to no purpose to keep her up, or to reclaim her by hard usage. Fair means peradventure may do somewhat.

Indulgence all the better restraint may prove.   (OVID)

Men and women are both in a predicament in this behalf, so sooner won, and better pacified. They will be led, not driven; though she be as arrant a scold as Xanthippe, as cruel as Medea, as clamorous as Hecuba, as lustful as Messalina, by such means (if at all) she may be reformed. Many patient Grizels by their obsequiousness in this kind, have re- claimed their husbands from their wandering lusts. In Nova Francia and Turkey (as Leah, Rachel, and Sarah did to Abraham and Jacob) they bring their fairest damsels to their husbands' beds; Livia seconded the lustful appetites of Augustus: Stratonice, wife to King Deiotarus, did not only bring Electra, a fair maid, to her goodman's bed, but brought up the children begot on her, as carefully as if they had been her own. Tertius Æmilius' wife, Cornelia's mother, perceiving her hus- band's intemperance, dissimulated the matter, made much of the maid, and would take no notice of it. A new married man, when a pick-thank friend of his, to curry favour, had shewed him his wife familiar in private with a young gallant, courting and dallying, &c., Tush, said he, let him do his worst, I dare trust my wife, though I dare not trust him. The best remedy then is by fair means; if that will not take place, to dissemble it, as I say, or turn it off with a jest: hear Guevara's advice in this case, either take in jest or ignore in silence; for if you take exceptions at every thing your wife doth, Solomon's wisdom, Hercules' valour, Homer's learning, Socrates' patience, Argus' vigilancy will not serve [your] turn. Therefore a less mischief, Nevisanus holds, to dissimulate, to be a buyer of cradles, as the proverb is, than to be too solicitous. A good fellow when his wife was brought to bed before her time, bought half a dozen of Cradles beforehand for so many children, as if his wife should continue to bear children at every two months. Pertinax the Emperor, when one told him a Fiddler was too familiar with his Empress, made no reckoning of it. And when that Macedonian Philip was upbraided with his wife's dishonesty, a Conqueror of Kingdoms could not tame his wife, (for she thrust him out of doors) he made a jest of it. Saith Nevisanus, wise men bear their horns in their hearts, fools on their foreheads. Eumenes, King of Pergamus, was at deadly feud with Perseus of Macedonia, insomuch that Perseus, hearing of a journey he was to take to Delphi, set a company of soldiers to intercept him in his passage; they did it accordingly, and as they supposed, left him stoned to death. The news of this fact was brought instantly to Pergamus; Attalus, Eumenes' brother, proclaimed himself King forthwith, took possession of the Crown, and married Stratonice the Queen. But by and by, when contrary news was brought, that King Eumenes was alive, and now coming to the City, he laid by his Crown, left his wife, as a private man went to meet him, and congratulated his return. Eumenes, though he knew all particulars passed, yet dissembling the matter, kindly embraced his brother, and took his wife into his favour again, as if no such matter had been heard of or done. Jocundo, in Ariosto, found his wife in bed with a knave, both asleep, went his ways, and would not so much as wake them, much less reprove them for it. An honest fellow finding in like sort his wife had played false at Tables, and borne a man too many, drew his dagger, and swore if he had not been his very friend, he would have killed him. Another hearing one had done that for him, which no man desires to be done by a Deputy, followed him in a rage with his sword drawn, and having overtaken him, laid adultery to his charge; the offender hotly pursued, confessed it was true, with which confession he was satisfied, and so left him, swearing, that if he had denied it, he would not have put it up. How much better is it to do thus, than to macerate himself, impatiently to rave and rage, to enter an Action (as Arnoldus Tillius did in the Court of Toulouse, against Martin Guerre his fellow-soldier, for that he counterfeited his habit, and was too familiar with his wife) so to divulge his own shame, and to remain for ever a Cuckold on record! How much better be Cornelius Tacitus, than Publicus Cornutus, to condemn in such cases, or take no notice of it! Saith Erasmus, better be a wittol, and put it up, than to trouble himself to no purpose. And though he will not nod for everybody, be an ass, as he is an ox, yet to wink at it, as many do, is not amiss at some times, in some cases, to some parties, if it be for his commodity, or some great man's sake, his Land-Lord, Patron, Benefactor (as Galba the Roman, saith Plutarch, did by Mæcenas, and Phayllus of Argos did by King Philip, when he promised him an office, on that condition he might lie with his wife) and so to let it pass; it never troubles me, said Amphitruo, to be cornuted by Jupiter; let it not molest thee then; be friends with her; let it, I say, make no breach of love betwixt you. Howsoever, the best way is to contemn it, which Henry the Second, King of France, advised a Courtier of his, jealous of his wife, and complaining of her unchasteness, to reject it, and comfort himself; for he that suspects his wife's incontinence, and fears the Pope's curse, shall never live a merry hour, or sleep a quiet night: no remedy but patience. When all is done, according to that counsel of Nevisanus, if it may not be helped, it must be endured. 'Tis Sophocles' advice, keep it to thyself, and which Chrysostom calls a domestic gymnasium, and a school of Philosophy, put it up. There is no other cure, but time to wear it out, the remedy for injuries is forgetting, as if they had drunk a draught of Lethe in Trophonius' den. To conclude, age will bereave her of it, time and patience must end it.

> The mind's affections Patience will appease,
> It passions kills, and healeth each disease. (R. T.)

SUBSECTION 2 — *By prevention before, or after marriage, Plato's community, marry a Courtesan, Philters, Stews, to marry one equal in years, fortunes, of a good family, education, good place, to use them well, &c.*

OF such medicines as conduce to the cure of this malady, I have sufficiently treated; there be some good remedies remaining, by way of prevention, precautions, or admonitions, which, if rightly practised, may do much good. Plato, in his Common-wealth, to prevent this mis-

chief belike, would have all things common, wives and children all as
one: and which Cæsar in his Commentaries observed of those old Britons, that first inhabited this Land, they had ten or twelve wives allotted
to such a family, or promiscuously to be used by so many men: not
one to one, as with us, or four, five or six to one, as in Turkey. The
Nicholaites, a Sect that sprung, saith Austin, from Nicholas the Deacon,
would have women indifferent; and the cause of this filthy sect was
Nicholas the Deacon's jealousy, for which, when he was condemned, to
purge himself of his offence, he broached his heresy that it was lawful
to lie with one another's wives, and for any man to lie with his: like
to those Anabaptists in Munster, that would consort with other men's
wives as the spirit moved them: or as Mahomet, the seducing Prophet,
would needs use women as he list himself, to beget Prophets; 205, their
Alcoran saith, were in love with him, and he as able as forty men.
Amongst the old Carthaginians, as Bohemus relates out of Sabellicus,
the King of the Country lay with the bride the first night, and once in
a year they went promiscuously altogether. Munster ascribes the beginning of this brutish custom (unjustly) to one Picardus, a French-man,
that invented a new sect of Adamites, to go naked as Adam did, and to
use promiscuous venery at set times. When the priest repeated that of
Genesis, " Increase and multiply," out went the candles in the place
where they met, and without all respect of age, persons, conditions,
catch that catch may, every man took her came next, &c. Some fasten
this on those ancient Bohemians and Russians: others on the inhabitants of Mambrium, in the Lucerne valley in Piedmont; and, as I read,
it was practised in Scotland amongst Christians themselves, until King
Malcolm's time, the King or the Lord of the Town had their maidenheads. In some parts of India in our age, and those Icelanders, as
amongst the Babylonians of old, they will prostitute their wives and
daughters (which Chalcocondylas, a Greek modern writer, for want of
better intelligence, puts upon us Britons) to such travellers or sea-faring
men, as come amongst them by chance, to shew how far they were from
this feral vice of Jealousy, and how little they esteemed it. The Kings
of Calicut, as Lod. Vertomannus relates, will not touch their wives, till
one of their Biarmi or high Priests have lain first with them, to sanctify
their wombs. But those Essenes and Montanists, two strange sects of
old, were in another extreme, they would not marry at all, or have any
society with women, because of their intemperance they held them all
to be naught [or naughty]. Nevisanus the Lawyer, would have him
that is inclined to this malady, to prevent the worst, marry a quean,

take a whore, so that at least he should not be deceived, knowing her
to be what she was, as he might not the others. A fornicator in Seneca
constuprated two wenches in a night; for satisfaction the one desired
to hang him, the other to marry him. Hieronymus, King of Syracuse in
Sicily, espoused himself to Peitho, keeper of the Stews; and Ptolemy
took Thais a common Whore to be his wife, had two sons, Leontiscus
and Lagus, by her, and one daughter Irene: 'tis therefore no such unlikely thing. A Citizen of Eugubine gelded himself to try his wife's
honesty, and to be freed from jealousy: so did a Baker in Basil, to the
same intent. But of all other precedents in this kind, that of Combabus
is most memorable: who to prevent his Master's suspicion, for he was
a beautiful young man, and sent by Seleucus his Lord and King, with
Stratonice the Queen, to conduct her into Syria, fearing the worst,
gelded himself before he went, and left his genitals behind him in a
box sealed up. His Mistress by the way fell in love with him, but he
not yielding to her, was accused to Seleucus of incontinency (as that
Bellerophon was in like case, falsely traduced by Sthenobœa, to King
Prœtus her husband, when she could not persuade him to bed with her)
and that by her, and was therefore at his coming home cast into prison:
the day of hearing appointed, he was sufficiently cleared and acquitted
by shewing his privities, which to the admiration of the beholders he
had formerly cut off. The Lydians used to geld women whom they
suspected, saith Leonicus, as well as men. To this purpose Saint Francis,
because he used to confess women in private, to prevent suspicion, and
prove himself a Maid, stripped himself before the Bishop of Assisi and
others: and Friar Leonard for the same cause went through Viterbo in
Italy without any garments.

Our Pseudo-Catholicks, to help these inconveniences which proceed
from Jealousy, to keep themselves and their wives honest, make severe
Laws; against adultery, present death; and withal [for] fornication, a
venial sin, as a sink to convey that furious and swift stream of concupiscence, they appoint and permit stews, those punks and pleasant sinners,
the more to secure their wives in all populous Cities, for they hold them
as necessary as Churches; and howsoever unlawful, yet to avoid a
greater mischief to be tolerated in policy, as usury, for the hardness of
men's hearts; and for this end they have whole Colleges of Courtesans
in their Towns and Cities. Of Cato's mind belike, that would have his
servants familiar with some such feminine creatures, to avoid worse mischiefs in his house, and made allowance for it. They hold it unpossible
for idle persons, young, rich, and lusty, so many servants, Monks, Friars,

to live honest, too tyrannical a burden to compel them to be chaste, and most unfit to suffer poor men, younger brothers and soldiers at all to marry, as also diseased persons, votaries, priests, servants. Therefore as well to keep and ease the one as the other, they tolerate and wink at these kind of Brothel-houses and Stews. Many probable arguments they have to prove the lawfulness, the necessity, and a toleration of them, as of usury; and without question in policy they are not to be contradicted: but altogether in Religion. Others prescribe philters, spells, charms to keep men and women honest. In order that a woman may not admit any man but her husband: Take the gall-bladder of a goat, and the fat, dry it, heat it in oil, &c., and she'll love none other but you. In Alexis, Porta, &c., you will find much more, and more absurd than these, as in Rhasis, to keep a woman from admitting others than her husband, and make her love him only, &c. But these are most part Pagan, impious, irreligious, absurd, and ridiculous devices.

The best means to avoid these and like inconveniences, are, to take away the causes and occasions. To this purpose Varro writ the Menippean Satire, but it is lost. Patricius prescribes four rules to be observed in choosing of a wife (which whoso will may read) ; Fonseca the Spaniard sets down six special cautions for men, four for women; Sam. Neander out of Shonbernerus, five for men, five for women; Anthony Guevara many good lessons ; Cleobulus two alone,* others otherwise ; as first to make a good choice in marriage, to invite Christ to their wedding, and which Saint Ambrose adviseth, and to pray to him for her, not to be too rash and precipitate in his election, to run upon the first he meets, or dote on every snowt-fair piece he sees, but to choose her as much by his ears as eyes, to be well advised whom he takes, of what age, &c. and cautelous [or cautious] in his proceeding.

An old man should not marry a young woman, or a young woman an old man,

>   *Old and young cattle plough not well together!*   (OVID)

such matches must needs minister a perpetual cause of suspicion, and be distasteful to each other.

>   *Night-crows on tombs, owl sits on carcass dead,*
>   *So lies a wench with Sophocles in bed.*   (ALCIATI)

For Sophocles, as Athenæus describes him, was a very old man, as cold as January, a bed-fellow of bones, and doted yet upon Archippe a young Courtesan, than which nothing can be more odious. An old man is a most unwelcome guest to a young wench, unable, unfit:

---

* Neither be too easy when alone with her, nor scold her too much in the presence of others. — Burton's note.

Maidens shun their embrace ; abhorrent they
To Venus, Love, and Hymen. (PONTANUS)

And as in like case a good fellow that had but a peck of corn weekly to grind, yet would needs build a new Mill for it, found his error eftsoons, for either he must let his Mill lie waste, pull it quite down, or let others grind at it : so these men, &c.

Seneca therefore disallows all such unseasonable matches, for that frequency in nuptial matters will be a curse. And as Tully farther inveighs, 'tis unfit for any, but ugly and filthy in old age. Amorousness in the old is unseemly, one of the three things God hateth. Plutarch rails downright at such kind of marriages, which are attempted by old men, who, already impotent in body, and laid waste by their pleasures, can sin only in fancy, and makes a question whether in some cases it be tolerable at least for such a man to marry.

Lust that desires the deed but lacks the power, (JUVENAL)

that is now past those venerous exercises, " as a gelded man lies with a Virgin and sighs," and now complains with him in Petronius, he is quite done, though once an Achilles in the fields of love.

Late a match for any maid,
I contended not ingloriously. (HORACE)

But the question is, whether he may delight himself as those Priapeian Popes, which in their decrepit age lay commonly between two wenches every night, touching and handling their beauties, whether he may pleasure himself thus far ; and as many doting Sires still do to their own shame, their children's undoing, and their families' confusion : he abhors it, it must be avoided as a Bedlam-master, and not obeyed.

————— *Alecto herself*
Holds the torch at such nuptials, and Hymen wails sadly,

the Devil himself makes such matches. Levinus Lemnius reckons up three things which generally disturb the peace of marriage : the first is when they marry intempestive or unseasonably, as many mortal men marry precipitately and inconsiderately, when they are effete and old : The second, when they marry unequally for fortunes and birth : The third, when a sick impotent person weds one that is sound ; the nuptial hopes are frustrate : many dislikes instantly follow. Many doting dizzards, it may not be denied, as Plutarch confesseth, recreate themselves with such obsolete, unseasonable and filthy remedies (so he calls them) with a remembrance of their former pleasures, against nature they stir up their dead flesh ; but an old lecher is abominable ; Nevisanus holds, a woman that marries a third time may be presumed to be no honester than she should. Of them both, thus Ambrose concludes in

his comment upon Luke, they that are coupled together, not to get
children, but to satisfy their lust, are not husbands, but fornicators,
with whom St. Austin consents: matrimony without hope of children, is
not a wedding but a jumbling or coupling together. In a word (except
they wed for mutual society, help, and comfort, one of another, in which
respects, though Tiberius deny it, without question old folks may well
marry) for sometimes a man hath most need of a wife, according to
Puccius, when he hath no need of a wife; otherwise it is most odious,
when an old Acherontick dizzard, that hath one foot in his grave, shall
flicker after a lusty young wench that is blythe and bonny,

> —————— *Lusty as the sparrow in spring,*
> *Or the snow-white ring-dove.* (PONTANUS)

What can be more detestable?

> *Thou old goat, hoary lecher, naughty man,*
> *With stinking breath, art thou in love?*
> *Must thou be slavering? she spews to see*
> *Thy filthy face, it doth so move.* (PLAUTUS)

Yet as some will, it is much more tolerable for an old man to marry a
young woman (Our Lady's match they call it) for she'll be a woman
tomorrow, as he said in Tully. Cato the Roman, Critobulus in Xenophon, Traquellus of late, Julius Scaliger, &c., and many famous precedents we have in that kind; but not to the contrary; 'tis not fit for an
ancient woman to match with a young man. For as Varro will, when an
old woman sports, she makes sport for death, 'tis Charon's match between Cascus and Casca, and the Devil himself is surely well pleased
with it. And therefore, as the Poet inveighs, thou old Vetustilla, bedridden quean, that art now skin and bones,

> *Thou hast three hairs, four teeth, a breast*
> *Like grasshopper, an emmet's crest,*
> *A skin more rugged than thy coat,*
> *And dugs like spider's web to boot.* (MARTIAL)

Must thou marry a youth again? And yet they would marry any number
of husbands; howsoever it is, as Apuleius gives out of his Meroe, a
pestilent match, abominable, and not to be endured. In such case, how
can they otherwise choose but be jealous? how should they agree one
with another? This inequality is not in years only, but in birth, fortunes,
conditions, and all good qualities,

> *If you would marry fitly, wed your equal.* (OVID)

'Tis my counsel, saith Anthony Guevara, to choose such a one. Let a
Citizen match with a Citizen, a Gentleman with a Gentlewoman: he that

observes not this precept (saith he) instead of a fair wife, shall have a fury, for a fit son-in-law a mere fiend, &c. Examples are too frequent.

Another main caution fit to be observed, is this, that though they be equal in years, birth, fortunes, and other conditions, yet they do not omit virtue and good education, which Musonius and Antipater so much inculcate in Stobæus.

> *Parental virtue is a splendid dowry,*
> *And chastity, that shrinks from others' arms*
> *And never breaks its compact.* (HORACE)

If as Plutarch adviseth, one must eat a bushel of salt with him before he choose his friend, what care should be had in choosing a wife, his second self, how solicitous should he be to know her qualities and behaviour! and when he is assured of them, not to prefer birth, fortune, beauty, before bringing up, and good conditions. Coquage, god of Cuckolds, as one [Rabelais] merrily said, accompanies the goddess Jealousy, both follow the fairest, by Jupiter's appointment, and they sacrifice to them together: beauty and honesty seldom agree; straight personages have often crooked manners; fair faces, foul vices; good complexions, ill conditions. Beauty (saith Chrysostom) is full of treachery and suspicion: he that hath a fair wife, cannot have a worse mischief, and yet most covet it, as if nothing else in marriage but that and wealth were to be respected. Francis Sforza, Duke of Milan, was so curious in this behalf, that he would not marry the Duke of Mantua's daughter, except he might see her naked first: which Lycurgus appointed in his Laws, and More in his Utopian Commonwealth approves. In Italy, as a traveller observes, if a man have three or four daughters, or more, and they prove fair, they are married eftsoons: if deformed, they change their lovely names of Lucia, Cynthia, Camæna, call them Dorothy, Ursula, Bridget, and so put them into Monasteries, as if none were fit for marriage but such as are eminently fair: but these are erroneous tenents: a modest Virgin well conditioned, to such a fair snout * piece, is much to be preferred. If thou wilt avoid them, take away all causes of suspicion and jealousy, marry a coarse piece, fetch her from Cassandra's Temple, which was wont in Italy to be a Sanctuary of all deformed Maids, and so thou shalt be sure that no man will make thee cuckold, but for spite. A Citizen of Byzantium in Thrace, had a filthy dowdy, deformed slut to his wife, and finding her in bed with another man, cried out as one amazed: O thou wretch! what necessity brought thee hither? as well he might; for who can affect such a one? But this is warily to be under-

* Snout, or snowt, good-looking.

stood, most offend in another extreme, they prefer wealth before beauty, and so she be rich, they care not how she look; but these are all out as faulty as the rest. Consider your wife's looks, as Sarisburiensis adviseth, that you may not despise her when you see other women, as that Knight in Chaucer, that was married to an old woman,

> And al day after hidde him as an owle.
> So wo was him, his wyf looked so foule.

Have a care of thy wife's complexion, lest whilst thou seest another, thou loathest her, she prove jealous, thou naught,

> *Though thy wife be ugly, thy maid beautiful,*
> *Yet from the maid abstain.*

I can perhaps give instance. It is a misery to possess that which no man likes: on the other side, what many love is not easily guarded. And as the bragging soldier vaunted in the Comedy, 'tis a great misery to be too handsome. Scipio did never so hardly besiege Carthage, as these young gallants will beset thine house, one with wit or person, another with wealth, &c. If she be fair, saith Guazzo, she will be suspected howsoever. Both extremes are naught, the one is soon beloved, the other loves: one is hardly kept, because proud and arrogant, the other not worth keeping; what is to be done in this case? Ennius in Menelippe adviseth thee as a friend to take one of a middle size, neither too fair nor too foul,

> *Not the fairest but the chastest doth me please,*   (MARULLUS)

with old Cato, though fit, let her beauty be, neither too choice nor too mean, between both. This I approve; but of the other two I resolve with Sarisburiensis, both rich alike, endowed alike, I had rather marry a fair one, and put it to the hazard, than be troubled with a blowze; but do thou as thou wilt, I speak only of myself.

Howsoever, I would advise thee thus much, be she fair or foul, to choose a wife out of a good kindred, parentage, well brought up, in an honest place. He that marries a wife out of a suspected Inn or Alehouse, buys a horse in Smithfield, and hires a servant in Paul's, as the diverb is, shall likely have a jade to his horse, a knave for his man, an arrant honest woman to his wife. Saith Nevisanus, such a mother, such a daughter; cat to her kind. If the mother be dishonest, in all likelihood the daughter will take after her in all good qualities; think you not Pasiphae will bring forth a bull-loving daughter? If the dam trot, the foal will not amble. My last caution is, that a woman do not bestow herself upon a fool, or an apparent melancholy person; jealousy is a symptom of that disease, and fools have no moderation. Justina, a Roman Lady, was much persecuted, and after made away by her jealous husband, she

caused and enjoined this Epitaph, as a caveat to others, to be engraven
on her tomb.

> *Learn parents all, and by Justina's case,*
> *Your children to no dizzards for to place.*

After marriage, I can give no better admonitions than to use their wives
well, and which a friend of mine told me that was a married man, I will
tell you as good cheap, saith Nicostratus in Stobæus, to avoid future
strife, and for quietness' sake, when you are in bed take heed of your
wives' flattering speeches overnight, and curtain sermons in the morning.
Let them do their endeavour likewise to maintain them to their means,
which Patricius ingeminates, and let them have liberty with discretion,
as time and place requires : many women turn queans by compulsion, as
Nevisanus observes, because their husbands are so hard, and keep them
so short in diet and apparel, poverty and hunger, want of means, makes
them dishonest, or bad usage ; their churlish behaviour forceth them to
fly out, or bad examples, they do it to cry quittance. In the other extreme some are too liberal, as the proverb is, they make a rod for their
own tails, as Candaules did to Gyges in Herodotus, commend his wife's
beauty himself, and besides would needs have him see her naked. Whilst
they give their wives too much liberty to gad abroad, and bountiful
allowance, they are accessory to their own miseries ; as Plautus jibes,
they have deformed souls, and by their painting and colours procure
their husband's hate, especially,

> *The wretched husband's lips are smeared with paint.*　(JUVENAL)

Besides, their wives (as Basil notes) impudently thrust themselves into
other men's companies, and by their undecent wanton carriage provoke
and tempt the spectators. Virtuous women should keep house ; and 'twas
well performed and ordered by the Greeks, that a matron should not be
seen in publick without her husband to speak for her ; which made
Phidias belike at Elis paint Venus treading on a Tortoise, a symbol of
women's silence and house-keeping. For a woman abroad and alone is
like a Deer broke out of a Park, whom every hunter follows ; and besides
in such places she cannot so well vindicate herself, but as that virgin
Dinah " going for to see the daughters of the land," lost her virginity,
she may be defiled and overtaken on a sudden.

> *Poor helpless does, what are we but a prey?*　(MARTIAL)

And therefore I know not what Philosopher he was, that would have
women come but thrice abroad all their time, to be baptized, married,
and buried ; but he was too strait-laced. Let them have their liberty in
good sort, and go in good sort ; as a good fellow said, so that they look

not twenty years younger abroad than they do at home; they be not spruce, neat, Angels abroad, beasts, dowdies, sluts at home; but seek by all means to please and give content to their husbands; to be quiet above all things, obedient, silent and patient; if they be incensed, angry, chide a little, their wives must not cample [or answer back] again, but take it in good part. An honest woman, I cannot now tell where she dwelt, but by report an honest woman she was, hearing one of her gossips by chance complaining of her husband's impatience, told her an excellent remedy for it, and gave her withal a glass of water, which when he brawled she should hold still in her mouth, and that as often as he chid; she did so two or three times with good success, and at length seeing her neighbour, gave her great thanks for it, and would needs know the ingredients, she told her in brief what it was, fair water, and no more: for it was not the water, but her silence which performed the cure. Let every froward woman imitate this example, and be quiet within doors, and (as M. Aurelius prescribes) a necessary caution it is to be observed of all good matrons that love their credits, to come little abroad, but follow their work at home, look to their household affairs and private business, be sober, thrifty, wary, circumspect, modest, and compose themselves to live to their husbands' means, as a good housewife should do.

One who delights in the distaff, and beguiles
The hours of labor with a song; her duties
Take on an air of virtuous loveliness
When with her maids she's busy at wheel and spindle. (CHALONER)

Howsoever 'tis good to keep them private, not in prison;

> *Whoever guards his wife with bolts and bars*
> *May be a learned man, but's sure a fool!* (MENANDER)

Read more of this subject in Arnisæus, Cyprian, Tertullian, Bossus, Godefridus, Levinus Lemnius, Barbarus, Franciscus Patricius, Fonseca, Sam. Neander, &c.

These cautions concern him; and if by those or his own discretion otherwise he cannot moderate himself, his friends must not be wanting by their wisdom, if it be possible, to give the party grieved satisfaction, to prevent and remove the occasions, objects, if it may be to secure him. If it be one alone, or many, to consider whom he suspects, or at what times, in what places he is most incensed, in what companies. Nevisanus makes a question whether a young Physician ought to be admitted in case of sickness, into a new married man's house, to administer a julip, a syrup, or some such physick. The Persians of old would not suffer a young Physician to come amongst women. Apollonides of Cos made Artaxerxes cuckold, and was after buried alive for it. A gaoler in Aristænetus had a fine young gentleman to his prisoner; in commiseration of his youth and person he let him loose, to enjoy the liberty of the prison, but he unkindly made him a Cornuto. Menelaus gave good welcome to Paris a stranger, his whole house and family were at his command, but he ungently stole away his beloved wife. The like measure was offered to Agis, king of Lacedæmon, by Alcibiades an exile, for his good entertainment, He was too familiar with Timæa his wife, begetting a child of her, called Leotychides; and bragging moreover, when he came home to Athens, that he had a son should be King of the Lacedæmonians. If such objects were removed, no doubt but the parties might easily be satisfied, or that they could use them gently, and intreat them well, not to revile them, scoff at, hate them, as in such cases commonly they do; 'tis an inhuman infirmity, a miserable vexation, and they should not add grief to grief, nor aggravate their misery, but seek to please, and by all means give them content, by good counsel, removing such offensive objects, or by mediation of some discreet friends. In old Rome there was a Temple erected by the Matrons to that Viriplaca Dea; another to Venus Verticordia, whither (if any difference happened betwixt man and wife) they did instantly resort: there they did offer sacrifice, a white Hart, Plutarch records, without the gall (some say the like of Juno's Temple) and make their prayers for conjugal peace: before some indifferent arbitrators and friends, the matter was heard betwixt man and wife, and commonly composed. In our times we want no sacred Churches, or good men, to end such Controversies, if use were made of them. Some say, that precious stone called Beryllus, others a Diamond, hath excellent virtue, to reconcile men and wives, to maintain unity and love; you may try this when you will, and as you see cause. If none of all these means and cautions will take place, I know not what remedy to prescribe, or whither such persons may go for ease, except they can get into the same Turkey Paradise, where they shall have as many fair wives as they will themselves, with clear eyes, and such as look on none but their own husbands, no fear, no danger of being Cuckolds; or else I would have them observe that strict rule of Alphonsus, to marry a deaf and dumb man to a blind woman. If this will not help, let them, to prevent the worst, consult with an Astrologer, and see whether the Significators in her Horoscope agree with his, that they be not in signs and parts that betoken hateful looks and domineering, but mutually loving and dutiful, otherwise (as they hold) there will be intolerable enmities between them: or else get him the Seal of Venus, a Characteristical Seal stamped in the day and hour of Venus, when she is fortunate, with such and such set words and charms, which Villanovanus and Leo Suavius prescribe, from the magick Seals of Solomon, Hermes, Raguel, &c., with many such, which Alexis, Albertus, and some of our Natural Magicians put upon us: in order that a woman may not be able to commit adultery with any one, take a lock of her hair, &c., and he shall surely be gracious in all women's eyes, and never suspect or disagree with his own wife, so long as he wears it. If this course be not approved, and other remedies may not be had, they must in the last place sue for a divorce: but that is somewhat difficult to effect, and not all out so fit. For as Felisacus urgeth, if that law of Constantine the great, or that of Theodosius and Valentinian, concerning divorce, were in use in our times, we should have almost no married couples left. Try therefore those former remedies: or as Tertullian reports of Democritus, that put out his eyes because he could not look on a woman without lust, and was much troubled to see that which he might not enjoy; let him make himself blind, and so he shall avoid that care and molestation of watching his wife. One other sovereign remedy I could repeat, an especial Antidote against Jealousy, an excellent cure; but I am not now disposed to tell it, not that like a covetous Empirick, I conceal it for any gain, but some other reasons, I am not willing to publish it; if you be very desirous to know it, when I meet you next, I will peradventure tell you what it is in your ear. This is the best counsel I can give; which he that hath need of, as occasion serves, may apply unto himself. In the meantime,

Ye gods, avert from earth the pest!   (VIRGIL)

As the Proverb is, from Heresy, Jealousy, and Frenzy, good Lord, deliver us.

SECTION 4   MEMBER 1

SUBSECTION I — *Religious Melancholy. Its object God; what his beauty is; how it allureth. The parts and parties affected*

THAT there is such a distinct species of Love-Melancholy, no man hath ever yet doubted; but whether this subdivision of Religious Melancholy be warrantable, it may be controverted.

Lead on, ye Muses, nor desert me now
Mid-journey, where no footsteps go before,
Nor wheel-tracks marking out a way for me.   (GROTIUS)

I have no pattern to follow, as in some of the rest, no man to imitate. No Physician hath as yet distinctly written of it, as of the other; all acknowledge it a most notable symptom, some a cause, but few a species or kind. Aretæus, Alexander, Rhasis, Avicenna, and most of our late Writers, as Gordonius, Fuchsius, Plater, Bruel, Montaltus, &c., repeat it as a symptom. Some seem to be inspired of the Holy Ghost, some take upon them to be Prophets, some are addicted to new opinions, some fore-tell strange things concerning the state of the world, Anti-Christ, saith Gordonius. Some will prophesy of the end of the World to a day almost, and the fall of the Antichrist, as they have been addicted or brought up; for so melancholy works with them, as Laurentius holds. If they have been precisely given, all their meditations tend that way, and in con-clusion produce strange effects, the humour imprints symptoms accord-ing to their several inclinations and conditions, which makes Guianerius and Felix Plater, put too much devotion, blind zeal, fear of eternal punishment, and that last judgment, for a cause of those Enthusiasticks and desperate persons; but some do not obscurely make a distinct species of it, dividing Love-Melancholy into that whose object is women; & into the other, whose object is God. Plato, in the Banquet, makes men-tion of two distinct Furies; and amongst our Neotericks, Hercules de Saxoniâ doth expressly treat of it in a distinct species. Love-Melancholy (saith he) is twofold; the first is that (to which peradventure some will not vouchsafe this name or species of Melancholy) affection of those which put God for their object, and are altogether about prayer, fasting, &c., the other about women. Peter Forestus in his Observations delivereth as much in the same words: and Felix Platerus, 'tis a frequent disease; and they have a ground of what they say, forth of Aretæus and Plato. Aretæus an old Author, doth so divide Love-Melancholy, and derives this second from the first, which comes by inspiration or otherwise. Plato in his Phædrus hath these words, Apollo's Priests at Delphi, and at Dodona, in their fury do many pretty feats, and benefit the Greeks, but never in their right wits. He makes them all mad, as well he might; and he that shall but consider that superstition of old, those prodigious effects of it (as in its place I will shew the several furies of our Seers, Pythonesses, Sibyls, Enthusiasts, Pseudo-prophets, Hereticks and Schis-maticks in these our latter ages) shall instantly confess, that all the world again cannot afford so much matter of madness, so many stupid symptoms, as superstition, heresy, schism hath brought out: that this species alone may be parallel'd to all the former, hath a greater latitude, and more miraculous effects; that it more besots and infatuates men, than any other above named whatsoever, doth more harm, works more disquietness to mankind, and hath more crucified the souls of mortal men (such hath been the Devil's craft) than wars, plagues, sicknesses, dearth, famine, and all the rest.

Give me but a little leave, and I will set before your eyes in brief a stupend, vast, infinite Ocean of incredible madness and folly: a Sea full of shelves and rocks, sands, gulfs, Euripuses, and contrary tides, full of fearful monsters, uncouth shapes, roaring waves, tempests, and Siren calms, Halcyonian Seas, unspeakable misery, such Comedies and Tragedies, such absurd and ridiculous, feral and lamentable fits, that I know not whether they are more to be pitied or derided, or may be believed, but that we daily see the same still practised in our days, fresh examples, new news, fresh objects of misery and madness in this kind, that are still represented unto us, abroad, at home, in the midst of us, in our bosoms.

But before I can come to treat of these several errors and obliquities, their causes, symptoms, affections, &c., I must say something necessarily of the object of this love, God himself, what this love is, how it allureth, whence it proceeds, and (which is the cause of all our miseries) how we mistake, wander, and swerve from it.

Amongst all those Divine Attributes that God doth vindicate to himself, Eternity, Omnipotency, Immutability, Wisdom, Majesty, Justice, Mercy, &c., his Beauty is not the least. One thing, saith David, have I desired of the Lord, and that I will still desire, to behold the beauty of the Lord. And out of Sion, which is the perfection of beauty, God hath shined. All other creatures are fair, I confess, and many other objects do much enamour us, a fair house, a fair horse, a comely person. I am amazed, saith Austin, when I look up to Heaven, and behold the beauty of the Stars; the beauty of Angels, Principalities, Powers, who can express it? who can sufficiently commend, or set out this beauty which appears in us? so fair a body, so fair a face, eyes, nose, cheeks, chin, brows, all fair and lovely to behold, besides the beauty of the soul, which cannot be discerned. If we so labour, and be so much affected, with the comeliness of creatures, how should we be ravished with that admirable lustre of God himself? — If ordinary beauty have such a prerogative and power, and what is amiable and fair, to draw the eyes and ears, hearts and affections, of all spectators unto it, to move, win, entice, allure: how shall this divine form ravish our souls, which is the fountain and quintessence of all beauty? If Heaven be so fair, the Sun so fair, how much fairer shall he be that made them fair? For by the greatness and beauty of the creatures, proportionally the maker of them is seen. If there be such pleasure in beholding a beautiful person alone, and, as a plausible Sermon, he so much affect us, what shall this beauty of God himself, that is infinitely fairer than all creatures, men, angels? &c. All other beauties are night itself, mere darkness, to this our inexplicable, incomprehensible, unspeakable, eternal, infinite, admirable, and divine beauty.

This lustre, a beauty of all things the most beautiful, this beauty and splendour of the divine Majesty, is it that draws all creatures to it, to seek it, love, admire, and adore it; and those Heathens, Pagans, Philosophers, out of those reliques they have yet left of God's Image, are so far forth incensed, as not only to acknowledge a God, but, though after their own inventions, to stand in admiration of his bounty, goodness, to adore and seek him; the magnificence and structure of the world itself, and beauty of all his creatures, his goodness, providence, protection, enforceth them to love him, seek him, fear him, though a wrong way to adore him: but for us that are Christians, Regenerate, that are his Adopted sons, Illuminated by his Word, having the eyes of our hearts and understandings opened; how fairly doth he offer and expose himself! Austin saith, he wooes us by his beauty, gifts, promises, to come unto him; the whole Scripture is a message, an exhortation, a love-letter to this purpose, to incite us, and invite us, God's Epistle, as Gregory calls it, to his creatures. He sets out his Son and his Church in that Epithalamium, or mystical Song of Solomon, to enamour us the more, comparing his head to *fine gold, his locks curled, and black as a Raven,* ———— *his eyes like doves on rivers of waters, washed with milk; his lips as lilies, dropping down pure juice; his hands as rings of gold set with Chrysolite:* ————and his Church to *a vineyard, a garden enclosed, a fountain of living waters, an orchard of Pomegranates, with sweet scents of saffron, spike, calamus and cinnamon, and all the trees of incense, as the chief spices; the fairest amongst women, no spot in her, his sister, his Spouse, undefiled, the only daughter of her mother, dear unto her, fair as the Moon, pure as the Sun, looking out as the morning;* ————that by these figures, that glass, these spiritual eyes of contemplation, we might perceive some resemblance of his beauty, the love betwixt his Church and him. And so in the 45th Psalm, this beauty of his Church is compared to *a Queen in a vesture of gold of Ophir, embroidered raiment of needlework,* that the King might take pleasure in her beauty. To incense us further yet, John in his Apocalypse, makes a description of that heavenly Jerusalem, the beauty of it, and in it the maker of it; likening it to a city of pure gold, like unto clear glass, shining and garnished with all manner of precious stones, having no need of Sun or Moon: for the Lamb is the light of it, the glory of God doth illuminate it: to give us to understand the infinite glory, beauty and happiness of it. Not that it is no fairer than these creatures to which it is compared, but that this vision of his, this lustre of his divine majesty, cannot otherwise be expressed to our apprehensions, *no tongue can tell, no heart can conceive it,* as Paul saith. Moses himself, when he desired to see God in his glory, was answered, that he might not endure it, no man could see his face and live. A strong object overcometh the sight, according to that axiom in Philosophy: if thou canst not endure the Sun beams, how canst thou endure that fulgor and brightness of him that made the Sun? The Sun itself, and all that we can imagine, are but shadows of it, 'tis a surpassing vision, as Austin calls it, the quintessence of beauty this, which far exceeds the beauty of Heavens, Sun and Moon, Stars, Angels, gold and silver, woods, fair fields, and whatsoever is pleasant to behold. All those other beauties fail, vary, are subject to corruption, to loathing; but this is an immortal vision, a divine beauty, an immortal love, an indefatigable love and beauty, with sight of which we shall never be tired, nor wearied, but still the more we see the more we shall covet him. For as one saith, where this vision is, there is absolute beauty; and where is that beauty, from the same fountain comes all pleasure and happiness; neither can beauty, pleasure, happiness, be separated from his vision or sight, or his vision from beauty, pleasure, happiness. In this life we have but a glimpse of this beauty and happiness: we shall hereafter, as John saith, see him as he is: thine eyes, as Isaiah promiseth, shall behold the King in his glory, then shall we be perfectly enamoured, have a full fruition of it, desire, behold and love him alone as the most amiable and fairest object, or chiefest good.

This likewise should we now have done, had not our will been corrupted; and as we are enjoined to love God with all our heart, and all our soul: for to that end were we born, to love this object, as Melancthon discourseth, and to enjoy it. And him our will would have loved and sought alone as our principal good, and all other good things for God's sake: and nature, as she proceeded from it, would have sought this fountain; but in this infirmity of human nature this order is disturbed, our love is corrupt: and a man is like that monster in Plato, composed of a Scylla, a lion, and a man. We are carried away headlong with the torrent of our affections: the world and that infinite variety of pleasing objects in it, do so allure and enamour us, that we cannot so much as look towards God, seek him, or think on him as we should: we cannot, saith

Austin, we cannot contain ourselves from them, their sweetness is so pleasing to us. Marriage, saith Gualter, detains many, a thing in itself laudable, good and necessary, but many deceived and carried away with the blind love of it, have quite laid aside the love of God, and desire of his glory. Meat and drink hath overcome as many, whilst they rather strive to please, satisfy their guts and belly, than to serve God and nature. Some are so busied about merchandise to get money, they lose their own souls, whiles covetously carried; and with an unsatiable desire of gain, they forget God; as much we may say of honour, leagues, friendships, health, wealth, and all other profits or pleasures in this life whatsoever. In this world there be so many beautiful objects, splendours and brightness of gold, majesty of glory, assistance of friends, fair promises, smooth words, victories, triumphs, and such an infinite company of pleasing beauties to allure us, and draw us from God, that we cannot look after him. And this is it which Christ himself, those Prophets and Apostles, so much thundered against. 1 John, 2 : 15, dehorts us from: *Love not the world, nor the things that are in the world : if any man love the world, the love of the Father is not in him. For all that is in the world, as the lust of the flesh, the lust of the eyes, and pride of life, is not of the Father, but of the world : and the world passeth away, and the lust thereof ; but he that fulfilleth the will of God abideth for ever. No man,* saith our Saviour, *can serve two masters,* but he must love the one and hate the other, Austin well infers: and this is that which all the fathers inculcate. He cannot (Austin admonisheth) be God's friend, that is delighted with the pleasures of the world: make clean thine heart, purify thine heart, if thou wilt see this beauty, prepare thyself for it. It is the eye of contemplation, by which we must behold it, the wing of meditation which lifts us up and rears our souls with the motion of our hearts, and sweetness of contemplation: so saith Gregory, cited by Bonaventure. And as Philo Judæus seconds him, He that loves God will soar aloft and take him wings; and leaving the earth fly up to Heaven, wander with Sun and Moon, Stars, and that heavenly troop, God himself being his guide. If we desire to see him, we must lay aside all vain objects, which detain us and dazzle our eyes, and as Ficinus adviseth us, get us solar eyes, spectacles as they that look on the Sun: to see this divine beauty, lay aside all material objects, all sense, and then thou shalt see him as he is. Thou covetous wretch, as Austin expostulates, why dost thou stand gaping on this dross, muck-hills, filthy excrements? behold a far fairer object, God himself wooes thee; behold him, enjoy him, he is sick for love. He invites thee to his sight, to come into his fair Garden, to eat and drink with him, to be merry with him, to enjoy his presence for ever. Wisdom cries out in the streets, besides the gates, in the top of high places, before the City, at the entry of the door, and bids them give ear to her instruction, which is better than gold or precious stones; no pleasures can be compared to it: leave all then and follow her. In Ficinus' words, I exhort and beseech you, that you would embrace and follow this divine love with all your hearts and abilities, by all offices and endeavours make this so loving God propitious unto you. For whom alone, saith Plotinus, we must forsake the Kingdoms and Empires of the whole earth, Sea, Land, and Air, if we desire to be engrafted into him, leave all and follow him.

Now forasmuch as this love of God is an habit infused of God, as Thomas holds, by which a man is inclined to love God above all, and his neighbour as himself, we must pray to God that he will open our eyes, make clear our hearts, that we may be capable of his glorious rays, and perform those duties that he requires of us, *to love God above all, and our neighbour as ourself,* to keep his commandments. *In this we know, saith John, we love the children of God, when we love God and keep his commandments.* ———— *This is the love of God, that we keep his commandments; he that loveth not, knoweth not God, for God is love,* ———— *and he that dwelleth in love, dwelleth in God, and God in him,* for love presupposeth knowledge, faith, hope, and unites us to God himself, as Leon Hebræus delivereth unto us, and is accompanied with the fear of God, humility, meekness, patience, all those virtues, and charity itself. For if we love God, we shall love our neighbour, and perform the duties which are required at our hands, to which we are exhorted. We shall not be envious or puffed up, or boast, disdain, think evil, or be provoked to anger, but suffer all things; endeavour to keep the unity of the Spirit in the bond of peace; forbear one another, forgive one another, clothe the naked, visit the sick, and perform all those works of mercy, which Clemens Alexandrinus calls the extent and complement of Love; and that not for fear or worldly respects, but for the love of God himself. This we shall do if we be truly enamoured; but we come short in both, we neither love God nor our neighbour as we should. Our love in spiritual things is too defective, in worldly things too excessive, there is a jar in both. We love the world too much; God too little, our neighbour not at all, or for our own ends.

The mob judges of friendships by their use.   (OVID)

The chief thing we respect is our commodity: and what we do, is for fear of worldly punishment, for vain-glory, praise of men, fashion, and such by-respects, not for God's sake. We neither know God aright, nor seek, love, or worship him as we should. And for these defects, we involve ourselves into a multitude of errors, we swerve from this true love and worship of God: which is a cause unto us of unspeakable miseries; running into both extremes, we become fools, madmen, without sense, as now in the next place I will shew you.

The parties affected are innumerable almost, and scattered over the face of the earth, far and near, and so have been in all precedent ages, from the beginning of the world to these times, of all sorts and conditions. For method's sake I will reduce them to a twofold division, according to those two extremes of Excess and Defect, Impiety and Superstition, Idolatry and Atheism. Not that there is any excess of divine worship or love of God; that cannot be, we cannot love God too much, or do our duty as we ought, as Papists hold, or have any perfection in this life, much less supererogate; when we have all done, we are unprofitable servants. But because we do go astray, are zealous without knowledge, and too solicitous about that which is not necessary, busying ourselves about impertinent, needless, idle, & vain ceremonies, to please the populace, as the Jews did about sacrifices, oblations, offerings, incense, new Moons, feasts, &c., but as Isaiah taxeth them, Who required this at your hands? We have too great opinion of our own worth, that we can satisfy the Law; and do more than is required at our hands, by performing those Evangelical Counsels, and such works of supererogation, merit for others, which Bellarmine, Gregory de Valentia, all their Jesuits and champions defend, that if God should deal in rigour with them, some of their Franciscans and Dominicans are so pure, that nothing could be objected to them. Some of us again are too dear, as we think, more divine and sanctified than others, of a better metal, greater gifts, and with that proud Pharisee, contemn others in respect of ourselves, we are better Christians, better learned, choice spirits, inspired, know more, have special revelation, perceive God's secrets, and thereupon presume, say and do many times which is not fitting to be said or done. Of this number are all superstitious Idolaters, Ethnicks, Mahometans, Jews, Hereticks, Enthusiasts, Divinators, Prophets, Sectaries, and Schismaticks. Zanchius reduceth such infidels to four chief sects; but I will insist and follow mine own intended method: all which, with many other curious persons, Monks, Hermits, &c. may be ranged in this extreme, and fight under this superstitious banner, with those rude Idiots, and infinite swarms of people that are seduced by them. In the other extreme or in defect, march those impious Epicures, Libertines, Atheists, Hypocrites, Infidels, worldly, secure, impenitent, unthankful, and carnal-minded

men that attribute all to natural causes, that will acknowledge no supreme power; that have cauterized consciences, or live in a reprobate
sense: or such desperate persons as are too distrustful of his mercies. Of
these there be many subdivisions, divers degrees of madness and folly,
some more than other, as shall be shewed in the symptoms: and yet all
miserably out, perplexed, doting, and beside themselves for religion's
sake. For as Zanchius well distinguished, and all the world knows, Religion is twofold, true or false; False is that vain superstition of Idolaters, such as were of old, Greeks, Romans, present Mahometans, &c.
Foolish fear of the gods, Tully could term it; or as Zanchius defines it,
when false gods, or that God is falsely worshipped. And 'tis a miserable
plague, a torture of the Soul, a mere madness, a religious madness,
Meteran calls it, or as Seneca, a frantick error; or as Austin, a furious
disease of the Soul; a quintessence of madness; for he that is superstitious can never be quiet. 'Tis proper to man alone; to him alone pride,
avarice, superstition, saith Pliny; which wrings his soul for the present
and to come: the greatest misery belongs to mankind, a perpetual servitude, a slavery, a fear born of fear, an heavy yoke, the seal of damnation,
an intolerable burthen. They that are superstitious, are still fearing,
suspecting, vexing themselves with auguries, prodigies, false tales,
dreams, idle, vain works, unprofitable labours, as Boterus observes, they
are driven hither and thither by their troubled minds, enemies to God
and to themselves. In a word, as Seneca concludes, superstition destroys,
but true Religion honours God. True Religion, where the true God is
truly worshipped, is the way to Heaven, the mother of all virtues, Love,
Fear, Devotion, Obedience, Knowledge, &c. It rears the dejected Soul of
man, and amidst so many cares, miseries, persecutions, which this world
affords, it is a sole ease, an unspeakable comfort, a sweet reposal, a light
yoke, an anchor, and an Haven. It adds courage, boldness, and begets
generous spirits: although tyrants rage, persecute, and that bloudy
Lictor or Serjeant be ready to martyr them, either sacrifice or die, (as
in those persecutions of the primitive Church, it was put in practise, as
you may read in Eusebius, and others) though enemies be now ready to
invade, and all in an uproar, though heaven should fall on his head, he
would not be dismayed. But as a good Christian prince once made answer to a menacing Turk, he easily scorns the wicked host of men, who is
safe in the protection of God: or as Phalaris writ to Alexander in a
wrong cause, he nor any other enemy could terrify him, for that he
trusted in God.

If God be with us, who can be against us? In all calamities, persecutions whatsoever, as David did, he will sing with him, The Lord is my rock, my fortress, my strength, my refuge, the tower and horn of my salvation, &c. In all troubles and adversities, God is my hope and help, still ready to be found, I will not therefore fear, &c., 'tis a fear expelling fear; he hath peace of conscience, and is full of hope, which is (saith Austin) the life of this our mortal life, hope of immortality, the sole comfort of our misery: otherwise as Paul saith, we of all others were most wretched, but this makes us happy, counterpoising our hearts in all misery; superstition torments, and is from the Devil, the author of lies; but this is from God himself, as Lucian that Antiochian Priest made his divine confession in Eusebius, God is the author of our Religion himself, his word is our rule, a lanthorn to us, dictated by the holy Ghost, he plays upon our hearts as so many harp-strings, and we are his Temples, he dwelleth in us, and we in him.

The part affected of superstition, is the brain, heart, will, understanding, soul itself, and all the faculties of it, all is mad, and dotes. Now for the extent, as I say, the world itself is the subject of it, (to omit that grand sin of Atheism) all times have been misaffected, past, present. There is not one that doth good, no not one, from the Prophet to the Priest, &c. A lamentable thing it is to consider, how many myriads of men this Idolatry and Superstition (for that comprehends all) hath infatuated in all ages, besotted by this blind zeal, which is Religion's Ape, Religion's Bastard, Religion's shadow, false glass. For where God hath a Temple, the Devil will have a chapel: where God hath sacrifices, the Devil will have his oblations; where God hath ceremonies, the Devil will have his traditions; where there is any Religion, the Devil will plant superstition; and 'tis a pitiful sight to behold and read, what tortures, miseries it hath procured, what slaughter of souls it hath made, how it raged amongst those old Persians, Syrians, Egyptians, Greeks, Romans, Tuscans, Gauls, Germans, Britons, &c. Saith Pliny (speaking of Superstition), the Britons are so stupendly superstitious in their ceremonies, that they go beyond those Persians. He that shall but read in Pausanias alone, those Gods, Temples, Altars, Idols, Statues, so curiously made, with such infinite cost and charge, amongst those old Greeks, such multitudes of them, and frequent varieties, as Gerbelius truly observes, may stand amazed, and never enough wonder at it; and thank God withal, that by the light of the Gospel, we are so happily freed from that slavish Idolatry in these our days. But heretofore almost in all Countries, in all places, superstition hath blinded the hearts of men. In all ages, what a small portion hath the true Church ever been!

The Devil divides the world's empire with God.

The Patriarchs and their families, the Israelites, a handful in respect [or comparison], Christ and his Apostles, and not all of them neither. Into what traits hath it been compinged, a little flock! how hath superstition on the other side dilated herself, error, ignorance, barbarism, folly, madness, deceived, triumphed, and insulted over the most wise, discreet, and understanding men! Philosophers, Dynasts, Monarchs, all were involved and over-shadowed in this mist, in more than Cimmerian darkness. So much doth superstition deprave ignorant minds and even lead astray the souls of the wise. At this present, how small a party is truly religious! How little in respect! Divide the world into six parts, and one, or not so much, is Christians; Idolaters and Mahometans possess almost Asia, Africa, America, Magellanica. The Kings of China, great Cham, Siam, and Bornaye, Pegu, Deccan, Narsinga, Japan, &c., are Gentiles, Idolaters, and many other petty Princes in Asia, Monomotopa, Congo, and I know not how many Negro Princes in Africa, all Terra Australis Incognita, most of America Pagans, differing all in their several superstitions; and yet all Idolaters. The Mahometans extend themselves over the great Turk's dominions in Europe, Africa, Asia, to the Xeriffes in Barbary, and his territories in Fez, Sus, Morocco, &c. The Tartar, the great Mogor, the Sophy of Persia, with most of their dominions and subjects, are at this day Mahometans. See how the Devil rageth! Those at odds, or differing among themselves, some for Alli, some Enbocar, for Acmar, and Ozimen, those four Doctors, Mahomet's successors, and are subdivided into seventy-two inferior sects, as Leo Afer reports. The Jews, as a company of vagabonds, are scattered over all parts; whose story, present estate, progress from time to time, is fully set down by Mr. Thomas Jackson, Doctor of Divinity, in his comment on the Creed. A fifth part of the world, and hardly that, now professeth CHRIST, but so inlarded & interlaced with several superstitions, that there is scarce a sound part to be found, or any agreement amongst them.

Presbyter John, in Africa, Lord of those Abyssines, or Æthiopians, is by his profession a Christian, but so different from us, with such new absurdities and ceremonies, such liberty, such a mixture of Idolatry and Paganism, that they keep little more than a bare title of Christianity. They suffer Polygamy, Circumcision, stupend fastings, divorce as they will themselves, &c., and as the Papists call on the Virgin Mary, so do they on Thomas Didymus, before Christ. The Greek or Eastern Church is rent from this of the West, and as they have four chief Patriarchs, so have they four subdivisions, besides those Nestorians, Jacobins, Syrians, Armenians, Georgians, &c., scattered over Asia Minor, Syria, Egypt, &c., Greece, Valachia, Circassia, Bulgary, Bosnia, Albania, Illyricum, Slavonia, Croatia, Thrace, Servia, Rascia, and a sprinkling amongst the Tartars. The Russians, Muscovites, and most of that Great Duke's [Czar's] subjects, are part of the Greek Church, and still Christians: but as one saith, in process of time they have added so many superstitions, they be rather semi-Christians than otherwise. That which remains is the Western Church with us in Europe, but so eclipsed with several schisms, heresies and superstitions, that one knows not where to find it. The Papists have Italy, Spain, Savoy, part of Germany, France, Poland, and a sprinkling in the rest of Europe. In America they hold all that which Spaniards inhabit, Hispania Nova, Castella Aurea, Peru, &c. In the East Indies, the Philippinæ, some small holds about Goa, Malacca, Zelan, Ormus, &c., which the Portuguese got not long since, and those land-leaping [or wandering] Jesuits have essayed in China, Japan, as appears by their yearly letters; in Africa they have Melinda, Quiloa, Mombaze, &c., and some few towns, they drive out one superstition with another. Poland is a receptacle of all religions, where Samisetans, Socinians, Photinians (now protected in Transylvania and Poland), Arians, Anabaptists are to be found, as well as in some German Cities. Scandia is Christian, but Damianus A-Goes the Portugal Knight complains, so mixt with Magick, Pagan Rites and Ceremonies, they may be as well counted Idolaters: what Tacitus formerly said of a like nation, is verified in them, a people subject to superstition, contrary to religion. And some of them as about Lapland and the Pilapians, the Devil's possession to this day, a miserable people (saith mine Author), and which is to be admired and pitied, if any of them be baptized, which the Kings of Sweden much labour, they die within seven or nine days after, and for that cause they will hardly be brought to Christianity, but worship still the Devil, who daily appears to them. In their Idolatrous courses, they rejoice in and worship the Gods of the country, &c. Yet are they [that is, they still are] very superstitious, like our wild Irish. Though they of the better note, the Kings of Denmark & Sweden themselves, that govern them, be Lutherans; the remnant are Calvinists, Lutherans, in Germany equally mixt. And yet the emperor himself, dukes of Lorraine, Bavaria, and the Princes Electors, are most part professed Papists. And though some part of France and Ireland, Great Britain, half the cantons in Switzerland, and the Low Countries, be Calvinists, more defecate [or purified], than the rest, yet at odds amongst themselves, not free from superstition. And which Brochard, the monk, in his description of the Holy Land, after he had censured the Greek church, and showed their errors, concluded at last, I say God grant there be no fopperies in our church. As a dam of water stopped in one place breaks out into another, so doth superstition. I say nothing of Anabaptists, Socinians, Brownists, Barrowists, Familists, &c. There is superstition in our prayers, often in our hearing of sermons, bitter contentions, invectives, persecutions, strange conceits, besides diversity of opinions, schisms, factions, &c. But as the Lord said to Eliphaz the Temanite, and his two friends, *his wrath was kindled against them, for they had not spoken of him things that were right,* we may justly of these Schismaticks and Hereticks, how wise soever in their own conceits, they speak not, they think not, they write not well of God, and as they ought. And therefore, as Erasmus concludes to Dorpius, what shall we wish them, but a sound mind, and a good Physician? But more of their differences, paradoxes, opinions, mad pranks, in the Symptoms: I now hasten to the Causes.

SUBSECTION 2 — *Causes of Religious Melancholy. From the Devil by miracles, apparitions, oracles. His instruments or factors, Politicians, Priests, Impostors, Hereticks, blind guides. In them simplicity, fear, blind zeal, ignorance, solitariness, curiosity, pride, vain-glory, presumption, &c. His engines, fasting, solitariness, hope, fear, &c.*

WE are taught in holy Scripture, that *the Devil rangeth abroad like a roaring Lion, still seeking whom he may devour:* and as in several shapes, so by several engines and devices, he goeth about to seduce us; sometimes he transforms himself into an Angel of Light; and is so cunning, that he is able, if it were possible, to deceive the very Elect. He will be worshipped as God himself, and is so adored by the Heathen, and esteemed. And in imitation of that divine power, as Eusebius observes, to abuse or emulate God's glory, as Dandinus adds, he will have all homage, sacrifices, oblations, and whatsoever else belongs to the worship of God, to be done likewise unto him, he will be like God, and by this means infatuates the world, deludes, entraps, and destroys many a thousand souls. Sometimes by dreams, visions (as God to Moses by familiar conference), the Devil in several shapes talks with them: in the Indies it is common, and in China nothing so familiar as apparitions, inspirations, oracles, by terrifying them with false prodigies, counterfeit miracles, sending storms, tempests, diseases, plagues (as of old in Athens there was Apollo Alexicacus, Apollo the bringer of pestilence and driver away of evils), raising wars, seditions by spectrums, troubling their consciences, driving them to despair, terrors of mind, intolerable pains; by promises, rewards, benefits, and fair means, he raiseth such an opinion of his Deity and greatness, that they dare not do otherwise than adore him, do as he will have them, they dare not offend him. And to compel them more to stand in awe of him, he sends and cures diseases, disquiets their spirits (as Cyprian saith), torments and terrifies their souls, to make them adore him: and all his study, all his endeavour is to divert them from true religion to superstition: and because he is damned himself, and in an error, he would have all the world participate of his errors, and be damned with him. The first mover, therefore, of all superstition, is the Devil, that great enemy of mankind, the principal agent, who in a thousand several shapes, after diverse fashions, with several engines, illusions, and by several names hath deceived the inhabitants of the earth, in several places and countries, still rejoicing at their falls. All the world over before Christ's time, he freely domineered, and held the souls of men in most slavish subjection (saith Eusebius) in diverse forms, ceremonies, and sacrifices, till Christ's coming, as if those Devils of the Air had shared the earth amongst them, which the Platonists held for gods (we are the sport of the gods), and were our governors and keepers. In several places, they had several rites, orders, names, of which read Wierus, Strozius, Cicogna, and others; Adonided amongst the Syrians: Adramelech amongst the Capernaites, Asiniæ amongst the Emathites: Astarte with the Sidonians; Astaroth with the Palestines; Dagon with the Philistines; Tartary with the Hanæi; Milcom amongst the Ammonites: Bel amongst the Babylonians; Beelzebub and Baal with the Samaritans and Moabites; Apis, Isis, and Osiris amongst the Egyptians; Apollo Pythius at Delphi, Colophon, Ancyra, Cumæ, Erythræ; Jupiter in Crete, Venus at Cyprus, Juno at Carthage, Æsculapius at Epidaurus, Diana at Ephesus, Pallas at Athens, &c. And even in these our days, both in the East and West Indies, in Tartary, China, Japan, &c., what strange Idols, in what prodigious forms, with what absurd ceremonies are they adored? What strange sacraments, like ours of Baptism and the Lord's Supper, what goodly Temples, Priests, Sacrifices, they had in America, when the Spaniards first landed there, let Acosta the Jesuit relate, and how the Devil imitated the Ark and the children of Israel's coming out of Egypt; with many such. For as Lipsius well discourseth out of the doctrine of the Stoicks, now and of old, they [that is, the Devils] still and most especially desire to be adored by men. See but what Verto-

mannus, Marco Polo, Lerius, Benzo, P. Martyr in his Ocean Decades,
Acosta, and Mat. Riccius in his Christian Campaign in China, relate.
Eusebius wonders how that wise City of Athens, and flourishing Kingdoms of Greece, should be so besotted; and we in our times, how those
witty China's [Chinese], so perspicacious in all other things, should be
so gulled, so tortured with superstition, so blind, as to worship stocks
and stones. But it is no marvel, when we see all out as great effects
amongst Christians themselves; how are those Anabaptists, Arians, and
Papists above the rest, miserably infatuated! Mars, Jupiter, Apollo, and
Æsculapius, have resigned their interest, names, and offices to S. George,

> *O greatest master of war, by our youths worshipped*
> *As though he were Mars himself!*   (MANTUAN)

S. Christopher, and a company of fictitious Saints, Venus [hath resigned
hers] to the Lady of Loretto. And as those old Romans had several distinct gods, for divers offices, persons, places, so have they Saints, as Lavater well observes out of Lactantius, the name only being changed, 'tis
the same spirit or Devil that deludes them still. The manner how, as I
say, is by rewards, promises, terrors, affrights, punishments: in a word,
fair and foul means, Hope and Fear. How often hath Jupiter, Apollo,
Bacchus, and the rest, sent plagues in Greece and Italy, because their
sacrifices were neglected!

> *Many misfortunes have the slighted Gods*
> *Imposed on poor Hesperia,*   (OVID)

to terrify them, to rouse them up, and the like: see but Livy, Dionysus
Halicarnasseus, Thucydides, Pausanias, Philostratus, Polybius, before
the battle of Cannæ, prodigies, signs and wonders abounded, both publickly in the temple and privately. Œneus reigned in Ætolia, and because he did not sacrifice to Diana with his other gods (see more in
Libanius his Diana), she sent a wild boar, to spoil both men and country,
which was afterwards killed by Meleager. So Plutarch in the Life of
Lucullus relates, how Mithridates, King of Pontus, at the siege of Cizi-
cum, with all his Navy was overthrown by Proserpina, for neglecting of
her holy-day. She appeared in a vision to Aristagoras in the night: To-
morrow, she said, I will cause a contest between a Libyan and a Pontick
minstrel; and the day following, this Enigma was understood; for with
a great South-wind which came from Libya, she quite overwhelmed
Mithridates' army. What prodigies and miracles, dreams, visions, predictions, apparitions, oracles, have been of old at Delphi, Dodona, Trophonius' Den, at Thebes, and Lebadea, of Jupiter Ammon in Egypt,
Amphiarus in Attica, &c.; what strange cures performed by Apollo and

Æsculapius! Juno's image and that of Fortune spake, Castor and Pollux fought in person for the Romans against Hannibal's army, as Pallas, Mars, Juno, Venus, for Greeks and Trojans, &c. Amongst our Pseudo-Catholicks, nothing so familiar as such miracles; how many cures done by our Lady of Loretto, at Sichem! of old at our S. Thomas' Shrine, &c. S. Sabine was seen to fight for Arnulphus, Duke of Spoleto. S. George fought in person for John, the Bastard of Portugal, against the Castilians; S. James for the Spaniards in America. In the battle of Bannockburn, where Edward the Second, our English King, was foiled by the Scots, S. Philanus' arm was seen to fight (if Hector Boethius doth not impose), that was before shut up in a silver capcase; another time, in the same author, S. Magnus fought for them. Now for visions, revelations, miracles, not only out of the Legend, out of purgatory, but every day comes news from the Indies, and at home, read the Jesuits' Letters, Ribadineira, Thurselinus, Acosta, Lippomannus, Xaverius, Ignatius' Lives, &c., and tell me what difference?

His ordinary instruments or factors which he useth, as God himself did good Kings, Lawful Magistrates, patriarchs, prophets, to the establishing of his Church, are Politicians, Statesmen, Priests, Hereticks, blind guides, Impostors, pseudo-Prophets, to propagate his superstition. And first to begin with Politicians, it hath ever been a principal axiom with them, to maintain religion, or superstition, which they determine of, alter and vary upon all occasions, as to them seems best, they make Religion mere policy, a cloak, a human invention; to rule the vulgar with, as Tacitus and Tully hold. Austin censures Scævola saying and acknowledging, that it was a fit thing cities should be deceived by religion, according to the diverb, If the world will be gulled, let it be gulled, 'tis good howsoever to keep it in subjection. 'Tis that Aristotle and Plato inculcate in their Politicks, Religion neglected brings plagues to the city, opens a gap to all naughtiness. 'Tis that which all our late Politicians ingeminate; Cromerus, Boterus, Clapmarius, Arneseus, Captain Machiavel will have a prince by all means to counterfeit religion, to be superstitious in shew at least, to seem to be devout, frequent holy exercises, honour divines, love the Church, affect priests, as Numa, Lycurgus, and such law-makers were, and did, not that they had faith, but that it was an easy way to keep power, to keep people in obedience. Though truly, as Cardan writes, the Christian law is the law of piety, justice, faith, simplicity, &c. But this error of his, Innocentius Jentilettus, a French Lawyer, and Thomas Bozius, in his book On the Downfall of Peoples and Kings, have copiously confuted. Many Politicians, I dare not deny, maintain Religion as a true means, and sincerely speak of it without hypocrisy, are truly zealous and religious themselves. Justice and Religion are the two chief props and supporters of a well-governed commonwealth; but most of them are but Machiavellians, counterfeits only for political ends; for kingship only (which Campanella in his Triumph of Atheism observes), as amongst our modern Turks, as knowing the greatest dominion is that over men's minds; and that as Sabellicus delivers, A man without Religion is like a horse without a bridle. No better way to curb than superstition, to terrify men's consciences, and to keep them in awe: they make new laws, statutes, invent new religions, ceremonies, as so many stalking-horses, to their own ends. If a religion be false, only let it be supposed to be true, and it will tame fierce minds, restrain desires, and make loyal subjects. Therefore (saith Polybius of Lycurgus) did he maintain ceremonies, not that he was superstitious himself, but that he perceived mortal men more apt to embrace Paradoxes than aught else, and durst attempt no evil things for fear of the gods. This was Zamolxis' stratagem amongst the Thracians, Numa's plot, when he said he had conference with the Nymph Ægeria, and that of Sertorius with an Hart; to get more credit to their Decrees, by deriving them from the gods; or else they did all by divine instinct, which Nicholas Damascen well observes of Lycurgus, Solon, and Minos, they had their laws dictated, by Jupiter himself. So Mahomet referred his new laws to the Angel Gabriel, by whose direction he gave out they were made. Caligula in Dion feigned himself to be familiar with Castor and Pollux, and many such, which kept those Romans under (who, as Machiavel proves, were most superstitious): and did curb the people more by this means, than by force of arms, or severity of human laws. Only the common people were deceived (saith Vaninus, speaking of Religion), your Grandees and Philosophers had no such conceit [or notion], save to establish and maintain their power, which had not been possible without the pretext of religion; and many thousands in all ages have ever held as much, Philosophers especially, they knew these things were fables, but they were silent for fear of Laws, &c. To this end that Syrian Pherecydes, Pythagoras his Master, broached in the East amongst the Heathens first the immortality of the Soul, as Trismegistus did in Egypt, with a many of feigned Gods. Those French and British Druids in the West first taught, saith Cæsar, that souls did not die, but after death went from one to another, that so they might encourage them to virtue. 'Twas for a politick end, and to this purpose the old Poets feigned those Elysian fields, their Æcus, Minos, and Rhadamanthus, their infernal Judges, and those Stygian lakes, fiery Phlegethons, Pluto's Kingdom, and variety of torments after death. Those that had done well went to the Elysian fields, but evil-doers to Cocytus, and to that burning lake of Hell, with fire and brimstone for ever to be tormented. 'Tis this which Plato labours for in his Phædo, and in the third book of his Republick. The Turks in their Alcoran, when they set down rewards and several punishments for every particular virtue and vice, when they persuade men, that they that die in battle shall go directly to Heaven, but wicked livers to eternal torment, and all of all sorts (much like our Papistical Purgatory), for a set time shall be tortured in their graves, as appears by that tract which John Baptista Alfaqui, that Mauritanian Priest, now turned Christian, hath written in his confutation of the Alcoran. After a man's death two black Angels, Nunquir and Nequir (so they call them) come to him to his grave and punish him for his precedent sins; if he lived well, they torture him the less; if ill, they incessantly punish him to the day of judgment. The thought of this crucifies them all their lives long, and makes them spend their days in fasting and prayer, lest these evils should come to pass, &c. A Tartar Prince, saith Marco Polo, called the Old Man of the Mountain, the better to establish his government amongst his subjects, and to keep them in awe, found a convenient place in a pleasant valley, environed with hills, in which he made a delicious Park full of odoriferous flowers and fruits, and a Palace of all worldly contents that could possibly be devised, Music, Pictures, variety of meats, &c., and chose out a certain young man, whom with a soporiferous potion he so benumbed, that he perceived nothing: and so fast asleep as he was, caused him to be conveyed into this fair Garden; where after he had lived awhile in all such pleasures a sensual man could desire, he cast him into a sleep again, and brought him forth, that when he awaked he might tell others he had been in Paradise. The like he did for Hell, and by this means brought his people to subjection. Because Heaven and Hell are mentioned in the Scriptures, and to be believed necessary by Christians: so cunningly can the Devil and his Ministers, in imitation of true Religion, counterfeit and forge the like, to circumvent and delude his superstitious followers. Many such tricks and impostures are acted by Politicians, in China especially, but with what effect I will discourse in the Symptoms.

Next to Politicians, if I may distinguish them, are some of our Priests, (who make Religion Policy) if not far beyond them, for they domineer over Princes and Statesmen themselves. One saith, they tyrannize over men's consciences more than any other torments whatsoever, partly for their commodity and gain; since (as Postellus holds) their livelihood, that corruption of all religions, is at stake; for sovereignty, credit, to maintain their state and reputation, out of Ambition and Avarice, which are their chief supporters. What have they not made the common people believe? Impossibilities in nature, incredible things; what devices, traditions, ceremonies, have they not invented in all ages to keep men in obedience, to enrich themselves? For their enrichment have men's minds been overcome with superstition, as Livy saith. Those Egyptian Priests of old got all the sovereignty into their hands, and knowing, as Curtius insinuates, the common people will sooner obey Priests than Captains, and nothing so forcible as superstition, or better than blind zeal to rule a multitude; have so terrified and gulled them, that it is incredible to relate. All nations almost have been besotted in this kind; amongst our Britons and old Gauls the Druids; Magi in Persia; Philosophers in Greece; Chaldæans amongst the Oriental; Brachmanni in India; Gymnosophists in Æthiopia; the Turditani in Spain; Augurs in Rome, have insulted; Apollo's Priests in Greece, Phæbades and Pythonissæ, by their oracles and phantasms; Amphiaraus and his companions; now Mahometan and Pagan Priests, what can they not effect? How do they not infatuate the world? Scaliger writes of the Mahometan Priests, so cunningly can they gull the commons in all places and Countries. But above all others, that High Priest of Rome, the dam of that monstrous and superstitious brood, the bull-bellowing Pope, which now rageth in the West, that three-headed Cerberus, hath played his part. Whose religion at this day is mere policy, a state wholly composed of superstition and wit, and needs nothing but wit and superstition to maintain it, that useth Colleges and religious houses to as good purpose as Forts and Castles, and doth more at this day by a company of scribbling Parasites, fiery-spirited Friars, Zealous Anchorites, hypocritical Confessors, and those Prætorian soldiers, his Janissary Jesuits, that dissociable society, as Langius terms it, the last effort of the Devil and the very excrement of time, that now stand in the fore-front of the battle, will have a monopoly of, and engross all other learning, but domineer in Divinity, and fight alone almost (for the rest are but his dromedaries and asses), than ever he could have done by garrisons and armies. What power of Prince, or penal Law, be it never so strict, could enforce men to do that which for conscience' sake they will voluntarily undergo? As to fast from all flesh, abstain from marriage, rise to their prayers at midnight, whip themselves, with stupend fasting and penance, abandon the world, wilful poverty, perform canonical and blind obedience, to prostrate their goods, fortunes, bodies, lives, and offer up themselves at their Superior's feet, at his command? What so powerful an engine as superstition? Which they right well perceiving, are of no religion at all themselves. For truly (as Calvin rightly suspects, [and as] the tenor and practice of their life proves) the first of the secrets of these theologians, by which they rule, and in chief, is that they hold there is no God, as Leo X. did, Hildebrand the Magician, Alexander VI., Julius II., mere atheists, and which the common proverb amongst them approves, the worst Christians of Italy are the Romans, of the Romans the Priests are wildest, the lewdest Priests are preferred to be Cardinals, and the baddest man amongst the Cardinals is chosen to be Pope, that is an epicure, as most part the Popes are, Infidels and Lucianists, for so they think and believe; and what is said of Christ to be fables and impostures, of Heaven and Hell, day of Judgment, Paradise, Immortality of the soul, are all dreams, toys, and old wives' tales. Yet as so many whetstones to make other tools cut, but cut not themselves, though they be of no religion at all, they will make others most devout and superstitious, by promises and threats, compel, enforce from, and lead them by the nose like so many bears in a line; when as their end is not to propagate the church, advance God's kingdom, seek His glory or common good, but to enrich themselves, to enlarge their territories, to domineer and compel them to stand in awe, to live in subjection to the See of Rome. For what otherwise care they? Since the world wishes to be gulled, let it be gulled, 'tis fit it should be so. And for which Austin cites Varro to maintain his Roman religion, we may better apply to them: some things are true, some false, which for their own ends they will not have the gullish commonalty take notice of. As well may witness their intolerable covetousness, strange forgeries, fopperies, fooleries, unrighteous subtilties, impostures, illusion, new doctrines, paradoxes, traditions, false miracles, which they have still forged to enthrall, circumvent, and subjugate them, to maintain their own estates. One while by Bulls, Pardons, Indulgences, and their doctrine of good works; that they be meritorious, hope of Heaven, by that means they have so fleeced the commonalty, and spurred on this free superstitious horse, that he runs himself blind, and is an Ass to carry burdens. They have so amplified Peter's patrimony, that from a poor Bishop he is become King of Kings, Lord of Lords, a Demi-god, as his Canonists make him (Felinus and the rest) above God himself. And for his wealth and temporalities, is not inferior to many Kings; his Cardinals Princes' companions; and in every Kingdom almost, Abbots, Priors, Monks, Friars, &c., and his Clergy have engrossed a third part, half, in some places all, into their hands. Three Princes Electors in Germany Bishops; besides Magdeburg, Spires, Salzburg, Bremen, Bamberg, &c. In France, as Bodine gives us to understand, their revenues are twelve millions, and three hundred thousand livres; and of twelve parts of the revenues in France, the Church possesseth seven. The Jesuits, a new sect begun in this age, have, as Midendropius and Pelargus reckon up, three or four hundred Colleges in Europe, and more revenues than many Princes. In France, as Arnoldus proves, in thirty years they have got £200,000 annually. I say nothing of the rest of their orders. We have had in England, as Armachanus demonstrates, above thirty thousand Friars at once, and, as Speed collects out of Leland and others, almost 600 religious houses, and near two hundred thousand pound in revenues of the old rent belonging to them, besides Images of Gold, Silver, Plate, furniture, goods and ornaments, as Weever calculates, and esteems them at the dissolution of the Abbies, worth a million of gold. How many Towns in every Kingdom hath superstition enriched! What a deal of money by musty reliques, Images, Idolatry, have their Mass-Priests engrossed, and what sums have they scraped by their other tricks! Loretto in Italy, Walsingham in England, in those days, where everything shines with gold, saith Erasmus, S. Thomas's shrine, &c., may witness. Delphi, so renowned of old in Greece for Apollo's oracle, Delos, a general meeting-place and market-town defended only by religion, Dodona, whose fame and wealth were sustained by religion, were not so rich, so famous. If they can get but a relic of some Saint, the Virgin Mary's picture, Idols, or the like, that City is for ever made, it needs no other maintenance. Now if any of these their impostures or juggling tricks be controverted, or called in question: if a magnanimous or zealous Luther, an heroical Luther, as Dithmarus calls him, dare touch the monks' bellies, all is in a combustion, all is in an uproar: Demetrius and his associates are ready to pull him in pieces, to keep up their trades, " Great is Diana of the Ephesians ": with a mighty shout of two hours long they will roar and not be pacified.

Now for their authority, what by auricular confession, satisfaction, penance, Peter's keys, thunderings, excommunications, &c., roaring bulls, this High Priest of Rome, shaking his Gorgon's head, hath so terrified the soul of many a silly man, insulted over Majesty itself, and swaggered generally over all Europe for many ages, and still doth to some, holding them as yet in slavish subjection, as never tyrannising Spaniards did by their poor Negroes, or Turks by their galley-slaves. The Bishop of Rome (saith Stapleton, a parasite of his) hath done that

without arms, which those Roman Emperors could never achieve with
forty legions of soldiers, deposed kings, and crowned them again with
his foot, made friends, and corrected at his pleasure, &c. 'Tis a wonder,
saith Machiavel, what slavery King Henry the Second endured for the
death of Thomas à Becket, what things he was enjoined by the Pope,
and how he submitted himself to do that which in our times a private
man would not endure, and all through superstition. Henry the Fourth,
deposed of his Empire, stood barefooted with his wife at the gates of
Canossa. Frederick the Emperor was trodden on by Alexander the Third.
Another held Adrian's stirrup. King John kissed the knees of Pandulph
the Pope's Legate, &c. What made so many thousand Christians travel
from France, Britain, &c., into the Holy Land, spend such huge sums
of money, go a pilgrimage so familiarly to Jerusalem, to creep and
crouch, but slavish superstition? What makes them so freely venture
their lives, to leave their native Countries, to go seek martyrdom in the
Indies, but superstition? to be assassinates, to meet death, murder
Kings, but a false persuasion of merit, of canonical or blind obedience
which they instil into them, and animate them by strange illusions, hope
of being Martyrs and Saints? Such pretty feats can the Devil work by
Priests, and so well for their own advantage can they play their parts.
And if it were not yet enough, by Priests and Politicians to delude mankind, and crucify the souls of men, he hath more actors in his Tragedy,
more irons in the fire, another Scene of Hereticks, factious, ambitious
wits, insolent spirits, Schismaticks, Impostors, false Prophets, blind
guides, that out of pride, singularity, vain-glory, blind zeal, cause much
more madness yet, set all in an uproar by their new doctrines, paradoxes,
figments, crotchets, make new divisions, subdivisions, new sects, oppose
one superstition to another, one Kingdom to another, commit Prince and
subjects, brother against brother, father against son, to the ruin and
destruction of a Commonwealth, to the disturbance of peace, and to make
a general confusion of all estates. How did those Arians rage of old!
How many did they circumvent! Those Pelagians, Manichees, &c., their
names alone would make a just volume. How many silly souls have Impostors still deluded, drawn away, and quite alienated from Christ!
Lucian's Alexander, Simon Magus, whose statue was to be seen and
adored in Rome, saith Justin Martyr, after his decease, Apollonius
Tyanæus, Cynops, Eumo, who by counterfeiting some new ceremonies
and juggling tricks of that Dea Syria, by spitting fire, and the like, got
an army together of 40,000 men, and did much harm: with Eudo de
Stellis, of whom Nubrigensis speaks, that in King Stephen's days imi-

tated most of Christ's miracles, fed I know not how many people in the
wilderness, and built castles in the air, &c., to the seducing of multitudes
of poor souls. In Franconia, 1476, a base illiterate fellow took upon him
to be a prophet, and preach, John Beheim by name, a neatherd at
Nicholhausen, he seduced 30,000 persons, and was taken by the commonalty to be a most holy man, come from Heaven. Tradesmen left their
shops, women their distaffs, servants ran from their Masters, children
from their Parents, scholars left their Tutors, all to hear him, some for
novelty, some for zeal. He was burnt at last by the Bishop of Wartzburg,
and so he and his heresy vanished together. How many such Impostors,
false Prophets, have lived in every King's reign? what Chronicle will
not afford such examples! that as so many false lights, have led men out
of the way, terrified some, deluded others, that are apt to be carried
about with the blast of every wind, a rude inconstant multitude, a silly
company of poor souls, that follow all, and are cluttered together like
so many pebbles in a tide. What prodigious follies, madness, vexations,
persecutions, absurdities, impossibilities, these impostors, hereticks,
&c., have thrust upon the world, what strange effects shall be shewed in
the Symptoms.

Now the means by which, or advantages the Devil and his infernal
Ministers take, so to delude and disquiet the world with such idle ceremonies, false doctrines, superstitious fopperies, are from themselves,
innate fear, ignorance, simplicity, Hope and Fear, those two battering
Cannons and principal Engines, with their objects, reward and punishment, Purgatory, the Limbo of the Fathers, &c., which now more than
ever tyrannise; for what province is free from Atheism, Superstition,
Idolatry, Schism, Heresy, Impiety, their factors and followers? Thence
they proceed, and from that same decayed image of God, which is yet
remaining in us.

> *God gave to man alone to stand erect*
> *And gaze on heaven.*   (OVID)

Our own conscience doth dictate so much unto us, we know there is a
God, and Nature doth inform us. No tribe so barbarous (saith Tully)
but that they believe in a God; not Scythia, nor Greece, nor the Hyper-
boreans doubt that, (as Maximus Tyrius the Platonist farther adds)
let him dwell where he will, in what coast soever, there is no Nation
so barbarous, that is not persuaded there is a God. It is a wonder to
read [in the missionary Acosta] of that infinite superstition amongst
the Indians in this kind, of their tenents in America, for there
they superstitiously worship plants, animals, mountains, &c., which they
love or fear (some few places excepted, as he grants, that had no God at

all). So the Heavens declare the glory of God, and the Firmament declareth his handiwork. Every creature will evince it; every blade of grass testifies to the presence of God. They know it in spite of themselves, as the said Tyrius proceeds, will or nill, they must acknowledge it. The Philosophers, Socrates, Plato, Plotinus, Pythagoras, Trismegistus, Seneca, Epictetus, those Magi, Druids, &c., went as far as they could by the light of Nature; writ many things well of the nature of God, but they had but a confused light, a glimpse. As he that walks by Moonshine in a wood, they groped in the dark; they had a gross knowledge, as he in Euripides,

O God, whatever thou art, whether the Sky,
Or the Earth, or somewhat else,

and that of Aristotle, Being of Beings, pity me! And so of the immortality of the Soul, and future happiness. Pythagoras (saith Hierom) imagined the immortality of the soul, Democritus believed it not, in the consolatory discourse on his condemnation which Socrates argued in his cell; India, Persia, the Goths, played the philosopher. So some said this, some that, as they conceived themselves, which the Devil perceiving, led them farther out (as Lemnius observes) and made them worship him as their God with stocks and stones, and torture themselves to their own destruction, as he thought fit himself, inspired his Priests and Ministers with lies and fictions to prosecute the same, which they for their own ends were as willing to undergo, taking advantage of their simplicity, fear and ignorance. For the common people are as a flock of sheep, a rude, illiterate rout, void many times of common sense, a mere beast, a many-headed beast, will go whithersoever they are led: as you lead a ram over a gap by the horns, all the rest will follow, they will do as they see others do, and as their Prince will have them, let him be of what Religion he will, they are for him. Now for those Idolaters, Maxentius and Licinius, then for Constantine a Christian. Who denies Christ perisheth miserably, the cry goes, for two hours' space, who does not worship Christ is an enemy of the Emperor, louder than ever; and by and by Idolaters again under that Apostate Julianus; all Arrians under Constantius, good Catholicks again under Jovinian. And little difference there is between the discretion of men and children in this case, especially of old folks and women, as Cardan discourseth, when as they are tossed with fear and superstition, and with other men's folly and dishonesty. So that I may say their ignorance is a cause of their superstition, a symptom, and madness itself:

Their prayers are cause and punishment at once.

Their own fear, folly, stupidity, to be deplored Lethargy, is that which gives occasion to the other, and pulls their miseries on their own heads. For in all these Religions and Superstitions, amongst our Idolaters, you shall still find that the parties first affected, are silly, rude, ignorant people, old folks, that are naturally prone to superstition, weak women, or some poor rude illiterate persons, that are apt to be wrought upon, and gulled in this kind, prone without either examination or due consideration (for they take up Religion a trust [or on trust], as at Mercers they do their wares) to believe any thing. And the best means they have to broach first or to maintain it when they have done, is to keep them still in ignorance : for Ignorance is the mother of devotion, as all the world knows, and these times can amply witness. This hath been the Devil's practice, and his infernal Ministers in all ages ; not as our Saviour, by a few silly Fishermen, to confound the wisdom of the world, to save Publicans and Sinners, but to make advantage of their ignorance, to convert them and their associates, and that they may better effect what they intend, they begin, as I say, with poor, stupid, illiterate persons. So Mahomet did when he published his Alcoran, which is a piece of work (saith Bredenbachius) full of nonsense, barbarism, confusion without rhyme, reason, or any good composition, first published to a company of rude rusticks, hog-rubbers, that had no discretion, judgment, art, or understanding, and is so still maintained. For it is a part of their policy to let no man comment, dare to dispute or call in question to this day any part of it, be it never so absurd, incredible, ridiculous, fabulous as it is, it must be believed implicitly upon pain of death, no man must dare to contradict it, God and the Emperor, &c. What else do our Papists but, by keeping the people in ignorance, vent and broach all their new ceremonies and traditions, when they conceal the Scripture, read it in Latin, and to some few alone, feeding the slavish people in the mean time with tales out of Legends, and such like fabulous narrations ? Whom do they begin with but collapsed Ladies, some few tradesmen, superstitious old folks, illiterate persons, weak women, discontent, rude, silly companions, or sooner circumvent ? So do all our schismaticks and hereticks. Marcus and Valentinian, hereticks in Irenæus, seduced first I know not how many women, and made them believe they were Prophets. Friar Cornelius of Dort seduced a company of silly women. What are all our Anabaptists, Brownists, Barrowists, Familists, but a company of rude, illiterate, capricious base fellows ? What are most of our Papists, but stupid, ignorant and blind Bayards ? How should they otherwise be, when as they are brought up, and kept still in darkness ? If their Pastors (saith Lavater) had done their duties, and instructed their flocks as they ought, in the Principles of Christian Religion, or had not forbidden them the reading of Scriptures, they had not been as they are. But being so misled all their lives in superstition, and carried hood-winked like Hawks, how can they prove otherwise than blind Idiots, and superstitious Asses? What shall we expect else at their hands? Neither is it sufficient to keep them blind, and in Cimmerian darkness, but withal, as a Schoolmaster doth by his boys, to make them follow their books, sometimes by good hope, promises and encouragements, but most of all by fear, strict discipline, severity, threats and punishment, do they collogue and sooth up their silly Auditors, and so bring them into a fool's paradise. Do well, thou shalt be crowned; but for the most part by threats, terrors and affrights, they tyrannize and terrify their distressed souls: knowing that fear alone is the sole and only means to keep men in obedience, according to that Hemistich of Petronius, the fear of some divine and supreme powers, keeps men in obedience, makes the people do their duties: they play upon their consciences; which was practised of old in Egypt by their Priests; when there was an Eclipse, they made the people believe God was angry, great miseries were to come; they take all opportunities of natural causes, to delude the people's senses, and with fearful tales out of purgatory, feigned apparitions, earthquakes in Japan or China, tragical examples of Devils, possessions, obsessions, false miracles, counterfeit visions, &c. They do so insult over, and restrain them, never Hobby [or Falcon] so dared [or fascinated] a Lark, that they will not offend the least tradition, tread, or scarce look awry. Good God, Lavater exclaims, how many men have been miserably afflicted by this fiction of purgatory!

To these advantages of Hope and Fear, ignorance and simplicity, he hath several engines, traps, devices, to batter and enthrall, omitting no opportunities, according to men's several inclinations, abilities, to circumvent and humour them, to maintain his superstitions; sometimes to stupify, besot them; sometimes again by oppositions, factions, to set all at odds, and in an uproar; sometimes he infects one man, and makes him a principal agent; sometimes whole Cities, Countries. If of meaner sort, by stupidity, canonical obedience, blind zeal, &c. If of better note, by pride, ambition, popularity, vain-glory. If of the Clergy and more eminent, of better parts than the rest, more learned, eloquent, he puffs them up with a vain conceit of their own worth, they begin to swell and scorn all the world in respect of themselves, and thereupon turn hereticks, schismaticks, broach new doctrines, frame new crochets, and the like; or else out of too much learning become mad, or out of curiosity they will search into God's secrets, and eat of the forbidden fruit; or out of presumption of their holiness and good gifts, inspirations, become Prophets, Enthusiasts, and what not? or else if they be displeased, discontent, and have not (as they suppose) preferment to their worth, have some disgrace, repulse, neglected, or not esteemed, as they fondly value themselves, or out of emulation, they begin presently to rage and rave, embroil Heaven and Earth, they become so impatient in an instant, that the whole Kingdom cannot contain them, they will set all in a combustion, all at variance, to be revenged of their adversaries.

Donatus, when he saw Cæcilian preferred before him in the Bishoprick of Carthage, turned heretick, and so did Arius, because Alexander was advanced: we have examples at home, and too many experiments of such persons. If they be laymen of better note, the same engines of pride, ambition, emulation and jealousy take place, they will be gods themselves: Alexander after his victories in India, became so insolent, he would be adored for a god: and those Roman Emperors came to that height of madness they must have Temples built to them, sacrifices to their deities, Divus Augustus, D. Claudius, D. Adrianus: Heliogabalus put out that Vestal fire at Rome, expelled the Virgins, and banished all other Religions all over the world, and would be the sole God himself. Our Turks, China Kings, great Chams, and Mogors, do little less, assuming divine and bombast titles to themselves; the meaner sort are too credulous, and led with blind zeal, blind obedience, to prosecute and maintain whatsoever their sottish leaders shall propose, what they in pride and singularity, revenge, vain glory, ambition, spleen, for gain, shall rashly maintain and broach, their disciples make a matter of conscience, of hell and damnation, if they do it not, and will rather forsake wives, children, house and home, lands, goods, fortunes, life itself, than omit or abjure the least tittle of it, and to advance the common cause, undergo any miseries, turn traitors, assassinates, pseudo-martyrs, with full assurance and hope of reward in that other world, that they shall certainly merit by it, win heaven, be canonized for Saints.

Now when they are truly possessed with blind zeal, and misled with superstition, he hath many other baits to inveigle and infatuate them farther yet, to make them quite mortified and mad, and that under colour of perfection, to merit by penance, going woolward, whipping, alms, fasting, &c. In the year 1320, there was a Sect of whippers in Germany, that to the astonishment of the beholders, lashed, and cruelly tortured themselves. I could give many other instances of each particular. But these works so done are meritorious (" meritorious works performed ") for themselves & others, to make them macerate and consume their bodies, the counterfeit of virtue, those Evangelical counsels are propounded, as our Pseudo-Catholicks call them, canonical obedience, wilful poverty, vows of chastity, monkery, and a solitary life, which extend almost to all religions and superstitions, to Turks, Chinese, Gentiles, Abyssinians, Greeks, Latins, and all Countries. Amongst the rest, fasting, contemplation, solitariness, are as it were certain rams by which the devil doth batter and work upon the strongest constitutions. Saith Peter Forestus some by fasting overmuch, and divine meditations, are overcome. Not that fasting is a thing of itself to be discommended, for it is an excellent means to keep the body in subjection, a preparative to devotion, the physick of the soul, by which chaste thoughts are engendered, true zeal, a divine spirit, whence wholsome counsels do proceed, concupiscence is restrained, vicious and predominant lusts and humours are expelled. The Fathers are very much in commendation of it, and, as Calvin notes, sometimes immoderate. The mother of health, key of heaven, a spiritual wing to erear us, the chariot of the holy Ghost, banner of faith, &c. And 'tis true they say of it, if it be moderately and seasonably used, by such parties as Moses, Elias, Daniel, Christ, and as his Apostles made use of it; but when by this means they will supererogate, and as Erasmus well taxeth, Heaven is too small a reward for it; they make choice of times and meats, buy and sell their merits, attribute more to them than to the ten commandments, and count it a greater sin to eat meat in Lent than to kill a man, and as one saith, respect roast fish more than Christ crucified, salmon more than Solomon, have Christ on their lips and Epicurus in their heart; when some counterfeit, and some attribute more to such works of theirs than to Christ's death and passion; the devil sets in a foot, strangely deludes them, and by that means makes them to overthrow the temperature of their bodies, and hazard their souls. Never any strange illusions of devils amongst hermits, Anachorites, never any visions, phantasms, apparitions, Enthusiasms, Prophets, any revelations, but immoderate fasting, bad diet, sickness, melancholy, solitariness, or some such things were the precedent causes, the forerunners or concomitants of them. The best opportunity and sole occasion the Devil takes to delude them. Marcilius Cognatus hath many stories to this purpose, of such as after long fasting have been seduced by devils: and 'tis a miraculous thing to relate (as Cardan writes) what strange accidents proceed from fasting; dreams, superstition, contempt of torments, desire of death, prophesies, paradoxes, madness; fasting naturally prepares men to these things. Monks, Anachorites, and the like, after much emptiness become melancholy, vertiginous, they think they hear strange noises, confer with Hobgoblins, Devils, rivell up their bodies, and (whilst we harass the enemy, saith Gregory, we slay those we love) they become bare Skeletons, skin and bones; abstaining from meats, they consume their own flesh. Hilarion, as Hierome reports in his life, and Athanasius of Antonius, was so bare with fasting, that the skin did scarce stick to the bones; for want of vapours he could not sleep, and for want of sleep became idle-headed, heard every night infants cry, oxen low, wolves howl, lions roar (as he thought), clattering of chains, strange voices, and the like illusions of devils. Such symptoms are common to those that fast long, are solitary, given to contemplation, over much solitariness and meditation. Not that these things (as I said of fasting) are to be discommended of themselves, but very behoveful in some cases and good: sobriety and contemplation join our souls to God, as that heathen Porphyry can tell us. Ecstasis is a taste of future happiness, by which we are united unto God, a divine melancholy, a spiritual wing, Bonaventure terms it, to lift us up to heaven: but as it is abused, a mere dotage, madness, a cause and symptom of Religious Melancholy. If you shall at any time see (saith Guianerius) a Religious person over-superstitious, too solitary, or much given to fasting, that man will certainly be melancholy, thou mayst boldly say it, he will be so. P. Forestus hath almost the same words, and Cardan, solitariness, fasting, and that melancholy humour, are the causes of all Hermits' illusions. Lavater puts solitariness a main cause of such spectrums and apparitions; none, saith he, so melancholy as Monks and Hermits, the devil's bath melancholy, none so subject to visions and dotage in this kind, as such as live solitary lives, they hear and act strange things in their dotage. Polydore Virgil holds that those prophesies, and Monks' revelations, Nuns' dreams, which they suppose come from God, do proceed wholly by the Devil's means: and so those Enthusiasts, Anabaptists, pseudo-Prophets from the same cause. Fracastorius will have all your Pythonisses, Sibyls, and pseudo-Prophets to be mere melancholy; so doth Wierus prove, and Arculanus, that melancholy is a sole cause, and the Devil together, with fasting and solitariness, of such Sibylline prophesies, if there were ever such, which with Casaubon and others I justly except at; for it is not likely that the Spirit of God should ever reveal such manifest revelations and predictions of Christ to those Pythonisses, Apollo's witches, priests, the Devil's ministers, (they were no better), and conceal them from his own prophets; for these Sibyls set down all particular circumstances of Christ's coming, and many other future accidents, far more perspicuous and plain than ever any prophet did. But howsoever there be no Phœbades or Sibyls, I am assured there be other Enthusiasts, prophets, Fortune Tellers, Magi, (of which read Jo. Boissardus, who hath laboriously collected them into a great volume of late, with elegant pictures, and epitomized their lives) &c., ever have been in all ages, and still proceeding from those causes, who relate their visions, dream of the future, prophetize, and agitated by such madness, think that the Holy Spirit is imparted to them. That which is written of Saint Francis' five wounds, and other such monastical effects, of him and others, may justly be referred to this our Melancholy; and that which Matthew Paris relates of the Monk of Evesham, who saw heaven and hell in a vision; of Sir Owen, that went down into Saint Patrick's Purgatory in King Stephen's days, and saw as much: Walsingham of him that was shewed as much by Saint Julian, Beda reports of King Sebba that saw strange visions; and Stumphius, a cobbler of Basil, 1520, that beheld rare apparitions at Augsburg in Germany. Alexander ab Alexandro [tells] of an Enthusiastical prisoner, (all out as probable as that of Eris the son of Armenius, in Plato's tenth dialogue of his Republic, that revived again ten days after he was killed in a battle, and told strange wonders, like those tales Ulysses related to Alcinous in Homer, or Lucian's True Story itself) was still after much solitariness, fasting, or long sickness, when their brains were addle, and their bellies as empty of meat as their heads of wit. Florilegus hath many such examples, one of Saint Guthlac of Croyland that fought with Devils, but still after long fasting, over-much solitariness, the Devil persuaded him therefore to fast, as Moses and Elias did, the better to delude him. In the same Author is recorded Carolus Magnus' vision, in the year 185, or ecstasis, wherein he saw heaven and hell after much fasting and meditation. So did the Devil of old with Apollo's priests. Amphiaraus, and his fellows, those Egyptians, still enjoin long fasting before he would give any Oracles, three days' abstinence from food and wine before they gave any answers, as Volateran records; and Strabo describes Charon's den, in the way betwixt Tralles and Nysa, whither the Priests led sick and fanatick men: but nothing performed without long fasting, no good to be done. That scoffing Lucian conducts his Menippus to hell by the directions of that Chaldæan Mithrobarzanes, but after long fasting, and such like idle preparation. Which the Jesuits right well perceiving of what force this fasting and solitary meditation is to alter men's minds, when they would

make a man mad, ravish him, improve him beyond himself, to undertake some great business of moment, to kill a King or the like, they
bring him into a melancholy dark chamber, where he shall see no light
for many days together, no company, little meat, ghastly pictures of
Devils all about him, and leave him to lie as he will himself, on the bare
floor in this chamber of meditation, as they call it, on his back, side,
belly, till by this strange usage they make him quite mad and beside
himself. And then after some ten days, as they find him animated and
resolved, they make use of him. The Devil hath many such factors,
many such engines, which what effect they produce, you shall hear in
these following Symptoms.

SUBSECTION 3 — *Symptoms general, love to their own sect, hate of all
    other Religions, obstinacy, peevishness, ready to undergo any dan-
    ger or cross for it; Martyrs, blind zeal, blind obedience, fastings,
    vows, belief of incredibilities, impossibilities: Particular of Gen-
    tiles, Mahometans, Jews, Christians; and in them, Hereticks old
    and new, Schismaticks, Schoolmen, Prophets, Enthusiasts, &c.*

IN attempting to speak of these Symptoms, shall I laugh with Democritus, or weep with Heraclitus? they are so ridiculous and absurd on the
one side, so lamentable and tragical on the other; a mixt Scene offers
itself, so full of errors, and a promiscuous variety of objects, that I
know not in what strain to represent it. When I think of that Turkish
Paradise, those Jewish fables, and pontificial rites, those pagan superstitions, their sacrifices, and ceremonies, as to make images of all matter,
and adore them when they have done, to see them kiss the pyx, creep
to the cross, &c., I cannot choose but laugh with Democritus: but when
I see them whip and torture themselves, grind their souls for toys and
trifles, desperate, and now ready to die, I cannot choose but weep with
Heraclitus. When I see a Priest say mass, with all those apish gestures,
murmurings, &c., read the customs of the Jews' Synagogue, or Mahometan Mosque, I must needs laugh at their folly, who can restrain his
laughter? but when I see them make matters of conscience of such toys
and trifles, to adore the Devil, to endanger their souls, to offer their
children to their Idols, &c., I must needs condole their misery. When I
see two superstitious Orders contend, tooth and nail, with such have
and hold, of goats' wool trifles, some write such great Volumes to no
purpose, take so much pains to so small effect, their Satires, invectives,
apologies, dull and gross fictions; when I see grave learned men rail
and scold like butter-women. methinks 'tis pretty sport, and fit for

Calphurnius and Democritus to laugh at. But when I see so much bloud spilt, so many murders and massacres, so many cruel battles fought, &c., 'tis a fitter subject for Heraclitus to lament. As Merlin when he sat by the lake side with Vortigern, and had seen the white and red dragon fight, before he began to interpret or to speak, fell a weeping, and then proceeded to declare to the King what it meant; I should first pity and bewail this misery of human kind with some passionate preface, wishing mine eyes a fountain of tears, as Jeremy did, and then to my task. For it is that great torture, that infernal plague of mortal man, superstition, of all pests the most pestilential, and able of itself alone to stand in opposition to all other plagues, miseries, and calamities whatsoever; far more cruel, more pestiferous, more grievous, more general, more violent, of a greater extent. Other fears and sorrows, grievances of body and mind, are troublesome for the time; but this is for ever, eternal damnation, hell itself, a plague, a fire: an inundation hurts one Province alone, and the loss may be recovered; but this superstition involves all the world almost, and can never be remedied. Sickness and sorrows come and go, but a superstitious soul hath no rest; superstition can give the soul no peace, no quietness. True Religion and Superstition are quite opposite, as Lactantius describes, the one erears, the other dejects; the one is an easy yoke, the other an intolerable burden, an absolute tyranny; the one a sure anchor, an haven; the other a tempestuous Ocean; the one makes, the other mars; the one is wisdom, the other is folly, madness, indiscretion; the one unfeigned, the other a counterfeit; the one a diligent observer, the other an ape; one leads to heaven, the other to hell. But these differences will more evidently appear by their particular symptoms. What Religion is, and of what parts it doth consist, every Catechism will tell you, what Symptoms it hath, and what effects it produceth: but for their superstitions, no tongue can tell them, no pen express, they are so many, so diverse, so uncertain, so unconstant, and so different from themselves. One saith, there be as many superstitions in the world, as there be stars in heaven, or devils themselves that are the first founders of them: with such ridiculous, absurd symptoms and signs, so many several rites, ceremonies, torments and vexations accompanying, as may well express and beseem the devil to be the author and maintainer of them. I will only point at some of them, the lion's toe-nail, guess at the rest, and those of the chief kinds of superstition, which beside us Christians now domineer and crucify the world, Gentiles, Mahometans, Jews, &c.

Of these symptoms some be general, some particular to each private sect: general to all, are, an extraordinary love and affection they bear and shew to such as are of their own sect, and more than Vatinian hate to such as are opposite in Religion, as they call it, or disagree from them in their superstitious rites, blind zeal, (which is as much a symptom as a cause,) vain fears, blind obedience, needless works, incredibilities, impossibilities, monstrous rites and ceremonies, wilfulness, blindness, obstinacy, &c. For the first, which is love and hate, as Montanus saith, no greater concord, no greater discord than that which proceeds from Religion. It is incredible to relate, did not our daily experience evince it, what factions, (as Rich. Dinoth writes), have been of late for matters of Religion in France, and what hurly burlies all over Europe for these many years. There is nothing so intemperately sweeps man along as an accepted opinion as to salvation; for it, forsooth, all nations are wont to sacrifice their bodies and souls, and bind themselves together in strictest bond of poverty. We are all brethren in Christ, servants of one Lord, members of one body, and therefore are or should be at least dearly beloved, inseparably allied in the greatest bond of love and familiarity, united partakers not only of the same cross, but coadjutors, comforters, helpers, at all times, upon all occasions: as they did in the primitive Church, they sold their patrimonies, and laid them at the Apostles' feet, and many such memorable examples of mutual love we have had under the ten general persecutions, many since. Examples on the other side of discord none like, as our Saviour saith, he came therefore into the world to set father against son, &c. In imitation of whom the Devil belike (superstition is still Religion's ape, as in all other things, so in this) doth so combine and glue together his superstitious followers in love and affection, that they will live and die together: and what an innate hatred hath he still inspired to any other superstition opposite! How those old Romans were affected, those ten persecutions may be a witness, and that cruel executioner in Eusebius, sacrifice or die. No greater hate, more continuate, bitter faction, wars, persecution in all ages, than for matters of Religion, no such feral opposition, father against son, mother against daughter, husband against wife, City against City, Kingdom against Kingdom: as of old at Tentyra and Ombos:

> *Immortal hate it breeds, a wound past cure*
> *And fury to the commons still to endure:*
> *Because one City t' other's gods as vain*
> *Deride, and his alone as good maintain.*   (JUVENAL)

The Turks at this day count no better of us than of dogs, so they commonly call us Giaours, infidels, miscreants, make that their main quarrel and cause of Christian persecution. If he will turn Turk, he shall be entertained as a brother, and had in good esteem, a Mussulman or a believer, which is a greater tie to them than any affinity or consanguinity. The Jews stick together like so many burrs, but as for the rest whom they call Gentiles, they do hate and abhor, they cannot endure their Messias should be a common Saviour to us all, and rather as Luther writes, than they that now scoff at them, curse them, persecute and revile them, shall be coheirs and brethren with them, or have any part of fellowship with their Messias, they would crucify their Messias ten times over and God himself, his Angels, and all his creatures, if it were possible, though they endure a thousand hells for it. Such is their malice towards us. Now for Papists, what in a common cause for the advancement of their Religion they will endure, our Traitors and Pseudo-Catholicks will declare unto us; and how bitter on the other side to their adversaries, how violently bent, let those Marian times record, as those miserable slaughters at Merindol and Cabriers, the Spanish Inquisition, the Duke of Alva's tyranny in the Low Countries, the French Massacres and Civil Wars.

So great the evils that religion prompts. (LUCRETIUS)
Not there only, but all over Europe, we read of bloody battles, racks and wheels, seditions, factions, oppositions, standards facing standards, eagles matching eagles, and spear threatening spear, invectives and contentions. They had rather shake hands with a Jew, Turk, or as the Spaniards do, suffer Moors to live amongst them, and Jews, than Protestants; my name (saith Luther) is more odious to them than any thief or murderer. So it is with all hereticks and schismaticks whatsoever: and none so passionate, violent in their tenents, opinions, obstinate, wilful, refractory, peevish, factious, singular and stiff in defence of them; they do not only persecute and hate, but pity all other Religions, account them damned, blind, as if they alone were the true Church, they are the true heirs, have the fee simple of heaven by a peculiar donation, 'tis entailed on them and their posterities, their doctrine sound, they alone are to be saved. The Jews at this day are so incomprehensibly proud and churlish, saith Luther, that they alone wish to be saved, they alone wish to be lords of the world. And, as Buxtorfius adds, so ignorant and self-willed withal, that amongst their most understanding Rabbins you shall find nought but gross dotage, horrible hardness of heart, and stupend obstinacy, in all their actions,

opinions, conversations: and yet so zealous withal, that no man living can be more, and vindicate themselves for the elect people of God. 'Tis so with all other superstitious sects, Mahometans, Gentiles in China, and Tartary; our ignorant Papists, Anabaptists, Separatists, and peculiar Churches of Amsterdam, they alone, and none but they can be saved. Zealous (as Paul saith) without knowledge, they will endure any misery, any trouble, suffer and do that which the Sun-beams will not endure to see, driven on by religious fury, all extremities, losses and dangers, take any pains, fast, pray, vow chastity, wilful poverty, forsake all and follow their Idols, die a thousand deaths, as some Jews did to Pilate's soldiers, in like case, thrusting forward their bared throats, and clearly showing (as Josephus hath it) that dearer than life to them was the observance of their country's law. Rather than abjure, or deny the least particle of that Religion which their Fathers profess, and they themselves have been brought up in, be it never so absurd, ridiculous, they will embrace it, and without further enquiry or examination of the truth, though it be prodigiously false, they will believe it: they will take much more pains to go to hell, than we shall do to heaven. Single out the most ignorant of them, convince his understanding, shew him his errors, grossness, and absurdities of his sect, he will not be persuaded. As those Pagans told the Jesuits in Japan, they would do as their fore-fathers have done; and with Ratholde the Frisian Prince, go to hell for company, if most of their friends went thither: they will not be moved, no persuasion, no torture can stir them. So that Papists cannot brag of their vows, poverty, obedience, orders, merits, martyrdoms, fastings, alms, good works, pilgrimages: much and more than all this, I shall shew you, is, and hath been done by these superstitious Gentiles, Pagans, Idolaters and Jews: their blind zeal and idolatrous superstition in all kinds is much at one; little or no difference, and it is hard to say which is the greatest, which is the grossest. For if a man shall duly consider those superstitious rites amongst the Ethnicks in Japan, the Bannians in Guzerat, the Chinese idolaters, Americans of old, in Mexico especially, Mahometan priests, he shall find the same government almost, the same orders and ceremonies, or so like, that they may seem all apparently to be derived from some heathen spirit, and the Roman Hierarchy no better than the rest. In a word, this is common to all superstition, there is nothing so mad and absurd, so ridiculous, impossible, incredible, which they will not believe, observe, and diligently perform as much as in them lies; nothing so monstrous to conceive, or intolerable to put in practice, so cruel to suffer, which they will not willingly undertake. So powerful a thing is super-stition! O Egypt (as Trismegistus exclaims) thy religion is fables, and such as posterity will not believe. I know that in true Religion itself many mysteries are so apprehended alone by faith, as that of the Trinity, which Turks especially deride, Christ's Incarnation, resurrection of the body at the last day, that should be believed (saith Tertullian) for the very reason that it is incredible, &c., many miracles not to be controverted or disputed of. True wisdom lieth in wonder, not inquiry, saith Gerhardus; and in matters divine (as a good Father informs us) some things are to be believed, embraced, followed with all submission and obedience, some again admired [or wondered at]. Though Julian the Apostate scoff at Christians in this point, saying that the Christian Creed is like the Pythagorean dictum, we make our will and understanding too slavishly subject to our faith, without farther examination of the truth; yet, as Saint Gregory truly answers, our Creed is of a higher excellence, and much more divine; and, as Thomas will, to one who gives pious thought, reasons are always at hand, proving credibility in supernatural mysteries; we do absolutely believe it, and upon good reasons, for, as Gregory well informeth us, that faith hath no merit, is not worth the name of faith, that will not apprehend without a certain demonstration: we must and will believe God's word; and if we be mistaken or err in our general belief, as Richardus de Sancto Victore vows he will say to Christ himself at the day of judgement, Lord, if we be deceived, thou alone hast deceived us: thus we plead. But for the rest I will not justify that pontifical transubstantiation, that which Mahometans and Jews justly except at, as Campanella confesseth, 'tis a most difficult dogma, nor can anything be found more exposed to the blasphemies of hereticks or the foolish mockeries of politicians. They hold it impossible, that God should be eaten in bread; and besides they scoff at it, Behold a people feeding on its God, says a certain Marius; flies and worms mock at this God, while devouring and defiling him; he is exposed to fire and water, and robbers steal from him; they cast his golden pyx on the ground, yet this God does not defend himself: how can it be that he be found whole in each of the particles of the Host, the same single body, be in so many places, in the sky, in the earth, &c. But he that shall read the Turks' Alcoran, the Jews' Talmud, and Papists' Golden Legend, in the mean time will swear that such gross fictions, fables, vain traditions, prodigious paradoxes and ceremonies, could never proceed from any other spirit, than that of the devil himself, which is the Author of confusion and lies; and wonder withal how such wise men as have been of the Jews, such learned understanding men as Averroes, Avicenna, or those Heathen Philosophers, could ever be persuaded to believe, or subscribe to the least part of them: not detect the fraud: but that as Vanninus answers, they durst not speak for fear of the law. But I will descend to particulars: read their several symptoms and then guess.

Of such symptoms as properly belong to superstition, or that irreligious Religion, I may say as of the rest, some are ridiculous, some again feral to relate. Of those ridiculous, there can be no better testimony than the multitude of their gods, those absurd names, actions, offices they put upon them, their feasts, holy days, sacrifices, adorations, and the like. The Egyptians that pretended so great antiquity, 300 Kings before Amasis: and as Mela writes, 13,000 years from the beginning of their Chronicles, that bragg'd so much of their knowledge of old, for they invented Arithmetick, Astronomy, Geometry: of their wealth and power, that vaunted of 20,000 Cities: yet at the same time their Idolatry and superstition was most gross: they worshipped, as Diodorus Siculus records, Sun and Moon under the name of Isis and Osiris, and after, such men as were beneficial to them, or any creature that did them good. In the city of Bubastis they adored Cats, saith Herodotus, Ibises and Storks, an Ox (saith Pliny), Leeks and Onions, Macrobius,

You, O Egypt, worship leeks and onions. (PRUDENTIUS)

Scoffing Lucian in his True History, which, as he confesseth himself, was not persuasively written as a truth, but in Comical fashion to glance at the monstrous fictions, and gross absurdities of writers and nations, to deride without doubt this prodigious Egyptian Idolatry, feigns this story of himself; that when he had seen the Elysian fields, and was now coming away, Rhadamanthus gave him a Mallow root, and bade him pray to that when he was in any peril or extremity; which he did accordingly; for when he came to Hydramardia in the Island of treacherous women, he made his prayers to his root, and was instantly delivered. The Syrians, Chaldæans, had as many proper Gods of their own invention; see the said Lucian, Mornay, Guliel. Stuckius, Peter Faber, Selden, Purchas' Pilgrimage, Rosinus of the Romans, and Lilius Giraldus of the Greeks. The Romans borrowed from all, besides their own gods which were of greater & lesser kinds, as Varro holds, certain and uncertain; some celestial select and great ones, others Indigetes [or home-made Gods], half-Gods, Lares [or House-Gods], Lemures [or Sprites], Dioscuri [Castor and Pollux, to swear by], Soters [Saviours, or Deliverers], Parastas [Pillars, or Under-Officers], tutelary deities amongst the Greeks: gods of all sorts, for all functions; some for the Land, some for Sea; some for Heaven, some for Hell; some for passions, diseases, some for birth, some for weddings, husbandry, woods, waters, gardens, orchards, &c. All actions and offices, Peace, Quiet, Health, Liberty, Happiness, Energy, Readiness for Love, Encouragement, Pan, Sylvanus, Priapus, Flora, Cloacina [Goddess of Sewers], Stercutius [God of Muck], Febris [Goddess of Fevers], Pallor [God of Fear], Invidia [Goddess of Hatred], Protervia [Goddess of Shamelessness], Risus [God of Mirth], Angerona [Goddess of Melancholy], Volupia [Goddess of Pleasure], Vacuna [Goddess of Leisure], Viriplaca [Appeaser of Husbands], Veneranda [Goddess of Reverence], Pales [God of Shepherds], Neptune, Doris [Sea-gods], Kings, Emperors, valiant men that had done any good offices for them, they did likewise canonize and adore for Gods, and it was usually done, among the ancients, as Jac. Boissardus well observes, and the Devil was still ready to second their intents, he crept into their temples, statues, tombs, altars, and was ready to give oracles, cure diseases, do miracles, &c., as by Jupiter, Æsculapius, Tiresias, Apollo, Mopsus, Amphiaraus, &c., Gods and Demi-gods. For so they were Demi-gods, some mediators between Gods and men, as Max. Tyrius, the Platonist, maintains and justifies in many words. When a good man dies, his body is buried, but his soul becomes forthwith a Demi-god, nothing disparaged with malignity of air, or variety of forms, rejoiceth, exults and sees that perfect beauty with his eyes. Now being deified, in commiseration he helps his poor friends here on earth, his kindred and allies, informs, succours, &c., punisheth those that are bad, and do amiss, as a good Genius to protect and govern mortal men appointed by the gods, so they will have it, ordaining some for provinces, some for private men, some for one office, some for another. Hector and Achilles assist Soldiers to this day, Æsculapius all sick men, the Dioscuri Seafaring men, &c., and sometimes upon occasion they shew themselves. The Dioscuri, Hercules and Æsculapius, he saw himself (or the devil in their likeness) not when sleeping but wide awake. So far Tyrius. And not good men only do they thus adore, but tyrants, monsters, devils, (as Stuckius inveighs) Neros, Domitians, Heliogables, beastly women, and arrant whores, amongst the rest. For all intents, places, creatures, they assign gods; to buildings, dwellings, baths, and horses, saith Prudentius. Cuna for cradles, Diverra for sweeping houses, Nodina knots, Prema, Premunda, Hymen, Hymenæus, for weddings; Comus the God of good fellows, gods of silence, of comfort, Hebe, goddess of youth; Mena of the monthly flow of women, &c., male and female gods, of all ages, sexes, and dimensions, with beards, without beards, married, unmarried, begot, not born at all, but as Minerva start out of Jupiter's head. Hesiodus reckons up at least 30,000 gods, Varro 300 Jupiters. As Jeremy told them, their gods were to the multitude of Cities.

Whatever heavens, sea, and land begat,
Hills, seas and rivers, God was this and that.

And which was most absurd, they made gods upon such ridiculous occasions; As children make babies (so saith Mornay) their Poets make Gods, worship them in temples, exhibit them in theatres, as Lactantius scoffs. Saturn, a man (gelded, himself), did eat his own children, a cruel tyrant driven out of his kingdom by his son Jupiter, as good a God as himself, a wicked lascivious paltry King of Crete, of whose rapes, lusts, murders, villanies, a whole volume is too little to relate. Venus, a notorious strumpet, as common as a barber's chair, Mars', Adonis', Anchises' whore, is a great she-goddess as well as the rest, as much renowned by their Poets; with many such: and these gods so fabulously and foolishly made, celebrated in Ceremonies, Hymns and Canticles; their errors, (as Eusebius well taxeth) weddings, mirth and mournings, loves, angers, and quarrelling they did celebrate in Hymns, and sing of in their ordinary songs, as it were publishing their villanies. But see more of their originals. When Romulus was made away by the sedition of the senators, to pacify the people, Julius Proculus gave out that Romulus was taken up by Jupiter into Heaven, and therefore to be ever after adored for a God amongst the Romans. Syrophanes of Egypt had one only son, whom he dearly loved, he erected his statue in his house, which his servants did adorn with crowns and garlands, to pacify their master's wrath when he was angry, so by little and little he was adored for a god. This did Semiramis for her husband Belus, and Adrian the Emperor by his minion Antinous. Flora was a rich harlot in Rome, and for that she made the Common-wealth her heir, her birthday was solemnized long after; and to make it a more plausible holiday, they made her Goddess of flowers, and sacrificed to her amongst the rest. The matrons of Rome, as Dionysius Halicarnasseus relates, because at their entreaty Coriolanus desisted from his Wars, consecrated a Church to Woman's Luck; and Venus Barbata [or Barber'd] had a temple erected, for that somewhat was amiss about [her] hair, and so the rest. The Citizens of Alabanda, a small town in Asia Minor, to curry favour with the Romans (who then warred in Greece with Perseus of Macedon, and were formidable to these parts) consecrated a temple to the City of Rome, and made her a goddess, with annual games and sacrifices: so a town of houses was deified, with shameful flattery of the one side to give, and intolerable arrogance on the other to accept, upon so vile and absurd an occasion. Tully writes to Atticus, that his daughter Tulliola might be made a goddess, and adored as Juno and Minerva, and as well she deserved it. Their Holydays and adorations were all out as ridiculous; those Lupercalia of Pan, Floralia of Flora, [those of] Bona Dea, Anna Perenna, Saturnalia, &c., as how they were celebrated, with what lascivious and wanton gestures, bald ceremonies, by what bawdy Priests, how they hang their noses over the smoke of sacrifices, saith Lucian, and lick blood like flies that was spilled about the altars. Their carved Idols, gilt Images of wood, iron, ivory, silver, brass, stone, a log of wood, &c., were most absurd, as being their own workmanship; for, as Seneca notes, they worship gods of wood and despise those who made them, they adore work, contemn the workman; and as Tertullian follows it, had it not been for men, they had never been gods, but blocks still, and stupid statues, in which mice, swallows, birds made their nests, spiders their webs, and in their very mouths laid their excrements. Those Images I say were all out as gross, as the shapes in which they did represent them: Jupiter with a ram's head, Mercury a dog's, Pan like a goat, Hecate with three heads, one with a beard, another without; see more in Carterius and Verdurius of their monstrous forms and ugly pictures: and which was absurder yet, they told them these Images came from heaven, as that of Minerva in her temple at Athens, which they believe came from the sky, saith Pausanias. They formed some like Storks, Apes, Bulls, and yet seriously believed; and that which was impious, and abominable, they made their Gods notorious whoremasters, incestuous Sodomites, (as commonly they were all, as well as Jupiter, Mars, Apollo, Mercury, Neptune, &c.), thieves, slaves, drudges, (for Apollo and Neptune made tiles in Phrygia,) kept sheep, Hercules emptied stables, Vulcan a black-smith, unfit to dwell upon the earth for their villanies, much less in heaven, as Mornay well saith, and yet they gave them out to be such; so weak and brutish, some to whine, lament, and roar, as Isis for her son and Cynocephalus, as also all her weeping Priests; Mars in Homer to be wounded, vexed; Venus run away crying, and the like; than which what can be more ridiculous? Is it not absurd you should lament over that you adore, or adore that you lament over (which Minucius objects); if gods, why, weep? if mortal, why worship? ———— that it is no marvel if Lucian, that adamantine persecutor of superstition, and Pliny could so scoff at them and their horrible Idolatry as they did: if Diagoras took Hercules' Image, and put it under his pot to seeth his pottage, which was, as he said, his 13th Labour. But see more of their fopperies in Cyprian, Chrysostom, Arnobius, Austin, Theodoretus, Clemens Alexandrinus, Minucius Felix, Eusebius, Lactantius, Stuckius, &c. Lamentable, tragical, and fearful those symptoms are, that they should be so far forth affrighted with their fictitious Gods, as to spend the goods, lives, fortunes, precious time, best days in their honour, to sacrifice unto them, to their inestimable loss, such Hecatombs, so many thousand Sheep, Oxen, with gilded horns, Goats, as Crœsus King of Lydia, Marcus Julianus, surnamed, for much sacrifice, Victimarius, & Tauricremus, and the rest of the Roman Emperors usually did with such labour and cost: and not Emperors only and great ones, for the common good, were at this charge, but private men for their ordinary occasions. Pythagoras offered an hundred Oxen for the invention of a Geometrical Problem, and it was an ordinary thing to sacrifice in Lucian's time, a heifer for their good health, four Oxen for wealth, an hundred for a Kingdom, nine Bulls for their safe return from Troy to Pylos, &c. Every God almost hath a peculiar sacrifice, the Sun horses, Vulcan fire, Diana a white hart, Venus a turtle, Ceres an hog, Proserpina a black lamb, Neptune a bull, (read more in Stuckius at large) besides sheep, cocks, corals, frankincense, to their undoings, as if their gods were affected with blood or smoke. And surely (saith he) if one should but repeat the fopperies of mortal men, in their sacrifices, feasts, worshipping their Gods, their rites and ceremonies, what they think of them, of their diet, houses, orders, &c., what prayers and vows they make; if one should but observe their absurdity and madness, he would burst out a laughing, and pity their folly. For what can be more absurd than their ordinary prayers, petitions, requests, sacrifices, oracles, devotions? of which we have a taste in Maximus Tyrius, Plato's second Alcibiades, Persius, Juvenal, there likewise exploded; Lactantius, as if their Gods were an hungry, athirst, in the dark, they light candles, offer meat and drink. And what so base as to reveal their counsels and give oracles out of the bowels and excremental parts of beasts? sordid Gods, Varro truly calls them therefore, and well he might. I say nothing of their magnificent and sumptuous temples, those majestical structures. To the roof of Apollo Didymæus' Temple, the Branchidian, as Strabo writes, a thousand oaks did not suffice. Who can relate the glorious splendour, and stupend magnificence, the sumptuous building of Diana at Ephesus, Jupiter Ammon's Temple in Africa, the Pantheon at Rome, the Capitol,

the Serapeum at Alexandria, Apollo's Temple at Daphne in the Suburbs of Antioch. The great Temple at Mexico, so richly adorned, and
so capacious (for 10,000 men might stand in it at once) that fair Pantheon of Cusco, described by Acosta in his Indian History, which
eclipses both Jews and Christians. There were in old Jerusalem, as
some write, 408 Synagogues; but new Cairo reckons up (if Radzivilius
may be believed) 6800 meskites [or mosques], Fessa 400, whereof 50
are most magnificent, like Saint Paul's in London. Helena built 300 fair
churches in the holy Land, but one Bassa hath built 400 meskites. The
Mahometans have 1000 Monks in a Monastery; the like saith Acosta of
Americans; Riccius of the Chinese, for men and women, fairly built;
and more richly endowed some of them than Arras in Artois, Fulda in
Germany, or Saint Edmundsbury in England with us; who can describe
those curious and costly Statues, Idols, Images, so frequently mentioned
in Pausanias? I conceal their donaries, pendants, other offerings, presents,
to these their fictitious Gods daily consecrated. Alexander the son of
Amyntas, King of Macedonia, sent two statues of pure gold to Apollo at
Delphi. Crœsus King of Lydia dedicated an hundred golden Tiles in the
same place, with a golden Altar: no man came empty-handed to their
Shrines. But these are base offerings in respect; they offered men themselves alive. The Leucadians, as Strabo writes, sacrificed every year a
man, to pacify their Gods, to be thrown down from a mountain, and they
did voluntarily undergo it. The tribe of Decius did so sacrifice to the
Infernal Deities, Curtius did leap into the gulf. Were they not all
strangely deluded to go so far to their Oracles, to be so gulled by them,
both in war and peace, as Polybius relates (which their Augurs, Priests,
Vestal Virgins can witness) to be so superstitious, that they would
rather lose goods and lives, than omit any ceremonies, or offend their
Heathen Gods? Nicias that generous and valiant Captain of the Greeks,
overthrew the Athenian Navy, by reason of his too much superstition,
because the Augurs told him it was ominous to set sail from the Haven
of Syracuse whilst the Moon was eclipsed, he tarried so long, till his
enemies besieged him, he and all his Army was overthrown. The Parthians of old were so sottish in this kind, they would rather lose a victory, nay, lose their own lives, than fight in the night, 'twas against their
Religion. The Jews would make no resistance on the Sabbath, when
Pompey besieged Jerusalem; and some Jewish Christians in Africa, set
upon by the Goths, suffered themselves upon the same occasion to be
utterly vanquished. The superstition of the Dibrenses, a bordering
Town in Epirus, besieged by the Turks, is miraculous almost to re-

port. Because a dead dog was flung into the only Fountain which the City had, they would die of thirst all, rather than drink of that unclean water,* and yield up the City upon any conditions. Though the Prætor and chief Citizens began to drink first, using all good persuasions, their superstition was such, no saying would serve, they must all forthwith die, or yield up the City. I myself (saith Barletius) scarcely dare credit so great a superstition, or attribute a cause so trivial to so great a matter; the story was too ridiculous, he was ashamed to report it, because he thought no body would believe it. It is stupend to relate what strange effects this Idolatry and superstition hath brought forth in these latter years in the Indies, and those bordering parts: in what feral shapes the Devil is adored, lest he should do them harm, as they say; for in the mountains betwixt Scanderoon and Aleppo at this day, there are dwelling a certain kind of people called Coords, coming of the race of the ancient Parthians, who worship the Devil, and allege this reason in so doing; God is a good man, and will do no harm, but the Devil is bad, and must be pleased, lest he hurt them. It is wonderful to tell how the devil deludes them, how he terrifies them, how they offer men, and women sacrifices unto him, an hundred at once, as they did infants in Crete to Saturn of old, the finest children, like Agamemnon's Iphigenia, &c. At Mexico, when the Spaniards first overcame them, they daily sacrificed the hearts of men yet living, 20,000 in a year (Acosta saith), to their Idols made of flour and men's blood, and every year six thousand infants of both sexes; and as prodigious to relate, how they bury their wives with husbands deceased, 'tis fearful to report, and harder to believe,

> *The widows even vie with one another*
> *Who shall die first; they are ashamed to live,*   (PROPERTIUS)

and burn them alive, best goods, servants, horses, when a grandee dies, 12,000 at once amongst the Tartars, when a great Cham departs, or an Emperor in America: how they plague themselves, which abstain from all that hath life, like those old Pythagoreans, with immoderate fasting, as the Bannians about Surat, they of China, that for superstition's sake never eat flesh nor fish all their lives, never marry, but live in deserts and by-places, and some pray to their Idols 24 hours together, without any intermission, biting off their tongues when they have done, for devotion's sake. Some again are brought to that madness by their superstitious Priests, (that tell them such vain stories of immortality, and the joys of heaven in that other life) that many thousands volun-

* They were of the Greek church. — Burton's note.

tarily break their own necks, as Cleombrotus Ambraciotes' Auditors of old, precipitate themselves, that they may participate of that unspeakable happiness in the other world. One poisons, another strangleth himself; and the King of China had done as much, deluded with this vain hope, had he not been detained by his servant. But who can sufficiently tell of their several superstitions, vexations, follies, torments? I may conclude with Possevinus, Religion makes wild beasts civil, superstition makes wise men beasts and fools; and the discreetest that are, if they give way to it, are no better than dizzards; nay more, if that of Plotinus be true, that's the drift of religion, to make us like him whom we worship: what shall be the end of Idolaters, but to degenerate into stocks and stones? of such as worship these Heathen gods, for such gods are a kind of Devils, but to become devils themselves? 'Tis therefore a most perilous and dangerous error of all others, as Plutarch holds, a pestilent, a troublesome passion, that utterly undoeth men. Unhappy superstition, Pliny calls it, death takes away life, but not superstition. Impious and ignorant are far more happy than they which are superstitious, no torture like to it, none so continuate, so general, so destructive, so violent.

In this superstitious row, Jews for antiquity may go next to Gentiles; what of old they have done, what Idolatries they have committed in their groves and high places, what their Pharisees, Sadducees, Scribes, Essenes, and such sectaries have maintained, I will not so much as mention: for the present, I presume, no Nation under Heaven can be more sottish, ignorant, blind, superstitious, wilful, obstinate and peevish, tiring themselves with vain ceremonies to no purpose; he that shall but read their Rabbins' ridiculous Comments, their strange interpretation of Scriptures, their absurd ceremonies. fables, childish tales, which they steadfastly believe, will think they be scarce rational creatures; their foolish customs, when they rise in the morning, and how they prepare themselves to prayer, to meat, with what superstitious washings, how to their Sabbath, to their other feasts, weddings, burials, &c. Last of all, the expectation of their Messias, and those figments, miracles, vain pomp that shall attend him, as how he shall terrify the Gentiles, and overcome them by new diseases; how Michael the Arch-Angel shall sound his trumpet, how he shall gather all the scattered Jews into the Holy Land, and there make them a great banquet, wherein shall be all the birds, beasts, fishes, that ever God made; a cup of wine that grew in Paradise, and that hath been kept in Adam's cellar ever since. At the first course shall be served in that great Ox, *that every day feeds on a thousand hills,* that great Leviathan, and a great bird, that laid an egg so big, that by chance tumbling out of the nest, it knocked down 300 tall Cedars, and breaking as it fell, drowned 160 villages: this bird stood up to the knees in the Sea, and the Sea was so deep, that a hatchet would not fall to the bottom in seven years: of their Messias' wives and children (every King of the world shall send him one of his daughters to be his wife, because it is written, " King's daughters shall attend on him "); Adam and Eve, &c., and that one stupend fiction among the rest: when a Roman Prince asked of Rabbi Jehosua ben Hanania, why the Jews' God was compared to a Lion; he made answer, he compared himself to no ordinary Lion, but to one in the wood Ela, which when he desired to see, the Rabbin prayed to God he might, and forthwith the Lion set forward. But when he was 400 miles from Rome, he so roared, that all the great-bellied women in Rome made aborts, the City walls fell down, and when he came an hundred miles nearer, and roared the second time, their teeth fell out of their heads, the Emperor himself fell down dead, and so the Lion went back. With an infinite number of such lies and forgeries, which they verily believe, feed themselves with vain hope, and in the mean time will by no persuasions be diverted, but still crucify their souls with a company of idle ceremonies, live like slaves and vagabonds, will not be relieved or reconciled.

Mahometans are a compound of Gentiles, Jews, and Christians, and so absurd in their ceremonies, as if they had taken that which is most sottish out of every one of them, full of idle fables in their superstitious law, their Alcoran itself a gallimaufry of lies, tales, ceremonies, traditions, precepts, stole from other sects, and confusedly heaped up to delude a company of rude and barbarous clowns. As how birds, beasts, stones, saluted Mahomet when he came from Mecca, the Moon came down from Heaven to visit him, how God sent for him, spake to him, &c., with a company of stupend figments of the Angels, Sun, Moon, and Stars, &c. Of the day of judgment, and three sounds to prepare to it, which must last 50,000 years, of Paradise, which wholly consists in wenching and feasting, and what is written about flocks [for provender], herds in Paradise, is so ridiculous, that Virgil, Dante, Lucian, nor any Poet can be more fabulous. Their Rites and Ceremonies are most vain and superstitious, Wine and Swine's-flesh are utterly forbidden by their Law, they must pray five times a day, and still towards the South; wash before and after all their bodies over, with many such. For fasting, vows, religious orders, peregrinations, they go far beyond any Papists, they fast a month together many times, and must not eat a bit till

Sun be set. Their Kalenders, Dervises, and Torlachers, [or idle Vaga-bonds] &c., are more abstemious some of them, than Carthusians, Franciscans, Anachorites, forsake all, live solitary, fare hard, go naked, &c. Their Pilgrimages are as far as to the River Ganges (which the Gentiles of those Tracts likewise do) to wash themselves, for that River, as they hold, hath a sovereign virtue to purge them of all sins, and no man can be saved that hath not been washed in it. For which reason they come far and near from the Indies; and infinite numbers yearly resort to it. Others go as far as Mecca to Mahomet's Tomb, which journey is both miraculous and meritorious. The ceremonies of flinging stones to stone the Devil, of eating a Camel at Cairo by the way; their fastings, their running till they sweat, their long prayers, Mahomet's Temple, Tomb, and building of it, would ask a whole volume to dilate; and for their pains taken in this holy Pilgrimage, all their sins are for-given, and they reputed for so many Saints. And divers of them with hot bricks, when they return, will put out their eyes, that they never after see any profane thing, bite out their tongues, &c. They look for their Prophet Mahomet, as Jews do for their Messias. Read more of their Customs, Rites, Ceremonies, in Lonicerus, Bredenbachius, Leo Afer, Busbequius, Sabellicus, Purchas, Theodorus Bibliander, &c. Many foolish Ceremonies you shall find in them; and which is most to be lamented, the people are generally so curious in observing of them, that if the least Circumstance be omitted, they think they shall be damned, 'tis an irremissible offence, and can hardly be forgiven. I kept in my house amongst my followers (saith Busbequius, sometime the Turk's Orator in Constantinople) a Turkey boy, that by chance did eat shell-fish, a meat forbidden by their Law, but the next day when he knew what he had done, he was not only sick to cast and vomit, but very much troubled in mind, would weep and grieve many days after, torment himself for his foul offence. Another Turk, being to drink a cup of wine in his Cellar, first made a huge noise, and filthy faces, to warn his soul, as he said, that it should not be guilty of that foul fact which he was to commit. With such toys as these are men kept in awe, and so cowed, that they dare not resist, or offend the least circumstance of their Law, for conscience sake, misled by superstition, which no human edict otherwise, no force of arms, could have enforced.

In the last place are Pseudo-Christians, in describing of whose super-stitious symptoms, as a mixture of the rest, I may say that which S. Benedict once saw in a vision, one Devil in the market-place, but ten in a Monastery, because there was more work; in populous Cities, they would swear and for-swear, lie, falsify, deceive fast enough of themselves, one Devil could circumvent a thousand; but in their religious houses, a thousand Devils could scarce tempt one silly Monk. All the principal Devils, I think, busy themselves in subverting Christians; Jews, Gentiles, and Mahometans are out of the fold, and need no such attendance, they make no resistance, for he troubleth not to scourge those whom he possesseth in peace, they are his own already; but Christians have that shield of Faith, sword of the spirit to resist, and must have a great deal of battery before they can be overcome. That the Devil is most busy amongst us that are of the true Church, appears by those several Oppositions, Heresies, Schisms, which in all ages he hath raised to subvert it, and in that of Rome especially, wherein Antichrist himself now sits and plays his prize. This mystery of iniquity began to work even in the Apostles' time, many Antichrists and Hereticks were abroad, many sprung up since, many now present, and will be to the world's end, to dementate men's minds, to seduce and captivate their souls. Their symptoms I know not how better to express, than in that twofold division, of such as lead, and are led. Such as lead are Hereticks, Schismaticks, false Prophets, Impostors, and their Ministers: they have some common symptoms, some peculiar. Common, as madness, folly, pride, insolency, arrogancy, singularity, peevishness, obstinacy, impudence, scorn, and contempt of all other sects:

Not bound to swear as any one master dictates.   (HORACE)

They will approve of nought but what they first invent themselves, no interpretation good, but what their infallible spirit dictates; none shall be second best, no not third, they are only wise, only learned in the truth, all damned but they and their followers; saith Tertullian, they make a slaughter of Scriptures, and turn it, as a nose of wax, to their own ends. So irrefragable, in the mean time, that what they have once said, they must and will maintain, in whole Tomes, duplications, triplications, never yield to death, so self-conceited, say what you can. As Bernard (erroneously some say) speaks of P. Aliardus, all the Fathers may say this, I say that. Though all the Fathers, Councils, the whole world contradict it, they care not, they are all one: and as Gregory well notes of such as are vertiginous, they think all turns round and moves, all err; when as the error is wholly in their own brains. Magallianus the Jesuit in his Comment on the first of Timothy, and Alphonsus de Castro, give two more eminent notes, or probable conjectures to know such men by (they might have taken themselves by the noses when they said it), First, they affect novelties and toys, and prefer falsehood before truth; Secondly, they care not what they say, that which rashness and folly hath brought out, pride afterward, peevishness and contumacy shall maintain to the last gasp. Peculiar symptoms are prodigious paradoxes, new doctrines, vain phantasms, which are many and divers, as they themselves. Nicholaites of old would have wives in common: Montanists will not marry at all, nor Tatians, forbidding all flesh, Severians wine; Adamians go naked, because Adam did so in Paradise, and some bare-foot all their lives, because God bid Moses so to do, and Isaiah was bid put off his shoes: Manichees hold that Pythagorean transmigration of souls from men to beasts; the Circumcelliones in Africa with a mad cruelty made away themselves, some by fire, water, breaking their necks, and seduced others to do the like, threatening some if they did not, with a thousand such; as you may read in Austin, (for there were fourscore and eleven Heresies in his time, besides Schisms and smaller factions) Epiphanius, Alphonsus de Castro, Danæus, Gab. Prateolus, &c. Of Prophets, Enthusiasts & Impostors, our Ecclesiastical stories afford many examples: of Eliases and Christs, as our Eudo de Stellis, a Briton in King Stephen's time, that went invisible, translated himself from one to another in a moment, fed thousands with good cheer in the wilderness, and many such; nothing so common as miracles, visions, revelations, prophecies. Now what these brain-sick Hereticks once broach, and Impostors set on foot, be it never so absurd, false, and prodigious, the common people will follow and believe. It will run along like Murrain in cattle, scab in sheep, as Jovianus Pontanus said: as he that is bitten with a mad dog bites others, and all in the end become mad; either out of affection of novelty, simplicity, blind zeal, hope and fear, the giddy-headed multitude will embrace it, and without farther examination approve it.

But these are old, these things that we complain of, they belong to the past. In our days we have a new scene of superstitious Impostors and Hereticks, a new company of Actors, of Antichrists, that great Antichrist himself: a rope * of Popes, that by their greatness and authority bear down all before them: who from that time they proclaimed themselves universal Bishops, to establish their own Kingdom, sovereignty, greatness, and to enrich themselves, brought in such a company of human traditions, Purgatory, the Limbo of the Fathers, of Infants, and all that subterranean Geography, Mass, adoration of Saints, alms,

* Rope, a Middle English form of " roop," noisy, blustering lot; but perhaps here a string or chain.

fastings, bulls, indulgencies, Orders, Friars, Images, Shrines, musty
Reliques, Excommunications, confessions, satisfactions, blind obedi-
ences, vows, pilgrimages, peregrinations, with many such curious toys,
intricate subtilties, gross errors, obscure questions, to vindicate the
better, and set a gloss upon them, that the light of the Gospel was quite
eclipsed, darkness over all, the Scriptures concealed, legends brought in,
religion banished, hypocritical superstition exalted, and the Church
itself obscured and persecuted: Christ and his members crucified more,
saith Benzo, by a few Necromantical, Atheistical Popes, than ever it
was by Julian the Apostate, Porphyry the Platonist, Celsus the Physician, Libanius the Sophister; by those Heathen Emperors, Hunns,
Goths, and Vandals. What each of them did, by what means, at what
times, by what support, superstition climbed to this height, traditions
increased, and Antichrist himself came to his estate, let Magdeburgenses, Kemnisius, Osiander, Bale, Mornay, Fox, Usher, and many others
relate. In the mean time he that shall but see their profane Rites and
foolish Customs, how superstitiously kept, how strictly observed, their
multitude of Saints, Images, that rabble of Romish Deities, for Trades,
Professions, Diseases, Persons, Offices, Countries, Places; St. George for
England; St. Denis, for France; Patrick, Ireland; Andrew, Scotland;
Jago, Spain, &c.; Gregory for Students; Luke for Painters; Cosmas and
Damian for Philosophers; Crispin, Shoe-makers; Katherine, Spinners,
&c.; Anthony for Pigs; Gallus, Geese; Wenceslaus, Sheep; Pelagius,
Oxen; Sebastian, the plague; Valentine, falling-sickness; Apollonia,
tooth-ache; Petronella, for agues; and the Virgin Mary, for sea and
land, for all parties, offices: he that shall observe these things, their
Shrines, Images, Oblations, Pendants, Adorations, Pilgrimages they
make to them, what creeping to Crosses, our Lady of Loretto's rich
Gowns, her Donaries, the cost bestowed on Images, and number of
suitors; S. Nicholas Burge in France; our S. Thomas' Shrine of old at
Canterbury; those Reliques at Rome, Jerusalem, Genoa, Lyons, Prato,
S. Denis; and how many thousands come yearly to offer to them, with
what cost, trouble, anxiety, superstition (for forty several Masses are
daily said in some of their Churches, and they rise at all hours of the
night to Mass, come bare-foot, &c.) how they spend themselves, times,
goods, lives, fortunes, in such ridiculous observations; their tales and
figments, false miracles, buying and selling of pardons, indulgences for
forty thousand years to come, their processions on set days, their strict
fastings, monks, anchorites, friar mendicants, Franciscans, Carthusians,
&c. Their Vigils and Fasts, their Ceremonies at Christmas, Shrovetide,

Candlemas, Palm-Sunday, S. Blase, S. Martin, S. Nicholas' day; their adorations, exorcisms, &c. will think all those Grecian, Pagan, Mahometan superstitions, gods, Idols, and Ceremonies, the Name, Time and Place, habit only altered, to have degenerated into Christians. Whilst they prefer Traditions before Scriptures; those Evangelical Councils, poverty, obedience, vows, alms, fasting, supererogations, before God's Commandments; their own Ordinances instead of his Precepts, and keep them in ignorance, blindness, they have brought the common people into such a case by their cunning conveyances, strict discipline, and servile education, that upon pain of damnation they dare not break the least ceremony, tradition, edict: hold it a greater sin to eat a bit of meat in Lent than kill a man: their consciences are so terrified, that they are ready to despair if a small ceremony be omitted; and will accuse their own Father, Mother, Brother, Sister, nearest and dearest friends, of heresy, if they do not as they do, will be their chief executioners, and help first to bring a fagot to burn them. What mulct, what penance soever is enjoined, they dare not but do it, tumble with S. Francis in the mire amongst hogs, if they be appointed, go woolward,* whip themselves, build Hospitals, Abbies, &c., go to the East or West-Indies, kill a King, or run upon a sword point: they perform all, without any muttering or hesitation, believe all.

> *As children think their babies live to be,*
> *Do they these brazen images they see.* (LUCILIUS)

And whilst the ruder sort are so carried headlong with blind zeal, are so gulled and tortured by their superstitions, their own too credulous simplicity and ignorance, their Epicurean Popes and Hypocritical Cardinals laugh in their sleeves, and are merry in their chambers with their Punks, they do indulge their genius, and make much of themselves. The middle sort, some for private gain, hope of Ecclesiastical preferment, (who taught the parrot to chirp his good-morning?) popularity, base flattery, must and will believe all their paradoxes and absurd tenents, without exception, and as obstinately maintain and put in practice all their traditions and Idolatrous ceremonies, (for their Religion is half a Trade) to the death; they will defend all, the Golden Legend itself, with all the lies and tales in it: as that of S. George, S. Christopher, S. Winifred, S. Denis, &c. It is a wonder to see how Nich. Harpsfield, that pharisaical Impostor, amongst the rest, puzzles himself to vindicate that ridiculous fable of S. Ursula, and the eleven thousand Virgins, as when they lived, how they came to Cologne, by whom mar-

* Wear wool next the skin for penance, like haircloth.

tyred, &c., though he can say nothing for it, yet he must and will approve it: Ursula with her companions ennobled (he saith) this age, whose history I would were as clear and certain as it is certain and clear in my mind that she is a happy virgin in heaven with her companions. They must and will (I say) either out of blind zeal believe, vary their compass with the rest, as the latitude of Religion varies, apply themselves to the times and seasons, and for fear and flattery are content to subscribe and do all that in them lies to maintain and defend their present government, and slavish religious School-men, Canonists, Jesuits, Friars, Priests, Orators, Sophisters, luxuriant wits, who either for that they had nothing else to do, knew not otherwise how to busy themselves in those idle times, for the Church then had few or no open adversaries, or better to defend their lies, fictions, miracles, transubstantiations, traditions, Popes' Pardons, Purgatories, Masses, impossibilities, &c., with glorious shews, fair pretences, big words, and plausible wits, have coined a thousand idle questions, nice distinctions, subtilties, Obs and Sols [Objections and Solutions], such tropological, allegorical expositions, to salve all appearances, objections, such quirks and quiddities, Quodlibetaries, as Bale saith of Ferribrigge and Strode, instances, ampliations, decrees, glosses, canons, that instead of sound Commentaries, good Preachers, are come in a company of mad sophisters, firstly and secondly fellows, Sectaries, Canonists, Sorbonists [Doctors of the Sorbonne], Minorites [Franciscan Friars], with a rabble of idle controversies and questions, Whether the Pope be God, or like to God? whether each shares the nature of Christ? Whether it be as possible for God to be an Humble-Bee, or a Gourd, as a man? Whether he can produce respect without a foundation or term, make a Whore a Virgin? Fetch Trajan's soul from hell, and how? with a rabble of questions about hell fire: whether it be a greater sin to kill a man, or to clout shoes upon a Sunday? Whether God can make another God like unto himself? Such, saith Kemnisius, are most of your School-men (mere Alchemists), 200 Commentators on Peter Lombard; (Pitsius reckons up 180 English Commentators alone, on the matter of the sentences); Scotists, Thomists, Reals, Nominals, &c., and so perhaps that of Saint Austin may be verified, the unlearn'd get heaven while the learn'd go down to hell. Thus they continued in such error, blindness, decrees, sophisms, superstitions; idle ceremonies and traditions were the sum of their new-coined holiness and religion, and by these knaveries and stratagems they were able to involve multitudes, to deceive the most sanctified souls, and if it were possible the very Elect. In the mean time the true Church, as wine and water mixt, lay hid and obscure to speak of till Luther's time, who began upon a sudden to defecate, [or purge], and, as another Sun, to drive away those foggy mists of superstition, to restore it to that purity of the Primitive Church. And after him many good and godly men, divine spirits, have done their endeavours, and still do.

> *And what their ignorance esteem'd so holy,*
> *Our wiser ages do account as folly.*   (DANIEL)

But see the Devil, that will never suffer the Church to be quiet or at rest: no garden so well tilled, but some noxious weeds grow up in it; no wheat, but it hath some tares; we have a mad giddy company of Precisians, Schismaticks, and some Hereticks, even in our bosoms in another extreme,

> *Fools run from one extreme into another,*   (HORACE)

that out of too much zeal in opposition to Antichrist, human traditions, those Romish rites and superstitions, will quite demolish all, they will admit of no ceremonies at all, no fasting days, no Cross in Baptism, no kneeling at Communion, no Church-musick, &c., no Bishop's-Courts, no Church-government, rail at all our Church-discipline, will not hold their tongues, and all for the peace of thee, O Sion. No not so much as Degrees will some of them tolerate, or Universities, all human learning ('tis the Devil's Sewer), hoods, habits, cap and surplice, such as are things indifferent in themselves, and wholly for ornament, decency, or distinction sake, they abhor, hate and snuff at, as a stone-horse [stallion] when he meets a Bear: they make matters of conscience of them, and will rather forsake their livings, than subscribe to them. They will admit of no holy-days, or honest recreations, as of hawking, hunting, &c., no Churches, no bells some of them, because Papists use them: no discipline, no ceremonies but what they invent themselves: no interpretations of Scriptures, no Comments of Fathers, no Councils, but such as their own phantastical spirits dictate, or right reason, as Socinians, by which spirit misled, many times they broach as prodigious paradoxes as Papists themselves. Some of them turn Prophets, have secret revelations, will be of privy council with God himself, and know all his secrets, hold the Holy Spirit by the hair, obstinate asses that they are. A company of giddy heads will take upon them to define how many shall be saved, and who damned in a parish, where they shall sit in Heaven, interpret Apocalypses (precipitate and giddy-pated Commentators, one calls them, as well he might) and those hidden mysteries to private persons, times, places, as their own spirit informs them, private revelations shall suggest, and precisely set down when the world shall come to an end, what year, what month, what day. Some of them again have such strong faith, so presumptuous, they will go into infected houses, expel devils, and fast forty days, as Christ himself did ; some call God and his Attributes into question, as Vorstius and Socinus, some Princes, Civil Magistrates, and their authorities, as Anabaptists, will do all their own private spirit dictates, and nothing else. Brownists, Barrowists, Familists, and those Amsterdamian sects and sectaries, are led all by so many private spirits. It is a wonder to reveal what passages Sleidan relates in his Commentaries, of Cretink, Knipperdoling, and their associates, those mad men of Munster in Germany ; what strange Enthusiasms, sottish Revelations they had, how absurdly they carried themselves, deluded others ; and as profane Machiavel in his Political Disputations holds of Christian Religion in general, it doth enervate, debilitate, take away men's spirits and courage from them, makes men more simple, breeds nothing so courageous Soldiers as that Roman : we may say of these peculiar sects, their Religion takes away not spirits only, but wit and judgment, and deprives them of their understanding : for some of chem are so far gone with their private Enthusiasms and Revelations, that they are quite mad, out of their wits.

What greater madness can there be, than for a man to take upon him to be God, as some do ? to be the Holy Ghost, Elias, and what not ? In Poland, 1518, in the Reign of King Sigismund, one said he was Christ, and got him twelve Apostles, came to judge the world, and strangely deluded the Commons. One David George, an illiterate Painter, not many years since, did as much in Holland, took upon him to be the Messias, and had many followers. Benedictus Victorinus Faventinus writes as much of one Honorius, that thought he was not only inspired as a Prophet, but that he was a God himself, and had familiar conference * with God and his Angels. Lavater hath a story of one John Sartorius, that thought he was the Prophet Elias, and of divers others that had conference with Angels, were Saints, Prophets ; Wierus makes mention of a Prophet of Groningen that said he was God the Father ; of an Italian and Spanish Prophet that held as much. We need not rove so far abroad, we have familiar examples at home ; Hacket that said he was Christ, Coppinger and Arthington, his disciples : Burchet and Hovatus, burned at Norwich. We are never likely seven years together without some such new Prophets, that have several inspirations, some to convert the Jews, some fast forty days, go with Daniel to the Lion's

* Hen. Nicholas, at Leyden, 1580, such a one. — Burton's note.

den ; some foretell strange things, some for one thing, some for another. Great Precisians of mean conditions and very illiterate, most part by a preposterous zeal, fasting, meditation, melancholy, are brought into these gross errors and inconveniences. Of these men I may conclude generally, that howsoever they may seem to be discreet, and men of understanding in other matters, discourse well, they have a diseased imagination, they are like comets, round in all places but only where they blaze, otherwise sane, they have impregnable wits many of them, and discreet otherwise, but in this their madness and folly breaks out beyond measure. They are certainly far gone with melancholy, if not quite mad, and have more need of physick than many a man that keeps his bed, more need of Hellebore than those that are in Bedlam.

SUBSECTION 4 — *Prognosticks of Religious Melancholy*

You may guess at the Prognosticks by the Symptoms. What can these signs foretell otherwise than folly, dotage, madness, gross ignorance, despair, obstinacy, a reprobate sense, a bad end? What else can superstition, heresy produce, but wars, tumults, uproars, torture of souls, and despair, a desolate land, as Jeremy teacheth, when they commit Idolatry, and walk after their own ways? how should it be otherwise with them? What can they expect but *blasting, famine, dearth,* and all the plagues of Egypt, as Amos denounceth; to be led into captivity? If our hopes be frustrate, *we sow much, and bring in little, eat, and have not enough, drink, and are not filled, clothe, and be not warm,* &c.; *we look for much, and it comes to little, whence is it? His house was waste, they came to their own houses, therefore the Heaven staid his dew, the Earth his fruit.* Because we are superstitious, irreligious, we do not serve God as we ought, all these plagues and miseries come upon us; what can we look for else but mutual wars, slaughters, fearful ends in this life, and in the life to come eternal damnation? What is it that hath caused so many feral battles to be fought, so much Christian blood shed, but superstition? That Spanish Inquisition, Racks, Wheels, Tortures, Torments, whence do they proceed? from superstition. Bodine the Frenchman accounts Englishmen Barbarians for their civil wars: but let him but read those Pharsalian fields fought of late in France for Religion, their Massacres, wherein by their own relations in four and twenty years I know not how many millions have been consumed, whole Families and Cities, and he shall find ours to have been but velitations [or skirishes] to theirs. But it hath ever been the custom of Hereticks and Idolaters, when they are plagued for their sins, and God's just judgments come upon them, not to acknowledge any fault in themselves, but still impute it unto others. In Cyprian's time it was much controverted betwixt him and Demetrius an Idolater, who should be the cause of those present calamities. Demetrius laid all the fault on Christians (and so they did ever in the primitive Church, as appears by the first book of Arnobius) that there were not such ordinary showers in Winter, the ripening heat in Summer, no seasonable Springs, fruitful Autumns, no Marble Mines in the Mountains, less gold and silver than of old; that husbandmen, sea-men, soldiers, all were scanted, justice, friendship, skill in Arts, all was decayed, and that through Christians' default, and all their other miseries from them, because they did not worship their gods. But Cyprian retorts all upon him again, as appears by his Tract against him. 'Tis true, the world is miserably tormented and shaken with wars, dearth, famine, fire, inundations, plagues, and many feral diseases rage amongst us, but not as thou complainest, that we do not worship your Gods, but because you are Idolaters, and do not serve the true God, neither seek him, nor fear him as you ought. Our Papists object as much to us, and account us hereticks, we them; the Turks esteem of both as Infidels, and we them as a company of Pagans, Jews against all; when indeed there is a general fault in us all, and something in the very best, which may justly deserve God's wrath, and pull these miseries upon our heads. I will say nothing here of those vain cares, torments, needless works, penance, pilgrimages, pseudo-martyrdom, &c. We heap upon ourselves unnecessary troubles, observations; we punish our bodies, as in Turkey (saith Busbequius) one did, that was much affected with Musick, and to hear Boys sing, but very superstitious; an old Sibyl coming to his house, or an holy woman (as that place yields many) took him down for it, and told him, that in that other world he should suffer for it; thereupon he flung his rich and costly Instruments which he had bedeckt with Jewels, all at once into the fire. He was served in silver plate, and had goodly household-stuff: a little after another religious man reprehended him in like sort, and from thenceforth he was served in earthen vessels. Last of all, a decree came forth, because Turks might not drink wine themselves, that neither Jew nor Christian then living in Constantinople might drink any wine at all. In like sort amongst Papists, fasting at first was generally proposed as a good thing; after, from such meats at set times, and then last of all so rigourously proposed, to bind the consciences upon pain of damnation. First Friday, saith Erasmus, then Saturday, and Wednesday now is in danger of a fast. And for such like toys some so miserably afflict themselves, to despair, and death itself, rather than offend, and think themselves good Christians in it, when as indeed they are superstitious Jews. So saith Leonardus Fuchsius, a great Physician in his time. We are tortured in Germany with these Popish edicts, our bodies so taken down, our goods so diminished, that if God had not sent Luther, a worthy man, in time to redress these mischiefs, we should have eaten hay with our horses before this. As in fasting, so in all other superstitious edicts, we crucify one another without a cause, barring ourselves of many good and lawful things, honest disports, pleasures and recreations; for wherefore did God create them but for our use? Feasts, mirth, musick, hawking, hunting, singing, dancing, &c. God not only ministers to our necessities but sheweth his love by providing for our pleasures also, as Seneca notes, God would have it so. And as Plato gives out, the gods, in commiseration of human estate, sent Apollo, Bacchus, and the Muses, to be merry with mortals, to sing and dance with us. So that he that will not rejoice and enjoy himself, making good use of such things as are lawfully permitted, is not temperate, as he will, but superstitious. *There is nothing better for a man, than that he should eat and drink, and that he should make his Soul enjoy good in his labour.* And as one said of hawking and hunting, I say of all honest recreations, God hath therefore indulged them to refresh, ease, solace and comfort us. But we are some of us too stern, too rigid, too precise, too grossly superstitious, and whilst we make a conscience of every toy, with touch not, taste not, &c., as those Pythagoreans of old, and some Indians now that will eat no flesh, or suffer any living creature to be killed, the Bannians about Guzerat; we tyrannize over our brother's soul, lose the right use of many good gifts, honest sports, games and pleasant recreations, punish ourselves without a cause, lose our liberties, and sometimes our lives. In the year 1270, at Magdeburg in Germany, a Jew fell into a Privy upon a Saturday, and without help could not possibly get out; he called to his fellows for succour, but they denied it, because it was their Sabbath, it was not permitted to do any work; the Bishop hearing of it the next day forbade him to be pulled out because it was our Sunday: in the mean time the wretch died before Monday. We have myriads of examples in this kind amongst those rigid Sabbatarians, and therefore not without good cause, Seneca calls it, as well he might, an intolerable perturbation, that causeth such dire events, folly, madness, sickness, despair, death of body and soul, and hell itself.

SUBSECTION 5 — *Cure of Religious Melancholy*

To purge the world of Idolatry and superstition, will require some monster-taming Hercules, a divine Æsculapius, or Christ himself to come in his own person, to reign a thousand years on earth before the end, as the Millenaries [those who expect the Millenium] will have him. They are generally so refractory, self-conceited, obstinate, so firmly addicted to that religion in which they have been bred and brought up, that no persuasion, no terror, no persecution can divert them. The consideration of which hath induced many commonwealths to suffer them to enjoy their consciences as they will themselves. A toleration of Jews is in most Provinces of Europe: in Asia they have their Synagogues: Spaniards permit Moors to live amongst them: the Mogullians, Gentiles: the Turks, all religions. In Europe, Poland and Amsterdam are the common Sanctuaries. Some are of opinion, that no man ought to be compelled for conscience sake, but let him be of what religion he will, he may be saved, as Cornelius was formerly accepted, Jew, Turk, Anabaptists, &c. If he be an honest man, live soberly and civilly in his profession, (Volkelius, Crellius, and the rest of the Socinians, that now nestle themselves about Cracow and Rakow in Poland, have renewed this opinion) serve his own God, with that fear and reverence as he ought. Let each state keep its own religion (saith Lælius) and let us keep ours; Tully thought fit every city should be free in this behalf, adore their own tutelary and local gods, as Symmachus calls them. Isocrates adviseth Demonicus, when he came to a strange city, to worship by all means the Gods of the place: which Cæcilius labours, and would have every nation keep their own ceremonies, worship their peculiar gods, which Pomponius Mela reports of the Africans, they worship their own gods according to their own ordination. For why should any one nation, as he there pleads, challenge that universality of God (this God of theirs, whom they neither display nor see, wandering about, forsooth, and everywhere present, inquiring into the habits, deeds, and hidden thoughts of all, &c.), as Christians do? Let every Province enjoy their liberty in this behalf, worship one God, or all, as they will, and are informed [inspired to do]. The Romans built Altars to the Gods of Asia, Libya, to unknown and wandering Gods: others otherwise, &c.; Plinius Secundus, as appears by his Epistle to Trajan, would not have the Christians so persecuted, and in some time of the reign of Maximin, as we find it registered in Eusebius, there was a decree made to this purpose, *Let no one be compelled against his will to worship any particular God,* and by Constantine in the 19th year of his reign, as Baronius informeth us, *Let no man shew arrogance against another, what each man chooseth, that let him do;* new gods, new law-givers, new Priests will have new ceremonies, customs and religions, to which every wise man as a good Formalist should accommodate himself.

> *Saturn is dead, his laws have perished with him:*
> *Obey now Jupiter, who rules the world.*   (OVID)

The said Constantine the Emperor, as Eusebius writes, flung down and demolished all the heathen gods, silver, gold statues, altars, Images and temples, and turned them all to Christian Churches (hostile to the popular memorials, he exposed them to ridicule); the Turk now con-verts them again to Mahometan Meskites [or Mosques]. The like Edict came forth in the reign of Arcadius and Honorius. Symmachus the Orator, in his days, to procure a general toleration, used this argu-ment, Because God is immense and infinite, and his nature cannot perfectly be known, it is convenient he should be as diversely wor-shipped, as every man shall perceive or understand. It was impossible, he thought, for one religion to be universal: you see that one small Province can hardly be ruled by one law civil or spiritual; and how shall so many distinct and vast Empires of the world be united into one? It never was, never will be. Besides, if there be infinite planetary and firmamental worlds, as some will, there be infinite Geniuses or commanding Spirits belonging to each of them: and so in consequence (for they will be all adored) infinite religions. And therefore let every Territory keep their proper rites and ceremonies, as their tutelary gods will, so Tyrius calls them, and according to the quarter they hold, their own institutions, revelations, orders, Oracles, which they dictate to from time to time, or teach their Priests or Ministers. This tenent was stiffly maintained in Turkey not long since, as you may read in the third Epistle of Busbequius, that all those should participate of eternal happiness, that lived an holy and innocent life, what religion soever they professed: Rustan Bassa was a great Patron of it; though Ma-homet himself was sent as the sword of virtue, to enforce all, as he writes in his Alcoran, to follow him. Some again will approve of this for Jews, Gentiles, Infidels, that are out of the fold, they can be content to give them all respect and favour, but by no means to such as are within the precincts of our own Church, and called Christians, to no Hereticks, Schismaticks, or the like; let the Spanish Inquisition, that fourth Fury, speak of some of them, the civil wars and Massacres in France, our Marian times. Magallianus the Jesuit will not admit of conference with an heretick, but severity and rigour to be used, one should not argue with them, but set up pillories for them; and Theodosius is commended in Nicephorus, that he put all Hereticks to silence. Bernard will have club law, fire and sword for Hereticks, compel them, stop their mouths, not with disputations, or refute them with reasons, but with fists; and this is their ordinary practice. Another company are as mild, on the other side, to avoid all heart-burning, and contentious wars and uproars, they would have a general toleration in every kingdom, no mulct at all, no man for religion or conscience be put to death, which Thuanus the French Historian much favours: our late Socinians defend; Vaticanus against Calvin, in a large Treatise in behalf of Servetus, vindicates; Castalio, &c., Martin Bellius, and his companions, maintained this opinion not long since in France, whose error is confuted by Beza in a just Volume. The medium is best, and that which Paul prescribes: " If any man shall fall by occasion, to restore such a one with the spirit of meekness, by all fair means, gentle admonitions " : but if that will not take place, after a second admonition shun the heretick, he must be excommunicate, as Paul did by Hymenæus, delivered over to Satan. A wound that cannot be cured, must be cut away (saith Ovid). As Hippocrates said in Physick, I may well say in Divinity, the fire cures what the sword cannot. For the vulgar, restrain them by laws, mulcts, burn their books, forbid their conventicles: for when the cause is taken away, the effect will soon cease. Now for Prophets, dreamers, and such rude silly fellows, that through fasting, too much meditation, preciseness, or by Melancholy are distempered: the best means to reduce them to a sound mind is to alter their course of life, and with conference, threats, promises, persuasions, to intermix Physick. Hercules de Saxoniâ had such a Prophet committed to his charge in Venice, that thought he was Elias, and would fast as he did: he dressed a fellow in Angel's attire, that said he came from heaven to bring him divine food, and by that means staid his fast, administered his Physick: so by the mediation of this forged Angel he was cured. Rhasis, an Arabian, speaks of a fellow that in like case complained to him, and desired his help: I asked him (saith he) what the matter was, he replied, I am continually meditating of Heaven and Hell, and methinks I see and talk with fiery spirits, smell brimstone, &c., and am so carried away with these conceits, that I can neither eat, nor sleep, nor go about my business: I cured him (saith Rhasis) partly by persuasion, partly by Physick, and so have I done by many others. We have frequently such Prophets and dreamers amongst us, whom we persecute with fire and fagot: I think the most compendious cure for some of them at least, had been in Bedlam. But enough of this.

MEMBER 2

SUBSECTION 1 — *Religious Melancholy in defect; Parties affected, Epicures, Atheists, Hypocrites, worldly secure, Carnalists, all impious persons, impenitent sinners, &c.*

IN that other extreme, or defect of this love of God, knowledge, faith, fear, hope, &c., are such as err both in doctrine and manners, Sadducees, Herodians, Libertines, Politicians; all manner of Atheists, Epicures, Infidels, that are secure, in a reprobate sense, fear not God at all, and such are too distrustful and timorous, as desperate persons be. That grand sin of Atheism or Impiety, Melancthon calls it, monstrous Melancholy; or poisoned Melancholy. A company of Cyclops or Giants, that war with the gods, as the Poets feigned, Antipodes to Christians, that scoff at all Religion, at God himself, deny him and all his attributes, his wisdom, power, providence, his mercy and judgment.

> *That there are ghosts, and an infernal realm,*
> *A ferry, black frogs in the Stygian whirlpool,*
> *And thousands passing over at a time,*
> *Not even boys believe.* (JUVENAL)

That there is either Heaven or Hell, resurrection of the dead, pain, happiness, or world to come, let he who likes believe; for their parts, they esteem them as so many Poet's tales, Bugbears; Lucian's Alexander, Moses, Mahomet, and Christ, are all as one in their Creed. When those bloody wars in France for matters of Religion (saith Richard Dinoth) were so violently pursued betwixt Huguenots and Papists, there was a company of good fellows laughed them all to scorn, for being such superstitious fools, to lose their lives and fortunes, accounting faith, religion, immortality of the soul, mere fopperies and illusions. Such loose Atheistical spirits are too predominant in all Kingdoms. Let them contend, pray, tremble, trouble themselves that will, for their parts, they fear neither God nor Devil; but with that Cyclops in Euripides,

> *They fear no God but one,*
> *They sacrifice to none,*
> *But belly, and him adore,*
> *For Gods they know no more.*

Their God is their belly, as Paul saith; satiety their goddess:
> *Their palate is their only reason for living.* (JUVENAL)

The Idol which they worship and adore is their Mistress, with him in
Plautus, they had rather have her favour than the Gods'. Satan is their
guide, the flesh is their instructor, Hypocrisy their Counsellor, Vanity
their fellow-soldier, their Will their law, Ambition their Captain, Custom their Rule: temerity, boldness, impudence their Art, toys their
trading, damnation their end. All their endeavours are to satisfy their
lust and appetite, how to please their Genius, and to be merry for the
present,
> *Eat, drink, and love; no pleasure after death.*

*The same condition is of men and of beasts; as the one dieth, so dieth
the other;* the world goes round,
> *Day follows day, and full moons haste to wane.* (HORACE)

They did eat and drink of old, marry, bury, bought, sold, planted, built,
and will do still. *Our life is short and tedious, and in the death of a man
there is no recovery, neither was any man known that hath returned
from the grave: for we are born at all adventure, and we shall be hereafter as though we had never been; for the breath is as smoke in our
nostrils, &c., and the spirit vanisheth as the soft Air. Come let us enjoy
the pleasures that are present, let us cheerfully use the creatures as in
youth, let us fill ourselves with costly wine and ointments, let not the
flower of our life pass by us, let us crown ourselves with Rose-buds, before they are withered,* &c. Lesbia mine, let's live and love. *Come let us
take our fill of love, and pleasure in dalliance, for this is our portion,
this is our lot.*
> *Time flies with noiseless foot, and we grow old.* (OVID)

For the rest of Heaven and Hell, let children and superstitious fools believe it: for their parts they are so far from trembling at the dreadful
day of judgment, that they wish with Nero, let it come in their times:
so secure, so desperate, so immoderate in lust and pleasure, so prone
to revenge, that as Paterculus said of some Caitiffs in his time in Rome,
it shall not be so wickedly attempted, but as desperately performed,
whate'er they take in hand. Were it not for God's restraining grace, fear
and shame, temporal punishment, and their own infamy, they would
Lycaon-like exenterate, as so many Cannibals eat up, or [as] Cadmus'
soldiers, consume one another. These are most impious, and commonly
professed Atheists, that never use the name of God, but to swear by it:
that express nought else but Epicurism in their carriage or hypocrisy;
with Pentheus, they neglect and contemn these rites and religious cere-

monies of the Gods, they will be Gods themselves, or at least companions of the Gods.

Cæsar divides the world's empire with Jove.

Apries an Egyptian tyrant, grew, saith Herodotus, to that height of pride, insolency and impiety, to that contempt of God and men, that he held his Kingdom so sure, neither God nor men could take it from him. A certain blasphemous King of Spain (as Lansius reports) made an edict, that no subject of his, for ten years' space, should believe in, call on, or worship any god. And as Jovius relates of Mahomet the Second, that sacked Constantinople, he so behaved himself, that he believed neither Christ nor Mahomet, and thence it came to pass, that he kept his word and promise no further than for his advantage, neither did he care to commit [care if he committed] any offence to satisfy his lust. I could say the like of many Princes, many private men (our stories are full of them) in times past, this present age, that love, fear, obey, and perform all civil duties, as they shall find them expedient or behoveful to their own ends; which Tacitus reports of some Germans, they need not pray, fear, hope, for they are secure to their thinking, both from God and men. Bulco Opiliensis, sometime Duke of Silesia, was such a one to an hair, he lived (saith Æneas Sylvius) at Uratislavia, and was so mad to satisfy his lust, that he believed neither Heaven nor Hell, or that the soul was immortal, but married wives, and turned them up as he thought fit, did murder and mischief, and what he list himself. This Duke hath too many followers in our days: say what you can, dehort, exhort, persuade to the contrary, they are no more moved,

Than were a pillar of flint or Marpesian cliff, (VIRGIL)

than so many stocks and stones; tell them of Heaven and Hell, 'tis to no purpose, 'tis washing a mudbrick; they answer, as Ataliba, that Indian Prince, did Friar Vincent, when he brought him a book, and told him all the mysteries of salvation, Heaven and Hell were contained in it: he looked upon it, and said he saw no such matter, asking withal how he knew it: they will but scoff at it, or wholly reject it. Petronius in Tacitus, when he was now by Nero's command bleeding to death, instead of good counsel and divine meditations, he made his friends sing him bawdy verses, and scurrile songs. Let them take Heaven, Paradise, and that future happiness that will, it is good being here: there is no talking to such, no hope of their conversion, they are in a reprobate sense, mere carnalists, fleshy-minded men, which howsoever they may be applauded in this life by some few Parasites, and held for worldly wise men, they seem to me (saith Melancthon) to be as mad as Hercules was, when he raved and killed his wife and children. A milder sort of these Atheistical spirits there are that profess Religion, but timidly and hesitantly, tempted thereunto out of that horrible consideration of diversity of Religions, which are and have been in the world (which argument Campanella both urgeth and answers), besides the covetousness, imposture and knavery of Priests which (as Postellus observes) makes people believe less in religion, and those religions some of them so fantastical, exorbitant, so violently maintained with equal constancy and assurance; whence they infer, that if there be so many religious sects, and denied by the rest, why may they not be all false? or why should this or that be preferred before the rest? The Scepticks urge this, and amongst others it is the conclusion of Sextus Empiricus: after many Philosophical arguments and reasons for and against, that there are Gods, and again that there are no Gods, he so concludes, when there are so many contradictions, one only can be true, as Tully likewise disputes: Christians say they alone worship the true God, pity all other sects, lament their case; and yet those old Greeks and Romans that worshipped the Devil, as the Chinese do now, their own gods; as Julian the Apostate, Cæcilius in Minucius, Celsus and Porphyry the Philosopher object; and as Machiavel contends, were much more noble, generous, victorious, had a more flourishing Commonwealth, better Cities, better Soldiers, better Scholars, better Wits. Their Gods often overcame our Gods, did as many miracles, &c., Saint Cyril, Arnobius, Minucius, with many other ancients, of late Lessius, Mornay, Grotius, Savanarola, well defend; but Zanchius, Campanella, Marinus Marcennus, Bozius, and Gentilettus answer all their Atheistical arguments at large. But this again troubles many, as of old, wicked men generally thrive, professed Atheists thrive.

> There are no Gods, Heavens are toys,
> Segius in public justifies;
> Because that whilst he thus denies
> Their Deities, he better thrives.   (MARTIAL)

This is a prime Argument: and most part your most sincere, upright, honest, and good men are depressed. *The race is not to the swift, nor the battle to the strong, nor yet bread to the wise, favour nor riches to men of understanding, but time and chance comes to all.* There was a great plague in Athens (as Thucydides relates) in which at last every man with great licentiousness did what he list, not caring at all for God's or men's Laws. Neither the fear of God, nor Laws of men (saith he) awed any man, because the plague swept all away alike, good and bad; they thence concluded, it was alike to worship or not worship the Gods, since they perished all alike. Some cavil and make doubts of Scripture itself, it cannot stand with God's mercy, that so many should be damned, so many bad, so few good, such have and hold about Religions, all stiff on their side, factious alike, thrive alike, and yet bitterly persecuting and damning each other. It cannot stand with God's goodness, protection and providence (as Saint Chrysostom in the dialect of such discontented persons) to see and suffer one man to be lame, another mad, a third poor and miserable all the days of his life, a fourth grievously tormented with sickness and aches to his last hour. Are these signs and works of God's providence, to let one man be deaf, another dumb? A poor honest fellow lives in disgrace, woe and want, wretched he is; when as a wicked Caitiff abounds in superfluity of wealth, keeps whores, parasites, and what he will himself. Do you hear this, Jupiter? Collecting many such things, they weave a tissue of reproaches against God's providence. Thus they mutter and object (see the rest of their Arguments in Marcennus, and in Campanella, amply confuted), with many such vain cavils, well known, not worthy the recapitulation or answering, whatsoever they pretend, they are meantime of little or no Religion.

Couzin-germans to these men are many of our great Philosophers and Deists, who, though they be more temperate in this life, give many good moral precepts, honest, upright, and sober in their conversation, yet in effect they are the same (accounting no man a good Scholar that is not an Atheist) too much learning makes them mad. Whiles they attribute all to natural causes, contingence of all things, as Melancthon calls them, a peevish Generation of men, that misled by Philosophy, and the Devil's suggestion, their own innate blindness, deny God as much as the rest, hold all Religion a fiction, opposite to Reason and Philosophy, though for fear of Magistrates, saith Vaninus, they durst not publickly profess it. Ask one of them of what Religion he is, he scoffingly replies, a Philosopher, a Galenist, an Averroist, and with Rabelais a Physician, a Peripatetick, an Epicure. In spiritual things God must demonstrate all to sense, leave a pawn with them, or else seek some other creditor. They will acknowledge nature and fortune, yet not God: though in effect they grant both: for as Scaliger defines, Nature signifies God's ordinary power; or as Calvin writes, Nature is God's order, and so things extraordinary may be called unnatural: Fortune his unrevealed will; and so we call things changeable that are beside reason and expectation. To this purpose Minucius, and Seneca well discourseth with them. They do not understand what they say; what is Nature but God?

Call him what thou wilt, Nature, Jupiter, he hath as many Names as Offices. It comes all to one pass, God is the fountain of all, the first Giver and Preserver, from whom all things depend. God is all in all, God is everywhere, in every place. And yet this Seneca that could confute and blame them, is all out as much to be blamed and confuted himself, as mad himself; for he holds to Stoick Fate, that inevitable necessity, in the other extreme, as those Chaldæan Astrologers of old did, against whom the Prophet Jeremiah so often thunders, and those Heathen Mathematicians, Nigidius Figulus, Magicians, and Pricilianists, whom S. Austin so eagerly confutes, those Arabian questionaries, Nine Judges, Albumazar, Dorotheus, &c., and our Countryman Estuidus, that take upon them to define out of those great conjunctions of Stars, with Ptolomæus, the periods of Kingdoms, or Religions, of all future Accidents, Wars, Plagues, Schisms, Heresies, and what not? all from Stars, and such things, saith Maginus, which God hath reserved to himself and his Angels, they will take upon them to fore-tell, as if Stars were immediate, inevitable causes of all future accidents. Cæsar Vaninus,* in his Book, is more free, copious & open in the explication of this Astrological Tenent of Ptolemy, than any of our modern Writers, Cardan excepted, a true Disciple of his Master Pomponatius; according to the doctrine of Peripateticks, he refers all Apparitions, Prodigies, Miracles, Oracles, Accidents, Alterations of Religions, Kingdoms, &c., (for which he is soundly lashed by Marinus Marcennus, as well he deserves), to natural causes (for spirits he will not acknowledge), to that light, motion, influences of Heavens and Stars, and to the Intelligences that move the Orbs. Intelligences do all: and after a long Discourse of Miracles done of old, If Devils can do these things, why not the Intelligences of the heavenly bodies? And as these great Conjunctions, Aspects of Planets, begin or end, vary, are vertical and predominant, so have Religions, Rites, Ceremonies and Kingdoms their beginning, progress, periods; with Cities, Kings, Religions, and individual men, these things are true and plain, as Aristotle seems to imply, and daily experience teaches to the reader of history; for what was more sacred and illustrious, by Gentile law, than Jupiter? what now more vile and execrable? Thus the celestial bodies set up religions for mortal benefits, and when the influence ceases, so doth the law, &c. And because, according to their Tenents, the world is eternal, intelligences

---

* Cæsar Vaninus (or Lucilio Vanini), an Italian free-thinker, was condemned as an atheist, had his tongue cut out, and was strangled at the stake, his body being burned to ashes, in 1619. His book was The Secrets of Nature (Paris, 1616).

eternal, influence of the Stars eternal, Kingdoms, Religions, Alterations shall be likewise eternal, and run round after many Ages; again great Achilles shall be sent against Troy; religions and their ceremonies shall be born again; human affairs relapse into the same track, there is nothing that was not of old time and shall not be again, saith Vaninus, the same in kind but not in person, as in Plato. These (saith mine Author), these are the Decrees of Peripateticks, which though I recite, as I am a Christian I detest and hate. Thus Peripateticks, and Astrologians held in former times, and to this effect of old in Rome, saith Dionysus Halicarnasseus, when those Meteors and Prodigies appeared in the Air, after the banishment of Coriolanus, men were diversely affected, some said they were God's just judgments for the execution of that good man, some referred all to natural causes, some to the Stars, some thought they came by chance, some by necessity decreed from the beginning, and could not be altered. The last two Opinions of Necessity and Chance were, it seems, of greater note than the rest.

> *All human things some do ascribe to Fortune,*
> *And think this world without a governor,*
> *That seasons come and go spontaneously.* (JUVENAL)

For the first of Chance, as Sallust likewise informeth us, those old Romans generally received. They supposed Fortune alone gave Kingdoms and Empires, Wealth, Honours, Offices; and that for two causes, first, because every wicked, base, unworthy wretch was preferred, rich, potent, &c. Secondly, because of their uncertainty, though never so good, scarce any one enjoyed them long: but after they began upon better advice to think otherwise, that every man made his own fortune. The last of Necessity was Seneca's tenent, that God was so tied to second causes, to that inexorable necessity, that he could alter nothing of that which was once decreed; thus 'twas fated, it cannot be altered, God hath once said it, and it must for ever stand good, no prayers, no threats, nor power, nor thunder itself can alter it. Zeno, Chrysippus, and those other Stoicks, as you may read in Tully, A. Gellius, &c., maintained as much. In all ages, there have been such, that either deny God in all, or in part; some deride him, they could have made a better world, and rule it more orderly themselves, blaspheme him, derogate at their pleasure from him. 'Twas so in Plato's times, Some say there be no gods, others, that they care not for men, a middle sort grant both. If there's no God, whence comes good? If there is a God, whence evil? So Cotta argues in Tully, why made he not all good, or at least tenders not the welfare of such as are good? As the woman told Alexander, if he be not

at leisure to hear Causes, and redress them, why doth he reign? Sextus
Empiricus hath many such Arguments. Thus perverse men cavil. So
it will ever be, some of all sorts, good, bad, indifferent, true, false,
zealous, Ambidexters [or people who would keep in with both parties],
Neutralists, lukewarm Libertines, Atheists, &c. They will see these religious Sectaries agree amongst themselves, be reconciled all, before
they will participate with, or believe any. They think in the mean time
(which Celsus objects, and whom Origen confutes) we Christians adore
a person put to death, with no more reason than the barbarous Getæ
worshipped Zamolxis, the Cilicians Mopsus, the Thebans Amphiaraus,
and the Lebadeans Trophonius; one religion is as true as another, new-
fangled devices, all for human respects; great witted Aristotle's works
are as much authentical to them, as Scriptures, subtil Seneca's Epistles
as Canonical as Saint Paul's, Pindar's Odes as good as the Prophet
David's Psalms, Epictetus' Enchiridion equivalent to wise Solomon's
Proverbs. They do openly and boldly speak this and more, some of
them, in all places and companies. Claudius the Emperor was angry
with Heaven, because it thundered, and challenged Jupiter into the
field; with what madness! saith Seneca; he thought Jupiter could not
hurt him, but he could hurt Jupiter. Diagoras, Demonax, Epicurus,
Pliny, Lucian, Lucretius,

And Mezentius, the despiser of the Gods,   (VIRGIL)

professed Atheists all in their times: though not simple Atheists neither,
as Cicogna proves, they scoffed only at those Pagan gods, their plurality,
base and fictitious Offices. Gilbertus Cognatus labours much, and so
doth Erasmus, to vindicate Lucian from scandal, and there be those
that apologize for Epicurus; but all in vain, Lucian scoffs at all, Epicurus he denies all, and Lucretius his Scholar defends him in it;

When human kind was drenched in superstition,
With ghastly looks aloft, which frighted mortal men, &c.

He alone, as another Hercules, did vindicate the world from that Monster. Uncle Pliny, in express words denies the Immortality of the Soul.
Seneca doth little less, or rather more. Some Greek Commentators
would put as much upon Job, that he should deny the resurrection, &c.,
whom Pineda copiously confutes. Aristotle is hardly censured of some,
both Divines and Philosophers. S. Justin, Gregory Nazianzen, Theodoretus, Origen, Pomponatius justifies in his Tract (so styled at least)
on the Immortality of the Soul, Scaliger (who would forswear himself
at any time, saith Patritius, in defence of his great Master Aristotle),
and Dandinus. acknowledge as much. Averroes oppugns all spirits and

supreme powers; of late Brunus (unhappy Brunus, Kepler calls him), Machiavel, Cæsar Vaninus lately burned at Toulouse in France, and Peter Aretine, have publickly maintained such Atheistical Paradoxes, with that Italian Boccaccio, with his Fable of three Rings, &c., from which he infers it cannot be known which is the true religion, Jewish, Mahometan, or Christian, since they have the same signs, &c. Marinus Marcennus suspects Cardan for his Subtilties, Campanella, and Charron's Book of Wisdom, with some other Tracts, to savour of Atheism: but amongst the rest that pestilent Book of the Three Impostors of the World, which you cannot read (he says) without horror, and the Cymbal of the World, in four dialogues, written by Perier in the year 1538, printed at Paris, &c. And as there have been in all ages such blasphemous spirits, so there have not been wanting their Patrons, Protectors, Disciples and Adherents. Never so many Atheists in Italy and Germany, saith Colerus, as in this age: the like complaint Marcennus makes in France, 50,000 in that one City of Paris. Frederick the Emperor, as Matthew Paris records (I use his own words), is reported to have said: Although it may not be told, three Prestidigitators, Moses, Christ, and Mahomet, in order that they might rule the world, befooled all the people living in their times. (Henry the Landgrave of Hesse heard him speak it.) If the Princes of the Empire (he said) would follow my teaching, I would lay out a much better way of believing and living.

To these professed Atheists we may well add that impious and carnal crew of worldly-minded men, impenitent sinners, that go to Hell in a lethargy, or in a dream, who though they be professed Christians, yet they will make a conscience of nothing they do, they have cauterized consciences, and are indeed in a reprobate sense, *past all feeling, have given themselves over to wantonness, to work all manner of uncleanness even with greediness.* They do know there is a God, a day of Judgment to come, and yet for all that, as Hugo saith, they are as merry for all the sorrow, as if they had escaped all dangers, and were in Heaven already.

> *He put all fears under our feet, and death,*
> *The debt we all must pay, and Acheron's roar.* (VIRGIL)

Those rude idiots and ignorant persons, that neglect and contemn the means of their salvation, may march on with these, but above all others, those Herodian temporizing States-men, politick Machiavelians and Hypocrites, that make a show of Religion, but in their hearts laugh at it. A pretended sanctity is a double iniquity; they are in a double fault, *that fashion themselves to this world,* which Paul forbids, and like Mercury the Planet, are good with good, bad with bad. When they are at Rome, they do there as they see done, Puritans with Puritans, Papists with Papists, all things to all men, Formalists, Ambidexters, lukewarm Laodiceans. All their study is to please, and their god is their commodity, their labour to satisfy their lusts, and their endeavours to their own ends. Whatsoever they pretend, or in publick seem to do, *With the fool, in their hearts, they say there is no God.*

You, sir, what think you about Jupiter? (PERSIUS)
" Their words are as soft as oil, but bitterness is in their hearts," like Alexander the Sixth, so cunning dissemblers, that what they think, they never speak. Many of them are so close, you can hardly discern it, or take any just exceptions at them; they are not factious, oppressors, as most are, no bribers, no simoniacal Contractors, no such ambitious, lascivious persons, as some others are, no drunkards, they rise sober, and go sober to bed, plain dealing, upright honest men, they do wrong to no man, and are so reputed in the world's esteem at least, very zealous in Religion, very charitable, meek, humble, peace-makers, keep all duties, very devout, honest, well spoken of, beloved of all men: but he that knows better how to judge, he that examines the heart, saith they are Hypocrites, they are not sound within. As it is with Writers oftentimes, more holiness is in the Book, than in the Author of it: So 'tis with them; many come to Church with great Bibles, whom Cardan said, he could not choose but laugh at, and will now and then read Austin, frequent Sermons, and yet professed Usurers, mere Gripes, all their life is Epicurism and Atheism, come to Church all day, and lie with a Courtesan at night.

Pretend to be Curii, and live like bacchanals. (JUVENAL)
They have Esau's hands, and Jacob's voice; yea, and many of those holy Friars, sanctified men, saith Hierom, conceal a bandit within their robes. They are wolves in sheep's clothing, fair without, and most foul within. Oft-times under a mourning weed lies lust itself, and horrible vices under a poor coat. But who can examine all those kinds of Hypocrites, or dive into their hearts? If we may guess at the tree by the fruit, never so many as in these days; shew me a plain dealing true honest man; shame and honesty and fear are fled. He that shall but look into their lives, and see such enormous vices, men so immoderate in lust, unspeakable in malice, furious in their rage, flattering and dissembling (all for their own ends) will surely think they are not truly religious, but of an obdurate heart, most part in a reprobate sense, as in this Age.

But let them carry it as they will for the present, dissemble as they can, a time will come when they shall be called to an account, their melancholy is at hand, they pull a plague and curse upon their own heads. Besides all such as blaspheme, contemn, neglect God, or scoff at him, as the Poets feign of Salmoneus, that would in derision imitate Jupiter's Thunder, he was precipitated for his pains, so shall they certainly rue it in the end (they spit on themselves, who spit at the sky), their doom's at hand, and Hell is ready to receive them.

Some are of Opinion, that it is in vain to dispute with such Atheistical spirits in the mean time, 'tis not the best way to reclaim them. Atheism, Idolatry, Heresy, Hypocrisy, though they have one common root, that is indulgence to corrupt affection, yet their growth is different, they have divers symptoms, occasions, and must have several cures and remedies. 'Tis true, some deny there is any God, some confess, yet believe it not ; a third sort confess and believe, but will not live after his Laws, Worship and obey him : others allow God and Gods subordinate, but not one God, no such general God, but several Topick [or Local] Gods for several places, and those not to persecute one another for any differences, as Socinus will, but rather love and cherish.

To describe them in particular, to produce their Arguments and reasons, would require a just volume, I refer them therefore that expect a more ample satisfaction, to those subtil and elaborate Treatises, devout and famous Tracts of our learned Divines (Schoolmen amongst the rest, and Casuists) that have abundance of reasons to prove there is a God, the immortality of the soul, &c., out of the strength of wit and Philosophy bring irrefragable Arguments to such as are ingenious and well disposed ; at the least, answer all cavils and objections to confute their folly and madness, and to reduce them, if possible, to a better mind ; though to small purpose many times. Amongst others consult with Julius Cæsar Lagalla, Professor of Philosophy in Rome, who hath written a large Volume of late to confute Atheists ; of the Immortality of the Soul, Hierome, Montanus, Lelius Vincentius of the same subject ; Thomas Giaminus, and Franciscus Collius, a famous Doctor of the Ambrosian College in Milan. Bishop Fotherby in his Atheomastix, Doctor Dove, Doctor Jackson, Abernethy, Corderoy, have written well of this subject in our mother tongue : in Latin, Colerus, Zanchius, Palearius, Illyricus, Philippus, Faber, Faventinus, &c. But above all, the most copious confuter of Atheists, is Marinus Marcennus in his Commentaries on Genesis : with Campanella's Atheism Triumphant. He sets down at large the causes of this brutish passion (seventeen in number

I take it) answers all their Arguments and Sophisms, which he reduceth to twenty-six heads, proving withal his own Assertion; There is a
God, such a God, the true and sole God, by five and thirty reasons. His
Colophon [or Conclusion] is how to resist and repress Atheism, and to
that purpose he adds four especial means or ways, which whoso will
may profitably peruse.

SUBSECTION 2 — *Despair. Despairs, Equivocations, Definitions, Parties
and Parts affected*

THERE be many kinds of desperation, whereof some be holy, some unholy, as one [Abernethy] distinguisheth; that unholy he defines out of
Tully to be a sickness of the soul without any hope or expectation of
amendment: which commonly succeeds fear; for whilst evil is expected,
we fear; but when it is certain, we despair. According to Thomas, it is
a restraint from the thing desired, for some impossibility supposed.
Because they cannot obtain what they would, they become desperate,
and many times either yield to the passion by death itself, or else attempt impossibilities, not to be performed by men. In some cases this
desperate humour is not much to be discommended, as in Wars it is a
cause many times of extraordinary valour; as Josephus, L. Danæus,
and many Politicians hold. It makes them improve their worth beyond
itself, and a forlorn impotent Company become Conquerors in a moment.

One safety to the vanquished — not to seek it.   (VIRGIL)

In such courses when they see no remedy, but that they must either kill
or be killed, they take courage, and oftentimes beyond all hope vindicate themselves. Fifteen thousand Locrians fought against a hundred
thousand Crotonians, and seeing now no way but one, they must all
die, thought they would not depart unrevenged, and thereupon desperately giving an assault, conquered their Enemies. Nor was there other
cause of the victory, (saith Justin mine Author) than their desperation. William the Conqueror, when he first landed in England, sent back
his ships, that his soldiers might have no hope of retiring back. Bodine
excuseth his Countrymen's overthrow at that famous Battle at Agincourt, in Henry the Fifth his time (which, saith Froissart, no History can parallel almost, wherein one handful of English-men overthrew a Royal Army of French-men) with this refuge of despair, a few
desperate fellows being compassed in by their Enemies, past all hope of
life, fought like so many Devils; and gives a caution, that no soldiers
hereafter set upon desperate persons, which after Frontinus and Vige-

tius, Guicciardini likewise admonisheth, not to stop an enemy that is going his way. Many such kinds there are of desperation, when men are past hope of obtaining any suit, or in despair of better fortune; despair makes the monk, as the saying is, and desperation causeth death itself; how many thousands in such distress have made away themselves, and many others! For he that cares not for his own, is Master of another man's life. A Tuscan Sooth-sayer, as Paterculus tells the story, perceiving himself and Fulvius Flaccus his dear friend, now both carried to prison by Opimius, and in despair of pardon, seeing the young man weep, said, do as I do; and with that knockt out his brains against the door-cheek, as he was entering into Prison, and so desperately died. But these are equivocal, unproper. When I speak of despair, saith Zanchius, I speak not of every kind, but of that alone which concerns God. It is opposite to hope, and a most pernicious sin, wherewith the Devil seeks to entrap men. Musculus makes four kinds of Desperation, of God, ourselves, our Neighbour, or any thing to be done; but this division of his may be reduced easily to the former: all kinds are opposite to hope, that sweet Moderator of Passions, as Simonides calls it; I do not mean that vain hope which phantastical fellows feign to themselves, which according to Aristotle is a waking dream; but this Divine hope which proceeds from confidence, and is an Anchor to a floating soul; hope drives the farmer; even in our temporal affairs, hope revives us, but in spiritual it further animateth; and were it not for hope, " we of all others were the most miserable," as Paul saith, in this life; were it not for hope, the heart would break; " for though they be punished in the sight of men," yet is their hope " full of immortality," yet doth it not so rear, as Despair doth deject; this violent and sour passion of Despair, is of all perturbations most grievous, as Patricius holds. Some divide it into final and temporal; final is incurable, which befalleth Reprobates; temporal is a rejection of hope and comfort for a time, which may befall the best of God's children, and it commonly proceeds " from weakness of Faith," as in David, when he was oppressed, he cried out, " O Lord, thou hast forsaken me," but this [is] for a time. This ebbs and flows with hope and fear; it is a grievous sin howsoever: although some kind of Despair be not amiss, when, saith Zanchius, we despair of our own means, and rely wholly upon God: but that species is not here meant. This pernicious kind of desperation is the subject of our Discourse, the murderer of the soul, as Austin terms it, a fearful passion, wherein the party oppressed thinks he can get no ease but by death, and is fully resolved to offer violence unto himself, so sensible of his burthen, and impatient of his cross, that he hopes by death alone to be freed of his calamity (though it prove otherwise) and chooseth with Job, " rather to be strangled and die than to be in his bonds." The part affected is the whole soul, and all the faculties of it; there is a privation of joy, hope, trust, confidence, of present and future good, and in their place succeed fear, sorrow, &c., as in the Symptoms shall be shewed. The heart is grieved, the conscience wounded, and the mind eclipsed with black fumes arising from those perpetual terrors.

SUBSECTION 3 — *Causes of Despair, the Devil, Melancholy, Meditation, Distrust, weakness of Faith, rigid Ministers, Misunderstanding Scriptures, guilty-consciences, &c.*

THE principal agent and procurer of this mischief is the Devil; those whom God forsakes, the Devil, by his permission, lays hold on. Sometimes he persecutes them with that worm of conscience, as he did Judas, Saul, and others. The Poets call it Nemesis, but it is indeed God's just judgment, late but great, he strikes home at last, and setteth upon them *as a thief in the night*. This temporary passion made David cry out, *Lord, rebuke me not in thine anger, neither chasten me in thine heavy displeasure; for thine arrows have lit upon me*, &c. *There is nothing sound in my flesh, because of thine anger*. Again, *I roar for the very grief of my heart ;* and *My God, my God, why hast thou forsaken me, and art so far from my health, and the words of my crying? I am like to water poured out, my bones are out of joint, mine heart is like wax, that is molten in the midst of my bowels*. So Psalms 88, 15th and 16th verses, and Psalm 102. *I am in misery, at the point of death, from my youth I suffer thy terrors, doubting for my life ; thine indignations have gone over me, and thy fear hath cut me off*. Job doth often complain in this kind; and those God doth not assist, the Devil is ready to try and torment, *still seeking whom he may devour*. If he find them merry, saith Gregory, he tempts them forthwith to some dissolute act ; if pensive and sad, to a desperate end. Sometimes by fair means, sometimes again by foul, as he perceives men severally inclined. His ordinary engine by which he produceth this effect, is the melancholy humour itself, which is the Devil's bath ; and as in Saul, those evil spirits get in, as it were, and take possession of us. Black choler is a shoeing-horn, a bait to allure them, insomuch that many writers make melancholy an ordinary cause, and a symptom of despair, for that such men are most apt by reason of their ill-disposed temper, to distrust, fear, grieve, mistake, and amplify whatsoever they preposterously conceive, or falsely apprehend. A scrupulous conscience comes of a natural defect, a melancholy habit (saith Navarrus). The body works upon the mind, by obfuscating the spirits and corrupted instruments, which Perkins illustrates by simile of an Artificer, that hath a bad tool, his skill is good, ability correspondent, by reason of ill tools his work must needs be lame and unperfect. But melancholy and despair, though often, do not always concur; there is much difference; melancholy fears without a cause, this upon great occasion; melancholy is caused by fear and grief, but this torment procures them all extremity of bitterness; much melancholy is without affliction of conscience, as Bright and Perkins illustrate by four reasons; and yet melancholy alone again may be sometimes a sufficient cause of this terror of conscience. Felix Plater so found it in his observations, they think they are not predestinate, God hath forsaken them; and yet otherwise very zealous and religious; and 'tis common to be seen, melancholy for fear of God's judgment and hell fire, drives men to desperation; fear and sorrow, if they be immoderate, end often with it. Intolerable pain and anguish, long sickness, captivity, misery, loss of goods, loss of friends, and those lesser griefs, do sometimes effect it, or such dismal accidents. Saith Marcennus, if they be not eased forthwith, they doubt whether there be any God, they rave, curse, and are desperately mad, because good men are oppressed, wicked men flourish, they have not as they think to their desert, and through impatience of calamities are so misaffected. Democritus put out his eyes, because he could not abide to see wicked men prosper, and was therefore ready to make away himself, as A. Gellius writes of him. Felix Plater hath a memorable example in this kind, of a Painter's wife in Basil, that was melancholy for her son's death, and for melancholy became desperate, she thought God would not pardon her sins, and for four months, still raved, that she was in hell fire, already damned. When the humour is stirred up, every small object aggravates and incenseth it, as the parties are addicted. The same Author hath an example of a merchant-man, that for the loss of a little wheat, which he had over-long kept, was troubled in conscience, for that he had not sold it sooner, or given it to the poor, yet a good Scholar and a great Divine; no persuasion would serve to the contrary, but that for this fact he was damned; in other matters very judicious and discreet. Solitariness, much fasting, divine meditations, and contemplations of God's judgments, most part accompany this melancholy, and are main causes, as Navarrus holds; to converse with such kind of persons so troubled, is sufficient occasion of trouble to some men. Many (saith P. Forestus) through long fasting, serious meditations of heavenly things, fall into such fits; and, as Lemnius adds, if they be solitary given, superstitious, precise, or very devout: seldom shall you find a Merchant, a Soldier, an Inn-keeper, a Bawd, an Host, an Usurer so troubled in mind, they have cheverel [kid-leather] consciences that will stretch, they are seldom moved in this kind or molested: young men and middle age are more wild, & less apprehensive; but old folks, most part, & such as are timorous, are religiously given. Peter Forestus hath a fearful example of a Minister, that through precise fasting in Lent, and overmuch meditation, contracted this mischief, and in the end became desperate, thought he saw devils in his chamber, and that he could not be saved; he smelled nothing, as he said, but fire and brimstone, was already in hell, and would ask them still, if they did not smell as much. I told him he was melancholy, but he laughed me to scorn, and replied, that he saw devils, talked with them in good earnest, would spit in my face, and ask me if I did not smell brimstone, but at last he was by him cured. Such another story I find in Plater. A poor fellow had done some foul offence, and for fourteen days would eat no meat, in the end became desperate, the Divines about him could not ease him, but so he died. Continual meditation of God's judgments troubles many. Many, for fear of the judgment to come, saith Guatinerius, and their uncertainty, are desperate. David himself complains that God's judgments terrified his Soul: " My flesh trembleth for fear of thee, and I am afraid of thy judgments." That day (saith Hierome) I tremble as often as I think of it. The terrible meditation of hell-fire, and eternal punishment, much torments a sinful silly soul. What's a thousand years to eternity? There mourning, tears, eternal sorrow; death undying, end without end: a finger burnt by chance we may not endure, the pain is so grievous, we may not abide an hour, a night is intolerable; and what shall this unspeakable fire then be that burns for ever, innumerable infinite millions of years! O eternity!

Eternity, that word, that tremendous word,
More threatening than all the artillery of heaven, —
Eternity, that word, without end or beginning, &c.
No torments can affright us that time will end;
Eternity, eternity, fills and inflames the heart;
This it is that daily augments our sufferings,
And multiplies our heart-burnings an hundred-fold.   (DREXELIUS)

This meditation terrifies these poor distressed souls, especially if their bodies be predisposed by melancholy, they religiously given, and have tender consciences, every small object affrights them, the very in-considerate reading of Scripture itself, and misinterpretation of some places of it as *Many are called, few are chosen. Not every one that saith Lord. Fear not, little flock. He that stands, let him take heed lest he fall. Work out your salvation with fear and trembling. That night two shall be in a bed, one received, the other left. Straight is the way that leads to Heaven, and few there are that enter therein.* The parable of the seed, and of the sower, *some fell on barren ground, some was choked. Whom he hath predestinated, he hath chosen. He will have mercy on whom he will have mercy. So then it is not of him that willeth, nor of him that runneth, but of God that sheweth mercy.* These and the like places terrify the souls of many; election, predestination, reprobation, preposterously conceived, offend divers, with a deal of foolish presump-tion, curiosity, needless speculation, contemplation, solicitude, wherein they trouble and puzzle themselves about those questions of grace, free-will, perseverance, God's secrets; they will know more than is revealed by God in his word, human capacity, or ignorance can apprehend, and too importunate inquiry after that which is revealed; mysteries, cere-monies, observation of Sabbaths, laws, duties, &c., with many such which the Casuists discuss, and School-men broach, which divers mis-take, misconstrue, misapply to themselves, to their own undoing, and so fall into this gulf. They doubt of their Election, how they shall know it, by what signs. And so far forth, saith Luther, with such nice points, torture and crucify themselves, that they are almost mad, and all they get by it is this, they lay open a gap to the Devil by Desperation to carry them to Hell. But the greatest harm of all proceeds from those thundering Ministers, a most frequent cause they are of this malady: and do more harm in the Church (saith Erasmus) than they that flatter; great danger on both sides, the one lulls them asleep in carnal security, the other drives them to despair. Whereas S. Bernard well adviseth, We should not meddle with the one without the other, nor speak of judgment without mercy; the one alone brings Desperation, the other Security. But these men are wholly for judgment, of a rigid disposition themselves, there is no mercy with them, no salvation, no balsam for their diseased souls, they can speak of nothing but reproba-tion, hell-fire, & damnation, as they did, Luke, 11 :46, *lade men with bur-dens grievous to be borne, which they themselves touch not with a fin-ger.* 'Tis familiar with our Papists to terrify men's souls with purgatory, tales, visions, apparitions, to daunt even the most generous spirits, to require charity, as Brentius observes, of others, bounty, meekness, love, patience, when they themselves breathe out nought but lust, envy, covetousness. They teach others to fast, give alms, do penance, and crucify their mind with superstitious observations, bread and water, hair-cloths, whips, and the like, when they themselves have all the dainties the world can afford, lie on a down bed with a Courtesan in their arms. Alas, what we endure for Christ, as he [Leo Decimus] said; what a cruel tyranny is this, so to insult over, and terrify men's souls! Our indiscreet Pastors many of them come not far behind, whilst in their ordinary Sermons they speak so much of election, predestination, reprobation from the beginning of the world, subtraction of grace, præterition, voluntary permission, &c., by what signs and tokens they shall discern and try themselves, whether they be God's true children elect, or reprobate, predestinate, &c., with such scrupulous points, they still aggravate sin, thunder out God's judgments without respect, intempestively rail at, and pronounce them damned in all auditories, for giving so much to sports and honest recreations, making every small fault and thing indifferent an irremissible offence, they so rent, tear, and wound men's consciences, that they are almost mad, and at their wits' ends.

These bitter potions (saith Erasmus) are still in their mouths, nothing but gall and horror, and a mad noise, they make all their auditors desperate, many are wounded by this means, and they commonly that are most devout and precise, have been formerly presumptuous, and certain of their salvation; they that have tender consciences, that follow Sermons, frequent Lectures, that have indeed least cause, they are most apt to mistake, and fall into these miseries. I have heard some complain of Parsons' Resolution, and other books of like nature (good otherwise) they are too tragical, too much dejecting men, aggravating offences; great care and choice, much discretion is required in this kind.

The last and greatest cause of this malady, is our own conscience, sense of our sins, and God's anger justly deserved, a guilty conscience for some foul offence formerly committed.

" *Wretched Orestes, what is wasting you?* "

" *Conscience, for I am conscious of ill deeds.*"   (EURIPIDES)

A good conscience is a continual feast, but a galled conscience is as great a torment as can possibly happen, a still baking oven, (so Pierius in his Hieroglyph, compares it) another hell. Our conscience, which is a great ledger book, wherein are written all our offences, a register to lay them up, (which those Egyptians in their Hieroglyphicks expressed by a mill, as well for the continuance as for the torture of it) grinds our souls with the remembrance of some precedent sins, makes us reflect upon, accuse and condemn our own selves. " Sin lies at door," &c. I know there be many other causes assigned by Zanchius, Musculus, and the rest ; as incredulity, infidelity, presumption, ignorance, blindness, ingratitude, discontent, those five grand miseries in Aristotle, ignominy, need, sickness, enmity, death, &c., but this of conscience is the greatest, like an ulcer continually festering in the body, this scrupulous conscience (as Peter Forestus calls it) which tortures so many, that either out of a deep apprehension of their unworthiness, and consideration of their own dissolute life, accuse themselves, and aggravate every small offence, when there is no such cause, misdoubting in the mean time God's mercies, they fall into these inconveniences. The Poets call them Furies, but it is the conscience alone which is a thousand witnesses to accuse us,

Night and day they carry this witness in the breast.   (JUVENAL)

A continual testor to give in evidence, to empanel a Jury to examine us, to cry guilty, a persecutor with hue and cry to follow, an apparitor to summon us, a bailiff to carry us, a Serjeant to arrest, an Attorney to plead against us, a gaoler to torment, a Judge to condemn, still accusing, denouncing, torturing and molesting. And as the statue of Juno in that holy city near Euphrates in Assyria will look still towards you, sit where you will in her temple, she stares full upon you, if you go by, she follows with her eye, in all sites, places, conventicles, actions, our conscience will be still ready to accuse us. After many pleasant days, and fortunate adventures, merry tides, this conscience at last doth arrest us. Well he may escape temporal punishment, bribe a corrupt judge, and avoid the censure of law, and flourish for a time ; for who ever saw (saith Chrysostom) a covetous man troubled in mind when he is telling of his money, an adulterer mourn with his mistress in his arms? we are then drunk with pleasure, and perceive nothing : yet as the prodigal Son had dainty fare, sweet musick at first, merry company, jovial entertainment, but a cruel reckoning in the end, as bitter as wormwood, a fearful visitation commonly follows. And the devil that then told thee that it was a light sin, or no sin at all, now aggravates on the other side, and telleth thee that it is a most irremissible offence, as he did by Cain and Judas, to bring them to despair ; every small circumstance before neglected and contemned, will now amplify itself, rise up in judgment and accuse, the dust of their shoes, dumb creatures, as to Lucian's tyrant the bed and candle, did bear witness, to torment their souls for their sins past. Tragical examples in this kind are too familiar and common : Adrian, Galba,

Nero, Otho, Vitellius, Caracalla, were in such horror of conscience for their offences committed, murders, rapes, extortions, injuries, that they were weary of their lives, and could get no body to kill them. Kenneth III., King of Scotland, when he had murdered his Nephew Malcolm, King Duff's son, Prince of Cumberland, and with counterfeit tears and protestations dissembled the matter a long time, at last his conscience accused him, his unquiet soul could not rest day or night, he was terrified with fearful dreams, visions, and so miserably tormented all his life. It is strange to read what Commines hath written of Lewis the XI., that French King, of Charles the VIII., of Alphonso King of Naples, in the fury of his passion how he came into Sicily, and what pranks he played. Guicciardini, a man most unapt to believe lies, relates how that Ferdinand his father's ghost, who before had died for grief, came and told him that he could not resist the French King, he thought every man cried France, France; the reason of it (saith Commines) was because he was a vile tyrant, a murderer, an oppressor of his subjects, he bought up all commodities, and sold them at his own price, sold Abbies to Jews and Falconers; both Ferdinand his father, and he himself, never made conscience of any committed sin; and to conclude, saith he, it was impossible to do worse than they did. Why were Pausanias, the Spartan Tyrant, Nero, Otho, Galba, so persecuted with spirits in every house they came, but for their murders which they had committed? Why doth the devil haunt many men's houses after their deaths, appear to them living, and take possession of their habitations, as it were, of their palaces, but because of their several villanies? Why had Richard the III. such fearful dreams, saith Polydore, but for his frequent murders? Why was Herod so tortured in his mind? because he had made away Mariamne his wife. Why was Theodoricus the King of the Goths so suspicious, and so affrighted with a fish-head alone, but that he had murdered Symmachus, and Boethius his son-in-law, those worthy Romans? (Cœlius). See more in Plutarch. Yea, and sometimes God himself hath a hand in it, to shew his power, humiliate, exercise, and to try their faith, (divine temptation Perkins calls it) to punish them for their sins. God the avenger, as David terms him, his wrath is apprehended of a guilty soul, as by Saul and Judas, which the Poets expressed by Adrastea, or Nemesis:

> *That you may do no evil, Nemesis*
> *Pursues and dogs the footsteps of ill-doers.*

And she is, as Ammianus describes her, the Queen of causes, and moderator of things, now she pulls down the proud, now she rears and encourageth those that are good; he gives instance in his Eusebius; Nicephorus in Maximin and Julian. Fearful examples of God's just judgment, wrath and vengeance, are to be found in all histories, of some that have been eaten to death with Rats and Mice, as Popelius the Second, King of Poland, in the year 830, his wife and children; the like story is of Hatto Archbishop of Mentz, in the year 969, so devoured by these vermin, which howsoever Serrarius the Jesuit impugns by 22 arguments, Trithemius, Munster, Magdeburgenses, and many others relate for a truth. Such another example I find in Giraldus Cambrensis, and where not?

And yet for all these terrors of conscience, affrighting punishments which are so frequent, or whatsoever else may cause or aggravate this fearful malady in other Religions, I see no reason at all why a Papist at any time should despair, or be troubled for his sins; for let him be never so dissolute a Caitiff, so notorious a villain, so monstrous a sinner, out of that Treasure of Indulgences and merits of which the Pope is Dispensator, he may have free pardon, and plenary remission of all his sins. There be so many general pardons for ages to come, 40,000 years to come, so many Jubilees, so frequent Gaol-deliveries out of Purgatory for all souls now living, or after dissolution of the body so many particular Masses daily said in several Churches, so many Altars consecrated to this purpose, that if a man have either money or friends, or will take any pains to come to such an Altar, hear a Mass, say so many Pater-nosters, undergo such and such penance, he cannot do amiss, it is impossible his mind should be troubled, or he have any scruple to molest him. Besides that Sale of Indulgences, which was first published to get money in the days of Leo Decimus, that sharking Pope, and since divulged to the same ends, sets down such easy rates and dispensations for all offences, for perjury, murder, incest, adultery, &c., for so many groschens or dollars (able to invite any man to sin, and provoke him to offend, methinks, that otherwise would not) such comfortable remission, so gentle and parable [procurable] a pardon, so ready at hand, with so small cost and suit obtained, that I cannot see how he that hath any friends amongst them (as I say) or money in his purse, or will at least to ease himself, can any way miscarry or be misaffected, how he should be desperate, in danger of damnation, or troubled in mind. Their ghostly Fathers can so readily apply remedies, so cunningly string and unstring, wind and unwind their devotions, play upon their consciences with plausible speeches, and terrible threats, for their best advantage settle and remove, erect with such facility and deject, let in and out, that I cannot perceive how any man amongst them should much or often labour of this disease, or finally miscarry. The causes above named must more frequently therefore take hold in others.

SUBSECTION 4 — *Symptoms of Despair, Fear, Sorrow, Suspicion, Anxiety, Horror of conscience, fearful dreams and visions*

As Shoe-makers do when they bring home shoes, still cry, Leather is dearer and dearer; may I justly say of those melancholy Symptoms, these of Despair are most violent, tragical and grievous, far beyond the rest, not to be expressed, but negatively, as it is privation of all happiness, not to be endured; *for a wounded spirit who can bear?* What therefore Timanthes did in his picture cf Iphigenia, now ready to be sacrificed, when he had painted Calchas mourning, Ulysses sad, but most sorrowful Menelaus, and shewed all his art in expressing variety of affections, he covered the maid's father, Agamemnon's head, with a veil, and left it to every spectator to conceive what he would himself; for that true passion and sorrow in the highest degree, such as his was, could not by any art be deciphered. What he did in his picture, I will do in describing the Symptoms of Despair; imagine what thou canst, fear, sorrow, furies, grief, pain, terror, anger, dismal, ghastly, tedious, irksome, &c., it is not sufficient, it comes far short, no tongue can tell, no heart conceive it. 'Tis an Epitome of hell, an extract, a quintessence, a compound, a mixture of all feral maladies, tyrannical tortures, plagues and perplexities. There is no sickness, almost, but Physick provideth a remedy for it; to every sore Chirurgery will provide a salve: friendship helps poverty; hope of liberty easeth imprisonment; suit and favour revoke banishment; authority and time wear away reproach: but what Physick, what Chirurgery, what wealth, favour, authority can relieve, bear out, assuage, or expel a troubled conscience? A quiet mind cureth all them, but all they cannot comfort a distressed soul: who can put to silence the voice of desperation? All that is single in other melancholy, horrible, dire, pestilent, cruel, relentless, concur in this, it is more than melancholy in the highest degree; a burning fever of the soul; so mad, saith Jacchinus, by this misery; fear, sorrow, and despair he puts for ordinary symptoms of Melancholy. They are in great pain and horror of mind, distraction of soul, restless, full of continual fears, cares, torments, anxieties, they can neither eat, drink, nor sleep for them, take no rest,

> *Neither at bed nor yet at board,*
> *Will any rest despair afford.* (JUVENAL)

Fear takes away their content, and dries the blood, wasteth the marrow alters their countenance, even in their greatest delights, singing, danc ing, dalliance, they are still (saith Lemnius) tortured in their souls. I' consumes them to nought, *I am like a Pelican in the wilderness* (saitl David of himself, temporally afflicted) *an Owl because of thine indig· nation. My heart trembleth within me, and the terrors of death havι come upon me; fear and trembling are come upon me*, &c., *at death'ς door. Their soul abhors all manner of meats.* Their sleep is (if it be any) unquiet, subject to fearful dreams and terrors. Peter in his bonds slept secure, for he knew God protected him; and Tully makes it an Argument of Roscius Amerinus' innocency, that he killed not his Father, because he so securely slept. Those Martyrs in the Primitive Church were most cheerful and merry in the midst of their persecutions; but it is far otherwise with these men, tossed in a Sea, and that continually without rest or intermission, they can think of nought that is pleasant, their conscience will not let them be quiet, in perpetual fear, anxiety, if they be not yet apprehended, they are in doubt still they shall be ready to betray themselves, as Cain did, he thinks every man will kill him; *and roar for the grief of heart,* as David did, as Job did. *Wherefore is light given to him that is in misery, and life to them that have heavy hearts? Which long for death, and if it come not, search it more than treasures, and rejoice when they can find the grave.* They are generally weary of their lives, a trembling heart they have, a sorrowful mind, and little or no rest. Fears, terrors, and affrights in all places, at all times and seasons. As Wierus writes, they refuse many of them meat and drink, can not rest, aggravating still and supposing grievous offences, where there are none. God's heavy wrath is kindled in their souls, and notwithstanding their continual prayers and supplications to Christ Jesus, they have no release or ease at all, but a most intolerable torment, and insufferable anguish of conscience, and that makes them through impatience, to murmur against God many times, to rave, to blaspheme, turn Atheists, and seek to offer violence to themselves. *In the morning they wish for evening, and for morning in the evening, for the sight of their eyes which they see, and fear of hearts.* Marinus Marcennus in his Comment on Genesis, makes mention of a desperate friend of his, whom amongst others he came to visit, and exhort to patience, that broke out into most blasphemous Atheistical speeches, too fearful to relate, when they wished him to trust in God. Who is this God, (he saith) that I should serve him? What will it profit me, if I pray to him? If he be present, why does he not succor me? Why does he not set me free, who am destroyed by imprisonment, fasting, squalor, filth? What have I done? Far be from me such a God! Another of his acquaintance brake out into like Atheistical blasphemies upon his Wife's death, raved, cursed, said and did he car'd not what. And so, for the most part, it is with them all, many of them in their extremity think they hear and see visions, out-cries, confer with Devils, that they are tormented, possessed, and in hell fire, already damned, quite forsaken of God, they have no sense or feel-ing of mercy, or grace, hope of salvation, their sentence of condem-nation is already past, and not to be revoked, the Devil will certainly have them. Never was any living creature in such torment before, in such a miserable estate, in such distress of mind, no hope, no faith, past cure, reprobate, continually tempted to make away themselves: Some-thing talks with them, they spit fire and brimstone, they cannot but blaspheme, they cannot repent, believe, or think a good thought, so far carried, said Felix Plater, that they are compelled against their will to harbour impious thoughts, to blaspheme against God, to the committing of many horrible deeds, to laying violent hands upon themselves, &c., and in their distracted fits, and desperate humours, to offer violence to others, their familiar and dear friends sometimes, or to mere strangers, upon very small or no occasion: for he that cares not for his own is mas-ter of another man's life. They think evil against their wills; that which they abhor themselves, they must needs think, do, and speak. He gives instance in a Patient of his, that when he would pray, had such evil thoughts still suggested to him, and wicked meditations. Another in-stance he hath, of a woman that was often tempted to curse God, to blas-pheme and kill herself. Sometimes the Devil (as they say) stands with-out and talks with them; sometimes he is within them, as they think, and there speaks and talks, as to such as are possessed: so Apollodorus, in Plutarch, thought his heart spake within him. There is a most mem-orable example of Francis Spira an Advocate of Padua, in the year 1545, that being desperate, by no counsel of learned men could be comforted; he felt (as he said) the pains of hell in his soul, in all other things he discoursed aright, but in this most mad. Frismelica, Bullovat, and some other excellent Physicians, could neither make him eat, drink, or sleep, no persuasion could ease him. Never pleaded any man so well for him-self, as this man did against himself, and so he desperately died. Scrim-ger, a Lawyer, hath written his life. Cardinal Cresence died so likewise desperate at Verona, still he thought a black dog followed him to his death-bed, no man could drive the dog away (Sleidan). Whilst I was writing this Treatise, saith Montaltus, a Nun came to me for help, well for all other matters. but troubled in conscience for five years last past;

she is almost mad, and not able to resist, thinks she hath offended God, and is certainly damned. Felix Plater hath store of instances of such as thought themselves damned, forsaken of God, &c. One amongst the rest, that durst not go to Church, or come near the Rhine, for fear to make away himself, because then he was most especially tempted. These, and such like symptoms, are intended and remitted, as the malady itself is more or less; some will hear good counsel, some will not; some desire help, some reject all, and will not be eased.

SUBSECTION 5 — *Prognosticks of Despair, Atheism, Blasphemy, violent death, &c.*

MOST part, these kind of persons make away themselves, some are mad, blaspheme, curse, deny God, but most offer violence to their own persons, and sometimes to others. " A wounded spirit who can bear? " as Cain, Saul, Ahitophel, Judas, blasphemed and died. Bede saith, Pilate died desperate, eight years after Christ. Felix Plater hath collected many examples. A Merchant's wife that was long troubled with such temptations, in the night rose from her bed, and out of the window broke her neck into the street: another drowned himself, desperate as he was, in the Rhine; some cut their throats, many hang themselves. But this needs no illustration. It is controverted by some, whether a man so offering violence to himself, dying desperate, may be saved, aye or no? If they die so obstinately and suddenly, that they cannot so much as wish for mercy, the worst is to be suspected, because they die impenitent. If their death had been a little more lingering, wherein they might have some leisure in their hearts to cry for mercy, charity may judge the best; divers have been recovered out of a very act of hanging and drowning themselves, and so brought to a sound mind, they have been very penitent, much abhorred their former fact, confessed that they have repented in an instant, and cried for mercy in their hearts. If a man put desperate hands upon himself, by occasion of madness or melancholy, if he have given testimony before of his Regeneration, in regard he doth this not so much out of his will, as from the violence of his malady, we must make the best construction of it, as Turks do, that think all fools and mad men go directly to heaven.

SUBSECTION 6 — *Cure of Despair by Physick, good counsel, comforts, &c.*

EXPERIENCE teacheth us, that though many die obstinate and wilful in this malady, yet multitudes again are able to resist and overcome, seek for help, and find comfort, are taken from the chops of Hell, and out of the Devil's paws, though they have by obligation given themselves to him. Some out of their own strength, and God's assistance, *though he kill me* (saith Job) *yet will I trust in him,* out of good counsel, advice, and Physick. Bellovacus cured a Monk, by altering his habit, and course of life: Plater many by Physick alone. But for the most part they must concur: and they take a wrong course, that think to overcome this feral passion by sole Physick; and they are as much out, that think to work this effect by good advice alone, though both be forcible in themselves, yet they must go hand in hand to this disease:

Each requires the other's aid. (HORACE)

For Physick, the like course is to be taken with this, as in other Melancholy: diet, air, exercise, all those passions and perturbations of the mind, &c., are to be rectified by the same means. They must not be left solitary, or to themselves, never idle, never out of company. Counsel, good comfort is to be applied, as they shall see the parties inclined, or to the causes, whether it be loss, fear, grief, discontent, or some such feral accident, a guilty conscience, or otherwise by frequent meditation, too grievous an apprehension, and consideration of his former life; by hearing, reading of Scriptures, good Divines, good advice and conference, applying God's Word to their distressed souls, it must be corrected and counter-poised. Many excellent Exhortations, paranetical Discourses are extant to this purpose, for such as are any way troubled in mind: Perkins, Greenham, Hayward, Bright, Abernethy, Bolton, Culmannus, Hemmingius, Cœlius Secundus, Nicholas Laurentius, are copious in this subject: Azorius, Navarrus, Sayrus, &c., and such as have written cases of Conscience amongst our Pontifical Writers. But because these men's works are not to all parties at hand, so parable [procurable] at all times, I will for the benefit and ease of such as are afflicted, at the request of some friends,* recollect out of their voluminous Treatises, some few such comfortable speeches, exhortations, arguments, advice, tending to this subject, and out of God's Word, knowing, as Culmannus saith upon the like occasion, how unavailable and vain men's counsels are, to comfort an afflicted conscience, except God's Word concur and be annexed, from which comes life, ease, repentance, &c. Presupposing first that which Beza, Greenham, Perkins, Bolton, give in charge, the parties to whom counsel is given be sufficiently prepared, humbled for their sins, fit for comfort, confessed, tried how they are more or less afflicted, how they stand affected, or capable of good

* My brother, George Burton, Mr. James Whitehall, rector of Checkley, in Staffordshire, my quondam chambers fellow, and late student in Christ Church, Oxon. — Burton's note.

advice, before any remedies be applied. To such therefore as are so throughly searched and examined, I address this following Discourse.

Two main Antidotes, Hemmingius observes, opposite to Despair, good Hope out of God's Word, to be embraced; perverse Security and Presumption from the Devil's treachery, to be rejected; one saves, the other kills, destroys the soul, saith Austin, and doth as much harm as Despair itself. Navarrus the Casuist reckons up ten special cures: 1. God. 2. Physick. 3. Avoiding such Objects as have caused it. 4. Submission of himself to other men's judgments. 5. Answer of all Objections, &c. All which Cajetan, Gerson, Sayrus, repeat and approve out of Emanuel Roderiques. Greenham prescribes six special rules, Culmannus 7: 1. To acknowledge all help comes from God. 2. That the cause of their present misery is sin. 3. To repent and be heartily sorry for their sins. 4. To pray earnestly to God they may be eased. 5. To expect and implore the prayers of the Church, and good men's advice. 6. Physick. 7. To commend themselves to God, and rely upon his mercy: others otherwise, but all to this effect. But forasmuch as most men in this malady are spiritually sick, void of reason almost, over-borne by their miseries, and too deep an apprehension of their sins, they cannot apply themselves to good counsel, pray, believe, repent, we must, as much as in us lies, occur and help their peculiar infirmities, according to their several Causes and Symptoms, as we shall find them distressed and complain.

The main matter which terrifies and torments most that are troubled in mind, is the enormity of their offences, the intolerable burthen of their sins, God's heavy wrath and displeasure so deeply apprehended, that they account themselves Reprobates, quite forsaken of God, already damned, past all hope of grace, uncapable of mercy, slaves of sin, and their offences so great, they cannot be forgiven. But these men must know, there is no sin so heinous, which is not pardonable in itself; no crime so great, but by God's mercy it may be forgiven. *Where sin aboundeth, grace aboundeth much more.* And what the Lord said unto Paul in his extremity, *My grace is sufficient for thee, for my power is made perfect through weakness;* concerns every man in like case. His promises are made indefinite to all Believers, generally spoken to all, touching remission of sins, that are truly penitent, grieved for their offences, and desire to be reconciled; *I came not to call the righteous, but sinners to repentance,* that is, such as are truly touched in conscience for their sins. Again, *Come unto me all ye that are heavy laden, and I will ease you. At what time soever a sinner shall repent him of his sins from the bottom of his heart, I will blot out all his wickedness out of my remembrance, saith the Lord. I, even I, am he that put away thine iniquity for mine own sake, and will not remember thy sins. As a father* (saith David) *hath compassion on his children, so hath the Lord compassion on them that fear him.* And will receive them again as the Prodigal Son was entertained. If they shall so come with tears in their eyes, and a penitent heart. When the sinner repents, then God relents. *The Lord is full of compassion and mercy, slow to anger, of great kindness. He will not always chide, neither keep his anger for ever. As high as the heaven is above the earth, so great is his mercy towards them that fear him. As far as the East is from the West, so far hath he removed our sins from us.* Though Cain cry out in the anguish of his soul, *my punishment is greater than I can bear,* 'tis not so: Thou liest, Cain (saith Austin), God's mercy is greater than thy sins. *His mercy is above all his works,* able to satisfy for all men's sins, a ransom for all. His mercy is a panacea, a balsam for an afflicted soul, a sovereign Medicine, an Alexipharmacum for all sin, a charm for the Devil; his mercy was great to Solomon, to Manasses, to Peter, great to all Offenders, and whosoever thou art, it may be so to thee. For why should God bid us pray (as Austin infers), *Deliver us from all evil,* if he did not intend to help us? He therefore that doubts of the remission of his sins, denies God's mercy, and doth him injury, saith Austin. Yea, but thou repliest, I am a notorious sinner, mine offences are not so great as infinite. Hear Fulgentius, God's invincible goodness cannot be overcome by sin, his infinite mercy cannot be terminated by any: the multitude of his mercy is equivalent to his magnitude. Hear Chrysostom, Thy malice may be measured, but God's mercy cannot be defined; thy malice is circumscribed, his mercy is infinite. As a drop of water is to the Sea, so are thy misdeeds to his mercy; nay, there is no such proportion to be given; for the Sea, though great, it may be measured, but God's mercy cannot be circumscribed. Whatsoever thy sins be then in quantity, or quality, multitude, or magnitude, fear them not, distrust not. I speak not this, saith Chrysostom, to make thee secure and negligent, but to cheer thee up. Yea, but thou urgest again, I have little comfort of this which is said, it concerns me not: 'tis to no purpose for me to repent, and to do worse than ever I did before, to persevere in sin, and to return to my lusts, as a Dog to his vomit, or a Swine to the mire: to what end is it to ask forgiveness of my sins, and yet daily to sin again and again, to do evil out of an habit? I daily and hourly offend in thought, word, and deed, in a relapse by mine own weakness and wilfulness: my good protecting Angel is gone, I am fallen from that I was, or would be, worse and worse, my latter end is worse than my beginning. Saith Chrysostom, If thou daily offend, daily repent : if twice, thrice, an hundred, an hundred thousand times, twice, thrice, an hundred thousand times repent. As they do by an old house that is out of repair, still mend some part or other ; so do by thy soul, still reform some vice, repair it by repentance, call to him for grace, and thou shalt have it ; *for we are freely justified by his grace.* If thine enemy repent, as our Saviour enjoined Peter, forgive him seventy seven times ; and why shouldest thou think God will not forgive thee ? Why should the enormity of thy sins trouble thee ? God can do it, he will do it. My conscience (saith Anselm) dictates to me, that I deserve damnation, my repentance will not suffice for satisfaction ; but thy mercy, O Lord, quite overcomes all my transgressions. The gods once (as the Poets feign) with a gold chain would pull Jupiter out of Heaven, but all they together could not stir him, and yet he could draw and turn them as he would himself ; maugre all the force and fury of these infernal fiends, and crying sins, his grace is sufficient. Confer the debt and the payment ; Christ and Adam ; sin and the cure of it ; the disease and the medicine ; confer the sick man to the Physician, and thou shalt soon perceive that his power is infinitely beyond it. God is better able, as Bernard informeth us, to help, than sin to do us hurt ; Christ is better able to save, than the Devil to destroy. If he be a skilful Physician, as Fulgentius adds, he can cure all diseases ; if merciful, he will. His goodness is not absolute and perfect, if it be not able to overcome all malice. Submit thyself unto him, as Saint Austin adviseth, he knoweth best what he doth ; and be not so much pleased when he sustains thee, as patient when he corrects thee ; he is Omnipotent, and can cure all diseases when he sees his own time. He looks down from Heaven upon Earth, that he may hear *the mourning of prisoners, and deliver the children of death. And though our sins be as red as scarlet, he can make them as white as snow.* Doubt not of this, or ask how it shall be done ; he is all-sufficient that promiseth ; saith Chrysostom, he that made a fair world of nought, can do this and much more for his part : do thou only believe, trust in him, rely on him, be penitent, and heartily sorry for thy sins. Repentance is a sovereign remedy for all sins, a spiritual wing to erear us, a charm for our miseries, a protecting Amulet to expel sin's venom, an attractive loadstone to draw God's mercy and graces unto us. Sin made the breach, repentance must help it ; howsoever thine offence came, by error, sloth, obstinacy, ignorance, this is the sole means to be relieved. Hence comes our hope of safety, by this alone sinners are saved, God is provoked to mercy. This unlooseth all that is bound, enlighteneth darkness, mends that is broken, puts life to that which was desperately dying : makes no respect of offences, or of persons. This doth not repel a fornicator, reject a drunkard, resist a proud fellow, turn away an idolater, but entertains all, communicates itself to all. Who persecuted the Church more than Paul, offended more than Peter? and yet by repentance (saith Chrysologus) they got both the magistery of Holiness. The Prodigal Son went far, but by Repentance he came home at last. This alone will turn a Wolf into a Sheep, make a Publican a Preacher, turn a Thorn into an Olive, make a deboist [debauched] fellow Religious, a Blasphemer sing Hallelujah, make Alexander the Copper-smith truly devout, make a Devil a Saint. And him that polluted his mouth with calumnies, lying, swearing, and filthy tunes and tones, to purge his throat with divine Psalms. Repentance will effect prodigious cures, make a stupend metamorphosis. An Hawk came into the Ark, and went out again an Hawk; a Lion came in, went out a Lion; a Bear, a Bear; a Wolf, a Wolf; but if an Hawk come into this sacred Temple of Repentance, he will go forth a Dove (saith Chrysostom), a Wolf go out a Sheep, a Lion a Lamb. This gives sight to the blind, legs to the lame, cures all diseases, confers grace, expels vice, inserts virtue, comforts and fortifies the soul. Shall I say, let thy sin be what it will, do but repent, it is sufficient?

Who's sorry that he sinned is almost innocent.   (SENECA)
'Tis true indeed, and all-sufficient this, they do confess, if they could repent, but they are obdurate, they have cauterized consciences, they are in a reprobate sense, they cannot think a good thought, they cannot hope for grace, pray, believe, repent, or be sorry for their sins, they find no grief for sin in themselves, but rather a delight, no groaning of spirit, but are carried head-long to their own destruction, *heaping wrath to themselves against the day of wrath.* 'Tis a grievous case this, I do yield, and yet not to be despaired; God of his bounty and mercy calls all to repentance. Thou mayest be called at length, restored, taken to his grace, as the Thief upon the Cross at the last hour, as Mary Magdalene, and many other sinners have been, that were buried in sin. God (saith Fulgentius) is delighted in the conversion of a sinner, he sets no time; deferring of time, or grievousness of sin, do not prejudicate his grace, things past and to come are all one to him, as present, 'tis never too late to repent. This Heaven of Repentance is still open for all distressed souls; and howsoever as yet no signs appear, thou mayest repent in good time. Hear a comfortable speech of St. Austin, Whatsoever thou shalt do, how great a sinner soever, thou art yet living; if God would not help thee, he would surely take thee away; but in sparing thy life, he gives thee leisure, and invites thee to repentance. Howsoever as yet,

I say, thou perceivest no fruit, no feeling, findest no likelihood of it in thyself, patiently abide the Lord's good leisure, despair not, or think thou art a Reprobate; he came to call sinners to repentance, of which number thou art one; he came to call thee, and in his time will surely call thee. And although as yet thou hast no inclination to pray, to repent, thy Faith be cold and dead, and thou wholly averse from all divine functions, yet it may revive, as Trees are dead in Winter, but flourish in the Spring; these Virtues may lie hid in thee for the present, yet hereafter shew themselves, and peradventure already bud, howsoever thou dost not perceive it. 'Tis Satan's policy to plead against, suppress and aggravate, to conceal those sparks of Faith in thee. Thou dost not believe, thou sayest, yet thou wouldest believe if thou couldest, 'tis thy desire to believe; then pray, *Lord help mine unbelief;* and hereafter thou shalt certainly believe: *It shall be given to him that thirsteth.* Thou canst not yet repent, hereafter thou shalt; a black cloud of sin as yet obnubilates thy soul, terrifies thy conscience, but this cloud may conceive a Rain-bow at the last, and be quite dissipated by repentance. Be of good cheer; a child is rational in power, not in act; and so art thou penitent in affection, though not yet in action. 'Tis thy desire to please God, to be heartily sorry; comfort thyself, no time is over-past, 'tis never too late. A desire to repent, is repentance itself, though not in nature, yet in God's acceptance; a willing mind is sufficient. *Blessed are they that hunger and thirst after Righteousness.* He that is destitute of God's Grace, and wisheth for it, shall have it. " The Lord (saith David) will hear the desire of the poor," that is, of such as are in distress of body and mind. 'Tis true, thou canst not as yet grieve for thy sin, thou hast no feeling of Faith, I yield; yet canst thou grieve thou dost not grieve? It troubles thee, I am sure, thine heart should be so impenitent and hard, thou wouldest have it otherwise; 'tis thy desire to grieve, to repent and believe. Thou lovest God's children and Saints in the mean time, hatest them not, persecutest them not, but rather wishest thyself a true Professor, to be as they are, as thou thyself hast been heretofore; which is an evident token thou art in no such desperate case. 'Tis a good sign of thy conversion, thy sins are pardonable, thou art, or shalt surely be reconciled. *The Lord is near them that are of a contrite heart.* A true desire of mercy in the want of mercy, is mercy itself; a desire of grace in the want of grace, is grace itself; a constant and earnest desire to believe, repent, and to be reconciled to God, if it be in a touched heart, is an acceptation of God, a reconciliation, Faith and Repentance itself. For it is not thy Faith and Repentance, as Chrysostom truly teacheth,

that is vailable, but God's mercy that is annexed to it, he accepts the
will for the deed. So that I conclude, to feel in ourselves the want of
grace, and to be grieved for it, is grace itself. I am troubled with fear
my sins are not forgiven, Careless objects; but Bradford answers, they
are; for God hath given thee a penitent and believing heart, that is, an
heart which desireth to repent and believe; for such a one is taken of
him (he accepting the will for the deed) for a truly penitent and believing heart.

All this is true, thou repliest, but yet it concerns not thee, 'tis verified
in ordinary offenders, in common sins, but thine are of an higher strain,
even against the Holy Ghost himself, irremissible sins, sins of the first
magnitude, written with a pen of Iron, engraven with the point of a
Diamond. Thou art worse than a Pagan, Infidel, Jew, or Turk, for thou
art an Apostate and more, thou hast voluntarily blasphemed, renounced
God and all Religion, thou art worse than Judas himself, or they that
crucified Christ: for they did offend out of ignorance, but thou hast
thought in thine heart there is no God. Thou hast given thy soul to the
Devil, as Witches and Conjurers do, explicitly and implicitly, by compact, band, and obligation (a desperate, a fearful case) to satisfy thy
lust, or to be revenged of thine enemies, thou didst never pray, come to
Church, hear, read, or do any divine duties with any devotion, but for
formality and fashion sake, with a kind of reluctancy, 'twas troublesome and painful to thee to perform any such thing, against thy will.
Thou never mad'st any conscience of lying, swearing, bearing false
witness, murder, adultery, bribery, oppression, theft, drunkenness,
idolatry, but hast ever done all duties for fear of punishment, as they
were most advantageous, and to thine own ends, and committed all such
notorious sins, with an extraordinary delight, hating that thou shouldest
love, and loving that thou shouldest hate. Instead of Faith, fear, and
love of God, repentance, &c. blasphemous thoughts have been ever har-
boured in his mind, even against God himself, the blessed Trinity: the
Scripture false, rude, harsh, immethodical: Heaven, hell, resurrection,
mere toys and fables, incredible, impossible, absurd, vain, ill contrived;
Religion, Policy, an human invention, to keep men in obedience, or for
profit, invented by Priests and Law-givers to that purpose. If there be
any such supreme power he takes no notice of our doings, hears not our
prayers, regardeth them not, will not, cannot help, or else he is partial,
an excepter of persons, author of sin, a cruel, a destructive God, to
create our souls, and destinate them to eternal damnation, to make us
worse than our dogs and horses, why doth he not govern things better,

protect good men, root out wicked livers? why do they prosper and flourish? as she raved in the tragedy,

> *Strumpets dwell in the sky,*

there they shine,

> *And Perseus hath his golden stars.*

Where is his providence? how appears it?

> *In a marble tomb Licinius lies, Cato in a mean one;*
> *And Pompey has none at all. Who says there are gods?*

Why doth he suffer Turks to overcome Christians, the enemy to triumph over his Church, Paganism to domineer in all places as it doth, heresies to multiply, such enormities to be committed, and so many such bloody wars, murders, massacres, plagues, feral diseases? why doth he not make us all good, able, sound? why makes he venomous creatures, rocks, sands, deserts, this earth itself the muckhill of the world, a prison, an house of correction?

> *When we say Jove reigns, we speak not the truth,*   (LUCAN)

with many such horrible and execrable conceits, not fit to be uttered; terrible things about religion, horrible things about God. They cannot some of them but think evil, they are compelled, willy nilly, to blaspheme, especially when they come to Church and pray, read, &c., such foul and prodigious suggestions come into their hearts.

These are abominable, unspeakable offences, and most opposite to God, foul and impious temptations, yet in this case, he or they that shall be tempted and so affected, must know, that no man living is free from such thoughts in part, or at some times, the most divine spirits have been so tempted in some sort, evil custom, omission of holy exercises, ill company, idleness, solitariness, melancholy, or depraved nature, and the Devil is still ready to corrupt, trouble, and divert our souls, to suggest such blasphemous thoughts into our phantasies, ungodly, profane, monstrous and wicked conceits. If they come from Satan, they are more speedy, fearful and violent, the parties cannot avoid them: they are more frequent, I say, and monstrous when they come; for the Devil he is a spirit, and hath means and opportunity to mingle himself with our spirits, and sometimes more slily, sometimes more abruptly, and openly, to suggest such devilish thoughts into our hearts; he insults and domineers in Melancholy distempered phantasies, and persons especially: Melancholy is, as Serapio holds, the Devil's bath, and invites him to come to it. As a sick man frets, raves in his fits, speaks and doth he knows not what, the Devil violently compels such crazed souls, to think such damned thoughts against their wills, they cannot but do it; sometimes more continuate, or by fits, he takes his advantage, as the subject is less able to resist, he aggravates, extenuates, affirms, denies, damns, confounds the spirits, troubles heart, brain, humors, organs, senses, and wholly domineers in their imaginations. If they proceed from themselves, such thoughts, they are remiss and moderate, not so violent and monstrous, not so frequent. The Devil commonly suggests things oppo-site to nature, opposite to God and his word, impious, absurd, such as a man would never of himself, or could not conceive, they strike terror and horror into the party's own heart. For if he or they be asked, whether they do approve of such like thoughts or no? they answer (and their own souls truly dictate as much) they abhor them as Hell, and the Devil himself, they would fain think otherwise if they could; he hath thought otherwise, and with all his soul desires so to think again; he doth resist, and hath some good motions intermixt now and then: so that such blasphemous, impious, unclean thoughts, are not his own, but the Devil's; they proceed not from him, but from a crazed phantasy, distempered humours, black fumes which offend his brain: they are thy crosses, the Devil's sins, and he shall answer for them, he doth enforce thee to do that which thou dost abhor, and didst never give consent to; and although he hath sometimes so slily set upon thee, and so far prevailed, as to make thee in some sort to assent to, to delight in such wicked thoughts, yet they have not proceeded from a confirmed will in thee, but are of that nature which thou dost afterwards reject and abhor. Therefore be not overmuch troubled and dismayed with such kind of suggestions, at least if they please thee not, because they are not thy personal sins, for which thou shalt incur the wrath of God, or his dis-pleasure: contemn, neglect them, let them go as they come, strive not too violently, or trouble thyself too much, but as our Saviour said to Satan in like case, say thou, *Avoid, Satan,* I detest thee and them. Saith Austin, as Satan labours to suggest, so must we strive not to give con-sent, and it will be sufficient: the more anxious and solicitous thou art, the more perplexed, the more thou shalt otherwise be troubled, and in-tangled. Besides, they must know this, all so molested and distempered, that, although these be most execrable and grievous sins, they are pardonable yet, through God's mercy and goodness they may be for-given, if they be penitent and sorry for them. Paul himself confesseth, *He did not the good he would do, but the evil which he would not do; 'tis not I, but sin that dwelleth in me.* 'Tis not thou, but Satan's sugges-tions, his craft and subtilty, his malice. Comfort thyself then, if thou be penitent and grieved, or desirous to be so, these heinous sins shall not be laid to thy charge; God's mercy is above all sins, which if thou do not finally contemn, without doubt thou shalt be saved. No man sins against the Holy Ghost, but he that wilfully and finally renounceth Christ, and contemneth him and his word to the last, without which there is no salvation, from which grievous sin, God of his infinite mercy deliver us. Take hold of this to be thy comfort, and meditate withal on God's word, labour to pray, to repent, to be renewed in mind, *keep thine heart with all diligence. Resist the Devil, and he will fly from thee,* pour out thy soul unto the Lord with sorrowful Hannah; *pray continually,* as Paul enjoins, and as David did, *meditate on his Law day and night.*

Yea, but this meditation is that that mars all, and mistaken, makes many men far worse, misconceiving all they read or hear, to their own overthrow; the more they search and read Scriptures, or divine Treatises, the more they puzzle themselves, as a bird in a net, the more they are intangled and precipitated into this preposterous gulf. Many are called, but few are chosen, with such like places of Scripture misinterpreted, strike them with horror, they doubt presently whether they be of this number or no: God's eternal decree of predestination, absolute reprobation, and such fatal tables [decrees] they form to their own ruin, and impinge upon this rock of despair. How shall they be assured of their salvation, by what signs? If the righteous scarcely be saved, where shall the ungodly and sinners appear? Who knows, saith Solomon, whether he be elect? This grinds their souls, how shall they discern they are not reprobates? But I say again, how shall they discern they are? From the Devil can be no certainty, for he is a liar from the beginning: if he suggest any such thing, as too frequently he doth, reject him as a deceiver, an enemy of human kind, dispute not with him, give no credit to him, obstinately refuse him, as S. Anthony did in the wilderness, whom the Devil set upon in several shapes, or as the Collier did, so do thou by him. For when the Devil tempted him with the weakness of his faith, and told him, he could not be saved, as being ignorant in the principles of Religion; and urged him moreover to know what he believed, what he thought of such and such points and Mysteries: the Collier told him, he believed as the Church did; but what (said the Devil again) doth the Church believe? as I do (saith the Collier) and what's that thou believest? as the Church doth, &c., when the Devil could get no other answer, he left him. If Satan summon thee to answer, send him to Christ: he is thy liberty, thy protector against cruel death, raging sin. that roaring Lion; he is thy righteousness, thy Saviour, and thy life. Though he [Satan] say, thou art not of the number of the Elect, a Reprobate, forsaken of God, hold thine own still,

Be this our wall of brass, (HORACE)

let this be as a Bulwark, a Brazen Wall to defend thee, stay thyself in that certainty of faith; let that be thy comfort, Christ will protect thee, vindicate thee, thou art one of his flock, he will triumph over the Law, vanquish Death, overcome the Devil, and destroy Hell. If he say thou art none of the Elect, no Believer, reject him, defy him, thou hast thought otherwise, and mayest so be resolved again; comfort thyself; this persuasion cannot come from the Devil, and much less can it be grounded from thyself; men are liars, and why shouldest thou distrust? A denying Peter, a persecuting Paul, an adulterous cruel David, have been received; an Apostate Solomon may be converted; no sin at all but impenitency can give testimony of final reprobation. Why shouldest thou then distrust, misdoubt thyself, upon what ground, what suspicion? This opinion alone of particularity? Against that, and for the certainty of Election and salvation on the other side, see God's good will toward men, hear how generally his grace is proposed to him, and him, and them, each man in particular, and to all. *God wills that all men be saved, and come to the knowledge of the truth.* 'Tis an universal promise, *God sent not his Son into the world, to condemn the world, but that through him the world might be saved.* He then that acknowledgeth himself a man in the world, must likewise acknowledge, he is of that number that is to be saved: *I will not the death of a sinner, but that he repent and live.* But thou art a sinner, therefore he will not thy death. *This is the will of him that sent me, that every man that believeth in the Son, should have everlasting life. He would have no man perish, but all come to repentance.* Besides, remission of sins is to be preached, not to a few, but universally to all men. *Go therefore and tell all Nations, baptizing them,* &c. *Go into all the world, and preach the Gospel to every creature.* Now there cannot be contradictory wills in God; he will have all saved, and not all, how can this stand together? be secure then, believe, trust in him, hope well, and be saved. Yea, that's the main matter, how shall I believe, or discern my security, from carnal presumption? my faith is weak and faint, I want those signs and fruits of Sanctification, sorrow for sin, thirsting for Grace, groanings of the Spirit, love of Christians as Christians, avoiding occasion of sin, endeavour of new obedience, charity, love of God, perseverance. Though these signs be languishing in thee, and not seated in thine heart, thou must not therefore be dejected or terrified; the effects of faith and the Spirit are not yet so fully felt in thee; conclude not therefore thou art a Reprobate, or doubt of thine Election, because the Elect themselves are without them, before their conversion. Thou mayest in the Lord's good time be converted; some are called at the eleventh hour. Use, I say, the means of thy conversion, expect the Lord's leisure, if not yet called, pray thou mayest be, or at least wish and desire thou mayest be.

Notwithstanding all this which might be said to this effect, to ease their afflicted minds, what comfort our best Divines can afford in this case, Zanchius, Beza, &c., this furious curiosity, needless speculation, fruitless meditation about election, reprobation, free-will, grace, such places of Scripture preposterously conceived, torment still, and crucify the souls of too many, and set all the world together by the ears. To avoid which inconveniences, and to settle their distressed minds, to mitigate those divine Aphorisms (though in another extreme somewhat) our late Arminians have revived that plausible doctrine of universal grace, which many Fathers, our late Lutherans and modern Papists do still maintain, that we have free-will of our selves, and that grace is common to all that will believe. Some again, though less orthodoxal, will have a far greater part saved, than shall be damned (as Cælius Secundus stiffly maintains in his Book, or some Impostor under his name). He calls that other Tenent of special Election and Reprobation, a prejudicate, envious, and malicious opinion, apt to draw all men to desperation. *Many are called, few chosen,* &c. He opposeth some opposite parts of Scripture to it, " Christ came into the world to save sinners," &c. And four especial Arguments he produceth, one from God's power. If more be damned than saved, he erroneously concludes, the Devil hath the greatest Sovereignty; for what is power but to protect? and Majesty consists in multitude. If the Devil have the greater part, where is his mercy? where is his power? Where is his greatness? where his goodness? He proceeds, We account him a murderer that is accessary only, or doth not help when he can; which may not be supposed of God without great offence, because he may do what he will, and is otherwise accessary, and the author of sin. The nature of good is to be communicated, God is good, and will not then be contracted in his goodness; for how is he the Father of mercy and comfort, if his good concern but a few? O envious and unthankful men to think otherwise! Why should we pray to God that are Gentiles, and thank him for his mercies and benefits, that hath damned us all innocuous for Adam's offence, one man's offence, one small offence, eating of an Apple? why should we acknowledge him for our Governor, that hath

wholly neglected the salvation of our souls, contemned us, and sent no
Prophets or Instructors to teach us, as he hath done to the Hebrews? So
Julian the Apostate objects. Why should these Christians (Cælius urgeth) reject us, and appropriate God unto themselves. But to return to
our forged Cælius. At last he comes to that, he will have those saved
that never heard of, or believed in Christ, from ignorance, with the
Pelagians, and proves it out of Origen and others. They (saith Origen)
that never heard God's word, are to be excused for their ignorance: we
may not think God will be so hard, angry, cruel or unjust as to condemn
any man without a hearing. They alone (he holds) are in the state of
damnation that refuse Christ's mercy and grace, when it is offered.
Many worthy Greeks and Romans, good moral honest men, that kept
the Law of Nature, did to others as they would be done to themselves,
are as certainly saved, he concludes, as they were that lived uprightly
before the Law of Moses. They were acceptable in God's sight, as Job
was, the Magi, the Queen of Sheba, Darius of Persia, Socrates, Aristides,
Cato, Curius, Tully, Seneca, and many other Philosophers, upright
livers, no matter of what Religion, as Cornelius, out of any Nation, so
that he live honestly, call on God, trust in him, fear him, he shall be
saved. This Opinion was formerly maintained by the Valentinian and
Basilidian Hereticks, revived of late in Turkey, of which sect Rustan
Bassa was Patron, defended by Galeatius Martius, and some antient
Fathers, and of later times favoured by Erasmus, by Zuinglius, whose
Tenent Bullinger vindicates, and Gualter approves in a just Apology
with many Arguments. There be many Jesuits that follow these Calvinists in this behalf, Franciscus Buchsius Moguntinus, Andradius, many
schoolmen, that are verily persuaded, that those good works of the
Gentiles did so far please God, that they might deserve eternal life, and
be saved in the end. Sesellius, and Benedictus Justinianus in his Comment on the first of the Romans, Mathias Ditmarsh the Politician, with
many others, hold a mediocrity, they may be not unworthy of salvation,
but they will not absolutely decree it. Hofmannus, a Lutheran Professor of Helmstadt, and many of his Followers, with most of our Church,
and Papists, are stiff against it. Franciscus Collius hath fully censured
all Opinions, and amply dilated this question, which who so will, may
peruse. But to return to my Author, his Conclusion is, that not only
wicked Livers, Blasphemers, Reprobates, and such as reject God's
grace, but that the Devils themselves shall be saved at last, as Origen
long since delivered in his works, and our late Socinians defend, Osto-
rodius, Smaltius, &c. Those terms of all and for ever in Scripture, are

not eternal, but only denote a longer time, which by many Examples they prove. The world shall end like a Comedy, and we shall meet at last in Heaven, and live in bliss altogether; or else in conclusion, fade away into nothing. For how can he be merciful that shall condemn any creature to eternal unspeakable punishment, for one small temporary fault, all posterity, so many myriads, for one and another man's offence; how have you sheep offended? But these absurd paradoxes are exploded by our Church, we teach otherwise. That this vocation, predestination, election, reprobation, was not " out of the corrupt mass," * " faith having been foreseen," as some of our Arminians [believe], or " because of works foreseen," as some of our Papists [believe], nor because of a " passing over " [of the non-elect by God], but [it was] God's absolute decree before the creation of the world (as many of our Church hold), ['t] was from the beginning, before the foundation of the world was laid, or man created (or from Adam's fall, as others will, it is man as fallen who is the object of reprobation); with the perseverance of saints, we must be certain of our salvation, we may fall, but not finally, which our Arminians will not admit. According to his immutable, eternal, just decree and counsel of saving men and Angels, God calls all, and would have all to be saved according to the efficacy of vocation: all are invited, but only the elect apprehended: the rest that are unbelieving, impenitent, whom God in his just judgment leaves to be punished for their sins, are in a reprobate sense; yet we must not determine who are such, condemn ourselves, or others, because we have an universal invitation; all are commanded to believe, and we

---

* " Out of the corrupt mass " refers to the disputed question: Did predestination precede the fall, or did God predestine some out of the corrupt mass (of mankind as fallen) — that is, did predestination follow the fall? The Arminians taught the second, Burton here asserts the first. " Faith having been foreseen ": the Arminians taught that God foresaw faith in some, and on that ground they were predestined; this Burton denies. " Or because of works foreknown ": the Catholics taught that God predestined those in whom he foresaw good works. " Nor because of a passing over " : some taught that the non-elect were not definitely so predestined, but that God simply passed them over. " It is man as fallen who is the object of reprobation " : the decree is subsequent and not antecedent to the fall. " The perseverance of the saints " : those whom God has elected cannot finally fall away from grace, although they may have lapses; this doctrine the Arminians rejected, and said that even the saints might finally fall away. Burton's argument is, if we are elect, we *must* be certain of our salvation finally, even if we have lapses. It is this certainty which Burton argues they will not admit. The following sentences are somewhat inconsistent: as the invitation is general, and God alone knows whom of them who accept or seem to accept it He has really elected, we need not assume that we are non-elect because we have not the certainty of which he speaks above. (This note is due to the kindness of the Rev. A. E. Garvie, of the Divinity School of the University of London.)

know not how soon or late before our end we may be received. I might have said more of this subject; but forasmuch as it is a forbidden question, and in the Preface or Declaration to the Articles of the Church, printed 1633, to avoid factions and altercations, we that are University Divines especially, are prohibited all curious search, to print or preach, or draw the Article aside by our own sense and Comments, upon pain of Ecclesiastical censure, I will surcease, and conclude with Erasmus of such controversies: Let who will dispute, I think that the laws of our ancestors should be received with reverence, and religiously observ'd, as coming from God; nor is it safe or pious to invent or spread evil suspicion as to the public authority. And should any Tyranny exist, if unlikely to drive men into wickedness, 'tis better to endure it than resist it by sedition.

But to my former task. The last main torture and trouble of a distressed mind, is, not so much this doubt of Election, and that the promises of grace are smothered and extinct in them, nay quite blotted out, as they suppose, but withal God's heavy wrath, a most intolerable pain and grief of heart se¹zeth on them: to their thinking they are already damned, they suffer the pains of Hell, and more than possibly can be expressed, they smell brimstone, talk familiarly with Devils, hear and see Chimeras, prodigious, uncouth shapes, Bears, Owls, Anticks, black dogs, fiends, hideous out-cries, fearful noises, shrieks, lamentable complaints, they are possessed, and through impatience they roar and howl, curse, blaspheme, deny God, call his power in question, abjure Religion, and are still ready to offer violence unto themselves, by hanging, drowning, &c. Never any miserable wretch from the beginning of the world, was in such a woful case. To such persons I oppose God's mercy, and his justice; the judgments of God are mysterious, not unjust; his secret counsel, and just judgment, by which he spares some, and sore afflicts others again in this life: his judgment is to be adored, trembled at, not to be searched or enquired after by mortal men: he hath reasons reserved to himself, which our frailty cannot apprehend. He may punish all, if he will, and that justly for sin; in that he doth it in some, is to make a way for his mercy that they repent and be saved, to heal them, to try them, exercise their patience, and make them call upon him, to confess their sins, and pray unto him, as David did, *Righteous art thou, O Lord, and just are thy judgments.* As the poor Publican, *Lord have mercy upon me a miserable sinner.* To put confidence, and have an assured hope in him, as Job had, *Though he kill me, I will trust in him.* Saith Austin, kill, cut in pieces, burn my body (O Lord) to save my soul. A small sickness, one lash of affliction, a little misery, many times, will more humiliate a man, sooner convert, bring him home to know himself, than all those parænetical discourses, the whole Theory of Philosophy, Law, Physick and Divinity, or a world of instances and examples. So that this, which they take to be such an insupportable plague, is an evident sign of God's mercy and justice, of his love and goodness: had they not thus been undone, they had finally been undone. Many a carnal man is lulled asleep in perverse security, foolish presumption, is stupified in his sins, and hath no feeling at all of them: *I have sinned* (he saith) *and what evil shall come unto me?* and *tush, how shall God know it?* And so in a reprobate sense goes down to Hell.

But here, God pulls them by the ear, by affliction, he will bring them to Heaven and Happiness; *Blessed are they that mourn, for they shall be comforted,* a blessed and an happy state, if considered aright, it is, to be so troubled. *It is good for me that I have been afflicted, Before I was afflicted I went astray, but now I keep thy word, Tribulation works patience, patience hope,* and by such like crosses and calamities we are driven from the stake of security. So that affliction is a School or Academy, wherein the best Scholars are prepared to the Commencements of the Deity. And though it be most troublesome and grievous for the time, yet know this, it comes by God's permission and providence, he is a spectator of thy groans and tears, still present with thee, the very hairs of thy head are numbered, not one of them can fall to the ground, without the express will of God: he will not suffer thee to be tempted above measure, he corrects us all, the Lord will not quench the smoking flax, or break the bruised reed; saith Austin, He suffers thee to be tempted for thy good. And as a Mother doth handle her child sick and weak, not reject it, but with all tenderness observe and keep it, so doth God by us, not forsake us in our miseries, or relinquish us for our imperfections, but with all piety and compassion, support and receive us; whom he loves, he loves to the end. Whom he hath elected, those he hath called, justified, sanctified, and glorified. Think not then thou hast lost the Spirit, that thou art forsaken of God, be not overcome with heaviness of heart, but as David said, *I will not fear, though I walk in the shadows of death.* We must all go, not from delights to delights, but from the Cross to the Crown, by Hell to Heaven, as the old Romans put Virtue's Temple in the way to that of Honour: we must endure sorrow and misery in this life. 'Tis no new thing this, God's best servants and dearest children have been so visited and tried. Christ in the Garden cried out, *My God, my God, why hast thou forsaken me?* his son by nature, as thou art by adoption and grace. Job in his anguish said, *The arrows of the Almighty God were in him, his terrors fought against him, the venom drank up his spirit.* He saith, *God was his enemy, writ bitter things against him, hated him.* His heavy wrath had so seized on his soul. David complains, *His eyes were eaten up, sunk into his head ; his moisture became as the drought in Summer, his flesh was consumed, his bones vexed :* yet neither Job nor David did finally despair. Job would not leave his hold, but still trusted in him, acknowledging him to be his good God. *The Lord gives, the Lord takes, blessed be the name of the Lord. Behold I am vile, I abhor myself, repent in dust and ashes.* David humbled himself, and upon his confession received mercy. Faith, hope, repentance, are the sovereign cures and remedies, the sole comforts in this case ; confess, humble thyself, repent, it is sufficient. Saith Chrysostom, the King of Nineveh's sackcloth and ashes did that which his Purple Robes and Crown could not effect ; Turn to him, he will turn to thee ; the Lord is near those that are of a contrite heart, and will save such as be afflicted in spirit. *He came to the lost sheep of Israel.* He is at all times ready to assist. He never rejects a penitent sinner ; though he have come to the full height of iniquity, wallowed and delighted in sin ; yet if he will forsake his former ways, he will receive him. Saith Austin, speaking for God, I will spare him, because he hath not spared himself ; I will pardon him, because he doth acknowledge his offence ; let it be never so enormous a sin, *his grace is sufficient.* Despair not then, faint not at all, be not dejected, but rely on God, call on him in thy trouble, and he will hear thee, he will assist, help, and deliver thee. *Draw near to him, and He will draw near to thee.* Lazarus was poor, and full of boils, and yet still he relied upon God, Abraham did hope beyond hope.

Thou exceptest, these were chief men, divine spirits, beloved of God, especially respected ; but I am a contemptible and forlorn wretch, forsaken of God, and left to the merciless fury of evil spirits. I cannot hope, pray, repent, &c. How often shall I say it ! thou mayest perform all these duties, Christian-offices, and be restored in good time. A sick man loseth his appetite, strength and ability, his disease prevaileth so far, that all his faculties are spent, hand and foot perform not their duties, his eyes are dim, hearing dull, tongue distastes things of pleasant relish, yet nature lies hid, recovereth again, and expelleth all those feculent matters by vomit, sweat, or some such like evacuations. Thou art spiritually sick, thine heart is heavy, thy mind distressed, thou mayest happily recover again, expel those dismal passions of fear and grief ; God did not suffer thee to be tempted above measure; whom he loves (I say) he loves to the end; hope the best. David in his misery prayed to the Lord, remembering how he had formerly dealt with him; and with that meditation of God's mercy confirmed his Faith, and pacified his own tumultuous heart in his greatest agony. *O my soul, why art thou so disquieted within me,* &c. Thy soul is eclipsed for a time, I yield, as the Sun is shadowed by a cloud; no doubt but those gracious beams of God's mercy will shine upon thee again, as they have formerly done; those embers of Faith, Hope and Repentance, now buried in ashes, will flame out afresh, and be fully revived. Want of Faith, no feeling of grace for the present, are not fit directions; we must live by Faith, not by feeling; 'tis the beginning of grace to wish for grace: we must expect and tarry David, a man after God's own heart, was so troubled himself; *Awake, why sleepest thou? O Lord, arise, cast me not off; wherefore hidest thou thy face, and forgettest mine affliction and oppression? My soul is bowed down to the dust. Arise, redeem us,* &c. He prayed long before he was heard, endured much before he was relieved. He complains, *I am weary of crying, and my throat is dry, mine eyes fail, whilst I wait on the Lord,* and yet he perseveres. Be not dismayed, thou shalt be respected at last. God often works by contrarieties, he first kills, and then makes alive, he woundeth first, and then healeth, he makes man sow in tears, that he may reap in joy; 'tis God's method: he that is so visited, must with patience endure and rest satisfied for the present. The Paschal Lamb was eaten with sour herbs; we shall feel no sweetness of his blood, till we first feel the smart of our sins. Thy pains are great, intolerable for the time; thou art destitute of grace and comfort, stay the Lord's leisure, he will not (I say) suffer thee to be tempted above what thou art able to bear, but will give an issue to temptation. He works all for the best to them that love God. Doubt not of thine election, it is an immutable decree; a mark never to be defaced; you have been otherwise, you may and shall be. And for your present affliction, hope the best, it will shortly end. *He is present with his servants in their affliction. Great are the troubles of the righteous, but the Lord delivereth them out of all. Our light affliction, which is but for a moment, worketh in us an eternal weight of glory. Not answerable to that glory which is to come; though now in heaviness, you shall rejoice.*

Now last of all to those external impediments, terrible objects, which they hear and see many times, Devils, Bugbears, and Mormoluches [or Hobgoblins], noisome smells, &c. These may come, as I have formerly declared in my precedent discourse of the Symptoms of Melancholy, from inward causes; as a concave glass reflects solid bodies, a troubled brain for want of sleep, nutriment, and by reason of that agitation of spirits to which Hercules de Saxoniâ attributes all Symptoms almost, may reflect and shew prodigious shapes, as our vain fear and crazed phantasy shall suggest and feign, as many silly weak women and children in the dark, sick folks, and frantick for want of repast and sleep, suppose they see that they see not: many times such terriculaments [things which produce fright] may proceed from natural causes, and all other senses may be deluded. Besides, as I have said, this humour is the Devil's Bath, by reason of the distemper of humours, and infirm Organs in us: he may so possess us inwardly to molest us, as he did Saul and others, by God's permission; he is Prince of the Air, and can transform himself into several shapes, delude all our senses for a time, but his power is determined [limited] ; he may terrify us, but not hurt: *God hath given his Angels charge over us. He is a wall round about his people.* There be those that prescribe Physick in such cases, 'tis God's instrument, and not unfit. The Devil works by mediation of humours, and mixt diseases must have mixt remedies. Levinus Lemnius is very copious in this subject, besides that chief remedy of confidence in God, prayer, hearty repentance, &c., of which, for your comfort and instruction, read Lavater, Wierus, and others, and that Christian armour which Paul prescribes; he sets down certain Amulets, herbs, and precious stones, which have marvellous virtues all, to drive away Devils and their illusions. Sapphires, Chrysolites, Carbuncles, &c., which have the marvellous virtue of keeping off ghosts, goblins, nightmares, spirits of the air, if faith can be put in the records of the antients. Of herbs, he reckons us Pennyroyal, Rue, Mint, Angelica, Piony: Richard Argentine adds hypericon or S. John's wort, which by a divine virtue drives away Devils, and is therefore called Expeller of Demons; all which rightly used, by their suffitus [or fumigation] expel Devils themselves, and all devilish illusions. Anthony Musa, the Emperor Augustus his Physician, approves of Betony to this purpose; the antients used therefore to plant it in Church-yards, because it was held to be an holy herb, and good against fearful visions, did secure such places it grew in, and sanctified those persons that carried it about them. Mattiolus says the same. Others commend accurate musick; so Saul was helped by David's harp. Fires to be made in such rooms where spirits haunt, good store of lights to be set up, odours, perfumes, and suffumigations, as the Angel taught Tobias,* of brimstone and bitumen, thus [or frankincense], myrrh, briony-root, with many such simples which Wecker hath col-

* Tobit, vi.

lected. Take of sulphur one drachm, boiled again in white vine water, that the sulphur may be diluted ; let it be given to the patient ; for diseases are devils (saith Richard Argentine). Vigetus hath a far larger receipt to this purpose, which the said Wecker cites out of Wierus. Take sulphur, wine, bitumen, opoponax, gambanum, castor oil, &c. Why sweet perfumes, fires and so many lights should be used in such places, Ernestus Burgravius, Lamps of Life and Death, and Fortunius Lycetus assigns this cause, because good spirits are well pleased with, but evil abhor them, And therefore those old Gentiles, present Mahometans, and Papists, have continual lamps burning in their Churches all day, and all night, lights at funerals, and in their graves ; burning lamps of molten gold, for many ages to endure (saith Lazius) lest Devils harm the body, lights ever burning, as those Vestal Virgins, Pythonisses maintained heretofore, with many such, of which read Tostatus, Thyreus, Pictorius, see more in them. Cardan would have the party affected wink altogether in such a case, if he see ought that offends him, or cut the Air with a sword in such places they walk and abide ; shoot a pistol at them, for being aerial bodies (as Cælius Rhodiginus, Tertullian, Origen, Psellas, and many hold) if strucken, they feel pain. Papists commonly enjoin and apply crosses, holy-water, sanctified beads, Amulets, musick, ringing of bells, for to that end are they consecrated, and by them baptized, Characters, counterfeit relicks, so many Masses, Peregrinations, oblations, adjurations, and what not ? Alexander Albertinus à Rocha, Petrus Thyreus, and Hieronymus Mengus, with many other Pontificial writers, prescribe and set down several forms of exorcisms, as well to houses possessed with Devils, as to demoniacal persons ; but I am of Lemnius' mind, 'tis but a mere mockage, a counterfeit charm, to no purpose, they are fopperies and fictions, as that absurd story * is amongst the rest, of a penitent woman seduced by a Magician in France, at S. Bawn, exorcised by Domphius, Michaelis, and a company of circumventing Friars. If any man (saith Lemnius) will attempt such a thing, without all those juggling circumstances, Astrological elections of time, place, prodigious habits, fustian, big, sesquipedal words, spells, crosses, characters, which exorcists ordinarily use, let him follow the example of Peter and John, that without any ambitious swelling terms, cured a lame man, *In the name of Jesus Christ rise and walk*. His Name alone is the best and only charm against all such diabolical illusions ; so doth Origen advise, and so Chrysostom, This will be your staff, this your impregnable tower, this your armour. Saith S. Austin, many men will desire my counsel and opinion, what's to be

* Done into English by W. B., 1613. — Burton's note. [See W. B. in Index.]

done in this behalf? I can say no more, they with true faith, which worketh through love, let them fly to God alone for help. Athanasius prescribes as a present charm against Devils, the beginning of the 67th Psalm, *Hear my voice, O God, in my prayer: preserve my life from fear of the enemy,* &c. But the best remedy is to fly to God, to call on him, hope, pray, trust, rely on him, to commit ourselves wholly to him. What the practice of the Primitive Church was in this behalf, and the way of expelling Devils, read Wierus at large.

Last of all: if the party affected shall certainly know this malady to have proceeded from too much fasting, meditation, precise life, contemplation of God's judgments (for the Devil deceives many by such means) in that other extreme he circumvents Melancholy itself, reading some Books, Treatises, hearing rigid Preachers, &c. If he shall perceive that it hath begun first from some great loss, grievous accident, disaster, seeing others in like case, or any such terrible object, let him speedily remove the cause, which to the cure of this disease Navarrus so much commends, turn away his thoughts from the painful subject, by all opposite means, art, and industry, let him ease the soul by all honest recreations, refresh and recreate his distressed soul; let him direct his thoughts, by himself and other of his friends. Let him read no more such tracts or subjects, hear no more such fearful tones, avoid such companies, and by all means open himself, submit himself to the advice of good Physicians, and Divines, which is a relief in uneasiness, as he calls it, hear them speak to whom the Lord hath given the tongue of the learned, to be able to minister a word to him that is weary, whose words are as flagons of wine. Let him not be obstinate, head-strong, peevish, wilful, self-conceited (as in this malady they are) but give ear to good advice, be ruled and persuaded; and no doubt but such good counsel may prove as prosperous to his soul, as the Angel was to Peter, that opened the Iron-gates, loosed his bands, brought him out of prison, and delivered him from bodily thraldom; they may ease his afflicted mind, relieve his wounded soul, and take him out of the jaws of Hell itself. I can say no more, or give better advice to such as are any way distressed in this kind, than what I have given and said. Only take this for a corollary and conclusion, as thou tenderest thine own welfare in this, and all other melancholy, thy good health of body and mind, observe this short Precept, give not way to solitariness and idleness. Be not solitary, be not idle.

HOPE, YE MISERABLE,
YE HAPPY, TAKE HEED

Dost thou wish to be free from doubt? dost desire to escape uncertainty? be penitent, then, while still sound, of wholesome mind;
      being so, thou art safe, I tell thee, because thou hast been
         penitent whilst thou mightest have been sinning: so
                           saith Austin.

                           FINIS

APPENDIX I

THE CONCLUSION OF THE AUTHOR
TO THE READER

[This, which appeared at the end of the first edition, was not reprinted in any subsequent issue. Much of it was later transferred to the prefatory " Democritus to the Reader." But we have deemed it of sufficient interest to warrant republication.]

HE last section shall be mine, to cut the strings of Democritus' visor, to unmask and show him as he is.

Why will you thus a mighty vase intend,

If in a worthless bowl your labors end? (HORACE)

Democritus began as a Prologue in this Tragi-comedy, but why doth the author end, and act the Epilogue in his own name? I intended at first to have concealed myself, but second thoughts, &c. For some reasons I have altered mine intent, and am willing to subscribe.

On me! on me! Here am I who did the deed:

Turn your eyes on me, O Reader, my work you read.

If ought be otherwise than it should be, since I have now put myself upon the stage, I must undergo and abide the censure of it, the die is cast, and I may not escape it. It is most true, the style proclaims the man, our style bewrayes us, and as hunters find their game by the trace, so is a man descried by his writings. I have laid myself open (I know it) in this Treatise, and shall be censured I doubt not, yet this is some comfort: our censures are as various as our palates. If I be taxed, exploded by some, I shall happily be as much approved and commended by others. It was Democritus' fortune, at once laughed at and admired, and 'tis the common doom of all writers: I seek not to be commended; nor am I indeed so very ugly, I would not be vilified. I fear good men's censures; the tongues of servants you may despise; as the barking of a dog I securely contemne the malicious and scurrile obloquies, flouts, calumnies of those railers and detractors; I scorn the rest. I am none of the best of you. I am none of the meanest; howsoever, I am now come to retract some part of that which I have writ —

When I peruse this tract which I have writ,

I am abash't, and much I hold unfit. (OVID)

073

I could wish it otherwise, expunged, and to this end I have annexed this Apologetical Appendix, to crave pardon for that which is amiss. I do suspect some precedent passages have been distastefull, as too Satyricall & bitter; some again as too Comical, homely, broad, or lightly spoken. For the first, I grant that of Tacitus to be true: a bitter jest leaves a sting behind it; and as an honourable & worthy man observes: They fear a Satyrist's wit, and he their memories (Sr. Fr. Bacon). I might therefore suspect, but I hope I have wronged no man. And though for this I have Apologized already, yet in Medea's words:

> *And in my last words this I do desire,*
> *That what in passion I have said or ire;*
> *May be forgotten and a better mind,*
> *Be had of us hereafter as you find.*

To the other of lightness, I make answer, — To the pure all things are pure, and as Augusta Livia sometimes said: A naked man to a modest woman is no otherwise than a picture. *Bad heart, bad disposition; Evil to him who evil thinks.* If in thy censure it be too light, I advise thee, as Lipsius did his reader for some places of Plautus: If they like thee not let them pass; or oppose that which is good to that which is bad, reject not therefore all. But, to invert that verse of Martial and apply it to my present use, which Jerome Wolfius did to his Translation of Suidas:

Some is bad, some indifferent, some good; I have inserted some things more homely or light, which I would request every man to interpret to the best, — and conclude in Scaliger's words to Cardan: If thou didst know me well, thou wouldst not only pardon these witticisms of mine, but would even consider it unworthy that so kindly a soul as I should find it necessary to avert even the slightest suspicion. But this likewise I have formerly excused withall those harsh compositions, Tautological repetitions, perturbations of tenses and numbers &c. I should indeed (had I wisely done) observed that precept of the poet: Let it be withheld up to the ninth year, and have taken more care; or as Alexander the Physician would have done by lapis lazuli, 50 times washed before it be used; I should have perused, corrected and amended this Tract, but I had not that happy leasure, no amanuenses, assistants; and was enforced as a Bear doth her whelps, to bring forth this confused lump, and had not space to lick it into form, as she doth her young ones; but even so to publish it, as it was written at first, once for all, in an extemporanean style, whatever came uppermost, as I do commonly all other exercises, standing on one leg, as he

made verses out of a confused company of notes; I poured forth whatever my genius dictated, and writ with as small deliberation as I do
ordinarily speak. So that as a river runs precipitate & swift, & sometimes dull and slow; now direct, now winding about; now deep, then
shallow; now muddy, then clear; now broad, then narrow, doth my
style flow, now more serious, then light, now more elaborate or remiss.
Comical, Satyrical, as the present subject required, or as at that time
I was affected. And if thou vouchsafe to read this Treatise, it shall seem
no otherwise to thee than the way to an ordinary traveller: sometimes
fair, sometimes foul, here Champion, there inclosed; barren in one
place, better soil in another; by woods, groves, hills, dales, plains, &c.
I shall lead thee over high mountains, & through dangerous valleys, &
dewy meadows, & plowed fields, through variety of objects, that which
thou shalt like and dislike.

For the matter itself or method, if it be faulty, consider I pray you
that of Columella: No one is perfect, or made perfect by zeal alone, no
man can observe all, much is defective, and may be justly taxed, altered
in Galen, Aristotle, and the very best. He is a good huntsman (one
observes) can catch some, not all. I have done mine indeavor. Besides,
I dwell not in these humane studies, or Physick, they are no part of
my profession, I do not draw this furrow, sweat in this field, I am but
a stranger, a smatterer in them, here and there I pull a flower. And I do
easily grant, if a rigid censurer should criticise on this which I have
writ, he should not find three faults, as Scaliger in Terence, but 300,
even as many as he hath done in Cardan's subtilties, or Borocius on
Sacro-Boscus. If ought be amiss, I require friendly admonition, no
bitter invective, otherwise as in ordinary controversies, we may contend, and likely misuse one another, but to what purpose? we are
both scholars, say Arcadians both, and adepts in part-singing. If we do
wrangle, what shall we get by it? trouble and wrong ourselves, make
sport for others.

When all is done, it may be, that which thou so much reprehendest
and in thy judgement dost so much condemn, is not faulty, not to be
condemned: So many men so many minds; I like it, so doth he, thou
dost not; is it therefore unfit, absurd and ridiculous? Every man
abounds in his own sense, and one man cannot express what every man
thinks, or please all. It is the common humour; to discommend that
which they dislike themselves; if ought be omitted, added, if he say not
point blank, as they would have it, he is an idiot, an ass, a nobody. An
easy matter it is to find fault, to censure, vilify, detract from others, a

thing of nothing when it is done; and who could not have done as much?

As for the end of the present Discourse, I refer you to that which hath been formerly said. In the mean time, if any man shall say: Physician Heal thyself, or, as in *Wisdom* (17.8) it was objected to those Wizards: — They that promised to drive away fear and trouble from the sick person, were sick for fear, and worthy to be laughed at. I reply with Sulpitius: They that cure others, cannot well prescribe Physick to themselves.

It now remains that I make thankful remembrance of such friends to whom I have been beholden for their approbation, or troubled in perusing several parts, or all of this Treatise. For I did impart it to some of our worthiest Physicians, whose approbations I had for matters of Physick, and to some Divines, and others of better note in our University, as well as to my more private Collegiate friends, whose censures when I had passed, and that with good encouragement to proceed, I was the bolder to hasten it, with the permission of the Higher authorities, to the Press. I will name no man, or prefix, as the custom is, any Encomiastick verses, which I thank my friends have been offered, lest if either whole or part should be misliked, I should prejudice their judgement, I acknowledge myself much beholding and bound to them: if ought be amiss, I take it wholly to myself, and say again:

> *On me! On me! Here am I who did the deed,*
> *Turn your tongues 'gainst me O scoffers,*
> *You naught approved: mine the faulty screed.*

But I am overtroublesome, I will conclude, if first I may request a favourable censure of such faults as are omitted in the Press. The Copy (as I have said) was once written and in haste, I could not always be there myself; or I had been still present. The Miller sees not all the water goes by his mill. Besides many letters mistaken, misplaced, added, omitted, as i for y, or a for e, or o, false points, &c. which are in some copies only, not throughout: (To point at each particular of which were to pick out the seeds of a foul bushel of corn) some of the chiefest, as thou shalt find them corrected, I desire thee to take notice of. My translations are sometimes rather Paraphrases, and that only taken which was to my purpose; quotations are often inserted in the text, which make the style more harsh, or in the Margin as it happened. Greek Authors, Plato, Plutarch, Athenaus, &c. I have cited out of their interpreters, because the Original was not so ready &c. I have indeed mingled Sacred with profane, but I hope not profaned; and in repetition of Authors' names, not according to Chronology, ranked them willy nilly; sometimes Neotericks, before Ancients, as my memory suggested.

These are the things which I thought good to mention in this Epilogue, the consideration of which I leave to thy favorable censure, and with all submissiveness, as I ought, my self and these my labours to a friendly Reader. Farewell & be kind.

From my Study in Christ
Church, Oxon. December 5,
1620.

Robert Burton

APPENDIX II

THE DATE OF BURTON'S BIRTH AS CALCULATED FROM HIS NATIVITY

[The date of Burton's birth has previously been uncertain. His elder brother, William, in his Description of Lincolnshire, gave it as Feb. 8, 1578 (Julian style, now called 1578-9). The nativity, or horoscope, above the bust in Christ Church cathedral, gives the date as Feb. 8, 1576 (now called 1576-7 *). But a nativity in Burton's own handwriting has recently come to light, and has been printed in the Proceedings of the Oxford Bibliographical Society, Vol. I, Part III, 1925, from which it is reproduced in this volume. We have asked Dr. Florian Cajori, professor of the history of mathematics at the University of California, to calculate, if possible, the date of Burton's birth from the astronomical data furnished in the nativity itself. This he has done, as described in the letter following, and the question may now be regarded as settled.]

Berkeley, Calif., Sept. 9, '27.

My dear Sir:

I find that the positions of Jupiter and Saturn in Burton's horoscope indicate the year 1577 as the date of Burton's birth.

Horoscope computation is usually arduous, but in this case I was able to get the desired result easily by the comparison of different horoscopes. In Burton's horoscope Jupiter appears in the " house " having the initial line Leo 24° 20', and the final line Libra 28° 46' (?). The question arises, " Is Jupiter in Virgo or in Libra ? " Being written down nearer to Virgo, the reading should be " Virgo 9° 59'." That this mode of interpretation is correct can be verified by reference to the Introduction to Astrology, by William Lilly, edited by Zadkiel, London, 1913, pp. 156 and 157, and many other places. In Burton's horoscope, Saturn appears in Capricorn 9° 58'.

---

* Perhaps it should be explained that the Gregorian calendar, introduced into Catholic countries in 1582, was not adopted in England till 1752; and not only was there a discrepancy of ten days, in the 16th c., between the two calendars, so that Feb. 8 in the Julian style would be equal to Feb. 18 in the Gregorian style, but also the legal New Year began in England on March 25, so that the year 1576 extended through the following March 24, including February of what we should now call 1577. This is the meaning of the date Feb. 8, 1576-7.

978

I chose the planets Jupiter and Saturn, rather than others, because they are furthest from the sun and therefore least affected, in their apparent positions in the Zodiac, by the motion of the earth. Jupiter completes an orbital revolution in 11.862 years, Saturn in 29.46 years. Taking the planet Jupiter, I compared Burton's horoscope with that of Edward VI. (Oct. 11, 1537), where Jupiter appears in Taurus, 18° 41'. In passing from Taurus 18° 41' through the intervening signs of Gemini, Cancer, and Leo, the number of degrees in the Zodiac is 11° 19' + 30° + 30° + 30° + 9° 59' = 111° 18'. The difference in time between the two horoscopes, taking 1577 as the year of Burton's birth, is 39.32 years. In that time Jupiter swept in the Zodiac over a number of degrees, x, as indicated by the following proportions: 11.862 : 39.32 = 360° : x = 1193.3°. This indicates that Jupiter made, in 39.32 years, three orbital revolutions and 113° 18' over. Taking the year 1578, that difference is 143° 42'; taking 1576, the difference is 83°. It follows, therefore, that the year 1577 is the one in which Burton was born. His horoscope writing indicates either 1576 or 1578. The date Feb. 8, 1576 agrees with the date Feb. 8, 1577, provided we interpret (as we may) Feb. 8, 1576 to mean " Feb. 8, 1576–77," by which we understand " Feb. 8 of the legal year 1576, which began the preceding March and ended March 1577." *

I copy the results of my computations with Jupiter and Saturn, in the comparison of horoscopes, —

Edward VI.	Burton	Computed difference	
Oct. 11, 1537 —	Feb. 8, 1576:	Jupiter, 82° 54';	Saturn, 108° 12'
" " "	" " 1577:	" 113° 18';	" 120° 27'
" " "	" " 1578:	" 143° 42';	" 132° 42'
	Horoscope difference	Jupiter, 111° 18';	Saturn, 113° 5'

Death of Charles I.	Burton	Computed difference	
Jan. 30, 1648–49 —	Feb. 8, 1576:	Jupiter, 55° ;	Saturn, 171° 36'
" " " "	" " 1577:	" 24° 24';	" 159° 30'
" " " "	" " 1578:	" −6° ;	" 147° 24'
	Horoscope difference	Jupiter, 28° 55';	Saturn, 149° 27'

Goethe	Burton	Computed difference	
Aug. 28, 1749 —	Feb. 8, 1576:	Jupiter, 228° ;	Saturn, 39° 24'
" " "	" " 1577:	" 198° ;	" 51° 30'
" " "	" " 1578:	" 168° ;	" 63° 36'
	Horoscope difference	Jupiter, 196° 12';	Saturn, 54° 54'

* See footnote on the Julian and Gregorian year, p. 978.

American *Independence*	*Burton*	*Computed difference*			
Jul. 4, 1776 —	Feb. 8, 1576:	Jupiter, 38° ;		Saturn,	71° 24'
" " "	" " 1577:	" 68° 18';		"	83° 48'
" " "	" " 1578:	" 98° ;		"	96° 12'
	Horoscope difference Jupiter, 64° 01'; Saturn, 85° 8'				

The Jupiter data point conclusively to 1577 as the year of Burton's birth. The Saturn data point to the same conclusion, but less convincingly, as was to be expected from the fact that Saturn moves over only 12° of the Zodiac in a year, and has a greater eccentricity of orbit than Jupiter.

FLORIAN CAJORI

APPENDIX III

A NOTE ON EMENDATIONS AND ERRATA

First, those places in the text of the 6th edition where the meaning is obscure or the grammar incorrect, and a correct text can be restored from an earlier edition: Page 100 * — " The Pope is more than a man, as his parats make him "; as Prof. Bensly has pointed out, the early editions read " parasites." Page 122 — " Alexander Tertullianus " has been corrected to " Alexander Trallianus." Page 264 — Of the scholar: " Like an ass, he wears out his time for provender, and can shew a stum rod, . . . an old torn gown " &c.; in all previous editions it is " stumpe rod," which, as Shilleto suggests, is probably a schoolmaster's rod worn by long use to a stump; perhaps we should print " stump rod," but we have merely restored the old reading with its archaic final " e." Page 330 — " Physicians, that study to cure diseases, catch them themselves, will be sick, and appropriate all symptoms they find related of others to their own persons." We restore the reading of the 4th and 5th editions, " Physicians, that studying " &c. Page 364 — Of magical deceptions: " But most part it is in the brain that deceives them." We follow earlier editions in reading " But most part is in the brain," — though this is not quite clear; perhaps the correct reading would be " But most part it is the brain that deceives them." Page 408 — " Whether . . . that hungry Spaniard's discovery . . . be as true as . . . his of Utopia, or his of Lucinia." From the 1st edition we restore " Lusinia," the name of John Barclay's imaginary country in his political allegory, Argenis. Page 723 — Of secret love, it is said that by its symptoms " it may be described "; from the 4th edition we restore " described." Page 758 — Concerning a company of young men and maids: " they might all three sing and dance "; again thanks is due to Prof. Bensly for finding in the earlier editions the correct reading, " all there." Page 785 — If the lover be a judge of female beauty, " he shall find many faults in Physiognomy, and ill colour; if form, one side of the face likely bigger than the other," &c.; the 3d edition supplies the correct reading, " ill colour,

---

* The quotation following the page-number represents, in every case, the unemended text, followed by the emendation.

ill form." Page 802 — " Oftentimes they may and will not, 'tis their own foolish proceedings that mars all "; earlier editions read " proceeding." Page 812 — Of the chastity of monks: " I am of Tertullian's opinion, few can continue but by compulsion." Earlier editions give us " few can contain." Page 817 — " behold a brief abstract of all that which I have said, . . . elegantly delivered in twelve motions to mitigate the miseries of marriage "; but a little below we are told " how easy it is to answer these motives," and the earlier editions give us " motives " instead of " motions " in the first passage as well. Page 832 — " He that marries a wife that is snowy fair alone "; as Prof. Bensly has pointed out, " snowt fair " is the correct reading.

Second are corrections of the text of the 6th edition, as reprinted by Shilleto, which have been made in other reprints of the 6th and 7th editions; they have been newly compared with the texts of the early editions, but not with the 1651–2 edition, and some of them may concern typographical errors which have crept into the Shilleto text: Page 401 — " the same is incalculcated by Crato "; it should be " inculcated." Page 624 — " Leon Hebræus, in his first dialogue, educeth them all to these three "; it should be " reduceth." Page 669 — " Wherefore did that royal Virgin in Apuleius, when she fled from the thieves' den, made such an Apostrophe to her Ass on whom she rode "; it should be " make such an Apostrophe." Page 733 — " For fire, saith Xenophon, burns them alone that stands near it "; " stand near it " is correct. Page 829 — Of the jealousy of elderly husbands: " Insomuch that she did not complain without cause, in Apuleius, of an old bald bedridded knave she had to her goodman." " Bedridden " is the right reading. Page 896 — Of wicked Jesuits who would persuade some one to assassinate a king: " they bring him into a melancholy dark chamber, . . . till by his strange usage they make him quite mad "; it should be " by this strange usage." Page 898 — " no greater concord, no greater discord then that which proceeds from Religion "; by the 5th edition, this and other " thens " have become " thans " (and we have used the modern spelling generally without referring in every case to earlier editions). Page 913 — " Of Prophets, Enthusians and Impostors "; " Enthusians " is a term which some will regret to lose, but it should be " Enthusiasts." Page 915 — " It is a wonder to see now Nich. Harpsfield . . . puzzles himself "; " to see how " is the correct reading. Page 960 — Of Christian consolation: " let his be as a Bulwark, a Brazen Wall to defend thee "; the correct reading is " let this be." Page 962 — " Galeatius, Martius " is rightly one man, " Galeatius Martius " (though here other reprints leave out Martius and the next ten words).

In looking up " set tippling " in the sentence, page 103, which reads in Shilleto's text, " When our countrymen sacrificed to their goddess Vacuna, and set tippling by their Vacunal fires," we found an interesting variation in the first edition: " When our Countrimen set turning an apple with a pot of ale and a toste by their Vacunal fires." Too bad the apple, ale, and toast were lost in Burton's subsequent revisions! But " set tippling " has become " sate tippling " by the 3d edition ; we print " sat tippling."

Next are emendations not based on the text of any early edition, but which we take to be corrections of fairly obvious typographical errors : Page 37 — " When Socrates had taken great pains to find out a wise man, . . . he concludes all men were fools "; we print " he concluded." Page 69 — We supply the necessary " I " before " love and honour in the mean time all good laws." Page 100 — " I must needs except Lipsius and the Pope, and expunge their name out of the catalogue of fools." We print " names." Page 103 — " to say and do what them list "; we print " what they list." Page 416 — " Is it from Topick stars "; we print " Tropick stars," which has a definite meaning and fits the context. Page 508 — " good men have wealth that we should not think it evil ; and bad men that they should not rely on or hold it so good "; we print " and bad men that we should not rely on or hold it so good." Page 511 — In the first line of Burton's translation of Lucretius : " men still attending fears "; we print " men's still attending fears." Page 681 — " a round black eye is the best, the Son of Beauty "; we print " Sun of Beauty." Page 736 — " and if thou werst not so indeed "; we print " wert." Page 808 — " If she have fortunes of her own, let her make a man "; " make " might be defended on several grounds, but the context, with its " take him for a husband " a few lines below, persuades us that this is merely a typographical error, and we print " take a man." Page 858 — We believe that " stout fair " is a misprint for " snout fair "; we print " snowt-fair," as on page 832.

There are some corrections of proper names — though we do not mention all the cases in which we have given a more familiar or a corrected spelling, as Marco Polo for M. Polus, Fuchsius for Fuschius, &c. Page 262 — " S. Bernard rode all day long by the Lemnian Lake "; we print " Lake Leman." Page 451 — " Cl. Bruxer's Philosophy Game "; Prof. Bensly having identified him for us, we print " Claude Boissiere's."

Page 948 — " Springer a Lawyer "; again following Prof. Bensly's identification, we print " Scrimger, a Lawyer."

Finally there are a few instances where we have arbitrarily made some slight change for the sake of greater intelligibility: Page 18 — " libraries and shops are full of our putid papers "; we print " putrid," which means the same and is more familiar. Page 22 — " not regarding what, but who write "; we print " who writes." Page 529 — " 'tis a fortune which some indefinitely prefer "; " indefinitely " here means " infinitely," and we print it so.

We also note here the following errata: On page 71, " grievances, which must disturb a body politick " was corrected by earlier editions to " much disturb," and then, by some editorial oversight, changed back again to " must disturb," as the 6th edition wrongly has it. On page 579, we should doubtless have translated the Greek " Zeus " and printed " that proud Jupiter Menecrates," as Burton has it on pages 258 and 382. It was doubtless unnecessary, on page 504, to alter " Adrian the Fourth Pope " into " Pope Adrian the Fourth "; a comma after Fourth, as in Shilleto's text, would have served the turn. Alterations of punctuation, and the general omission of titles of books from the text, are dealt with in our editorial preface. The very broad editorial privileges of omission there claimed with regard to Burton's long and repetitive lists of names was only once taken liberal advantage of, on page 579, in the omission of Amatus Lusitanus, Godefridus Stegius, and Hollerius, before " and all our Herbalists." And we confess an error on page 160, where " Alexander " should read " Alexander ab Alexandro." The discovery of further errors we must now leave to others.

INDEX

INDEX [1013

his nephew, a student at Padua, against the dangers of love), 264, 612, 709, 713, 730, 744, 761, 778, 786

Haggesius, Thaddæus, 182

Hakluyt's Voyages, 456

Hal, the Virgin of, 387 note

Hall, Bishop Joseph, 230 note

Halyabbas (Haly Abbas, Persian phys., 10th c., auth. The Royal Book, a med. textbk.), 148, 189, 204, 320, 406

Hammel, pied piper of, 173

Hammer of Witches, see Springer, Jacob

Hare, whether a merry meat or not, 190

Harington, Sir John (Eng. writer, 16th–17th c., transl. of Orlando Furioso, 1591, of Salernitan Regimen of Health, 1607, inventor of the modern water-closet, auth. epigrams, &c.), 484

Hart, a meat that hath an evil name, 190

Hatto, Archbishop of Mentz, and the rats, 945

Hawking, 441

Hegesippus (supposed auth. Latin adaptation of Josephus' Jewish Wars and Antiquities), 234, 441, 653, 718

Heinsius, Daniel (Dutch scholar & poet, libr. of Leyden university), 14, 457, 755, 774, 831

Heliodorus (Greek writer of romance, 3d c., auth. Æthiopica), 221, 455, 614, 669, 670, 671, 675, 676, 681, 683, 722, 759

Heliodorus of Carthage (Burton has a note on him: " I, Heliodorus of Carthage, have ordered in my will that I be put in a sarcophagus at the ends of the world, so that I might see whether any madder than I would betake himself thus far for the sake of looking at me," from Ortelius, in his description of Gades), 97

Hellebore, white, 575; black, 578; 32 note, &c.

Heloise, see Abelard

Hemingius, 176, 950, 951

Henninges, Hieronymus (Eng. divine & genealogist, auth. Saxon Genealogies, 1587, and Theatre of Genealogies, 1598), 29

Heraclitus, 15, 38, 48, 105, 261, 360, 425, 896, &c.

Herbastein, Baron (Siegmund von Herberstein, Austrian diplomat & histor.,

16th c., auth. Muscovy, 1550), 410, 411, 434, 447, 827

Hercules de Saxonia (phys., 16th–17th c., prof. med. at Venice, auth. Pantheon, or Practice of Medicine, and a posth. Treatise on Melancholy, 1620), 120, 148, 149, 150, 151, 152, 153, 154, 179, 205, &c.

Hermes Trismegistus, see Trismegistus

Hero Alexandrinus, 461

Herodotus, 79, 409, 441, 561, 650, 863, 902, 927

Hesiod, 787, &c.

Hessus, Eobanus (German Latin poet & med. writer, 16th c., auth. Concerning the Preservation of Health, Frankfurt, 1582), 485

Heurnius, Johannes (Dutch phys., 16th c., auth. treatise on Diseases of the Head), 20, 120, 122, 123, 124, 153, &c.

Heuter, Pontus (auth. Burgundian History), 48, 452, 687

He-woman, she-man (hic mulier, hæc vir: apparently from the anonymous books, Hic Mulier, or the Man-Woman, Being a Medicine to cure the Coltish Disease of the Staggers in the Masculine-feminines of the Times, London, 1620, and Hæc Vir, or the Womanish Man, same date), 462

Heydon, Sir Christopher, 179

Hiera, 581, &c.

Hierologodium, or Hierologadium (from hiera, medicine, and perh. logos, wisdom, or logas, logados, picked, chosen), 581, 586, 589

Hierom, or Hierome, or Hieronymus (St. Jerome), 19, 31, 143, 159, 160, 162, 163, 215, &c.

Hilarius (St., bishop of Pictavium, 4th c., anti-Arian controversialist), 19

Hilary's term (St. Hilary's feast was in January; a term at Oxford and in the Eng. judicial sitting was named for it, but why Hilary's term should be proverbially hilarious does not appear), 252

Hildesheim (phys., writer on melancholy & madness, auth. bk. of Gleanings from the best med. authors.), 20, 120, 123, 124, 149, 179, 204, 226, &c.

Hill, Nicholas (Eng. philos., 16th–17th c., accused of a Romanist plot against

and they took them wives of all which they chose "), 162, 179, 650

Peresius, 143

Perez, Anthony (Spanish statesman & exile under Philip II), 244

Persius (Roman satirist, 1st c.), 22, 56, 94, &c.

Peter and his daughter's ague (this story is from Augustine's qtn. from some apocryphal Acts of Peter, in which she is stricken with palsy at Peter's prayer, to save her from a worse evil miraculously foreknown to him; a similar story exists in a Coptic fragment of the Acts of Peter, now at Berlin; and there is another apocryphal story of a gardener's daughter struck dead by Peter's prayer for like reasons), 115

Peter of Abano, see Apponensis

Peter Comestor (French eccles. histor., 12th c.), 504

Peter Martyr, see Peter Martyr Anglerius

Peter Martyr Anglerius (histor., 15th c., bishop of Jamaica, auth. Ocean Decades, 1516-1525, and The Babylonian Embassy, 1516, an account of his embassy to Cairo), 90, 165, 411, 415, 456, 825, 880

Petrarch, 43, 215, &c.

Petronius, 60, 94, 101, 198, 699, 891

Peucer, Caspar (German phys. & math., 16th c., auth. bk. pub. Viteburg, 1563, transl. as The Soothsayer, a Commentary on the Principal Kindes of Divination, 1584), 91, 123, 805

Pezelius, Christopher (astrol., 17th c., auth. History of Sorcery, 1629), 809

Pherecydes Syrius (Greek philos., 6th c. B.C.), 142, 882

Philænis, a writer on the art of love, 701

Philelphus, Francis (Francesco Filelfo, Ital. scholar, 15th c.), 832

Philip (auth. bk. on the soul), 135, 142

Philo, 25, 61, 218, 228, &c.

Philolaches (in Plautus), 213

Philonium Romanum, 597 note

Philonius, 88, 571

Philosophaster (Burton's Latin comedy was not printed during his lifetime, but was edited by W. E. Buckley for the Roxburghe Club, 1862, together with some of his poems), 279 note

Philostratus (the Athenian, 2d-3d c. A.D.,

auth. Life of Apollonius of Tyana, Lives of the Stoics, and erotic Epistles), 25 note, 218, 748, 786

Philters, 796 et seq.

Phocion (Athenian general, 4th c. B.C.), 64

Phryne, 255, 668, 669, 672

Picatrix, 382

Piccolomineus, Alexander (? Alessandro Piccolomini, Ital. eccles. & philos., 16th c.), 135, 217, 218, 233, 411, 617, 622

Pictorius, 167, 170, 171, 969

Picus, Francis (Gian Francesco Pico della Mirandola, 16th c., nephew of Giovanni Pico della M., whose philos. ideas he followed closely, & whose works he pub.; auth. life of Savonarola the martyr), 144

Picus, John (Giovanni Pico della Mirandola, Ital. philos. & mystic, 15th c.), 135, 144, 179, 275, 612

Picus Mirandula, see Picus, John

Pied Piper of Hammel, 173

Pierius, Valerianus (Ital. philol., 16th c., auth. Hieroglyphics, or the Secrets of Egypt, 1576), 123, 337 note, 646, 942

Pinzonus (Pinzon, Spanish navigator, one of Columbus' companions), 532

Pirckheemerus, Bilibaldus (Willibad Pirckheimer, German humanist, 16th c.; his Praise of Gout, or the Gout's Apologie, was pub. London, 1617), 500, &c.

Pirovanus, 179

Piso, Nicholas (phys., auth. Practica), 120, 193, &c.

Pituita, 127, 129

Plater, Felix (F. Platter, Swiss phys., 16th-17th c., prof. med. at Basle, auth. Observations, treatise on Mental Aberrations, &c.; his works were pub. Basle, 1625), 16, 98, 124, 204, 206, 225, 229, &c.

Platerus (prob. Felix Plater, but poss. Joannes Platerus or Platearius, prof. med. at Salerno, 11th c., auth. Practica, much reprinted: or Matthew P., 11th c., or John P. the Younger, 12th c., both Salernitan), 124

Platina, Baptista (real name Bartolomeo de Sicchi, Ital. man of letters, 15th c., libr. of the Vatican library, auth. many bks., incl. a misogynistic Dialogue of

17th c., auth. The Noble Art of Venerie, or Huntinge, 1576), 646

Turnebus, Adrian (Adrien Turnèbe, French classical scholar, 16th c., re-ferred to several times by Montaigne), 13

Turner, Dr. William (Eng. phys. 16th c., auth. The Newe Herbal, 1538–1562, and a Booke of Bathes, 1568), 405, 575

Turrianus, Baptista, 363

Tusser, Thomas (Eng. poet & farmer, 16th c., auth. A Hundreth Good Pointes of Husbandrie, 1557, in verse: Burton probably qts. from a later enlarged ed., the Five Hundreth Pointes, 1577), 84 note, 433

T. W. Jes, see Wright, Thomas

Tyreus, see Thyræus

Tyrius, see Maximus Tyrius

Ubaldus, Guidus, see Guidus Ubaldus

Ulricus Molitor, see Molitor, Ulricus

Utopia, his own, set forth, 82–91

Vacuna, goddess of rural leisure, 103, 903

Valentinus Andreas, see Andrea

Valentius (Basil Valentine, German alchemist & Hermetic philos., 15th c., Benedictine monk, prior of St. Peter's in Erfurt, reputed auth. The Triumphal Chariot of Antinomy, and other works on chemistry & pharmacy), 577

Valerius Maximus (Roman rhetorician, 1st c., auth. bk. of Memorable Deeds), 119, 125, 228, 246, 247, 813

Valescus de Taranta (Portug. phys. & med. writer, phys. to Charles VI of France; auth. Tract on Epidemics and the Pest, 1473, an Epitome of Surgery, a bk. of Antidotes, &c.), 229, &c.

Valesius, Franciscus (Francisco Valles, Spanish phys., 16th c., auth. Commentary on Hippocrates in regard to Sacred Diseases), 148, 151, 152, 157, 224, &c.

Valleriola, Francisco (auth. Medical Observations, Lyons, 1605, and Surgical Observations), 223, 361, 394, 419, 612, 613, 683, 721, 723, 733, 764, 765, 769, 771, 820

Vaninus, Cæsar (Lucilio Vanini, Ital.

free-thinker, 17th c., pupil of Pomponatius; auth. Concerning the Wonderful Secrets of Nature, the Queen and Goddess of Mortal Affairs, 1616; executed as an atheist, 1619), 220, 223, 882, 902, 929, 930 note, 931, 933

Varchi, Benedetto (Florentine histor. & poet, 16th c., auth. bk. transl. by Robert Toíte as The Blason of Jealousy, 1615), 821, 827, 838

Varro (Roman scholar, 2d–1st c. B.C., auth. various works incl. one on the Latin Language, and one on Rustic Matters), 19, 94, 164, 227, &c.

Vascus Gama, see Gama, Vascus

Vatinian hatred, 52, 233 note

Vaughan, Mr. (Sir William Vaughan, Eng. poet & colonial pioneer, 17th c., auth. The Golden Fleece, a bk. written to coax emigrants to his settlement in Newfoundland: he wrote under the name of Orpheus Junior), 416, 812

Vectius (Vettius Praetextatus, the host in Macrobius' Saturnalia), 16

Vega, Christophorus à, see Christophorus à Vega

Vegetius (Latin military writer, 4th c. A.D., much studied in the middle ages, printed in Eng. by Caxton, 1489), 87, 398, 415, 431, 936–7

Venetian courtesans, their elegancy of speech, 699

Venison, a melancholy meat, 190

Venus, use of (sexual intercourse), **203**, 204, 205, 405, 406, 407, &c.

Venus Barbata, 904

Verdeur, Anthony de, or Verdurius (Verdier, French biographer & bibliographer, 16th c., auth. Pictures of the Gods), 343, 797, 905

Verjuice and oatmeal is good for a parrot, 80 note

Vertomannus, Lodovicus (Barthema, or Varthema, Ital. traveller & writer, 16th c., auth. Journeys, pub. Rome, 1510, transl. into Eng. by Richard Eden as The Navigation and Voyage of Lewes Vertomannus to the Regions of Arabia, Ægypte, Syria, Ethiopia and East Indies, both within and without the Ryver of Ganges: Conteyning many notable and straunge Thinges, both hystoricall and naturall, London, 1576),

ERRATA

Page ix (Introduction)

Line 9 should read: "had gone into *eight* when Dr. Johnson's famous"

Line 22: "1811" is probably wrong: it is more likely the edition of 1800 to which Lamb referred, that being the year in which Coleridge suggested to him the writing of his imitation of Burton's Anatomy. However several octavo reprints had appeared prior to the publication of Lamb's essay, *Detached Thoughts on Books and Reading,* where he raised the complaint. The edition read by Keats was that of 1813.

Page 600 (prose)

Line 25: *Randoletius* should read—*Rondoletius.*

Page 628 (the footnote)

Line 1: the first name should read, Julius Cæsar Scaliger.

Line 5: "Bordone" should read *Burdone.*

Line 6: "Bordone" should read *Burdone.*

—the point being that Gaspar Scioppius, in his book (published in 1607), made a wretched pun on the word *Burdon,—Burdonis* being the Latin equivalent of "from a mule."

ADDITIONS AND CORRECTIONS TO INDEX

Page 986

Afer, Leo (Traveller and historian, 16th c., auth. Description of Africa.), 207, 300, 302, 456, 656, 844, 849, 876, 911.

Page 990

Atwater, B, should read,—*Atwater, William* (Bishop Eng. ch. 16th c.).

Page 996

Burton, George (Robert's brother), 950 note.

Page 997

Line 2 should read: Bensly's **articles** in Notes & Queries,

Page 1009

Faventinus should have been entered as: Victorius Benedictus Faven-tinus Empiric phys. 1481-1561: wrote De curandis morbis, important in Burton's study of melancholia.

Page 1009

Fienus, should read: Fienus, Thomas.

Page 1011

Add to "Gemma, Cornelius" (*16th c. Astrol. and phys.*)

Page 1013 (second column)

Hildesheim. Change to: Hildesheim, Franciscus (Germ. Med. writer, 16th & 17th cent., from whose "De cerebri et capitis morbis internis Spicilegia," Frankfurt, 1612, Burton so often quotes).

Page 1014

Jason Pratensis. Change "Dutch" to *Swiss:* His book, "De cerebri Morbis" (Basle, 1549), is often quoted by Burton.

Page 1016

On this page are two entries of *"Laurentius."* There should be but one, viz.: Laurentius Andre du Laurens, auth. "De Morbis Melancholicis tractabus, 1599; phys. to Henry IV., and great anatomist. Died at Paris in 1609.

Page 1016

Leon the Hebrew (Don Judah Abravanel [1565-1630], auth. "Dialoghi di Amore," Rome 1535), 612, 618, 621, 622, 644, 872.

Page 1018

Melanelius, Matthias Theodorus (16th cent. phys. auth. "De Melancholia ex Galeni, Rufi, etc. 1540).

Page 1020

Montaltus, Ælianus. Should be Montaltus, Ælianus. Portuguese phys. died at Tours, 1616. His book on mental pathology, "Archipathologia," Paris 1614, was one of Burton's most useful sourcebooks.

Page 1020

Montanus. Should read: Montanus, John Bapt. Veronese phys. & poet, 1498-1551, called "the second Galen"; his *Consultations,* Basle, 1563, contain a large section devoted to melancholy.

Page 1023
  Picatrix. Celebrated medieval book
  of magic; prob. 12th or 13th cent.
  compilation. Never printed, but
  widely circulated in Ms. form.
Page 1023
  Platerus is same as *Plater* above,
  viz.: Felix Plater.
Page 1026
  Rondoletius, Guillame (referred to
  by Rabelais under the name of
  "Rondibilis"; he was one of the
  first scientific zoologists; 1509-
  1566).
Page 1026
  Roeslin, Helisaeus; Eliseo Roeslin;
  Germ. phys. and astron. 16th c.
  His "Theoria Nova cœlestium
  Meteorum"—Strassburg, 1578—, is
  referred to by Burton. 420, 421,
  422, 427, 428.
Page 1029
  Thuanus. Jacques August De Thou.
  (French hist. 1553-1617.)

The Anatomy of Melancholy
By Robert Burton

ON DECEMBER FIFTH, three hundred and more years ago, in his study at Christ Church, Oxford, a curious, middle-aged scholar wrote the last lines of one of the most entertaining and amazing books in the world.

It is a sort of literary cosmos, an omnium gatherum, a compendium of everything that caught the fancy of the scholar who lived in an unspecialized age. Poetry, medicine, "morbid psychology", philosophy, old wives' tales, philology, wars, antiquarian lore, theology, morals, history, climatology, travel, food, love, hate, ambition, pride, astrology, art, politics, and a scheme for the establishment of Utopia — all these and more are poured forth helter-skelter by this 17th century reckoner of human frailties, in a style abounding in quaint conceits and hundreds of rare excerpts and quotations.

The *Anatomy* is one of the most comfortable books that ever graced a library, as entrancing as Rabelais, or its own step-child, Tristram Shandy; the "bed book" par excellence that delighted and influenced Dr. Johnson, Milton, Sterne, Keats and Lamb; a source of incomparable literary delight, as he who reads will find.

This handsome large-type library edition is complete with the Latin passages translated into modern English.